LAN TIMES Encyclopedia of Networking

About the Author...

Tom Sheldon has worked in the computer industry for fifteen years and is a fully authorized Novell service and support technician and Novell Certified Network Engineer (CNE). He is the author of eighteen books, including **Novell Network 386: The Complete Reference, Novell NetWare 4: The Complete Reference** and **Windows NT Inside and Out.**

LAN TIMES Encyclopedia of Networking

Tom Sheldon

Osborne **McGraw-Hill**
Berkeley New York St. Louis San Francisco
Auckland Bogotá Hamburg London Madrid
Mexico City Milan Montreal New Delhi Panama City
Paris São Paulo Singapore Sydney
Tokyo Toronto

Osborne **McGraw-Hill**
2600 Tenth Street
Berkeley, California 94710
U.S.A.

For information on software, translations, or book distributors outside of the U.S.A., please write to Osborne McGraw-Hill at the above address.

LAN TIMES Encyclopedia of Networking

7890 DOC 99876

ISBN 0-07-881965-2

This book is printed on acid-free paper.

To Christopher and Kelsey

Stay Updated!
Keep In Touch!

We want to keep you updated with the latest information about networks, networking technology, and the Internet, so we periodically provide free update notes on this growing and changing industry. It's our way of keeping this book on the cutting edge.

If you would like to be included on our mailing list, drop us a card at the address listed below, or call 1-800-280-9555.

Write:

Network Update Notes
c/o Tom Sheldon
P. O. Box 947
Cambria, CA 93428

Contents

Introduction

This encyclopedia provides anyone involved in the field of computer networking with a broad list of reference topics. Each topic is designed to provide a definition of a particular term, concept, technology, or standard that is more detailed than you would find in a dictionary, yet honed to provide the most important information. This book is useful to:

- people who work with computer networks, such as network managers, network administrators, engineers, systems integrators, network installers, service technicians, technical writers, users, and students of computer science.

- people who are indirectly associated with computer networks, such as department managers, resellers, buyers, planners, architects, and others.

- people who need to read technical articles and papers related to networking and are not versed in the latest terminology used in the field.

This book is designed to be extremely easy to use and easy to find information in. It provides extensive cross-referencing to related topics so readers can quickly locate directly or indirectly related information. It also includes a detailed index so readers can locate information that does not warrant a heading. By using the cross-references and index, and by referring to the section, "Important Topics of General Interest" later in this introduction, you should be able to find most any topic you need.

The topics are alphabetized in letter-by-letter order, rather than word-by-word order—that means the space or hyphen that separates words is ignored, so that "LANtastic" comes before "LAN Troubleshooting," and "Object-Oriented Technology" comes before "Object Request Broker." Commas, on the other hand, are *not* ignored, so that "Directory Services, NetWare" comes before "Directory Services Naming."

This book also contains, in Appendix A, an extensive list of the most common network-related acronyms.

Important Topics and Emerging Trends

The topics discussed in this book detail the current and cutting-edge trends of the computer networking industry today. For a general overview of these emerging technologies and networking trends, readers should refer to "Client-Server Computing," "Distributed Computing," "Distributed Database," and "Enterprise Networks."

As networks grow to encompass many different remote sites over wide areas, security becomes more of a problem, and the need to authenticate and authorize user access increases. The topic "Security" covers methods for providing security in distributed computing environments. Additional information on security and related topics is provided in sections such as "Authentication and Authorization," "Data Encryption Standard," "Digital Signatures," "Distributed File Systems," "Kerberos Authentication," and "Key Encryption Technology."

The 1990s have been referred to as the decade of the wide area network (WAN) by many industry analysts. This is because the cost of WANs is coming down—public network providers implement fiber-optic networks and new communication standards provide more flexibility at lower costs for customers who want to build networks that interconnect many remote sites. Refer to "Carrier Services," "Cellular Data Communication Systems," "Data Communications," "Metropolitan Area Networks," "Public Data Networks," "Telecommunication," "Wide Area Networks," and "Wireless Mobile Communication" for more information.

Today, new network cabling strategies are providing a better way to plan, maintain, and expand the cabling system of an organization. The bandwidth of cabling systems has been boosted to support new applications like multimedia and real-time videoconferencing. Structured wiring systems like those discussed under "Cabling" and "EIA/TIA 568 Commercial Building Wiring Standard" are designed to provide new services and growth and make it easy to accommodate reorganization of computers and users.

Electronic mail and workflow applications are also emerging in the enterprise network environment. For information on these applications, readers should refer to topics such as "Compound Documents," "Document Interchange Standards," "Document Management," "Electronic Mail," "Groupware," "Hierarchical Storage

Management Systems," "Imaging," "Message-Enabled Applications," Messaging Application Programming Interface," "Multimedia," and "Workflow Software."

This book covers a number of other important industry trends in addition to the subjects already listed. In particular, readers should refer to topics such as "IBM Networking Blueprint," "Information Warehouse," "Internet," "Middleware," "Mobile Computing," "Object-Oriented Interfaces and Operating Systems," "Object-Oriented Technology," and many others listed in the following section, "Important Topics of General Interest."

Important Topics of General Interest

The following is a list of major topics covered in this book. Many of these topics also contain a list of related entries you can look up for more in-depth information. It is worthwhile to spend a few minutes looking over this list to find areas of particular interest to you.

Access Rights
Analog Transmission Systems
Application Program Interface (API)
Archiving
Asynchronous Communications
Asynchronous Transfer Mode (ATM)
Auditing
Authentication and Authorization
Backbone Networks
Backup and Data Archiving
Bridging
Cable Installation
Cabling
Carriers
Carrier Services
Cell Relay
Cellular Data Communication Systems
Circuit-Switching Services
Client-Server Computing
Compound Documents
Compression Techniques
Configuration Management
Connection-Oriented and Connectionless Protocols
Database Management System (DBMS)
Data Communications
Data Encryption Standard (DES)
Datagram Network Services

Alphabetical Reference of Terms

Access Control

Access control provides a way to control user access to resources on a network. Control includes login password schemes, time and computer restrictions, and control over resources such as files and printers. *Access control lists (ACLs)* are small databases that describe the type of access a user has to a service. ACLs are usually attached to file system directories and specify access permissions for users such as Read, Write, Delete, and so on. In object-oriented systems, objects that represent resources like file servers and printers contain ACLs. Each user can have different access rights to files and resources on the network based on ACLs.

ACLs are used in Novell NetWare, Microsoft Windows NT, and other operating systems to control access to network information. In NetWare 4.x, users are authenticated when they first log on to the system. This process sets up a relationship in which other services on the network "trust" that the authentication system has properly verified the user. An *access token* is then assigned to the user for the duration of the user's logon session. This token is used to validate the user and determine his or her rights to use resources based on the ACL.

RELATED ENTRIES   Access Rights; Authentication and Authorization; Permissions in Windows NT; Rights (several headings); *and* Security

Access Method, Network

Local area networks (LANs) are typically shared by a number of attached systems, and only one system at a time can use the network cable to transmit data. Access methods are the rules defined within a specific network type that determine how each station accesses the cable. Simultaneous access to the cable is either prevented by using a token passing method, or tolerated and managed with a carrier sensing and collision detection method.

The primary access methods are *carrier sensing* and *token passing*. There are two carrier sensing methods, each with a different way of handling multiple, simultaneous cable access. A new *demand priority access method* is implemented in a new Ethernet standard that provides 100 Mbits/sec throughput, rather than 10 Mbits/sec.

- *Carrier Sense Multiple Access/Collision Detection (CSMA/CD)* Carrier sensing implies that network nodes listen for a carrier tone on the cable and send information when other devices are not transmitting. Multiple access means that many devices share the same cable. If two or more devices sense that the network is idle, they will attempt to access it simultaneously (contention), causing collisions. Each station must then back off and wait a certain amount of time before attempting to retransmit. Delays caused by contention are lowered by reducing the number of workstations on the LAN.

- *Carrier Sense Multiple Access/Collision Avoidance (CSMA/CA)* This access method is a variation on the CSMA/CD method. Nodes estimate when a collision might occur and avoid transmission during that period. This method is cheaper to implement since collision detection circuitry is not required; however, it imposes more delay and can slow network throughput.

■ *Demand Priority Access Method*   This is a new access method for 100 Mbits/sec Ethernet. It turns over network access management to a central hub, rather than relying on individual workstations to determine when they should access the cable. Workstations request permission to transmit data based on priority, and the hub transmits the highest-priority data first. Demand priority access was proposed by Hewlett-Packard and AT&T for use in the Ethernet 100VG-AnyLAN (IEEE 802) networking scheme.

■ *Token Passing*   ARCNET and token ring networks use the token passing access method. A workstation must have possession of a token before it can begin transmission. The token is passed around the network and acquired by any station that needs to transmit. See "Token and Token Passing Access Methods".

Carrier sensing methods tend to be faster than token passing methods, but collisions can bog down the network during heavy traffic loads. Token ring does not suffer from cable contention problems.

RELATED ENTRIES   ARCNET; Distributed Queue Dual Bus; Ethernet (several headings); *and* Token Ring Network

Access Rights

Access rights are the "keys" that define a user's ability to access a computer network, a particular network server, or the directories and files located on a network or server. Access rights are assigned by network administrators, supervisors, or department managers, depending on the management structure. They include:

■ Login access rights may define the hours during which the user can log in, or the specific computers the user can operate.

■ Access rights control user access to system resources like printers, fax machines, and communication services.

■ Directory and file rights define a user's ability to read and change files, or execute program files. Users without the proper rights (or permissions) can be prevented from changing or deleting files.

As an example, access rights and permissions in Novell NetWare and Microsoft Windows NT are discussed and compared in the following sections.

Access Rights in NetWare

In NetWare, users who have rights to access files, directories, or objects (NetWare 4 Directory Services) are *trustees*. The login process requires that users enter a password to gain access to a server or, in NetWare 4.x, to the internetwork. Login restrictions can prevent users from logging in after hours, or on unauthorized systems.

Directory and file rights give users access to the filing system. These rights are granted to users or groups of users and include the ability to read a file but not change it, or the ability to read and change files. Users are granted rights to directories and files, and the rights "flow down" into subdirectories unless they are specifically changed in those subdirectories by system administrators or supervisors.

Access Rights in Windows NT

In Microsoft Windows NT, users have rights and permissions, as described here:

- *Rights*   Rights control the actions a user can perform on the system, and come in sets, such as logon rights, manager rights, and backup rights. Rights are typically granted to groups, and users gain the rights by being made members of groups. Groups include the Administrator group, the Power User group (assistant administrators), Users group (normal users), Backup Operators group, and others. For example, the Backup Operators group has the Backup and Restore rights.

- *Permissions*   Permissions give users access to directories, files, and resources such as printers. Permissions are assigned by members of the Administrator group and Power User group, or by owners of directories and files. Permissions include the ability to read, write (change), execute, and delete files, among others. Permissions also come in groups so administrators don't need to assign several rights to a user so they can perform a task. For example, the set of permissions called Read gives users the ability to read files or execute program files, but not change or delete them.

RELATED ENTRIES   Access Rights; Permissions in Windows NT; Rights in Novell NetWare; *and* Rights in Windows for Workgroups

Account, User Network

Network computer users typically have accounts that hold information such as their name, password, and restrictions to the network. Network administrators control user access by changing values in user accounts. For example, the account can be temporarily disabled if a user fails to enter the correct password after three tries. The account can also have a time limit, so that a temporary employee might be granted access for a two-week period. An account can also restrict a user to logging in only during a specific time period (8:00 am to 5:00 pm), or on a specific machine. Account information can also hold general information, such as the address of the user's workstation or the user's phone number for reference.

Accounting Services

Accounting services are provided by some network operating systems to track the usage of resources and the users who access those resources. Accounting systems also provide network asset tracking. Typical network resources tracked by accounting systems are listed here:

- Files accessed
- Disk space used
- User logons and logoffs
- Messages transferred by users
- Bytes transferred by users
- Applications started
- Access to peripheral and resources like printers and data bases

In most cases, it is possible for the administrator or supervisor of a network or server to set limits on the amount of time a user can access the system, the amount of disk space a user can use, and the resources a user can access.

In some network operating systems, users are granted a certain amount of time or resources that get used up as the user accesses the network. The user can then request or purchase additional time or resources. The values are tracked in the user's account. The accounting system in NetWare can track and charge users for blocks read and written to disk, connect time, or service requests.

RELATED ENTRIES   Access Rights; Auditing; *and* Users and Groups

Accumaster Integrator, AT&T

Accumaster Integrator is part of AT&T's Unified Network Management Architecture (UNMA) model. UNMA defines an enterprise-level management system with various subsystems, such as network elements and an element management systems that handles the management of the network elements. Above these elements is an integration system that lets administrators get a full view of all the elements. The interface is based on the Open Systems Interconnection (OSI) management standard called CMIP (Common Management Information Protocol).

Accumaster is the management software package that provides administrators with a view of subsystems. Information regarding performance and faults is collected from the network elements to help administrators locate potential or real problems. An inventory of all network elements and their relationships is also maintained. As of this writing, AT&T was putting more marketing energy into the NCR StarSENTRY network management system.

RELATED ENTRY   Management Standards and Tools

ACCUNET

AT&T's ACCUNET digital services are high-speed data transmission offerings that first appeared in 1983 as ACCUNET T1.5 and in 1986 as ACCUNET T45. The services provide dedicated point-to-point digital channels operating at the speeds described in the following list. The services are designed to provide communications backbones to consolidate geographically dispersed voice, data, and video networks.

- *T1.5 Service*   This provides a 1.544 Mbits/sec leased line with twenty-four 64 Kbits/sec circuits for voice or data transmissions.

- *T45 Service*   AT&T's highest-capacity domestic digital service provides dedicated 44.736 Mbits/sec digital capabilities.

- *ACCUNET T1.5 Reserved Digital Services and ACCUNET T45 Reserved Digital Services*   These provide high-volume transmission rates on as as-needed basis by calling an AT&T reservations center 24 hours in advance. The service is useful for periodic high-volume data transfers.

- *ACCUNET Spectrum of Digital Services*   This is basically AT&T fractional T1 offerings. Users can access digital leased lines in increments of 64 Kbits/sec, up to 1.544 Mbits/sec. For example, customers can lease 64, 128, or 256 Kbits/sec, or other increments to match their data transmission requirements. There are 24 fractional 64 Kbits/sec lines in a T1 line.

- *ACCUNET Switched 1536 Service*   This service lets users dial into 1.536 Mbits/sec lines on AT&T's digital switched network. An Integrated Services Digital Network (ISDN) primary rate interface is required. The service was initially launched in 10 cities and is supported from AT&T's Switched Digital Services Network Control Center in Chicago. Charges for a call's initial 30 seconds range from $3.10 for 1 to 10 miles to $5.17 for 3,000 or more miles.

- *Dataphone Digital Service (DDS)*   DDS is offered in a variety of major cities and provides links to Canadian digital networks. It is a dedicated, two-way transmission line that operates at synchronous data transfer rates of 2.4, 4.8, 9.6, 19.2, and 56 Kbits/sec.

- *ACCUNET Switched 56 Service*   In 1980, the ACCUNET Switched 56 Service was introduced to provide nondedicated dialup (switched) lines at 56 Kbits/sec to use as backup lines for the dedicated DDS services or to supplement those services during peak periods. Users gain access to this service by dialing 700 numbers in host cities.

To protect users against failed facilities, AT&T offers redundancy and protection features in its lines for those that need it. Diversity of lines ensures that different geographic routes are used in the transmission to prevent total disruption of communications services. Protection features can automatically reroute lines in subseconds should a line fail.

RELATED ENTRIES   AT&T; Backbone Networks; Carrier Services; Circuit-Switching Services; Leased Line; *and* Wide Area Networks

Acknowledgments

In various communications protocols and file transfer utilities, an acknowledgment is sent by a receiving device to a transmitting device to indicate that it is ready to begin transmissions or that a block of data was received without error. In packet networks, acknowledgments can provide reliable service, but add to overhead. As networks become more reliable, acknowledgments are eliminated and end-stations take on more responsibility for error checking.

RELATED ENTRIES   Asynchronous Communications; Connection-Oriented and Connectionless Protocols; *and* Flow Control Methods

Active Hub, ARCNET

In the ARCNET networking system, an active hub (as opposed to a passive hub) is a repeater device that regenerates and retransmits bits exactly as they are received. The repeated signal extends the distance of the network up to 2,000 feet. The maximum total distance is 20,000 feet. A typical active hub has 8 to 12 ports for the attachment of coaxial cable-connected workstations, but hybrid devices have ports for twisted-pair and fiber-optic cable, as well as lamps that indicate whether a port is operating correctly. Active hubs are now common in other network systems with the increasing use of twisted-pair wire and wiring centers.

RELATED ENTRIES   ARCNET; Hubs

Active Star Topology

Star topology networks are either active or passive. In *passive star topology*, the star is configured with a box that simply serves to organize the wiring, such as a telephone punch-down block. In *active star topology*, a hub is a device that regenerates and repeats signals. The active hub may contain diagnostic features that indicate faulty ports or that report fault information back to a management station. A failure of a node or break in a node's cable does not disable the rest of the network.

RELATED ENTRIES   ARCNET; Hubs; Networks; Token Ring Network; *and* Topology

Adaptive Differential Pulse Code Modulation (ADPCM)

ADPCM defines the digitizing method called pulse code modulation (PCM) used to transmit analog voice on digital channels. Organizations that establish digital lines between remote sites can transmit both voice and data over those lines by digitizing the voice signals before transmitting. ADPCM uses a lower bit rate that permits more voice channels to be transmitted over a typical digital line. The difference between samples is used and the coding scale can be dynamically changed to compensate for amplitude and frequency variations.

RELATED ENTRIES   Analog-to-Digital Conversion; Modulation Techniques; Multiplexing; *and* Transmission Media, Methods, and Equipment

Address Resolution Protocol (ARP)

On Transmission Control Protocol/Internet Protocol (TCP/IP) networks with Ethernet nodes, there is a physical network address, and an Internet Protocol (IP) address that resides in software. An Ethernet physical address consists of a code built right onto the network adapter. The purpose of ARP is to determine which physical network address corresponds to the IP address in a packet. When a node sends an IP packet, it is necessary to determine the physical address on the network for the IP address specified. The node broadcasts an ARP packet containing the destination IP address and the destination node then returns its physical address to the requesting node.

The information is kept in an address resolution cache. The next time the node needs to send an IP packet, it first looks in the address resolution cache to see if the physical address for the destination workstation is in the cache. If so, that address is used and an ARP request is not necessary, thus reducing network traffic.

RELATED ENTRY   Transmission Control Protocol/Internet Protocol

Addresses, Electronic Mail

Electronic mail systems have specific addressing schemes that identify users and resources on the network. These addressing schemes identify the area or domain where a user or resource exists, and the specific node within the area or domain.

The Internet, a global network of users, employs a hierarchical naming scheme. An address for a user attached to a local area network or a network attached to the organization's E-mail hub might be the following, which addresses John Doe (jdoe) at the library, University of California, Berkeley. The last portion, "edu," is an Internet-type code indicating an educational institution.

jdoe@library.berkeley.edu

Many networks provide directory naming services, some of which follow the X.500 set of standards. Users can access these directory services to determine the address of a user or resource anywhere on the network. In most cases, the process of addressing a message automatically accesses the naming service in the background.

The X.400 specifications are a set of electronic mail communications standards developed by the CCITT.

RELATED ENTRIES   Addresses, Network; Directory Services Naming, NetWare 4.x; Domain Name Service; Internet; Transmission Control Protocol/Internet Protocol; X.400 Message Handling System; *and* X.500 Directory Services

Addresses, Network

Every node on a network has an assigned address that other nodes use when communicating with it. For Ethernet and token ring network adapters, unique addresses are assigned at the factory. ARCNET networks have user-definable addresses. For example, the address of an Ethernet and token ring network adapter consists of a 6-byte address, half of which is a special number identifying the board's manufacturer. The last half of the address is a unique number for the board assigned at the factory. This strategy virtually guarantees that no two Ethernet or token ring network interface cards will ever have the same address, and prevents conflicts.

When separate networks are connected into an internetwork, a new addressing scheme is required. On interconnected NetWare networks, each network segment has its own address, which is used for routing purposes and to differentiate each segment from the others.

In TCP/IP networks such as the Internet, every node has a numeric address that identifies both a network and a local host or node on the network. This address is written as four numbers separated by dots, for example, (191.31.140.115). The assignment of addresses is arbitrary within a company or organization, but if the company plans to connect with the Internet, it is important to obtain registered addresses from an outside agency to conform with international addressing standards. Applications running in computers also have addresses that other applications, either local or remote, use to communicate with the application. On TCP/IP networks, a *socket* is a combination of an Internet address plus an application address.

RELATED ENTRIES   Directory Services Naming, NetWare 4.x; Domain Name Service; Internet; Sockets; *and* X.500 Directory Services

Administrators, NetWare 4.x

The NetWare Directory Services feature in NetWare 4.x changes the management structure and rules for users who manage NetWare servers and the networks attached to them. In previous versions of NetWare, the person installing the operating system on a server basically becomes the supervisor for that server if that person specifies the password for the supervisor account. The supervisor account has unlimited rights to the file system and management functions on the server. NetWare 4.x does not use this server-centric view.

In NetWare 4.x, because of NetWare Directory Services, the network and its resources are managed by an administrative user at the highest level and supervisor-like users at the division, department, or server levels. The person installing the first NetWare 4.x server can sign on as the ADMIN user and create a password for the account. The ADMIN account initially has full and unrestricted rights to the server and any other servers added to the directory services tree unless those rights are relinquished. Technically, the ADMIN account is at the base of the directory services tree and has unlimited rights. These rights then flow down into all branches of the tree.

One of the first tasks of the ADMIN user is to create branches in the hierarchical directory services tree that represent divisions or departments within the company. The ADMIN user then creates user accounts for supervisors of those divisions or departments and grants them a management set of rights. Part of the supervisors' tasks is to create user accounts and assign rights to those accounts. Servers, printers, and other resources are represented as objects in the directory tree. The managers of these divisions or departments also have control over the resources in them.

An administrator has many tasks; some are listed here. Keep in mind that many of these tasks are delegated to supervisors at the department or division level.

- Install servers.
- Create the initial administrator password.
- Change the administrator password periodically for security reasons.
- Administer the NDS (NetWare Directory Services) directory.
- Administer the security of servers and of the entire internetwork.
- Create directory structures for programs and data within volume objects.
- Install applications.
- Create, manage, and delete user and resource objects.
- Assign passwords to users or require them to periodically change their passwords.
- Designate users as managers with special rights to manage other users.
- Monitor the performance and integrity of the network.
- Recommend new equipment or manage the expansion of the network when it becomes overloaded.
- Ensure that data is properly protected with backup procedures and system fault tolerance (SFT) features, as well as by physically securing servers.

The ADMIN user should also have a normal logon account that he or she uses to access the network for nonadministrative tasks. Administrator-level access should not be taken lightly. If the administrator's workstation is left unattended, an intruder could walk up to it and gain unrestricted access to the entire internetwork.

The system administrator's password is the master key to the system. Write it down and place it in a locked safe or give it to a trusted person of authority for safekeeping. Another suggestion is to create a two- or three-word password and then give a portion of the password to two or three people in the company. This "fail-safe" approach ensures that others can gain administrative access to the server should something happen to the administrator, but to gain access, they must do so together.

RELATED ENTRIES   Directory Services, NetWare; NetWare; NetWare 4.x Enhanced Features; *and* Users and Groups

Advanced Data Communications Control Procedure (ADCCP)

A Data-Link layer protocol that places data on a network and ensures proper delivery to a destination. ADCCP is similar to the IBM Synchronous Data Link Control (SDLC) protocol and is the American National Standards Institute (ANSI) X3.66 standard.

RELATED ENTRIES   High-level Data Link Control; Synchronous Data Link Control

Advanced Interactive Executive (AIX), IBM

AIX is IBM's version of UNIX that runs on System 370/390 mainframes, RS/6000 systems, and PS/2 desktop computers. With the growing popularity of UNIX as an open system, IBM views AIX as an important product in its new client-server, open system strategy that supports Transmission Control Protocol/Internet Protocol (TCP/IP) and Open Systems Interconnection (OSI) communication protocols.

AIX includes the IBM Customer Information Control System (CICS). CICS is a transaction processing system that operates in a distributed environment. In the AIX/6000 environment, CICS uses the Open Software Foundation (OSF) Distributed Computing Environment (DCE) remote procedure call (RPC) and its implementation of Transarc's Encina transaction processing system.

- AIX is positioned as a NetView/6000 management platform.

- AIX provides gateway features between the IBM Systems Application Architecture (SAA) environment and UNIX or OSI environments.

- AIX/6000 provides a gateway between file systems in the TCP/IP environment and the OSI environment; specifically, it provides a gateway between File Transfer Protocol (FTP) and File Transfer Access and Management (FTAM).

- AIX/6000 also provides an E-mail gateway between the TCP/IP world and the OSI X.400 MHS (mail handling system) world.

IBM AIX is built around the Carnegie Mellon University Mach operating system, a relatively small microkernel that is designed to handle critical functions such as interrupts, messaging, thread scheduling, and virtual memory. Other functions such as file management are modular and layered on top of the microkernel. These modules can be added and removed as necessary to accommodate changes and updates, or reduce memory requirements.

RELATED ENTRIES   IBM; IBM Networking Blueprint; Transaction Processing; *and* UNIX

Advanced National Radio Data Service (ARDIS)

ARDIS is a nationwide radio data communication service that enables field workers, using hand-held terminals from almost any location in 400+ metropolitan areas in the United States, to access centralized host computer applications. Portable, hand-held data terminals and similar devices with radio frequency (RF) modems can access the ARDIS system and communicate with home office systems. In 1993, service applications made up 80 percent of ARDIS's customer activity. Field technicians can use portable data terminals in their vehicles and at commercial and residential customer sites to access dispatch and diagnostic information as well as service call, service history, and parts availability data.

Competing services include cellular services such as GTE Mobilnet and similar offerings from the regional Bell operating companies (RBOCs). However, cellular networks were not designed to transmit data and are based on analog technologies used for voice transmissions. Cellular technology is also not as reliable for in-building communications as ARDIS.

ARDIS is a communications system developed by a partnership between IBM and Motorola. It was originally used by 15,000 IBM field engineers. IBM's Netview system and the Codex 9800 network management system are integrated so the health of the ARDIS network can be managed, all the way from the radio transmitter component on a remote rooftop to the modem attached to a host computer.

ARDIS provides a nationwide radio data communication service in which more than 1,250 radio base stations are deployed. They are typically co-located with their antennae on the tops of multistory buildings or on towers. They incorporate a 40-watt transmitter and operate in the 800 MHz band of frequencies. Depending on the antenna height and surrounding terrain, each site provides a coverage radius of 15 to 20 miles. Multiple sites providing overlapping coverage are deployed throughout a typical metropolitan area in order to provide wide-area coverage, and to penetrate buildings. The user has seamless access to the network while traveling, because all the base stations operate at the same frequency.

Base stations are connected to one of more than 30 radio network controllers located at various points across the U.S. via dedicated leased lines. Each controller is responsible for the radio communications in one or more metropolitan areas. Each controller holds registration information for terminals that are authorized to communicate on the network. The controllers also hold last-known-location information for terminals for message forwarding.

There are three network hubs, located in Chicago, Los Angeles, and Lexington, Kentucky. These hubs serve as the point of access to ARDIS for customer host applications. They also perform message routing, network management, and accounting/billing functions. The hubs are interconnected via dedicated leased lines with alternate communication paths for redundancy. Lexington is the primary operation center, but a duplicate center is maintained in Chicago for backup. Customers can connect to ARDIS either through dedicated leased lines to one of the hubs, or through a value added network (VAN).

RELATED ENTRIES   Mobile Computing; Radio Networks; *and* Wireless Mobile Communication

Advanced Peer-to-Peer Networking (APPN)

IBM's advanced peer-to-peer networking (APPN) was introduced by IBM in 1985 and integrated into Systems Network Architecture (SNA). It provides peer-to-peer networking services similar to but not quite the same as Transmission Control Protocol/Internet Protocol (TCP/IP). One of the main reasons IBM introduced APPN was to provide client-server computing services to users who might have moved to TCP/IP or other services. APPN is basically link-layer independent. It can run over token ring, Ethernet, Fiber Distributed Data Interface (FDDI), Frame Relay, Integrated Services Digital Network (ISDN), X.25, Synchronous Data Link Control (SDLC), and ultra high-speed networks such as B-ISDN and ATM.

APPN is based on the concept that computers on the network have enough processing power of their own to handle session management and routing. APPN moves various services from central control (such as that provided by a host mainframe computer), to decentralized control points that operate in a peer-to-peer relationship. In the old SNA model, a mainframe was required to control sessions. In the APPN model, user stations setup and maintain their own sessions.

APPN is part of IBM's revision to SNA and is often called the "new SNA." APPN is still tightly integrated with SNA and it uses the SNA LU 6.2 protocol that is formally marketed as APPC (advanced program-to-program communications). In addition, APPN implements a newer application interface, the Common Programming Interface for Communications (CPI-C). APPN is compared to Open Systems Interconnection (OSI) and TCP/IP in Figure A-1.

- *APPC*   Introduced in the early 1980s, APPC is also called LU 6.2. It is the application interface for APPN. By providing a way for applications on separate

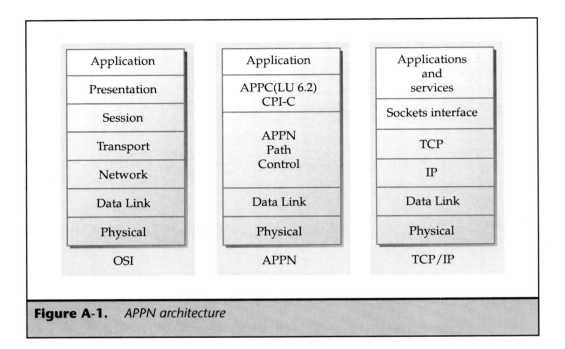

Figure A-1. *APPN architecture*

systems to communicate without involving a host system, APPC forged the way for APPN. It provided the shift away from centralized mainframe control and allowed programmable devices like computers to control their own sessions.

■ *CPI-C*   CPI is a set of application program interfaces (APIs) that provide a common environment for the execution of programs on different IBM platforms. Recently, IBM has implemented CPI-C in its Networking Blueprint and included support for OSI and TCP/IP protocols.

APPN provides routing services for APPC sessions. The routing environment consists of the following hierarchy as pictured in Figure A-2:

■ *End Nodes (ENs)*   An EN is a computer with its own operating system. It transmits information about itself and any locally attached resources to network nodes (NNs) when it logs into the network. The NN then holds this information and provides it to other nodes on the APPN network. This reduces the need to search every EN when establishing sessions. IBM mainframe and midrange computers as well as AIX or UNIX systems and desktop computers running OS/2 are end nodes. These systems can also be network nodes, as discussed next.

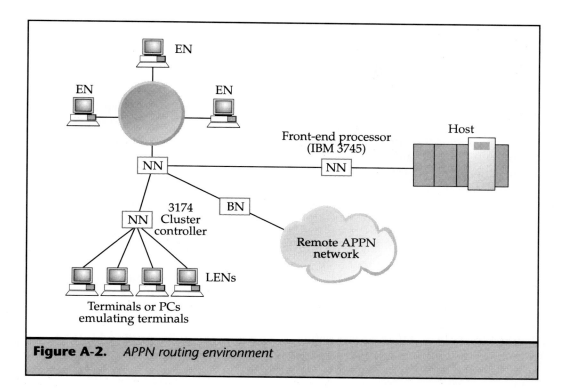

Figure A-2. *APPN routing environment*

- *Network Nodes (NNs)* An NN is a routing node that moves traffic between end nodes. NNs exchange routing information with other NNs about the topology of the network as changes occur. To conserve network bandwidth, only information about recent changes is exchanged, rather than entire routing tables. NNs also locate resources and store the resource information for later use. Thus, NNs serve as distributed depositories for information about the network. This caching feature "improves with age" as more routes are added to the list, reducing the number of required route searches. IBM 6611 routers and 3174 terminal controllers are devices that can serve as NNs.

- *Low-Entry Nodes (LENs)* An LEN can participate in a session with another LEN node on the network, but it requires the services of a network node to do so. This network node can be part of a local area network or directly connected to the LEN. PCs running DOS are examples of LEN nodes because they don't have the capability of operating as end nodes. OS/2, on the other hand, has full end-node capabilities.

- *Border Nodes (BNs)* Subdivision of an APPN network is possible if network broadcast becomes excessive. Division of the network isolates broadcast to specific subnetworks. The BN routes information among subnetworks.

APPN NNs dynamically locate resources on the network and store the routing information locally. In older SNA networks, network elements were defined in a Virtual Telecommunications Access Method (VTAM) table stored in a mainframe. In contrast, APPN networks can configure themselves using route discovery methods. NN work together to establish a path through a network so two end stations can set up a communication session. Each node contains a routing table used to establish the pathway for the link. One potential problem with APPN is that the selected path remains fixed for the duration of the session. If a node fails along the path, the session is not rerouted and fails as well. IBM plans to fix this with APPN+, also called High Performance Routing (HPR), by late 1994.

Applications establish sessions with other destination nodes on the network by accessing logical unit software interfaces that correspond roughly to OSI Session layer protocols. These high-level interfaces provide names for software entities that reside in ENs and NNs on the network. Note that applications go through logical units (LUs) to establish sessions, not directly to APPN. Basically, an LU in one station uses APPN services to locate a destination LU and set up a session. Think of LU sessions like pipes for transmitting data across the network from one application to another. Multiple applications can access a single LU, or applications can access multiple LUs.

High Performance Routing will provide enhanced router functions, support for gigabit-speed networks, and other services. Eventually, APPN may replace the hierarchical SNA architecture altogether. IBM's Networking Blueprint and Information Warehouse strategy already delegate host systems as back-end network "superservers."

RELATED ENTRIES   Advanced Program-to-Program Communications; IBM; Systems Application Architecture; *and* Systems Network Architecture, IBM

Advanced Program-to-Program Communications (APPC)

APPC is part of IBM's Systems Application Architecture (SAA). It is a session layer protocol, in relation to the Open Systems Interconnection (OSI) protocol model that allows separate programs running on different computers in an IBM Systems Network Architecture (SNA) network to communicate in a peer-to-peer mode. APPC is actually the marketing name—the actual protocol is called *LU 6.2*. This protocol represented a major strategy change for IBM when it was introduced. It demonstrated a shift in network control away from the centralized host systems to the systems that were attached to the network. Systems running LU 6.2 sessions do not need the services of a host system when establishing sessions.

LU 6.2 was developed to allow computers on the network with their own processing power to set up their own sessions. In the older hierarchical approach, terminals attached to host computers relied completely on the host to set up and maintain sessions. LU 6.2 provides peer-to-peer communications between systems other than hosts and allows those systems to run distributed applications like file sharing and remote access. The entire range of IBM platforms is supported by LU 6.2, including local area networks (LANs), desktop systems, and mainframes.

LU 6.2 relies on Systems Network Architecture (SNA) Type 2.1 nodes. Type 2.1 nodes are different than other SNA nodes in that they run Control Point (CP) software that allows them to engage in peer-to-peer connections with other Type 2.1 nodes. This arrangement became increasingly important as LANs were installed in IBM SNA environments. While the LAN provided a connection from a network node to a connected host, those LAN nodes could also use LU 6.2 to communicate directly with other LAN nodes, rather than go through the host.

Applications using the LU 6.2 protocols are called *transaction programs (TPs)*. Examples of TPs are IBM Distributed Data Management (DDM), which provides file sharing and database sharing among systems that implement DDM, and Document Interchange Architecture (DIA), which is a document exchange standard that defines searching, browsing, printing, and the distribution of documents.

A TP opens a session, performs data transfers, and closes. A TP performs a "unit of work" on a channel that interconnects IBM systems. The sessions are designed to be short lived because some systems cannot perform other tasks until they complete the transactions. A transaction is like a conversation, and a TP can hold multiple conversations with multiple systems. Each conversation has a name and buffers for sending and receiving data, along with a code that is returned to indicate success or failure of the transaction. The parameters are simple so code can be portable among systems.

Programs use LU 6.2 services through an interface called the *LU 6.2 Protocol Boundary* or through the Common Programming Interface for Communications (CPI-C). CPI-C is the current preferred method. CPI provides a common environment for the execution of programs on different IBM platforms, and the C version provides the LU 6.2 communication interface. Recently, IBM has implemented CPI-C in its Networking Blueprint, which supports OSI (Open Systems Interconnection) and Transmission Control Protocol/Internet Protocol (TCP/IP).

RELATED ENTRIES   Advanced Peer-to-Peer Networking; IBM; Systems Application Architecture; *and* Systems Network Architecture, IBM

Advanced Research Projects Agency Network (ARPANET)

ARPANET was a packet-switching network developed in the early 1970s. ARPANET was funded by ARPA (Advanced Research Projects Agency), which later became DARPA (Defense Advanced Research Projects Agency). The ARPANET network linked defense facilities, government research laboratories, and university sites. It evolved into the backbone of the Internet, and the term ARPANET was officially retired in 1990. However, ARPANET spurred the development of one of the most important protocol suites available today, Transmission Control Protocol/Internet

Protocol (TCP/IP). TCP/IP is a set of communications procedures and standards that provide a basis for interconnecting dissimilar computers.

DARPA was interested in interlinking the many different computer systems that were spread out across the country as part of the nation's research and development effort. DARPA's goal was to create a set of nonproprietary communications protocols that would make it easy to connect many different computers together. Much of the original work was done at the Massachusetts Institute of Technology, and with the help of companies such as Bolt, Beranek, and Newman, Inc. In 1980, the first TCP/IP modules were installed.

One of the most important aspects of TCP/IP's development was the program of testing and certifying carried out by the government to ensure that developers met published TCP/IP standards, which were (and still are) available to the public free of licensing arrangements. This ensured that developers did not alter the standard to fit their own needs, and possibly cause confusion in the rest of the TCP/IP community. Today, the use of TCP/IP protocols virtually assures interconnection, and in some cases, interoperability, among systems that use it for communications.

RELATED ENTRIES   Defense Advanced Research Projects Agency; Internet; *and* Transmission Control Protocol/Internet Protocol

ADVANTAGE-NETWORKS, DEC

ADVANTAGE-NETWORKS is Digital Equipment Corporation's program to integrate Open Systems Interconnection (OSI) standards as set by the International Organization for Standardization (ISO), Transmission Control Protocol/Internet Protocol (TCP/IP), and DECnet protocols. It is the basis of Digital's networking strategy for the 1990s while maintaining backward-compatibility with DECnet Phase IV. There are three main goals:

- Multivendor connectivity through the use of OSI and TCP/IP protocols
- Removal of addressing limitations so computer networks can support millions of nodes
- Management of very small to very large multivendor networks using a network management entity model that is modular and extensible

The ADVANTAGE-NETWORKS program gives Digital's customers the ability to build a single multivendor network using open system strategies. An open system is a vendor-neutral computing environment, compliant with international and de facto standards that permits system and network interoperability while maintaining a somewhat consistent user interface.

OSI SUPPORT   The ADVANTAGE-NETWORKS program provides support for OSI and Government OSI Profiles (GOSIP) with a wide variety of products, such as DECnet/OSI for ULTRIX (DEC's UNIX), DENnet/OSI for VMS, which provides

OSI-based products for VMS systems, and a variety of other products for local and wide area networking.

TCP/IP SUPPORT   The TCP/IP protocols suite is the predominant communications protocol used for multivendor network interconnection. It is the primary protocol of the Internet, which connects thousands of networks worldwide. Digital provides TCP/IP bundled in the ULTRIX operating system and includes the Network File System (NFS) with the package. Other products include DEC TCP/IP Services for VMS, PATHWORKS software for PC integration with ULTRIX or VMS systems via TCP/IP, and a variety of other networking products that provide TCP/IP support over local or wide area networks.

SNA SUPPORT   Digital provides Digital-to-IBM connectivity through a set of products that allow information flow between the two environments. The IBM MVS, VM, and VSE/SP operating environments are supported. The Digital IBM Interconnect products are made up of a series of gateways and access routines that support network transport, interactive access, information transfer, and database access.

DISTRIBUTED COMPUTING SUPPORT   Distributed computing gives users access to resources available throughout an enterprise network environment and minimize equipment costs, while giving users greater access to information. ADVANTAGE-NETWORKS supports the Open Software Foundation's distributed computing environment (DCE), which is a comprehensive integrated set of services that supports the development, use, and maintenance of distributed applications. DCE provides remote procedure calls (RPCs), threads, directory services, time synchronization, security, distributed file services, and other features as described in "Distributed Computing Environment, OSF."

WIDE AREA NETWORKING ENHANCEMENTS   ADVANTAGE-NETWORKS includes new routing software that supports the Integrated IS-IS (intermediate system-to-intermediate system) routing protocol, which is an enhancement of the adaptive routing capabilities in DECnet Phase IV. Additional wide area support includes enhanced X.25 services, efficient packet fragmentation and reassembly that maximizes the use of various circuit speeds throughout the network, and Multilink End Systems, which provides fault-tolerant networking with multiple circuits to a computer.

ADVANTAGE-NETWORKS also provides compatibility with the existing DECnet family of products and software. All DECnet Phase IV systems, applications, and network components function in the DECnet/OSI environment

RELATED ENTRIES   DECnet; Digital Equipment Corporation

Agent

In general, an *agent* is a background process that performs an action when an event occurs. In the realm of networking, an agent is part of a network management system that resides in workstations or other network devices (called *managed elements*) and collects information to report back to a management system about those devices. The management system runs at a central location, but in a distributed management system, management subsystems may reside at various points in the network to collect local information that is periodically collected by the main management system.

In the Simple Network Management Protocol (SNMP) system, which provides a tool for tracking workstations and compiling information about them, agents are called *network agents*. As shown in Figure A-3, these agents reside in routing and bridging devices and monitor activities on the network, such as packet transmissions, error conditions, and connections. The agents then make this information available to network management stations (NMSs). The NMS is the controlling device that gathers information from network agents, stores it in a management information base (MIB) on disk, and presents it to network administrators or supervisors for evaluation. Statistical information can show how the network is reacting to its current load and provide a way to detect potential problems.

RELATED ENTRY   Management Standards and Tools

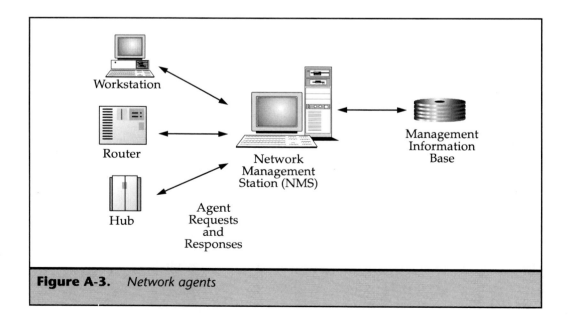

Figure A-3.   *Network agents*

Alpha AXP, DEC

Alpha AXP represents of family of computer systems developed and manufactured by Digital Equipment Corporation. The architecture is designed, according to Digital, to "last well into the 21st century." Specifically, Alpha AXP is a 64-bit, Reduced Instruction Set Computer (RISC) processor architecture. The 64-bit design allows addressing of up to 4 billion times more information than is possible with 32-bit systems. The first implementation is the DECchip 21064—currently the fastest processor in the industry. The chip has the following features:

- Fully pipelined and capable of issuing two instructions per clock cycle
- Capable of executing up to 400 million operations per second
- An 8-KB instruction cache
- An 8-KB data cache
- Two associated translation buffers
- Four-entry 32-byte/entry write buffer
- A pipelined 64-bit integer execution unit with 32-entry register file
- A pipelined floating-point unit with an additional 32 registers

The Alpha AXP architecture is not biased toward any operating system or language. The DEC OSF/1, OpenVMS AXP, and Microsoft Windows NT operating systems will work on the first generation of systems built around the architecture. Because these systems are industry standard, developers can use standardized application program interfaces (APIs) to create applications that are portable and interoperable for Alpha AXP and other systems. The Alpha AXP architecture is also scalable, meaning that it can be deployed at a range of levels, from desktop systems to servers to minicomputer/mainframe-capacity systems.

To ensure success of the new architecture, Digital has realigned its business practices with a new openness. DEC is licensing the Alpha AXP architecture and the operating systems that run on it. It has also developed partnerships with hardware and software companies that will develop Alpha AXP products. This policy should attract a broad range of applications and ensure that Alpha AXP systems are available in large numbers.

Alpha AXP systems from Digital include a range of desktop systems with a single DECchip 21064 processor running at 100 MHz to 150 MHz. The low-end model has an Extended Industry Standard Architecture (EISA) bus and holds from 16 MB to 128 MB of memory. Higher-end desktop systems use the TURBOchannel bus and have memory capabilities of 32 MB to 512 MB. A newer Alpha processor known as the DECchip 21066 has a built-in Peripheral Component Interconnect (PCI) bus and operates at 166 MHz with a peak performance of 330 million instructions per second (MIPS). The Intel 66 MHz Pentium is rated at 105 MIPS.

Computer room systems such as the Model 7000 and 10000 have from 1 to 6 DECchip processors running at 182 MHz to 200 MHz. These systems have a variety of bus options with up to 36 slots and support memory from 128 MB to 14 GB.

RELATED ENTRY   Digital Equipment Corporation

American National Standards Institute (ANSI)

ANSI is an organization that defines coding standards and signalling schemes in the United States and represents the United States in the International Organization for Standardization (ISO) and within the Consultative Committee for International Telegraph and Telephone (CCITT). ISO is the developer of the Open Systems Interconnection (OSI) model. The Institute of Electrical and Electronic Engineers (IEEE) has conforming standards in some cases. Several major ANSI specifications and standards are listed here:

- ANSI 802.1-1985 and IEEE 802.5 are specifications that define the access protocols, cabling, and interface for **token ring local area networks**. IBM made the standard popular.

- ANSI/IEEE 802.3 defines coaxial cable carrier sense multiple access/collision detection (CSMA/CD) **Ethernet networks**. 10Base5 is the thick cable Ethernet standard and 10Base2 is the thin cable Ethernet standard. 10BaseT is the twisted-pair, star-configured Ethernet standard.

- ANSI X3.135 is the **Structured Query Language (SQL)** specification that defines standardized data-base query methods for front-end clients and back-end database services.

- ANSI X3.92 is a standard that defines an **encryption algorithm** that creates privacy and security in data transmissions.

- ANSI X12 is the **electronic data interchange** (EDI) specification that defines how a company exchanges purchase orders, bills of lading, invoices, and many other transaction forms with its vendors.

- ANSI X3T9.5 is the **Fiber Distributed Data Interface (FDDI) specification** that defines 100 Mbits/sec transmissions over fiber-optic networks that have dual counter-rotating rings and a token-passing scheme. Copper wire may also be used as the medium, but distances are greatly reduced. FDDI supports up to 500 nodes over 2 kilometers. FDDI-I defines data networking while FDDI-II defines voice and data transmissions.

- The **Synchronous Optical Network (SONET)** is the ANSI specification for fiber-optic transmissions and defines a common global infrastructure for the transmission of synchronous and isochronous (time-sensitive data such as real-time video) information. SONET can transmit in the multimegabit and multigigabit range and provides for the insertion of lower-speed channels.

RELATED ENTRIES   IEEE Computer Society; IEEE 802 Standards; International Organization for Standardization; *and* Standards Organizations

American Wire Gauge (AWG)

AWG is a measurement system for wire that specifies its thickness. As the thickness of the wire increases, the AWG number decreases. Some common cable conductor gauges are listed here:

- RS-232 serial cable: 22 AWG and 24 AWG
- Telephone cable: 22 AWG, 24 AWG, and 28 AWG
- Coaxial thick Ethernet cable: 12 AWG
- Coaxial thin Ethernet cable: 20 AWG

Amplitude Modulation (AM)

In AM, a carrier signal is varied (modulated) in amplitude based on the data signal, which is usually an audio-frequency signal. The carrier signal maintains the same frequency, but its amplitude changes over time by the signal that is blended with it. A similar technique is used for AM radio broadcasting. To represent digital information using amplitude modulation, the signal is amplified with a voltage to represent a binary 1. The absence of the voltage or a negative voltage represents a binary zero, as shown in Figure A-4. AM is normally combined with phase modulation to improve data transfer rates.

RELATED ENTRY   Modulation Techniques

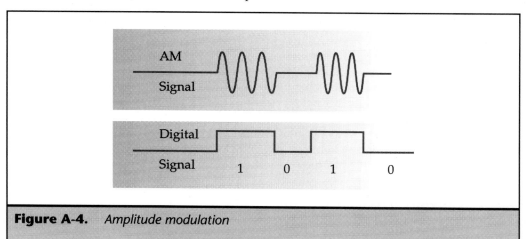

Figure A-4.   *Amplitude modulation*

Analog Signals

Analog values are *continuously* variable voltages or waves that can represent an infinite number of values within the range of the device that is producing, measuring, or recording the signals. Contrast this with the digital representation of analog values, in which a signal is recorded and converted to numeric values. The resolution of recorded signals depends on the amount of information collected and is limited by the recording technique.

RELATED ENTRIES   Analog-to-Digital Conversion; Signals, Analog and Digital; *and* Transmission Media, Methods, and Equipment

Analog-to-Digital Conversion (ADC)

ADC, or *digitizing,* converts analog waveforms to digital representations that can be processed and stored in computers. The analog wave is "sampled" or read hundreds or thousands of times per second to determine the position and value of the sound waves. Digital music requires extremely high sampling rates (44,100 samples/sec), while voice sampling is acceptable at 11,000 samples/sec or higher. There is also a factor that determines the precision of the captured signal—the more bits used to record the value of the sampled signal, the higher its resolution and the better its sound when played back; however, more disk space is required. For example, one minute of sampling at 44.1 KHz using 16 bits per sample (the compact disc specification) requires 5.292 MB of disk space.

Analog-to-digital converters are used in a variety of information processing applications. Information collected from an analog phenomena such as sound, light, temperature, and pressure can be digitized and made available for digital processing. A *codec* (coder/decoder) is the device that transforms the analog signals to digital signals. The process involves sampling, quantizing, and digitizing. The amplitude of a signal is measured at various intervals. The closer these intervals, the more accurate the recording. Figure A-5 illustrates how a wave is sampled 16 times per second, which implies a sampling rate of 16 hertz. While sampling at this rate is impractical for voice or music, it illustrates how each sample records a different amplitude value for the sound. Generally, a rate of 8,000 samples per second or higher using 8 bits per sample is adequate for voice quality signals. *Quantizing* is the process of replacing the sampled value with the nearest value within the range of the device and the sampling rate. Digitizing completes the process.

Scanners are devices that record the differences in dark and light areas in photographs and convert them to digital values. The picture becomes a matrix of dots, and each dot is represented in memory as a color or gray-scale value that can be displayed on a screen or transmitted to another device. Fax machines have built-in scanners.

RELATED ENTRY   Adaptive Differential Pulse Code Modulation

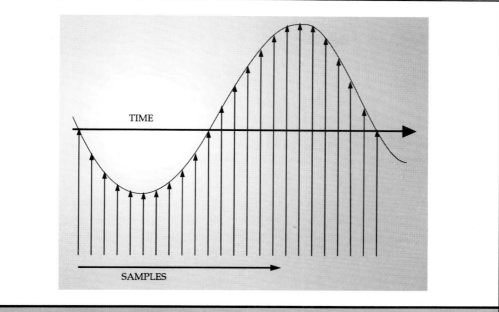

Figure A-5. *Analog-to-digital conversion*

Analog Transmission Systems

An analog transmission system can transmit information using continuously variable voltages or waves that represent an infinite number of values within the range of the device that is producing, measuring, recording, or transmitting the signal. A *channel* is a path that connects two or more points in a transmission system. In the analog telephone system, a channel is formed by a pair of twisted wires. Circuits in the "local loop" between the telephone company and user sites are either two-wire or four-wire. Channels can also be separated using multiplexing techniques, in which signals from several sources share a single wire.

Analog lines can transmit digital computer information by first converting the digital data to analog signals with a modem, or modulator-demodulator. A modem is required on both sides of the line. The modem at the sending system performs a digital-to-analog conversion, transmitting a modulated signal over the phone lines. The receiving modem converts the analog signal back to digital and sends them to the attached computer. In this arrangement, the computers are called data terminal equipment (DTE) and the modems are called data communications equipment (DCE). Today's modems employ a number of performance-improving techniques such as encoding and compression that boost data transfer rates.

Analog transmission methods have some problems that limit their usefulness in high-speed data transmissions:

- Analog lines are subject to transmission impairments that can distort signals. This requires error correction and detection mechanisms and data retransmissions that can reduce performance.

- Analog transmission in the telephone network has limited data transfer speeds. Digital transmissions can attain multimegabit transfer rates.

Applications such as imaging and video require higher bandwidth than analog services can provide, even with new modem signaling and compression techniques in place. This is where the high-speed carrier services come into play.

RELATED ENTRIES   Carrier Services; Digital Circuits and Services; Multiplexing; Signals, Analog and Digital; *and* Transmission Media, Methods, and Equipment

Andrew File System (AFS)

AFS was developed by the Information Technology Center (ITC) at Carnegie Mellon University; its current development and marketing is in the hands of Transarc Corporation. A version of AFS called the Distributed File System (DFS) is a component in the Open Software Foundation (OSF) Distributed Computing Environment (DCE). AFS is architecturally similar to the Network File System (NFS), but unlike NFS, AFS is designed for large-scale networks with thousands of users, so it relies heavily on the client to handle much of the processing load.

RELATED ENTRY   Distributed File Systems

Anonymous File Transfer Protocol (FTP)

On the Internet system, Anonymous FTP provides Internet sites that have information to share with a way to publish information for other network users to access. A host system is set up with an account called "anonymous," and this account usually doesn't have a password, so anyone can access it. Anonymous FTP is an extension of the FTP command. The Internet has an enormous amount of information available on Anonymous FTP servers, such as public domain software, abstracts, published papers, and other documents. There are reportedly over 1,500 Anonymous FTP hosts.

You can use the Archie system, which is an Internet resource discovery tool, to search for and list Internet Anonymous FTP sites, along with the resources available at each site. Files at Anonymous FTP sites can be downloaded using the FTP. The procedure is to use the FTP user's client program to connect with the desired Anonymous FTP host, then log on with the user name *anonymous* and the password *guest.* You can then use various file transfer commands or operating system features to list and download files on the system.

RELATED ENTRY   Internet

AnyNet, IBM

A series of IBM networking products that use the Multiprotocol Transport Network (MPTN) protocols. MPTN decouples applications from underlying transport protocols, removing the need for multiprotocol routers.

RELATED ENTRY   Multiprotocol Transport Network, IBM

Apple Computer

Apple Computer is the manufacturer of the Macintosh line of computers and developed the AppleTalk networking system that works over LocalTalk, EtherTalk, and TokenTalk. Apple is involved extensively in networking and distributed management. Its products are widespread and can be used as nodes on almost every available network operating system and topology. Apple's strategic networking goals and products are outlined here:

- *Virtually Integrated Technical Architecture Lifecycle (VITAL)* represents the key components of Apple's enterprise networking strategy. It outlines a plan for distributed client-server computing environments.

- *AppleTalk* is Apple's networking architecture and is built into every Macintosh computer.

- *AppleShare* is a centralized file server and print server operating system extension that provides shared files and resources to AppleTalk users. It is built on the AppleTalk protocols.

- *Macintosh System 7* is the latest version of the Macintosh operating system. It provides distributed file sharing services that operate in a peer-to-peer arrangement.

- *A/UX,* a UNIX environment, is the foundation for Apple's open-systems line of Macintosh workstations. It provides the familiar System 7 interface, but with a UNIX foundation.

- *Taligent* is the name of a company formed by Apple and IBM to develop an object-oriented operating system that is code-named Pink.

RELATED ENTRIES   Apple Open Collaborative Environment; AppleShare, AppleTalk; LocalTalk; *and* Virtually Integrated Technical Architecture Lifecycle

Apple Open Collaborative Environment (AOCE)

The AOCE is a set of technology available from Apple Computer that is designed to consolidate workgroups and workflow within a network environment. The environment is implemented as a set of application program interfaces (APIs) and software modules that let applications communicate with services. AOCE technology is a key component of Apple's Virtually Integrated Technical Architecture Lifecycle (VITAL) model. Common services are listed here:

- *Message exchange* between applications.

- *E-mail enabled applications* so users can send electronic mail from within their applications. A user can send an E-mail message while working in a word processor, thus eliminating the need to switch out of the word processor and start up the E-mail application.

- *Directory naming services* that store the names and locations of users and resources on the network, a sort of telephone book for the network. When addressing an E-mail message, for example, a user locates the name in the naming service. The naming service then appends all the pertinent addressing and routing information.

- *Authentication services* that verify logon and provide global access authorization for users.

- *Digital signatures* that allow users to attach legal electronic signatures to documents by dragging the document to a "signer" utility. Once signed and approved, the identity of the signer stays with the document. In addition, any alterations can be detected after the signature has been attached.

With these services available in system software, and the tools to implement them, software developers can quickly create collaborative applications that are built on AOCE's messaging, directory, and security infrastructure.

While AOCE will ensure the fast development of network-aware applications, from the users point of view, AOCE features will allow users to operate network and communications services from inside their applications and make workgroup collaboration easier. Users can execute multiple tasks at once from any application, and a common communications environment lets groups of users work together on projects. Group scheduling, document flow, and intergroup communications are handled by applications that are AOCE-compliant.

Apple envisions the following three types of applications growing out of its AOCE strategy:

- *Integrated Personal Communication* Applications that automate electronic mail, fax, and voice messaging. AOCE simplifies and consolidates the procedures for these tasks by placing appropriate commands on the Macintosh file menu. Users won't need to switch applications to perform these tasks.

■ *Workflow Automation* Workflow software imitates paper routing procedures by displaying electronic documents that need digital signatures for verification and processing. AOCE provides secure digital signature technology to enable these applications.

■ *Team Productivity* Applications that provide workgroup communications over wide areas. For these applications, AOCE provides a common directory of users and services that collaborative applications can share.

AOCE is available as an upgrade to Macintosh System 7 and as modules supplied by Apple or third-party software vendors. A series of products based on AOCE technology is being introduced for Apple Macintosh and Powerbook computers. AOCE-compliant products from other vendors are also available. Apple will also provide AOCE servers in which messaging, directory services, and authentication services can be centralized and provided to all network users so collaborative applications such as scheduling and project management can be implemented.

Similar environments are Digital Equipment Corporation's network applications support (NAS) and Microsoft's Windows Open System Architecture (WOSA).

AOCE Components

AOCE consists of many components that are arranged into three separate architectural layers, as pictured in Figure A-6. These layers are described in the following sections.

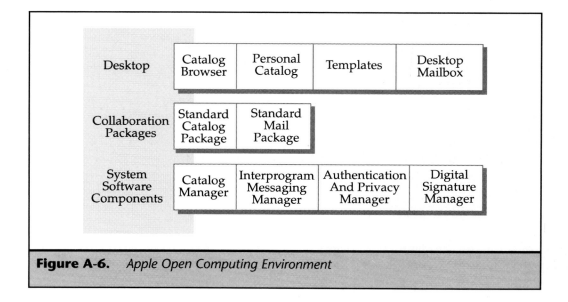

Figure A-6. *Apple Open Computing Environment*

System Software Component

The components at this level include the APIs that developers use to provide AOCE capabilities in their applications. The modules are described here:

- *Catalog Manager* provides access to many different types of directory storage systems.

- *Interprogram Messaging Manager* provides store-and-forward message delivery between programs.

- *Authentication and Privacy Manager* authenticates (verifies) the authenticity of users at the other end of a network connection, provides authentication of users accessing applications, and provides data encryption algorithms developed by RSA Data Security, Inc.

- *Digital Signature Manager* provides a way to attach an electronic signature to a document to verify its authenticity. AOCE's digital signature capability is based on public-key encryption technology provided by RSA Data Security. Inc.

Collaboration Packages

The collaboration packages provide the user interface elements for applications. The packages include the tools required to add dialog boxes and other interface elements as well as the access elements for electronic mail, digital signatures, and directory services. Two packages are currently available:

- *Standard Catalog Package* provides tools to create a standard interface for access directory services from within any Macintosh application.

- *Standard Mail Package* includes the tools to enable electronic-mail features in any Macintosh application through a standard interface called the *mailer*.

Desktop Capabilities

The desktop capabilities provided by AOCE include a catalog browser icon used to search for collaborative information, a personal catalog icon used to manage personal information for collaborative environments, a template icon used to customize the way information is displayed, and a mailbox icon used to manage electronic mail, faxes, and messages.

RELATED ENTRIES   Apple Computer; Distributed Computing; *and* Virtually Integrated Technical Architecture Lifecycle

AppleShare

Apple Computer provides AppleShare as its centralized server solution. AppleShare is built on the AppleTalk protocols and thus provides access to users over LocalTalk, EtherTalk, or TokenTalk physical network topologies. AppleShare is part of Apple's long-term commitment to enterprise computing. Another part of that commitment is defined by the Virtually Integrated Technical Architecture Lifecycle (VITAL) model, Apple's architecture for distributed client-server computing. While AppleShare is Apple's centralized file server software, Macintosh System 7 provides peer-to-peer networking services in which any system can share its data with other users on the network. AppleShare Server 3.0 was designed to work with Macintosh System 7.

AppleShare Server 3.0 is the latest version of AppleShare. It provides a range of functions, including file and printer sharing services. It has the following features:

- Operates concurrently in the same system with print services, administrative services, and electronic mail services.

- Supports 120 concurrent users.

- Provides queue services for up to five network printers.

- Provides security in the form of password access and file or folder locking. The network administrator can set various password features such as aging, and also set time limits on user accounts.

- Provides network administrators with accounting information, such as when users logged on and what resources they accessed.

- Can be combined with System 7 to provide an optimized file server environment that takes advantage of System 7's muiltitasking features, so administrators can install and run multiple network services such as electronic mail and management software.

Print Services

Print sharing in AppleShare is an extension of the printer-sharing features already available in AppleTalk. With AppleTalk, a printer can attach directly to a LocalTalk network and workstation users can access the printer without the need for a special print server. Users choose a network printer with the Chooser. On busy networks, System 6 and System 7 software can hold a file for printing if a printer is available, but a more practical method is to set up a separate print server.

AppleShare provides print services that can store print jobs from network nodes and queue the jobs to available printers. The software also provides features that let users or administrators view and change the queue, or defer printing to another time. Administrators can rearrange the queue to prioritize jobs or delete jobs in it. In addition, the network administrator can bypass the print server if necessary.

Administrative Features

AppleShare Server 3.0 includes a management program called AppleShare Admin. Admin contains network administrative tools that help network administrators create new user accounts and groups, administer system security, and establish volume and folder sharing privileges.

AppleShare allows up to 120 concurrent users to access the server at once and can maintain accounts for up to 8,129 users. Users can be placed in groups to simplify E-mail addressing and administrative functions. Groups also make it easier for users to interact with other users on the network. A user can belong to 42 groups.

While each workstation on an AppleTalk network has a specific station address, Macintosh computers and AppleShare let users address these systems by name. AppleShare includes the Namer application that administrators use to name devices on the network. AppleShare follows the Macintosh naming convention, which allows any character in a name of up to 32 characters except the colon. The administrator is usually responsible for naming hard disks and printers.

Logon Restrictions

Network administrators can control access to AppleShare resources. This is done through user accounts that require password logon. The password aging feature requires users to enter new passwords periodically. A history of recent passwords can be kept to prevent users from using a recent password. AppleShare can lock the account after a specified number of failures to prevent intruders from attempting to gain access by trying different passwords. The following is a list of the password management options that appear in the Admin program:

- Minimum number of characters in password
- Number of days until password expires
- Number of failed logon attempts before logon disabled
- Allow user to save password for automatic logon

Administrators can control the number of users that can access the server at any one time to prevent performance degradation. For the same reason, administrators can restrict the number of users starting a particular program. When the number of concurrent logons is restricted, users attempting to logon after the maximum value is reached see a message that the server is unavailable. Administrators can also log off any user at any time.

Administrators can also install a network startup service that allows Macintoshes to start from the server, providing more control over the work environment for users and the network.

Access Privileges

Access privileges let users view or change the files on the AppleShare Server. Administrators can set access privileges for any folder on a volume, while users can set privileges for the folder they own. By setting the privileges listed here, owners or administrators can share files with other users:

- *See Folders* This privilege lets other users see, but not change, the folders contained within a volume or within another folder.

- *See Files* This privilege lets other users see the files within a volume or folder, but not change them. However, users can copy the files to their own system and change them there.

- *Make Changes* With this privilege, users can change folders and their contents. This includes adding and removing information in a folder. It also includes moving, renaming, or deleting the folder. If a folder has this privilege only, it is a drop box and anything placed in it cannot be removed.

Administrators have unlimited rights and can override privileges set by users. If a folder is created without privileges, the folder is assigned the privileges of the folder in which it resides. The privileges of a folder change when the folder is moved into another folder. The new privileges assigned to it are called *inherited privileges*. However, explicit privileges can be assigned to override inherited privileges— they travel with the folder.

Administrator Messaging

AppleShare lets administrators send four messages to users of the AppleShare file server. These are messages that greet users when they log on and messages that warn of impending server shutdown or user disconnection. Administrators can also send a message to a specific user. It is important to follow proper shutdown or workstation disconnection procedures, which includes warning users so they can save open files and close their work in progress.

Accounting Features

Accounting functions let administrators collect data about user accounts, and use that data to monitor system usage and security. Administrators can also use the information to validate the need for new equipment in their budgetary requests. The Admin utility provides limited accounting features, but third-party packages are available if sophisticated auditing is needed in the AppleShare environment. The Admin program provides a log of the following:

- A list of drives and the space available on those drives

- A list of users and the groups they belong to

- A count of the files and folders belonging to each user and the amount of disk space they occupy

- Optionally, a complete list of file names and folders along with the owner names, access privileges, and locked status

RELATED ENTRIES   Apple Computer; AppleTalk; AppleTalk Filing Protocol; LocalTalk; Networks; *and* Peer-to-Peer Communication

AppleTalk

AppleTalk is a set of specifications that describe how to connect Apple Macintosh computers, printers, and other resources or computers into a communications network. AppleTalk is the architecture that defines a set of protocols used by devices to communicate over the network. Networking with the Macintosh is extremely simple because networking functions are built directly into the Macintosh. Originally, AppleTalk was designed to use the *LocalTalk cabling system*, but AppleTalk now supports Ethernet and token ring topologies. AppleTalk was also designed for small local workgroups, and so its performance is not adequate for large local area networks (LANs) and wide area networks (WANs), although some improvements have been made for WAN connections.

The LocalTalk cabling system consists of a set of simple connectors that attach to Macintosh systems and provide plug attachments for LocalTalk cable or telephone wire, as shown in Figure A-7. Transmission rates are a relatively slow 230.4 Kbits/sec, but the total installation cost is low since network adapter cards and workstation software are not required. LocalTalk was originally called AppleTalk, but Apple changed the name in 1989 to LocalTalk and now refers to the networking protocols as AppleTalk. Organizations that need higher-speed networks can install EtherTalk (Ethernet) or TokenTalk (token ring) network segments. Special adapters and cabling systems are required for these networks.

AppleShare is a centralized file-sharing system that runs on top of AppleTalk on a Macintosh system that has been dedicated for server use. Other Macintosh systems access AppleShare servers through the AppleShare Client module. Services provided

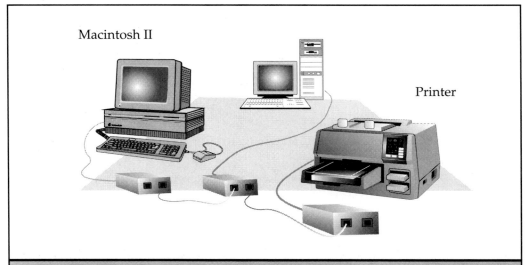

Figure A-7.   *LocalTalk cabling in an AppleTalk environment*

by AppleShare include file sharing, printer sharing, and electronic-mail handling. Additional modules such as management systems are available.

With the advent of the Macintosh System 7 operating system, peer-to-peer (distributed) file sharing became available in the AppleTalk environment, whether an AppleShare server is available or not. A user can share files with other users by designating which files to share and access files on other systems that have been shared. However, the file-sharing features in System 7 lack security and are somewhat deficient.

AppleTalk Basic Operation

Devices attached to AppleTalk networks dynamically assign themselves an address when first attached. The address is randomly selected from a range of allowable addresses. The address is then broadcast out over the network as a check to see if another device is already using the address. A device stores its selected address for use the next time it is turned on.

Node addresses are mapped to names that make the network easier to access by humans. When users want to access resources on the AppleTalk network, they do so by looking up the name of the resource using features of the Macintosh graphic interface. This makes it much easier to find exactly the printer you want to use or the user you want to send an electronic message to.

AppleTalk Phase 2 was introduced in 1989 with the primary addition of *extended addressing*. Extended addressing increases the node identification number from 8 bits to 16 bits on EtherTalk and TokenTalk networks only. This overcame the previous restrictions of 254 nodes per network and allowed up to 16 million nodes. LocalTalk is still limited to 254 nodes.

Zones are an important AppleTalk concept. They are logical areas that primarily exist to make access to resources easier for users. A zone may extend across multiple networks. The whole network of zones is collectively called an *internet*. Routers can separate networks into segments that become zones. The router is then responsible for keeping track of network addresses and the cable systems associated with them.

Zones make it easier for users to find services. For example, rather than seeing a list of all users on the network, you can view a list of users in your own zone, which might be a department, a workgroup, or the floor you work on. Zones are assigned names, such as Accounting or Sales and appear in the Macintosh Chooser when a user goes to search for someone or do research. Choosing a zone reveals the names of devices attached in the zone.

AppleTalk Protocol Suite

AppleTalk is a suite of protocols that stack one upon another into layers. Figure A-8 illustrates the AppleTalk protocols and how they are positioned in the protocol stack. Functions available at each layer are briefly described in the following sections, starting with the lowest physical layer and working up to the application layer.

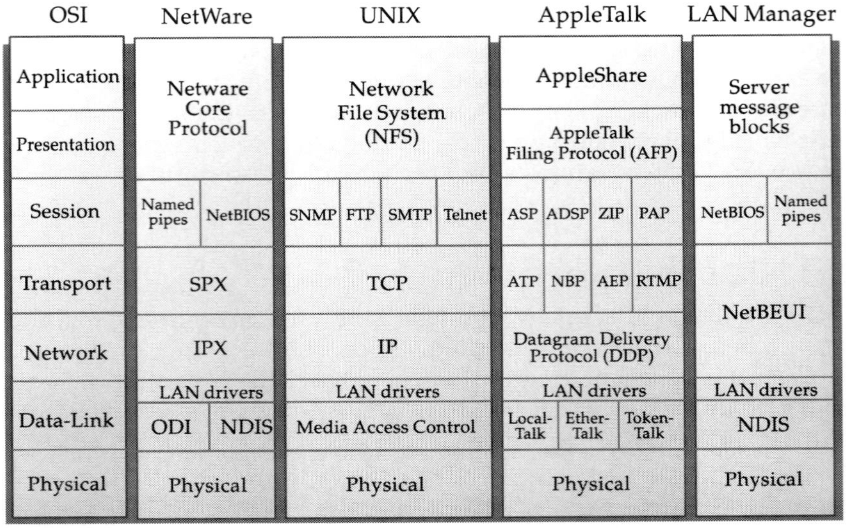

OSI	NetWare	UNIX	AppleTalk	LAN Manager
Application	Netware Core Protocol	Network File System (NFS)	AppleShare	Server message blocks
Presentation			AppleTalk Filing Protocol (AFP)	
Session	Named pipes / NetBIOS	SNMP / FTP / SMTP / Telnet	ASP / ADSP / ZIP / PAP	NetBIOS / Named pipes
Transport	SPX	TCP	ATP / NBP / AEP / RTMP	NetBEUI
Network	IPX	IP	Datagram Delivery Protocol (DDP)	
Data-Link	LAN drivers / ODI / NDIS	LAN drivers / Media Access Control	LAN drivers / Local-Talk / Ether-Talk / Token-Talk	LAN drivers / NDIS
Physical	Physical	Physical	Physical	Physical

Figure A-8. *AppleTalk protocol suite (compared to other suites)*

The Physical Layer

Physical layer specifications define hardware connections and access methods. Ethernet, token ring, and LocalTalk are defined in the AppleTalk physical layer. LocalTalk is a synchronous RS-422A communications system that encodes bits using frequency modulation (FM) 0 encoding. Unused ports on LocalTalk connectors are terminated with a 100-ohm resister.

Data-Link Layer Protocols

Link Access Protocols (LAPs) for each Ethernet, LocalTalk, and token ring reside in the Data-Link layer. The protocols for Ethernet and token ring are called EtherTalk and TokenTalk respectively; LocalTalk uses the carrier sense multiple access/collision avoidance (CSMA/CA) access method. Contentions for the cable are handled by an avoidance method

A LAP manager in the Data-Link layer is responsible for hiding the type of network in use from upper protocols. It packages data packets produced by upper protocols for transmission over whatever network the workstation is attached to.

Network Layer Protocols

Protocols in the network layer package data for delivery over the network and send it to the LAP manager in the Data-Link layer. The Datagram Delivery Protocol (DDP)

exists in this layer. It packages up to 586 bytes of data in a datagram, inserts addresses and error-checking information in a packet header, and forwards the packet to the LAP manager. The DDP packet contains a hop count that increments every time a packet passes through a router. The maximum count is 15.

Transport Layer Protocols

The transport layer contains four protocols, each of which is described in the following sections.

- *Routing Table Maintenance Protocol (RTMP)* This protocol is responsible for maintaining address tables and communicating with other routers about the status of the network. This protocol is inefficient on WANs because it sends entire tables across the WAN. A new version called AppleTalk Update Routing Protocol (AURP) reduces the amount of updating that takes place over a WAN connection.

- *AppleTalk Echo Protocol (AEP)* This is responsible for determining whether a destination node is available for a communications session before it begins. The destination node returns an *echo* datagram to the sender with a response.

- *AppleTalk Transaction Protocol (ATP)* This is responsible for three types of transactions. A transaction *request* (TREQ) and a transaction *response* (TRESP) work together, while a transaction *release* (TREL) closes a transaction session when it is complete. TREQ and TRESP can determine whether requests are lost or delayed, or whether the responder is unreachable.

- *Name Binding Protocol (NBP)* This is responsible for translating the numeric internet address of a node into a named entity. NBP can broadcast packets over the network to locate the network address that matches the named entity. Nodes listen for the packet and search their name tables, then respond when a match is found.

Session Layer Protocols

The main purpose of protocols in the session layer is to establish and maintain communications sessions between two nodes. AppleTalk contains four protocols in this layer, as described here:

- *AppleTalk Data Stream Protocol (ADSP)* This protocol manages data transmission between two sockets on separate machines, providing a full-duplex byte-stream if necessary. With full duplex, both computers can transmit at the same time. Once a connection is established, ADSP manages the flow of data.

- *AppleTalk Session Protocol (ASP)* This is responsible for opening and closing sessions between two nodes and transmits session commands as necessary. ASP called on NBP to obtain node addresses and ATP to provide transport services for its packets.

■ *Printer Access Protocol (PAP)* This protocol is responsible for maintaining communication between a user's workstation and a printer.

■ *Zone Information Protocol (ZIP)* This protocol works with RTMP to maintain a mapping of the network. It creates Zone Information Tables (ZITs) in routers that define network numbers and zone names.

Presentation Layer Protocols

Protocols defined in this layer are related to file translations, file formatting, data encryption, and data compression. The AppleTalk Filing Protocol (AFP) provides access to remote files on the shared disks of network servers. AFP uses ASP in the session layer to establish a communications session, then relies on ADSP to ensure the accuracy of file transfers of the network.

Application Layer

The applications layer does not have protocols of its own. It is where applications reside that interact with the lower protocols in the stack. Depending on the user's interaction, the application makes requests for services from other systems or resources and passes those requests to the presentation layer.

AppleTalk Phase 2

Originally, AppleTalk was designed for LocalTalk, a relatively low-speed transmission medium. Support for Ethernet and token ring were added later. A set of separate LocalTalk LANs can be interconnected with routers, thus forming an internet. Each network segment in the internet can have its own cable type.

To route data packets between LAN segments, an addressing system is used that uniquely identifies each node. AppleTalk consists of older addressing techniques and newer extended addressing techniques that were introduced in 1989 with AppleTalk Phase 2. The old scheme used 8 bits for the address and allows 254 stations per network.

AppleTalk Phase 2 added support for 16 million nodes and enhanced AppleTalk for large networks. The most important aspect of AppleTalk Phase 2 network system enhancements were the AppleTalk Internet Router and the addition of hardware/software support for Ethernet and token ring.

Problems associated with AppleTalk relate to the fact that the networks start small, then grow large or require interconnection with other AppleTalk networks. Joining two networks often causes duplicate address problems that must be resolved. Other problems are related to AppleTalk's routing protocols, although these were improved with Phase 2. The older AppleTalk Routing Table Maintenance Protocol (RTMP) sent full routing information tables (often up to 1 MB in size) every 10 seconds. With only a few devices on the network, this strategy was not a problem, but with large interconnected networks, performance problems were excessive due to this overhead.

In 1992, Apple improved RTMP by providing a routing protocol called AppleTalk Update-Based Routing Protocol (AURP). While RTMP is sufficient for small LANs, it is inefficient for WAN connectivity. AURP does not replace RTMP, but complements it. The main difference between the two is that, as long as the internet is stable, there is little or no routing update traffic over the AURP link. With AURP, routing information is transmitted only when changes actually occur on the internet and only the changes are sent. AURP also automates the mapping of addresses which helps eliminate duplicate addresses when two AppleTalk networks are joined.

AppleTalk routes in an internetwork are selected based on the least number of hops a packet must make to reach its destination. AURP provides an improved routing mechanism and a way to encapsulate AppleTalk into Transmission Control Protocol/Internet Protocol (TCP/IP) or Open Systems Interconnection (OSI) packets. It is possible that Apple will replace AURP with a link-state routing algorithm like Open Shortest Path First (OSPF) or OSI's Intermediate System-to-Intermediate System (IS-IS).

RELATED ENTRIES   Apple Computer; AppleShare; AppleTalk Filing Protocol; LocalTalk; *and* Networks

AppleTalk Filing Protocol (AFP)

AFP resides in the presentation and application layers of the AppleTalk protocol stack. AFP lets users communicate with AppleTalk file servers. It passes user commands down to lower-layer protocols that handle establishing connections and monitoring data flow between systems. AFP has the following features:

- AFP sets up an environment for a user that appears as if files on a remote file server are available locally.

- Access to server files is handled using the same procedures as access to local files, except that a user must initially establish a connection to the remote file server.

- AFP provides security features that can restrict user access to files.

AppleShare is based on AFP. Macintosh systems can access AppleShare servers through built-in AppleShare Client software. Macintosh System 7's File Sharing utility adds distributed files service features by allowing users to access files on other users systems or make files on their own system available to other users.

RELATED ENTRIES   Apple Computer; AppleShare; *and* AppleTalk

Apple VITAL

This is Apple's distributed network computing model. It defines how users in workgroups share information with other users and access a variety of resources on the network.

RELATED ENTRY   Virtually Integrated Technical Architecture Lifecycle

Application Layer, OSI Model

The application layer is part of the Open Systems Interconnection (OSI) model. The OSI model guides software developers and hardware vendors in the design of network communications products. When two systems need to communicate, they must use the same network protocols. The OSI models divide protocols in seven layers, with the lowest layer defining the physical connection of equipment and electrical signalling. The highest layer defines how an application running on one system can communicate with an application on another system. Middle layers define protocols that set up communication sessions, keep sessions alive, provide reliable delivery, and perform error checking to ensure that information is transmitted correctly. See "Open Systems Interconnection Model" for more information on the complete OSI stack.

The application layer is the top layer in the OSI protocol stack. Applications that provide network features reside at this layer and access underlying communication protocols. Examples include file access and transfer over the network, resource sharing, and print services. The OSI model specifies that applications must provide their own layer 7 protocols. The OSI File Transfer, Access, and Management (FTAM) utility and the X.400 electronic mail standard provide services at the application layer.

RELATED ENTRIES   Layered Architecture; Open Systems Interconnection Model; *and* Protocol Stack

Application Program Interface (API)

The API is the language and messaging format that defines how programs interact with functions in other programs, with communications system, or with hardware drivers. For example, tasks such as accepting user input, writing information to the screen, or managing files are handled by a computer operating system. The APIs for that operating system provide the program with the interface to communicate with it. If a graphical user interface like Microsoft Windows is used, a set of APIs is available for integrating pull-down menus, icons, scroll bars, and other features in programs. On networks, APIs provide interfaces to network services. These APIs communicate with protocols that are at lower levels in the protocol stack used by the network. In database management systems, APIs bind the user applications with the data management system.

Programmers see APIs as a set of routines they can use to quickly build programs to a specific system. A cross-platform API defines programming commands that can be used to develop applications that work on many different operating systems. An operating system-based API is defined for use on only one operating system. The OS-based API is more adaptable to the front-end applications of client-server computing, while cross-platform APIs are more useful for back-end server

A

applications. Because of the growing importance of distributed computing and client-server applications, cross-platform APIs are growing.

There are three types of APIs for communications between applications and communications between applications and servers in a client-server environment. These are the *conversation, remote procedure call (RPC),* and *message* APIs. IBM's Advanced Program-to-Program Communications (APPC) model is conversational. RPC models have been developed by Sun Microsystems and the Open Software Foundation (OSF). Messaging models, such as the *Message Queuing Interface (MQI)* in IBM's Networking Blueprint, are growing in popularity in distributed environments.

The OSF Distributed Computing Environment (DCE) provides tools that developers can use to create distributed applications that work with a variety of back-end systems and front-end clients. Cross-platform E-mail APIs like Vendor Independent Messaging (VIM) from Lotus and Common Mail Calls (CMC) allow developers to create mail applications that work on many different platforms and share mail among platforms. Microsoft's Messaging Applications Programming Interface (MAPI) was originally designed as a cross-platform API, but Microsoft then developed it as a distinct Windows-based API. Microsoft's direction is to support CMC.

A UNIX API called Common Open Software Environment (COSE)—sponsored by Hewlett-Packard, IBM, SunSoft Inc, Santa Cruz Operation, and Novell—will define interoperability of desktop computing, networking, graphics, multimedia, object technology, and system management applications across the vendors' UNIX environments.

RELATED ENTRIES   Database Connectivity APIs and Middleware; Distributed Computing Environment, OSF; Messaging API, E-mail; Messaging API, Inter-Application; *and* Remote Procedure Call

Archiving

Archiving defines the process of moving files to a near-line or offline storage device, usually a magnetic tape or optical disk system. Files that are candidates for archives are those that are rarely accessed or never accessed. In addition, imaged documents are candidates for offline storage. All of these files are stored for historical reasons. In contrast, backups are duplicate file copies on magnetic disk, made to protect current data from disasters.

Archived files often remain available to users, depending on the system used, although access to those files is slower than access to files on magnetic storage. The storage medium must remain attached to the network and requires a management software system that can locate archived files and make them available to users. When a user requests a file, it is moved online, which can take a few seconds, especially if the file is on a disk that must be mounted by an autochanger device.

The Novell High Capacity Storage System (HCSS) is an archiving system that "migrates" files that have been flagged by an administrator to an offline optical jukebox storage device. A list of these files remains available to users in a special directory, and the files appear as if they are still stored online. If a user needs a migrated file, he or she simply accesses the file as normal. The HCSS system demigrates the file to magnetic disk where the user can access it. Except for a slight access delay, the user may be unaware that an archived file has been accessed. After a certain period, the file is de-migrated back to optical disk.

Archiving systems are ideal for the insurance, legal, and medical industries, which typically handle large numbers of documents and must have those documents available at any time to check records or case histories. Archiving systems also figure into document imaging systems.

RELATED ENTRIES   Backup and Data Archiving; Hierarchical Storage Management Systems; Imaging; *and* Optical Libraries

ARCNET

The Attached Resource Computing Network (ARCNET) is a baseband, token-passing network system that offers flexible star and bus topologies at a low price. Transmission speeds are 2.5 Mbits/sec. ARCNET uses a token-passing protocol on a token bus network topology, but ARCNET itself is not an IEEE standard. ARCNET was developed by Datapoint in 1977 and was licensed to other companies. In 1981, Standard Microsystems Corporation (SMC) developed the first single-chip LAN controller based on the ARCNET token-passing protocol. In 1986, a new chip set supporting bus topology was introduced. Most industry-standard ARCNET configurations are now based on the new chip set technology.

A typical ARCNET configuration is shown in Figure A-9. Although ARCNET is generally considered to have a slow throughput, it does support cable lengths of up to 2,000 feet when using active hubs. It is suitable for office environments that use text-based applications and where users don't often access the file server. Newer versions of ARCNET support fiber-optic and twisted-pair cable. Because its flexible wiring scheme allows long trunks, and because you can have star configurations on the same local area network (LAN), ARCNET is a good choice when speed is not a factor but price is. In addition, the cable is the same type used to connect IBM 3270 terminals to IBM mainframes and may already be in place in some buildings.

ARCNET provides a robust network that is not as susceptible to failure as coaxial cable Ethernet if cable comes loose or is disconnected. This is partly due to its topology and partly due to its slow transfer rate. If the cable that attaches a workstation to a hub is disconnected or cut, only that workstation goes down, not the entire network. The token-passing protocol requires that every transaction be acknowledged, so there is virtually no chance of errors, although throughput is much slower than other networking schemes.

In Figure A-9, note the flexibility in workstation cabling arrangements. First, ARCNET is a distributed star topology, which means that workstations attach to hubs and hubs can attach to other hubs. This arrangement is well suited to multistory office

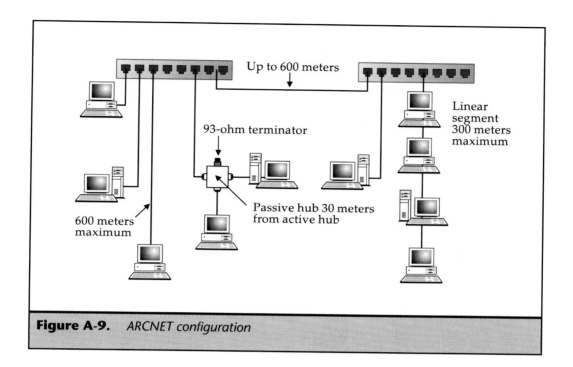

Figure A-9. *ARCNET configuration*

layouts in which long trunks provide connections between floors and departments. Departments are then wired in a star configuration that branches from active or passive hubs. The ability to connect groups of workstations with one single trunk provides cost savings.

Despite ARCNET's flexibility, it never caught on as a major networking product like Ethernet and token ring, partly because it was never standardized and marketed by major companies. However, several ARCNET vendors recently announced ARCNET Plus, a 20 Mbits/sec version of ARCNET that is compatible with 2.5 Mbits/sec ARCNET. Both versions can be on the same LAN. Basically, each node advertises its transmission capabilities to other nodes so that if a fast node needs to communicate with a slow node, it steps down to the slower speed for the extent of that session. ARCNETplus supports larger packet sizes and eight times as many stations. Another new feature is the ability to connect with Ethernet, token ring, and Transmission Control Protocol/Internet Protocol (TCP/IP) networks using bridges and routers. This is possible because the new version supports the IEEE 802.2 logical link control standard.

The components that are typically part of a standard ARCNET network are described in the next sections.

NETWORK INTERFACE BOARD   ARCNET boards are available from many vendors, including Standard Microsystems Corporation and Thomas-Conrad. Standard coaxial boards should have a BNC connector attached to the back. When ARCNET is configured as a linear bus, T-connectors are used on the cards, and jumpers must be set to specify the configuration. If the card is installed in a diskless workstation, a remote-boot chip must be installed on the card. ARCNET interface boards have a dip switch on which you set the node address for the workstation. You must assign each node on the network a unique address in the range of 1 to 255. It is important to write this station number on the outside faceplate of each card as well as in a log book, in case you want to add more stations. The lowest numbered station broadcasts a permission token to each workstation, which grants them permission to access the cable. Other stations then access the cable based on their address numbers.

ACTIVE HUB   An *active hub* is a network relay that conditions and amplifies the signal strength. Workstations can be a maximum of 2,000 feet from active hubs. Most active hubs have eight ports to which workstations, passive hubs, or additional active hubs can be attached. It is not necessary to terminate unused ports on an active hub since they are self-terminating.

PASSIVE HUB   A *passive hub* is a four-port connector with BNC jacks that is used as a wiring center and simple signal splitter. Workstations cannot be further than 100 feet from a passive hub. Each unused port on a passive hub must be terminated. Figure A-10 illustrates a three-station network using a passive hub.

ARCNET CABLING   The standard cabling used for ARCNET is 93-ohm RG-62 A/U coaxial cable, although many vendors provide twisted-pair and fiber-optic cable. A configuration that uses fiber-optic cable backbones between active hubs and for

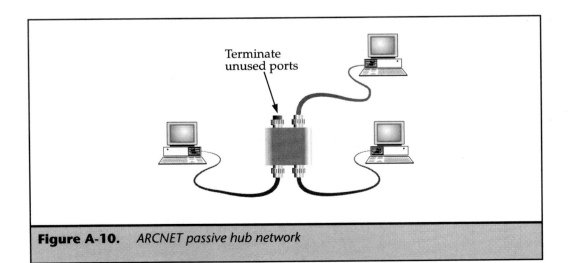

Terminate unused ports

Figure A-10.   *ARCNET passive hub network*

outside runs is possible. You attach coaxial cable segments to active hubs, passive hubs, and network interface cards with BNC-type connectors. ARCNET coaxial cable is available from many vendors who have precut standard lengths ready to ship. Bulk cable is also available, but you must mount the BNC connectors yourself using a coaxial cable stripping and crimping tool, which are available from cable suppliers. Note that cable is available as firesafe plenum cable, nonplenum interior cable, underground rated cable, and aerial rated cable. If dissimilar media are used, you'll need appropriate media connectors.

BNC COAXIAL CONNECTORS   Connectors can be purchased to mount on the ends of specially cut bulk cable. The BNC coaxial connector kits include a center pin, a housing, and a clamp-down sleeve.

BNC T-CONNECTORS   A T-connector is attached to the BNC connector on the back of an ARCNET interface card when it is used in a bus topology. The T-connector provides two cable connections for signal-in and signal-out. You will need a T-connector for each workstation, plus two for each repeater being used.

BNC TERMINATORS   A 93-ohm BNC terminating cap must be placed on all passive hub ports that are not in use.

The following rules and limitations apply to ARCNET networks:

- Most active hubs have eight nodes. Workstations on active hubs can extend as far as 600 meters (2,000 feet) from the hub.

- You can connect active hubs to form a hierarchical configuration. The maximum distance between two active hubs is 600 meters (2,000 feet).

- Up to three workstations can be grouped around a four-port passive hub. One connection leads back to an active hub or file server. Each workstation cannot be farther than 30.5 meters (100 feet) from the hub.

- Passive hubs cannot be connected to other passive hubs. They can attach to active hubs at a maximum distance of 30.5 meters (100 feet).

- You must terminate unused nodes on passive hubs with 93-ohm terminator caps.

- The maximum distance between stations at opposite ends of a multisegment network is 20,000 feet, about 4 miles.

- When stations are wired in a bus configuration, the maximum trunk length of the bus segment is 305 meters (1,000 feet).

- The maximum number of stations is 255.

Problems with ARCNET networks are relatively easy to isolate. They are sometimes related to the absence of terminating resistors, or duplication of network addresses. So check those items first. Also check the lights on hubs to make sure station connections are working. The problem might be a faulty active or passive hub, or a faulty network interface card. You can isolate these problems by segmenting the network, which involves disconnecting cables from a hub and adding terminators where necessary. If the problem clears up, you've located the branch that is having a problem. If not, you need to segment the network in another place and continue this process until you've located the problem. Replace defective network interface cards, cable segments, or hubs, as necessary. Of course, most ARCNET vendors provide network management software that can more easily detect faulty network nodes and other problems.

ARCNET Frame Formats

ARCNET packets have five different types of frame formats as specified in the ARCNET protocol. All the frames start with an alert burst that contains six binary ones. The data packet frame is illustrated in Figure A-11. The frames are summarized here:

■ The invitation to transmit (ITT) is the token frame. Workstations obtain the token when they want to transmit.

■ The free buffer enquiry (FBE) frame determines whether a destination node can accept data from the transmitting node.

■ The acknowledgment (ACK) frame is a positive response to an FBE.

■ The negative acknowledgment (NAK) frame, which a destination node sends to a transmitting node to indicate it can't receive.

■ The data packet frame, as pictured in Figure A-11, holds the data being transmitted, along with the source and destination address, and error checking information.

RELATED ENTRIES   Networks; Topology

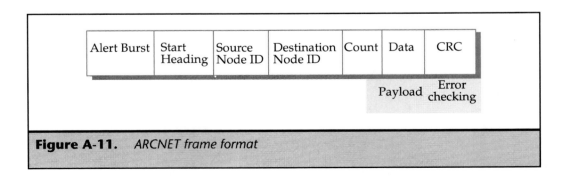

Figure A-11.   *ARCNET frame format*

ARPANET

The first packet-switched network. It offers datagram services in which packets are sent along varying routes through a mesh of network connections.

RELATED ENTRIES   Advanced Research Projects Agency Network; Internet

Artisoft LANtastic

See LANtastic

Asymmetrical Digital Subscriber Line (ADSL)

ADSL can transmit digital signals over the existing copper-based lines that provide telephone service at speeds as high as 1.544 Mbits/sec (T1) in one direction. It opens the possibility for services such as video-on-demand, interactive information, telecommuting, and tele-education to home and business users.

This service is under development and was initiated after the Federal Communications Commission (FCC) rules in July of 1992 that telephone companies could transmit video entertainment into the home. Along with the standard line, ADSL permits a low-speed connection of 16 Kbits/sec to 64 Kbits/sec for the transmission of program and menu functions. This second channel is a return datastream that lets users enter keyboard and data input.

ADSL has been an American National Standards Institute (ANSI) study project in the T1E1.4 working group. It is seen as an interim step to fiber-optic cabling. The first trials took place in early 1993 by Bell Atlantic. As of this writing, three encoding techniques were proposed—16-point quadrature amplitude modulation (QAM), carrierless amplitude/phase modulation (CAP), and discrete multitone (DMT). QAM and CAP are passband technologies that can provide different services like voice and video on the same wire, using frequency multiplexing. DMT is a method under development that attempts to reduce line noise.

ADSL is related to Integrated Services Digital Network (ISDN) and High bit-rate Digital Subscriber Line (HDSL), which both support symmetric two-way communication. HDSL is available now. Some experts see "copper-boosting" technologies like HDSL and ADSL as a method for phone companies to compete with cable companies in the home entertainment business. A third encoding scheme, called Very High bit-rate Digital Subscriber Line (VHDSL), can provide 3- to 6-Mbits/sec service over two twisted pairs.

Asymmetrical Multiprocessing

Computer systems with multiple processors can utilize the processors in one of two ways. In *asymmetrical* multiprocessing, each CPU is dedicated to a specific function, such as network interface card input/output (I/O), or file operations. In *symmetrical* multiprocessing, which is generally agreed to be superior to asymmetrical multiprocessing (but harder to implement), any CPU can handle any task if it is available to do so. Depending on the operating system and/or applications, tasks can be split up and simultaneously handled by multiple processors. Microsoft Windows NT and other new-generation operating systems perform symmetric multiprocessing.

RELATED ENTRY   Multiprocessing

Asynchronous Communications

A form of communication in which information is transmitted as a serial stream of bits. Each character is coded as a string of bits and separated by a "start-of-character" bit and "stop" bit. A parity bit is sometimes used for error-detection and correction. Asynchronous implies that a timing mechanism such as a clock is not used to synchronize events between the sender and the receiver, such as the start of a new character. In contrast, synchronous communication relies on a clocking mechanism to separate groups of bits. Synchronous communication is more efficient since the bits of one character follow the bits of another. Start and stop bits are not required.

This start-stop mode of transmission means that transmission starts over again for each new character, which eliminates any timing discrepancies that may have occurred during the last transmission. When discrepancies do occur, error detection and correction mechanisms can request a retransmission.

Asynchronous transmissions can take place between two nearby computers by connecting a null-modem cable between the asynchronous communications ports of each computer. If computers are at distant locations, a modem is required on each end to convert computer digital signals for transmission over analog phone lines. Asynchronous transmission can take place at speeds up to 28,800 bits/sec over normal switched (dialup) or leased telephone lines. Rates up to 38,400 bits/sec are possible over directly connected systems or by using data compression.

A channel is a single communication path between two communicating devices that is created by physical connections or by multiplexing techniques. A circuit is an actual physical connection that provides a communication channel. The dialup phone system provides circuits for channel communication between two systems. A *simplex* circuit is a unidirectional transmission path that transmit signals in one direction. A *half-duplex* circuit is a bidirectional transmission path that provides transmission in both directions, but only one direction at a time. A *full-duplex* circuit is a bidirectional transmission path that can transmit both ways at the same time.

Error Correction Methods

All transmission media are susceptible to interference and problems introduced by the medium itself, such as current resistance and signal attenuation. Outside interference may be introduced by background noise, atmospheric radiation, machinery, or even faulty equipment. As transmission rates increase, the number of bits affected by disturbances increases because there are more bits involved in the time frame of the disturbance. To correct these problems, error detection and correction methods are used.

In parity checking, the numbers of 1s in groups must always be the same, either even or odd, to indicate that a group of bits was transmitted without error. Checking on a per-character basis is called vertical redundancy checking (VRC). Checking on a block-by-block basis is called longitudinal redundancy checking (LRC). Both systems must agree on the parity method before transmission begins. There is even parity (number of 1s must be even), odd parity (number of 1s must be odd), space parity (parity bit is always 0), and mark parity (parity bit is always 1).

Newer modems provide advanced error checking and correcting methods that are much more practical and efficient than those just discussed.

Interface Standards

The connections used for asynchronous communication are defined in the physical layer of the Open Systems Interconnections (OSI) reference model. This layer defines specifications related to connector types, pin-outs, and electrical signalling. Standards such as RS-232, RS-449, CCITT V.24, and others define these interfaces for various requirements.

RELATED ENTRIES   Modems; Modulation Techniques; Serial Communication; Synchronous Communication; *and* "V-dot" Standards, CCITT

Asynchronous Transfer Mode (ATM)

ATM is a data transmission technology that has the potential to revolutionize the way computer networks are built. Viable for both local and wide area networks, this technology provides high-speed data transmission rates and supports many types of traffic including voice, data, facsimile, real-time video, CD-quality audio, and imaging. The carriers such as AT&T and US Sprint are already deploying ATM over a wide area and offering multimegabit data transmission services to customers. Over the 1994 to 1995 time frame, ATM products will emerge from almost every hardware vendor to provide:

- ATM routers and ATM switches that connect to carrier ATM services for building enterprise-wide global networks.

- ATM devices for building internal private backbone networks that interconnect all the local area networks (LANs) within organizations.

- ATM adapters and workgroup switches for bringing high-speed ATM connections to desktop computers that run emerging multimedia applications.

ATM takes advantage of the high data throughput rates possible on fiber-optic cables. In the carrier systems, high-speed ATM implementations (155 Mbits/sec to 622

Mbits/sec) use the Synchronous Optical Network (SONET), which is implemented on optical cable and provides a common global telecommunication standard. While fiber networks implementing ATM are built for the public telecommunication systems, ATM is also considered an appropriate technology for private internal switching networks that reach all the way to the desktop. As ATM becomes more established and competition for customers increases, it is probable that 155 Mbits/sec ATM boards will be common in desktop multimedia computers by the middle of the decade. With the number of vendors getting into ATM, competition will surely be fierce.

Current LAN technology does not provide enough bandwidth for the enterprise-wide use of emerging applications such as multimedia and real-time video. The latter requires data transmission capabilities in which a certain amount of bandwidth must be guaranteed to prevent dropouts that appears as jittery images. Shared LAN media like Ethernet can quickly become saturated with traffic loads that prevent real-time applications from getting their transmissions through on a timely basis. ATM can handle real-time applications, because of its high bandwidth, its ability to dedicate a certain bandwidth to an application, and its fixed-size packets (called cells).

ATM has the potential to become the standard data transmission method that replaces most of today's voice and communications devices with ATM switching devices. It is interesting to note that during early standardizations, many assumed ATM would not be widely implemented until the next century. However, the need for high-bandwidth services in the carrier networks and in LAN enviornments has driven vendors to produce products well ahead of schedule.

ATM Technical Aspects

ATM is a broadband technology for transmitting voice, video, and data over LANs or WANs. It is a cell relay technology, implying that the data packets have a fixed size. You can think of a cell as a sort of vehicle that transports blocks of data from one device to another across an ATM switching device. All the cells are the same size, unlike Frame Relay and LAN systems in which packets can vary in size. Using same-size cells provides a way of predicting and guaranteeing bandwidth for applications that need it. Variable-length packets can cause traffic delays at switches, in the same way that cars must wait for long trucks to make turns at busy intersections.

The switching device is the important component in ATM. It can serve as a hub within an organization that quickly relays packets from one node to another, or it can serve as a wide area communication device, transmitting ATM cells between remote LANs at high speeds. Conventional LANs like Ethernet, Fiber Distributed Data Interface (FDDI), and token ring use shared media in which only one node can transmit at any one time. ATM, on the other hand, provides any-to-any connections and nodes can transmit simultaneously. Information from many nodes is multiplexed as a stream of cells, as shown in Figure A-12. In this system, the ATM switch may be owned by a public service provider or be part of an organization's internal network.

    NOTE: An ATM switch simply relays cells. It looks at the header and immediately begins forwarding the cell. The time-consuming store-and-forward methods used by routers is eliminated.

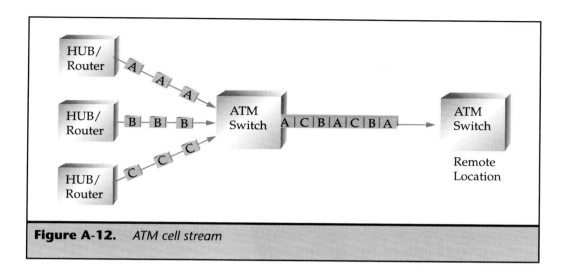

Figure A-12. *ATM cell stream*

An Analogy

Let's use the analogy of vehicles on a bridge to illustrate how ATM works and why it is so efficient. Think of the bridge as the ATM connection between two remote LANs. If every vehicle were exactly the same size, as ATM cells are, they could be spaced equally apart in traffic and driven at the same speed across the bridge. Consequently, you could accurately predict when a vehicle would reach the other side of the bridge. In real life, however, vehicles come in many different sizes, making traffic predictions difficult. In data communication, variable-sized data packets that provide uncertain delays are not suitable for video and voice applications (unless prioritization methods are used).

Taking this analogy further, suppose you want to transport a busload of people across the bridge. Buses aren't allowed, so groups of four people climb into cars, traverse the bridge, then climb back into another bus on the other side. Likewise, in ATM, packets of data from upper-level applications might need to be split apart, inserted into a number of ATM cells, transmitted, then recombined at the other side of the ATM transmission.

If several buses arrive at the same time, all can begin traversing the bridge simultaneously—it's not necessary to unload one bus first, then the next. Like the ATM cells pictured in Figure A-12, cars holding passengers from each bus are allowed to traverse the bridge one after the other. In communication, this technique is used in multiplexing; in ATM, it is used to transfer data from multiple connections simultaneously.

NOTE: *An ATM switch typically has many input and output ports. Because all the cells are the same size, the delay caused by variable-length cells is eliminated.*

The fixed cell size and multiplexing provide bandwidth on demand to devices that need it. LAN traffic is often "bursty" due to file transfers or other activities that cause peaks in activity. An ATM switch can detect bursts in traffic and dynamically allocate more cells to handle a burst from a particular source. In Figure A-12, a burst from hub A might translate into a cell stream that consists of three A cells, one B cell, and one C cell, followed by three more A cells and so on until the transfer is complete.

ATM Switches and Networks

An ATM network contains ATM switches, which are generally multiport devices that perform cell switching. When a cell arrives at one port, the ATM switch looks at the cell's destination information and sends it to an appropriate output port. There are *fabric-type* ATM switch designs as pictured in Figure A-13 that have many ports and are used by the public carriers, and there are *bus-based* switches with fewer ports that are more suitable for LANs. If multiple ATM switches are connected together, a routing protocol is needed so the switches can exchange look-up connection tables.

One reason for the high switching speeds in ATM switches is that they perform their switching operations in hardware. ATM switches avoid the Network layer (relative to the OSI protocol). Instead, ATM simply places information into cells and sends it off. ATM is a so-called "fast-packet" technology like frame relay and Switched Multimegabit Data Service (SMDS), in that it performs no error checking and is not bogged down by such matters. A receiving station is responsible for making sure it received everything from a sender. If a cell is lost or corrupted, the end station must

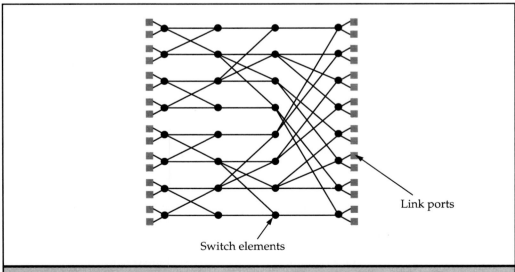

Link ports

Switch elements

Figure A-13. *An ATM switch can provide connections between any link port*

request another from the sender. ATM is not responsible for recovering the cell. In contrast, X.25 uses extensive error checking as packets traverse the network. A packet must be fully received and error-checked at a node before it is forwarded. This overhead limits throughput. X.25 is designed for older analog phone systems that were prone to error. The error checking was designed to detect corrupted packets as soon as possible. ATM assumes the use of high-quality, error-free transmission facilities.

ATM is a transport protocol that operates roughly at the media access control (MAC) sublayer of the Data-Link layer in the Open Systems Interconnection (OSI) protocol stack. Because of this, it can work above many Physical-layer topologies and map any kind of packet into its 53-byte cell and transport it over a backbone or a WAN.

ATM transfer rates are scalable, depending on the capacity of the physical layer. With ATM, there is no standard that locks the transmission rate as there is with Fiber Distributed Data Interface (FDDI)—100 Mbits/sec, for example. The small cell size does not require special processing, which is required with FDDI. ATM cells are easy to build, whereas FDDI requires protocol conversions that cause delays. ATM can be used now on existing T1 lines, fractional T1 lines, and T3 lines. A conversion is required to do the same for FDDI.

ATM desktop connections are in the works, but users should shop carefully. ATM is difficult to implement for workstation-to-workstation communications in the LAN environment. However, hubs that provide about a dozen 100 Mbits/sec ATM connections to workstations are under development by several vendors, including IBM and Hewlett-Packard. Users of scientific workstations and those who handle images and modeling are likely candidates for this type of equipment. Uses for ATM at the desktop and in LANs include imaging, multimedia, graphics, and computer-aided design/computer-aided manufacturing (CAD/CAM). High definition television (HDTV), for example, requires 100 to 150 Mbits/sec of dedicated bandwidth, which is possible with ATM.

ATM Roots and Architecture

ATM was originally defined as part of the Broadband-Integrated Services Digital Network (B-ISDN), which was developed in 1988 by the Consultative Committee for International Telegraph and Telephone (CCITT). B-ISDN is an extension of narrowband ISDN, which defined public digital telecommunications networks. B-ISDN provides more bandwidth and can attain higher data throughput. The B-ISDN reference model is shown in Figure A-14.

- ■ The physical layer defines the electrical or physical interface, line speeds, and other physical characteristics.
- ■ The ATM layer defines the cell format.
- ■ The ATM adaptation layer defines the process of converting information from upper layers into ATM cells.

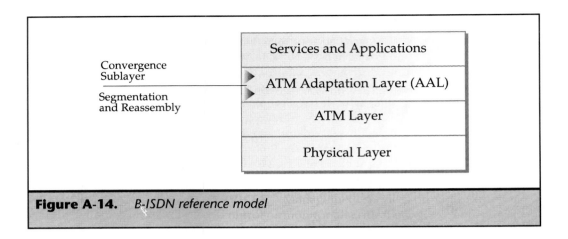

Figure A-14. *B-ISDN reference model*

While the B-ISDN model broadened support for ATM, many specifics still required attention. A consortium of hardware vendors and telecommunication service providers formed the ATM Forum in 1991 to further define physical interface standards for ATM in LANs and WANs. The ATM Forum does not set standards, but is committed to clarifying and setting the goals of ATM development. The ATM Forum defined two physical interface methods:

- *User-to-Network Interfaces (UNIs)*   The UNI is the point of connection for endstations to an ATM network. For example, an ATM access switch can form the UNI connection to a public (such as the telephone company) ATM network.

- *Network-to-Network Interfaces (NNIs)*   These are the interfaces between ATM switches in public ATM networks like those provided by local telephone companies. NNIs basically govern the interoperability of ATM switches. NNIs may also refer to Network-to-Node Interfaces.

In this arrangement, carrier services have their own ATM switches to handle wide area traffic from many different customers. Each customer has his or her own in-house private ATM switches handling local area network traffic, and connections to the public ATM networks.

The ATM Forum is also working to define other portions of ATM, such as management methods, traffic control, different media types, and testing methods. The Internet Engineering Task Force (IETF) is working on defining how ATM will handle converting LAN packets to ATM cells.

In the ATM environment, logical connections between end stations are called *virtual channels (VCs)*. A *virtual path (VP)* is a bundle of VCs, as pictured in Figure A-15. Think of a VP as a cable that contains a bundle of wires. The cable connects two points and wires within the cable provide individual circuits between the two points. The advantage of this method is that connections sharing the same path through the

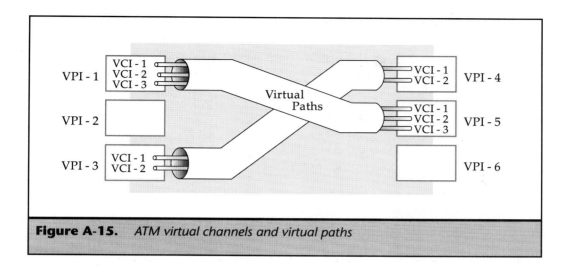

Figure A-15.   *ATM virtual channels and virtual paths*

network are grouped together and take advantage of the same management actions. If a VP is already set up, adding a new VC is easy since the work of defining paths through the network is already done. In addition, if a VP changes to avoid congestion or a downed switch, all the VCs within the VP change with it.

In an ATM cell header, a *virtual path identifier (VPI)* identifies a link formed by a virtual path and a *virtual channel identifier (VCI)* identifies a channel within a virtual path. The VPI and VCI are identified and correspond to termination points at ATM switches. For example, in the previous illustration, a virtual path connects VPI-1 and VPI-5. Within this path are three virtual channels. Note that VPIs identify the equivalent of a port specific to the network, while channels within virtual paths are identified relative to that path.

The Physical Layer

The most interesting thing about the physical layer of ATM is that it does not define any one specific media type. LANs were designed for coaxial or twisted-pair cable and have rigid specifications that define the exact bandwidth. The specifications were established to match the electrical components available at the time of design. ATM supports many different media, including existing media used by other communications systems.

Industry experts are endorsing the Synchronous Optical Network (SONET) as the ATM physical transport media for both LAN and WAN applications. SONET is a BellCore specification that is currently being installed for use in worldwide public data networks. The ATM Forum is recommending FDDI (100 Mbits/sec), Fibre Channel (155 Mbits/sec), OC3 SONET (155 Mbits/sec), and T3 (45 Mbits/sec) as the physical interface for ATM. Currently, most carriers are providing T3 links to their ATM networks.

The ATM Layer

The ATM layer defines the structure of the ATM cell, which is pictured in Figure A-16. It also defines virtual channel and path routing, as well as error control. ATM cells are packets of information that contain a "payload" (data) and header information that contain channel and path information to direct the cell to its destination.

The cell is 53 bytes in length, 48 bytes of which is the payload and 5 bytes of which is the header information. Note that header information is almost ten percent of the cell, which adds up to extensive overhead on long transmissions, as pointed out by some ATM detractors. They advocate variable-length technologies like Frame Relay for this reason. The information held by each field in the header is explained here:

- *Generic Flow Control (GFC)*   This field is still being defined, but the ATM Forum has defined it to provide a way for multiple workstations to use the same User Network Interface (UNI). Other possibilities include a definition for the type of service.

- *Virtual Path Identifier (VPI)*   Identifies virtual paths between users, or users and networks.

- *Virtual Channel Identifier (VCI)*   Identifies virtual channels between users, or users and networks.

- *Payload Type Indicator (PTI)*   Indicates the type of information in the payload area, such as user, network, or management information.

- *Cell Loss Priority (CLP)*   Defines how to drop certain cells if network congestion occurs. The field holds priority values, with 0 indicating that a cell cannot be dropped.

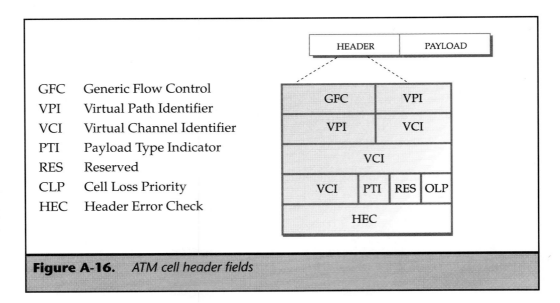

GFC	Generic Flow Control
VPI	Virtual Path Identifier
VCI	Virtual Channel Identifier
PTI	Payload Type Indicator
RES	Reserved
CLP	Cell Loss Priority
HEC	Header Error Check

Figure A-16.   *ATM cell header fields*

■ *Header Error Control (HEC)*   Provides information for error detection and correction of single bit errors.

ATM Adaptation Layer (AAL)

AAL converges packets from upper layers into ATM cells. Recall that each cell has a 48-byte "payload bay." The AAL would segment a 1,000-byte packet into 21 fragments and place each fragment into a cell for transport. The layer is divided into two sublayers. The convergence sublayer (CS) accepts the higher layer data and passes it down to the segmentation and reassembly (SAR) sublayer. The SAR is responsible for breaking the data up into 53-byte ATM cells. If cells are arriving, the SAR reassembles the data in the cells and passes it to upper layers. There are several AAL types:

■ *Type 1* is an isochronous, constant bit-rate service for audio and video applications. It is similar to T1 or T3 and provides a variety of data rates.

■ *Type 2* is an isochronous variable bit-rate application like compressed video. The carriers have not implemented this interface.

■ *Type 3/4* supports bursty LAN-type variable bit-rate data that supports frame relay and SMDS interfaces.

■ *Type 5* supports a subset of Type 3/4 functions, providing message mode and nonassured operation. This mode will most likely be quickly deployed.

Service Classes

ATM accommodates different types of traffic such as voice, video, and data by providing four classes of service. The service classes categorize applications based on how bits are transmitted, the required bandwidth, and the types of connections required. These classes are shown in Figure A-17.

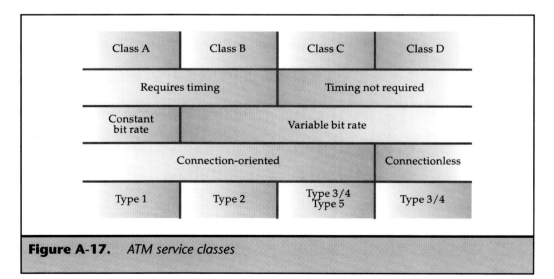

Class A	Class B	Class C	Class D
Requires timing		Timing not required	
Constant bit rate	Variable bit rate		
Connection-oriented			Connectionless
Type 1	Type 2	Type 3/4 Type 5	Type 3/4

Figure A-17.   *ATM service classes*

■ Class A is a connection-oriented service that provides a constant bit rate. The timing compensations make it suitable for video and voice applications.

■ Class B is a connection-oriented service and is timed for transmitting variable bit rate voice and video. The interface to the AAL is Type 2.

■ Class C is a connection-oriented, variable, bit-rate service without timing, suitable for services like X.25, Frame Relay, and TCP/IP. The interface to the AAL is Type 3/4 or Type 5.

■ Class D is connectionless service, with variable rate data traffic that does not require timing relationships between end-nodes. LAN packet traffic is an example of data supported by this class. The interface to the AAL is Type 3/4.

ATM and the Carrier Services

ATM is defining the future of wide area network (WAN) communication. It will remove the barrier between local area networks (LANs) and WANs. That barrier is the drop in throughput currently associated with data transfers over public networks. Store-and-forward WAN connection devices like routers are another barrier. LECs (local exchange carriers) and IXCs (interexchange carriers) must install integrated ATM/SONET digital networks to offer economical virtual private data network services. ATM carries more traffic at reduced cost, which will pass down to the consumer. Users only pay for the information they transfer.

Switched Multimegabit Data Service (SMDS), is a service provided by Bellcore based on the IEEE 802.6 metropolitan area network (MAN) standard. It is a cell-based, connectionless, packet-switched network built on ATM that lets users create their own internetworked LANs within a specific metropolitan area. Services are provided on demand and customers pay for only what they use, which helps customers eliminate underutilized dedicated, point-to-point lines. The throughput of SMDS is 45 Mbits/sec.

SMDS is good for customers who need to connect LANs in metropolitan areas. However, AT&T's plans do not include SMDS. Instead, AT&T is moving quickly to install ATM technology and services. An experimental ATM network is set up between the University of Wisconsin and the University of Illinois that provides 622 Mbits/sec transmission rates. According to AT&T, the entire contents of the *Encyclopedia Britannica* can be transferred in under one second, compared to two and one-half days using a 2400 baud modem. AT&T is also developing high-speed ATM switches for service providers of video and multimedia formats.

Other carriers are installing ATM switches that implement frame relay, SMDS, and X.25 interfaces. Since ATM can handle almost all transmission requirements, including voice and video, experts see the division between circuit and packet switching disappearing by the end of the decade.

A

Planning for ATM

While ATM will be initially deployed as a wide-area technology to improve transmissions rates outside the local area network, ATM technology will eventually be cost-effective for in-house networks. Meanwhile, fast Ethernet technologies and switching hubs may be preferable and more cost-effective. On the other hand, IBM has invested over $100 million per year in the development of ATM products, including its own ATM chip set. The product line includes ATM interface cards for personal computers and desktop systems, as well as ATM hubs, all of which should be available in 1994. While some consider desktop ATM adapters premature, IBM insists that there is already a demand.

Organizations considering a migration to ATM should follow a step-by-step approach employing a hierarchical distributed wiring structure. In a multistory office building, you would start by installing a main ATM switch as a backbone that links the connections from each floor. These connections might be existing Ethernet or Fiber Distributed Data Interface (FDDI) backbones. In the next phase, you install ATM switches on each floor to connect the high-performance servers installed there. In the last phase, when ATM is relatively inexpensive, you connect end-user systems directly to the ATM switches.

You can build ATM backbone topologies in a number of ways. ATM is not tied to one specific topology like Ethernet or FDDI. While the hierarchical star will most likely predominate, other topologies are possible if necessary.

ATM makes network management easier when used as a corporate backbone, eliminating a lot of the problems introduced by complex internetworks that have different addressing schemes and routing mechanisms. ATM hubs provide connections between any two ports on the hub, independent of the type of device attached to it. The addresses of these devices are premapped, making it easy to send a message for example, from one node to another, regardless of the network type the nodes are connected to. ATM management software makes it easy to move users and their physical workstations from one place to another.

ATM Forum

The ATM Forum (415/926-2585) is an industry-wide organization based in Mountain View, California that promotes ATM. The organization was formed in October of 1991 and has over 300 members. The ATM Forum consists of committees that implement and document specifications, committees that market ATM in North America and Europe, and a roundtable committee that promotes ongoing discussions about ATM with end users.

AT&T

In 1913, the Department of Justice brought an antitrust suit against AT&T that resulted in the Kingsbury Commitment. It forced AT&T to divest itself of Western Union and allow independent carriers to use the long distance network it had established. In 1956, the Justice Department limited AT&T to providing only regulated services to customers and, in 1968, ruled that customers could attach non-AT&T equipment to the public telephone network. The 1969 MCI Decision allowed MCI and other carriers to compete with AT&T for long-distance communications. From 1982 to 1984, the Justice Department finalized its antitrust suit by forcing AT&T to break up and reform into seven regional holding companies called the regional Bell operating companies (RBOCs). A manufacturing, research, and long distance operation called AT&T Corporation was allowed to continue operation. The RBOCs are listed later in the book, under the heading "Regional Bell Operating Companies."

The RBOCs provide their services within specific geographic areas called LATAs (Local Access and Transport Areas). A LATA basically separates local and long distance telephone markets. A local exchange carrier (LEC) has a franchise within a LATA (intraLATA) to provide services. An LEC may be a BOC or an independent telephone company.

InterLATA telecommunication refers to services provided between LATAs by *interexchange carriers (IXCs)* such as AT&T, MCI, US Sprint, and others.

RBOC and AT&T services are regulated and prices are fixed for services. For example, tariffs that control interLATA service rates cannot be changed without approval from the federal government. IntraLATA tariffs are controlled at the state level. RBOCs can provide cellular communication, Yellow Pages publications, voice messaging, electronic mail, and other services.

RBOCs must provide all interexchange carriers with equal access to their LATA facilities. Users can therefore choose which interexchange carrier (AT&T, MCI, US Sprint, and others) they want to use. That carrier then provides switching services between LATAs.

AT&T provides a number of services for network connections, based around a core technology platform that uses Asynchronous Transfer Mode (ATM) switches. Its "integrated services" platform allows service providers to construct new networks or mix and match equipment with their existing networks and provide new business and residential services, including:

- Connecting personal computers and local area networks (LANs) over extremely high-speed networks
- Multimedia videoconferencing capabilities
- Medical imaging services that let doctors at remote locations perform common diagnoses
- Interactive distance learning services
- Telecommuting services

ATM is the key to AT&T's communication system. The GCNS-2000 is an ATM switch that AT&T makes available as a common technology product for companies that want to create end-to-end video systems that deliver movies, and other video services. Other ATM products provide various types and speeds of access and trunk interfaces so service providers can build the "gigabit" data highways for future networking systems.

AT&T has also set up the fastest wide area network in the nation. It uses ATM technology over a 500-mile, fiber-optic network that runs at 622 Mbits/sec between the University of Wisconsin at Madison and University of Illinois at Urbana-Champaign. This new network is an enhancement of a previous experimental network that will test the ability to transmit complex imaging, multimedia, and supercomputer information.

RELATED ENTRIES   ACCUNET; Carrier Services; *and* Regional Bell Operating Companies

Athena Project

The Athena Project was a test environment for an enterprise-wide computing system at the Massachusetts Institute of Technology. The project, which took place from 1983 to 1991, was sponsored by IBM and Digital Equipment Corporation. One project goal was to map out the strategies, problems, and solutions encountered when building and scaling a large enterprise network. The project connected over 1,500 workstations with gigabytes of storage onto a network that supported thousands of logins and mail messages per day. For practical purposes, the system was and is still used to manage the educational environment at the Massachusetts Institute of Technology, but it also serves as a prototype for a distributed computing environment.

Attenuation

Attenuation is signal loss, measured in decibels, of a signal transmission over distance. The opposite of attenuation is amplification. On network cables, attenuation is the degradation of the digital signal or a loss of amplitude of an electric signal. Repeaters are used to regenerate signals by amplifying them but not changing their information content in any way. With a repeater, a network can be extended beyond its normal range.

RELATED ENTRIES   Cabling; Transmission Media, Methods, and Equipment

Attributes

Attributes define user access to files and directories, and the properties of files and directories. A common attribute is "Archive Needed," which indicates that a file has been modified and needs to be included in the next back up. This attribute is then turned off when the file is backed up, but is set on again if a user changes the file. Read Only attributes found on most network operating systems prevent users from changing the contents of files or deleting them.

NetWare 4.x has some interesting attributes. Delete Inhibit (DI) prevents a user from deleting a file or directory. Immediate Compress (IM) causes a file, or the files in a directory to be compressed as soon as possible. Don't Compress (DC) prevents a file, or the files in a directory from being automatically compressed.

Objects within object-oriented filing systems, databases, and programming languages have attributes called *properties.* If an object is compared to a record within a database, its properties are like the fields within a record that hold values.

At Work Architecture, Microsoft

See Microsoft At Work Architecture.

Auditing

A network auditing system logs details of what users are doing on the network so that malicious or unintended activities can be tracked. When auditing is in place, vast amounts of information are often recorded. Most goes unscrutinized, however, the information is available to track illicit activities if necessary. Some audit systems provide special views of auditing information to make browsing much simpler. Event alarms are also important to warn administrators when certain levels or conditions are met.

NetWare 4.x provides a good example of an auditing system. It designates a network user known as the *auditor* to track events on the network. The events fall into two categories: *volume tracking* and *container tracking.* Each auditing category can have a distinct password, so, for example, the auditor who tracks volume events cannot track container events if they don't have the container password. However, one auditor can track all events if necessary.

One of the primary users to track with the auditing system is the network administrator, who basically has unlimited rights to the system. An auditor can keep administrators "honest" by passively tracking and monitoring all their activities. Initially, the network administrator creates a special auditor account, usually as directed by higher-level management. The auditor then logs into the account and immediately changes the password, effectively blocking all access to the account, even by the network administrator.

The auditor can then set up auditing features, view audit logs, and work in designated audit directories. A record is kept for every activity that is designated for tracking. Events that can be tracked are listed here:

■ Directory creation and deletion

■ Creating, opening, closing, deleting, renaming, writing, and salvaging files

- Modifying directory entries
- Queue activities
- Server events, such as changing the date and time, downing the server, and mounting or dismounting volumes
- User events, such as logon, logoff, connection termination, space restrictions, granting of trustee rights, and disabling of accounts
- Directory Services events, such as changes in passwords, security, and logon restrictions
- Activities of a specific user, such as a supervisor or network administrator

Auditing records can be viewed using special filters to produce reports that show specific activities. Filters can be applied to show specific date and time ranges, specified events, file and directory events, or user events.

The **syslog** facility exists in the UNIX operating system to create audit trails. It is necessary to protect the audit records from alteration or destruction. They can, for example, be copied to another system that is accessible only by administrators or an auditor.

Administrators should be on the lookout for a large number of failed logon attempts, or logins that take place at odd hours, which usually indicate that an intruder is attempting to access the system.

RELATED ENTRY   Security

Authentication and Authorization

In a distributed computing environment, users typically access resources besides those attached to their local servers. Traditionally, a user logs on to access local resources. When accessing remote resources (that may be in other cities), the user must log on again. This method of logging in for each resource is not only cumbersome, but hard to manage. A user account with current passwords must be kept at each server. In addition, the connection to the remote device is not reliably secure and intruders could monitor the line and intercept the logon information for their own use. Clearly, better methods are needed. Password encryption methods can also fail if an intruder masquerades as another legitimate user and captures the encrypted password.

UNIX, NetWare 4.x, and other network operating systems use the "trusted host" concept, in which one system trusts that another system has properly verified the identity of a user. Methods for doing this are discussed in the next paragraphs, but once a user has been authenticated, that user can access any resource that he or she has authorization to use. The information used to verify a user's access to remote resources is different every time the user logs in, so if the information is intercepted, it can't be used once the user logs out.

Authentication techniques must determine whether a request originated from the correct user or application and that the request has not been modified in some way. Once the request is verified as authentic, *authorization* procedures then determine the type of access a user has to a resource.

There are two important products that provide authentication services in distributed network environments, as discussed in the next paragraphs.

Kerberos

The Kerberos Authentication service was developed by the Massachusetts Institute of Technology's Project Athena as an authentication mechanism for open systems in distributed environments. It is used in the Open Software Foundation (OSF) Distributed Computing Environment (DCE) and by various network operating system vendors.

RSA Data Security

The RSA Cryptosystem is a product of RSA Data Security Inc., of Redwood City, California. It is available for licensing and incorporation in a variety of products. RSA is a public key encryption scheme with authentication that is perhaps best known as the provider of authentication services in NetWare 4.x. The size of the key used in the RSA system virtually guarantees that it can never be deduced.

While conventional encryption methods use one key, public key systems use two keys. The private key maintains confidentiality while the public key is published for public use. The public key is used to encrypt information and the private key is used to decrypt it. The RSA system uses this technique to provide authentication, signature verification, and other security requirements.

NetWare 4.x Authentication

NetWare 4.x uses the RSA security system to authenticate users and authorize them to use the network. It works in conjunction with the Access Control List, which contains information about objects. Users are not aware of authentication; it works in the background. Authentication assigns a unique identification to each user for each logon session. The identification, not the user's password, is used to authenticate each of the user's network requests. Authentication guarantees that a user's password never goes beyond the logon process. It is immediately converted to a different code that identifies the user and the station they are logged into during the user's current session. Authentication also guarantees that messages are from the correct user at his or her workstation in the current session and not corrupted, counterfeited, or tampered with.

RELATED ENTRIES   Kerberos Authentication; RSA Data Security; *and* Security

Backbone Networks

A backbone is a network that connects two or more local area network (LAN) segments or subnetworks and provides a data path for packets transmitting information among them. A bridge or router connects each network segment to the backbone. Fiber-optic cable systems such as Fiber Distributed Data Interface (FDDI) are often used for the backbone connection. The backbone cable can extend throughout the premises. Alternatively, a hub device that serves as a "collapsed backbone" can provide a single connection point for all the subnetworks. Backbones handle internetwork traffic while local traffic is handled by subnetworks. Servers attached directly to the backbone provide better access for internetwork users than if they are attached to subnetworks.

A NetWare server-based backbone is illustrated in Figure B-1. Each server contains two or more network adapters. One of the adapters connects the server to the backbone and provides the connection to the other LAN segments that are attached to the backbone. The other adapters in the server attach to local segments. Server-based backbones provide bridge and routing functions for small networks.

A router-based backbone is shown in Figure B-2. The router is the connection point to the backbone cable. In this case, a dual-ring fiber-optic cable is used. The dual-fiber ring provides redundancy—if the cable is cut, it loops back on itself to keep traffic flowing. On the left, a router provides the connection for LAN users. On the right, a server provides a bridge between the backbone and the LAN attached to it.

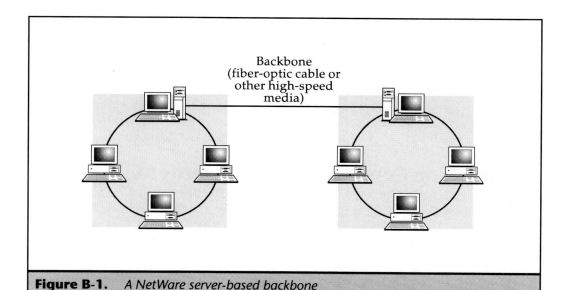

Figure B-1. *A NetWare server-based backbone*

B

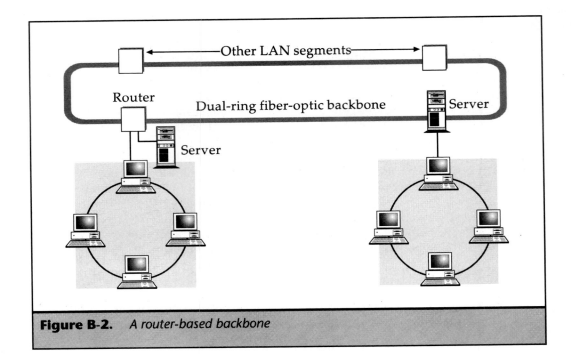

Figure B-2.   *A router-based backbone*

Figure B-3 illustrates another way to configure a backbone. In this case, the LAN segments on each floor of an office building are connected to a backbone that runs through the conduit from one floor to the next. In this example, LANs are attached to servers, which are then attached to the backbone.

Because many network operating systems contain bridge and routing functions, there is a tendency to use file servers as network interconnection devices. The server must have adequate processing power to handle these tasks, as well as its file management responsibilities. For busy networks, it is best to dedicate file servers to file management tasks and build backbones with bridges or routers. Wiring centers and hubs that provide collapsed backbone features are also recommended.

Backbones for Centralized Management

Figure B-4 illustrates a centralized network design that provides better management of network resources. Departmental servers are moved to a central management area and connected to a high-speed network such as FDDI. Department LANs are linked to the backbone with bridges. Centralized networks are easier to monitor and manage as described here:

■ Hardware repairs and replacements are easier, since all the parts and personnel are at the same location.

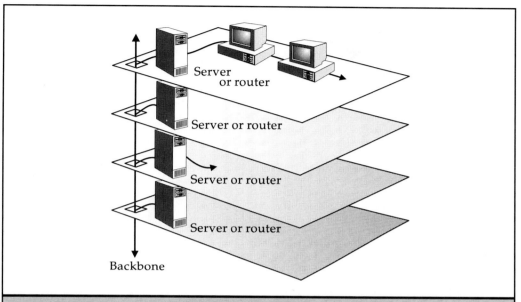

Figure B-3.   *A backbone connection for a multistory office building*

- Security is enhanced because the server area can be locked and fireproofed.
- Servers are not locked into individual departments where maintenance personnel may have trouble accessing them during off-hours.
- Performance can be optimized over the backbone.
- Backups, archiving, and other data protection methods are performed in one area by trained personnel.
- All hardware can take advantage of power and grounding enhancements.
- Connections to metropolitan area networks (MANs) and wide area networks (WANs) are simplified.

Collapsed Backbones and Structured Wiring

A "collapsed backbone" is a backbone that is reduced to fit within a single box. Instead of deploying the backbone cable throughout the enterprise, a cable is attached to the hub from each subnetwork. The trend is natural. Once you've moved servers and other types of network equipment to a central location for management purposes, it makes sense to simply connect them to a single box, called a *hub*, that replaces the backbone cable. Hubs are built on a chassis with high-speed, often proprietary, backplanes that provide a high-speed bus for expansion boards. Hubs are modular

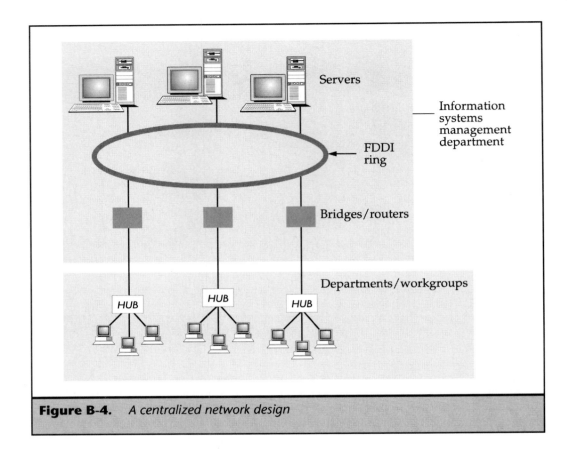

Figure B-4.   *A centralized network design*

and expandable. Many accept Ethernet, token ring, FDDI, and WAN modules, as well as diagnostic and management modules.

As shown in Figure B-5, a central hub can provide attachments for department hubs in a hierarchical arrangement. Department hubs then provide ports for workstations. Departmental hubs are "wiring closet devices" that usually provide connections for only one type of network topology, such as Ethernet. Alternatively, central backbone hubs are designed to accept many different types of networks, such as Ethernet, token ring, and FDDI, as well as WAN modules and management modules.

Hierarchical network designs are built with structured wiring systems. "Horizontal" wiring provides workstation connections to department hubs and "vertical" wiring provides department hub connections to a central enterprise hub.

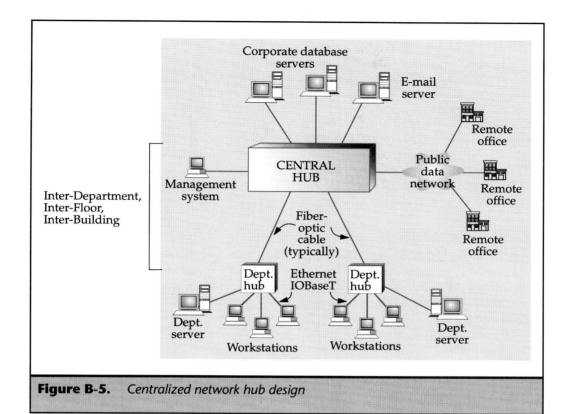

Figure B-5. *Centralized network hub design*

- ■ The *central hub* controls the flow of information between departments and also provides a connection point for corporate database servers, management systems, and wide area connections as shown in Figure B-5.

- ■ *Department hubs* may be located on separate floors of a single building, or in separate buildings in a campus environment. High-speed fiber-optic cable is the common connecting medium for central hubs because it has high throughput and distance advantages.

- ■ *Workstations* connections are typically made with copper twisted-pair cable.

- ■ *Servers* accessed only by a specific department are attached to department subnetworks. Servers with shared enterprise data are attached to central hubs.

Structured backbone systems make distributed computing easier to implement, configure, secure, and manage. Expansion and changes are easier to implement. Monitoring and troubleshooting structured systems is easier. Problems related to cable are quickly identified and fixed or bypassed. Without structure, the cabling system becomes cumbersome and confusing, and it is difficult to move users from one location to another. This is a big issue in today's workgroup-oriented organization.

While 10BaseT (twisted-pair Ethernet at 10 Mbits/sec) has been a popular cabling scheme for structured wiring systems, new 100 Mbits/sec Ethernet cabling schemes for twisted-pair copper wire are now standardized and growing in popularity.

One of the downsides of interconnecting diverse LANs is the possibility of creating ground loops in the electrical system. Pathways created by copper network cables between once isolated departments attached to their own power supplies can cause load differences that cause electrical disturbances in delicate electronic equipment. Fiber-optic cable is the preferred medium for interconnecting diverse LANs because it does not conduct electrical signals that could form ground loops. See the "Power and Grounding Problems and Solutions" section later in this book for more details.

Public Backbones

While collapsed backbones and structured wiring systems are providing solutions for in-house enterprise systems, alternative connection methods are required to create offsite links. Solutions include satellite, microwave, and public carrier backbones. For more details, see the headings "Telecommunications" and "Wide Area Networks" later in this book.

The public carriers such as AT&T, US Sprint, MCI, Ameritech, Pacific Bell, and other companies such as CompuServe are providing new types of services for WAN connections that have higher bandwidth, lower cost, and more flexibility than the dedicated, private leased lines that were popular in the 1980s. Leased lines provide dedicated connections between two points over a high-quality circuit that provides a constant bandwidth. Dedicated lines are justified for continuous traffic between two sites. Many organizations build private backbone networks over wide areas using T1, T3, or other dedicated lines.

New switched services like Switched-56, Frame Relay, Switched Multimegabit Data Service (SMDS), and Asynchronous Transfer Mode (ATM) are providing new ways for network managers to build wide-area networks without resorting to dedicated leased lines. These high-speed switching services provide "bandwidth-on-demand," and "pay-for-use" wide area networking. Customers contract for a certain bandwidth, and more is available at an additional rate if it is required. In addition, connections can be made to many different sites.

The Future

While "collapsed backbone" hub devices present a single point of failure that can cripple the entire enterprise network, the collapsed backbone-in-a-box is still appealing to managers, and it has its place. Some vendors see its benefits and are already designing "super-hubs" built on ATM that include bridges, routers, management modules, and high-speed ATM switching. The architecture of such a device is shown in Figure B-6. ATM cell switching connects the bridges and the routers, and in more advanced units, provides connections for workstations and other LAN segment nodes as well.

RELATED ENTRIES   Bridging; Carrier Services; EIA/TIA 568 Commercial Building Wiring Standard; Enterprise Networks; Hubs; Routers; *and* Wide Area Networks

Back-End Systems

Back-end systems are the server portion in client-server relationships. Client-server computing splits processing between a front-end system that runs on the clients

B

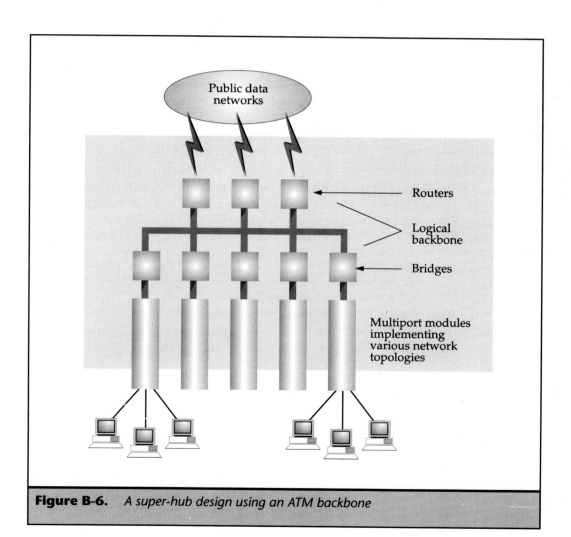

Figure B-6.   *A super-hub design using an ATM backbone*

workstation, and a back-end system that runs on one or more servers. The client is a user who typically runs an application in order to access data from a server over a network connection. A database management system (DBMS) typically runs on the back-end system.

The front-end application runs in the memory of the user's workstation. It displays screens and provides user prompts, although a graphical user interface such as Microsoft Windows is now commonly used at the front end. The user creates queries for the back-end system through this interface. The back-end system then takes the query statements sent over the network and processes them, searching for data, sorting the data, or providing other services. The back-end system performs these data operations because it is close to the data. This strategy is based on the fact that it is not efficient or secure to send large amounts of data to the front-end for processing. You can think of the back-end system as an "engine" that performs the major data-processing functions.

When the back-end server system has completed the client's request, it returns the results to the client. The client system then displays those results and handles further input from the user.

RELATED ENTRY   Client-Server Computing

Backplane

A backplane is the board that holds the bus interface in modular hub devices such as those used to create collapsed backbones, structured wiring systems, and star-configured network topologies. For the purposes of this discussion, a hub is a chassis in the middle of a star-configured, structured wiring scheme. Workstation and other node connections emanate from the hub. Hubs are usually modular and expandable, which means you can install additional multiport repeater modules when you need more network connections. It is the bus on the backplane that these modules plug into. The bus is analogous to the Industry Standard Architecture (ISA) or Extended Industry Standard Architecture (EISA) bus inside a PC, into which you plug expansion cards. Buses form *channels* through which signals are transferred.

The design of the backplane is critical to the performance of the hub in routing packets among modules installed in the hub. In most cases, backplane designs are proprietary. Vendors use various techniques to boost data transfers (in some cases to the gigabits-per-second range), and there are several different bus architectures. Some hubs are designed for only one type of network, such as Ethernet or token ring, so the bus in these systems simply passes signals between modules. Hubs of this design are typically used in departmental local area networks (LANs) that use one type of topology, such as Ethernet 10BaseT with twisted-pair wire. Some vendors use standard bus designs like ISA and EISA.

More advanced bus designs consist of separate physical channels for each different type of network topology. For example, SynOptics' hubs have three channels, one each for Ethernet, token ring, and Fiber Distributed Data Interface (FDDI). ADC/Fibermux hubs follow a similar approach with four channels for either Ethernet or AppleTalk and one channel for token ring or Apollo Domain token ring.

The backplane is getting more sophisticated, especially with the increased use of Asynchronous Transfer Mode (ATM) switching. Hubs that support different network topologies such as Ethernet and token ring provide bridging and routing functions on a shared bus so any node can communicate with any other node, or over wide area links. Newer designs use ATM switching matrices that quickly relay cells of information between any two stations. Stations can set up a dedicated, not-shared communication channel with any other station attached to the switch.

RELATED ENTRIES   Hubs; Matrix Switch; *and* Routers

Backup and Data Archiving

Backup and archiving strategies are critical for data protection. Without proper backups, the enterprise could loose thousands or millions of dollars every day in downtime. The purpose of this section is not to convince you to implement backup strategies—that is obvious. This section describes backup terminology, techniques, media, and devices.

Today, departmental networks are merging into the organization-wide enterprise networks that are often managed from central locations. Department managers now rely on the information managers at these central locations to ensure that data is properly backed up and secure. The strategies, timing, management, and security aspects of backing up company-wide data has become more complex. There are many issues to consider, such as when and how to back up data files that are constantly accessed and constantly changing.

Many organizations today have gigabyte storage requirements that seem small by tomorrow's requirements. Future backups will require hundreds or thousands of gigabytes of storage to accommodate voice mail, multimedia, document imaging, and video. As an example, a single voice-mail message lasting only a few seconds can take up to 10 MB of disk storage space.

To accommodate these backup requirements, new tape drives and optical storage systems are emerging that can handle gigabytes of information. Data compression and technology advancements are making this possible. Hierarchical storage systems provide methods for moving little-used data from fast-access magnetic media to high-capacity archiving devices. Finally, network operating systems now incorporate data-protection techniques that provide real-time backup of data to secondary magnetic storage devices.

Note the following terms:

■ A *backup* is a copy of online storage information that provides fault protection. An *archive* is an historical backup.

■ An *online* storage device is a high-performance magnetic disk that stores information users access most often. *Nearline* and *offline* storage devices are slower, secondary storage devices that provide backup services or archiving services.

■ *Hierarchical file systems* move little-used files or large image files from online storage to nearline storage systems such as optical disk, where they remain available to users.

■ *Tape backup systems* are the traditional backup medium while *optical disk systems* provide archiving and nearline storage requirements.

■ A backup system must follow a schedule and set of procedures to guarantee the integrity of backed up data. Backup might occur daily, hourly, or even continuously.

■ *Incremental backups* are used to back up files that have changed since the last full-system backup. During a restore, you restore the last major full-system backup, then each incremental backup, one after the other in order.

■ *Differential backups* are similar to incremental backups, except that each backup following the last full backup contains all the files that have changed or been added since the full backup. During a restore, you restore the full backup, then the last differential backup since it contains all the changes.

■ *Real-time backups* take place at any time and must have a procedure for handling files that are open by users. In most cases, the backup system tracks open files and returns to back them up later.

■ *Mirroring* provides real-time data protection as an adjunct to normal backup strategies. With mirroring, data is written to two or more magnetic disk drives simultaneously. If one fails, the other can take over. A *RAID, redundant arrays of inexpensive disks,* system spreads data writes over an array of disks along with parity information so that if one disk in the array fails, others remain operational.

■ The network administrator must take steps to protect the backup media and ensure the media are not exposed to the same disasters that might destroy online data, such as fire, floods, and earthquakes. This usually involves a *rotation scheme* in which backup tapes are carried offsite to a secure location. Backups might also take place over wide area connections in which data is copied over a high-speed data link to a remote location. But keep in mind that data is exposed to monitoring during the transmission.

Backup Media and Devices

There are several methods you can use to back up network data. The media you choose depend on the access requirements, portability, read/write performance, and other factors.

Floppy Disks

Floppy disks are sufficient for some workstation backup requirements, but they are inadequate for server backup. The method requires time and attention from a human operator, is not cost-effective, and has more potential for failure (for example, the operator gets bored with the procedure and occasionally skips it). Automated procedures using tape or other media are best.

Quarter-Inch Cartridges (QIC)

The QIC tape is well established in the computer industry as a backup solution. It was first introduced by 3M Company in 1972 as a medium for recording continuous serial data streams from test equipment and information-gathering devices. Today, it is a primary backup method for thousands of organizations. Data is sequentially recorded on parallel tracks of a tape, first in one direction, then on the next track and in the other direction. As shown in Figure B-7, each tape has a rubber wheel that contacts and is driven by a capstan in the drive. A belt system is attached to this wheel, which drives the supply and take-up spools in the cartridge. The drives themselves include a motor and read/write head. The tapes are 6×4×5/8 inches in size.

There are many vendors with many different types of systems and backup strategies. Early systems attached to floppy disk controllers while more recent systems use proprietary accelerator adapters or Small Computer System Interface (SCSI) adapters to increase performance. Current tape formats hold anywhere from 250 megabytes to 1 gigabyte of data. The original cartridge, called the CD300A, held 300

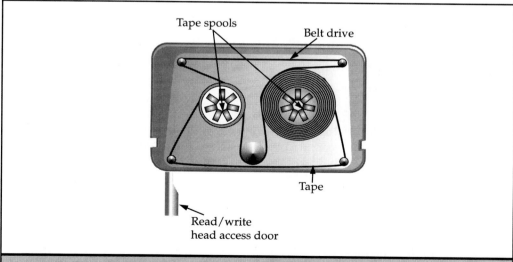

Figure B-7.   *Tape cartridge for backup system*

feet of tape and had a data capacity of 2 to 15 megabytes. A 600-foot version called the DC600 was introduced later, with much larger data capacities. Today, an industry organization called the QIC Committee has defined a whole series of QIC tapes. Each tape provides increased numbers of tracks and data densities. The newest standards use DC6000 cartridges with capacities in the gigabyte ranges. There are proposed standards for 10- and 35-gigabyte tapes with 144 tracks and 216 tracks respectively. Special encoding techniques and a precision tape mechanism will be required to read and write these tapes.

Minicartridges

Minicartridges use the same belt drive systems as the previously mentioned QIC cartridges, but are only 3.25×2.5×0.625 inches in size. The cartridges are collectively named DC2000, and format standards range from the original QIC-40 tape (20 tracks, 60 megabytes) to the QIC-80 tape (32 tracks, 80 or 120 megabytes). A special high-performance, low-capacity tape called the QIC-100 (40 megabytes) was designated, but it was never widely used. Emerging tape formats will hold as much as 500 megabytes and future standards may hold as much as 10 to 35 gigabytes.

Helical-Scan Tape Systems

In a helical-scan system, magnetic tape wraps around a moving drum that reads and writes data in parallel, diagonally adjoining paths. The combination of the moving tape and moving drum provide a high data-transfer rate. The technique was first used in the television industry as a way to record television pictures on tape. The rotating read/write head (or drum) is tilted at a slight angle to the tape, which traces a repeating helix pattern on the tape and optimizes tape surface tracking. The drum is part of the recording device, and tape feeds out of the cartridge around it. One interesting feature is that tracks can overlap because data can be written into each track at different angles. Thus, when the head reads a track, it only reads data written at a specific angle. Data written at other angles has a weaker signal with respect to the head.

Two standard tape formats use helical-scan technology: digital audio tape (DAT) and 8 mm tape.

DIGITAL AUDIO TAPES (DATS)   DATs were originally designed for music, but were quickly adopted for data backup because of their high transfer rates and capacities. The cassettes are 2.9×2.1×0.4 inches in size with a tape width of 4mm. Tapes can hold up to 2.5 gigabytes of uncompressed data. DATs use the Digital Data Storage (DDS) storage format, which writes data sequentially. A new format called *Data/DAT* is planned. Data/DAT will allow quicker random file updates and retrieval.

EIGHT-MILLIMETER TAPE SYSTEMS   Eight-millimeter helical-scan tape systems use a tape that is 8mm wide (obviously) in a cassette that measures 3.75×2.5 inches. Since the tape is twice as big as DAT tape, it can hold twice their capacity. All 8 mm devices are manufactured by Exabyte Corporation, although Sony was the original developer. Various vendors repackage the 8 mm Exabyte devices and provide special backup software and other add-ons to go with the drives. It is possible to store up to 2.5 to 5 megabytes of data on a single tape without compression and up to 10 megabytes with compression.

Optical Storage Devices

Optical storage technologies provide relatively quick access to backups and archives because they provide random access capabilities. Disk lifetimes are estimated in centuries. Write once, read-many (WORM) drives and rewritable optical drives are required for backup systems. While rewritable optical disk technology is still fairly expensive and slow, it offers convenience. In addition, speed is not a factor if backups take place during off-hours.

Some optical disk systems designed for data archiving purposes provide *jukebox* capabilities. A jukebox has an *autochanger* mechanism that mounts and dismounts disks upon requests for files. A typical jukebox might have up to four optical drives and a device that picks disks from a bay and inserts them in the drives. Hierarchical management systems use jukeboxes such as those made by Hewlett-Packard.

WORM DRIVES   WORM drives are capable of permanently writing spots corresponding to digital data on the substrate sandwiched between the compact disk's plastic layers. A laser light causes a chemical reaction that darkens the media. Some disks are double-sided. Each WORM drive vendor produces its own specialized products. While industry standards exist, vendors have produced devices that use different disk sizes and write patterns. Thus, it is usually not possible to interchange disks between different vendor's devices. If you do need to interchange disks, check with the vendor for compatible devices.

REWRITABLE OPTICAL DISKS   The rewritable optical disk provides a permanent or changeable data storage solution for backup or archiving. While rewritable optical disk technology stores large amounts of information, there are limitations in the number of times you can actually rewrite the disks. The three main rewritable optical disk technologies are described here:

■ *Magnetic-Optical Technology* This technology is currently used in most rewritable drives. The recording medium in the disks is a magnetic material. The write heads of the drive change the magnetic field of the material to record digital information with the assistance of a laser. The material is highly resistant to change, but when heated with a laser, a high magnetic flux can be applied to change the magnetic state of the very small area heated by the laser. Thus, the technology combines the permanence of magnetic media with the data-packing benefits of optical technology. Because the magnetic material is highly resistant to change, it has a much longer shelf-life than other magnetic media such as floppy disks, hard drives, and tape, and is less susceptible to accidental erasure by an outside source. The magnetically altered disk is read by using a laser that reflects a polarized beam of light off the magnetically aligned particles of the disk.

■ *Phase-change technology*   This technique uses a laser to change a crystalline material to an amorphous state, altering the reflectivity of the material, and thus providing a way to record digital information. A problem with this technology is that the material has limitations in the number of times it can be changed (a few thousand times), so disks must be occasionally retired.

■ *Dye polymer technology*   In this technique, the heat of a laser causes a spot on a die-tinted polymer material sandwiched between the disk's outer casing to physically change its state. The change of state can represent binary information. To erase the disk, the material is reheated with another laser and returns to its original state. Some vendor's systems use disks that can be played on industry-standard CD-ROM players. As with phase-change technology, disks can endure only a limited number of changes, and must be retired based on the manufacturer's specifications.

Backup Procedures

If you are not using a continuous backup system, your backups should follow a regular schedule to ensure that data is adequately protected. There are several types of backups and backup procedures, all of which are important in any backup strategy:

■ Back up the entire server on a regular basis or as often as a system has major changes to its software, user, directory structure, or data configurations.

■ Perform incremental backup procedures to back up files that change between major backup.

■ Rotate backups to protect from local disasters such as fire and use caution when transporting tapes to protect them from theft.

■ Run a restoration test to ensure that your backup and restore procedures work. Use a "spare" server to tests backups on a regular basis.

Maintaining a spare server is not a far-fetched idea. Remember, a downed network can cost your company thousands or millions of dollars, depending on how long it takes you to get the system back up and running. The server can be used for testing, spare parts, or emergency service. In fact, using both servers simultaneously is the basis of fault tolerant strategies, such as NetWare SFT III, as discussed under the heading "NetWare SFT Level III" later in this book.

Tape Rotation Methods

It's important to maintain more than one backup tape set for any system you back up. Storing some of those tapes at an offsite location, preferably in an insured tape storage facility, reduces the chance that a fire, flood, or other disaster will destroy all your

B

chances of re-creating a server from the tape backup. Assign the task of delivering the backup tapes to an employee or delivery service.

There are a number of tape backup strategies that vendors advocate. Some are very complex; others are very simple. Just about every tape and operating system vendor provides you with at least a few ideas on how to rotate your tapes. The least complex tape-rotation scheme uses three tape sets, assumes a five day work week, and assumes that data is backed up during off-hours when no one else is accessing the system. The tape sets are the current backup, the previous backup, and backup from two weeks ago. Each tape contains one week's worth of information. You start with a full backup on Monday, then create an incremental backup each day until Friday. The following Monday you insert a new tape and start the process over again. The current backup stays with the machine, you store the previous backup in a nearby vault, and store the two-week-old tape in an offsite location.

Another common tape backup rotations is the "Grandfather" method. It uses 22 tapes or tape sets, depending on the amount of data to back up:

1. You label five tape sets DAILY, five tape sets WEEKLY, and 12 tape sets with the months of the year.

2. Every Monday you start with the DAILY tapes that correspond to the week of the month (the first Monday of the month you use DAILY1, the second Monday you use DAILY2, and so forth).

3. Tuesday, Wednesday, and Thursday you make incremental backups.

4. Friday you retrieve tapes from offsite storage, create another full backup, and send it to offsite storage.

5. Always use the tapes that correspond to the current week of the month.

6. At the end of every month, you make another backup and place it in offsite storage.

This strategy allows you to retrieve data from a year ago if necessary and ensures that you will never lose more than one week's worth of data. Keeping the daily backups nearby allows you to retrieve up to a month's worth of data without waiting for a tape to be retrieved from offsite storage.

Whatever tape-rotation strategy you use, make sure it allows for both onsite and offsite storage. You need to keep more than one tape set near your machine in case your current tape breaks or fails in some other way. Ideally, you should have backups in both places, because waiting for someone to retrieve tapes from offsite storage is inconvenient—but losing your data to fire is devastating.

You also need to consider replacement of the actual tapes. There are two schools of thought in this area. The first method replaces a tape after a certain date. This method compensates for the environmental factors that break down the tape media. Most technicians agree that a tape is good for five years—at most— with correct onsite storage. High humidity and/or heat reduce the life span of your tapes, so you need to adjust replacement dates accordingly. If you use the tape on a regular basis, consider replacing it within two years of first use. The combination of tape wear and environmental factors breaks down the media even faster than if you only use the tape occasionally. The other tape replacement technique is to replace the tape after a certain number of uses. This method uses as its determining factor the amount of wear that a tape receives during use. Most technicians that use this method replace the tape after a maximum of 40 uses.

Real-Time Backup

Most backup procedures assume that backups are made at night when no one is accessing the system. But when servers are constantly accessed, the backup system must deal with files that are opened by users. To make matters worse, some files are constantly in use. Backups of such files are only good until the next change is made, which might be during the backup procedure.

To solve the open file problem, most backup utilities will keep track of open files, then periodically check to see if the files have closed. When a file closes, it is added to the backup. There are several methods for backing up files that constantly change, some being more secure (and more expensive) than others:

- ■ *Periodic backup*   A periodic backup is made at regular intervals, say every five or ten minutes. Then if the system goes down, data is restored from the last backup and users re-key information that might have been lost. Transaction tracking systems available in most server operating systems "roll-back" incomplete transactions.

- ■ *Perpetual backup*   This strategy maintains a master backup and a backup of every file that has changed. With this method, the state of the file system can be restored at any time, or before or after any particular file change.

- ■ *Mirroring*   A mirrored system has two or more hard drives. File changes are written to both systems simultaneously. If one drive fails, the other provides service to users. Backups are still required if mirroring is used to protect against system loss.

Hierarchical Storage Management (HSM)

HSM provides a way to move little used or unused files from fast magnetic storage to tape backup, optical disk systems (jukeboxes), or other archiving systems. They are also used in imaging systems to store scanned documents. Files are migrated after a specific period of time, and specific files can be marked for migration. Files that have been migrated are still available for use, and can be de-migrated back to magnetic disk for faster access. After a certain period of nonuse, these de-migrated files are migrated back to archive storage.

In Novell's High Capacity Storage System (HCSS), the migration can be controlled in intermediate steps, so that over time, little used data is eventually moved to the least expensive media (such as archive tapes). For example, if a file on a server's magnetic disk system is not used in 30 days, it is moved to optical disk, which still provides relatively efficient access. Files are easily de-migrated from optical disk back to magnetic disk if necessary. If files on optical disk are not accessed within 30 days, they can be further migrated to tape storage. File headers for de-migrated files are kept in the directories where the files were originally stored. To users, files appear to be on magnetic disk, and except for a slight delay in access, users may be unaware that a file has been de-migrated.

Backup in Selected Server Environments

Each server environment has its own backup procedures and commands. You can use the procedures and commands or take advantage of third-party alternatives in many cases.

Keep in mind that server operating systems create special files to hold user and group information, security information, access rights, and other information. These files are often hidden and sometimes left out of backup procedures. Some examples are listed in the following paragraphs. Be sure to check the documentation of server operating systems to determine the location of hidden system files that might not be included in your normal backup procedure.

AppleShare

In the AppleShare environment, the Users & Groups Data File created by the Admin program holds account and security information for users. Be sure to back up this file separately to floppy disk on a regular basis. The information restores the user environment in the event that the server must be restored. AppleShare does not include automatic backup utilities, but several are available from third-party developers. You can back up from the server or over the network.

Novell NetWare

A large number of vendors supply hardware and backup software that is compatible with NetWare. All major devices are supported. Both server-based and workstation-based backup methods are available, depending on the operating system version.

NetWare 3.x backup procedures must include backup of the hidden bindery files called NET&BIND.SYS and NET$BVAL.SYS, which are located in the SYS:SYSTEM directory. These files hold user and groups account information, as well as security and related information. In NetWare 4.x, user, group, security, and other information is stored in the Directory Services database, which can be automatically replicated in whole or in part to other servers on the network. See "Replication."

Novell has recently attempted to standardize the tape market with its Storage Management System (SMS). SMS is a set of specifications for backing up information on multiple operating systems. Many major system manufacturers are already supporting the standard, and backup device vendors are including SMS support within their packages. The main goals of SMS are to centralize and simplify the backup of NetWare data, no matter where it is on the network, and to support many different file types (other operating systems). SMS may be on its way to industry standardization since Novell has made it easy for vendors to integrate their hardware or applications into the specification. A strong feature of SMS is that it provides support for old hardware and backups, even if the standard changes well in the future.

Microsoft Products

Backing up Windows for Workgroups systems is a simple procedure that can use any DOS-based backup system. Windows NT provides its own backup utility that includes built-in support for a number of industry standard backup devices. Windows NT Advanced Server software includes the same backup utility in addition to providing disk mirroring, data striping, and support for parity (RAID 5).

RELATED ENTRIES   Archiving; Disk Mirroring and Duplexing; Disk Storage Systems; Fault Tolerance; Hierarchical Storage Management Systems; High Capacity Storage System, Novell NetWare; Jukebox Optical Storage Devices; Mirroring; Optical Libraries; Power and Grounding Problems and Solutions; Redundant Arrays of Inexpensive Disks; Storage Management System Novell; *and* Striping

Balun (BALanced UNbalanced)

Transmission lines can be "balanced" or "unbalanced." A balanced line is typically a twisted-pair or twinax cable that contains two conductors. An unbalanced line is typically a coaxial cable. In a balanced line, both wires are connected to the generator (sender) and receiver and each of the wires has an equal current, but the currents are in opposite directions. In an unbalanced line, current flows through the signal conductor and returns on the ground.

A balun (balanced/unbalanced) provides a way to join these two different types of cables when connecting terminals to IBM hosts. Network installers who want to convert from coaxial to twisted-pair cable for a particular cable run can do so by installing balun transformers. A balun is required on each side of the twisted-pair run.

Bandwidth

Bandwidth in a communication channel is the difference between the highest and lowest frequencies in a specific range of frequencies. The range of frequencies is usually specified in hertz (cycles-per-second). For example, the analog signals for telephone communication occupy the voice frequency range of 300 to 3,300 Hz. Thus, the voice bandwidth, or passband, is 3,000 Hz wide as pictured in Figure B-8.

Note that while these numbers define the speech range, a voice-band channel is defined as having a 4 KHz bandwidth. The extra bandwidth is used to insert a guard band on both sides of the speech channel to reduce interference with other channels

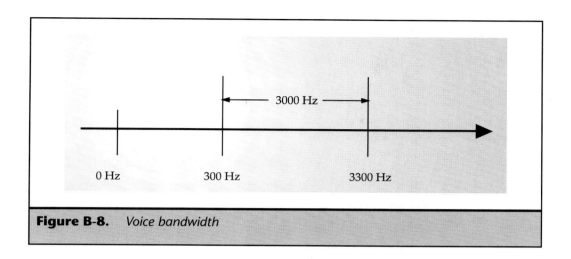

Figure B-8.   *Voice bandwidth*

on the line. Incidentally, this narrow band was originally used to efficiently implement frequency division multiplexing, which transmits multiple calls on a single circuit.

The Federal Communications Commission (FCC) is in charge of allocating the electromagnetic spectrum and thus the bandwidth of various communication systems. In the electromagnetic spectrum, sound waves occupy low ranges while microwaves, visible light, ultraviolet, and X-rays occupy upper ranges. The bandwidth occupied by various communication technologies is discussed below.

- Bandwidths in the 500 to 929 MHz range are allocated to television and radio broadcast, as well as transportation radio (taxis, for example).
- The bandwidth from 932 to 1,999 MHz is allocated to planes and ships.
- Spread-spectrum radio used for security and paging systems occupies 902 to 928 MHz.
- Wireless mobile communications is allocated to the 930 to 931 MHz and 2,000 to 2,400 MHz (2 to 2.4 GHz) ranges.

RELATED ENTRIES   Data Transfer Rates; Radio Networks; Transmission Media, Methods, and Equipment

Bandwidth on Demand

Bandwidth on demand is a feature of data communication networks that accommodates bursts in data traffic and the need for additional bandwidth. Most network traffic does not flow in steady predictable streams, and therefore it is often difficult for managers to determine the type of wide area network connections they need. Dialup modems might provide adequate service for occasional file transfers, but real-time access to databases and other applications will drive up demand for bandwidth on wide area connections.

Dedicated T1 lines (1.544 Mbits/sec) or T3 lines (45 Mbits/sec) can handle higher traffic requirements, but the lines have a set bandwidth that is often underused, then overloaded during traffic peaks. Some experts estimate that T1 activity peaks only 20 percent of the time. Decisions to add more dedicated bandwidth to handle peaks are difficult. AT&T provides services to accommodate extra traffic loads, but 24-hour advance notice is required in some cases.

A solution is available in switched data services such as Frame Relay, Switched Multimegabit Data Service (SMDS), and Asynchronous Transfer Mode (ATM). The public data network (PDN) community, which includes AT&T, CompuServe, US Spring, MCI, and others, are deploying switched data services that provide bandwidth on demand so customers can build *virtual data networks* that connect outlying offices on a metropolitan or global scale. Since connections are not dedicated, customers can connect to any point at any time, accommodating worker reassignments, office moves, and temporary connections. And because the lines are switched, customers only pay for services used. In addition, bandwidth is immediately available to accommodate bursts in traffic. A virtual data network provides a way to fully interconnect all systems at all sites in an organization at much lower costs.

Another solution is the use of inverse-multiplexing. In this technique, an inverse multiplexer splits a signal over several switched lines that have the same end points. The signals are recombined at the other end. If more bandwidth is required, the inverse multiplexer connects another line to handle the traffic load, then disconnects the lines when traffic stabilizes. Dial-up analog lines and Switched-56 lines are often used in this technique.

RELATED ENTRIES   Carrier Services; Data Transfer Rates; Fast Packet Switching; Frame Relay; Multiplexing; Switched-56 Services; Switched Multimegabit Data Service; Switched Services; *and* Wide Area Networks

Banyan VINES

Banyan VINES is a networking operating system that allows users of popular PC desktop operating systems such as DOS, OS/2, Windows, and those for Macintosh systems to share information and resources with each other and with host computing systems. VINES is based on UNIX, and it first appeared in the 1980s. VINES provides full UNIX Network File System (NFS) support in its core services and the Transmission Control Protocol/Internet Protocol (TCP/IP) for transport.

Like other networks, VINES is built around servers that provide services to client workstations. It is designed to help organizations build fully distributed computing environments around a suite of enterprise network services, including security, messaging, administration, host connectivity, and wide area network communication. StreetTalk provides directory services to help managers and users keep track of users and resources on the network.

VINES provides enterprise network services that are not server-centric, but services-centric. Users on Banyan networks access and view resources logically, without needing to know where resources are physically located. Users see the entire network and need only log on once. The following sections define the key core network services in VINES.

Global Directory Services

Banyan's StreetTalk Directory service is designed to integrate and manage a growing variety of heterogeneous environments including Banyan networks, UNIX, and NetWare. It extends peer-to-peer client workgroups to encompass every user and resource on the network. StreetTalk integrates with all VINES core services so that network services and applications always know a user's physical location and security privileges. Users can log on from any location and their network environment remains the same. In addition, users log on to the network, not to an individual server.

StreetTalk Directory Assistance (STDA) provides distributed directory services. It collects information about network-wide services and places the information in databases that users can search when looking for other users or services on the network. The data includes information about users, printers, files, and gateways. Administrator-defined attributes are preconfigured with the standard attribute types defined in the X.500 specification.

Banyan Services

The following services are provided in the Banyan VINES operating system, which includes the following product lineup:

- *VINES 5, VINES 10, VINES 20*   Provide Banyan's enterprise network services to 5, 10, or 20 users, respectively.
- *VINES Unlimited*   Provides VINES services to an unlimited number of users.
- *VINES Symmetric Multiprocessing (SMP)*   Provides VINES services on multiprocessing platforms and delivers higher levels of performance using symmetric multiprocessing
- *VINES on UNIX*   Provides VINES services on SCO (The Santa Cruz Operation) UNIX.

SECURITY SERVICES   Banyan's security services work constantly to authenticate user requests and determine user authorization with every attempt to access a network resource. Security services provide login restrictions, password control, directory access controls, and internetwork security for all items in all groups maintained on that particular server. These are the key security components:

- *VINES Security Service (VSS)*   This service verifies a user's StreetTalk name and password by examining the user profile and any security information associated with the user or groups the user belongs to.

- *User Profiles*   This is the control mechanism for user access to the network. A user profile is created for each new user account and hold information about the resources a user can access, as well as any restrictions they have to the network, such as login location and login times.

- *Access Rights Lists (ARL)*   An ARL is associated with every directory and file in the VINES File Service and define who can access directories and files based on access rights such as Control, Scan, Read, Write, and Delete.

NETWORK MANAGEMENT SERVICES   Management services provide a way for central staff or administrators to control or monitor all critical network connectivity or performance-related data and events in real time from any location on the network. Management of the network can be centralized or distributed throughout the organization.

SYSTEM ADMINISTRATION SERVICES   These services provide a way to administer users and user profiles on the network. Tasks such as moving or adding services, managing lists and allocating resources are simplified.

Messaging Services

These services provide electronic mail capabilities to every user in the enterprise. Messaging is integrated with StreetTalk so users can quickly locate user names and addresses.

Baseband

Baseband is a transmission method in which voltage pulses are applied directly to the cable and use the full signal spectrum of that cable. Compare baseband to broadband transmission, in which radio signals from multiple channels are modulated onto separate "carrier" frequencies, and in which the bandwidth is subdivided into separate communication channels that occupy a specific frequency range.

LocalTalk and Ethernet are baseband networks; they transmits only one signal at a time. The signals applied to the cable change its voltage level to indicate the digital value 0 or 1. A communication session is established between two systems using the entire bandwidth of the cable. Each system then transmits in turn. Other systems that share the cable cannot transmit during this period.

The direct-current signals placed on a baseband transmission system have a tendency to degrade over distance due to resistance, capacitance, and other factors. In addition, outside interference from electrical fields generated by motors, fluorescent lights, and other electrical devices can further corrupt the signal. The higher the data transmission rate, the more susceptible the signal is to degradation. For this reason, networking standards such as Ethernet specify cable types, cable shielding, cable distances, transmission rates, and other details that are known to work and provide relatively error-free service in most environments.

RELATED ENTRIES   Cabling; Ethernet; *and* Transmission Media, Methods, and Equipment

Baud

Baud is a measure of signal changes per second in a device such as a modem. It represents the number of times the state of a communication line changes per second. The name comes from the Frenchman Baudot, who developed an encoding scheme for the French telegraph system in 1877.

Baud is no longer used to refer to modem speeds because it does not have a relationship to the number of bits transferred per second. If a modem transferred 1 bit for every signal change, then its bits-per-second rate and baud rate would be the same. However, encoding techniques are employed to make 1 baud or signal change represent 2 or more bits. Two bits per baud is known as dibit encoding and 3 bits per baud is known as tribit encoding.

RELATED ENTRIES   Modems; Modulation Techniques; *and* Telecommunication

Bellman-Ford Distance-Vector Routing Algorithm

An internetwork is a collection of subnetworks connected by routers. Routers exchange routing information so they know the current status of the network and how to route packets to their destination. One method for merging router information is the Bellman-Ford distance-vector routing algorithm. It is well defined and used on a number of popular networks. The Bellman-Ford algorithm provides reasonable performance on small- to medium-sized networks. On larger networks, the algorithm can provide slow updates. In some cases, looping occurs in which a packet goes through the same node more than once. Distance-vector routing (DVR) is not suitable for larger networks that have thousands of nodes, dynamic network configurations that require constant updating, and networks that put more focus on routers to handle such tasks as security and congestion management. A more efficient routing protocol is Open Shortest Path First (OSPF).

RELATED ENTRIES   Open Shortest Path First Protocol; Routing Protocols

Bell Modem Standards

The Bell standards were the first methods used to control the communication process between two modems. The first of these standards was Bell 103, which paved the way for today's complex and efficient modem standards, such as V.32bis and V.42bis. While AT&T largely controlled the standardization of the original modem standards, the Consultative Committee for International Telegraph and Telephone (CCITT), established as part of the United Nations International Telecommunications Union (ITU), controls most standardization today. The Bell standards are summarized here:

- *Bell 103* Supports 300 baud transmissions.
- *Bell 113A and 113D* A originates calls, and D answers calls.
- *Bell 201B* Supports synchronous 2,400 bits/sec full-duplex transmissions.
- *Bell 202* Supports asynchronous 1,800 bits/sec full-duplex transmissions.
- *Bell 208* Supports synchronous 4,800 bits/sec transmissions.
- *Bell 209* Supports synchronous 9,600 bits/sec full-duplex transmissions.
- *Bell 212A* Supports 1,200 bits/sec full-duplex transmissions (equivalent CCITT V.22 standard).

Many other standards have been developed since these initial standards, such as the CCITT "V dot" series standards. Microcom, a modem and communications software vendor, developed several standards on its own that have also come into widespread use or been integrated into ITU standards.

RELATED ENTRIES Microcom Networking Protocol; Modems; Modulation Techniques; Telecommunication; *and* "V dot" Standards, CCITT

Bell Operating Companies

See AT&T; Carriers; Carrier Services; Local Access and Transport Area; *and* Regional Bell Operating Companies.

Binary Synchronous Communications (BISYNC)

Binary synchronous communications, or BISYNC, is a form of communication developed by IBM in the 1960s. It was originally designed for batch transmissions between the IBM S/360 mainframe family and IBM 2780 and 3780 terminals. It supports online and remote job entry (RJE) terminals in the CICS/VSE (Customer Information Control System/Virtual Storage Extended) environment. BISYNC provides the rules for the transmission of binary-coded data between a terminal and a host computer's BISYNC port. BISYNC has the following features:

- BISYNC operates with both ASCII and EBCDIC character sets.
- While BISYNC is a half-duplex protocol, it will synchronize in both directions on a full-duplex channel.

- BISYNC supports both point-to-point (over leased or dialup lines) and multipoint transmissions.
- Each message must be acknowledged, adding to its overhead.

BISYNC is character-oriented, meaning that groups of bits (characters) are the main elements of transmission, rather than a stream of bits. The BISYNC frame is pictured in Figure B-9. It starts with two sync characters that the receiver and transmitter use for synchronizing. This is followed by a start of header (SOH) command, and then the header. Following this are the start of text (STX) command, and the text. Finally, an end of text (EOT) command and a cyclic redundancy check (CRC) end the frame. The CRC provides error detection and correction.

Most of the bisynchronous protocols, of which there are many, provide only half-duplex transmission and require an acknowledgment for every block of transmitted data. Some do provide full-duplex transmission and bit-oriented operation. BISYNC has largely been replaced by the more powerful Synchronous Data Link Protocol (SDLC).

Bindery

The bindery is a database file in NetWare operating systems previous to NetWare 4.x that holds security, accounting, and name management information for a server. The bindery has the following features and properties:

- Every server on the network maintains its own bindery.
- The bindery contains *object* records. Objects are server entities, such as users, groups, and the server name.
- Object have attributes, called *properties* such as passwords, account restrictions, account balances, group membership, and so on.
- Properties have values, which are kept in a separate but related file.

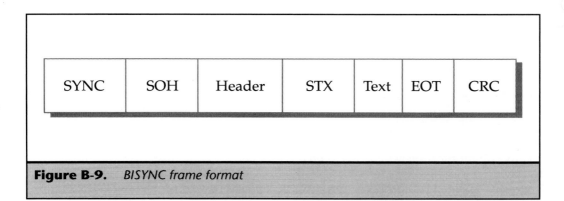

| SYNC | SOH | Header | STX | Text | EOT | CRC |

Figure B-9. *BISYNC frame format*

■ The bindery includes two files stored in the SYS:SYSTEM directory. NET$BIND.SYS holds the bindery object and property information. NET$BVAL.SYS holds the property values.

■ The bindery files are hidden, therefore it is essential that backup operators make sure they are included in backups. It's also a good idea to create a separate backup of the bindery.

The bindery is critical to NetWare's operation, and it is referenced often. The SYS:SYSTEM directory and its bindery files should be placed on the fastest drive possible, or the bindery files should be kept in cache memory at all times by ensuring that the server has more than enough memory to do so.

Objects in the bindery have object type codes associated with them that identify what kind of object they are. With appropriate applications, users access the bindery to list or search for objects that have specific names. Objects are referenced using 4-byte ID codes, and once found, the property values of the objects are used to determine access to the system or the type of action that can take place.

Two NetWare utilities are related to the bindery. BINDFIX.EXE attempts to repair a damaged bindery. BINDREST.EXE restores the bindery to its previous state when BINDFIX.EXE is unsuccessful at fixing the bindery.

BITNET

The *Because It's Time Network (BITNET)* is an international network managed by the Corporation for Research and Educational Networking (CREN). CREN also provides BITNET with information services. BITNET is used mainly for electronic mail services, but offers other services as well. There are gateways between BITNET and the Internet that allow the exchange of electronic mail and other services. BITNET consists of over 2,500 host computers at sites in the U.S., Canada, Mexico, South America, Europe, and Japan. The host sites are typically universities.

BITNET was established in the early 1980s as an outgrowth of the ARPANET. The ARPANET was funded by ARPA (Advanced Research Projects Agency), which later became DARPA (Defense Advanced Research Projects Agency). The ARPANET network linked defense facilities, government research laboratories, and university sites and later evolved into the Internet. BITNET was established as a separate academic network without DARPA funding because DARPA was restricted from providing support outside of the military establishment.

RELATED ENTRY   Internet

Bit-Oriented Protocol

In any communication session between devices, control codes are used to control another device or provide information about the status of the session. Byte- or character-oriented protocols use full bytes to represent established control codes such as those defined by the American Standard Code for Information Interchange (ASCII). Bit-oriented protocols rely on individual bits for control information.

In a bit-oriented transmission, data is transmitted as a steady stream of bits. The transmission is synchronous and the transmitting and receiving devices use a clocking signal to determine where each character begins and ends in the data stream. This is in contrast to asynchronous communications, in which each character is separated by a start bit and stop bit.

Before actual data transmission begins, special *sync* characters are transmitted by the sender so the receiver can synchronize its clock. This bit pattern is usually in the form of a specially coded 8-bit string. IBM Synchronous Data Link Control (SDLC) protocol is bit-oriented. The sync character is the bit string 01111110, and this is followed by an 8-bit address, an 8-bit control field, and the data. The clock at the receiving end provides the timing signal that separates the data into characters. Following the data is an error check and an ending flag.

IBM's SDLC and High-level Data Link Control (HDLC) are bit-oriented protocols that control synchronous communication. HDLC is used in X.25 packet switching networks; SDLC is a subset of HDLC.

RELATED ENTRIES   Byte-Oriented Protocol; Synchronous Communications; *and* Synchronous Data Link Control

Block Suballocation

This NetWare 4.X feature maximizes disk space. If there are any partially used disk blocks (usually a block is 8 kilobytes in size), NetWare divides them into 512-byte suballocation blocks for the storage of small files or fragments of files.

RELATED ENTRY   Disks, Partitions, and Volumes Under NetWare

BNC Connector

BNC connectors are used to connect, extend, or terminate coaxial cable networks such as Ethernet and ARCNET. There are various connectors, such as the BNC T-connector, BNC barrel connector, and the BNC terminator, as pictured in Figure B-10.

■ The BNC connector attaches directly to the cable. It has a center pin that is soldered onto the center wire of the cable, and an outer casing, to which the shielding ground wire is attached. BNC connectors are pushed onto the ends of T-connectors, then the outer housing is twisted to lock it into place.

■ The BNC T-connector provides the cable attachment to the network interface card. Cables branch from either side of the T to the next stations up or down in the trunk cable.

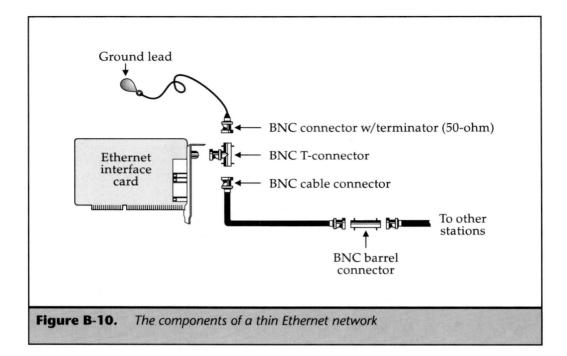

Figure B-10.   *The components of a thin Ethernet network*

■ The BNC terminator has a resistor to terminate the coaxial cable. Each end of the coaxial cable trunk requires a terminator, and one end requires a ground lead, as shown in the illustration.

■ The BNC barrel connector is used to join two cable segments.

RELATED ENTRIES   Cabling; Ethernet; *and* Transmission Media, Methods, and Equipment

Border Gateway Protocol (BGP)

BGP is an Internet exterior gateway routing protocol that accumulates information about the reachability of neighbors from packets as they traverse the network. Route attributes such as the cost or security of a path are also added. BGP reduces the bandwidth required to exchange routing information because the information is exchanged incrementally, rather than by sending the entire database.

RELATED ENTRIES   Domains; Routing, Internet; *and* Routing Protocols

Breakout Box

See Testing Equipment and Techniques.

Bridging

A *bridge* is an internetworking device that provides a communication pathway between two or more network segments or subnetworks. A network segment or subnetwork has the same network address and the same type of networking technology. For example, Figure B-11 illustrates how a server provides bridging between two network adapters. The bridge provides a way for a station on one network to broadcast messages to stations on the other network. It is therefore a two-port (or more) device that joins network segments. On the other hand, a bridge can be used to split a busy network into two segments, thus reducing the amount of traffic on each and improving performance. Bridges can filter broadcasts on one network from reaching another, allowing only essential internetwork traffic to cross the bridge. Other internetworking devices discussed in this book include *repeaters*, *routers*, and *gateways*.

You install bridges for the following reasons:

- To expand the distance or number of nodes for the entire network.
- To reduce traffic bottlenecks caused by an excessive number of attached nodes.
- To link unlike networks such as Ethernet and token ring and forward packets between them, assuming they run the same network protocol.

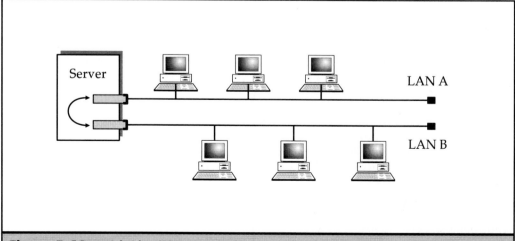

Figure B-11.   *A bridge joins two similar networks to extend their maximum length and increase performance by segmenting network traffic*

A bridge is a stand-alone device or is created in servers by installing one or more network interface cards, assuming the server operating system supports bridging. Each local area network (LAN) segment connected by a bridge has a distinct network number. As an analogy, the network number is like a street name, and workstation numbers are like house numbers. A bridge forwards packets between attached network segments. Novell NetWare, Banyan VINES, and Microsoft networks provide server bridging. External bridging is required if bridging functions bog down a server. External bridges are manufactured by Cisco, 3COM, Cabletron, and many others vendors.

Bridges provide filtering functions by reading the address in the Ethernet or token ring frame to determine which LAN segment data packets belong to. However, bridges don't have access to Network layer protocol information so they can't provide best-path routing. Routers can be programmed (or will learn) to route packets over specific paths to reduce costs or avoid traffic congestion and multiprotocol routers can be used to handle network traffic that consists of multiple communications protocols.

As networks grow, the number of bridged connections grows, opening up the possibility that loops or inefficient paths will appear. The avoidance of loops in bridged networks is discussed later. Bridges also lack congestion management besides being incapable of determining optimal data pathways. Congestion occurs when many workstations need to broadcast. In a bridged network, flow control is relegated to the end system. Bridges may actually add to the congestion problems by transmitting excess packets in an attempt to recover congestion problems. These problems are discussed later in this section under "The Spanning Tree Algorithm."

Types of Bridges

There are generally two types of bridges: *local* and *remote*. A local bridge provides connection points for LANS, and is used to interconnect LAN segments within the same building or area as shown on the bottom in Figure B-12. Remote bridges have ports for analog or digital telecommunication links to connect networks at other locations, as shown on the top in Figure B-12. Connections between remote bridges are made over analog lines using modems, or over digital leased lines like T1 that provide 1.544 Mbits/sec throughput.

An analog line is basically a voice-grade, dialup telephone line that provides a circuit to connect bridges on a temporary dialup basis (see "Circuit-Switching Services" later in this book) or on a permanent basis (see "Leased Line" later in this book). A dedicated leased line can provide faster and better quality service than is possible on dialup connections because the phone company can guarantee the connection. However, the lease rate may not be in line with the requirements of the network. A dialup line is appropriate for occasional use, such as file transfers or a bulk transfer of electronic mail between company locations. Leased lines are best for continual use.

B

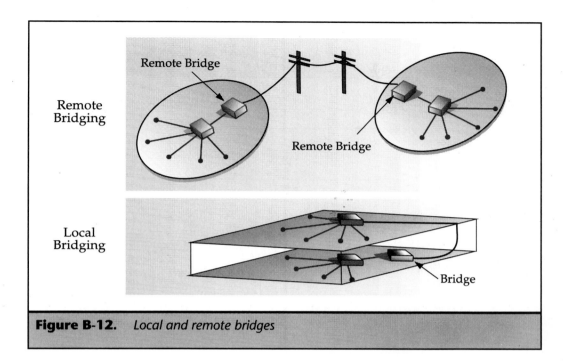

Figure B-12.   *Local and remote bridges*

Bridge Functionality

A bridge can join two similar or dissimilar LAN segments. You can think of a bridge as a mail sorter that looks at the addresses of packets and places them on the appropriate network segments. Bridging takes place in the Data-Link layer relative to the Open Systems Interconnection (OSI) protocol model. Any device that conforms to the media access control (MAC) specifications of the IEEE 802 standard can bridge with other IEEE MAC devices. Ethernet, token ring, and Fiber Distributed Data Interface (FDDI) are examples of networks that conform to IEEE 802 standards for MAC-level bridging. Because of this, bridging devices that join Ethernet or token ring networks to FDDI backbones are common, as discussed under Backbones.

The Data-Link layer is subdivided into the upper logical link control (LLC) sublayer and the lower MAC sublayer. Devices that support the IEEE 802 standard have a modular MAC sublayer that can handle multiple network types, such as Ethernet, or token ring, as shown in Figure B-13. The upper LLC sublayer then serves as a "switchboard" that moves data packets among the network modules in the MAC sublayer. In this example, the data is removed from the Ethernet frame and repackaged with token ring frame formats. This extra processing does introduce some slowdown, so bridges are usually rated according to the number of packets they can process per second.

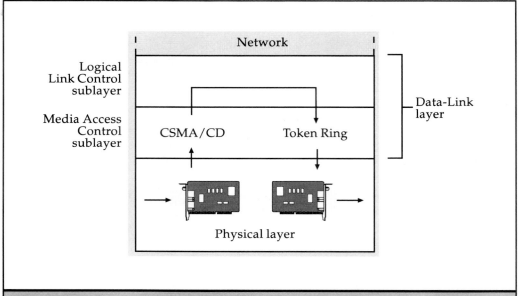

Figure B-13. *A bridge links media access control sublayer devices through the logical link control sublayer*

Bridges provide the following functions:

■ *Frame forwarding* Frame forwarding is a form of filtering. A bridge will forward packets to other LAN segments if their address matches the segments address. This prevents locally addressed packets from crossing a bridge. Without filtering, packets are sent everywhere on a network. When a packet arrives at a bridge, the bridge reads the destination address in the packets and determines whether it should forward the packet across the bridge.

■ *Loop resolution* Large-bridged LANs may have loops that could cause a packet to travel continuously. Some bridges will detect such looping packets and intercept them.

■ *Learning techniques* Bridges build address tables that describe routes by either examining packet flow or obtaining information from "explorer packets" that have learned about the network topology during their travels. The first method is called *transparent bridging,* and the second is called *source routing.* These learning techniques are discussed next.

Early bridges required that network managers hand-enter the address tables. This was a tedious task, and the tables had to be periodically updated if a workstation or user moved to another location. Today's advanced bridges can learn the address of other stations on the network using techniques discussed here. Note that transparent bridges are often called learning bridges, and they use the spanning tree algorithm, which is the IEEE 802.1 standard. Transparent bridging is found in the Ethernet environment while source routing is found in the token ring environment.

Transparent Bridging

Transparent bridges automatically set about learning the topology of the network environment as soon as they are installed and powered up. As packets arrive on bridge ports, transparent bridges look at the source address and add entries to bridging tables. These entries associate the source address with the network address from which the packet arrived. A typical table for two LAN segments (segment 123 and segment 456) is shown in Figure B-14. The bridging table is constantly updated with new source addresses and updates as the network changes.

Arriving packets are forwarded based on table information and may be repackaged if the destination network is different. A discovery process is initiated if an address is not found in the table. A frame is sent to all LAN segments except the one from which the frame originated. When the destination responds back with a network

Network	Source address
123	32156
123	16584
456	30925
123	93643
456	89621
456	66329
123	54615
⋮	⋮

Figure B-14.   *Bridging table*

address, the bridge makes a new entry in its bridging table. Given time, a bridge will learn the address of every node on the network.

The number of interconnected network segments is an issue in the learning process. If a bridge only connects two network segments, it is relatively easy to build a table that defines which stations are on one side and which are on the other. However, the bridge must first learn the address of each connected network by forwarding packets from one side of the bridge to the other and listening for a response from the destination.

How do you interconnect multiple LAN segments? The network at the top in Figure B-15 must transmit packets from the left segment through the middle segment to reach the right segment. This can cause performance problems in the middle; however, only two bridges are required. An alternate method is to attach a bridge to each LAN segment and connect the bridges to a backbone network such as an FDDI ring, as shown at the bottom in Figure B-15.

On large interconnected networks, multiple bridge paths are possible that can form a closed loop and cause packets to circle endlessly, reducing performance or crippling the network. In the worst case, *broadcast storms* occur when new packets are endlessly generated to correct the problem. But multiple paths are necessary to provide fault tolerance, as shown in Figure B-16. If the link between LAN A and LAN B goes down, an alternate link is still available indirectly through LAN C. The spanning tree algorithm (STA) provides a way to create multiple paths while preventing loops. However, STA does this by blocking one path until it is needed. This

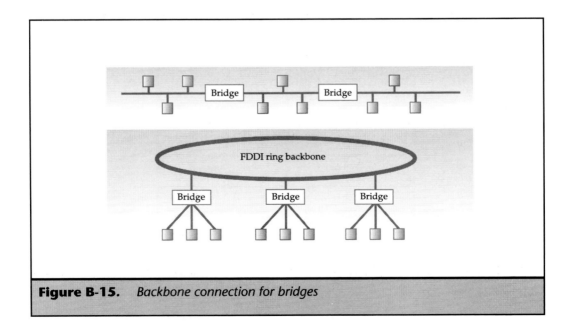

Figure B-15.   *Backbone connection for bridges*

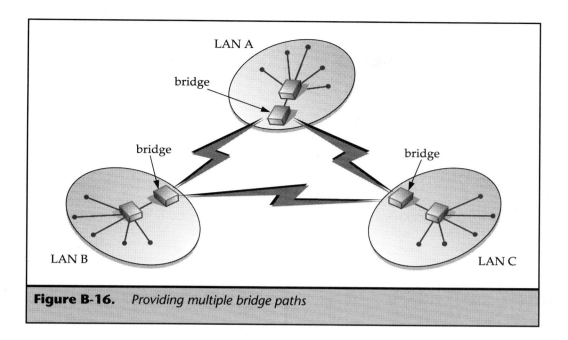

Figure B-16. *Providing multiple bridge paths*

blocked path should be a switched analog or digital line that is put into service only when needed. An alternate strategy called load sharing solves this problem somewhat.

The Spanning Tree Algorithm

Spanning tree bridges detect and break circular traffic patterns by disabling certain links in Ethernet networks. The IEEE 801.2-D spanning tree protocol (STP) inhibits loops in redundant bridges by maintaining the secondary bridge as a backup. If the first bridge goes down, the secondary bridge takes over.

- The algorithm assigns unique *identifiers* to each bridge, which is usually the bridge's MAC address.

- A *priority value* is also assigned to each bridge.

- Each port on every bridge is assigned a unique *identifier*.

- Each bridge port is then assigned a *path cost* that assigns a value to ports. The network administrator can change cost values manually to assign preferences for a particular port.

As the algorithm proceeds, a root bridge is selected from the set of bridges. The bridge with the lowest identifier is selected as the root. Once the root bridge is selected, other bridges determine which of their ports provides access to the root bridge at the least cost. This port becomes the *root port* of the bridge. If ports have the same costs, then the one with the least number of bridge-to-bridge hops is used.

The last step is to determine which bridges and bridge ports will provide a pathway through the network to the root based on the least path cost. This process enables some ports to ensure forwarding paths for some bridges and disables other ports to prevent loops. The disabled ports are attached to dial-on-demand modems or bridges that establish connections of switched telecommunications links only in the event the path is required or if the line can safely be used with causing loops.

Load-Sharing Bridges

When bridges use leased lines to span wide areas, it is not economically feasible in the minds of most network managers to block the line and only use it for a backup. Some bridge manufacturers provide load-sharing bridges that are capable of using the backup link to share the network load without causing loops. The load-sharing bridge is the most efficient form of bridge. It uses a spanning tree-type algorithm, and it uses a dual link to transfer packets, thus improving internetwork performance.

Source Route Bridging

IBM Token Ring networks use a special source routing method that tells the bridge not only where packets should go but how to get to their destination. In source routing, the packets themselves hold the forwarding information. Path information is placed directly in packets so they can find their way through the network on their own.

Bridges that do source routing use a *discovery* method to first determine the route a packet should take to a destination. Note that although this sounds like routing, the source routing bridge is simply a forwarding device that knows the addresses of other bridges. Best-path routing information is contained within the packet. This has advantages for wide area networks. In transparent bridging, it is necessary to block some links to prevent loops. In source routing, loops are avoided so it is much easier and safer to create parallel redundant paths over wide-area links to remote locations.

Explorer packets are released by a source to discover a path through the network. If there are multiple bridges on the network, multiple explorer packets arrive at the destination from each intermediate bridge. The destination node forwards these responses to the original source node. The source node then picks the best path based on factors such as the number of bridge-to-bridge hops. This path is saved by the bridge and placed in all subsequent packets sent to the destination.

Initially, this discovery process requires some work, but eventually, the bridge learns the most commonly used paths. If the token ring network is large, there is a potential for creating explorer packet storms that can cripple the network. Token ring hardware imposes a seven-hop limit, which helps reduce these storms, but also imposes a limit on the size of the network.

Bridging Ethernet and Token Ring

So far, we've assumed that bridges are created in an all-Ethernet or all-token ring environment. However, this is rarely the case. Organizations usually need to bridge departmental LANs that are a mixture of both topologies. Some of the problems in doing this are listed here:

■ Ethernet uses learning bridges with spanning tree algorithms while token ring uses source routing techniques. Ethernet bridges maintain address tables while token ring maintains path information.

■ Information about frame status and errors is encoded within Ethernet and token ring frames differently.

■ There is no corollary for some frame information between the two network types. For example, token ring uses a priority mechanism to designate some frame as more important than others. Ethernet does not have this feature.

■ There is a difference in the packet structure between Ethernet's 1,500-byte packet and token ring 4,000- to 17,800-byte packet.

To solve these problems, translation bridges are required such as the IBM 8209. The 8209 has an Ethernet port and a token ring port and provides translation services so both networks can exchange packets. It solves the frame problem by forcing token ring networks to use 1,500 byte frames. To token ring nodes, the bridge appears as a source routing bridge and to Ethernet nodes, it appears as a spanning tree bridge.

FDDI Backbone Bridges

The Fiber Distributed Data Interface (FDDI) standard is an excellent backbone medium for a building or a campus environment. Bridges that have FDDI interfaces can provide a link for LAN segments to such a backbone. When bridging Ethernet networks onto an FDDI backbone, the Ethernet frame must be repackaged for transport over the network. This is done in one of two ways:

■ *Encapsulation* This method simply places an FDDI envelope around the Ethernet frame and sends it across the backbone network as a packet. When the packet reaches the bridge for the destination network, it is unpackaged and sent to the destination. Encapsulation is normally implemented in most Ethernet-to-FDDI bridges. This method assumes that nodes on the Ethernet will never need to communicate with nodes attached directly to the FDDI LAN, except for the bridge. Encapsulation makes the frames unusable until they are unpackaged at the receiving bridge.

■ *Translation* A translation bridge converts Ethernet packets to FDDI packets with most of the associated problems and some of the solutions discussed in the last section. Translation is not as efficient as encapsulation, but it does allow nodes on the Ethernet network to communicate with nodes on the FDDI network. If FDDI is used simply as a backbone, encapsulation is preferable to translation.

Remote Bridging Techniques

There are a number of connection methods for remote bridges. The topic "Data Transfer Rates" (later in this book) defines rates for common network applications and activities that can help you determine transmission requirements.

ASYNCHRONOUS BRIDGES   The dialup modem and asynchronous link are adequate for occasional low-volume internetwork traffic. For heavier traffic, dedicated analog lines or the digital lines discussed next are necessary. Asynchronous bridging devices have an RS-232 and V.35 ports for the attachment of high-speed modems. V.32bis modems can operate at 14.4 Kbits/sec, and emerging standards are providing even higher rates using compression methods. See "Modems" later in this book.

DEDICATED OR SWITCHED DIGITAL CIRCUITS   Digital lines are available at rates of 64 Kbits/sec or above, up to T1 rates of 1.544 Mbits/sec to T3 rates of 45 Mbits/sec. T1 provides 24 channels that can handle voice or data transmissions. A channel service unit/data service unit (CSU/DSU) links the bridge to the digital line, as shown in Figure B-17. If you plan to mix voice and data, you'll need a multiplexer. See "Multiplexing," "T1/T3 Services," and "Wide Area Networks" later in this book.

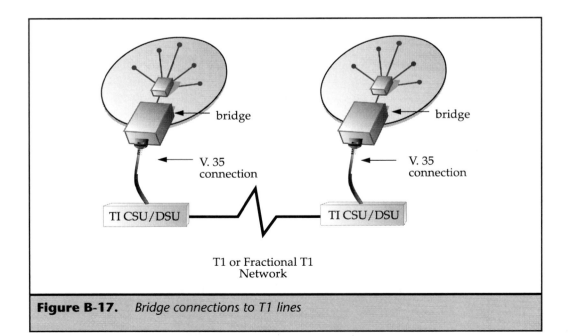

Figure B-17.   *Bridge connections to T1 lines*

PACKET-SWITCHED SERVICES   Packet-switched services provide any-to-any connections, which are the opposite of dedicated point-to-point connections. The bridge can establish links to multiple remote sites through the packet-switched network. Because the lines are switched, connections can be short-lived so customers only pay for what is used. Some packet-switched services are listed below.

- X.25 packet switching provides 56 Kbits/sec transmission speeds.

- Frame Relay is a streamlined frame delivery service that operates at speeds of 1.544 Mbits/sec or higher. It eliminates extraneous error checking on the assumption that modern transmission facilities are reliable and relatively error free.

- Switched Multimegabit Data Service (SMDS) is a metropolitan area network service that operates over fiber-optic ring networks.

Bridging versus Routing

Routers are often preferred over bridges because they provide better traffic management through complex networks. Routers can bypass congested or failed connections by sharing network status information with one another. This information is available to network layer protocols (relative to the Open Systems Interconnection [OSI] protocol stack). Bridges can't see this information. Because routers work at the network layer, they have access to more information in packets and can use this information to improve packet delivery.

RELATED ENTRIES   Campus Network; Carrier Services; Circuit-Switching Services; Digital Circuits and Services; Enterprise Networks; Metropolitan Area Networks; Routers; *and* Wide Area Networks

Broadband ISDN (B-ISDN)

Broadband Integrated Services Digital Network (B-ISDN) is a Consultative Committee for International Telegraph and Telephone (CCITT) recommendation that defines data, voice, and video transmission operating in the megabit-to-gigabit range. B-ISDN subscriber interfaces operate over fiber-optic cable, which are connected all the way to the customer premises site. Existing twisted-pair wiring is not suitable for the higher transmission rates available with B-ISDN. Those rates are much higher than narrowband ISDN service (see "Integrated Services Digital Network" later in this book). Initial B-ISDN offering will be in the 150 to 600 Mbits/sec range.

B-ISDN was created to overcome some of the limitations of ISDN. While ISDN connections are suitable for home and small business users, B-ISDN is designed for high-speed data transmissions such as wide area network connections, video conferencing, and scientific or medical transmissions. However, B-ISDN requires a network that can handle megabits-to-gigabits of information. This network is just being put into place by the carrier services. At its base is an optical cable transport network called Synchronous Optical Network (SONET) and an Asynchronous Transfer Mode (ATM) switching service, as shown in Figure B-18.

SONET is the physical transport backbone of B-ISDN. It is a fiber-optic-based networking standard that defines a hierarchy of transmission rates and data framing formats that comply with the international Synchronous Digital Hierarchy (SDH) standard. It is used as a transmission medium to interconnect carrier switching offices worldwide, and so will define future global communications. B-ISDN, FDDI, and SMDS can be transported on SONET networks. SONET is now used as the medium between carrier-switching offices and many customer premises sites. SONET transmission rates start at 51.4 Mbits/sec and increase in 52-Mbits/sec building blocks. Speeds up to 50 gigabits/sec are possible.

ATM is the switching technology for B-ISDN and provides B-ISDN users access to the SONET fiber-optic network. Information received at the ATM layer is placed in fixed-length packets, addressed, and transmitted over the SONET network. ATM provides very high-speed switching of these packets between the links attached to the SONET network. ATM takes full advantage of the transmission speeds available on fiber-optic cable.

ATM is a packet-oriented and multiplexing service. Thus it offers a unique combination of switching services to many points, and multiplexing of information from many different sources. Unlike time division multiplexing, ATM does not have dedicated time slots in the multiplexed stream. Thus, a burst from one source can use slots not in use by other sources. ATM can handle all types of information, including variable-length video information and burst information from local area networks.

RELATED ENTRIES   Asynchronous Transfer Mode; Integrated Services Digital Network; *and* Synchronous Optical Network

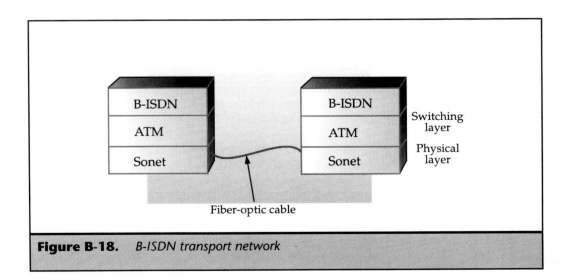

Figure B-18.   *B-ISDN transport network*

Broadband Services

Broadband packet-switching services, or "fast packet" services, provide data rates at T1 (1.544 Mbits/sec) rates or higher. Broadband networks get part of their performance boost because they don't provide error checking. Packet sequencing and the recovery of lost packets is handled by protocols in the source and destination stations, not by the network. Broadband packet switching services are Frame Relay, Switched Multimegabit Data Service (SMDS), and Asynchronous Transfer Mode (ATM). These services offer some of the following benefits:

■ Bandwidth on demand to accommodate bursts of traffic. A burst uses bandwidth that is not in use by other connections.

■ Transmission rates above common leased line rates of 1.544 Mbits/sec.

■ Customers pay for only the bandwidth used, unlike point-to-point dedicated leased lines that are expensive, often underused, and don't accommodate burst activities.

In a packet-switching network, datastreams are divided into segments and each segment is then placed in a packet. Packets are addressed and sent out over the network. The packet network is often pictured as a "cloud" because it may consist of many different routes that a packet can traverse to its destination. These multiple routes provide redundancy that can handle traffic bursts and keep the network running in case a route fails. Keep in mind, however, that switched or dedicated lines are required between the customer site and the carrier-switching networks.

RELATED ENTRIES   Asynchronous Transfer Mode; Broadband ISDN; Carrier Services; Frame Relay; High-bit-rate Digital Subscriber Line; Switched Multimegabit Data Service; *and* Wide Area Networks

Broadcast

In radio communication, a broadcast is a one-to-many signal transmission. *Transmitters* broadcast signals to *receivers.* In networks such as Ethernet, stations broadcast packet transmission on shared media. Other stations listen to these broadcasts, but receive only packets addressed to them.

When a user sends a message to another user on an Ethernet network, the message gets broadcast to all stations. An eavesdropper with the right monitoring equipment could intercept the message. Encryption techniques can provide some levels of privacy. Broadcast is also used when discussing videoconferencing. A video signal from one workstation can be broadcast to multiple destination workstations.

Broadcast Storm

A broadcast storm occurs when a host system responds to a packet that is continuously circulating on the network, or attempts to respond to a system that never replies.

Typically, request or response packets are continuously generated to correct the situation, often making it worse. As the number of packets on the network increases, congestion occurs that can reduce network performance or cripple it.

Brouter (Bridge/router)

A brouter is a hybrid device that represents the merging of bridge and router technology. Brouters can bridge multiple protocols and provide routing for some of those protocols. In this sense, a brouter is a device that forwards packets between networks at the network layer and the data link layer in the Open Systems Interconnection (OSI) protocol stack.

RELATED ENTRIES   Multiprotocol Router; Routers

Bulletin Board System (BBS)

A BBS is a host computer system that other users can connect to. A BBS provides message and file exchange services. A dialup telephone link is the normal means of accessing a BBS. Users log onto the system to read and post messages, or to upload and download files. An individual might operate a BBS out of his or her home, or a company might set up a BBS as a way to provide messages, files, and updates to its customers or employees. Many BBSs provide special interest information. For example, Macrocosm USA operates a BBS in Cambria, California (805/927-1987) to provide environmental and social change information.

BBSs provide messaging systems that let users have electronic conversations. Messages are dropped off and read by users when they log on. Some systems allow multiple users to log on at the same time and such users can carry on "live conferences" in which text typed by any user appears on the screen for others to read and respond to. Organizations can create private BBS systems so employees at remote sites can exchange messages and files. Many product vendors have created public BBS systems so customers can access help information and download updates.

The administrator of a BBS is called the system operator (SYSOP). Typically, the SYSOP has unlimited security rights to change and customize the system, or to access files and other information. BBSs use a variety of file transfer protocols such as XMODEM, YMODEM, and ZMODEM. Advanced BBS systems provide the ability to set up networks of BBSs and include FidoNet or PCRelay technology for doing this. In one scenario, one BBS system calls another at preset times to exchange any store-and-forward messages that may have been left by users. In another scenario, several BBS systems call a central BBS hub to drop off messages.

Features to look for in BBS software include :

■ The ability to support multiple users at the same time, including users who want to have online conversations.

- The ability to connect with FidoNet or PCRelay networks for message sharing among BBSs.
- Security features that prevent unauthorized users from intruding on the system and prevent users from viewing unauthorized files and messages.

Examples of BBS software include *PCBoard* from Clark Development (Murray, Utah), *TBBS* from eSoft, Inc. (Aurora, Colorado), and *RBBS-PC*, which is available free by downloading it from the Technology Consultants BBS at 407/627-6969.

Burst Mode, NetWare

Burst mode technology was added to NetWare in early 1993 to enhance NetWare's native Internetwork Packet Exchange (IPX) protocol for use over wide area links. Burst mode lets a workstation make one request for a file. The server then responds with a continuous stream of packets without the need for a reply, thus improving throughput. A single acknowledge response is sent after the burst of packets has been received. Burst mode greatly reduces the amount of traffic on the network and is essential for improving performance over wide area links.

Burst mode improves performance in the following environments:

- LAN segments that typically transmit large files
- WANs with slower (9,600-baud or less) asynchronous links
- Internetworks linked with bridges and routers
- WANs using X.25 packet switching or T1 and satellite links

The size of the burst mode packets is negotiated between the workstation and server. Slow machines like older PCs don't benefit from burst mode because they cannot transfer information over their own bus fast enough to keep up with burst mode. You'll need to disable burst mode in these machines if the network has problems or the workstation loses packets.

RELATED ENTRY   Internetwork Packet Exchange

Bursts

A burst is a continuous transfer of data without interruption from one device to another. Microprocessors such as the Intel 80486 and the Motorola 68030 allow burst mode block transfers of data to memory and onboard caches. IBM's Micro Channel bus provides a burst mode in which an adapter can control the bus to send multiple block of data.

In a multiplexing bus device or data communication channel that normally merges and transfers data from several sources, burst mode provides a way to dedicate the entire channel for the transmission of data from one source. Devices with burst mode features usually provide a maximum throughput rating for burst mode operations. For example, the Extended Industry Standard Architecture (EISA) bus used in Intel-based PCs has a burst mode of 33 Mbits/sec in which data is moved every clock cycle, rather than the normal two-cycle transfers.

Bus Topology

The layout of a network's cable system and the methods that workstations use to access and transmit data on the cable are part of the topology of a network. A bus topology network consists of a single cable trunk that connects one workstation to the next in a daisy-chain configuration, as shown in Figure B-19. In an actual installation, the cable snakes its way through a building from office to office. All nodes share the same media, and only one node can broadcast messages at a time. While bus topologies are easy to install because they conform well to office layouts, a break in the trunk cable will disable the entire network.

The most common bus topology network is Ethernet. Coaxial cable has been its primary transmission media, although twisted-pair wire is now used in most new installations. Twisted-pair Ethernet (10Base-T) is a star-configured bus topology. The bus itself is collapsed into a small box called a concentrator. Wires branch out to workstations from the connection in a star configuration as shown in Figure B-20.

RELATED ENTRIES   Ethernet; Topology

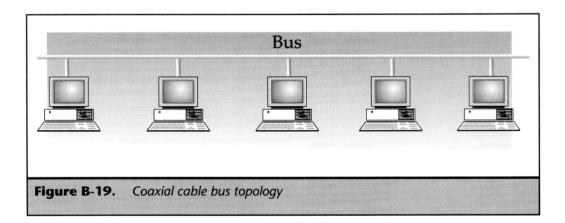

Figure B-19.   *Coaxial cable bus topology*

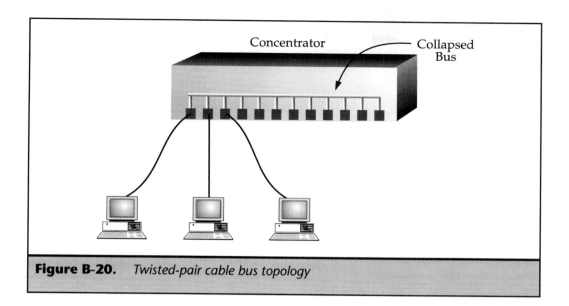

Figure B-20.   *Twisted-pair cable bus topology*

Byte-Oriented Protocol

In any communication session between devices, control codes are used to control another device or provide information about the status of the session. Byte- or character-oriented protocols use full bytes to represent established control codes such as those defined by the American Standard Code for Information Interchange (ASCII) scheme. In contrast, bit-oriented protocols rely on individual bits for control codes.

Byte-oriented protocols transmit data as strings of characters. The transmission method is asynchronous. Each character is separated by a start bit and stop bit and no timing mechanism is needed. Asynchronous protocols used with most modems and IBM's Binary Synchronous Communications (BISYNC) protocol are byte-oriented protocols.

RELATED ENTRIES   Asynchronous Communications; Bit-Oriented Protocol; *and* Modems

Cable Installation

Most organizations rely on third-party vendors to install cable. These installers have equipment and expertise, and guarantee their work. They can determine if existing cable is suitable, or whether new cable is required. Cable installers bid on the complete cable installation job, including the installation of wallplates, conduits, and other components.

Managers who plan to perform their own cable installation (or closely monitor a third-party installer) should keep the following tips in mind:

- Check local building codes before starting and consult with a building inspector.
- Follow a plan and have the building blueprints available.
- Locate cable runs, risers, conduit, wiring closets, and existing equipment you want to attach to the network.
- Document and map the entire installation. Documentation for existing telephone wiring might be available from the original cable installer. Log all problems for future reference.
- Talk with people who have installed similar network cabling systems.
- Avoid surprises by familiarizing yourself with other side of walls and ceilings. Solid concrete walls or fire blocks might be hiding in unexpected places.
- Do not run data cables next to power cables.
- Label all cables as they are installed.
- Avoid running cable near electrical equipment such as air conditioners, power cables, and fluorescent lighting fixtures, and in walkways or other high traffic areas.
- Make sure workstation attachment points are near a source of electric power.
- Schedule the cable installation to avoid conflict with the schedules of people who will be affected by it.
- Check wire with testing equipment to make sure it meets specifications while it's still on the roll.
- Avoid bending, creasing, pulling, or stretching cable. This changes its electrical characteristics and may cause transmission errors later.
- Category 5 data-grade cable requires special handling and must conform to strict rules to avoid excessive bending or stress on the cable. As pictured in Figure C-1, the geometry of the cable is drastically altered when excessively bent or flattened. Conductors are pushed closer together and may cause crosstalk.
- Category 5 data-grade cable twisted pairs must remain twisted up to .5 inch from the termination point. Don't unravel the wires unnecessarily.

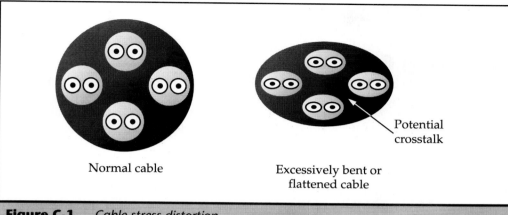

Figure C-1.   *Cable stress distortion*

■ Rubber balls are a cable installer's best friends. Attach a string to a tennis ball and then throw it to a coworker in a crawl space so that you can drag a cable across the space. A string attached to a heavier object can be dropped down to a hole in a wall to where you plan to mount a wallplate. Lightweight rods or poles are useful when you need to push wire through a cable housing.

■ Walkie-talkies are useful when you need to communicate with a coworker on the other side of a wall or floor.

■ Avoid running cable near fluorescent lights in drop ceilings. Plan on running extra cable so that you can avoid fixtures.

■ Prop up coaxial cable with fasteners, staples, or clamps, but don't crush the cable.

■ Moisture can damage cable, so protect outside cable runs from the elements by using conduit or other casing materials.

■ Avoid long cable runs if possible, especially through areas that contain heavy machinery or equipment that might produce interference.

■ Keep a look out for interesting and unique gadgets that can solve simple network problems and make your life easier. Contact the distributors listed here for free catalogs:

    Black Box, Pittsburgh, Pennsylvania, 412/746-5500
    Inmac, Santa Cruz, California, 800/547-5444
    Specialized, Irving, Texas, 800/527-5018

These catalogs are essential reading material for network managers and maintenance personnel.

Cable Testing Equipment

Defective or incorrectly installed cable is a common source of failed networks. There are a number of devices you can use to test cable runs. Some are quite affordable and should be part of any cable installer's toolkit. More expensive equipment can be rented, or you can rely on the services of consultants and professional cable installers.

A simple voltage meter is a useful cable-testing tool. To test the continuity of bulk cable, set the meter to its ohm or resistance setting and touch the leads against the ends of each wire. The meter should jump to the resistance value. If a cable run is already installed, you can still check continuity. For coaxial cable, attach a terminator to one end of the cable, and then at the other end, touch the ground with one lead and the center wire with the other. You should get a reading that matches the terminating resistor's value.

Cable Tracers

You *trace* a cable to determine its path in a wall or ceiling, or its source and destination. A cable tracer is useful if you need to determine the destination of one wire in a bundle of wires. A tone generator is attached to one end of the cable and an amplifier is then used to listen for the tone at the other end, which is typically a punchdown block. The amplifier indicates when it is near the wire that is producing the signal.

A popular product is the Microtest Tracer. With it, you can locate any coaxial, twisted-pair, or other type of wire hidden inside a floor, wall, or ceiling. The Tracer's sending unit is connected to the wire or cable, and then its pocket-size receiving unit is run over the areas where you suspect the wire runs. When the Tracer's receiving unit passes over the wire, an alarm sounds; the alarm grows stronger as you get closer to the wire.

Time Domain Reflectometers

A time domain reflectometer (TDR) determines the locations of breaks and shorts in cables. It sends a high-frequency pulse down the length of the cable and then measures the time it takes for the reflection of the signal to return. Reflections occur at shorts and breaks, and the time and amplitude of the reflection indicates the distance to the problem. In addition, the polarity indicates whether the problem is a short or an open connection. TDRs are now available for as little as $1,000 from Black Box.

The Microtest Cable Scanner (approximately $1,500) is a stand-alone, hand-held TDR. Its 32-character display reports fault problems in plain English, such as "Short at 306 ft." The Cable Scanner can print a hard copy to any serial printer and save test results in memory for later review. You can test Ethernet, ARCNET, and token ring networks that use coaxial or twisted-pair cable. The Cable Scanner also provides real-time monitoring of a LAN's activity to help determine when a bridge or repeater might need to be added, and you can attach the Cable Scanner to an oscilloscope to analyze waveforms. The Tracer product described in the previous section is included with the Cable Scanner.

Protocol Analyzers

Protocol analyzers are diagnostics tools that monitor and track the activity of networks. They can come in the form of software or a combination of software and hardware. Hardware protocol analyzers are self-contained, portable units. Protocol analyzers run on a network workstation and typically perform the following tasks:

- Display information about the types of packets traversing the network so that you can determine the accuracy of transmission

- Query all nodes and perform point-to-point communication testing between any specified node and all other nodes on the internetwork

- Determine the entire internetwork configuration

- Analyze critical data from one or all nodes and report only unusual activity based on a user-defined set of thresholds

- Display performance data such as traffic volume and packets serviced

- Provide useful information about network efficiency, network performance, possible hardware errors, noise problems, and problems with application software

Protocol analysis products are available from Novell (LANalyzer) at 800/243-8526, Gateway Communications (EtherStat) at 800/367-6555, Triticom (LANdecoder) at 612/937-0772, and Intel (NetSight Analyst) at 800/538-3373.

RELATED ENTRIES   Cabling; EIA/TIA 568 Commercial Building Wiring Standard; *and* Testing Equipment and Techniques

Cabling

Managers who need to cable networks face critical decisions. Cable and cable equipment must meet current and future requirements for data transmission, electrical characteristics, and topology. Fortunately, manufacturers have boosted data transfer rates on relatively inexpensive copper twisted-pair wire where it should meet future demands for high-bandwidth to the desktop. Fiber-optic cable is a good choice for backbones. To help managers make informed decision and design workable cable systems, a new wiring standard has emerged from the Electronic Industries Association/Telecommunications Industries Association (EIA/TIA) called the EIA/TIA 568 Commercial Building Wiring Standard (see "EIA/TIA 568 Commercial Building Wiring Standard").

There are two types of media for data transmission:

- *Guided media* include metal wire (copper, aluminum, and so on) and fiber-optic cable. Cable is normally installed within buildings or underground conduit. Metal wires include twisted-pair wire and coaxial cable, with copper being the preferred core transmission material for networks. Fiber-optic cable is available with either single or multiple strands of plastic or glass fiber.

- *Unguided media* refers to techniques for transmitting signals through air and space from transmitter to receiver. Infrared and microwave are included in this category.

    For a discussion of unguided media types, see "Satellite Telecommunication," "Wireless LAN Communication," and "Wireless Mobile Communication."

Copper cable is a relatively inexpensive, well-understood technology that is easy to install. It is the cable of choice for the majority of network installations. However, copper cable suffers from various electrical characteristics that impose transmission limits. For example, it is resistant to the flow of electrons, which limits its distance. It also radiates energy in the form of signals that can be monitored and is susceptible to external radiation that can distort transmissions. However, current products support Ethernet transmission speeds up to 100 Mbits/sec, and AT&T is reportedly working on technology that will boost twisted-pair transmission rates above 500 Mbits/sec.

In contrast, *fiber cable* transmits light signals (photons) through a core of pure silicon dioxide that is so clear, a 3-mile thick window of it would not distort the view. Photonic transmissions produce no emissions outside the cable and are not affected by external radiation. Fiber cable is preferred where security is an issue. Computer signals are transmitted through fiber-optic cable by converting electronic 1s and 0s to light flashes. A light-emitting diode at one end flashes light through the cable that is collected at the other end with a simple photodetector and converted back to electrical signals. Because there is virtually no resistance to signals and no emissions, fiber cable transmission rates are many times higher than copper cable.

One other overall characteristic of cable has to do with where it gets installed. In order to comply with the National Electrical Code (NEC), all cable installed in the plenum space, which is the airspace between the ceiling and the next floor or roof, must be installed in metal conduit, or must meet local fire codes. If the cable should burn, it must not produce noxious or hazardous gases that are pumped to other parts of a structure through the plenum. Consequently, there are normal cables types that are insulated with polyvinyl chloride (PVC) materials and plenum-rated cables that are insulated with fluoropolymers such as Du Pont's Teflon.

The remainder of this discussion concentrates on copper cable types. See "Fiber-Optic Cable" for a discussion of optical cable types.

Copper Cable Characteristics

Binary data is transmitted over copper cable by applying a voltage at one end and receiving it at the other. Typically, a voltage of +V volts represents a digital 1, and a voltage of -V represents a digital 0. The three primary types of copper cable used to transmit digital signals are discussed next.

STRAIGHT CABLE   Straight copper cable consists of copper wires surrounded by an insulator. It is used to connect various peripheral devices over short distances and at low bit rates. Serial cables used to connect modems or serial printers use this type of wire. This wire suffers from crosstalk (signals emanating from nearby wires) over long distances. It is not suitable for networks.

TWISTED-PAIR CABLE   Twisted-pair cable consists of copper core wires surrounded by an insulator as shown in Figure C-2. Two wires are twisted together to form a pair, and the pair forms a circuit that can transmit data. A cable is a bundle of one or more twisted pairs surrounded by an insulator. Unshielded twisted pair (UTP) is common in the telephone network. Shielded twisted pair (STP) provides protection against external crosstalk. The twisting prevents interference problems. High data rates (100 Mbits/sec) are possible if data grades cable (Category 5) is installed. The twists must be maintained all the way to the connection points. Twisted-pair cable is now commonly used in Ethernet, token ring, and other network topologies.

COAXIAL CABLE   Coaxial cable consists of a solid copper core surrounded by an insulator, a combination shield and ground wire, and an outer protective jacket, as pictured in Figure C-3. In the past, coaxial cable had higher bit rates (10 Mbits/sec)

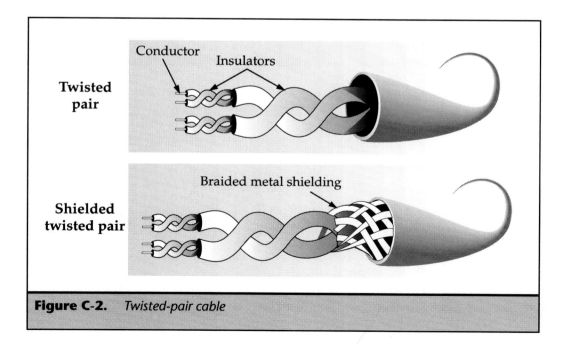

Figure C-2.   *Twisted-pair cable*

than twisted-pair cable, but newer transmission techniques for twisted-pair cable equal or surpass coaxial cable rates. However, coaxial cables can connect devices over longer distances than twisted-pair cable. While coaxial cable is the traditional media for Ethernet and ARCNET networks, twisted-pair and fiber-optic cable are common today. New structured wiring system standards call for data-grade twisted-pair cable wire that transmits at 100 Mbits/sec, ten times the speed of coaxial cable. Coaxial cable is most likely a dead-end cabling scheme for large office environments. It is discussed briefly later in this section and also under the "Ethernet" and "ARCNET" headings in this book.

Balanced and Unbalanced Circuits

Metal cables that conduct electrical signals are either "balanced" or "unbalanced." Twisted-pair cable is balanced—it consists of two wires that are individually surrounded by an insulator. Each wire in the pair has an equal current, but in opposite directions so that one wire provides a signal return to balance the circuit. A single twisted pair forms a circuit which can, for example, handle a telephone call. The twisting helps reduce electrical noise as well as external interference, which tends to be cancelled by the opposing currents of the wire pair.

Coaxial cable is an unbalanced media in which current flows through the signal conductor and returns on the ground. In coaxial cable, mesh shielding that surrounds the conductor serves as the ground and shield.

Electrical Parameters

Copper cable is subject to the following parameters that are related to the materials used to create the cable and the construction design. These parameters are attenuation, capacitance, delay distortion, and noise. The longer a cable, the more likely you will find signal distortion caused by these parameters. In addition, increasing the

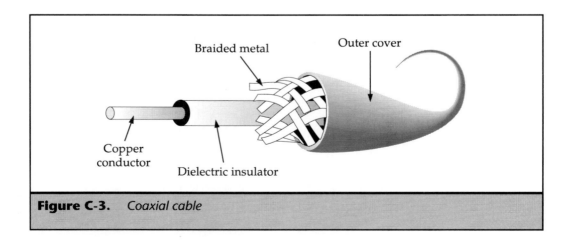

Figure C-3. *Coaxial cable*

frequency of the signal to boost data transfer rates will require a reduction in cable lengths to avoid signal distortion.

ATTENUATION Signal transmissions over long distances are subject to attenuation, which is a loss of signal strength or amplitude, as shown in Figure C-4. Attenuation is also caused by broken or damaged cables. Attenuation is the main reason why networks have various cable-length restrictions. If a signal becomes too weak, the receiving equipment will interpret it incorrectly or not at all. This causes errors that require retransmission and loss of performance. Repeater or amplifier devices are used to extend the distance of a network beyond the distance limitation of its cable type. Attenuation is measured by devices that inject signals at one end of the line and measure them at the other end.

CAPACITANCE Capacitance can distort the signal on a cable. The greater the length of a cable or thickness of the insulator, the greater the capacitance and resulting distortion. Capacitance is a measure of the energy (electric charge) stored by the cable, including the insulator. Adjoining wires in wire bundles contribute to the capacitance of a wire, as does the outer covering of the wire. Cable testers can check capacitance values to determine if a cable has kinks or has been stretched. All cable has known capacitance values that are measured in pico Farads (pF). Twisted-pair wire used for networks is rated at 17 to 20 pF.

IMPEDANCE AND DELAY DISTORTION A signal made up of various frequencies is prone to delay distortion caused by impedance, which is resistance that changes at different frequencies. It can cause the different frequency components within a signal to arrive out of step at the receiver. If the frequency is increased to boost data throughput, the effect worsens and the receiver may not be able to interpret data signals correctly. Decreasing the cable length and/or lowering the transmission frequency can solve the problem. Note that the impedance value of a cable can be measured to detect breaks or faulty connections. Data-grade cable should have an impedance value of 100 ohms at the frequency used to transmit data.

BACKGROUND NOISE Transmission lines will have some amount of background noise that is generated by external sources, the transmitter, or adjacent lines. This noise

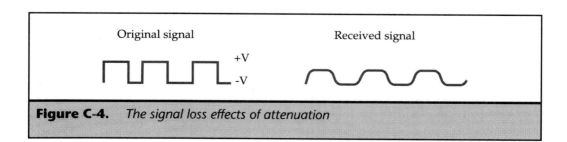

Figure C-4. *The signal loss effects of attenuation*

combines with the transmitted signal. The resulting distortion may be minor, but attenuation can cause the amplitude level of the digital signal to decrease to the level of the background noise. As shown in Figure C-5, the *signal-to-noise ratio* is high at the transmitter, but about equal at the receiver, due to distance. It is important to maintain a high signal-to-noise ratio. A major source of noise in twisted-pair cables with multiple wire pairs is *crosstalk*. Crosstalk is signal "leakage" from adjacent wires and is not typically a problem with coaxial cable unless the cable is placed directly next to other cables. A faint background conversation on your telephone line is an example of crosstalk. Ambient noise on digital circuits is caused by florescent lights, motors, microwave ovens, and office equipment such as computers, phones, and copiers. Technicians can certify wire by testing for noise levels and crosstalk. To test crosstalk levels, the technician injects a signal of known value into a wire and measures crosstalk on adjacent wires.

Twisted-Pair Cable

As mentioned, twisted-pair cable is available as unshielded twisted pair (UTP) or shielded twisted pair (STP). UTP is the most commonly used twisted-pair cable; it is specified in the EIA/TIA 568 Commercial Building Wiring Standard, discussed briefly in the next section and more fully under its own entry in this book. Because the EIA/TIA 568 standard put to rest much confusion about twisted-pair cabling in the industry, the cable specifications and requirements pertaining to it are discussed in this book.

Twisted-Pair Cable Categories

The EIA/TIA has defined the EIA/TIA 568 specification to standardize the installation of premises wiring. It applies to all UTP wiring schemes that work with Ethernet 10Base-T, token-ring, Private Branch Exchange (PBX), Integrated Services Digital Network (ISDN), and Twisted Pair-Physical Media Dependent (TP-PMD) networks.

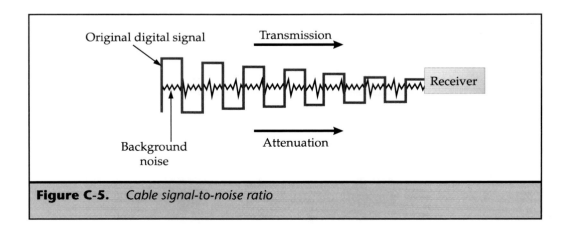

Figure C-5. *Cable signal-to-noise ratio*

EIA/TIA-568 has benefits for customers because it standardizes network cabling and installation, opening the market for competing products and services such as design, installation, and management of premises wiring.

EIA/TIA 568 defines the following cable categories:

- *Category 1* Traditional unshielded twisted-pair telephone cable that is suited for voice but not data. Most telephone cable installed before 1983 is Category 1 cable.

- *Category 2* Unshielded twisted-pair cable certified for data transmissions up to 4 Mbits/sec. Similar to IBM Cabling System Type 3. This cable has four twisted pairs and costs less than 10 cents per foot. Plenum cable costs about 30 to 40 cents per foot.

- *Category 3* Supports 10-Mbits/sec transmission rates and is required for token ring (4 Mbits/sec) and 10-Mbits/sec Ethernet 10Base-T. The cable has four pairs and three twists per foot. Costs are around 7 cents per foot. Plenum cable costs about 50 cents per foot.

- *Category 4* Certified for 16-Mbits/sec transmission rates and is the lowest grade acceptable for 16 Mbits/sec token ring. The cable has four pairs and costs around 11 cents per foot. Plenum cable costs about 60 cents per foot.

- *Category 5* Defines 100-ohm, four-wire twisted-pair copper cable that can transmit data at 100 Mbits/sec to support emerging technologies such as Ethernet and Asynchronous Transfer Mode (ATM), if installed according to specifications. The cable is low-capacitance and exhibits low crosstalk. It costs about 16 cents per foot. Plenum cable costs about 60 cents per foot.

The high transmission rates of Category 5 and other standards in the works that deliver hundreds of megabits-per-second are attributable to tighter twisting of copper pairs, better materials, improved hardware designs, and new access methods. All cables, patch panels, and terminations must conform to the specifications to eliminate crosstalk between wire pairs. Older modular connectors and jacks are not suitable for Category 5 installations. In addition, the twists in the wire must be maintained all the way up to the connection point.

The performance characteristics of Category 5 cabling and connections can provide 100 Mbits/sec network throughput. Any network that operates at this rate can take advantage of the cabling scheme. The standard is designed to support current and future networking needs. Recent studies by AT&T Paradyne indicate that Category 5 UTP cable can transmit up to 950 Mbits/sec over 100-meter distances.

With the possibility of such high data rates in the future, it would seem that Category 5 UTP is the most logical cable to install, preferable even to optical cable when compared in price and ease of installation. However, many organizations cannot afford to pay now for what might be needed in the future, even though installing lower-grade cable will limit future growth. Managers will need to carefully evaluate

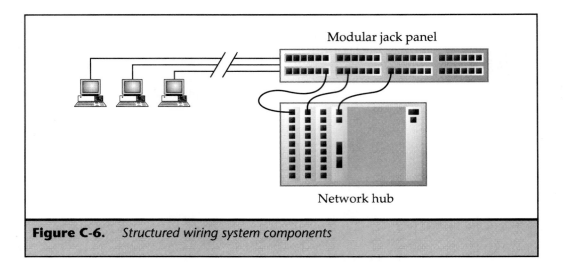

Figure C-6. *Structured wiring system components*

current and future needs and the requirements of emerging high-bandwidth multimedia, videoconferencing, and imaging applications.

Cabling Components

All components within the Category 5 cabling systems must comply with the specifications. That includes the connectors, wallplates, cables, and such things as maintaining the twists in the cable all the way to the connector. Due to those specifications, many existing cable plants must be upgraded.

The components of a structured cabling system is illustrated in Figure C-6. It consists of computers connected over horizontal cabling to a modular jack panel. Cables on the front of the panel then connect to network devices such as hubs and routers. The cabling components are discussed next.

Wallplates and Cable Connectors

The wall jacks and cable connectors for a Category 5 cabling system are pictured in Figure C-7. The right side of the picture illustrates the pin/wiring schemes for the two types of eight-pin jacks. The wallplate is a Siemens design that is oriented to keep debris out of the jack opening when a cable is not connected. It has both telephone and data connectors.

The EIA/TIA 568 standard calls for four twisted pairs in each cable to accommodate the diverse needs of current and future network and telecommunication applications. Some of the applications are noted in the following list. There are two pin configurations for the cable connectors as shown in Figure C-7: T568A should be used unless the T568B configuration is required to accommodate existing equipment that uses it.

- *Pins 4/5*   Voice
- *Pins 4/5, 3/6*   ISDN
- *Pins 4/5, 3/6*   Token ring
- *Pins 3/6, 1/2*   Ethernet 10Base-T
- *All pins*   Ethernet 100VG-Any LAN (100 Mbits/sec)
- *Pins 1/2, 7/8*   Future ATM applications

Wiring Closet Termination Hardware

Horizontal wiring extends from workstations to wallplates, then to wiring closets and equipment rooms. A *modular jack panel* such as the AT&T 1100 contains up to 48 termination points for workstations. Wire pairs are connected to the back of the panel as shown in Figure C-8. The front of the panel provides modular connector ports. Patch cables connect these ports with ports on network hub devices. Changes such as moving a workstation to a different workgroup on the local area network (LAN) are made by simply moving the patch cable.

Another approach for terminating the workstation in the wiring closet is the *cross-connect block.* The standard wiring block called the Type 66 was designed by AT&T for telephone wiring. Blocks contain scissor-like clips into which cable installers insert wires. A special tool forces the clip to cut through the insulation of the wire and

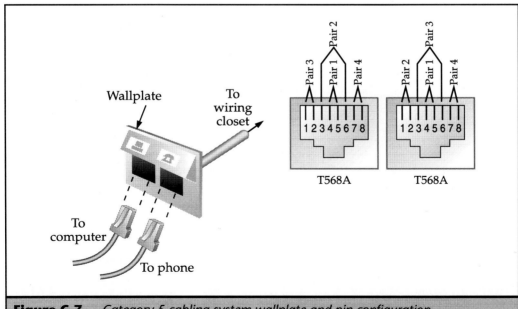

Figure C-7.   *Category 5 cabling system wallplate and pin configuration*

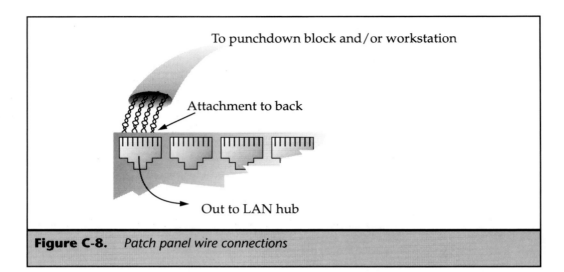

Figure C-8. *Patch panel wire connections*

contact the conductor. Blocks for Category 5 cable deviate from the traditional Type 66 block. The top portion of the Siemens S66M1-50 block is shown in Figure C-9. It increases the space between wire pairs to reduce crosstalk.

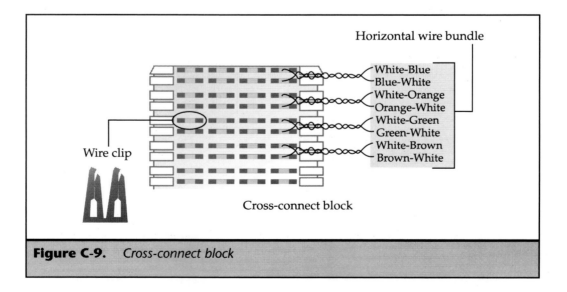

Figure C-9. *Cross-connect block*

RELATED ENTRIES   Cable Installation; EIA/TIA 568 Commercial Building Wiring Standard; *and* Testing Equipment and Techniques

Cache

A *cache* is a block of memory that holds frequently used data or data that is waiting for another process to use it. When a process needs information, it first checks the cache. If the information is already in the cache, performance is improved. If the information is not in the cache, it is retrieved from alternate storage and placed in the cache where it might be accessed again. There are several types of caches and applications that use caches:

- *Processor cache*   A processor cache is a block of memory that is part of the processor itself. Information in a processors cache is much more accessible than information in random access memory (RAM) because it requires fewer cycles to access, may be available on a wider bus, and is usually accessible at the clock rate of the processor rather than a slower external bus rate.

- *Disk cache*   A disk cache is located in a computer's RAM memory. It holds information read from disk and makes it available to the processor. Disk caches hold blocks of information, rather than whole files. When information is requested, blocks are moved from disk to cache. In some cases, several blocks are moved in anticipation of future needs.

- *Client-server cache*   In a client-server system, large chunks of data are "shipped" to a cache in the client workstation. This data is manipulated by the client; however, the server must ensure consistency of the data if more than one user is making changes to it.

- *Remote cache*   Users who access information on remote file servers over wide area networks may experience delays that can be resolved by caching information from remote servers on the local system. In this way, frequently accessed information only needs to cross the link once.

- *Distributed directory caching*   Some distributed file systems cache directory services information in users' workstations so that users can quickly locate servers where files are stored. This reduces network traffic and other overhead since workstations can look in their own memory cache for file information.

- *Intermediate server cache*   In a distributed, client-server environment, an intermediate server can provide cache information from a primary server to a set of clients, such as a local workgroup. When clients request files, they are retrieved from the primary server and cached on the intermediate server. This arrangement is useful if the primary server is at a remote location.

In some distributed file systems (such as the Andrew File System), client workstations maintain a cache on a local hard disk (rather than in RAM memory) for information requested from servers. This cache can become quite large, which introduces consistency problems. There are two methods that help overcome this problem. One model has the client constantly checking with the server to see if information has changed, but this adds a great deal of overhead. Another model uses a *call back* approach, in which the server informs clients when information they have in their cache is changed by someone else.

RELATED ENTRIES   Client-Server Computing; Distributed File Systems

Cairo

Cairo is the code name of a distributed object-oriented operating system under development by Microsoft. Its expected release date is 1995. Cairo is built on top of Windows NT and adds important new features such as an object-oriented file system, Kerberos security, replication services, and directory services. Cairo presents itself to the user as a Windows-like graphical user interface.

The object-oriented capabilities of Cairo are perhaps its most important features. Object technology is considered vital to implementing distributed systems. The complexity of such systems is simplified with object models that implement messaging services such as those available in Cairo. Cairo competes with *Taligent*, the object-oriented operating system jointly developed by Apple and IBM, as well as Common Object Request Broker Architecture (CORBA), which is a development of the Object Management Group.

In an object-oriented system, the focus is not on any one "main program" but on the data that is manipulated by that program. Data is seen as *objects* that have a particular structure and type definition. In the case of an operating system, the focus is on files, processes, and memory. This makes the operating system easy to expand and change. System resources that are shared, such as files, memory, and physical devices are viewed as *objects* that can be controlled with *object services.* Changes in the operating system involve changing object services, not the objects themselves. If new resources are added, new object services are added to support them. This modular approach does not require major changes to existing services, but provides a way to easily expand those services or the operating system. This modular approach can be seen in Cairo's use of installable file systems and services such as security and electronic mail.

Although still under development as of this writing, Cairo is expected to have these features:

- Cairo will have many of the features of the Open Software Foundation (OSF) Distributed Computing Environment (DCE).

- Cairo's underlying object model will be based on a distributed version of the Component Object Model (COM) of OLE 2.0, which means that Object Linking and Embedding (OLE) will work over networks.

- Cairo will include a file, print, and program management application called Explorer for browsing file systems.
- Cairo will be made available in client and server versions similar to Windows NT.
- Cairo will provide workgroup and workflow features similar to the Lotus Notes environment.

Figure C-10 illustrates the architectural plan for the Cairo operating system. At the base is Windows NT with its microkernel and modular design. Users can install the file system they are familiar with, such as the NT File System (NTFS) or the DOS File Allocation Table (FAT) system. Users are encouraged to use the new OFS file system which contains more database-like capabilities. The object filing system and distributed object linking and embedding layer will provide object "brokering" services that allow objects to communicate across networks with objects on other Cairo systems, and within domains set up by network administrators. Using a query language that has natural-language commands, users will be able to quickly locate objects such as files, resources, and users in a distributed environment. Artificial intelligence technology will automate future searches based on a user's previous search patterns.

As mentioned, Cairo will provide powerful services to support workgroup applications. These services include advanced electronic mail messaging and the ability to create complex compound documents that take advantage of networks. The object-oriented design of Cairo is also suitable for binary large objects (BLOB) databases that hold many different types of data such as voice, video, and graphics—not just record-oriented data.

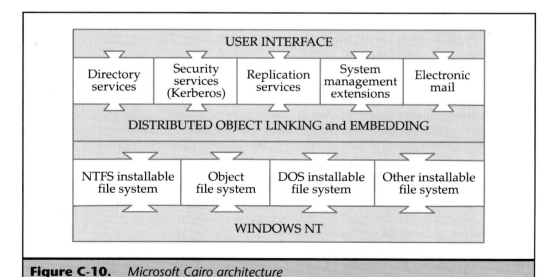

Figure C-10. *Microsoft Cairo architecture*

RELATED ENTRIES   Microkernel; Object Linking and Embedding; Object-Oriented Interfaces and Operating Systems; *and* Windows NT, Microsoft

Campus Network

A campus network interconnects local area networks (LANs) to create subnetworks within a small geographic area, such as a university or a business park. The networks are typically connected to a backbone network that consists of buried fiber-optic cable although microwave systems are also used. The network topology is typically Fiber Distributed Data Interface (FDDI).

FDDI is a 100 Mbits/sec token ring network that uses optical fiber cable as its medium. Copper Distributed Digital Interface (CDDI) is a copper-wire-based version of the FDDI standard. FDDI is a token-passing network. Stations act as repeaters, receiving packets and passing them on to the next station if necessary. FDDI supports up to 1,000 connections over a fiber cable that can span 200 kilometers. In the campus environment, bridges connect LANs to the FDDI network.

A network topology that is similar, but larger in geographic scope is the metropolitan area network (MAN), which is defined by the IEEE 802.6 standard and implemented by local carriers. It uses a Distributed Queue Dual Bus (DQDB) architecture that consists of two buses. Nodes on the network connect to both buses—one for receive and one for send. The buses are configured as a ring, but the ring is not closed up except in the event of a break elsewhere on the bus. Switched Multimegabit Data Service (SMDS) is a service provided over MANs by telephone carriers.

RELATED ENTRIES   Backbone Networks; Bridging; Cabling; Fiber Distributed Data Interface; *and* Routers

Carriers

A carrier is a company that provides telephone and data communication services in local geographic areas or between local geographic areas (wide areas). The carriers form the business units of the national and international telecommunication network. The primary carrier in the United States was AT&T until 1982, when it was broken up into the "baby" Bells, also called the regional Bell operating companies (RBOCs).

A carrier owns and operates the following facilities:

■ A switching system for telephone or data communication connections

■ Facilities for maintenance equipment, billing systems, and other internal components

■ Transmission facilities that provide communication pathways using either guided media (copper wire and fiber-optic cable), or unguided media (radiowaves)

In the United States, the equipment located at a customer's site is called *premises equipment,* and it is typically owned by the customer. The link between the customer site and the local carrier's switching office is called the *local loop,* and it is owned by the carrier.

There are local exchange carriers (LECs) and long-distance carriers, which are often called interexchange carriers (IXCs). LECs operate within specific franchised service areas (basically service monopolies) called a Local Access and Transport Area (LATA). LATAs were defined during the split-up of AT&T. The border of a LATA defines where local service ends and long-distance service begins. A LATA is generally associated with a telephone area code. LECs may be one of the RBOCs or an independent company that competes with a RBOC inside a LATA. The local carrier may have several switching offices within the same LATA, as shown in Figure C-11. Carriers like the RBOCs are not restricted to just one LATA. Pacific Bell, for example, operates franchises in all the California LATA areas.

IXCs are carriers that provide long distance services, such as MCI, US Sprint, AT&T, ITT, ATC/Microtel, and many others. Part of the 1982 judgment that broke up AT&T was an order for the RBOCs to provide access points (called *points-of-presence,* or POP) into their networks for the IXCs. Telephone customers can then be given a choice as to which long distance carrier they want to use. In late 1993, MCI announced plans

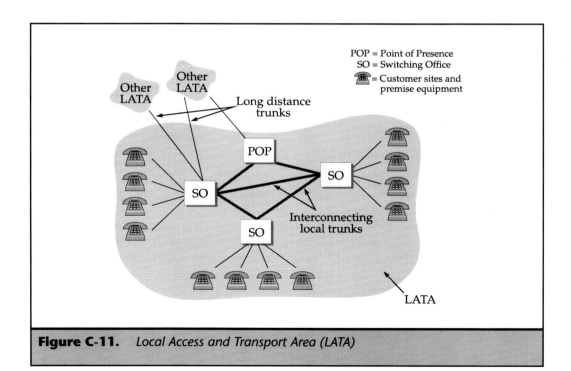

Figure C-11. *Local Access and Transport Area (LATA)*

to move into local areas and provide bypass facilities for its customers. It is estimated that long distance carriers pay almost half of their revenues to local exchange carriers for access at the POP. Further, these payments may constitute one-quarter to one-third of a LECs revenue. Competition in the local area will bring about some major changes in long distance rates. However, with loss of revenue, the RBOCs may increase charges in other areas to make up the difference.

To set up long distance telecommunication links, you go through a LEC to get to a preferred IXC, or use bypass services which are available in some metropolitan areas to route traffic directly to an IXC and avoid charges incurred by a LEC. These services use microwave system and private optical-cable networks. Some companies go so far as to create their own private wide area networks using satellite communication systems, thus bypassing both the LECs and IXCs. Value added carriers (VACs) create public data networks (PDNs) and offer "packages" that provide added services for their customers. For example, a VAC might provide protocol conversion and packet-switching services.

LEC services are regulated by the Federal Communications Commission (FCC) or state public-utility commissions. In addition, AT&T must file its rates (tariffs) with the FCC, while its competitors, such as MCI and US Sprint, do not. There is some talk that the AT&T restrictions will be lifted since they are largely unfair in today's market.

RELATED ENTRIES   AT&T; Carrier Services; Interexchange Carriers; Public Data Networks; Telecommunication; Value-Added Carrier; *and* Wide Area Networks

Carrier Sense Multiple Access (CSMA)

CSMA is a network access method used on shared network topologies such as Ethernet to control access to the network. Devices attached to the network cable listen (carrier sense) before transmitting. If the channel is in use, devices wait before transmitting. Multiple access (MA) indicates that many devices can connect to the network, which is a single wire. All devices have equal access to use the network when it is clear. There are two methods for avoiding "collisions" that occur when two or more stations attempt to access the cable at the same time.

CARRIER SENSE MULTIPLE ACCESS/COLLISION DETECTION (CSMA/CD)

Collision detection (CD) defines what happens when two devices sense a clear channel, then attempt to transmit at the same time. A collision occurs, and both devices stop transmission, wait for a random amount of time, then retransmit. This is the technique used to access the 802.3 Ethernet network channel. This method handles collisions as they occur, but if the bus is constantly busy, collisions can occur so often that performance drops drastically. It is estimated that network traffic must be less than 40 percent of the bus capacity for the network to operate efficiently. If distances are long, time lags occur that may result in inappropriate carrier sensing, and collisions.

CARRIER SENSE MULTIPLE ACCESS/COLLISION AVOIDANCE (CSMA/CA)   In collision avoidance (CA) collisions are avoided because each node signals its intent to transmit before actually doing so. This method is not popular because it requires excessive overhead that reduces performance.

RELATED ENTRIES   Access Methods, Network; Ethernet; *and* IEEE 802 Standards

Carrier Services

Organizations build wide area enterprise networks to link remote users and create LAN-to-LAN links that allow users in one geographic area to use resources on local area networks (LANs) in other areas. A variety of carrier services are available to create these links, as categorized here.

- *Circuit switching (analog)*   Provides dialup lines with relatively low throughput for point-to-point connections. This type of service is best for occasional traffic between two points, such as a single user connection or file transfer.

- *Circuit switching (digital)*   Provides temporary connections between two points with rapid setup times. This type of service is preferred for periodic connections between a number of different points.

- *Dedicated line*   Provides a permanent connection between two points on a leased, month-to-month basis, usually with an initial setup charge. Dedicated lines are available in digital formats starting at 56 Kbits/sec and ranging as high as 45 Mbits/sec. They are suitable for handling constant traffic between two points.

- *Packet switching*   Provides the most flexible service for companies that need to connect with many different sites and transmit data in varying amounts. A packet-switched network provides simultaneous connections to many points and bandwidth on demand.

SWITCHED VERSUS DEDICATED (LEASED)   Managers must evaluate the volume of network traffic and its destination to determine the type of services to use. The following table lists the transmission requirements for various types of activities. If traffic is light, dialup services are sufficient. If traffic is continuous between two points, dedicated lines are necessary. New "fast packet" switching services such as Frame Relay and Asynchronous Transfer Mode (ATM) provide unique services that can scale up as user requirements grow.

Application	Rate
Personal communications	300 to 9,600 bits/sec or higher
E-mail transmissions	2,400 to 9,600 bits/sec or higher
Remote control programs	9,600 bits/sec to 56 Kbits/sec
Database text query	Up to 1 Mbit/sec
Digital audio	1 to 2 Mbits/sec
Access images	1 to 8 Mbits/sec
Compressed video	2 to 10 Mbits/sec
Medical transmissions	Up to 50 Mbits/sec
Document imaging	10 to 100 Mbits/sec
Scientific imaging	Up to 1 gigabit/sec
Full-motion video (uncompress)	1 to 2 gigabits/sec

ONSITE VERSUS OFFSITE SWITCHING   Switching can be done on the customer's site (private networking) or by the carrier (public networking). If the customer does switching, appropriate equipment is installed, and the customer sets up dedicated lines between all the points that require connections. This private networking strategy gets more expensive as distance between sites grows. If the carrier provides switching, the customer funnels all its traffic to the carrier, which then routes the traffic to various destinations. Carriers are providing switching services in the form of Frame Relay, Switched Multimegabit Data Service (SMDS), and emerging Asynchronous Transfer Mode (ATM) services.

DEALING WITH CARRIERS   If you decide to install dedicated leased lines between two geographically remote locations, you might have to deal with a number of carriers. A LEC (local exchange carrier) is the telephone company that operates within a specific LATA (Local Access and Transport Area), typically associated with a telephone area code. If a customer requires a line outside of the local LATA, the LEC at the remote site and an IXC (interexchange carrier) must be involved. An IXC is a long distance carrier such as MCI, US Sprint, and AT&T that can provide transmission facilities between LATAs. Every LEC is required to provide a point of presence (POP) within a LATA so the various IXCs can access the long distance traffic generated by its customers within the LATA. Customers can choose any IXC that provides service at a POP.

Traditional Switched Analog Lines

Traditional analog voice lines provide a convenient and relatively inexpensive way to interconnect networks. Modems that conform to the new CCITT (ITU) V.34 (formerly V.fast) standard can operate at 28,800 bits/sec with compression. Analog lines are available as follows.

DIALUP LINES   Connections are made only when needed for file transfers, E-mail connections, and remote users sessions. See "Modems."

PERMANENT LEASED LINES   These analog lines provide the same data rates as dialup lines, except that customers contract with the carrier to keep the lines available for immediate use when necessary. See "Leased Line."

Circuit-Switched Services

A circuit-switched service provides a temporary dedicated path through a carrier's switching systems. Customers can contract for various types of services, depending on their anticipated bandwidth needs. Each of the services discussed in the following paragraphs are covered in more detail under separate headings.

SWITCHED-56 SERVICES   A common switched service is *Switched-56*, which operates at 56 Kbits/sec and requires a special Switched-56 channel service unit/data service unit (CSU/DSU) at each site. Switched-56 services were originally intended to provide an alternate backup route for higher-speed leased lines such as T1. If a leased line failed, a Switched-56 line would quickly establish an alternate connection. Switched-56 can still be used in this way, but it is also used to handle peaks in traffic, fax transmissions, backup sessions, bulk E-mail transfers, and LAN-to-LAN connections. Rates are calculated by the minute in most cases.

INTEGRATED SERVICES DIGITAL NETWORK (ISDN)   ISDN is a service that provides all-digital services on the *local loop,* which is the cable that runs between the home or business user and the LEC's switching office. ISDN has three channels: two that provide 64 Kbits/sec and a third that provides signalling to control the channels. ISDN is offered in selected areas. See the main entry for "Integrated Services Digital Network" and "Broadband ISDN" for more details.

EMERGING SERVICES   Some emerging standards will boost data rates and lower prices on the local loop. *High-bit-rate Digital Subscriber Line* (HDSL) permits transmission over the existing copper-based lines between 784 Kbits/sec to T1 rates of 1.544 Mbits/sec. A related product, *Asymmetrical Digital Subscriber Line* (ADSL) works over twisted pairs, offering a 1.544 Mbits/sec circuit in one direction and a lower-speed (typically 16 Kbits/sec) data channel in the other direction. ADSL is designed for interactive video to the home using existing copper telephone lines. HDSL can offer the same services and provide a full-duplex line. A third encoding scheme, *Very High bit-rate Digital Subscriber Line* (VHDSL), will provide 3- to 6-Mbits/sec service over two twisted pairs. HDSL is being deployed, ADSL is in the trial stages, and VHDSL may be available in 1994. See the appropriate headings for more details.

Dedicated Digital Services

Digital circuits provide data transmission speeds up to 45 Mbits/sec. Currently, digital lines are made possible by "conditioning" normal lines with special equipment to handle higher data rates. The lines are leased from the telephone company and installed between two points (point-to-point) to provide dedicated, full-time service. You'll need bridges or routers to connect local area networks (LANs) to digital lines. Voice and data multiplexers are also required if you plan to mix both voice and data channels.

The standard digital line service is the *T1 channel,* which provides transmission rates of 1.544 Mbits/sec. T1 lines can carry both voice and data, so they are often used to provide voice telephone connections between an organization's remote sites. The lines are fractional, meaning that they can be divided into channels for voice or data. T1 can be divided into 24 channels of 64 Kbits/sec bandwidth each, for example. Alternatively, a T3 line can provide the equivalent of 28 T1 lines for users who need a lot of bandwidth. See "T1/T3 Services."

AT&T offers a number of digital services under its ACCUNET label. ACCUNET T1.5 provides a dedicated point-to-point digital T1 channel while ACCUNET T45 Service provides dedicated 44.736 Mbits/sec digital rates. T45 is equivalent to 28 T1 channels. ACCUNET also provides protection from line failures by immediately switching to another circuit and it can provide temporary bandwidth for high-volume data transfers (bursts), which are common in LAN environments.

Packet-Switching Services

A packet-switched network is a "mesh" of interconnections provided by carrier services through which packets travel from source to destination, as shown in Figure C-12. There are *datagram* services, in which every packet is routed through the network as a self-contained entity. The physical path between two end points may change often because packets take advantage of least-cost routes or avoid congested areas. A *virtual circuit* service sends packets through a predefined path on the network. Organizations can use these services to create virtual data networks over wide areas that connect every site in the organization at much lower cost than dedicated leased lines, which are rapidly being replaced by switched services that provide bandwidth-on-demand and pay-for-what-you-use rates.

X.25

X.25 is a standard, well-tested, and often revised protocol that has been a workhorse packet-switching service since 1976. It is suitable for light loads and was commonly used to provide remote terminal connections to mainframe systems. X.25 packet-switched networks are not suitable for most LAN-to-LAN traffic because they are slow and require a large portion of the bandwidth to handle error checking. This error checking was important in the days of low-quality analog telephone lines, but is not needed today. Frame Relay provides a better choice.

Frame Relay

Frame Relay provides services similar to X.25, but is faster and more efficient. Frame Relay assumes that the telecommunications network is relatively error-free and does not require the extensive error checking and packet acknowledgment features of X.25.

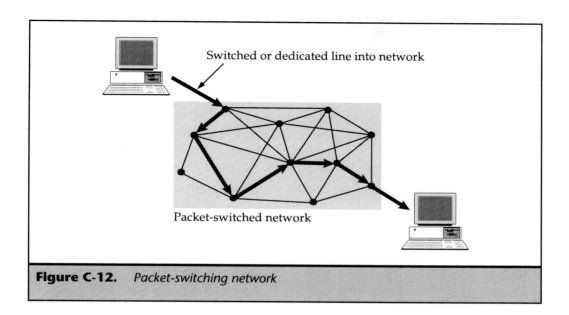

Switched or dedicated line into network

Packet-switched network

Figure C-12. *Packet-switching network*

Frame Relay is an excellent choice for organizations that need any-to-any connections on an as-needed basis. A customer connection into a public Frame Relay network takes the form of a switched or dedicated leased line like T1. Customer traffic is forwarded through this line to the Frame Relay provider and switched across the network. See "Frame Relay" for more details.

Cell Switching

Cell switching networks, namely Asynchronous Transfer Mode (ATM), provide "fast-packet" switching services that can transmit data at megabit- and potentially gigabit-per-second rates. Carriers are already installing ATM switches in their own networks. Customers simply use switched or dedicated lines to funnel traffic into the network and the carrier provides all the switching services. See "Asynchronous Transfer Mode" and "Cell Relay" for more details.

Switched Multimegabit Data Service (SMDS)

SMDS is cell-based service provided by the regional Bell operating companies (RBOCs) in selected areas. SMDS uses ATM switching and provides services such as usage-based billing and network management. The service will eventually grow from MAN use to wide area network use and take advantage of SONET networks. See "Switched Multimegabit Data Service."

Public Data Networks (PDNs)

PDN providers (called value added carriers or VACs) have created data networks that they make available to organizations at leased-line rates (monthly charge) or at dialup rates (per-use charge). A typical PDN network forms a web of global connections between the PDN's switching equipment. Circuits consist of the PDNs own private lines or lines leased from major carriers such as AT&T. Dialup or dedicated lines are used to connect with a PDN at access points that are available in most metropolitan areas. Services provided typically include X.25, Frame Relay, and even Asynchronous Transfer Mode (ATM). Some of the major PDNs offering these services are listed here:

■ CompuServe Information Services offers access points in hundreds of locations throughout the United States for X.25 and Frame Relay services.

■ GE Information Services provides packet switching and high-speed services, as well as asynchronous and synchronous services.

■ Infonet Services Corp provides an array of international services.

■ Tymenet Global Network has close to 5,000 global access points.

Using a PDN saves you the trouble of contracting for the lines and setting up your own switching equipment. The service provider handles any problems with the network itself and can guarantee data delivery through a vast mesh of switched lines.

Other Services

There are a variety of other services that network managers can choose for wide area connections or other types of network activity. These are listed below.

INTERNET CONNECTIVITY   The Internet provides access to a wide range of information services, electronic mail services, and connectivity services. There are a whole range of these value-added network providers, some of which are listed in the Internet entry.

WIRELESS SERVICES   Wireless communication consists of either local-area services or wide-area services. Local-area services involve wireless communication between workstations that are in a fixed position within an office. Wide-area services involve mobile workstations that communicate using technologies such as packet-radio, cellular networks, and satellite stations. See "Advanced National Radio Data Service" and "Wireless Mobile Communications."

Carrier Signal

A carrier is a specific frequency in a communication channel that is modulated to carry information. Carrier signals are commonly used in AM, FM, and other radio transmissions to differentiate the signals of each transmitting station. When you turn the dial of a radio, you are selecting a carrier frequency. The radio then amplifies the signal carried on the selected frequency. In amplitude modulation (AM), modulation changes the strength or amplitude of the carrier signal. In frequency modulation (FM), the frequency of the carrier signal is modulated.

CCITT

The Consultative Committee for International Telegraph and Telephone (CCITT) is a committee of a United Nations treaty organization called the International Telecommunications Union (ITU). The committee is made up of members from governments and has the task of studying, recommending, and standardizing technical and operational issues for telecommunications. The United States is involved with the CCITT through the U.S. State Department.

NOTE: Current terminology refers to CCITT standards as ITU standards.

The CCITT is organized into 15 study groups that prepare recommendations. The groups study services, maintenance, tariffs, data communication networks, transmission facilities, and other issues, then meet every four years to review work in progress, make proposals, prepare drafts, make new recommendations, and approve recommendations. Approved recommendations are then published. While approved standards are not mandatory, some countries adopt them as laws. The CCITT is currently working to decrease the time span of the approval process to accommodate rapidly evolving technologies.

There are a number of categories ranging from A through Z under which recommendations are made. These are some of the more interesting ones:

A and B	Working procedures, terms, and definitions
D and E	Tariffs
F	Telegraph, telematic, and mobile services
G and H	Transmissions
I	Integrated Services Digital Network (ISDN)
J	Television transmissions
K and L	Protection of facilities
M and N	Maintenance
P	Telephone transmission
R - U	Terminal and telegraph services
V	Data communication over telephone networks
X	Data communication networks

The V series covers transmission over telephone networks and defines modem communications. The X series covers Open Systems Interconnection (OSI) standards. Some of the more interesting standards are listed here.

Popular V CCITT Standards

V.22	1,200 bits/sec full-duplex modem standard
V.22bis	2,400 bits/sec full-duplex modem standard
V.28	Defines circuits in RS-232 interface
V.32	Asynchronous and synchronous 4,800/9,600 bits/sec standard
V.32bis	Asynchronous and synchronous standard up to 14,400 bits/sec
V.35	Defines high data-rates over combined circuits
V.42	Defines error checking standards
V.42bis	Defines modem compression using Lempel Ziv method
V.terbo	An emerging standard that provides 19.2 Kbits/sec rates
V.34 (formerly V.fast)	A proposed standard for 28 Kbits/sec transmission rates

Popular X CCITT Standards

X.200 (ISO 7498)	OSI Reference Model
X.25 (ISO 7776)	Packet-switching network interface
X.400 (ISO 10021)	Message handling (E-mail)
X.500 (ISO 9594)	Directory Services
X.700 (ISO 9595)	Common Management Information Protocol (CMIP)

RELATED ENTRY   Standards Organizations

CD-ROM
(Compact Disc, Read-Only Memory)

CD-ROM is an optical data disc that is an adaptation of the audio compact disc. The disc sizes and formats are the same. In fact, computer CD-ROM drives will play an audio compact disc with appropriate software or controls (but audio CD drives don't play CD-ROMs). As the name implies, CD-ROMs are read-only—you can't write data to them. CD-ROMs hold up to 600 megabytes of information, which is over 300,000 pages of information.

All CD-ROM discs are "pressed" using a master disc, then encased in a polycarbonate outer protective shell. Data is initially recorded on the master disc in a spiral pattern that starts from the center. Millions of tiny pits that represent digital information are recorded on the surface of the master, then copies are pressed from this master. When these copies are "played" in a CD-ROM drive, a laser beam scans the tracks and obtains digital information based on the changes in reflectivity produced by the pits.

CD-ROM disc manufacturing has become quite common and inexpensive. The real costs are for gathering or developing the information on the disc, and paying author royalties. CD-ROMs have extremely long shelf life, but ironically, the information on them is usually outdated long before the disc itself.

CD-ROM Players

Manufacturers have built optical disc systems that conform to the CD-ROM standard but these systems have slower transfer rates because the standard was originally designed for music. The transfer rate for CD-ROMs is about 150 Kbits/sec, compared to hard disk transfer rates of 8 Mbits/sec to 40 Mbits/sec (SCSI interface).

CD-ROM drives spin at a constant linear velocity, meaning that the spin rate of the disc varies as the read head moves from the center of the disc to the outside of the disc. While this technique was adequate for playing music, it doesn't provide much performance for the random-access requirements of data systems. When playing music, the spin rate changes slowly as the information on the disc is read sequentially. In computer applications, random access to data requires the drive to change its speed every time the read head is repositioned. There is always a slight pause before reading actually begins to adjust for the new spin rate. Another factor is the size of the read head, which has more mass than typical hard disk read/write heads, and thus takes more time to move.

With these factors in mind, the quality of a CD-ROM drive is important. Low-quality drives don't have efficient mechanisms for varying the drive speed or moving the read head and average access times are as high as 300 milliseconds. Typical hard drives operate in the range of 10 to 40 milliseconds. Some of these problems are being solved, however. NEC doubles the spin rate in its drives to improve performance.

CD-ROM drives are available in a number of configurations. The most popular drives simply mount in disc drive bay slots. External devices are also available, including drives with multiple trays and autochanging mechanisms. Drives that hold multiple discs are more appropriate for network applications. The interface for CD-ROM drives is almost always the Small Computer Systems Interface (SCSI). For single-disc drives, a CD-ROM disc is placed in a special carrier that gets inserted in the drive. The carriers are relatively inexpensive, and serious users purchase one for each of their CD-ROM discs to make loading easier and protect discs.

When a CD-ROM drive is installed in a DOS system, it is assigned a drive letter like any other disk drive, but this requires that you load a Microsoft software driver called MSCDEX.EXE during the boot process. This driver usually comes with the drive, or is available free on most bulletin boards. Most CD-ROMs include a software program for accessing the information on the disc. Unfortunately, there is no standardization in the programs, and you'll probably need to load one on your hard disk for each CD-ROM you use.

Networking CD-ROMs

There are three methods for sharing CD-ROM drives with users on a network. The first is to let other users access the drives located on workstations in peer-to-peer environments. Peer-to-peer networks such as Microsoft Windows for Workgroups and Artisoft LANtastic provide this capability. The CD-ROM drive is "published," or made available for use by other users in the same way as any other drive. The second method is to install CD-ROM drives in file servers, then install appropriate drivers that make that drive available to network users. That third method is similar to the second, except that you install one or more CD-ROM drives in a dedicated CD-ROM server.

In the Novell NetWare environment, the NetWare Loadable Module (NLM) called CDROM.NLM provides the support for mounting CD-ROM drives, which then appear as volumes for users to access. Other products include CD Connection from CBIS (Norcross, Georgia), which provides dedicated CD-ROM server capabilities on NetWare IPX networks, NetBIOS networks (Microsoft and others), and Banyan VINES networks. Corel Systems (Ottawa, Ontario) provides NetWare NLMs and drivers for other server environments that support the use of multiple CD-ROM drives from multiple vendors. Meridian Data Systems (Scotts Valley, California) provides NetWare NLMs and drives for NetBIOS networks.

RELATED ENTRIES   Backup and Data Archiving; Jukebox Optical Storage Devices; *and* Optical Libraries

Cell Relay

A cell is a fixed-size packet of data with a header that contains path information used to relay it through switching devices or local or wide area networks. This relay can be performed in hardware at very high speeds. An important characteristic of cell relay is that it takes place in only the lowest two levels of the OSI protocol stack and dispenses with error checking and acknowledgment features. Software running at end nodes is responsible for managing problems such as lost, corrupted, or out-of-sequence packets.

Asynchronous Transfer Mode (ATM) is the CCITT(ITU) cell relay standard. Cell relay is accomplished over switched networks that provide a mesh of connections through which cells can travel to reach their destination. The mesh provides reliability since many paths are available.

In a cell relay network, both multiplexing and switching techniques are used to divide the available bandwidth among many users. Data, voice, and video are supported. Cell relay networks are useful for real-time applications like full-motion video and applications that are sensitive to delays. The small fixed size of the cells (53 bytes) provides predictable performance that keeps time-sensitive information synchronized and on time. Technologies that use variable-length frames (like Frame

Relay) can produce delays at switching devices when long frames hold up other frames. Picture how a long truck holds up traffic while making a turn at an intersection. For voice and video, delays cause packets to fall out of synchronization and arrive late. If the transmission is live video, dropped packets make the video appear jittery.

The traditional bus design is not appropriate for cell switching. Instead, a multiport device with a mesh (fabric) of connections as shown in Figure C-13 can provide a dedicated path from any one port to any other. Thus, it's possible to set up channels that appear as dedicated circuits between end-systems. Such switches are also parallel processing devices that let traffic flow simultaneously between many ports.

Public data network providers like AT&T are busy installing ATM cell switching devices with Synchronous Optical Network (SONET) interfaces that operate in the multigigabit range. At the same time, carriers are providing Switched Multimegabit Data Services (SMDS) that provide usage-based billing and network management. SMDS defines services on top of a cell-switching system. A customer's data packets are encapsulated in SMDS packets, then placed into cells to take advantage of the greater speed of cell switching. However, the SMDS packet provides additional services such as the ability to screen addresses and provide custom connections.

RELATED ENTRIES   Asynchronous Transfer Mode; Packet-Switching Networks; *and* Switched Services

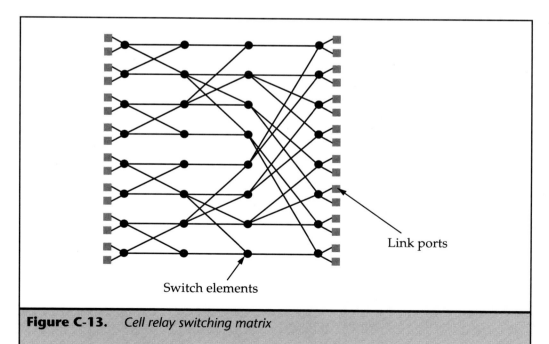

Figure C-13.   *Cell relay switching matrix*

Cellular Data Communication Systems

Cellular digital systems provide wireless telephone and data services to mobile users. They differ from older radio-telephone systems in that they provide more communication channels for users. This is done by limiting frequencies to specific areas, called *cells*, which form a hexagonal grid within a geographic area, as shown in Figure C-14. Each cell is assigned a set of frequencies and no adjoining cells have the same frequencies. While adjoining cells never use the same frequency, cells elsewhere in the grid might do so. But, the transmission power of each cell is limited to the specific area it covers.

An antenna is located in the middle of each cell. As users drive from one cell to the next, a hand-off procedure switches calls from a frequency in one cell to a different frequency in another cell. Radio-telephone systems used a single set of frequencies for an entire metropolitan area, and these frequencies often became overbooked.

Initially, only one cell may exist within a geographic area, but as needs grow and competition increases, cells are subdivided into seven smaller cell segments. Further subdivision is possible as requirements grow and it is possible to have cells that are as small as city blocks, or even floors on a building. Also, cells can be laid out in sizes and patterns that accommodate the traffic patterns of a geographic area. In other words, the downtown area might have numerous small cells while outlying areas might have fewer large cells. Apple Computer and other developers of emerging personal data assistants (PDAs) and portable computing devices are pushing these "microcellular" networks to accommodate the new devices.

The entire system consists of a mobile telephone switching office, the mobile control unit and antennae at the cell site, and the mobile transceivers owned by users. The switching office provides long distance connections. The Federal Communications Commission licences two cellular communication systems in each area. One goes to the Bell operating company local exchange carrier (LEC) and the other goes to an independent service that is selected by lottery.

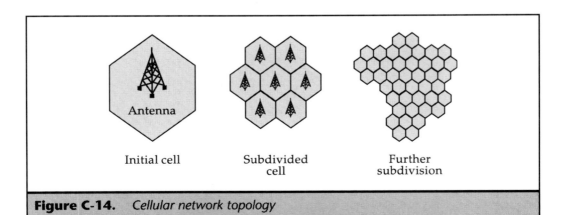

Initial cell   Subdivided cell   Further subdivision

Figure C-14. *Cellular network topology*

Data Communication on Cellular Networks

Data communication on cellular networks is handled by attaching cellular modems to communication devices. Cellular modems have data rates up to 9.6 Kbits/sec. While there are some problems associated with keeping a data connection alive as a device moves from one cell to another, techniques are used that overlap frequencies between cells until the transition is complete. Cellular modems provide enhanced error detection and correction as well as compression. They can also change the transmission speed on the fly and perform other tricks to maintain connections.

The advantage of cellular data communication systems is that the infrastructure such as antennae and switching offices is already in place. Users are familiar with cellular technology and already have necessary equipment.

Packet Switching on Cellular Networks

The traditional method of sending data over a cellular network is to use an entire voice channel and a modem to convert digital signals to analog signals. This is the same technique used to transmit data over normal telephone lines. However, data transmission uses a lot of the available bandwidth, so cellular companies came up with a technique called Cellular Digital Packet Data (CDPD) that optimizes the cellular system for both voice and data transmissions.

When CDPD is used, data packets are simply merged into the existing voice network when there is idle time between voice calls. Idle time on cellular channels is prevalent because calls are regularly handed off between cells, calls are terminated, or calls are reassigned to new channels. All of this switching takes time which the data packets use. Channel-hopping techniques can help the data call jump to another channel when a voice call needs bandwidth.

RELATED ENTRIES   Cellular Digital Packet Data; Mobile Computing; *and* Wireless Mobile Communications

Cellular Digital Packet Data (CDPD)

CDPD is a specification that defines a cellular radio network that lets users send computer data over existing cellular networks without tying up an entire voice channel. CDPD defines packet transmission methods, which are better able to handle the types of traffic that are expected from mobile computer users, such as the exchange of electronic mail or database queries. Users are billed in sub-minute billing units to accommodate short data bursts. In contrast, cellular voice is billed to the nearest minute.

CDPD basically takes advantage of unused time on voice cellular networks to send data packets. The standard is based on IBM CellPlan II technology. The full 30 KHz of a voice channel is used, but the data "hops" from channel to channel to avoid interference with voice transmissions. This strategy works because there is always unused capacity on a cellular system. The capacity is made available when voices switch from cell-to-cell, or when calls are set up and terminated. For example, a time interval of 10 seconds must elapse after a voice call is terminated before another voice call can be set up. Bandwidth for data transmission on CDPD-based cellular networks can go up to 19 Kbits/sec when compression is used.

CDPD is defined by a consortium of cellular carriers and computer companies, including eight of the nine regional Bell operating companies (RBOCs), McCaw Cellular Communications, Contel Cellular, and GTE Mobilnet. The consortium published its first specifications in July 1993. These first specifications define how network providers and equipment manufacturers will design and build products and services for the cellular networks. These are some of the items in the specification:

■ Architectural structure

■ Support and application services

■ Encryption and authentication techniques

■ External network interfaces

■ Radio access control

■ Airlink methods

■ Resource management

CDPD equipment and service providers include AT&T Network Systems, Hughes Network Systems, Motorola, and a number of other companies. Apple Computer, EO, Inc., and IBM are developing CDPD-enabled portable devices. These portable devices, often called personal digital assistants (PDAs) typically have a pen-based graphical user interface.

McCaw Cellular Communications has developed a wireless internetworking system called Mobile Database Station (MDBS) in conjunction with IBM, GTE Mobile Communications, and some of the RBOCs. Developers of mobile computing devices like Apple and EO Inc. are also involved. It provides 19,200 bits/sec transmission rates using existing cellular technology and the CDPD standard. MDBS includes accounting services, authentication, and control software provided by Inet Inc., X.400 and X.500 message-handling services from Retix Corp., and fault-tolerant systems provided by Tandem Computer Inc.

RELATED ENTRIES   Mobile Computing; Packet-Radio Communication; *and* Wireless Mobile Communication

Certification Systems

Certificates and certification servers provide a way to authenticate clients who wish to access servers in distributed environments without the need to authenticate users every time they access a secured service. The certificate procedure was first developed at the Massachusetts Institute of Technology and is implemented in the Kerberos security system. They are now defined in the Consultative Committee for International Telegraph and Telephone (CCITT) X.509 security standard.

Consider a large network in which many users need to access applications and data on many servers. In this large environment, it is unrealistic to authenticate a user every time he or she attempts to access one of the servers. Keep in mind that passwords, even those that are encrypted, must be kept off the line where they might be intercepted by an intruder to gain access to the system. Certification provides a way to authenticate users one time, when they log on to the system, and then verify to other servers that the user is who he or she claims to be. This is the basis of a "trust relationship."

The verification comes from a trusted third party, which is called the *certification server*. The certification server, the client, and the application server use a certification process that consists of the exchange of certificates in locked (encrypted) messages that give users access to other servers.

RELATED ENTRIES   Authentication and Authorization; Cryptography; Data Encryption Standard; Digital Signatures; Distributed File System Security; Kerberos Authentication; Key Encryption Technology; *and* Security

Channel

A channel is essentially a communication path between two or more devices. In a computer system, a channel provides an input/ouput interface between the processor and some peripheral device. In telecommunication, a channel may take one of the following forms:

- One channel carried on a physical circuit (such as copper wire) between two systems

- *Time-division multiplexed channels,* in which signals from several sources such as telephones and computers are merged into a single stream of data and separated by intervals of time

- *Frequency-division multiplexed channels,* in which signals from many sources are transmitted over a single cable by modulating each signal on a carrier at different frequencies

RELATED ENTRY   Modulation Techniques

Channel Service Unit/Data Service Unit (CSU/DSU)

Channel service units (CSUs) and data service units (DSU) are actually two separate devices, but they are used in conjunction and often combined into the same box. The devices are part of the hardware you need to connect computer equipment to digital transmission lines, as shown in Figure C-15.

CHANNEL SERVICE UNIT This inexpensive device connects with the digital communication line and provides a termination for the digital signal. The CSU provides various loop-back tests on the line and keeps the line connected if the other communication equipment attached to it fails.

DATA SERVICE UNIT This device, sometimes called a *digital service unit,* is the hardware component you need to transmit digital data over the hardware channel. The device converts signals from bridges, routers, and multiplexers into the bipolar digital signals used by the digital lines. Multiplexers mix voice signals and data on the same line.

CHORUS Nucleus

The CHORUS Nucleus is a microkernel operating system developed by Chorus Systems Inc. of Beaverton, Oregon. The company has developed a microkernel version of UNIX System V, Release 4 called CHORUS/MX V.4 that runs on top of the CHORUS microkernel. The microkernel itself provides fundamental services such as synchronization and premption management, asynchronous interprocess communication (IPC), remote procedure calls (RPCs), and a low-level hardware supervisor. A virtual memory manager is also available that assists in the movement of objects in distributed environments.

The operating system runs as a set of modules on top of the microkernel, and modules communicate through a message-based interface. These modules handle file management, memory management, applications, and networking in distributed environments.

RELATED ENTRY Microkernel; UNIX

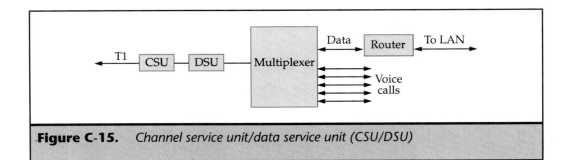

Figure C-15. *Channel service unit/data service unit (CSU/DSU)*

Circuit-Oriented Transport Services

See Connection-Oriented and Connectionless Protocols.

Circuit-Switching Services

A *circuit* is a path that can carry signals from one device to another. The most common analogy is the telephone. When you call someone, a dedicated circuit is established between two telephone devices. The telephone system is a circuit-switched network because the local telephone company provides the switching capabilities to connect your telephone with many other phones. Circuits are set up for the duration of the call and disconnected when the call is complete.

In the context of computer networks and data communication, there are two types of switched data communication circuits provided by the telephone companies:

Analog Telephone Lines

Analog telephone lines are dialup switched circuits that provide temporary connections using modems (*mo*dulator/*dem*odulator). Modems convert digital signals to an analog signal for transmission over analog telephone lines. A modem is required at each end of the connection and the speed of the modem determines transmission rates. Analog telephone lines are sometimes used to transfer files or a block of E-mail messages from one local area network (LAN) to another, or to provide connections into the LAN for remote and mobile users. They are usually inappropriate for real-time access to remote resources by multiple users.

Switched Digital Services

Switched digital services provide more flexibility than leased dedicated lines (see "Leased Line"). They are basically dialup lines that provide better quality service than comparable analog switched lines and are more suitable for LAN-to-LAN transmissions. Carriers provide switched digital services under special contract because the lines must handle higher data-rates than customers would normally transmit over analog lines.

Switched services have a big advantage over dedicated lines. They provide route flexibility so customers can get high-quality, high-speed digital services between any two points when it's needed. In contrast, dedicated lines are set up between two specific points and do not accommodate moves. In addition, customers often end up paying for more than they need, then do not have enough service during peaks in traffic.

A common switched service is *Switched-56*, which operates at 56 Kbits/sec and requires a special Switched-G   56 channel service unit/data service unit (CSU/DSU) at each site. Switched-56 services were originally intended to provide an alternate backup route for higher-speed leased lines such as T1. If a leased line failed, a Switched-56 line would quickly establish an alternate connection. Switched-56 can still be used in this way, but it is also used to handle peaks in traffic, fax transmissions, backup sessions, bulk E-mail transfers, and LAN-to-LAN connections. Rates are calculated by the minute in most cases.

Some carriers provide *Switched-T1* services, which provide all the benefits of high-speed, high-quality digital lines with switching capabilities. Some companies only need high-speed lines on an occasional basis, to handle month-end accounting or set up videoconferences, for example. Some carriers require 24-hour advance reservations for Switched-T1 services, however.

Another circuit-switched service is *Integrated Services Digital Network* (ISDN), which provides all digital service. ISDN represents an attempt to convert the telephone system to all-digital service. With ISDN, a home user could connect with a remote site over a digital connection and get all the advantage that digital service provides, including higher transmission rates and better quality service. ISDN is currently offered by carriers in selected areas.

An alternative to circuit-switching services is *packet-switched services*, which provide connections for multiple simultaneous users to multiple locations.

RELATED ENTRIES   Carrier Services; Packet-Switching Networks; *and* Switched Services

Client-Server Computing

In the client-server computing model, users work at intelligent computers called front-end systems and interact with back-end server systems that provide services, such as database access, network management, and centralized file storage. A computer network provides the communication platform on which many clients can interact with one or more servers. The interaction between the users' front-end application and the program (typically a database or network operating system) at the back-end server is called a *client-server relationship*. This implies that the user has a computer with its own processing capability, which runs a program that can handle user interaction and data presentation. Thus, client-server computing replaces the centralized computing paradigm.

- In centralized computing, users at dumb terminals communicate with central host computers. All processing takes place at the host—users simply type commands to send to the host and view the results on the screen.

- In client-server computing, the client system runs an application that interacts with another program running on a server.

The client-server model applies to operating systems and applications. Network operating systems such as Novell NetWare are client-server oriented because users at workstations make requests to NetWare servers. The client runs a requester program that redirects requests for network services to the appropriate servers on the network and directs requests for local services to the local operating system. In client-server database management systems, clients make requests using a front-end application, and servers fulfill those requests.

In the client-server relationship, processing is split between the client and the server. The client systems run an application that displays an interface for the user. It formats requests for network services and displays information or messages it received back from the server. The server performs back-end processing, such as sorting data or performing extracts. Because the data is close at hand, it performs this processing efficiently. After sorting, extracting, or performing some other service on data for a user, the server sends the results back to the client. Network traffic is reduced because the client only gets requested information, not large blocks of data to sort through.

The servers in a client-server environment are often powerful superserver systems, minicomputers, or mainframes that can adequately handle the multiple and simultaneous requests they receive from clients, along with security and network management tasks. Some large organizations have replaced mainframe systems that provide five million instructions-per-second (MIPS) with a pool of superserver systems that collectively provide a total of 1,000 MIPS. Client-server strategies provide a way to create relatively inexpensive computing platforms that are easy to customize for specific applications.

The software of a client-server system is usually a database management system (DBMS) in which clients query back-end servers using Structured Query Language (SQL). An online transaction processing (OLTP) system is particularly suited to the client-server model. While file servers and database servers are most common, a back-end server might also provide dedicated communication and print services, as well.

Client-Server Architecture

Client-server architecture defines a relationship between a user's workstation (the front-end client) and a back-end file server, print server, communication server, fax server, or other type of system that provides services. The client must be an intelligent system with its own processing power to take some of the load off the back-end system—that is the basis of the client-server model. The relationship consists of a request and a response, followed by more requests and responses. Placing file services and other services on back-end dedicated systems has several advantages. The servers are easier to secure and maintain in one location, and backups are simplified if the data is in one location and managed by the same authority.

There are several possible client-server configurations. In Figure C-16, several clients access a single server. This is the usual configuration of a small local area network (LAN). Figure C-17 is a distributed database model in which clients access data located on several servers.

In a peer-to-peer network such as Microsoft Windows for Workgroups, NetWare Lite, Artisoft LANtastic, or the Network File System (NFS), workstations can be both clients and servers, as shown in Figure C-18. A user can share files on his or her hard disk with other users on the network. Thus the workstation becomes a server to other

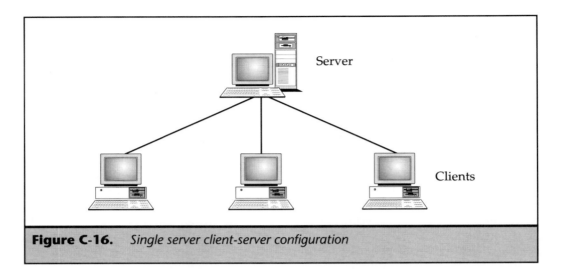

Figure C-16. *Single server client-server configuration*

clients. At the same time, the user can access shared files on other workstations as a client.

Let's elaborate on these models even further to see current and future trends in client-server computing. On the left in Figure C-19, a database is copied (replicated) to a remote system so that users at the remote site can access data at their local site, rather than over a wide area network (WAN) link. The two servers periodically synchronize with each other to ensure that users are working with the latest

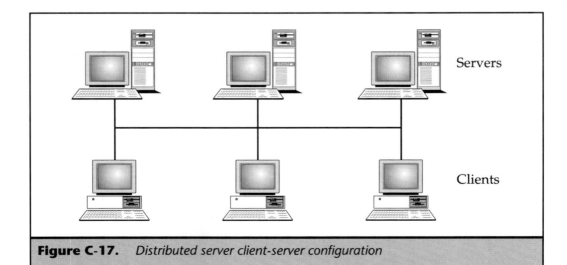

Figure C-17. *Distributed server client-server configuration*

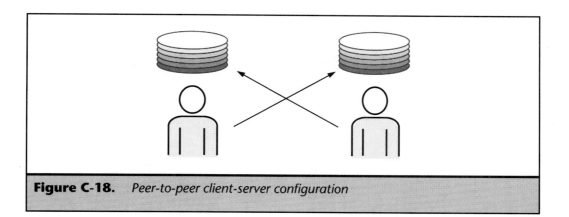

Figure C-18. *Peer-to-peer client-server configuration*

information. On the right in Figure C-19, vast amounts of data for the enterprise are stored in a "data warehouse." Workgroups don't normally access the warehouse data directly, although that is possible. Instead, a staging system accesses blocks of commonly used data for users in the workgroup and stores it for access by the workgroup. This cuts down on traffic over the enterprise network and assumes the workgroup users are accessing common data. At the same time, the data warehouse

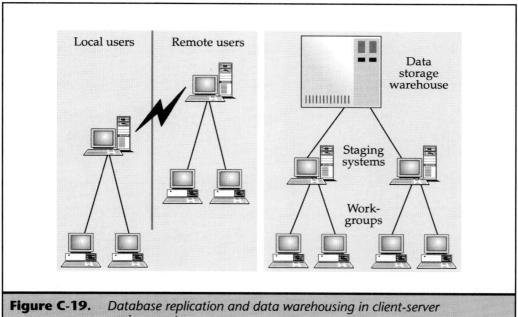

Figure C-19. *Database replication and data warehousing in client-server environments*

provides all the management, backup, and other benefits of centralized storage. For more on this topic, see "Information Warehouse."

These discussions have assumed that the client is software-compatible with the server, but this is not always the case when an enterprise network is constructed from previously installed departmental LANs. Two models are available for sharing data throughout the enterprise, as shown in Figure C-20.

■ On the left, a common gateway is installed to translate client requests to incompatible servers.

■ On the right, a common protocol layer is installed that provides an interface using a single standardized protocol between the incompatible clients and the servers. Many vendors are taking this approach.

Internally, the client and the server are divided into several processes that are pictured in Figure C-21. Note that client redirection software determines whether the client's requests are for a local service or for a network server. Depending on the operating system and/or application, there are variations in the amount of work the server performs. In some cases, the server performs as little work as possible to optimize its performance for an increased number of clients. In other cases, the server works as a powerful engine, handling most of the processing load.

In most configurations, communication takes place over the LAN. Servers can be part of a department or local workgroup, or located in a central area for access by the entire organization. These centrally accessed servers are called *enterprise servers*. Servers can also be at remote locations that users access over a telecommunication

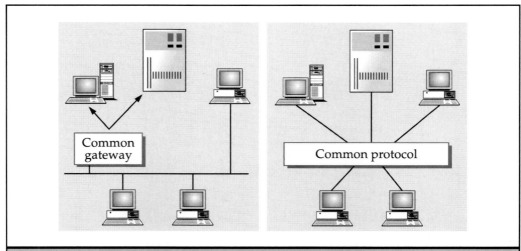

Figure C-20.   *Gateway and common protocol client-server models*

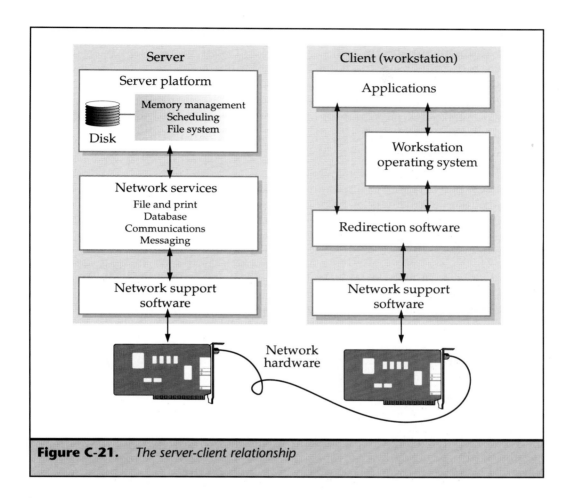

Figure C-21. *The server-client relationship*

link. Depending on the type of link, response time between client and remote servers may take a while, and this is something that managers need to take into consideration. If real-time access is not required, messaging techniques can be employed in which a user sends a requests to the server and the server sends a response back in the form of a message to the user's mailbox. The response may arrive in seconds, minutes, or even hours, depending on the connection type and time constraints allowed by the system designers.

Advantages of Client-Server Architecture

Here are some of the advantages in the client-server model:

- Client-server computing helps organizations "downsize" from mainframes and minicomputers to LAN-based servers and workstations, with networks serving as the enterprise-wide communication platform.

- The workload imposed by applications is split among computing systems. Client systems handle much of their own processing; thus processing is distributed over a large number of desktop systems.

- Server systems handle tasks related to centralized data on directly attached storage devices, thus minimizing the amount of information sent over the network.

- A large percentage of information is cached once into the server's memory, rather than the memory of every workstation that needs it.

- Network traffic is reduced because the server only gives the client the information requested, not large blocks of information that the workstation must process.

- Large server systems can offload applications that are better handled by personal workstations.

- Data is safe and secure in one location. Data warehousing provides a way to make specific data available at intermediate workgroup servers while maintaining control of the data.

- With centralized data, administrators can apply security controls to restrict data access and use tracking mechanisms to monitor data access.

- Client-server mechanisms promote multi-system parallel processing, in which multiple computers cooperate in the completion of a processing task. Each system is allocated a portion of the task, and the results are recombined. The task is completed much faster than if a stand-alone system handled it.

The Client-Server Model in Stand-Alone Operating Systems

While the client-server model is commonly discussed in terms of front- and back-end systems attached to networks, it also applies to the architectural design of most modern operating systems. For example, Microsoft Windows NT implements the client-server model as the standard method for user interaction with the operating system. The server process is implemented as a background *kernel* that handles low-level functions such as scheduling of tasks and synchronization processes. The front end is the user interface, the file system, and the application that the user runs. This strategy provides a modular, plug-and-play approach to operating systems. For example, you can plug-in a DOS file system, a Windows file system, or an OS/2 file system, depending on your preference. The back-end kernel doesn't care which operating system you are using, because it sees a common interface through which it can provide its services. See "Kernel" and "Microkernel" for more information.

The Object-Oriented Model

The new paradigm for distributed systems is the object-oriented model in which data and procedures are encapsulated in objects. Objects communicate with one another using message-passing procedures, and this communication can take place over a network. Message passing is handled by an Object Request Broker (ORB). The Object Management Group (OMG) has created the Common Object Request Broker Architecture (CORBA), which defines an ORB that accepts requests from objects, locates another object that can service the request, and forwards it. It also handles the response in a similar manner. The power of the ORB lies in its ability to locate services on the network, and it can be programmed to find the best providers of services (for example, a high-performance system or an idle system).

Object-oriented operating systems are also easier to build since objects are modular components. An existing modular system is easy to expand by simply adding new modules or modifying existing modules. The entire system does not need to be rebuilt. Objects represent shared system resources such as files, memory, and devices, and these devices are manipulated with the object services provided in the operating system. Object-oriented operating systems include Microsoft Cairo, Taligent products co-developed by IBM and Apple, and products based on CORBA. See "Object-Oriented Interfaces and Operating Systems" and "Object-Oriented Technology."

Implementing Client-Server Applications

In a distributed network environment, the goal is to provide shared data to all users on the enterprise. Data stored on many different systems is made accessible to clients and ideally this data appears as a single logical database. The implementation of a shared data environment will typically involve the following functions:

- *Security* measures are necessary to control who can access the data.
- *Integrity* measures are required to ensure that transactions are committed if complete, or rolled-back if incomplete.
- *Concurrency* and *availability* measures are necessary to allow many users to access and update the data.
- *Reliability and recoverability* of data are necessary using backups and fault tolerant features.

Each of these functions must be implemented if you intend to share data over the enterprise with many users. Consider the following situations:

- Which clients simply read the data on a server, and which clients both read and write the data?
- If two users are accessing the same data and one writes changes, should the other user's data also be updated? Is this even feasible?

■ When several users are manipulating the same data, does one user's write operation take precedence over another's, or does the last write have precedence?

Solutions to these problems are implemented in most client-server systems, but distributing data over many servers in an enterprise can pose insurmountable logistics problems that make real-time access to the same data by multiple users impractical in many environments. Locking mechanisms can prevent a user from accessing a block of records until another user is finished making changes, but these solutions introduce their own problems. For example, in a time-sensitive environment, waiting for another user to free up a block of records is impractical. Interleaved update can help the server keep track of changes on an ongoing basis. If multiple users are working with the same block of data, methods are needed so that clients know when the data has been changed by another user. Two techniques are:

■ Clients periodically check with the server to see if the data they are caching has been changed by another user. This method creates excessive network traffic.

■ The server sends updates to clients when mutually accessed data is changed by one of the clients.

Servers must make data available but also be concerned with concurrency of data. In distributed systems, these problems multiply if databases on various systems are interdependent. Various methods can be employed to keep the systems synchronized, but this can add delays. What happens if one of the servers crashes during a write operation? The crashed server must be updated when it is brought back online. In addition, any incomplete transactions must be rolled back, not just on the crashed server, but on all servers that received the transaction to maintain synchronization. Transaction processing mechanisms for doing this are discussed later in this section under "Transaction Processing."

DBMSs and SQL

The majority of client-server applications are database management systems (DBMSs) that use Structured Query Language (SQL). SQL is a standard relational database language first implemented by IBM as a way to access its DB2 database management system. Over the years, various improvements to the standard have been proposed and implemented. These include American National Standards Institute (ANSI) standards such as SQL'89 and SQL'92, as well as a proposed standard to support object-oriented technology called SQL3. A consortium of database vendors called SQL Access Group (SAG) and the X/Open group are attempting to enforce standards and develop new ones.

The database standards described in the following list were developed by Microsoft and an industry consortium to provide connectivity between a variety of front-end database applications and a variety of back-end database servers. Both are based on SAG standards. These standards and others are discussed in more detail under the entry "Database Connectivity APIs and Middleware".

■ Open Database Connectivity (ODBC), a Microsoft standard for interfacing databases that defines Windows interfaces to front-end and back-end data base services.

■ Integrated Database Application Program Interface (IDAPI), a Borland standard database API.

While there is ample standardization activity in the SQL environment, a uniform standard has not yet been developed. With the lack of standards, the primary focus will be on gateway drivers that allow clients to access many different databases in a distributed computing environment using translation methods.

The use of SQL is growing as the number of enterprise networks grows. It is becoming more a mechanism for accessing data on multivendor enterprise networks than a query language to access a single vendor's database management system. This is happening because SQL is available on a large number of systems, and protocols and gateways are widely available to link all the different versions. In addition, several tools simplify and automate client-server application development. These tools include PowerBuilder from Powersoft Corporation, Uniface from Uniface Corporation, and SQL Windows from Microsoft. These tools help resolve multivendor connectivity problems in distributed environments.

There are several ways to build client-server applications, depending on how much work load you want to give to the front end and the back end, as described next.

STANDARD MODEL   The standard model for client-server computing has already been described in the previous paragraphs. The client portion handles the user's keyboard inputs and display data, and presents an interface to the user for creating and sending SQL statements. SQL statements are sent to the server, which responds with data, sometimes in large blocks. This model can generate a lot of network traffic, thus stored procedure techniques were developed.

STORED PROCEDURES   In this model, a DBMS system not only accepts SQL statements from a client, it has a set of procedures that perform some of the processing normally performed by the client. For example, a stored procedure called *cust_bal* might execute a procedure at the server that would produce a list of customers with unpaid balances. Traffic is reduced because a single call to execute the stored procedures is sent to the server from the client. Stored procedures can contain security controls that prevent some users from executing the procedures. This model moves closer to the object-oriented model in which procedures are stored with data.

WAREHOUSE MODEL   In this model, data for the entire enterprise is stored in a back-end mainframe system or superserver system. Users can access this data directly using SQL statements. However, an intermediate system can stage data from the warehouse and transform the data in various ways for use by workgroups and people who use special tools and applications to view the information. You can think of the intermediate system as a "multiplexer" that handles requests from many users. It formulates its own requests to the warehouse servers and stores the data resulting from the requests. Since the intermediate system may already have some information on its disks or in its cache, it can satisfy some requests on its own. Part of this strategy is to reduce the number of user requests to the main server and use the intermediate system to optimize those requests.

Transaction Processing

A transaction is a discrete unit of work that is typically part of a business transaction. An *online transaction processing* (OLTP) system operates in real-time to collect and process transaction-related data and post changes to shared databases and other files. Online transaction processing implies that a transaction is executed immediately. In contrast, a connectionless transaction is a non-real-time transaction—it is executed by a command from a user in a store-and-forward message. The results of an online transaction are immediately available in the database, assuming that transaction's complete. Connectionless transactions appear once the message arrives at the server and is processed. The most common examples of OLTP systems are airline reservation systems, banking transactions systems, and accounting systems.

A *transaction* is commonly defined as an indivisible unit of work that is either fully completed and written to the database, or incomplete and not written anywhere in the database. This concept is important for these reasons:

- If the server goes down during a write operation, the write will be incomplete and the database must be rolled back to its original state.

- If the transaction is written to multiple servers, and one of those servers goes down, transactions on all servers must be rolled back to ensure data synchronization and integrity.

- An operator might need to halt a transaction in progress. Any changes made to the database must be rolled back to ensure that the database does not contain partial or incomplete information.

You can view transactions as single units of work executed by SQL statements. Each transaction is seen as an atomic, indivisible unit that is applied to the database in a consistent way. Consistency implies that the unit of work is written only if all the affected parts of the database have committed to it. In addition, each unit of work must be isolated from other transactions until it completes or is rolled back. This poses some problems in a shared system that many users access simultaneously, and where one user's transactions may depend on another user's transactions. Mechanisms must be in place to allow simultaneous transactions, but prevent those transactions from interfering with each other while providing users with a consistent view of the data.

Two-phase commit provides a way to ensure integrity when a transaction affects data located at multiple sites. In this scheme, all sites first prepare to commit the transaction and signal to a coordinator that they are ready. If all sites respond, the coordinator signals a commit; if one or more do not respond, the coordinator signals an abort. In the second phase, the data is committed and all sites send a confirmation message. If one or more of the sites do not respond at this point, the transaction is rolled back on all servers involved.

The Front End

So far, this discussion has focused on the back end of the client-server relationship. What about the front end? There are a number of applications and development tools to consider, as listed next.

QUERY TOOLS   A number of tools are available to help users access back-end data with predefined queries and built-in reporting capabilities. Query tools are available from most DBMS vendors. A special type of query tool called an Executive Information System (EIS) can present back-end data as tables and graphs. A popular EIS is Forest & Trees from Channel Computing.

USER APPLICATIONS   Common applications such as Lotus 1-2-3, Microsoft Excel and Access, Borland Paradox, and others can provide front-end access to back-end databases. Some include their own Structured Query Language (SQL). Microsoft Access uses the Open Database Connectivity (ODBC) standard to provide an interface to multivendor database management systems.

PROGRAM DEVELOPMENT TOOLS   Several tools are available for programmers and information systems managers to help them develop front-end applications for accessing back-end data. Programmer products include Microsoft Windows-based, graphics-oriented tools such as Microsoft Visual Basic, and tools from various DBMS vendors.

In all cases, users should ensure that front-end products are compatible with back-end products. If an organization has a diversity of multivendor back-end database systems, select front-end products that include support for the products through common protocols or direct compatibility. So-called "middleware" products can solve many incompatibility problems.

Connection and Communications Methods

The actual mechanisms for transmitting information between client and server systems in distributed multivendor environments has been called *middleware*. There is a wide range of these products, including store-and-forward messaging, and remote procedure calls (RPC):

■ A remote procedure call (RPC) is a call that connects two computers over a synchronous connection. The connection is maintained to ensure data integrity between the two systems on a real-time basis. This type of connection is important in mission-critical applications such as banking transactions.

■ In a message-passing system, information and requests are sent between computers in much the same way E-mail messages are sent between users. The message is stored and forwarded along a path to its destination. While message systems are not adequate for real-time database updating, they provide efficient read services.

Microsoft's Windows Open System Architecture (WOSA) is a strategy to build middleware directly into its operating systems so that information flows more easily throughout the enterprise. Client systems can connect to a variety of back-end services such as databases, communication, applications, and mail servers. In Microsoft Windows NT, RPCs are incorporated directly into the operating system.

IBM and other vendors are relying on the Open Software Foundation (OSF) Distributed Computing Environment (DCE) to help integrate multivendor distributed applications. The DCE provides an extensive set of services through which applications can communicate and users can connect with the wide variety of data services available in an enterprise network.

RELATED ENTRIES   Database Connectivity APIs and Middleware; Distributed Computing; Distributed Database; Middleware; *and* Transaction Processing

Client-Server LAN Protocols

Client-server LAN protocols are used in network operating systems in which a workstation, acting as a client, makes requests for services from a back-end server. The following protocols are optimized for workgroups and 802.x access methods. They are generally inadequate for wide area networking, although multiprotocol routers are removing some of the problems in using the protocols over wide areas.

■ Microsoft Server Message Blocks (SMB) and NetBIOS
■ AppleTalk
■ Novell NetWare Core Protocol (NCP) using Internetwork Packet Exchange (IPX)

Protocols suitable for enterprise networking and wide area networking are:

■ Advanced Peer-to-Peer Networking (APPN)
■ Transmission Control Protocol/Internet Protocol (TCP/IP)
■ Open Systems Interconnection (OSI) model protocols

Each protocol is discussed under its respective heading.

Client Software

Client software runs in workstations attached to networks. It is sometimes called the *shell* or *requester* software. It provides a way for applications running on a workstation to make requests for services provided by network servers attached to the network. The software acts as a redirector, forwarding requests for local services to the local operating system and requests for remote services to network servers.

NetWare Client Software

In the NetWare environment, the client software is referred to as the requester software. NetWare is a server-centric operating system—clients make requests from systems that are specifically set up to provide those services. In contrast, the peer-to-peer environment of Windows for Workgroups, Windows NT, LANtastic, and others is designed to allow users to share the resources on their own systems at will. Dedicated servers may also exist in the network.

In the NetWare environment, there is a requester for DOS and for OS/2. The DOS requester modules are installed using a special installation disk at each machine. The DOS requester loads several modules in a special directory that are typically loaded when the computer boots. These are the modules for NetWare 4.x:

- **LSL (Link Support Layer)** Loads the driver that supports multiple network interface cards and switches packets between them.

- **LAN Driver** Loads a driver that is specific to each of the installed network interface cards. The drivers are selected during the setup phase.

- **IPXODI** Loads the IPX driver to support communications between servers over the specified network interface card. Other drivers are available for AppleTalk and TCP/IP.

- **VLMs (Virtual Loadable Modules)** A variety of VLMs are loaded to support functions for the workstation, such as encryption and authentication, directory services, DOS redirection, and more.

A utility called WSUPDATE is available to automate client software updates from the central management workstation. Systems with outdated shells, utilities, and applications are automatically updated by the utility.

Microsoft Client Software

In the Microsoft Windows for Workgroups and Windows NT environment, the client software is built in. During software installation, the setup procedure asks for the type of interface card installed in the workstation and configures it accordingly.

The primary method for network communications involves the NetBIOS and NetBEUI protocols. These protocols are installed by default. NetBEUI establishes and maintains communication sessions between workstations, and NetBIOS provides an interface to the network for applications so they can request files and printers from other workstations. Note that IPX/SPX and TCP/IP are also supported through the Network Device Interface Specification (NDIS).

The setup utility loads various drivers in the WINDOWS directory and then makes changes to the startup files (in Windows for Workgroups). Startup settings are specified in a file called PROTOCOL.INI in the WINDOWS directory.

The client software allows workstations to act as redirectors, receivers, and servers. The Server Message Blocks (SMBs) protocol provides a way for workstations to communicate with other workstations through the NetBIOS interface. SMB operates in the Applications layer relative to the Open Systems Interconnection (OSI) model. It has the following features:

- The *redirector* translates requests and routes them to network servers.

- The *receiver service* lets a workstation listen for SMB messages from other workstations that are addressed to it.

- The *server service* lets any Windows for Workgroups and Windows NT system provide file and print services for other workstations on the network.

TCP/IP Clients

Transmission Control Protocol/Internet Protocol (TCP/IP) is a common communication protocol implemented in the UNIX environment and on the Internet. Most client software now provides TCP/IP support, either built-in or as an option. The TCP/IP protocol stack can run alongside the IPX or NetBIOS protocol stacks for NetWare and Windows NT clients. For example, the Open Data-Link Interface (ODI) in Novell NetWare provides a way to load multiple protocol stacks so workstations can run applications to access multivendor systems. Microsoft's Network Device Interface Specification (NDIS) provides these same functions, allowing clients to load NetBEUI/NetBIOS, SPX/IPX, TCP/IP, and other protocols simultaneously.

RELATED ENTRIES   DOS Requester, NetWare; LAN WorkPlace Products, Novell; Network Driver Interface Specification; *and* Open Data-link Interface

Cluster Controllers, IBM

A *cluster controller* is an IBM-manufactured or compatible device used to channel-attach 3270 terminals to a host system. A cluster controller may also communicate with a host via a Synchronous Data Link Control (SDLC) link, or a bisynchronous link to a host-attached communication controller. There are channel-attached cluster controllers and link-attached cluster controllers:

CHANNEL-ATTACHED CLUSTER CONTROLLER   These controllers are directly attached to the multiplexer channel of the host system. Model numbers for this type of cluster controller end in A (Systems Network Architecture [SNA] controller) or D (non-SNA controller), such as IBM 3274 Model 41D.

LINK-ATTACHED CLUSTER CONTROLLER   These controllers are connected to communication controllers. The communication controller is then attached to a channel of the mainframe. The link between the cluster controller and the communication controller is either a modem for analog circuits or channel service unit/data service unit (CSU/DSU) for digital circuits. Model numbers for this type of controller end in C, such as IBM 3274 Model 41C.

SNA cluster controllers are called physical unit (PU) Type 2 devices and terminals attached to the cluster controller are called logical unit (LU) type 2 devices. A printer device attached to a PU Type 2 is either an LU Type 1 or LU Type 3, depending on the printer type.

The 3274 series cluster controllers are actually the older series IBM cluster controllers. New models are the IBM 3174 series. The new models provide advanced features like IBM Token Ring attachment interfaces, management, and monitoring. Various models are listed here. Note that models with numbers ending in L connect directly to a host's channel (channel-attached) and models with numbers ending in R are designed for remote use and provide telecommunication link ports.

- *IBM 3174 Model 1L*   An SNA or non-SNA device with optional token ring, token ring 3270 Gateway, or Asynchronous Emulation Adapter that supports up to 24 ASCII devices.

- *IBM 3174 Model 1R or Model 51R*   Same as model 1L, but an SNA/SDLC or BISYNC device. The Model 1R supports 32 terminal devices and the Model 51R supports 16.

- *IBM 3174 Model 2R or Model 52R*   Same as Model 1R, but has X.21 physical interface. The Model 2R supports 32 terminal devices and the Model 52R supports 16.

- *IBM 3174 Model 3R or Model 53R*   Same as Model 1R, but includes Token Ring attachment. The Model 3R supports 32 terminal devices and the Model 53R supports 16.

- *IBM 3174 Model 81R*   Provides serial connections to modems for eight terminal devices.

- *IBM 3174 Model 82R*   Provides X.21 (CCITT V.11) connections for eight terminal devices.

RELATED ENTRIES   Communication Controller; IBM; IBM Mainframe Environment; IBM Networking Blueprint; *and* Systems Network Architecture

Coaxial Cable

Coaxial cable is commonly used to connect bus-topology networks such as Ethernet and ARCNET. The cable consists of a copper wire core surrounded by insulation. This is then wrapped by braided copper wire or metallic foil, which provides shielding from outside signals and the radiation of interior signals. These components are surrounded by a plastic outer covering.

RELATED ENTRIES ARCNET; Cabling; Ethernet; *and* Transmission Media, Methods, and Equipment

Commercial Building Wiring Standard (EIA/TIA 568)

See EIA/TIA 568 Commercial Building Wiring Standard.

Common Carrier

See Carriers; Carrier Services.

Common Mail Calls (CMC)

Common Mail Calls (CMC) is a cross-platform messaging application program interface (API) released by the X.400 API Association based on work done by Microsoft with its Simple MAPI (Messaging Application Programming Interface). X.400 is a standard for exchanging electronic messages among mail systems running on a wide variety of computing platforms. The X.400 API Association is responsible for creating interfaces to the X.400 standard.

A cross-platform message API is used by developers to build electronic mail functions into their software applications that are compatible with many different platforms. For example, a developer of scheduling software could use the API to add network-wide group scheduling functions so that users can view each other's schedules and plan meetings. Cross-platform messaging services are provided by the API. Cross-platform means that the application will be compatible with a variety of applications on a variety of operating systems.

CMC provides a basic set of services, including send, receive, and address lookup capabilities. Advanced functions were left out to promote wide acceptance from vendors who could add their own customized features. Advanced messaging functions include the ability to attach documents to E-mail messages. As an example, CMC has only 12 function calls, compared to 60 in the Vendor Independent Messaging (VIM) standard.

CMC is widely accepted, which ensures that a variety of applications include a method for integrating common messaging functions. Novell and other companies are supporting CMC as follows:

- The Novell Global Message Handling Service includes CMC support.
- Microsoft includes CMC in Windows.
- Lotus and the VIM committee include CMC in the VIM standard and the VIM Simple Mail Interface calls.

RELATED ENTRIES Electronic Mail; Message Handling Service, Novell; Messaging API, E-mail; Messaging Application Programming Interface; Vendor Independent Messaging; *and* X.400 Message Handling System

Common Management Information Protocol (CMIP)

The Common Management Information Protocol (CMIP) is an Open Systems Interconnection (OSI) model that defines how to create a common network management system. While both CMIP and the Internet SNMP (Simple Network Management Protocol) define network management standards, CMIP is much more complex and provides features that are sought after by network administrators. However, CMIP acceptance has been slow and few CMIP products exist. Additionally, some of the supporting components have not been standardized. In contrast, SNMP is common, primarily because it is an Internet design that has been well tested. In addition, it is easy to implement.

Some of the telephone companies are using CMIP for public network management, and CMIP is included, along with SNMP, in the Open Software Foundation (OSF) Distributed Management Environment (DME). The government has also ordered the use of OSI protocols for its agencies with the Government OSI Profile (GOSIP) and CMIP is part of OSI. CMIP may eventually surface as a major management standard, especially since it offers many more features than SNMP.

The OSI management model defines systems that are *managed* and it defines *management systems.* Managed systems run agents that gather information about processes and communicate with management systems.

A process runs in nodes that collect management information from processes running at each layer of the OSI protocol stack. Changes can also be applied in the layers. Each node has a *management information base* (MIB), which is a collection of objects that hold node information.

A System Management Application-Process (SMAP) provides the interface through which MIBs share information. SMAPs talk to other SMAPs over the network. A System Management Application Entity (SMAE) supports SMAP communication and SMAEs use CMIP to exchange data between nodes. CMIP forms a road map for designing a network management system, but the actual interface specifications are in CMIS (Common Management Information Service).

CMIP is divided into the following functions:

- *Accounting management* Provides a way to monitor network usage and charge users for the use of network resources. It can be used to monitor costs and prevent overruns of budgets. The information it produces can justify a need to purchase new equipment for example. The information is also useful for tracking a user's activity on the network for security reasons.

- *Configuration management* Provides a way to view and manage system resources and management information. In a graphical user interface environment, managers could point to icons of bridges, routers, or other devices and click to view information and modify settings.

- *Fault management* Detects and corrects faults in the network. Analysis features can help determine the cause of faults. Alarms are available to alert managers when usage or other thresholds are met.

- *Performance management* Provides services for monitoring the network and tuning its performance with the resulting information. Gathering statistics is the primary function of performance management.

- *Security* Provides high-level security services that can authenticate users, detect and alert managers to possible intrusions, and ensure the confidentiality of transmitted data, among other areas.

RELATED ENTRIES Desktop Management Interface; Management Standards and Tools; *and* Simple Network Management Protocol

Common Management Information Service (CMIS)

CMIS provides a way to share management information in the Common Management Information Protocol (CMIP) environment.

Common Object Model (COM)

COM is a set of object-based distributed networking interfaces designed to allow Windows applications to access applications and objects on other platforms. COM is a joint development effort of Microsoft and Digital Equipment Corporation (DEC). COM basically integrates Microsoft's Object Linking and Embedding (OLE) with DEC's ObjectBroker technology. OLE and ObjectBroker are similar technologies that provide a way for application to exchange information through active links.

ObjectBroker runs on DEC OpenVMS, ULTRIX, and OSF/1 platforms, as well as UNIX from Sun, Hewlett-Packard, and IBM. Microsoft OLE gains access to the enterprise environments with COM. OLE is part of Microsoft's operating system strategy that includes the fully object-oriented operating system code-named Cairo.

OLE and ObjectBroker will communicate with the remote procedure call (RPC) mechanisms developed by the Open Software Foundation (OSF) and implemented in its Distributed Computing Environment (DCE). COM competes with OMA (Object Management Architecture) developed by the Object Management Group.

RELATED ENTRIES   Common Object Request Broker Architecture; Object Linking and Embedding; Object Management Architecture; *and* Object-Oriented Interfaces and Operating Systems

Common Object Request Broker Architecture (CORBA)

C

CORBA is the basic object messaging technology specification defined by the Object Management Group (OMG) in its Object Management Architecture (OMA). The OMG is a consortium of about 200 companies, many of which have contributed major technologies to the OMA. These companies include Digital Equipment Corporation, Hewlett-Packard, HyperDesk Corporation, and SunSoft. The architecture has also been adopted by the X/Open Group, which has a common goal of developing multivendor common application environments, and the Open Software Foundation (OSF), which is developing portable system software called the Distributed Computing Environment (DCE) and the Distributed Management Environment (DME).

Readers should be aware that CORBA competes with Microsoft's Object Linking and Embedding (OLE), which is implemented in its Windows products and forthcoming object-oriented operating system code-named Cairo. However, OLE is concerned with sharing objects among Windows desktop applications, while CORBA focuses on internetwork and interoperable (cross-platform) object communication. In a round-about way, Microsoft has gained access to CORBA technology through its alliance with Digital and the formation of the Common Object Model (COM).

As described under the heading Object Management Architecture, OMA is comprised of four major components:

- *Application objects,* which are optional plug-and-play applications such as spreadsheet programs and word processors.
- *Common facilities,* which are procedures placed in common area so that any application can access them. Common facilities reduce redundant code.
- *Object services,* which provide the essential services to implement object technology.
- *Object Request Broker (ORB),* which is the common interface that objects use to communicate with other objects.

The ORB provides the interface through which objects communicate to one another. It also provides message formatting so that objects with different interfaces can communicate. You can think of the ORB as an intelligent message transfer bus that performs the following:

- Accepts requests from objects
- Locates "provider" objects that can service the request
- Formats the message for the destination object
- Formats and returns the results to the requester

The interesting part of this procedure is that the ORB locates the provider object over the distributed environment, even if the object is located over a wide area network (WAN) link in another city. Programmers and managers can specify which object should be used, and the ORB can optimize the distributed system by using objects on idle systems or high-performance systems.

Object technology is considered vital to implementing future distributed systems. The complexity of such systems is simplified with object models that implement messaging services such as the ORB. Objects simply request services and other objects provide those services. It is not necessary for developers to know much in advance about the systems on which objects will communicate. In fact, object technologies provide a way to design applications for local use that can expand to distributed environments at a later time.

CORBA includes the following:

- ORB engine
- Dynamic Invocation Interface
- Interface Definition Language (IDL)
- Object adapter
- ORB interface
- Implementation repository
- Interface repository

The ORB is implemented differently by many vendors, so future developments will focus on providing ORB-to-ORB interoperability. This will be available in CORBA version 2.0. OMG is also working to provide a standard interface to CORBA.

RELATED ENTRIES   Object Linking and Embedding; Object Management Architecture; Object Management Group; Object-Oriented Interfaces and Operating Systems; Object-Oriented Technology; Object Request Broker; *and* Objects

Common Open Software Environment (COSE)

COSE is a consortium of vendors including IBM, Hewlett-Packard, SunSoft, and Novell. These vendors are cooperating to deliver a common desktop environment

(CDE) to UNIX that can rival Microsoft Windows. The objectives of the organization are:

- Develop a specification that provides application program interfaces (APIs) for a common desktop graphical environment that is supported on the vendor's systems.
- Adopt common networking environments.
- Identify graphics, multimedia, and object technology for endorsement.
- Define system management and administration for distributed systems.

The specification addresses communication and message passing among applications; the display of data; editing; object management; window management; desktop integration; cut and paste; and drag and drop. Specifications are submitted to X/Open (Menlo Park, California) for evaluation. For the most part, the COSE specification defines an environment that is very close to Microsoft Windows. With the emergence of Microsoft Windows NT and its Windows interface, both UNIX and the COSE initiative are facing more competition.

The COSE specification includes elements of the following environments and technologies:

- Hewlett-Packard's Visual User Environment (VUE)
- IBM's Common User Access model and the OS/2 Release 2.0 Workplace Shell, which is an object-oriented user interface
- Open Software Foundation's Motif Tool kit and Windows Manager
- SunSoft's OpenLook and Deskset productivity tools (ToolTalk) and a set of distributed computing services and networking protocols called Open Network Computing Plus (ONC+)
- UNIX System Laboratories' (USL) Desktop Manager
- Remote procedure calls (RPCs) from Sun's Open Network Computing (ONC) environment and the Open Software Foundation (OSF) Distributed Computing Environment (DCE)
- Standard Generalized Markup Language (SGML), which provides ways to integrate and share document information that was created in other environments
- Multipurpose Internet Mail Extension (MIME), a compound document standard in the Internet environment

With the purchase of USL, Novell gained control of UNIX SVR4 to the dismay of other UNIX vendors. In an attempt to consolidate the industry on a common UNIX operating system, Novell gave the source code and the UNIX trademark to the X/Open organization. X/Open will grant the UNIX trademark to UNIX implementations that are compatible with a set of specifications defined by the COSE group. This set of specifications, called the *COSE Spec 1170 APIs*, defines programming interfaces that promote the portability of applications between operating systems.

RELATED ENTRY UNIX

Common Programming Interface for Communication (CPI-C), IBM

CPI-C is a high-level communication interface. It is one of the interfaces in the broader Common Programming Interface family that is part of IBM's Systems Application Architecture (SAA). CPI-C is designed to provide a common environment for the execution of applications across SAA platforms, such as IBM MVS (Multiple Virtual Storage), VS (Virtual Storage), OS/400, and OS/2-based systems.

CPI-C's most important feature is that it provides an interface to LU 6.2 (logical unit 6.2) services. LU 6.2 is the technical name for IBM Advanced Program-to-Program Communications (APPC). LU 6.2 was developed to allow computers in IBM environments to set up their own communication sessions, rather than rely on a host computer to do so. LU 6.2 provides peer-to-peer communications between systems other than hosts, and allows those systems to run distributed applications such as file sharing and remote access. LU 6.2 supports the entire range of IBM platforms, including local area networks, desktop systems, and mainframes.

CPI-C is the current preferred method for interfacing to LU 6.2. An older interface called the *LU 6.2 Protocol Boundary* also exists. IBM has implemented CPI-C in its Networking Blueprint and provides mapping to Open Systems Interconnection (OSI) and Transmission Control Protocol/Internet Protocol (TCP/IP) transport protocols as well. IBM also submitted CPI-C to the X/Open organization, which adopted it as a standard for developing client-server transaction processing applications.

IBM guides X/Open in its implementation of CPI-C and supports features such as full-duplex communications between CPI-C applications so programs can send and receive data at the same time. Multivendor distributed directory services are also supported, including X.500 and the directory services in the Open Software Foundation (OSF) Distributed Computing Environment (DCE). These services let applications locate users and resources without the need to know physical location information.

RELATED ENTRIES Advanced Program-to-Program Communications; IBM Networking Blueprint; *and* Systems Application Architecture

Communication

See Data Communications.

Communication Controller

A communication controller manages data input and output to a host computer or computer network. The units may be complex front-end mainframe interfaces or simpler devices such as multiplexers, bridges, and routers. The devices convert parallel computer data to serial data for transmission over communication lines and perform all the necessary control functions, error checking, and synchronization. Modern devices perform data compression, route selection, security functions, and collect management information. Some examples are listed here:

- Terminal servers provide a way to connect large numbers of terminals to host systems. The terminals connect into a single box that has a connection to the host over a network or remote link.

- Front-end processors provide the connection of terminals and networks to host systems.

- Multiplexers merge the data streams from a number of devices into a single line for transmission over long distances using various media.

- Repeaters, bridges, and routers are used to interconnect local area networks.

In the IBM mainframe environment, a communication controller is an IBM 3705, IBM 3720, IBM 3725, and IBM 3745. These devices provide a way to link cluster controllers at remote sites to an IBM host. There are two possible connection methods. In the first, the cluster controller at the remote site is connected via a telecommunication link to the communication controller at the main site, which is itself connected to the host. In the second method, the communication controller is at the remote site and provides a connection point for multiple cluster controllers. The communication controller then manages the flow of information from these cluster controllers over a telecommunication link to a communication controller at the main site, which is itself connected to the host.

The communication controller is often called a *front-end processor,* because it is a separate device from the host system that handles all communication with external devices such as terminals. This frees the host computer from being continuously interrupted by external devices and allows it to process applications more efficiently. Communication controllers handle the following functions:

- Establish communication sessions with terminals and network nodes.

- Manage data communication over communication links and control the flow of data.

- Concentrate cluster controller connections, and poll those controllers to see if they have data to transmit.

- Buffer incoming or outgoing data.

- Detect and correct errors.

■ Provide routing functions to get data to its destination.

A communication controller is really a computer in itself with a bus, memory, and central processing unit (CPU). It also contains the adapter to connect with the host channel and interface units that connect with the cluster controllers. The CPU manages the flow of information between the channel adapter and the interface units.

IBM communication controllers include the older, discontinued 3705 and new models with advanced features:

■ *IBM 3705* Provides from 128 to 352 communication lines with line speeds up to 230.4 Kbits/sec and can handle BISYNC, SDLC, or ASCII protocols. Supports eight channel-attached hosts. This unit relies on the host for control and diagnostics.

■ *IBM 3725* Designed as a replacement for the IBM 3705; comes in two models. The Model 1 supports up to 256 full-duplex communication lines and eight hosts. The Model 2 supports 80 full-duplex lines and four hosts.

■ *IBM 3720* Designed as a low-cost controller that is ideal for less-expensive hosts, such as IBM 9370 hosts. Various models provide direct or remote connection with 16 to 28 communication lines. A token ring interface is also available.

■ *IBM 3745* First introduced as communication controller in 1988; comes in two models. The Model 210 has one control unit. The Model 410 has two control units, which allows it to run as two separate communication controllers, or in modes that provide standby or backup support to guard against failures in software or hardware. The 210 can be upgraded to a 410 and supports up to 16 hosts and eight token ring adapters. The units also include hard disks that store the software modules required to restart the unit.

RELATED ENTRIES IBM Mainframe Environment; Systems Network Architecture

Communication Server

A communication server is a dedicated system that provides communication services for users on a network who need to transfer files or access information on systems or networks at remote locations over telecommunication links. The communication server provides communication channels for one or more users simultaneously, depending on the software and the hardware capabilities. Communication servers may provide one or more of the following functions:

■ *Gateway functions* These provide users with connections to host computers by translating between data formats, communication protocols, and cable signals.

■ *Access services*   These enable remote users to dial into the network from their home or other remote locations. This type of system is discussed further in this section, under "Remote Control Software."

■ *Modems*   Communication servers may provide internal users with a bank of asynchronous modems that they can access to dial out to remote systems, information services, or other resources.

■ *Bridge and router functions*   These maintain dedicated or dialup (intermittent) lines with remote LANs and automatically transfer data packets between the LANs.

■ *Electronic mail servers*   These automatically connect with other LANs or electronic "post offices" to pick up and deliver E-mail. The systems may call at timed intervals, or whenever there is enough outgoing mail to make the call worthwhile.

Remote Control Software

A remote workstation is a single PC at a remote site that dials into a LAN by using an asynchronous communication method and modems. The workstation might be used by an employee working at home, a manager at a remote site, or a field representative who needs to check the company database. Two methods for establishing remote workstation sessions are described next.

REMOTE EXECUTION   With the remote execution method (sometimes called "remote node"), all processing takes place at the remote workstation. All programs and data files the user needs must be transferred over the communication lines for processing in the user workstation unless the files are copied to the workstation in advance. This method is not recommended for real-time interaction with information systems.

LOCAL EXECUTION   The local execution method connects a dedicated workstation on the LAN to a remote workstation. All processing takes place at the dedicated workstation; screen displays are echoed at the remote workstation, and the user can enter keyboard commands. This method is efficient because only keyboard and screen information is transferred over the remote connection. However, a computer must be set up on the LAN to run the remote user's communication session.

Products such as Carbon Copy from Microcom, Close-Up from Norton-Lambert, and Norton pcANYWHERE from Symantec Corp. provide remote control capabilities such as these:

■ Users at remote workstations operate as if they were sitting at a workstation attached to the LAN.

■ Users can access database files in real time, with little delay in response.

■ File and database access are performed at LAN speeds because all processing is handled by the local network workstation. Only keystrokes and screen displays are sent from the local PC to the remote workstation.

A pcANYWHERE connection is illustrated in Figure C-22. It requires a dedicated computer on the network that runs the server software and a remote workstation that runs the client software.

NetWare Access Server Software

Novell's NetWare Access Server (NAS) provides a dedicated communication server that runs up to 15 remote sessions. The software runs on 80386 or faster systems, and an 80486 is recommended if you plan to run more than five simultaneous sessions. The software takes advantage of the 80386's ability to divide its processing time into 15 virtual 640 KB PCs. This provides 15 virtual computers for multiuser remote access. You install multiport serial cards in the system to accommodate the modems. Figure C-23 illustrates this configuration.

The NetWare Access Server provides the same features as remote control software, but in a single system that supports up to 15 users. Local network stations are not tied up performing tasks for remote users. The software provides a dial-back security feature that calls users back to verify the telephone numbers of the locations they are calling from. This ensures that an unauthorized user at another location is not

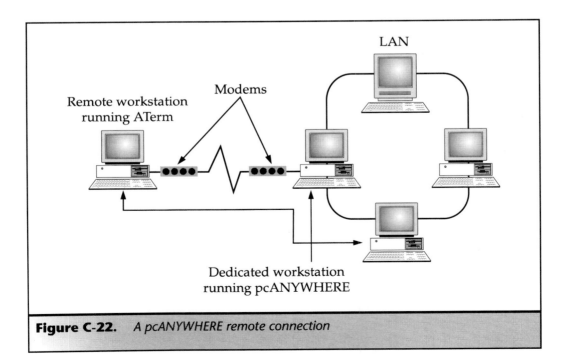

Figure C-22.   *A pcANYWHERE remote connection*

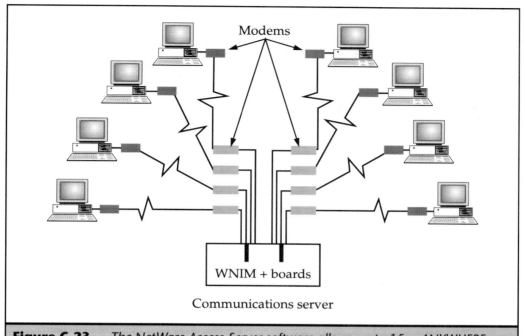

Communications server

Figure C-23. *The NetWare Access Server software allows up to 15 pcANYWHERE sessions to take place within a dedicated 80386 communications server*

attempting to dial in. A newer product called NetWare Connect provides these and other features.

Communication Services

See Carrier Services.

Complex Instruction Set Computer (CISC)

The microprocessor is the basic processing component of desktop computer systems and at the heart of every microprocessor is circuitry that performs instructions. Instructions consist of various steps that complete a task, such as moving a value into a register or adding values. The instructions are called the microprocessor's *microcode*. Each manufacturer's microprocessors have different sets of microcode. Manufacturers are free to make the microcode as simple or as complex as they want. The richer the instruction set, the easier it is to write programs for the microprocessor. However, the richer the microcode set, the slower the performance. This trade-off differentiates the two categories of microprocessors:

- *Complex Instruction Set Computer (CISC)* designs include a rich set of microcode that simplifies the creation of programs that run on the processor.

- *Reduced Instruction Set Computer (RISC)* designs, as the name implies, have a reduced set of instructions that improves the efficiency of the processor, but requires more complex external programs.

RISC designs are based on work performed at IBM by John Cocke, who found that about 20 percent of a computer's instructions did about 80 percent of the work. Thus, RISC-designed systems are generally faster than CISC cystems. His 80/20 rule spawned the development of RISC architecture.

Most desktop microprocessor designs such as the Intel and Motorola chips are CISC designs. Workstation processors such as the MIPS chips, the DEC Alpha, and the IBM RS family of chips use RISC architectures. Current and future processor designs seem to favor RISC over CISC.

RELATED ENTRY   Reduced Instruction Set Computer

Compound Documents

A compound document contains not only text, but a variety of elements, including text, graphics, spreadsheet data, sound, video, and other information. You can think of a compound document as a container that holds text, graphics, and multimedia information like sound and video. Current trends for building compound documents use object-oriented technologies in which nonstandard information such as sound and video can be included in documents as standalone, self-contained objects. Popular desktop environments such as Microsoft Windows and the Macintosh use this technology, as described here:

- *Microsoft Object Linking and Embedding (OLE)* is an object technology included with Windows products. It contains network linking features so users can share an object.

- *Apple Amber* is a compound document architecture that uses a document content standard called Bento. Amber is an open standard that will be fully interoperable with Microsoft OLE 2.0. If a developer creates an application that is Amber compatible, it will also be OLE 2.0 compatible. Bento is a document interchange format for multimedia information.

- *Lotus Development's Link, Embed, and Launch-to-Edit (LEL)* is an object linking standard that provides a Microsoft-like OLE enviornment for Lotus Notes users in UNIX environments. LEL is used on Sun, HP, IBM, and Novell versions of UNIX. Documents created in Windows can be read in UNIX.

- *Common Object Request Broker Architecture (CORBA)* is a standard developed by the Object Management Group to provide a way for objects to exchange information over multivendor environments. Objects in this case refers to elements within compound documents.

Along with these object standards, there are document architectures and languages that provide a way to create compound documents that are portable among a variety of systems. Consider an ASCII (American Standard Code for Information Interchange) document. It contains standard text characters. All desktop computers recognize ASCII, so you can transfer an ASCII file created on a DOS computer to a Macintosh computer. Document architectures and languages strive to create universal documents that you can move from one platform to another, retaining any formats such as fonts applied to that document. See "Document Interchange Standards" later in this book for more information.

Object-Oriented Compound Documents

An *object* is a self-contained block of information with additional information that describes the data, how to format it, the application that created it, and the location of related information if it is stored in a separate disk file. Compound documents are collections of objects and text. Figure C-24 illustrates a compound document created in Microsoft Windows using Object Linking and Embedding (OLE) technology. Other operating environments are implementing similar technology, and so the term can be considered generic. For example, Multipurpose Internet Mail Extension (MIME) is a compound document standard in the Internet environment for exchanging mail that contains text, graphics, sound, and video.

The remainder of this section describes compound documents in the Windows environment. There are a number of related topics that describe document architectures, document description languages, and electronic document exchange: see "Document Interchange Standards," "Document Management," "Electronic Data Interchange," "Groupware," "Object Management Architecture," "Standard Generalized Markup Language," and "Workflow Software."

Compound documents change the approach that users take to assembling documents and working with other users on a network. They provide a new view of documents. In the old *application-centric view,* users focused on the features of a single application at one time. To create a document with multiple graphic, text, and other elements, it was necessary to jump from one application to the next, then print each element separately. OLE provides a *document-centric view* in which the document itself becomes the place where users assemble and manipulate all the different elements of a presentation, project, or report. The elements are stored in one document, and when the document is printed, all the elements print together. To edit any element within a compound document, a user simply double-clicks the element with the mouse. The application used to create the element then appears on the screen. In version 2.0 of OLE, components of the application needed to edit the element actually replace components like pull-down menus and tools of the current application until the editing is complete. This basic feature is called *embedding.*

C

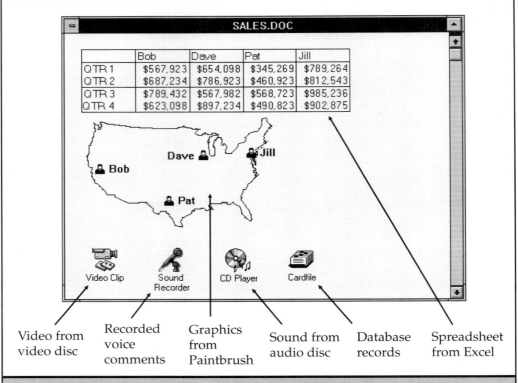

Figure C-24. *A compound document contains information from many sources*

 TIP: *The main benefit of embedding is that elements created in other applications are stored together in a single document, rather than separate files, reducing disk clutter and cross-references.*

Linking is more dynamic than embedding, but each element must exist as a separate disk file. In this arrangement, a user opens the disk file of an element and changes it. Changes to the linked files are automatically made for the references to those files in the compound document. The files that represent objects in compound documents can be at any location on a network. For example, an artist in the graphics department can submit a graphic element for a compound document created by the marketing department. At any time, the artist can change the original file, which is located on his or her computer. When a user in the marketing department opens the compound document, the application checks to see if the file on the artist's computer has been changed and updates the compound document if necessary.

In the Windows for Workgroups and Windows NT environments, a utility called the ClipBook provides cut-and-paste features that work over a network. You place objects to share with other users on the ClipBook. Users then open the ClipBook at their computer and paste the objects into their documents. The objects maintain a link to the file located on your computer, so if you make changes to the file, the copy in other users' documents also changes. However, if your computer is not on, users won't be able to get updates from it.

RELATED ENTRIES   Document Interchange Standards; Object Linking and Embedding; *and* Workflow Software

Compression Techniques

Data compression has become an important topic for network administrators as multimedia, video, document imaging, and other technologies emerge. Data compression basically squeezes data so it requires less disk space for storage and less time to transmit during a file transfer. Compression takes advantage of the fact that digital data contains a lot of repetition. It replaces repeating information with a symbol or code that represents the information in less space. Basic compression techniques are listed here:

- *Null compression*   Replaces a series of blank spaces with a compression code, followed by a value that represents the number of spaces.

- *Run-length compression*   Expands on the null compression technique by compressing any series of four or more repeating characters. The characters are replaced with a compression code, one of the characters, and a value that represents the number of characters to repeat.

- *Key-word encoding*   Creates a table with values that represent common sets of characters. Frequently occurring words like *for* and *the* or character pairs like *sh* or *th* are represented with tokens used to store or transmit the characters.

- *Huffman statistical method*   This compression technique assumes there is a varied distribution of characters in the data. In other words, some characters appear more than others. The more frequently occurring the character, the fewer bits used to encode it. A table is created to store the encoding scheme and, in the case of a data transmission, this table can be passed to a receiving modem so it knows how to decode the characters.

Because compression algorithms are software-based, overhead exists that can cause problems in real-time environments, but compression during backup and archiving of files usually poses few problems. The use of high-performance systems can help eliminate most of the overhead and performance problems. Another consideration is that compression removes portability from files unless the decompression software is shipped with the files.

Note that some files are already compressed to begin with and don't benefit from any further external compression techniques. Some graphics file formats, such as the tagged image file format (TIFF) include compression.

Storage System Compression

Before discussing compression algorithms for file storage, you should understand that file compression is different from disk encoding, which is commonly employed by disk drives to pack more digital 1s and 0s onto the physical surface of a disk. File compression squeezes the characters and bit-strings in a file down to a smaller size and takes place in software before the file information ever gets to the write head of the hard drive. Modern hard drives that use encoding simply accept the stream of 1s and 0s from the CPU and pack them into a much smaller space than is possible if encoding is not used. Disk encoding is discussed briefly here, followed by a more expanded discussion of file compression.

A magnetic recording system such as a hard drive records information by changing a magnetic field over the disk surface. A change in the field between two possible states is called a *flux transition*. In simple terms, a flux transition can represent a digital 1 and the absence of a transition can represent a digital 0. Encoding provides a way to represent more digital information per flux transition. *Modified frequency modulation (MFM)* stores digital 1s as a flux transition and 0s as the absence of a flux transition. Encoding techniques include the following:

- *Run length limited (RLL)*   Represents bit patterns as codes, which can be stored with fewer changes in magnetic flux, improving on MFM storage capabilities by 50 percent.

- *Advanced run length limited (ARLL)*   Doubles the density of MFM recording by converting patterns into codes that can be stored in flux transitions that are four times as dense.

Because disk encoding is automatically handled by the disk drive at the hardware level, it is of no further importance to this discussion. When you purchase a disk drive, it has a certain capacity that is obtained using an encoding scheme, but this encoding scheme is rarely of interest after the purchase as long as the drive has the capacity you need.

File Compression Techniques

File compression is handled in several ways. Various utilities are available that let you compress files one at a time, or as a group. Groups of files can be compressed into a single file that is much easier to send to another user. A decompression utility unpacks the files. A popular shareware utility called PKZIP (PKWARE, Inc., Glendale, Wisconsin) is used on CompuServe and other bulletin boards to compress files. You can download PKZIP from most bulletin board services.

Most operating systems, including DOS, NetWare, Windows NT, and others now include compression software. In the case of NetWare 4.x, you can enable automatic compression for specific files, or all files that reside on a volume or in a specific directory. Special file attributes can be set to flag the files you want the system to automatically compress when not in use. Be careful when enabling automatic compression systems. Some applications may not work properly with files in a compressed state.

Two important concepts in file compression are *lossless* and *lossy*:

- *Lossless compression*   A lossless compression system assumes you want to get everything back from a file that you have compressed. Every bit in the file is critical, so the compression algorithm meticulously compresses and uncompresses the file.

- *Lossy compression*   A lossy system assumes that some loss of information during compression and uncompression is acceptable. Many high-definition graphics files contain information that will not be missed if it is dropped during the compression cycle. For example, if you scan a color picture at high resolution, but your display is not capable of displaying that resolution, you can use a lossy compression scheme, since you won't miss the details. Sound and video files are also appropriate for lossy compression, since loss of some information produces subtle changes that may not be detectable when played back.

While no information is lost in lossless compression, compression ratios usually only achieve a 2:1 compression. Lossy compression can provide compression ratios of 100:1 to 200:1, depending on the type of information being compressed. Voice and video information compresses well because it usually contains a lot of redundant information.

Graphics, Video, and Voice Compression

With the advent of multimedia and video conferencing, highly efficient compression systems have become important. A typical color graphic image can consume 2 megabytes or more of disk space, depending on the video resolution, and a single second of uncompressed full-motion video requires about 10 megabytes of disk space. Network administrators are concerned about multimedia file sizes because they consume network bandwidth when copied to servers or other users.

Fortunately, most multimedia images can use lossy compression techniques as discussed in the preceding section. In video compression, each frame is an array of pixels that must be reduced by removing redundant information. Video compression is usually done with special integrated circuits, rather than with software, which operates too slowly. Standard video is normally about 30 frames/sec, but some studies have found that 16 frames/sec is acceptable to many viewers, so methods that remove frames can provide another form of compression.

Several compression standards for handling multimedia information are described below.

■ *Joint Photographic Experts Group (JPEG) compression* JPEG uses a generic algorithm to compress still images. The three-dimensional color and coordinate image information is first translated into a format that is more responsive to compression. Color information is also encoded, and some is discarded if a system is incapable of using it. Values are user-selectable, depending on the amount of image degradation that can be tolerated. Once these initial settings are made, the file is compressed using either lossless or lossy compression techniques. JPEG was not designed to handle video, but it does so to some extent by compressing frames and reducing the frame size and rate.

■ *Fractal Compression* In the fractal compression technique developed by Iterated Systems, images are broken into smaller and smaller tiles as the compression engine (a dedicated board) searches for matching patterns in the image using a mathematical transformation that manipulates tiles in various ways. Repetitive patterns are saved to reconstruct the original, and unmatched data that is considered unimportant is discarded. The amount of time the process runs is user-selectable and determines the amount of compression applied to the data.

■ *Audio-Video Interleave (AVI)* AVI was developed by Microsoft as a way to store motion video on CD-ROM discs. Software decompression is used to read the information. The technique combines lossless techniques and a special compression algorithm that is fast, but not effective. AVI images have a reduced number of frames per second, which produces an unpleasing image. However, the technique is acceptable for some applications.

■ *Digital Video Interactive (DVI)* DVI is an Intel-developed motion-video compression scheme that is considered a de facto standard. Like AVI, it is primarily used in CD-ROM applications and has been successful in bringing video to the desktop in that format.

■ *Indeo Video* Indeo video is a digital video recording format and compression software technology that can reduce video files from five to ten times their uncompressed size. For example, Indeo can reduce a 50-magabyte file to about 9 megabytes. Indeo is included with products like Microsoft Video for Windows, the OS/2 operating system, and Apple QuickTime for Macintosh and Windows. Playback is optimized for the type of hardware available so frame rate is increased on faster systems. Recording is optimized with the Intel i750 Video Processor because video is compressed as it is received, rather than being first stored, then compressed. Multiple compression techniques are used, including lossy and lossless techniques.

■ *Motion Picture Experts Group (MPEG)* MPEG is developing several video compression standards that define formatting, data rates, and compression techniques for international use. The MPEG-1 specification defines video and audio and how to access full-motion video from disk at 1.5 to 2 Mbits/sec. MPEG-2 strives to provide full-motion video quality that surpasses NTSC, PAL, and SECAM broadcast systems.

Other compression methods are on the way and many existing methods are being revised. CCITT committees are working on standards for video phones and videoconferencing over Integrated Services Digital Network (ISDN) and other services.

Compression for Data Communication

Compression provides a way to improve throughput on wide area links. In the case where you need to make a decision as to whether a link requires an inexpensive dialup line connected by modems, or a more expensive dedicated connection, a modem that has data compression features might provide the added throughput you need to decide on the cheaper solution.

If full-time connections are required, data compression can help you get the most out of those connections, as well. However, there are limitations. Performing data compression automatically at the connection point to the wide area network is impractical if the transmission speed is above 64 Kbits/sec, because compression cannot keep up with the line speed. An alternative is to manually compress files to reduce their size before they are sent using a compression utility like PKZIP. The resulting compressed file is transmitted, and the recipient unpacks the file on receipt.

Modem manufacturers have used many of the data-compression techniques mentioned earlier, but the Lempel-Ziv technique has become popular with the acceptance of the CCITT V.42 bis data-compression standard and its incorporation in most modems. Motorola Codex has tested data rates over 100 Kbits/sec using compression, although 28.8 Kbits/sec is the current limit.

In the Lempel-Ziv data-compression algorithm, all single character strings occupy the table. As new strings appear, a tree structure is created, similar to Figure C-25, which shows the "T" branch of the tree. Note that a three-character word can be deduced by following any branch of the tree. Each branch of the tree is identified by a codeword and the codeword is sent in any transmissions. If a new string appears, nodes are added to an appropriate branch of the tree and a new codeword is generated to represent it.

There are other methods of compression, such as the Microcom Networking Protocol (MNP) Class 5 and Class 7 series, but the V.42 standard has taken off in recent years as the compression method used by most modem vendors.

RELATED ENTRIES   Modems; Videoconferencing and Desktop Video

Concentrator Devices

A *concentrator* is a device that provides a central connection point for the connection of terminal, computer, or communication devices. It can be a central point where cables

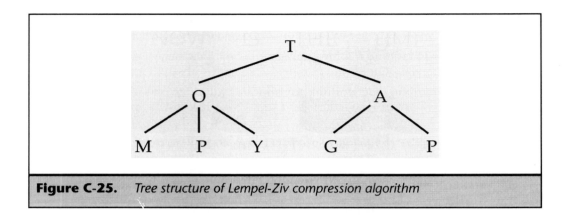

Figure C-25.   *Tree structure of Lempel-Ziv compression algorithm*

converge. Technically, a concentrator merges a certain number of incoming lines with a number of outgoing lines, or provides a central communication link for a number of devices. Various types of concentration equipment, most of which originated in the mainframe world, are covered next.

CONCENTRATORS   In the mainframe environment, a concentrator can merge the lines from a number of terminals and provides a link to another concentrator in a hierarchical arrangement, or links directly to the front-end processor of a host computer. Data from the low-speed terminal lines is transferred over a high-speed line using a multiplexing method or a contention method. In the multiplexing method, a terminal gets a fixed time slot in the multiplexed stream. In the contention method, each low-speed line gets full access to the high-speed line for a brief period.

FRONT-END PROCESSORS   A front-end processor is similar to the concentrator just described in function, but it is usually a dedicated computer in its own right that performs concentration functions at higher speeds and supports more attached devices.

LAN CONCENTRATORS   In the LAN environment, concentrators have grown from simple wire management facilities to hub devices that provide "collapsed backbone," bridging, and routing functions. A collapsed backbone is equivalent to shrinking a bus cable system like thinwire coaxial Ethernet down to the size of a small box. A separate wire of inexpensive twisted-pair wire then runs to each workstation. Instead of running coaxial cable in a daisy-chain configuration from one workstation to the next, you run twisted-pair wire from each workstation to a central point, the concentrator or hub. Hubs are modular devices into which you can plug a number of multiport concentrator cards. Modular cards usually have from 8 to 12 RJ-type jacks for the connection of workstations, so the more cards you add, the more connections you can concentrate at the hub. See "Hubs" for more details.

PORT-SHARING AND SELECTOR UNITS   Port-sharing units provide a way for multiple terminals at a remote site to share a modem connection to a computer or host system. The device fits in between the terminals and the modem.

MULTIPLEXERS   The original design of a multiplexer was based on a need to reduce the cost of data transmissions for terminal devices that needed to communicate with a host device over a telecommunication link. A multiplexer is a device that merges the data from multiple terminals into one line, and then ships the merged data over the link where it is de-multiplexed at the other end. Multiplexing cost-justifies the leasing of a high-speed digital line such as T1. The alternative would be to lease a low-speed analog dedicated line for each terminal, along with the modem equipment required to connect them to the lines. There are many different types of multiplexers. A time division multiplexer provides a block of time in the data stream for each device, one after the other. A frequency division multiplexer provides multiple frequency channels on which each device communicates. See "Multiplexing" for more details.

Conditioning

A conditioned line is a normal telephone line that has been amplified and attenuation-equalized to reduce transmission problems caused by noise, phase jitters, and distortion. Telephone companies provide line conditioning upon request, and it is often necessary to improve transmission performance when communicating at higher rates, such as 19,200 bits/sec. Leased digital lines such as T1 and T3 lines are conditioned.

Configuration Management

Configuration management covers a wide range of network administration topics. In its simplest form, network managers maintain a database that has a wide variety of information about bridges, routers, workstations, servers, and other equipment on the network. They can refer to this information when they need to change the configuration of the network or determine the cause of some failure. The database can hold important infrastructure information, such as physical connections and dependencies.

In advanced configuration management systems, changes to settings in the central database are implemented on network devices. For example, it might be necessary to change the identification number of a subnetwork on the enterprise network. Doing so would also require an update in all routers so they can address the subnetwork. In an automated system, the change is made in the database and the routers are automatically updated by the management software which sends update commands over the network.

Configuration management for networks deals with such issues as password management, printing configurations, and user or group management. This information is managed at a central location and distributed to outlying systems if necessary.

On the software side, configuration management may provide software installation, updates, and reconfiguration from a single location. The process should track version numbers and licensing and apply updates when they arrive to systems that require it. The information database provides this information since it keeps track of version numbers for nodes.

On the hardware side, configuration management provides a way to configure systems once new hardware is installed and to report this information to dependent systems. Information such as serial numbers, settings, and version information are reported back to the management database. Once the management system knows where hardware is located, it can automatically update drivers and driver updates.

As the size of networks grows, configuration management software, along with other centrally located management software (security, accounting, and performance tracking, for example) are becoming more important. It becomes impossible for network managers to perform these functions on site due to travel time and expenses. Automating the procedures to take advantage of the network that is already in place is a natural and cost-effective step.

The Desktop Management Task Force (DMTF)

The DMTF is a group of vendors working on a cooperative strategy for managing networked desktop systems. Charter members of the group include Digital Equipment Corporation, Hewlett-Packard, IBM, Intel, Microsoft, Novell, Sunconnect, and SynOptics.

The primary focus of the DMTF is to specify a method to access desktop information that could be integrated into a variety of management environments. The DMTF plans to create a set of open application program interfaces (APIs) for desktop management. It also is going to specify methods for managing desktop components. The APIs and related specifications are called the Desktop Management Interface (DMI).

The DMI creates a common set of rules for accessing hardware and software on a network-attached desktop computer. The interface runs on multivendor desktop systems but provides information to a variety of multivendor management systems. DMI can be implemented in a variety of components, such as video cards, fax modems, printers, mass storage devices, and network interface cards, as well as Simple Network Management Protocol (SNMP) and Common Management Over LCC (CMOL) management consoles.

RELATED ENTRIES   Desktop Management Interface; Desktop Management Task Force; Distributed Management; Distributed Management Environment; *and* Management Standards and Tools

Connectionless and Connection-Oriented Transactions

A transaction is a discrete unit of work that is typically part of a business transaction. It includes changes to databases on mainframe computers or back-end server system. *Online transaction processing (OLTP)* operates in real-time to collect and process transaction-related data and post changes to shared databases and other files. Online transaction processing implies that a transaction is executed immediately, thus it is a *connection-oriented transaction.* Connection-oriented transactions may use remote procedure calls (RPCs) or conversational communications mechanisms like IBM's Common Programming Interface for Communications (CPI-C). Also, named pipes is a mechanism in OS/2 that synchronizes exchanges between two network nodes.

Transactions can also be batch-oriented, in which a batch of transactions is stored over a period of time, then executed later. In addition, SQL (Structured Query Language) databases use stored procedures, in which a client invokes a set of procedures that are stored at the server as a single function. Stored procedures help minimize the traffic between client and server.

A *connectionless transaction* is a message-oriented transaction that uses store-and-forward techniques. The user sends a request or command in the form of a message, then waits for a reply. The important point is that there is no communication "session" or connection between the client and the server. The server may respond at a much later time. Messaging systems include IBM's Message Queuing Interface, Mail Slots (in OS/2 and Windows), and Novell's Message Handling Service (MHS).

A messaging model requires queue managers at both ends of the data exchange—that is, at the client and the server. A message is formulated at the source and it is delivered to the queue associated with the destination. Message queueing is typically asynchronous—one event must complete before another event occurs. However, messages can be delivered from one source to multiple destinations. For example, messages might be distributed among multiple processors so that each can work on a task in parallel.

RELATED ENTRIES   Encina; On-Line Transaction Processing; Transaction Processing; *and* Tuxedo, UNIX System Laboratories

Connectionless Network Protocol (CLNP)

CLNP is the equivalent of the Internet Protocol (IP) for Open Systems Interconnection (OSI) networks, with the primary difference being the size of the address. CLNP's address size is 20 bytes, as compared to IP's 4 bytes, so it is under consideration for use on the Internet as a way to solve the problem of not enough addresses. CLNP exists in the network layer of the OSI protocol stack. As the name implies, it provides connectionless datagram services over OSI networks.

RELATED ENTRY   Connection-Oriented and Connectionless Protocols

Connection-Oriented and Connectionless Protocols

Communication protocols are either *connection-oriented* or *connectionless*, depending on whether the sender of a message needs to contact and maintain a dialog (connection-oriented) with the recipient, or simply send a message without any prior contact (connectionless) and with the hope that the recipient receives everything in order. These methods reveal the two ways that communication is implemented on networks:

- In the *connection-oriented method,* the network takes responsibility for delivering packets in order and in a reliable way that detects loss and corruption. This method is used by "reliable" transport services.

- In the *connectionless method,* the network does not need to do anything except transmit packets to the destination. Error checking and flow control are handled by sender and receiver. The method is used by so-called "best-effort" or "unacknowledged" transport protocols.

Assume you want to send a series of letters to a friend in another town. The letters are analogous to the packets of data sent across a computer network. Two delivery methods are available. One method is to give the letters to a trusted friend who personally delivers the letters and calls you to confirm delivery. In this way, you maintain contact at both ends of the delivery. Your friend is providing a connection-oriented service. Alternatively, you could address each envelope and simply drop them in the mail. You have no guarantee that each letter will arrive at the destination, and if they do, they might arrive on different days and out of sequence. This is like a connectionless service.

Connection-Oriented Communication

In the *connection-oriented method,* a channel (circuit) for data communication is set up between the two end nodes. This channel provides a predefined pathway through the network for sending packets in an orderly manner. The connection is analogous to a voice telephone call. The sender and receiver maintain contact to coordinate the session and signal receipt of packets or failure to receive packets. This does not imply, however, that a connection-oriented channel uses more bandwidth than a connectionless channel. Both methods only use bandwidth when packets are transmitted.

The communication channel established for connection-oriented sessions is logical in nature, and often called a *virtual circuit.* It is focused on the end stations. The channel is more concerned with keeping the two end stations in touch with each other than tracing an actual physical path through some network. In networks that have multiple paths to a destination, the physical path may actually change during the session to accommodate traffic patterns, but the end stations (and intermediate nodes) keep track of the path. Logical paths exist on multiplexed circuits as shown in Figure C-26.

An application in one computer initiates a connection-oriented session with another computer. It requests such a session by contacting underlying communication protocols. In the Transmission Control Protocol/Internet Protocol (TCP/IP) suite, TCP provides connection-oriented services, while IP (a lower-level protocol) provides transport services. In the NetWare SPX/IPX protocol suite, SPX provides connection-oriented services.

Because packets are transmitted over a virtual circuit, full packet addresses are not required since the source and destination addresses are known by the network. Each node along the path in the network keeps track of virtual circuits and the ports required to switch packets. Sequencing numbers are used to ensure an orderly flow of packets. A circuit does require a setup procedure, but once the circuit is set up, it provides an efficient path for processes that operate over long periods of time, like the continuous monitoring of network stations by a management program or the transfer of many large files. In contrast, connectionless methods are designed for bursty, short-lived communications in which circuit setup would be inefficient.

The setup of a connection-oriented session goes something like this:

1. The source application requests a connection-oriented communication session.

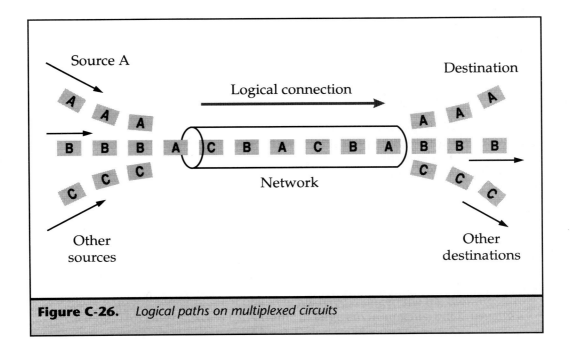

Figure C-26. *Logical paths on multiplexed circuits*

2. The session is set up (which, by the way, takes time, and is one reason why connectionless protocols are used instead).

3. Data transmission begins over the logical connections.

4. When the transmission is complete, the channel is disconnected.

In packet-switched telecommunications networks, some channels are never disconnected. A permanent channel is established between two points called *permanent virtual circuits (PVCs)*. PVCs are similar to dedicated telephone lines.

Connection-oriented protocols exist largely in the Transport layer protocols, relative to the Open Systems Interconnection (OSI) protocol model. Common connection-oriented protocols include TCP (Transmission Control Protocol) in the Internet and UNIX environments, Novell Sequenced Packet Exchange (SPX), IBM/Microsoft NetBIOS, and the OSI Connection Mode Network Protocol (CMNP).

Connectionless Communication

In the *connectionless method*, the network does not need to do anything except transmit packets to the destination. If a packet is lost, the receiver must detect the problem and request a retransmission. If the packets arrive out of sequence because they took different paths through the network, the receiver must put them back in order. Connectionless protocols are the IP portion of the TCP/IP protocol suite, the IPX portion of NetWare's SPX/IPX protocols, and the OSI Connectionless Network Protocol (CLNP). These protocols exist in the Network layer, relative to the OSI protocol model.

In a connectionless communication session, each data packet is an independent unit called a *datagram* that travels on its own over the network. There is no initial negotiation between the sender and receiver. The sender simply starts sending datagrams on the network. Each packet contains a source and destination address.

There is also no acknowledgment from the receiver that it has received a packet or not, and flow control is absent, so packets may arrive out of sequence and the receiver must resequence the packets. If a packet is received that has been corrupted, it is simply discarded. When the packets are reassembled, the discarded packet is discovered and a retransmission is requested.

There are benefits in using connectionless protocols. When it comes to performance, the connectionless strategy usually wins. This is because there are relatively few errors on most networks in the first place so corrupted or lost packets are rare enough that end stations don't spend alot of time retransmitting.

Comparing the Protocols

Connection-oriented services are preferable for applications that require a steady stream of data. For example, the remote monitoring program provided with Novell NetWare uses the SPX connection-oriented protocol. Connection-oriented services also provide more reliability and can more effectively recover from problems.

While connectionless services have more overhead in each packet, connection-oriented services require a little more processing at the end nodes to set up and maintain the connections. There are times when this overhead is not justified, however, such as the short bursty transmissions associated with a LAN user's interaction with a server.

RELATED ENTRIES Connectionless Network Protocol; Datagram Delivery Protocol; Datagram Network Services; Fast Packet Switching; Packets; *and* Virtual Circuits

Container Objects

Container objects are part of a directory services structure such as NetWare Directory Services, a feature in Novell NetWare 4.x. Container objects hold other objects, including other containers, and so form branches in a hierarchical directory tree used to organize the user accounts and resources of an organization. Container objects usually represent the divisions or departments of a company and contain the user accounts and resources belonging to the division or department. The managers or supervisors of the department have special management rights to the containers, which automatically give them rights to manage the objects within the container.

RELATED ENTRIES Directory Services; X.500 Directory Services

Contention

Contention occurs on networks that use a shared media and the carrier sense multiple access (CSMA) method, primarily Ethernet. Stations share the media and compete to use its communication channel. Contention occurs when two or more devices attempt to use the channel at the same time. When contention does occur, all stations wait for a random amount of time, then attempt access again. If many stations are competing for the cable, the situation becomes worse because the wait time reduces performance in addition to the need for workstations to continually attempt to access the cable.

Controlled Access Unit (CAU)

A CAU is similar to a token ring multistation access unit, but it contains management features for disabling and enabling ports.

RELATED ENTRY Token Ring

Cooperative Processing

Cooperative processing occurs in distributed computing systems in which two or more computers share the processing of a program or computational task. Cooperative processing requires sophisticated programs that can share workloads, data files, and memory contents over the network while maintaining synchronization, security, and accuracy of information.

The platform that enables cooperative processing is a distributed, client-server system in which systems can communicate with one another. The process is easiest to implement in an environment that uses common communication protocols and compatible processing platforms and peripheral devices. With the emergence of the remote procedure call (RPC), which can invoke procedures on other machines, cooperative processing is becoming more of a reality, even in heterogeneous environments.

RELATED ENTRY   Enterprise Networks

Copper Distributed Data Interface (CDDI)

CDDI is a version of Fiber Distributed Data Interface (FDDI) designed to run on shielded and unshielded twisted-pair cable. It is currently a standard that was developed separately by Cabletron and Crescendo, who combined their technology work and received ANSI standards approval in 1993. A typical CDDI network consists of concentrators with a number of ports for the connection of workstations. Because CDDI has limited cable distances, a CDDI concentrator can connect to an FDDI ring as a subnetwork.

RELATED ENTRY   Fiber Distributed Data Interface

Corporation for Open Systems (COS)

The Corporation for Open Systems (COS) is a nonprofit organization that strives to ensure interoperability between vendors following Open Systems Interconnection (OSI) and Integrated Services Digital Network (ISDN) standards. COS is a vendor of OSI protocols and provides conformance testing, certification, and promotion of OSI products. COS underwrites the OSInet Corp in McLean, Virginia, which performs interoperability tests and places COS Mark stamps on products that pass its tests.

RELATED ENTRY   Open Systems Interconnection Model

Cryptography

See Security.

DARPA

See Defense Advanced Research Projects Agency.

Database Connectivity APIs and Middleware

An organization that has consolidated its departmental networks into an enterprise network usually finds itself with a variety of autonomous database systems that are structured on different models. Most are probably relational databases, but some may be object-oriented, or hierarchical. All may be from different vendors, and all may have incompatible interfaces. This situation exists because, in the past, individual departments built their own database management systems. Since users within those departments had appropriate front-end applications to access the databases, problems with data access did not exist. However, differences in interfaces, protocols, procedures, and platforms have made enterprise data harder to get at and manipulate.

The interface between the client and the server consists of a *data access language* that is usually *Structured Query Language (SQL),* an *application program interface (API)* to interface the client to the server and allow SQL exchanges, and *formats and protocols (FAPs),* which define the communication procedures and formats between client and server for sending messages across a network. SQL is currently not in standard form, although there are a number of standards under development. Vendors have typically developed the language to fit their own needs.

The problem is getting the many different client applications to communicate with servers, and getting servers to communicate with other servers. One solution is to wait for front-end application developers to include interfaces to any back-end server. Another solution is to wait for back-end developers to include interfaces for any front-end applications. Both solutions are unlikely to occur in the short term.

The International Organization for Standardization (ISO) and an organization called the SQL Access Group (SAG) are working to create standards that will allow interoperability among a variety of front-end and back-end systems. SAG's goal is to promote and develop specifications for SQL APIs and FAPs that have their basis in the ISO Remote Database Access (RDA) specification which defines how SQL-based clients access remote database servers. The group has developed three technical specifications:

- *Structured Query Language*   A specification for implementing the SQL language following international specifications.
- *SQL Remote Database Access*   A specification that defines communication between an SQL-based client and a remote database server.
- *Call-Level Interface*   A set of APIs for interfacing with SQL-based products.

The SQL Access Call-Level Interface is the core of Microsoft's Open Database Connectivity (ODBC) standard, and the Independent Database Application Program Interface (IDAPI), which is a specification developed by Borland International, IBM, and Novell. Both ODBC and IDAPI provide a common interface between clients and multivendor, multiplatform database servers. The interfaces consist of drivers that intercept requests from clients and translate those requests into statements or calls that are appropriate for the server that the client needs to access. In this respect, ODBC and IDAPI are considered *middleware* products. ODBC, IDAPI, and a number of other interfaces and standards are discussed next.

MICROSOFT ODBC   ODBC provides common functions that are performed by most back-end database systems. Front-end applications are then written to ODBC and take advantage of these functions. This approach may not take advantage of special features available in every back-end system, but it is a step toward interoperability that will let users gain access to back-end data that was previously inaccessible. Microsoft delivers ODBC as a set of drivers that provide access from applications such as Microsoft Access, Microsoft Excel, FoxPro, Btrieve, dBASE, and Paradox to IBM, Oracle, Paradox, and other back-end database systems. The drivers are available for redistribution to software vendors and can be packaged with applications. The purpose of ODBC, from Microsoft's viewpoint, is to make Windows the most popular client platform.

IDAPI   IDAPI was originally developed by Borland, and other vendors later provided support for the standard. IDAPI is similar to ODBC in functionality and is designed around the Call-Level Interface as well. According to Borland, IDAPI supports more servers than ODBC. However, at this writing, industry support was more on the side of ODBC.

DISTRIBUTED RELATIONAL DATABASE ARCHITECTURE (DRDA)   DRDA is an IBM standard for accessing database information across IBM and non-IBM platforms. DRDA follows SQL standards, and it is a key component in IBM's Information Warehouse framework. DRDA is concerned with providing a way to interconnect LAN-based database systems with IBM mainframe-based database systems such as DB2, DBM, SQL/DS, and SQL/400 database systems.

APPLE'S DATA ACCESS LANGUAGE (DAL)   Apple developed DAL to provide Macintosh users with access to a variety of back-end database products, including IBM mainframe and midrange databases. DAL is related to SQL. DAL client software is available for Windows and allows ODBC applications to access all the databases and platforms accessible by DAL.

ORACLE'S GLUE   Glue is a communication API that includes a number of commands for accessing back-end database servers and connecting information systems across platforms. Glue reportedly requires fewer steps to access data than ODBC. It is primarily designed to provide access to Oracle's databases for a large number of front-end applications.

RELATED ENTRIES   Distributed Database; Middleware; *and* Open Database Connectivity, Microsoft

Database Management System (DBMS)

A DBMS is a software program that typically operates on a database server or mainframe system to manage data, accept queries from users, and respond to those queries. It has the following features:

- Provides a way to structure data as records, tables, or objects.

- Accepts data input from operators and stores that data for later retrieval.

- Provides query languages for searching, sorting, reporting, and other "decision support" activities that help users correlate and make sense of collected data.

- Provides multiuser access to data, along with security features that prevent some users from viewing and/or changing certain types of information.

- Provides data integrity features that prevent more than one user from accessing and changing the same information simultaneously.

- A DBMS may be located on a mainframe system and accessed by dumb terminals. However, in the client-server model, the DBMS is accessed by smart front-end clients that perform some of the processing and follow the DBMS to concentrate on data processing tasks.

A simple database is a collection of records that contains fields of information. A phone book is an example of a printed database. Each line represents a record that contains "field" information such as the name, address, and phone number. An actual computer database of this information would be called a flat-file database, since all the information could be stored in one file. Flat-file databases are usually inadequate for business applications. Instead, relational or object-oriented database systems are required as described here.

- *Relational database* This type of database contains separate tables of data that can be related with other tables for the purpose of correlating information. Tables consist of rows that list people or things and columns that describe attributes of those people or things. The intersection of a row and column holds a data value. Interrelated tables are joined on columns. One table might hold customer name and address information while another might hold account balance or purchase information. By joining these tables, you could produce a report with customer name, phone number, and overdue account balance to hand to a collection agency. A typical database for an accounting system might contain up to 100 tables with many columns of information.

■ *Object-oriented database*   In this type of database, things to track such as customers or inventory are categorized as *objects*. An object contains data about the "thing," and also contains functions (methods) that operate on the data. For example, a customer object contains name, address, and account information, along with procedures to produce reports on the account information. These procedures are located within the object, not as outside procedures, so they move with the object and are easily invoked by many types of external processes or applications. See "Object-Oriented Technology" for more details.

A network-based DBMS is typically a client-server program in which the DBMS is a database engine located on a server that handles requests for data and provides data manipulation such as sorting and extracting. These tasks are handled by the DBMS "engine" running at the server, and because data is stored on directly-attached devices, the DBMS has rapid access to the data. The results of a request are then passed back to the client that made the request. Consequently, network traffic is reduced because the server only responds with appropriate data, not large blocks of data the client manipulates. Clients access a DBMS in either a *production mode* or *decision support mode*. Production workers enter data and make basic queries. Decision support is typically a management-level function in which complex programs correlate and extract data.

The common language for accessing a DBMS is Structured Query Language (SQL). The interface between the front-end and the back-end is a specific application program interface (API) provided by the DBMS vendor. The current trend is to provide so-called *middleware* products between the clients and servers to allow users to access any back-end server using a variety of front-end applications. Middleware hides the differences between access languages and database APIs. Microsoft introduced its Open Database Connectivity (ODBC) standard and Borland developed its Integrated Database Application Program Interface (IDAPI). In addition, IBM developed the Distributed Relational Database Architecture (DRDA) SQL standard.

RELATED ENTRIES   Database Connectivity APIs and Middleware; Distributed Database; and Structured Query Language

Database Server

A database server is a computer attached to a network that runs a client-server database management system (DBMS). Workstations, acting as clients, can send requests to the server over the network. The server then responds. Client workstations handle the presentation of data and interact with users while the server performs the workhorse operations such as sorting, indexing, and delivering data to users.

A database server is a central depository for information that many users access. In fact, most of the database architectures and query languages (such as Structured Query Language or SQL) used to access the DBMS on a database server have roots in the mainframe world. However, LAN database servers use client-server models in which the processing load is divided between the back-end database server and the front-end client. This model takes advantages of the processing power of client computers.

The hardware components of a database server are typically high-performance systems running Intel 80486 or Pentium processors, or special multiprocessor systems that have two or more of these processors. Other systems are RISC-based designs from IBM and Sun Microsystems, or super-server systems with special proprietary high-speed busses and multiple processors such as systems from Tricord Systems, Parallan Computers, and NetFrame.

Popular server platforms are DEC VAX/VMS, IBM AIX, IBM MVS, Sun Microsystems, NCR 3000 UNIX, and systems running Novell NetWare, IBM OS/2, Microsoft Windows NT, UNIX, and other popular operating systems. Popular client-server database management systems are listed here:

Interbase	Borland International, Scotts Valley, CA
AccessWorks	Digital Equipment Corporation, Maynard, MA
Gupta SQLBase Server	Gupta Corporation, Menlo Park, CA
Informix OnLine	Informix Software, Inc., Menlo Park, CA
Microsoft SQL Server	Microsoft Corp., Redmond, WA
NetWare SQL	Novell, Inc., Provo, UT
Oracle7	Oracle Corp., Redwood Shores, CA
SQL Server	Sybase, Inc., Emeryville, CA

New approaches to client-server computing in distributed environments take advantage of data on multiple servers at multiple locations. There are client-server relationships and server-server relationships. In the server-server relationship, networks of servers can appear as a single system to users. Oracle SQL*Net V2 is such a product. It provides a transparent network architecture that allows the Oracle7 distributed database product to connect different types of computers, operating systems, and networks into one unified cooperative computing environment. Systems can be located at different sites, but users can access data as if it were on a single system. The product supports Transmission Control Protocol/Internet Protocol (TCP/IP), SPX/IPX, Advanced Program-to-Program Communications (APPC) LU 6.2, DECnet, AppleTalk, and other industry-standard protocols for the connection of most popular network operating systems.

RELATED ENTRIES   Client-Server Computing; Database Management System; Distributed Computing; *and* Distributed Database

Data Communication Equipment (DCE)

Data Communication Equipment (DCE) is typically a modem or other type of communication device. The DCE sits between the *Data Terminal Equipment (DTE)* and a circuit that transfers information to another site. Originally, the DTE was a dumb terminal or printer, but today it is a computer, or a bridge or router that interconnects local area networks. In an IBM mainframe environment, a *communication controller* and a link-attached *cluster controller* are examples of DTEs.

A DCE provides a connection for the DTE into a communication network and back again. In addition, it terminates and provides clocking for a circuit. When analog telephone lines are the communication media, the DCE is a *modem.* When the lines are digital, the DCE is a *channel service unit/data service unit (CSU/DSU).*

DTE and DCE interfaces are defined by the physical layer in the Open Systems Interconnection (OSI) model. The most common standards for DTE/DCE devices are Electronic Industries Association (EIA) RS-232-C and RS-232-D. Outside the United States, these standards are the same as the Consultative Committee for International Telegraph and Telephone (CCITT) V.24 standard. Other DTE/DCE standards include the EIA RS-366-A as well as the CCITT X.20, X.21, and V.35 standards. The later standards are used for high-speed communication over telephone lines.

DTE and DCE devices send and receive data on separate wires that terminate at a 25-pin connector. It is useful to know that DTE devices transmit on pin connector 2 and receive on pin 3. DCE devices are just the opposite—pin 3 transmits and pin 2 receives. Note that DB-9 connectors on the back of IBM-AT computers use pin 3 to send and pin 2 to receive.

Data Communications

Computers communicate over data communication media such as copper wires, fiber-optic cable, and radio waves to exchange data and control remote devices. Applications for data communication are listed here:

- File exchanges

- Electronic mail exchanges

- Remote business transactions, such as the update of an inventory after a sale at a retail outlet

- Banking activities, such as when users access their personal bank account from an automated teller machine (ATM)

- Management and monitoring, in which remote devices such as sensors are controlled and data from readings is collected

There are two ways to move information from one place to another. *Parallel* communication techniques use multiple paths or wires between two points, like a multilane freeway. *Serial* communication methods use a single wire, like a one-lane bridge. A parallel channel might consist of 8, 16, 32, or even 64 side-by-side wires for transmitting information. For example, a 32-bit processor has an internal data bus (transmission pathway) that can send 32 bits simultaneously from one place to another. If you consider that a character of the alphabet is represented by an 8-bit code, you can see that it is possible to send 4 characters in one step. In contrast, a serial line has only one wire for trasmitting, so the bits must be lined up in a single file and transferred as a stream over the wire, then reassembled back into discernable blocks of bits at the receiving end. Consequently, data transmissions over telephone wires are considerably slower than data transfers that occur inside a microprocessor, or over a parallel cable that connects a printer to a computer.

Typical configurations for the transmission of data are shown in Figure D-1 and described here.

- A point-to-point connection exists between two computer systems or a computer and a peripheral such as a printer or modem.

- A local area network (LAN) is a shared data-communication facility. A number of computers can attach to the network, but only one can transmit at a time, in most cases. Data is packeted and transmitted in serial streams.

- A wide area network (WAN) typically involves the telephone network of a national or international telecommunication company. The lines are used to transmit data in serial streams.

A point-to-point connection is made with a parallel or serial cable. A parallel cable has multiple wires for transmitting data bits in parallel, but it has distance limitations since bits tend to desynchronize over distance. A parallel connection is limited to about 10 feet.

In all the cases listed here, the interface between systems must be the same or appropriate translation is necessary to convert the coding, formatting, framing, and

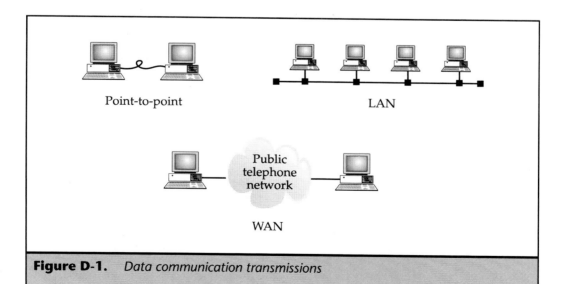

Point-to-point

LAN

Public telephone network

WAN

Figure D-1. *Data communication transmissions*

protocols between systems. Even if two computers successfully exchange files, applications in the receiving system may not be able to open a file or use its data. However, this has to do more with operating system and application *interoperability* than data communication and is covered later in this book under the heading "Interoperability."

The link between two devices over which data flows is called a *channel* or a *circuit*. The two terms are similar, but their origin is different. A channel, such as a TV or radio channel, implies that parallel channels exist, and each channel forms a separate data stream. Channels are separated by time or frequency. A circuit (in terms of this discussion) is best understood as the wire that connects a phone to the telephone company switching system, where it is connected with other phone wires. A circuit forms a dedicated path through the switching system for the duration of the call. In either case, channel or circuit is often used interchangeably to refer to data communication pathways. A *baseband* system transmits one channel over a cable, while a *broadband* system can transmit multiple channels over a wire using *multiplexing* techniques, as discussed under the heading "Multiplexing" later in this book.

The system on the receiving end of a transmission places data in a buffer or holding area, then transfers the data to the processor or sends it to disk for storage. If the buffer fills with incoming data, the receiving system must signal the sender to temporarily stop transmitting to prevent overflow. This process is called *flow control*.

To transmit text, the data stream must be delineated to differentiate the original byte-oriented (characters) structure. In *asynchronous communications,* each character is coded as a string of bits and separated by a "start-of-character" bit and "stop" bit. A parity bit is sometimes used for error detection and correction. In contrast, *synchronous communication* relies on a clocking mechanism to separate groups of bits. Synchronous communication is more efficient since stop and start bits are not required. For more information on these topics, see "Asynchronous Communications," "Bit-Oriented Protocol," "Byte-Oriented Protocol," and "Synchronous Communications."

Transmitted data is subject to corruption caused by outside interference, attenuation, and other problems associated with transmission facilities. *Error detection and correction* techniques can detect corrupted data and request a retransmission. The underlying communication hardware may perform this error checking, but some wide-area communication systems take advantage of the fact that transmission facilities are largely error free and perform no error checking. This improves performance. It is then up to the receiving system to determine if data is missing or corrupted, and to request a retransmission if so. The receiver or nodes along the communication pathway do not need to constantly error-check and acknowledge data.

A communication system has a certain *bandwidth,* which is a measure of data throughput. The measure is typically in bits per second (bps). Analog telephone circuits transmit in the kilobits-per-second (thousands of bits) range, while LANs transmit in the megabits-per-second (millions of bits) range. New fiber-optic systems in the public telephone networks transmit in the gigabits-per-second (billions of bits) range. Data transmitted through voice telephone systems is limited to 64 Kbits/sec, although, digital lines are available that transmit at much higher rates.

Most LANs and WANs transmit information in *packets,* or *datagrams* as they are often called. A packet is a package of data with header information that contains the source and destination address, error correction information, sequence numbers, and other information. Packets are limited in size, so for lengthy data transmissions, such as the transfer of a large file, data is split and placed in two or more packets. Packaging data in this way has several benefits:

- Interference on the network may only affect a specific packet, not the entire transmission. Only the affected packet is resent.

- Packets are independent data-carrying entities, that can be transmitted over multiple paths through a mesh-type network. This allows best path routing and congestion avoidance.

- On shared networks, it is not feasible to allow one station to send one long transmission that could congest the network. Small packets allow many stations to transmit by interleaving their packets on the network.

These points basically describe a "connectionless" link in which the sender does not first notify the recipient that it is sending data. The sender simply starts transmitting packets and the recipient receives those packets. This provides a highly efficient data transmission method that is suited for bursty LAN traffic and short transmissions. The opposite scheme is the "connection-oriented" method in which the sender and the receiver establish a communication session with each other to monitor and manage the flow of packets between stations. Connection-oriented sessions require a set-up phase, but provide more reliable data transmissions. They are useful when the session lasts a relatively long time and consists of a steady flow of data. For more information on these topics, see "Connection-Oriented and Connectionless Protocols," "Datagram Network Services," and "Packets."

Local and Wide Area Networks

The local area network (LAN) is the primary method of transmitting data among desktop computers in most organizations today. A cable system or wireless media is deployed in a building and computers are attached to it. A wide area network (WAN) typically involves a public switched telephone network (PSTN) or possibly a private communication facility that is built by the organization or leased from another organization.

LANs

LANs employing cable connection methods use either coaxial cables or twisted-pair cables. A coaxial cable is typically strung between each computer in an office using a daisy-chain configuration. Twisted-pair cable systems connect each computer to a central box called a concentrator or hub. If the network is large, one hub may connect to another. These configurations are shown in Figure D-2. Ethernet and token ring are common LAN standards.

Various limitations of the network may require that several separate networks be deployed, then connected using devices such as repeaters, bridges, and routers. These limitations include cable distance, a restriction on the number of workstations, or simply the inability to easily connect dispersed computers.

- *Repeater* Extends the distance of a cable segment by amplifying the signal.
- *Bridge* Interconnects two dissimilar LAN types, such as Ethernet to token ring.
- *Router* Provides a way to interconnect many different network segments and control traffic along multiple paths among those segments.

LANs are shared communication systems that provide connections for potentially hundreds of users. A mechanism is needed to ensure that only one workstation transmits data on the cable at a time. These mechanisms are called access methods, and there are several:

- *Carrier sense multiple access* Stations listen to see if the cable is in use and transmit only if it is available.
- *Token passing* Stations take possession of an electronic "token" and transmit only while in possession of the token.
- *Demand priority* A central hub determines which station can access the cable and can grant some station priority over others, depending on the time-sensitivity of the data to transmit.

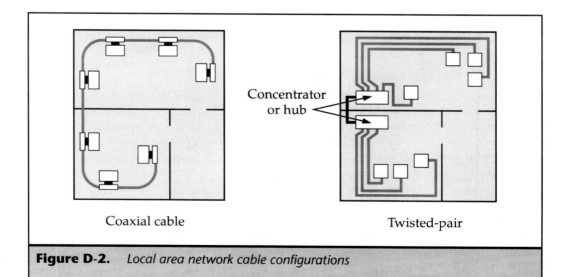

Concentrator or hub

Coaxial cable

Twisted-pair

Figure D-2. *Local area network cable configurations*

- *Slotted bus*   A continuous stream of data slots (such as a train of boxcars) are available in which any station can place data for transmission to another station.

For more information, see "Bridging," "Ethernet," "Local Area Networks," "Repeater," "Routers," and "Token Ring Network."

WANs

Communication between computers located at different sites requires the involvement of a public communication service such as the local and long distance telephone companies or other providers. An exception is the campus network, which interconnects networks between buildings in a campus or industrial park setting, and in which the owners can deploy their own cable systems among buildings.

There are a number of wide area connection options as summarized here. Modems are employed when analog telephone lines are used. They convert computer digital signals to analog signals. Digital lines are also available from the carriers that provide faster and more reliable service as either dedicated or dialup lines. A *dedicated line* is a permanent connection between two points that is usually leased on a monthly basis. Any-to-any connections provide a way for users to connect with a number of different sites, not just one dedicated site.

- A *switched* point-to-point connection using modems. The line is connected only during the call.
- A *dedicated* point-to-point connection over *analog* lines using modems.
- A *switched* point-to-point *digital* line.
- A *dedicated* point-to-point *digital* line.
- *Any-to-any* digital lines over *circuit-switched* networks.
- *Any-to-any* digital lines over *packet-switched* networks.

Modems are not required on digital lines. Instead, a channel service unit/data service unit (CSU/DSU) device provides the connection between local equipment and data communication network. These devices are called data communication equipment (DCE). DCE devices sit between data terminal equipment (DTE) devices, such as computers, and the communication network.

Other methods for connecting systems over wide geographic areas include microwave and satellite communication systems. Microwave systems consist of transmitters on top of earth-based towers that transmit signals from one tower to the next. Satellite systems transmit signals over large global areas. For more information on these topics, see "Local Area Networks," "Microwave Communication," "Modems," "Satellite Telecommunication," and "Wireless Mobile Communication."

Communication Protocols

A communication protocol is a set of rules and procedures that enable systems to exchange information. There are proprietary protocols that are used by a single vendor, and there are standard protocols that are recognized worldwide. Consider the simple protocols that a computer uses to send documents to a printer. The procedure is for the computer to notify the printer of its intent to send data. The printer sends an acknowledgment back to the computer and the computer starts sending data. During data transfer, the printer can use defined methods to halt the transmission from the computer if its buffers are overflowing. All printers generally follow the same procedures, so any printer can be attached to any computer. Without these defined procedures, connecting even the simplest devices would be impossible.

Computer network communication is quite complicated. There are rules and procedures that define the electrical transmission of signals at the physical connection level. There are also procedures for managing a communication session so two workstations can keep a channel open even when they aren't sending data. There are also procedures that applications use to access the data communication facilities of the network. These procedures are defined in a *network architectural model.*

The most commonly referenced model is the Open Systems Interconnection (OSI) model, which has been defined by the International Organization for Standardization (ISO). It defines a layered architecture that categorizes the different processes performed by systems that communicate. Each layer of the model defines protocols that control communication relative to the needs of that layer. For example, the lowest layer, called the *Physical layer*, defines protocols that control electrical transmission of bit streams over physical networks. The top layer, called the *Application layer*, defines how applications access the communication subsystem. An intermediate layer called the *Transport layer* handles connection-oriented communication sessions while the underlying *network layer* handles connectionless datagram services. For more information, see "Open Systems Interconnection Model," "Telecommunications," and "Wide Area Networks."

Data Compression

See Compression Techniques.

Data Encryption Standard (DES)

DES is a private-key encryption scheme developed by IBM in the 1970s. It was adopted by the National Bureau of Standards, which is now called the National Institute of Standards and Technology (NIST). DES was the United States government's standard for data encryption during the 1980s. The government is involved in security for its own use, and to provide security systems that can be trusted. You put your faith in the competence of the vendors who created the algorithms. DES, as a national published standard, has been exposed to many years of evaluation and "attack" and is considered stable. While DES suffered from lack of public confidence, it has shown no weaknesses to date.

The purpose of any encryption scheme is to secure private communication. The growth of international networks, public and private E-mail systems, and radio communication requires a greater need for security. Fortunately, advances in microelectronics are making security measures easier and cheaper to implement. Perhaps the use of protocol analyzers by technicians to monitor network traffic has enlightened managers to the fact that their data transmissions are not secure. Anyone with such a device can view selected data streams on the network.

Private-key encryption methods are called *symmetric* ciphers, and public-key methods are called *asymmetric* ciphers, as shown in Figure D-3.

D

- *Private-key scheme* Information is encrypted with a key that both the sender and receiver hold privately. This system assumes that both parties have already exchanged keys using some manual method and that the exchange did not compromise security.

- *Public-key scheme* Everyone has a public and private key, which use the same encryption and decryption codes. One is held privately and the other is placed in a public area such as a network security server. If someone wants to send you

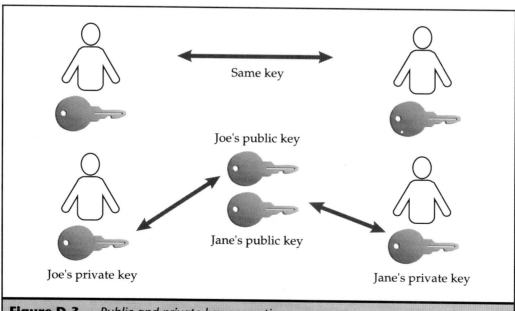

Figure D-3.   *Public and private key encryption*

a message, he or she gets a copy of your public key and encrypts the message with it. You can then decrypt the message with your private key.

The problem with private keys is getting a copy of the key to both users without compromising security. You would need to rely on a paper method or word of mouth and hope that both parties can keep the secret. The public-key method solves this problem by using two keys, one of which is placed in a public area such as a server dedicated to security functions. This solves many security problems in distributed computing environments and on international public networks such as the Internet, where users are exchanging electronic mail and files with people at remote locations and outside their own organization. For example, typical electronic mail systems that keep an address book would contain the public key for each person you normally communicate with.

DES's private key technique uses an algorithm that encrypts data in 64-bit blocks using a key that is 56-bits long. In contrast, the popular RSA public key encryption method (named after its designers, Rivest, Shamir, and Adleman) uses 512-bit keys. However, the 56-bit key provides quadrillions of possible key combinations. In addition, every block in the data stream can be encoded using a different key, which reduces the chance that a coding scheme might be revealed over a lengthy transmission.

Encryption algorithms are relatively slow, and the public key method is the slowest. Implementing algorithms in hardware improves performance and provides another level of security (software-based algorithms are exposed to hackers who might change the algorithms). Some users make use of both methods. Since DES is faster than public-key methods, it is often used to encrypt the text of a message itself. The key for the DES encryption is then itself encrypted using a public-key encryption method and sent to the receiving party along with the message. This strategy works because the public-key method provides a secure way to distribute the key over a public network while the DES method offers encryption speed advantages.

New Encryption Standard

Recently, the U.S. government has been interested in standardizing an encryption method referred to as *key escrow,* in which the key for decrypting the communication of any organization the government wishes to monitor is held in trust. The method breaks keys into parts and each part is given to a separate trustee. In this way, a key is only useful when it is reassembled by bringing the trustees together and getting them to hand over their part of the key. The U.S. Attorney General would supervise access to the keys and law enforcement agencies could get keys only with court orders. Needless to say, this has the security community in a tizzy.

In mid-1993, the National Institute of Standards and Technology (NIST) proposed the key escrow technology as the core of a Federal Information Processing Standard (FIPS) and the Justice Department committed to using the standard. Initially, telephones in federal agencies will be the target for the technology. Mykotronix Inc. (Torrance, California) has been contracted by NIST to develop key escrow chips, and AT&T will install them in telephones it sells to the government.

RELATED ENTRIES   Authentication and Authorization; Certification Systems; Digital Signatures; Public Key Cryptographic System; *and* Security

Datagram Delivery Protocol (DDP)

DDP is a routing protocol developed by Apple Computer for its AppleTalk networks.

RELATED ENTRY   AppleTalk

Datagram Network Services

A datagram is the packet of information in a *connectionless* network service, such as the Internetwork Packet Exchange (IPX) protocol in the NetWare SPX/IPX suite, or the Internet Protocol in the Transmission Control Protocol/Internet Protocol (TCP/IP) suite. Datagrams contain header information that provides routers with the destination addresses required to deliver a datagram.

Communication protocols are either connection-oriented or connectionless, depending on whether the sender of a message needs to contact and maintain a dialog (connection-oriented) with the recipient, or simply send a message without any prior contact (connectionless) and with the hope that the recipient receives everything in order. These methods reveal the two ways that protocols use networks:

■ In the *connection-oriented method*, the network takes responsibility for delivering packets in order and in a way that detects loss and corruption. This method is used by "reliable" transport services. In a connection-oriented session, end-nodes stay in contact so packets don't need full addressing information. Packets follow predefined paths (called "virtual circuits" in some cases) through the network and arrive in order so the recipient doesn't need to resequence them. Acknowledgments ensure that packets have been delivered and provide a way for the sender to know whether it needs to retransmit a packet.

■ In the *connectionless method,* the network does little but transmit packets (datagrams) to the destination. Error checking and flow control are handled by the receiving system although network nodes can detect packet corruption, in which case, the packets are discarded. The method is used by so-called "best-effort" or "unacknowledged" transport protocols. If datagrams fail to arrive, it is the job of the receiving station to contact the sender and request a retransmission. In addition, packets arriving out of order are resequenced by the receiving station.

There are advantages to both methods. Datagram network protocols are best for bursty traffic like that generated on local area networks. There is no active conversation between the sender and receiver about the status of the transmission, and so the protocols tend to be more efficient. Connection-oriented protocols are useful when a connection is required over a period of time for a long data transfer.

D

The datagram in the connectionless approach carries header information that identifies the source and destination, along with information about the data in its payload, such as length. The source of the datagram creates the headers before sending the datagram. Routers examine this information to determine how to route the packet and may change it to help the packet reach its destination. One interesting field in the Internet Protocol (IP) is called Type of Service. IP had its origins in the Defense Advanced Research Projects Agency (DARPA), which is a military-related organization. The Type of Service field was meant to provide a way to designate packets for priority service in the event of a national emergency.

RELATED ENTRIES   Connection-Oriented and Connectionless Protocols; Internet Protocol; Internetwork Packet Exchange; *and* Packets

Data Highways

"Data highways" and "information superhighway" refer to the National Information Infrastructure (NII). The NII is a proposed national computer network that will provide electronic information as well as voice and video to anyone with a computer or other device that can tap into the line. Resources on the network are provided by libraries, universities, and commercial providers. The system is being built on existing interstate fiber-optic backbones, and using the coaxial TV cable system. The existing Internet, which was developed with government funding, not only serves as a model, but is one of the primary components of the network infrastructure.

RELATED ENTRY   National Information Infrastructure

Data-Link Layer, OSI Model

The Open Systems Interconnection (OSI) model is a standard defined by the International Organization for Standards (ISO). It was designed to help developers create applications that are compatible across multivendor product lines, and to promote open, interoperable networking systems. The OSI model defines a layered architecture for differentiating each of the communication processes required to transmit data between networked systems and applications. During a communication session, processes running in each layer on each computer communicate with one another. The bottom layer defines the actual physical components, such as connectors and cable and the electrical signals for transmitting data bits. Above this layer is the Data-Link layer, which defines how data is packaged for transport over the physical network, as described further here. The next upper layer handles error detection and correction, as well as methods for keeping the communication session alive. Each layer provides a higher level of functionality. Finally, the uppermost layers define how applications use network communication services.

The Data-Link layer sits just above the Physical layer. Therefore it defines the protocols that directly interact with the physical components of the network such as the network adapters and cable. It controls the flow of information across the link, and adds its own error checking to the packets it sends out across the links. *Bridges* operate in the Data-Link layer.

The Institute of Electrical and Electronics Engineers (IEEE) has split the Data-Link layer into two sublayers called the *media access control (MAC)* sublayer and the *logical link control (LLC)* sublayer, as shown in Figure D-4. The lower MAC layer defines the media access method, which can be either carrier sense multiple access/collision detection (CSMA/CD), token ring, or other IEEE physical interface. The LLC sublayer provides a way to pass information between these different network types by repackaging the data with new headers, thus providing the linking functionality implied in the Data-Link layer's name. This is an important feature that provides a level of modularity to the network. For example, when running Novell NetWare, you can install Ethernet or Token Ring cards in the server. The Data-Link layer functions running in the server automatically forward packets between networks as needed, and thus serves as a bridge.

You can bridge devices that use different protocols, but the Data-Link layer doesn't see the network addresses in the packet. Thus it can't perform the optimal-path routing that routers provide. Some bridges provide filtering functions to restrict packets from traveling to other networks where they don't belong.

In the AppleTalk protocol stack, the Link Access Protocols (LAPs) exist in this layer. They are the LocalTalk LAP, EtherTalk LAP, or the Token Ring LAP. The LAP is responsible for creating its node number when the system starts, and for handling the

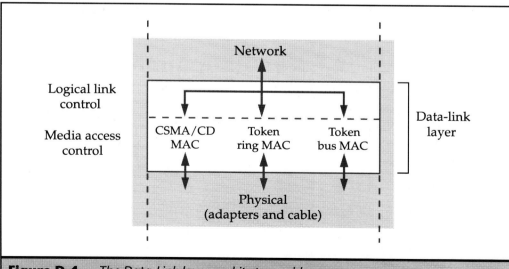

Figure D-4. *The Data-Link layer and its two sublayers*

access protocol, which is either CSMA/CA, Carrier Sense Multiple Access/Collision Detection (CSMA/CD), or the token access scheme.

Some interesting Data-Link layer protocols and interfaces are defined here:

■ *Open Data-link Interface (ODI)*   This Novell standard provides a way to run two or more communication protocols in one computer on one network adapter, or multiple network adapters. For example, it's possible to transfer both TCP/IP and IPX protocols over a single network card.

■ *Network Driver Interface Standard (NDIS)*   This Microsoft standard provides the same multiple protocol support as the Novell ODI standard. The two standards essentially compete in the LAN world.

RELATED ENTRIES   Layered Architecture; Open Systems Interconnection Model; *and* Protocol Stack

Data Management

Data management is concerned with the distribution of data to users and the protection of that data from loss such as fire or theft, or unauthorized access. Data management includes these areas:

■ *Archiving*   Copying files that are no longer needed to archival storage.

■ *Backup*   Backing up current files for protection.

■ *Data migration*   Similar to archiving, but provides a way for users to quickly access files that have been archived.

■ *Client-server system*   A client-server system is implemented on networks. It gives users, working at client workstations, access to DBMSs on back-end servers.

■ *Database management system (DBMS)*   A database is a file that contains records with information in fields. A DBMS is a complete package that provides a query language and provides access to the data.

■ *Distributed database*   A distributed database is stored on multiple servers over a network, but viewed and accessed as a single database by users.

■ *Security*   User access rights, directory rights, and file rights all deal with restricting user access to specific files, directories, and servers.

RELATED ENTRIES   Archiving; Backup and Data Archiving; Client-Server Computing; Data Migration; Database Management System; Distributed Database; *and* Security

Data Migration

Data migration is an archiving process that moves little-used or unused files to a secondary storage system, such as magnetic tape or optical disk. The files are typically imaged documents or historical information that clients might need to view at any time in the future. Migration works in conjunction with backup strategies— regular backups are still required.

Migration (and de-migration) is a process that moves files off valuable high-speed magnetic disk space and onto secondary, high-volume media, primarily optical disk. Files remain available offline, but are accessible to users over the network. This is accomplished by keeping a list of names for archived files in a directory on the primary media. When users need an archived file, they look in this directory, find the file, and open it as normal. The file is then *de-migrated* from secondary storage (optical disk) to primary storage (magnetic disk). This process happens in the background, and users may not be aware that the file has been de-migrated from optical disk. When users are done with the file, the file is migrated back to secondary storage. This migration can take place immediately, after a specific amount of time, or at the discretion of users or network administrators.

The Novell NetWare High Capacity Storage System (HCSS) is a data archiving system that supports an offline optical jukebox storage device. A jukebox is an autochanger device that can select from a stack of rewritable optical disks. The HCSS system migrates files marked by users and network administrators and de-migrates files as they are requested by users. Except for a slight delay in access, there is little indication that a file has been de-migrated.

RELATED ENTRIES   Hierarchical Storage Management Systems; High Capacity Storage System, Novell NetWare; Imaging; *and* Optical Libraries

Data Objects

See Objects.

Data Protection

Besides people, data is the most important asset to most organizations. Everything else can be replaced. If someone walks off with your server or the server goes down, you can replace the hardware in a day, but you can't bring your network back up and running if you don't have proper data backups. In addition, if your company is like most, even a day of downtime is intolerable, and thousands or millions of dollars could be lost while a system is not operating. There are many different solutions for protecting data, depending on the amount of money and effort you want to spend. The following sections cover steps you can take to guard against costly equipment and data loss.

PROTECTING AGAINST THEFT   You must protect servers from theft, not only because the equipment is valuable, but because the downtime it takes to replace the servers can cost many times more than the equipment. Consider the amount of time you would need to replace servers and restore backups. Here are a few server security options:

- Bolt the server chassis to a table and lock the case to the chassis. This prevents removal of the hard drive, which could easily be carried out of the building.
- Lock the server in a protective case that contains an adequate cooling system to prevent the server from overheating.
- Lock the server and associated equipment in the wiring closet. Make sure the closet is adequately cooled.
- Create a data center that requires a keycard or fingerprint verification for access.
- Place the server in a central management facility that is staffed 24 hours a day.
- Ensure that your personnel are trustworthy, competent, and know the security procedures.

You can justify the costs of elaborate data security techniques by including them in security measures required for other company assets, such as paper records and telecommunication equipment.

PROTECTING AGAINST FIRE AND NATURAL DISASTERS   Protecting valuable equipment and data against fire is a prime concern. Consider placing equipment in a vault or room that has internal or external fire protection. Many organizations already have banks of fireproof filing cabinets in rooms with sprinkler systems or halon gas systems to reduce fire loss.

Protect equipment from natural disasters such as earthquakes and floods. You might need to reinforce or elevate the server area and develop plans so users can access server data in case there is a disaster. Gas-powered generators can supply power to servers and workstations when electricity is cut off.

CENTRALIZE MANAGEMENT OR DISTRIBUTE MANAGEMENT   Both centralized management and distributed management have advantages. To centralize management, move network resources—servers, wiring centers, concentrators, routers, and even printers—to central locations where trained staff can manage the systems in secure and protected areas. However, doing so puts you at risk of catastrophes, such as earthquakes and fires. An alternative is to distribute network resources and automatically replicate data to remote sites on a regular basis. These sites are connected with high-speed data links to ensure that data is properly synchronized and up-to-date.

USING FAULT TOLERANCE TECHNIQUES   Network operating systems should provide fault tolerance techniques such as disk mirroring and disk duplexing for quick recovery from disk failures. Disk mirroring and duplexing techniques protect data by writing updates to multiple disks at the same time. Duplexing is a strategy of duplicating hardware components as well as disk storage. For example, NetWare System Fault Tolerance (SFT) Level III duplicates data onto another server and provides protection against both software and hardware failures. While fault tolerance at this level is expensive, it can protect against downtime.

KEEPING ADEQUATE BACKUPS   Ensure that data is properly backed up. Implement a backup plan that rotates backup to offsite storage. Backups can be classified as follows:

- Backups to restore an entire server in case of a disaster.
- Backups to restore blocks of data that have been corrupted or accidentally altered. For example, you might need to restore the accounting information from a previous day and re-enter data because of data entry errors.
- Backups that archive unused data to tape or optical disks.
- Backups that provide a way to recover single files that were accidentally deleted or copied over by users.

USING DISKLESS WORKSTATIONS   Diskless workstations don't have disk drives, so users can't download valuable company data or upload information that might contain viruses or clutter the server's disk. Diskless workstations are also less expensive than systems with disks and most can be upgraded to complete systems at a later time, making them practical for organizations with tight budgets. While these systems provide security at unsupervised or remote sites, they increase network traffic because users must access the network drive for all programs and files. Operating environments like Windows require swap files on disk. If a disk is not available, the swap file information must be stored on the server, which further adds to the network traffic problem.

PROTECTING AGAINST VIRUSES   Computer viruses are common and have the potential to infiltrate your network whenever a user logs on. This is especially true for users who work on a local area network (LAN) remotely from their home systems or take laptop computers on the road. Bulletin boards, public domain utility disks, and demonstration disks can carry viruses. It is essential that you have and use virus-detection software. Viruses are sometimes even found in the software that comes in shrink-wrapped packages. You should install all new software and updates on a test system and check for viruses before installing the software for use on the network server. You should also use appropriate file and directory rights to ensure that users can't alter executable files in program directories. There are other steps you can take. Advanced security techniques can eliminate the threat of viruses. These techniques authenticate users or any process that attempts to access a system and its files.

PROTECTING AGAINST INTRUDERS   Intruders can use various methods to gain access to a network. You can prevent intruders from accessing a local LAN by ensuring that users log off when done. Most network operating systems provide

D

features that restrict the station that users log on at and the time they log on. You can also add time restrictions to prevent access before or after normal working hours. An intruder who gains access to the system with a supervisor-level password can create another supervisor-level account, and then erase the tracks by altering the system log. Auditing features can log user activities and reveal security breaches to an independent auditor.

Unauthorized access by users at remote workstations poses another threat, but a call-back system can provide a level of security against these intruders. When a user dials in from a remote station, the system hangs up the call and calls the user back to ensure that he or she is at the designated location. However, this call-back feature cannot be used to protect a remote LAN or system that has a full-time connection. In that case, an intruder could find a way to set up an account that appears legitimate to your system. Take steps to prevent intruders from discovering passwords or back-door methods of entering your network.

ADMINISTERING ACCESS RIGHTS   Logon restrictions and directory or file access rights are important techniques that administrators and supervisors have to protect data against malicious or accidental loss or corruption by users. Users should never be given more rights than they need in program and data directories. Most users don't need more than the right to read in a program directory. Anything more opens program files to corruption, overwrites, and virus attack. Administering access to data directories is a little more complicated. You can assign clerks or temporary users the right to read files and databases, but not change the contents. Users who are authorized to update files are assigned Read, Write, and other appropriate rights, depending on the operating system. Use caution when granting rights that let users erase files, modify file attributes, or modify the rights of other users.

In database management systems, stored procedures can prevent users from accessing data they are not authorized to view or use. Instead of giving users access to the data itself, you give them access to procedures that perform common operations on the data. For example, a procedure might list customers with unpaid balances by customer number only and hide personal information such as the customer name, address, and phone number. Users who have no right to view this information never get a chance to see it. Stored procedures can also contain checks that ensure the user running the procedure is authorized to do so, and provide privileged users with higher levels of access.

TRAINING USERS   Train users to properly log on and log off of the network and to protect their passwords. If they need to leave their computers unattended, make sure they log off or know how to activate a password-protected screen saver that locks the computer (but maintains logon) while they are gone. Screen savers also provide a way to run unattended tasks without possibility of disturbance. In most network operating systems, you can set options in user accounts that force users to change their passwords at a predetermined interval, prevent them from reusing recent passwords, or require them to use passwords that haven't been used before.

One of the most common causes of data loss on a network is accidental erasure or corruption by an untrained user. Use security rights to prevent users from issuing potentially destructive commands, or make sure they are properly trained in the use of the commands to avoid accidents. Although users typically have full access rights in their own personal directories, you might want to prevent users from installing any files or software on the server. This not only protects against virus infection, but prevents users from filling a disk with unnecessary files.

TRACKING USERS   Keep track of users. Have department administrators inform you of users who have left the company or changed roles so that you can remove or alter their user accounts appropriately. Audit trails created by an auditing system can help you track users who disrupt the network either accidentally or on purpose.

RELATED ENTRIES   Access Rights; Backup and Data Archiving; Fault Tolerance; *and* Security

Data Service Unit/Channel Service Unit (DSU/CSU)

A data service unit (DSU) is a communication device that connects a company's telephone premises equipment to digital communication lines, such as a T1. A channel service unit (CSU) provides line termination and signal regeneration. The DSU and the CSU are often combined in one device and connected to a channel bank, which provides analog-to-digital conversion and multiplexing of voice transmissions.

RELATED ENTRIES   Channel Service Unit/Data Service Unit; Circuit-Switching Services; Switched Services; *and* T1/T3 Services

Data Striping

Data striping is a technique used in RAID (redundant arrays of inexpensive disks) systems to write data evenly across a series of disk drives. Striping divides data over two or more drives, as shown by the simplified example in Figure D-5. Data striping can occur at the bit level or sector level. A sector is a block of data. Striping improves throughput and provides a form of redundancy that protects against the failure of one disk in the array.

This protection comes from a technique that encodes the scattered data to a parity drive. Should one drive fail, the parity drive provides the information to fill in the missing bits from the lost drive and rebuild the data. The strategy assumes that it is unlikely that two drives will fail at the same time. RAID systems usually have a hot replacement feature that lets you immediately replace a drive without bringing the system down. Once the replacement drive is installed, the system starts rebuilding the data on the replaced drive using the parity information on the parity drive. The

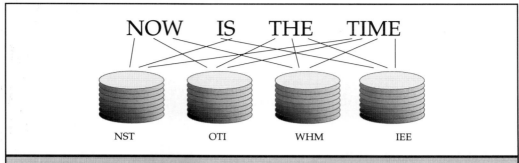

NOW   IS   THE   TIME

NST   OTI   WHM   IEE

Figure D-5.   *Data-striping distributes data over two or more drives*

operating system can continue to provide user access to the drive array during the rebuilding operation.

RELATED ENTRY   Redundant Arrays of Inexpensive Disks

Data Switches

A device that links terminals, computers, and other computing devices to host computers. They are basically concentrator devices that provide a way for a large number of devices to share a limited number of ports.

RELATED ENTRIES   Cluster Controllers, IBM; Concentrator Devices

Data Terminal Equipment (DTE)

See Data Communication Equipment.

Data Transfer Rates

The *bandwidth* of a data communication channel defines the rate of information exchange between two data systems, or the capacity of the line. The *bit rate* or *throughput* of a channel is the bits-per-second transfer rate supported by the channel. A 10- megabit-per-second Ethernet cable provides 10 times the bit-rate or throughput of a 1-megabit-per-second communication line. Telecommunication systems and networks such as Ethernet have specific bit-rates defined by standards to ensure that communication systems do not exceed the capacity of the specified equipment.

The bandwidth requirements of various applications are listed here. Data transfer rates measure the amount of digital information that can be transmitted through a channel per second. The rates are shown in bits-per-second (bits/sec), thousands of bits-per-sec (Kbits/sec), millions of bits-per-second (Mbits/sec), and even billions of bits-per-second (Gbits/sec or gigabits/sec).

Application	Rate
Personal communications	300 to 9,600 bits/sec or higher
E-mail transmissions	2,400 to 9,600 bits/sec or higher
Remote control programs	9,600 bits/sec to 56 Kbits/sec
Digitized voice phone call	64,000 bits/sec
Database text query	Up to 1 Mbit/sec
Digital audio	1 to 2 Mbits/sec
Access images	1 to 8 Mbits/sec
Compressed video	2 to 10 Mbits/sec
Medical transmissions	Up to 50 Mbits/sec
Document imaging	10 to 100 Mbits/sec
Scientific imaging	Up to 1 Gbit/sec
Full-motion video	1 to 2 Gbits/sec

The transmission rates of various communication media are listed here. Compression techniques can boost some rates. For example, modem rates have been boosted above 1 Mbit/sec in some studies, although these rates are not possible using existing serial ports on most computers.

Type	Rate
Dialup modem connection	1,200 to 28,800 bits/sec
Serial port file transfers	2,000 bits/sec
Fractional T1 digital WAN link	64,000 bits/sec
Parallel port	300,000 bits/sec
T1 digital WAN link	1.544 Mbits/sec
ARCNET LANs	2.5 or 20 Mbits/sec
Token ring LANs	4 or 16 Mbits/sec
Ethernet LANs	10 or 100 Mbits/sec
T3 digital WAN link	44.184 Mbits/sec
High-Speed Serial Interface (HSSI)	52 Mbits/sec
Fiber Distributed Data Interface (FDDI)	100 Mbits/sec
High Performance Parallel Interface (HIPPI)	800 to 1,600 Mbits/sec
Synchronous Optical Network (SONET)	51.9 Mbits/sec to 2.5 Gbits/sec
Potential future SONET	13.2 Gbits/sec

RELATED ENTRIES   Bandwidth; Transmission Media, Methods, and Equipment

Data Transmission Equipment

See Transmission Media, Methods, and Equipment.

DEC (Digital Equipment Corporation)

See Digital Equipment Corporation.

DECdns (DEC Distributed Name Service)

A Digital Equipment Corporation product that provides distributed network applications with a consistent, network-wide set of names (called name spaces) so that users and applications can refer to network resources such as disks, files, and nodes with a single name and not need to know where the resource is located. The product runs on DEC Virtual Address Extension (VAX) systems that run the Virtual Memory System (VMS) operating system.

DECdns, like other naming services, uses a client-server model. The names are stored in a database; a DECdns server is a node that physically holds some or all of the database. DECdns clients are applications such as the VAX Distributed File Service, Remote System Manager, and other applications. The DECdns database can be distributed across the network on more than one node to provide fault tolerance, availability, and performance benefits, especially when the network spans geographically distant areas. Keeping a copy of the database near user sites helps reduce wide area network link costs.

RELATED ENTRY   Digital Equipment Corporation

DEC Enterprise Management Architecture (EMA)

EMA is Digital Equipment Corporation's plan to provide network management for enterprise, multivendor networks. The architecture is two-tiered. It includes *entities*, which are physical devices such as bridges and routers, and *directors*, which are software applications that administrators use to manage the entities. EMA provides for a modular "plug-and-play" structure that has the following four components:

■ The *EMA executive* provides the management features and interface for the multivendor environment, and a management information repository (MIR) that collects data and stores it.

■ *Access modules* provide management links for entities on the network using the protocol implemented by the entity.

■ *Functional modules* are "plug-in" applications that address the five OSI management areas of configuration, fault, performance, accounting, and security.

■ *Presentation modules* provide the common user interface.

DECmcc

DECmcc (DEC Management Control Center) is DEC's first implementation of EMA. It is a family of software products that provide system and network management for multivendor computing environments. Administrators can manage single-site department LANs to global enterprise networks.

DECmcc runs on the DEC Virtual Memory System (VMS) operating system and Ultrix (DEC's UNIX) platforms and uses industry-standard protocols, such as Simple Network Management Protocol (SNMP), operate on Transmission Control Protocol/Internet Protocol (TCP/IP), Open Systems Interconnection (OSI), and DECnet networks. DECmcc is modular, allowing the management system to expand as the network grows. DECmcc has the potential to manage all enterprise networks and all components connected to them.

The EMA framework that DECmcc is built on divides the enterprise into two basic components: entities and directors. Entities are managed objects that communicate with the director according to a specified management protocol. Directors are the management components such as the modules described earlier (executive, access, functional, and presentation). Figure D-6 illustrates the modules.

There are three DECmcc packages:

DECMCC DIRECTOR   An entry-level package for managing ADVANTAGE-NETWORKS that is available for VAX VMS and RISC Ultrix systems. The DECmcc Director can register DECnet, OSI, and TCP/IP entities, separate them into manageable domains, and display a map of the network.

DECMCC BASIC MANAGEMENT SYSTEM (BMS)   The DECmcc BMS includes the DECmcc Director and local area network components and a number of management applications. BMS can automatically configure a network, monitor the network and create alarms, calculate network performance statistics, store and export historical management data, and react to alarm conditions.

DECMCC ENTERPRISE MANAGEMENT STATION (EMS)   The DECmcc EMS is a fully-loaded software package that includes most of DEC's EMA-based modules. It operates only on VMS systems and includes pre-EMA management tools. The entire network can be managed from a single integrated system.

OPTIONAL PACKAGES   The following optional packages are also available for specific network functions. Note that these options are included in the BMS and EMS packages. Also note that modules are available from other vendors.

D

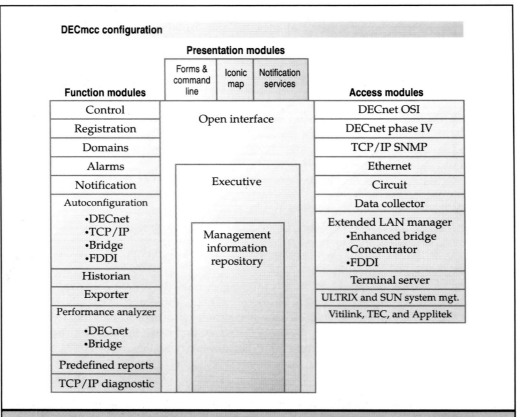

Figure D-6. *DEC's Management Control Center configuration*

■ *Configuration* This module permits automatic discovery, registration, and mapping of network objects.

■ *Notification* This module creates alarm rules, collects events, and provides customized notification techniques related to conditions anywhere in the network.

■ *Historical data* This module collects data over time for developing customized reports to track and tune system and network performance.

■ *Performance statistics* This module automatically calculates meaningful statistics for DECnet and TCP/IP networks and LAN bridges.

■ *Fault diagnostics* This module assists in diagnosing TCP/IP network problems.

- *Extended LAN manager*   This module manages Digital's LAN Bridge and FDDI products.

- *Terminal server access*   This module manages Digital's Terminal Server products.

RELATED ENTRIES   Digital Equipment Corporation; Management Standards and Tools

DECmcc (DEC Management Control Center)

DECmcc is the first implementation of DEC's Enterprise Management Architecture (EMA). It is a family of software that offers systems and network management for multivendor computing environments. Because DECmcc is based on the published EMA interface, it is not limited to system and network management. It can be extended to any manageable entity that can be reached through the data network, from a PBX to a building's air conditioning system.

RELATED ENTRIES   DEC Enterprise Management Architecture; Digital Equipment Corporation

DECnet

DECnet is Digital Equipment Corporation's name for the set of hardware and software products that implement the Digital Network Architecture (DNA). DECnet defines communication networks over Ethernet local area networks, Fiber Distributed Data Interface (FDDI) metropolitan area networks, and wide area networks that use private or public data transmission facilities. It can use Transmission Control Protocol/Internet Protocol (TCP/IP) and Open Systems Interconnection (OSI) protocols, as well as Digital's DECnet protocols.

DECnet was first announced in 1977 along with the introduction of the DEC VAX 11/780. It was originally designed for parallel interfaces that connected nearby systems (within 30 feet). In 1980, Digital, Xerox, and Intel announced Ethernet as a way to interconnect computer systems. The protocol layers of DECnet (which later influenced the OSI protocol stack) worked well in implementing the signaling and access scheme for nodes attached to Ethernet. Digital makes a number of Ethernet products; they are described under "Digital Equipment Corporation."

DECnet has evolved over the years in phases. DECnet Phase III implemented many advanced networking features, including adaptive routing that could detect link failures and reroute traffic as necessary. DECnet Phase IV, introduced in 1982, provided various enhancements, including the ones listed here, and an announcement that Digital would begin merging the OSI protocols into the architecture. Phase IV enhancements include:

D

- A virtual terminal that let users log on to a remote node
- Support for up to 64,000 nodes (1,023 nodes in 63 areas)
- Implementation of Routing Information Protocol (RIP), a distance-vector routing algorithm
- An IBM SNA gateway

NOTE: *The protocol stack for DECnet Phase IV is discussed under "DEC Network Architecture."*

DECnet Phase V was announced in 1987. It provided full compliance with the OSI model and backward compatibility to Phase IV. In Phase V, networks are broken up into routing domains that provide more flexibility in management than the backbone structure of Phase IV networks. The size of node addresses was increased to accommodate the domain number where a node exists.

In 1991, DEC announced ADVANTAGE-NETWORKS, a strategy that adds support for other protocols, backing away from its total commitment to OSI in Phase V. Most important, DEC provides support for TCP/IP and the ability to build multiprotocol backbones that can transport DECnet, TCP/IP, and OSI data. For example, users can transmit data between TCP/IP applications using OSI transport protocols, or between OSI applications using TCP protocols.

DECnet interconnects Digital PDP and VAX minicomputers systems, as well as desktop personal computers and workstations. Fundamental to DECnet is the idea of interconnecting machines that have their own processing power, rather than connecting terminals to a central system. These "intelligent" systems can then communicate with one another.

DECnet systems participating in a network are either full-function systems or end-node systems. A full-function system provides routing of messages beyond the local area network. An end-node system has full DECnet capabilities with the exception of the routing function. End-nodes access DECnet routers, X.25 gateways, or full-function nodes to send messages beyond the local area network. Data can originate and terminate at end-nodes, but data destined for other nodes cannot transit the node. Because end-nodes do not route, their performance is not affected.

DECnet-VAX

DECnet-VAX is a package for VMS systems that lets them participate as a full-function (routing) or end-node in DECnet computer networks. It is possible for DECnet-VAX networks to contain up to 1,023 nodes per network area, and up to 63 areas per network. DECnet-VAX interfaces are standard components of the VMS operating system for use on a local, stand-alone system.

DECnet-VAX offers task-to-task communication, file management, downline system and task loading, network command terminals, and network resource sharing capabilities using the Digital Network Architecture (DNA) protocols. Communication with Phase III, Phase IV, and DECnet/OSI nodes is supported.

DECnet-VAX Extensions

The DECnet-VAX Extensions provide an OSI end system stack that is co-resident with the DECnet Phase IV stack. Other enhancements include:

- Optional support for the DEC Distributed Name Service (DECdns) to manage network node names and addresses
- DEC Distributed Time Service (DECdts) to synchronize time among distributed systems
- ADVANTAGE-NETWORKS management of the OSI layers and remote ADVANTAGE-NETWORKS systems, multiprotocol routers and gateways

The extensions are designed to provide a transition path to DEC's ADVANTAGE-NETWORKS and enhance OSI with the following components that provide support for Government OSI Profiles (GOSIPs):

- File Transfer, Access, and Management (FTAM)
- OSI Application Kernel (OSAK)
- VAX OSI Transport Service (VOTS)
- VAX Packetnet System Interface Access (X.25 network access)
- VAX Wide Area Network Device Drivers (synchronous communication drivers)

Other DECnet Products

The following DECnet products provide nonrouting, end-node implementations of the Digital Network Architecture (DNA) in various operating systems:

DECNET FOR SCO UNIX   Provides the basic network to SCO UNIX clients and allows SCO UNIX users to participate as full peers in new and existing DECnet networks.

DECNET FOR RSX   Allows a DEC PDP-11 running the RSX operating system to participate as a Phase IV nonrouting, end-node in a DECnet network. Features include network terminal, file transfer, remote resource access, downline loading, and upline dumping.

DECNET FOR DOS   This product is a component of PATHWORKS for DOS and it allows DOS-compatible systems to participate as nonrouting, end-nodes in DECnet networks via Ethernet connections.

DECNET FOR OS/2   This product is a component of PATHWORKS for OS/2 and it allows OS/2 systems to participate as nonrouting, end-nodes in DECnet networks via Ethernet connections.

ADVANTAGE-NETWORKS

ADVANTAGE-NETWORKS represents Digital's merging of the DECnet, OSI, and TCP/IP protocols. The merging process is still underway as of this writing, but the specifications are available in the public domain so that other vendors can build products that support DECnet. These are the three main goals of ADVANTAGE-NETWORKS:

- Multivendor connectivity through the use of OSI and TCP/IP protocols

- Removal of addressing limitations for the support of computer networks with millions of nodes

- Management of very small to very large multivendor networks using a network management entity model that is modular and extensible

ADVANTAGE-NETWORKS fully supports the VMS operating system and DEC's Ultrix (UNIX) operating system. The architecture includes these important features:

- Numerous LAN and WAN communication options

- Enterprise Management Architecture (EMA), which provides a modular and expandable network management system

- DECdns, a VMS product that provides distributed network applications with a consistent, network-wide set of names (called name spaces) so that users and applications can refer to network resources such as disks, files, and nodes with a single name and not need know where the resource is located

- DECdts, a method for ensuring the synchronization of time over DECnet networks

- OSI-based network applications that provide interoperability

DECnet/OSI Products

DECnet/OSI is available in two packages for general-purpose DECnet systems: full-function and end-node. The full-function package includes routing capabilities.

The end-node package offers full DECnet capabilities with the exception of the routing function. End nodes access DECnet routers, X.25 gateways, or full-function nodes so they can send messages beyond the LAN. Data can originate and terminate at end nodes, but data destined for other nodes cannot transit the node. Because end nodes do not route, their performance is not affected.

DECnet/OSI for general-purpose systems is currently available in the end-node package only.

The DEC software products that support OSI have the following intrinsic features:

- Data exchange for cooperating programs using different operating systems
- Virtual terminal capabilities that enable users on a host system to log onto other network systems as though the terminals were directly connected
- Files transfer between network systems
- Enables users at local systems to execute command files at remote systems
- User access to remote resources such as printers
- Access to X.25 services
- Ability to access IBM SNA networks
- Ability to support IBM Binary Synchronous Communications (BISYNC) between Digital and IBM systems.

DECNET/OSI FOR VMS   This product supersedes the DECnet-VAX product. It implements both OSI and DECnet protocols for VMS and provides support for multivendor connectivity, larger networks, and EMA-based network management products. It also supports backward compatibility with DECnet Phase IV implementations. The release also includes integrated naming service, FDDI support, and the components included in the DECnet-VAX Extensions mentioned earlier that make it GOSIP-compliant.

DECNET/OSI FOR ULTRIX   Ultrix is DEC's version of UNIX. DECnet/OSI for Ultrix implements both OSI and DECnet protocols for the operating system. It includes most of the features in DECnet/OSI for VMS, with the addition of an Internet standard that allows OSI applications to run over TCP/IP.

DECnet System Services

DECnet System Services is a set of networking products that make a network of VAX systems (including single systems, VAXclusters, and Local Area VAXclusters) appear to be a single system for many key functions.

- VAX Distributed File Service (DFS) provides network-wide file operations.
- VAX Distributed Queuing Service (DQS) provides distributed use and management of network printing resources.
- Remote System Manager (RSM) lets a system administrator manage multiple distributed VMS and Ultrix systems. Automates recurring tasks such as operating system installation and updates, file backup and restore, and system administration.
- DECdns provides a consistent, network-wide set of names for distributed applications. See "DECdns" for more information.

D

DECnet Network Management

Digital's strategy for network management is designed around its Enterprise Management Architecture (EMA). EMA goes beyond typical network management, which focused on physical links such as modems, cables, and multiplexers, to the management of the systems, applications, and data that reside on the network.

Digital's architecture is open and extensive, and the company is working with the International Organization for Standardization (ISO) and many vendors to ensure that multivendor hardware and software products can be managed with Digital's management systems.

The first implementation of EMA is the DECmcc (DEC Management Control Center) family of management products.

RELATED ENTRIES   DEC Enterprise Management Architecture; DEC Network Architecture; *and* Digital Equipment Corporation

DECnet to IBM SNA Connectivity

Digital Equipment Corporation provides three transport products that provide DECnet connection to the IBM Systems Network Architecture (SNA) environment. All three products support Multiple Virtual Storage/System Product (MVS/SP) and Multiple Virtual Storage/Extended Architecture (MVS/XA), Virtual Machine (VM) both /SP and /XA, and Virtual Storage Extended /System Product (VSE/SP) operating systems.

- VMS SNA is a software product that provides a system-to-network connection over a synchronous communication line. It is designed for a single system with a single link to the SNA environment.

- DECnet SNA Gateway for Synchronous Transport is a software product that runs on DEC MicroServer dedicated servers. It provides network-to-network communication through Ethernet to up to four remote SNA networks over synchronous lines.

- DEC SNA Domain Gateway for Channel Transport connects to a dedicated high-speed IBM channel and is used for high-traffic links between DECnet and the SNA environment.

If the amount of traffic between a DEC system and IBM mainframe is low, Digital's Binary Synchronous Communications (BISYNC) Protocol Emulator is appropriate. It provides point-to-point emulation between the systems.

Other connectivity products are available, such as terminal emulators, remote job entry access routines, data transfer facilities, programming interfaces, database front-ends, and protocol emulators. Interested readers should consult DEC's *Networks Buyer's Guide* (available from DEC at 800/DIG-ITAL) for more information.

RELATED ENTRY Digital Equipment Corporation

DEC Network Applications Support (NAS)

Network Applications Support (NAS) was DEC's strategy for providing interoperability and cross-platform connectivity at all computing levels. It is similar to Apple Computer's Apple Open Collaborative Environment (AOCE) and Microsoft's Windows Open Service Architecture (WOSA). NAS specified such things as communication protocols, operating system interoperability, and the creation of compound document creation.

In 1993, DEC revised NAS to provide the following:

- Support for their new systems, such as Digital's Alpha AXP
- Support for workgroup computing using Digital's own products and third-party products, and support for X.400 and X.500 electronic mail and messaging standards
- Support for the Open Software Foundation's OSF/1
- Support for industry products and standards such as middleware, which lets a variety of client applications access a variety of back-end database server products
- Enterprise computing with sophisticated transaction-processing software
- Support for network management software

RELATED ENTRY Digital Equipment Corporation

DEC Network Architecture (DNA)

DNA is Digital Equipment Corporation's architecture that defines protocols, formats, and control message exchange over networks. DNA was first introduced in the mid-1970s. It serves as Digital's blueprint for past, present, and future communication products. The DNA model is similar to the Open Systems Interconnection (OSI) model developed by the International Organization for Standardization (ISO). DNA is arranged in layers, as shown in Figure D-7, where it is compared with IBM Systems Application Architecture/Systems Network Architecture (SAA/SNA) and Transmission Control Protocol/Internet Protocol (TCP/IP) protocols.

DECnet is Digital's family of software and hardware products that implements DNA to link systems into a single network. DECnet has evolved over the years, and the protocol layers of DNA have evolved with it. Refer to the "DECnet" for more information.

The Data-Link layer supports Digital Data Communication Messaging Protocol (DDCMP), an error-checking data-link protocol, as well as X.25 packet-switched networks, Ethernet, and High-level Data Link Control (HDLC). At the Open Systems

	DECnet/DNA	SNA/SAA	TCP/IP
Application (Presents User's Application)	VAX Software Remote Terminal	Document Content Architecture (DCA)	File Transfer Protocol (FTP), Simple Mail Transfer Protocol (SMTP)
Presentation (Translates Data)	Data Access Protocol (DAP)	SNADS, Dist. Data Management (DDM), Doc. Interchange Arch (DIA)	Network Filing System (NFS), Domain Name Service (DNS)
Session (Controls Dialog)	Distributed Naming Service (DNS)	LU 6.2 Network Services	TELNET
Transport (Ensures Message Integrity)	Network Services Protocol (NSP)	Path Control (Routes Data to Destination)	Transport Control Protocol (TCP), User Datagram Protocol (UDP)
Network (Routes Transmissions)	Routing Protocol (Integrated IS-IS)		Internet Protocol (IP) Address Resolution Protocol (ARP)
Data Link (Detects Errors)	DDCMP Ethernet, HDLC, X.25	SDLC, Token Ring, X.25	
Physical (Connects Devices to Network)	Primarily Ethernet		

Figure D-7. *DEC network architecture compared to SNA/SAA and TCP/IP*

Interconnection (OSI) Network layer are the DECnet protocols responsible for routing packets to destinations. The protocols use adaptive routing techniques that update routing tables as the network topology changes.

The Network Service Protocol at the OSI Transport layer provides management of logical network links between two nodes on DECnet networks. It controls the flow of data and handles errors. The protocol provides handshaking services so the linked nodes can have a two-way communication session. It segments information in the communication and sequences it to ensure delivery in the correct order.

The OSI Session layer includes DECdns (DEC distributed name service), an addition that manages names for network nodes. At the OSI Presentation level is DEC's Data Access Protocol (DAP), which provides remote file access and transfer capabilities. At the top level that corresponds to the OSI Application layer are network management protocols that handle peer-to-peer sessions.

In DECnet Phase V, DEC changed the DNA architecture to correspond as closely as possible to the OSI architecture. The names of the layers were made the same and support was added for X.400, File Transfer Access and Management (FTAM), and the Network File System (NFS).

RELATED ENTRIES   ADVANTAGE-NETWORKS, DEC; DECnet; *and* Digital Equipment Corporation

DEC PATHWORKS

DEC's PATHWORKS family of products creates a client-server environment where multivendor PCs, diverse communication protocols, networks, and applications can work together. PATHWORKS is based on Microsoft LAN Manager and uses the LAN Manager file protocol. In addition to providing standard file and printer sharing services, PATHWORKS also provides the following:

- A choice of Windows, DOS, OS/2, and Macintosh clients, as well as DEC Alpha machines running Windows NT, OpenVMS, and OSF/1 (a UNIX-like system)

- A choice of servers that use either Intel, RISC, or VAX architectures and that run operating systems such as OS/2 LAN Manager, NetWare, UNIX, and VMS

- A choice of networking transport mechanisms

- Interoperability with a range of personal and desktop systems, including VMS workstation users and PC users on non-DEC LANs

- File sharing on a peer-to-peer basis with other clients, or with dedicated file servers

- Network management facilities that allow remote software installation and updates, centralized file backups, and other management features

PATHWORKS is a client-server networking system in which clients access system software, applications, mass storage, and printer resources on PATHWORKS servers located anywhere on the network. Once links are established, users access files on server disks as if the drives were local.

PATHWORKS includes client software for the following:

- DOS and DOS (TCP/IP)
- Windows
- OS/2 and OS/2 (TCP/IP)
- Macintosh

In addition, server software is available for DEC VAX systems, Apple Macintosh, Intel platforms, and servers running OS/2.

RELATED ENTRIES   Digital Equipment Corporation; LAN Manager, Microsoft

Dedicated Circuits

A *dedicated circuit* is a data communication pathway between two communicating systems, that in some cases, comes with a guaranteed quality of service. The circuit may exist as a physical cable between two systems, or may exist logically within a multiplexed or switched system.

Dedicated circuits used in wide area networks (WANs) are leased on a monthly basis and maintain a constant point-to-point connection between two sites. They are often called leased lines and are used to create private networks. A dedicated circuit can be a voice-grade line requiring modems at each end, or a digital line such as a T1-type service that provides transmission speeds up to 1.544 Mbits/sec or a T3 line at 45 Mbits/sec.

A dedicated circuit can also exist *logically* in packet-switching networks such as X.25 and Frame Relay. A logical circuit is also called a *virtual circuit*. Two systems maintain contact with each over the network and predefine a path through the network before transmitting data. A virtual path offers advantages such as sequential packet delivery and acknowledgment of delivery if necessary. Such services are often less expensive than leased T1 lines because customers pay for packets delivered. They also provide bandwidth on demand, which accommodates bursts in traffic and connections to many sites.

Network administrators evaluating the use of these lines must weigh the cost of a leased line based on the amount of traffic that will traverse it, and whether an uninterrupted connection must be maintained at all times. If traffic is light, or only required during certain times of the day, a dialup line is more practical and less expensive. Dialup lines are appropriate for occasional transmissions such as E-mail. Dedicated lines are best when traffic is constant and service is required on an immediate basis.

RELATED ENTRIES   Circuit-Switching Services; Digital Circuits and Services; Fast Packet Switching; Logical Links, *and* Virtual Circuits

Dedicated Server

A *dedicated server* is a computer system that is used exclusively to provide services to network users. In contrast, a *nondedicated* server is set up in environments with light network loads, in which local users run processes and applications on a system that is running the server process. Peer-to-peer operating systems can operate in this way. Each workstation can share its resources with other network users while allowing the local user to access those resources as well.

Dedicated servers are recommended in busy network environments. When a server is dedicated, there is little chance that users or applications will disturb the network operating system or slow down its performance. For example, a user might run an application that locks up the system. In this case, the server would require rebooting and any users who were accessing the server could lose work in progress.

The decision to run a computer in dedicated or nondedicated mode is not much of an issue with the drastic price drops in computer hardware. It is best to purchase a separate system, load the operating system in dedicated mode, and lock the server in a secure location.

Defense Advanced Research Projects Agency (DARPA)

In 1972, the Advanced Research Projects Agency (ARPA) became the Defense Advanced Research Projects Agency (DARPA). DARPA is an extension of the Department of Defense assigned to fund basic research. The DARPA funded most of the basic research for the Transmission Control Protocol/Internet Protocol (TCP/IP) protocol suite and the Internet in the early 1970s. In fact, some of the original work took place at the Massachusetts Institute of Technology as far back as 1965 under a subcontract MIT had with ARPA.

DARPA does not conduct its own research. It funds universities and commercial or nonprofit organizations to do the research the Department of Defense needs. In the mid-1970s, DARPA saw a need to interlink computers used by organizations that were doing government research. The interconnection specification eventually became the TCP/IP protocols, which are nonproprietary and available for all to use without charge. At the same time, the ARPANET, which later became the Internet, was growing. By 1983, DARPA mandated that all computers attached to this network must use TCP/IP.

In 1981, DARPA organized an advisory group called the Internet Configuration Control Board (ICCB) that would manage the research activities for the Internet. In 1984, DARPA reorganized the ICCB into the Internet Activities Board (IAB), which was split up into task forces that handled such things as applications, interoperability, security, and testing. Most recently, DARPA reformed these groups into the Internet Engineering Task Force (IETF) and the Internet Research Task Force (IRTF). These groups get the most publicity today and are responsible for engineering the Internet and researching future trends. They organize meetings and conferences and provide publication services.

RELATED ENTRIES   Internet; National Information Infrastructure; National Research and Education Network; *and* Transmission Control Protocol/Internet Protocol

Demand Priority Access Method

Demand priority is a new access method designed for the 100 Mbits/sec Ethernet standard called 100VG-AnyLAN, which has been standardized by the IEEE 802.12

D

committee. Demand priority takes advantage of the structured wire design and hub-centric approach of the 100VG-AnyLAN topology. Unlike hubs in Ethernet 10Base-T, the 100VG-AnyLAN hubs control access to the network, eliminating the need for workstations to sense for a carrier signal as in done with the carrier sense multiple access/collision detection (CSMA/CD) access method of standard Ethernet. When a workstation needs to transmit, it sends a request to the hub. If the network is not busy, the workstation gets permission to transmit. All transmissions are directed through the hub, which provides rapid switching to the destination node. Transmissions are between sender and receiver only, unlike CSMA/CD in which a transmission is broadcast over the entire network. This reduces the chance that other attached devices can listen to private messages.

If multiple requests for transmission arrive at the hub, the highest priority is serviced first. If two workstations request the same priority at the same time, both are serviced by alternating between the two. This transmission method is superior to CSMA/CD. In CSMA/CD, workstations compete for access to the cable on their own, rather then under the direction of a central hub. Contention occurs when two or more workstations attempt access at the same time. Each workstation backs off and waits for a period of time before attempting access again. This reduces performance and causes more contention because workstations still need to compete for access to the cable.

It is possible to designate priority service for time-sensitive local area network traffic, particularly real-time video. In this way, the video is delivered on time before other traffic. If the network does not have enough bandwidth to deliver the video, packets are dropped and the image appears jerky to the viewer.

With the demand priority method, workstations can receive at the same time they transmit. This is possible through the use of four pairs of wires, and the use of quartet signaling. The quartet signaling method uses the same frequencies as 10Base-T, but transmits 25 MHz signals on each of the wire pairs in the cable. An encoding scheme called 5B6B replaces the Manchester encoding used in 10Base-T. The lower-signal frequencies in 100VG-AnyLAN, split across the wires, keep radio-frequency emissions within required standards and allow use of voice grade cable. The 10Base-T standard transmits a 20MHz signal split over two wire pairs.

RELATED ENTRY   Ethernet 100VG-AnyLAN (Voice Grade)

Demodulation

Demodulation is the opposite of modulation, which is the process of changing a carrier signal so that it carries information. For example, an AM radio broadcast modulates a carrier signal located at the frequency to which you tuned the dial. The modulation of the signal is converted to audible sound waves by the receiving device.

In computer communication, a sending modem (**mo**dulator/**de**modulator) modulates a digital signal into an analog wave for transmission over a voice telephone line. A modem at the receiving end demodulates the signal back into digital information.

RELATED ENTRIES   Modems; Modulation Techniques

Desktop Management Interface (DMI)

The DMI is a programming and reporting standard for managing desktop workstations. It was defined by the Desktop Management Task Force (DMTF), which is a consortium of industry vendors including Digital Equipment Corporation, Hewlett-Packard, Intel, Microsoft, SunConnect, SynOptics Communications, and other companies.

The DMI is an application program interface (API) that provides network managers with information about workstations on the network. The primary objective is to reduce network managers' workload by providing them with vital workstation information and assisting them with configuration and updating tasks. Managers can view information and carry out management tasks from their office, saving time and even eliminating travel in some cases.

The DMI defines how manufacturers of hardware products such as network interface cards or networking software can integrate "agents" into their products that collect information and report back to a management utility. Manufacturers don't need to worry about which protocols and operating systems end users will run with their management products. This is all handled by management software. The DMI is open to any management application or protocol, and all applications that adopt the DMI can call the same interface. IBM-compatible PCs, Macintosh, and UNIX systems are part of the DMI plan.

Automation is the primary advantage. The agents can perform tasks in the background and compile information that a normal network manager would never have time to gather using manual processes. This information can provide vital information required for network troubleshooting or to monitor changing conditions on the network that might present problems in the future, such as subtle increases in traffic problems or disks that are becoming full.

Local area network administrators can determine the following through the DMI interface:

- Basic information such as the processor type, available memory, and disk space information

- Hardware and software components installed in network systems

- How components are configured

- How well the components are working

- Whether the components are due for an upgrade

This information can help managers quickly resolve problems and provide upgrades.

DMI Architecture

The DMI provides a common method for issuing requests and commands called the Management Interface (MI). Management systems that are DMI-compliant use this interface to access management information. The Component Interface (CI) allows products to be managed by applications calling the DMI. The CI lets product manufacturers define the level of management needed for their products.

One component defined in the DMI is the management information format file (MIFF). The MIFF is a text file that collects information about systems and makes it available to management programs. Vendors will provide MIFFs with their DMI-compliant products. Microsoft Hermes uses MIFFs to configure software for the individual desktop.

RELATED ENTRIES   Electronic Software Distribution and Licensing; Hermes, Microsoft; *and* Management Standards and Tools

Desktop Management Task Force (DMTF)

The DMTF is a group of vendors that is defining a standard for managing and tracking resources on network workstations. The standard is called the Desktop Management Interface (DMI). The DMTF group consists of Digital Equipment Corporation, Hewlett-Packard, Intel, Microsoft, SunConnect, SynOptics Communications, and other companies.

RELATED ENTRIES   Desktop Management Interface; Management Standards and Tools

Dial-on-Demand Routing (DDR)

DDR provides a way to link two sites over a public network and provide needed bandwidth by setting up additional lines as required. DDR is a feature of Cisco routers that establishes a circuit-switched analog or digital connection to a remote location. Switched connections can provide alternate routes to back up primary communications lines that might fail. Switched lines are also used to handle peaks in traffic, fax transmissions, backup sessions, bulk E-mail transfers, and LAN-to-LAN connections.

A Cisco router running the DDR utility issues a dialup command to the connected DCE when it receives packets destined for remote networks. The network administrator can designate which packets can initiate a dial-on-demand sequence. Cisco routers use the CCITT V.25 bis protocol to initiate calls on automatic calling devices. DDR provides an alternative to leased lines, assuming your network can handle the brief pause that occurs while the dial-on-demand connection is made. Managers who need to decide between leased lines or traditional dialup lines may choose dialup lines when this feature is available.

RELATED ENTRY   Circuit-Switching Services

Dialup Line

A dialup line is a connection or circuit between two sites through a switched telephone network and is most commonly associated with a voice telephone call between two locations. In the data communication world, a dialup line forms a link between two distant computers or local area networks. Features that are important in data communication are listed here:

- Dialup lines provide any-to-any connections. The originating site can call any other site, unlike leased lines, which permanently connect two sites.

- Modems are required on both ends of a dialup line to convert digital signals to analog signals for transmission over the voice telephone network.

- A call setup and disconnect sequence is required for dialup lines. For online transactions, the setup phase may cause unacceptable delays necessitating a dedicated line.

- Dialup lines are inexpensive and charges are incurred only during connection time. They are useful for occasional file transfers and E-mail transmissions.

- The maximum transmission rate is currently 28,800 bits/sec with the V.34 standard and the use of compression.

- Leased digital lines can provide higher transmission rates, but are more expensive and require dedicated connections.

Differential Phase Shift Keying (DPSK)

See Modulation Techniques.

Digital Circuits and Services

See Circuit-Switching Services; Switched Services

Digital Equipment Corporation (DEC)

Digital Equipment Corporation, usually called DEC, was founded in 1957 in Maynard, Massachusetts by Kenneth Olsen. The company initially sold a set of computer systems for scientists and engineers and soon began competing with IBM in the business environment. DEC is best known for its minicomputer systems, which provided departments within companies with their own affordable computers so those departments didn't need to rely on a single, all powerful information systems department. This trend of making computer power more accessible to people continued in the 1980s with the development of personal computers, but that's a story that DEC does not play into as much as IBM and Apple Computer do.

In 1959, DEC announced the Programmed Data Processor (PDP-1), an 18-bit computer with a relatively inexpensive price tag of $120,000 and a very innovative idea—a built-in CRT. This model evolved into the PDP-8 minicomputer and other PDP systems with 12-, 18-, and 32-bit architectures. The most popular PDP system is the 16-bit PDP-11, but the Virtual Address Extension (VAX) 32-bit family of computers, first introduced in 1977, makes up the current DEC minicomputer line.

VAX systems are available in a range of sizes, from desktop systems to large-scale multiprocessing mainframes that service thousands of users. The VAX systems use the Virtual Memory System (VMS) operating system, a multiuser, multitasking, operating system that provides virtual memory capabilities. VAX systems will also run software written for PDP systems.

> **NOTE:** *The DEC Alpha AXP processors have a 64-bit design and are rated as the fastest processors in their size and price range.*

With the introduction of the VAX, DEC also announced its DECnet networking product. DECnet is built around the Digital Networking Architecture (DNA), and provides a way for multiple computers to link and share resources. DECnet was originally designed for parallel interfaces that connected nearby systems within about 30 feet of one another. In 1980, DEC, Xerox, and Intel announced Ethernet as a way to interconnect computer systems. The protocol layers of DECnet, which later influenced the Open Systems Interconnection (OSI) protocol stack, worked well in implementing the signaling and access scheme for nodes attached to Ethernet. DEC makes a number of Ethernet products, and they are described in the following sections. For more information, see the heading "DECnet" presented earlier in this book.

Today, DEC's minicomputer systems run either VMS or ULTRIX, which is a version of UNIX. A family of products called PATHWORKS provide client-server networking environments in which DEC minicomputers systems operate as servers and Windows, DOS, OS/2, and Macintosh computers operate as clients to access the servers. See "DEC PATHWORKS" for more information.

DEC's Strategy for the 1990s

Digital's current strategy is to support open networking environments that allow customers to mix and match systems and software, integrating systems, and applications across multivendor networks. This strategy is called Open Advantage, and it provides the following:

■ Compliance with industry and de facto standards

■ Support for the Open Software Foundation (OSF), of which DEC is one of the seven founding members. OSF's goal is to develop specifications for completely open software environments.

■ Network Application Support (NAS), which enables new and existing applications running in multivendor environments to share information and resources. See "DEC Network Applications Support" earlier in this book.

DEC's networking strategy integrates proprietary protocols such as DECnet and SNA, de facto standards such as TCP/IP, and international standards such as OSI. The DEC PATHWORKS family of products integrates DOS, OS/2, Apple Macintosh, VMS, ULTRIX (DEC's version of UNIX), and other platforms.

DEC's computing philosophy is based on distributed processing, which provides an organization total computing power to all users over computer networks. Distributed computing lets small systems access the resources of large systems and lets large systems off-load applications to smaller systems in order to free up processing power. DEC bases its LAN products on the following technologies:

■ Ethernet 802.3, which provides 10 Mbits/sec transmission rates over coaxial cable or twisted-pair wire. DEC will also support new Fast Ethernet standards.

■ Token Ring 802.5, which provides 4 Mbits/sec or 16 Mbits/sec transmission rates over various media.

■ FDDI, which provides 100 Mbits/sec transmission over fiber-optic cable.

■ OSI, which defines networking standards for local and wide area networks.

DEC embraces the OSI standards as a way to integrate equipment manufactured by different vendors. OSI provides a way for multivendor equipment to communicate, assuming vendors follow the rules for information exchange the standard specifies.

DEC's networking capabilities are built around DNA (DEC Network Architecture), which was developed in the 1970s. Like the OSI reference model, DNA is arranged in layers that define protocols for communication. DECnet, DEC's family of software and hardware products, implements DNA. One of the most important DNA developments is the merging of DECnet and the OSI standards, which provides multivendor communication for network-attached devices. Refer to "DEC Network Architecture" elsewhere in this book.

DEC's networking strategy began with the announcement of DNA in 1975. Through this architecture, every device that DEC ever manufactured will communicate with every device Digital now manufactures. DEC was instrumental in the development of Ethernet in 1980, along with Intel and Xerox. A plan to integrate OSI standards into DNA was launched in 1985. DEC announced DECnet OSI Phase V in 1987, becoming one of the first companies to comply fully with OSI standards. The ADVANTAGE-NETWORKS product family, announced in 1991, integrates OSI standards with DNA. The base protocols are DECnet, OSI, and TCP/IP with access to DECnet Phase IV and SNA.

Client-Server Networking Software

The following software products are available for use on DEC's networks:

DEC PATHWORKS

PATHWORKS is the name for DEC's family of client-server networking products. Similar to Microsoft's LAN Manager in functionality, it provides for Windows, DOS, OS/2, and Macintosh clients. Servers can include Intel, RISC, and VAX systems running the OS/2, UNIX, and VMS operating systems. Refer to "DEC PATHWORKS" earlier in this book.

DEC MAILworks

MAILworks is DEC's electronic mail software system that takes advantage of PATHWORKS networks. DEC MAILworks supports the X.400 standard for public and private electronic mail systems, as well as many proprietary mail systems. It has the following features:

- Available for Microsoft Windows, Macintosh, and DOS systems
- Adheres to CCITT X.400 User Agent recommendations for multinational, multivendor mail interconnection
- Integrates with multivendor mail systems through DEC's MAILbus.
- Includes Personal Address Book to track mail addresses and names, and integrates with Distributed Directory Services.
- Allows file or other message attachments to E-mail messages
- Provides for local or remote message storage
- Provides remote dial-in services for users on the road

TeamLinks for PATHWORKS

DEC TeamLinks integrates personal productivity tools such as word processors, spreadsheets, and other applications with electronic mail, workflow automation, document routing, conferencing, reference libraries, database access, document management, and other tools to facilitate the flow of information throughout the work group. TeamLinks is a distributed, client-server technology designed for the Microsoft Windows environment. Features include the following:

- Electronic mail that complies with the X.400 standard
- Electronic conferencing that provides a way to discuss issues with other users separated by space and time and to keep an audit trail of the discussions
- Browsing that provides a simple way to view and use information, such as content-based retrieval for searching by subject, plus copy, mail, and delete operations
- Group filing that provides a way to share data and documents in real time across and between work groups, and across and between multiple LANs

- Document conversion that provides a way to view and use information found on many different systems attached to the LAN

- Workflow automation and document routing that provides a way to track and audit activities, forms, and business practices

- Personal productivity software includes Microsoft Word for Windows, PowerPoint, and Excel with X.400 Mail services

RELATED ENTRIES   Alpha AXP, DEC; DECdns; DECmcc; DECnet; *and* DEC Network Architecture

Digital Service Unit

See Channel Service Unit/Data Service Unit.

Digital Signals

See Transmission Media, Methods, and Equipment.

Digital Signatures

Digital signatures are encryption methods that serve two purposes: First, they validate the contents of an electronic message and can be used at a later time to prove that a message was in fact sent from the sender (that is, prevents the sender from disavowing knowledge of the message). Second, they prove that a message has not been tampered with during its delivery. Digital signatures back up the authenticity of electronic mail, accounting transactions, company directives, workgroup documents, and other messages and files that move from one system, user, or organization to another.

Digital signatures are based on the fact that two parties can authenticate themselves to each other for the secure exchange of documents, but the relationship between the two parties is not based on complete trust. For example, a person could send you a message to wager on a racehorse, then later deny ever sending the message if the horse lost the race! While you know through the authentication process that this person actually sent you the message, without a digital signature, you can't technically prove that the message wasn't altered. The sender could say, "yes, I sent you a message, but you changed it."

Digital signatures provide message authenticity and are used to validate purchases, funds transfers, and other business transactions. A form with digital signature must include the sender's name, date, and time, along with an identification or sequence number that positively identifies the person or transmission. A procedure using public-key encryption is outlined here and pictured in Figure D-8.

1. The sender creates the digital signature using his or her private key by encrypting specific identifying information in the document.

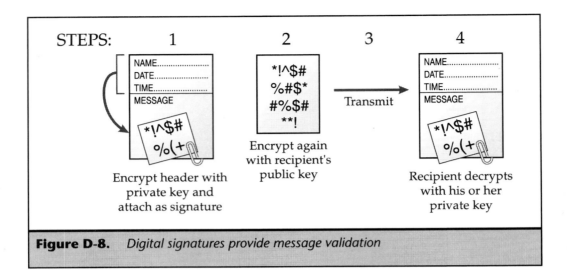

Figure D-8. *Digital signatures provide message validation*

2. Before sending the message, the sender encrypts the entire document *again* using the recipient's public key. The original encrypted message is now embedded in the newly encrypted document.

3. The message is sent to the recipient, who decrypts it using his or her private key.

The first encryption protects the sender's signature and identifying information from tampering and provides a way to authenticate the message. The second encryption protects the text or information portion of the document for transmission and allows the recipient to unencrypt and read the information upon receipt.

The security of a digital signature, like other encryption methods, is based on a mathematical algorithm that ensures that no two signatures are ever the same. Estimates of the time it would take to unlock modern computer-generated encryption codes are in the decades using supercomputers. In fact, the most trusted security systems are those under constant "attack" by security experts. With encryption algorithms provided by RSA Data Security (Redwood City, California) the probability that different documents will have the same code by coincidence is less than 1 in a trillion trillion.

Security requirements are growing daily due to the growth of distributed computing, which places computer and database resources at remote locations. Authentication, certification, public/private key encryption, and other topics discussed elsewhere in this book provide various types of security. See "Security."

Currently, RSA Data Security is the primary supplier of digital signature software. It is used in Novell NetWare 4.x, Sun Microsystems environments, Microsoft operating systems, and in Lotus Notes electronic messaging.

RELATED ENTRIES   Authentication and Authorization; Certification Systems; Privacy Enhanced Mail; Public Key Cryptographic System; *and* Security.

Digital Switched Services

See Switched Services.

Digitize

See Analog-to-Digital Conversion.

Dijkstra Routing Protocol Algorithm

The Dijkstra routing algorithm enables routers to find a pathway through a mesh of network connections based on the path with the least cost. The algorithm runs through a series of calculations that eventually develops the cost of pathways to nodes and the pathway that has the least cost.

RELATED ENTRIES   Link State Routing; Routing Protocols

Directory Agents

See Agent; X.500 Directory Services.

Directory Attributes, NetWare

See File and Directory Attributes, NetWare.

Directory Management

This section provides tips for organizing file server directories and administering user access to those directories with rights and attributes. The discussion here is appropriate for NetWare servers, Windows NT servers, and other systems that have hierarchical directory structures.

Organizing Directories

You can organize directory structures to simplify user access, to provide a more consistent data structure, and to simplify management. Whenever possible, separate document files from program files and organize the structure in a way that makes backup easier, as shown in Figure D-9. You can perform periodic backups on program files, but data files require a more intensive backup cycle. Keeping program and data files separate lets you implement different backup schedules for the two categories of files. It doesn't make sense to back up all the files every day.

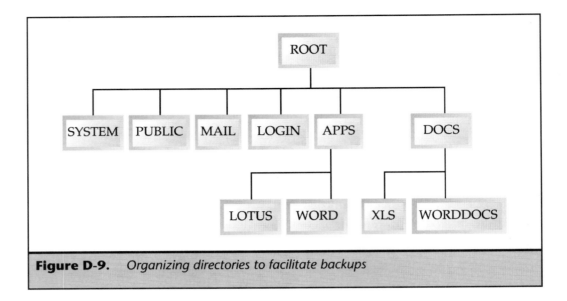

Figure D-9.   *Organizing directories to facilitate backups*

Security and Access Rights

Network operating systems have access rights (called *permissions* in Windows) that grant users specific rights in directories. For example, the Read right allows a user to open but not change a file, while the Write right lets the user change the file. Every network operating system has a specific set of rights. When a right is granted in one directory, users typically have the same right in subdirectories of that directory. This is called *rights inheritance*. However, administrators and supervisors can "block" these rights from being inherited in subdirectories.

In Figure D-9, the APPS directory has branching subdirectories for all the programs available on the server. The DOCS directory has branching subdirectories for the data files created by users. There are basically two groups of rights.

■ *Program rights*   In NetWare, you grant users the Read and File Scan rights in the APPS directory so they can run programs. In Windows NT, you grant users the Read permission to the APPS directory, and by inheritance, they get these same rights in the subdirectories.

■ *Document rights*   In NetWare, you grant users the Read, Create, Write, and File Scan rights in the DOCS directory so they can create and edit files. In Windows NT, you grant users the Change permission for the DOCS directory.

Rights inheritance is designed to make the management of rights easier. The rights you grant users at the top of a hierarchical tree carry through to subdirectories unless specifically changed. Plan directory structures to take advantage of this inheritance. Major branches in the tree can represent the points where different access rights apply.

User Directories

Create a private directory for each new user added to the network. This directory can branch from a directory called USERS or HOME. You can grant users full rights in their personal directory, which lets them create subdirectories and share those directories with other users if necessary. Alternatively, you can create a shared "public" directory where users place files they want to send to other users. If the system has a lot of users, install a separate server for users' personal directories.

Network operating systems typically provide mechanisms for limiting the amount of disk storage space that users have available. Implement this feature to prevent users from filling the drive with unnecessary programs, utilities, files, and other information.

Directory Permissions in Windows NT

See Permissions in Windows NT.

Directory Services

Distributed networks have resources and users at many locations. If a user needs to send a message to a person in a remote area, or access a server in that area, how does he or she locate the user or server? What is needed is a service that can provide users with a list of resources and addresses. Almost every major distributed network operating system vendor now has or is implementing a *directory service*. The CCITT X.500 directory services standard provides a model for others to follow. Most proprietary directory services follow its basic design with the intention of evolving into future X.500 designs.

Users of small workgroup local area networks have no problems identifying the one or two servers or printers in their area. As networks grow to an enterprise-wide and global scale, identifying and locating users and resources becomes increasingly difficult. The three primary pieces of information needed to locate a user or resource are the name, address, and route to get to that address. There are three types of services that can provide this type of information:

- *Name services*   Name services basically map a network address, which is usually a cryptic number, to a user's name.

- *Electronic mail address books*   E-mail applications such as Lotus cc:Mail and Microsoft Mail have built-in address books that help users address messages and merge their address books with others if necessary.

- *Directory services*   Directory services include name and address services managed at a central location by a central authority. Through the service, users can search for resources on an intra-network (organization-wide) or inter-network (global network such as the Internet) basis. This category includes X.500.

Distributed directory services provide a way for users and programs to locate and describe people and applications on large, multivendor networks. Directory services are similar to telephone books. Names are placed in database lists and made available to users. Users and resources on the network are called *objects*. The way the directory services user interface is implemented makes the system either simple and intuitive, or complex. Some examples follow:

■ *Graphical user interface* In this approach, users may see a graphical map of the organization. They click an icon that represents an organization, for example. This action displays a list of departments in the organization. They then click a department, which shows a list of users or resources. This approach is used in NetWare 4.x Directory Services. It helps managers locate and manage users or system resources. It also helps users locate other users to whom they want to send E-mail, or resources they want to access such as disks and printers.

TIP: *Refer to "Directory Services, NetWare" for an example of this method.*

■ *Address book* Users may access address books that hold the list of users and resources in their department or other departments they often contact or connect with.

■ *Search method* Users can query the directory services interface to find resources that have a particular class of services, or users with specific roles, such as "trainer" or manager. For example, a user could request a list of servers that provide information on a particular topic.

■ *Search agents* On large networks such as the Internet, special agents (often called *knowbots*) can search the network, looking for resources that match specific search criteria.

Replication and Partitioning

Because directory services are essential to locating services on the network, they must be available at all times. Some implementations use replications and partitioning methods to store the database or parts of it on multiple servers in multiple locations. Networks that are separated geographically benefit from replication because a copy of the database can be kept locally so users don't have to access the database at a location that is remote to them over wide-area links when looking up information. Replication also ensures that a copy of the database is available should one of the directory services systems go down.

Partitioning is useful for large databases and provides a way to store parts of the database on different computers. The database is typically partitioned according to geographic locations for wide area networks. For example, the Chicago division of a New York-based company stores the Chicago partition on its own server. A master copy of the entire database is stored and maintained in New York. Any updates to the master database or the partition are automatically copied to the other.

Replicating and partitioning a database introduces synchronization problems. Changes made in one database must be made as soon as possible in replicas. Fortunately, a database that provides a list of services for users' convenience can tolerate a few seconds' delay in getting its updates, unlike other types of distributed databases, such as online transaction processing systems.

Security Issues

Most of the discussion above has assumed that a company maintains a directory service of internal users and resources. This would be an intra-company directory service. However, the X.500 goal is to make all users on global networks accessible using directory services. The Internet is an example of an international system in which millions of users can exchange electronic mail and users can search for services that might be available on Internet-connected networks. However, many organizations are not ready to expose their internal employee and resource lists to outsiders. Why would an organization want to make its employee list available to head-hunters in the high-technology arena? Why would they open themselves up to a potential flood of electronic junk mail? Time will tell. For now, intercompany directory services and the X.500 standard has limited acceptance due to these questions.

Available Services

The following directory services are described in more detail under matching headings in this book. Services differ in the methods they use to look up information. There are descriptive naming services and primitive naming services. For example, X.500 is a descriptive naming service that lets users look up by a known name or search for special attributes if the name is not known. Primitive naming services assume the user knows the name of the person or resource they want to connect with, and simply provides the full address from the database upon request.

X.500 DIRECTORY SERVICES   CCITT X.500 is an emerging naming standard that allows organizations to globally share names and the objects associated with them. X.500 has been adopted as an international standard to provide worldwide directory services. It is closely linked to the X.400 electronic mail standard. X.500 is hierarchical in that there are administrative domains (organizations, divisions, departments, and workgroups) that provide information about the users and resources in those domains. X.500 is considered the best way to implement a directory service, but it costs more to implement and is slower than some of the other methods discussed here.

INTERNET OR "TCP/IP" NAMING SERVICES   The Internet is a worldwide network of networks that connects universities, research institutes, private companies, and other organizations. Currently, an overall structured system for finding users and resources does not exist. Instead, you use one of the following utilities and services. The Internet community is in the process of implementing the X.500 naming standard.

- **FINGER** is an Internet command that returns information about a specific user on a host system, such as their name, address, and phone number.

- **WHOIS** provides information about domains, networks, hosts, and users that have been officially registered with various Internet agencies.

- **NETFIND** is a utility that first searches a database that might contain information leading to the location of an object or service. It then uses the information to continue its search. The database is constructed from address information gathered during the monitoring of E-mail and other transmissions.

- **Domain Name Service (DNS)** is not a user command such as FINGER and WHOIS. It is a global system of distributed databases that contain names and addresses to represent the Internet numeric addresses. DNS is hierarchical; the upper-most level is divided into broad categories such as GOV (government) and EDU (education).

In addition, there are utilities for finding information, such as GOPHER, ARCHIE, WAIS (Wide Area Information Service), and W3 (World Wide Web). In GOPHER, information is presented in hierarchical form. ARCHIE lets you browse a database that lists common information and WAIS lets you search for documents based on keywords. W3 uses menus to provide access to information.

APPLE OPEN COLLABORATIVE ENVIRONMENT (AOCE)   Apple established AOCE as a foundation for developing applications that let users work in groups and collaborate on projects. It provides services such as messaging, electronic mail, authentication, digital signatures, and catalogs. This last item provides information about applications, resources, and users on the system. AOCE is an architecture and set of modules that help developers create applications. The Catalog Manager is a module that provides access to any kind of catalog/directory system, regardless of the storage format, via standard programming interfaces. It provides the interface elements for browsing, finding, and selecting catalog/directory records from within applications.

STREETTALK   StreetTalk is the directory service built into the Banyan VINES network operating system. It is designed to integrate and manage a growing variety of heterogeneous environments including Banyan enterprise networks, SCO UNIX, and Novell NetWare. StreetTalk extends beyond individual server or peer-to-peer client workgroup communities to encompass an entire enterprise network. StreetTalk integrates with all core services so that network services always know a user's physical location and security privileges. Users can log on once to gain access to all services, and they can log on from many different sites and their network environment remains the same.

The StreetTalk Directory Assistance (STDA) delivers distributed directory services. STDA collects information about available services on an ongoing basis and places that information in a database. Users can then call up STDA data on their screens and browse through its contents by an object's name or descriptive information. Users, printers, file volumes, gateways, and other network entities are listed in the database so users can locate users and services quickly. StreetTalk lets administrators define objects with attributes that closely follow X.500 naming standards.

DECdns (DEC DISTRIBUTED NAME SERVICE)   DECdns provides distributed applications with a consistent, network-wide set of names called *name spaces.* This corporate name space makes it possible for users and applications to refer to resources in the network such as files, disks, and nodes by using a single name without having to know where the resource is located. DECdns, like other naming services, uses a client-server model.

DIRECTORY SERVICES, NETWARE   NetWare Directory Services (NDS) is a feature in NetWare 4.x that implements a distributed directory service similar to the X.500 specification. The service keeps track of all network users, servers, and resources in a global database that network administrators and users access when they need to manage or use objects and services on the network.

DIRECTORY SERVICES, OPEN SOFTWARE FOUNDATION (OSF)   The OSF DCE directory services integrates with other DCE components as described under Distributed Computing Environment (DCE), OSF.

RELATED ENTRIES   Apple Open Collaborative Environment; Banyan VINES; DECdns; Directory Services, Netware; Directory Services, Open Software Foundation; Domain Name Service; Domains; *and* X.500 Directory Services

Directory Services, NetWare

NetWare Directory Services (NDS) is a feature in NetWare 4 that implements a distributed directory service similar to the International Organization for Standards (ISO) X.500 specification. The service keeps track of all network users, servers, and resources, even on large internetworks that use wide area network links. This information is kept in a global database that network administrators and users access when they need to manage or use objects and services on the network.

NDS was designed with large internetworks in mind. It provides centralized management of the entire network directory with a common naming service. It has the following features:

- NDS treats all network users and resources as *objects. User objects* hold the name, address, computer node address, logon script, and other vital administrative information about a network user. *Resource objects* (servers, printers, volumes, and so on) have properties that specify who can use and change them.

■ The directory forms a hierarchical structure in which objects are either *containers* that hold other objects, or *leaf* objects that define entities like user accounts, printers, servers, and other network devices. Containers form the branches of the hierarchical tree, much like directories form branches in hierarchical file systems. Containers can hold other containers to form sub-branches of the tree, or hold leaf objects.

■ Objects are stored in the NetWare Directory Database (NDB). A Windows-based application provides access to the database objects, and displays them in a tree structure as shown on the left in Figure D-10. This tree shows a company, a department, and users within a department. To view information about an object, administrators simply double-click the object.

■ The directory services database can be partitioned and replicated to other locations, making its information more readily available to users at those sites. NDS automatically keeps the partitions of the database synchronized with the master database.

■ The service provides gateways to other directory services, including Apple Name Binding Protocol, Sun Microsystems' Yellow Pages (NFS support), and the TCP/IP Domain Name Service.

Objects are stored in the NDB and organized in a hierarchical tree structure as shown on the left in Figure D-10. It's not necessary to organize the tree structure to resemble the physical location of users and resources in an organization. Instead, you can organize it to reflect the management organization of a company. For example, in

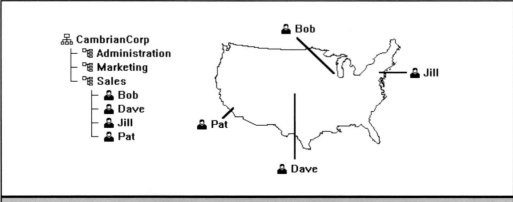

Figure D-10. *NetWare Directory Services provides location-independent organization of users and resources*

the illustration, salespeople are grouped under an organization called Sales in the directory services tree although they are physically located at remote locations, as shown on the right.

Grouping users and resources together in the directory services tree can simplify network management. For example, if the Sales object is granted access rights to files on a particular volume, all the user objects in the Sales container inherit those access rights.

The Directory Tree

The directory tree is made up of NDS named objects that represent the organization of the network. A named object can belong to one of four categories. Figure D-11 illustrates a typical directory tree structure. The meanings of the abbreviations are:

C = Country Name
O = Organization Name
OU = Organizational Unit Name
CN = Common Name

The picture of the directory tree shown in the figure is taken from the display you would see when running the Windows-based NetWare Administrator utility. This utility shows the tree in graphical form and lets you expand and collapse parts of the tree. Country, Organization, and Organizational Unit objects can contain other objects. For example, the Sales branch is expanded to show user and resource objects within it, and the Administration and Marketing branches are collapsed. The ability to view branches of the directory tree in this way makes it easy to locate and manage objects.

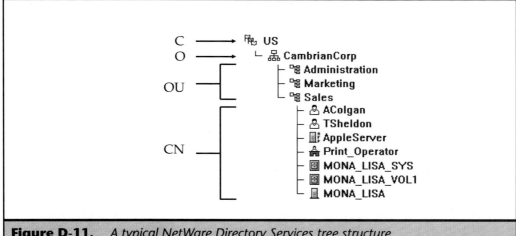

Figure D-11.   *A typical NetWare Directory Services tree structure*

Users and Resources as Objects

In NetWare Directory Services, objects are used to track and locate users and resources on the network. Resources are network servers, printers, and other devices, and objects hold information about a user or resource. This information forms the *properties* of the object. For example, a user object holds the logon script for a network user, among other things. If the network administrator or supervisor needs to change a user's logon script, he or she starts the Windows-based NetWare Administrator (or NetWare NETADMIN text-based utility), selects the user object, and changes the logon script.

Administrators and supervisors can simplify the task of granting access rights to users by granting those rights to the objects that contain user objects. For example, if all users in a department or division need Read and Write access rights to a directory called BBS, the rights can be granted to the organizational object that contains the users. In Figure D-11, if you granted the rights to the CambrianCorp organizational object, the rights would be inherited by the organizational unit objects Administration, Marketing, and Sales, as well as the objects they contain. It is also possible to block some or all of the rights that are inherited in this way at any branch in the tree.

Objects hold information about the users or resources they represent, so the NDS system can be used to document the network as well as to organize it and grant users access to it. You can also perform searches on this information to locate objects anywhere in the directory tree.

An important aspect of objects is that other users can be granted access to view and change the properties of objects. In this way, top-level administrators can delegate object management responsibilities to lower-level department managers or supervisors.

Types of Objects

As mentioned, an object is either a container object that holds other objects, or a leaf object that is contained within a container object. Container objects are the *country container, organization container,* and the *organizational unit* container. Leaf objects represent physical entities such as users, printers, and servers. A leaf object cannot contain objects of its own, and is therefore sometimes referred to as a terminal object.

The first three objects described next are used to organize the directory tree. The remaining objects are leaf objects. They are illustrated in Figure D-12 as they appear in the Windows-based NetWare Administrator.

THE COUNTRY CONTAINER The country container is the organizational unit that specifies which country an object is located in. It can hold information about one or more organizations. The name of the country object must be two characters long, such as US for the United States. The country container is optional. In fact, Novell recommends that you not use it to avoid adding unnecessary complexity to directory names. Instead, use organization containers to organize international divisions of an organization.

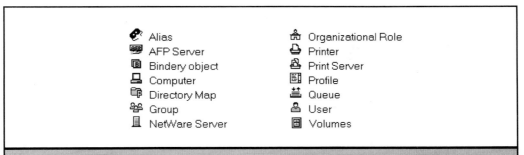

Figure D-12. *Object icons as they appear in the NetWare Administrator*

THE ORGANIZATION CONTAINER   There is usually one organization container, and a company assigns it the company name. Even if a company has different divisions around the world, the organization container is the preferred top-level container for the divisions, rather than the country container.

THE ORGANIZATIONAL UNIT CONTAINER   Organizational unit containers are the departments or divisions within an organization container.

THE ALIAS LEAF OBJECT   An alias object points to an object elsewhere in the directory tree. You create an alias in one branch of the tree for an object located in another branch of the directory tree. Users can then access the alias as if they were accessing the original object without the need to search through the tree.

THE AFP SERVER LEAF OBJECT   An AFP server is an Apple file server running the AppleTalk Filing Protocol.

THE BINDERY LEAF OBJECT   A bindery is an object that was upgraded from a version of NetWare that used server-specific binderies. Any object that was not identified during the upgrade is given the bindery object classification.

THE COMPUTER LEAF OBJECT   A computer object holds information about a workstation on the network, such as its serial number, node address, users, and location or department and is primarily used for documentation purposes.

THE DIRECTORY MAP LEAF OBJECT   A directory map object specifies the locations of applications and simplifies the mapping of directories for a large number of users. Directory maps are used in logon scripts to map directories for users. If the location of an application changes, you change the directory map rather than changing each user's logon script.

THE GROUP LEAF OBJECT   A group object is used to group users into mail groups, project groups, management groups, or other types of groups you might need for your organization. Groups simplify the assignment of directory and file rights and make it easy to add new users to the network. For example, you might create a group that works on a special project, and then assign the group access rights to directories and create a specific logon script. If new users need to work on the project, you simply add them to the group. The new users then gain all the rights of the group.

THE NETWARE SERVER LEAF OBJECT   A NetWare server object represents a NetWare server on the network.

THE ORGANIZATIONAL ROLE LEAF OBJECT   An organizational role is an object with specific rights that is assigned to a person such as an administrator, project leader, or temporary employee. If a different person takes over the job, a new person can be made a trustee of the object and thus inherit its rights.

THE PRINTER LEAF OBJECT   A printer object represents a printer that is attached to a print server or workstation and shared on the network.

THE PRINT SERVER LEAF OBJECT   A print server object represents a network print server. It can be part of the NetWare server or a stand-alone print server.

THE PROFILE LEAF OBJECT   A profile is a special logon script that is shared by more than one user. The profile script is executed after the script of the user's container, but before the user's logon script. Profile scripts make it easy to set up a network environment for a group of users who don't belong to the same containers (departments).

THE QUEUE LEAF OBJECT   A queue object represents a queue, which holds print jobs that are directed to one or more printers. Users send print jobs to queues.

THE USER LEAF OBJECT   A user object holds information about a user on the network.

THE VOLUME LEAF OBJECT   A volume object represents a physical volume on the hard drive of a file server. It also holds statistics about the volume. The name you assign to a volume object does not need to be the same as the hard disk volume name.

Properties of Objects

Objects have properties with the name being the most important. You specify the properties of an object when you create the object, and you can change them at any time by using the NetWare Administrator or NETADMIN text-based utility. An example of the NetWare Administrator window used to change the properties of a user object is shown in Figure D-13. You click the buttons on the right to view different property fields, such as logon restrictions and rights to the file system. You can then

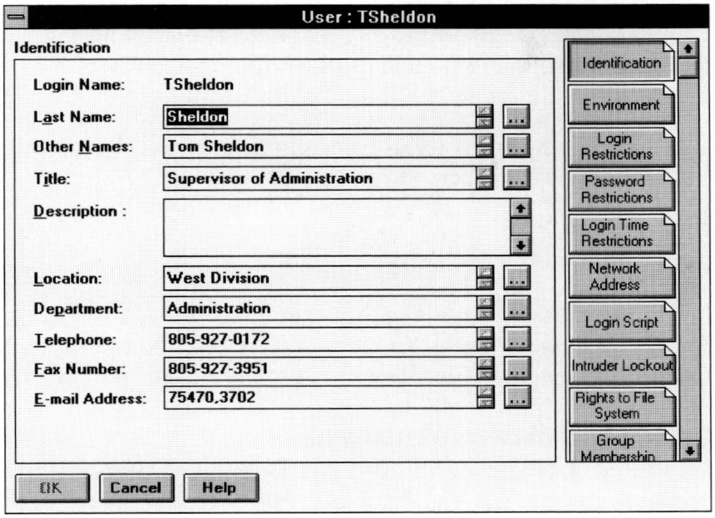

Figure D-13. *This window is used to change the properties of a user object*

change information about the selected properties. The network administrator can change any property field for any object. Other users can be restricted from changing or even viewing these fields.

Some of the property fields for a user object that you would see when working with the NetWare Administrator are listed here:

- The user's name, address, phone number, and fax number
- Account information, such as the balance amount
- Logon restrictions, such as the allowed time, the allowed workstations, and password requirements
- The default server of the user
- The groups the user belongs to
- The user's print job configuration and printer controls
- The profile object used by the user
- The user's identification number

In contrast, some of the properties of a physical object such as a server are listed here:

- The organizational unit name assigned to the server
- A description of the server, which is used for reference only
- The location of the server, which is used for reference only
- The network address of the server
- The trustees of the server, which is basically a list of users who can change the properties of the server object
- A list of server operators
- Status information about the server's operation

The network administrator can make any user a trustee of an object and set which of the object's properties that trustee can view and change. As mentioned earlier, department managers are usually granted rights to create and manage objects.

NDS Partition Management

NDS uses a distributed database called NetWare Directory Database (NDB) to track objects. On multiserver networks, the database resides on a network of servers, not just on one server, to ensure its survival in the event a server crashes. This is accomplished by segmenting the database into partitions and storing each partition on an appropriate server on the network. You can copy or replicate partitions to other servers to provide backups and increase performance. Administrators use the Partition Management utility to create, remove, join, divide, synchronize, and rebuild partitions. Partitions normally correspond to container objects in the NDS directory tree.

In order for partitions to operate concurrently, time synchronization is used. NDS uses time of day stamps to establish an order of events and ensure that updates to partitions by administrators are handled correctly and in order.

RELATED ENTRIES Directory Services; Directory Services Naming, NetWare 4.X; Distributed Computing; *and* X.500 Directory Services

Directory Services, Open Software Foundation (OSF)

OSF Distributed Computer Environment (DCE) Directory Services integrates with other DCE components (see "Distributed Computing Environment, OSF") and provides security, is readily available to all users, and is compatible with recognized naming standards. The service is based on DEC's DECdns and Siemen's DIR-X naming service. It supports networks with millions of computers and provides partitioning, caching, replication, authentication, and authorization functions. DCE Directory Services complies with X.400 worldwide Directory Services and the X/Open

Directory Service programming interface. However, OSF's Directory Services are not as robust as the X.500 standard.

DCE Directory Services provide high availability in the form of a replication mechanism. If a server fails, a copy of the database stored on another system is used. Replicas require updating whenever changes are made to the database, but replicas are beneficial for geographically dispersed networks. Users at remote locations can access a replica of the database in their own area, rather than use expensive wide area links to access the master database.

DCE Directory Services provide security features to prevent unauthorized users from accessing information about other users or resources. It also provides partition management so managers in geographic areas of a wide area network can more easily manage the objects they control. Partitioning a Directory Services database over separate computers improves performance by spreading the Directory Services processing load across computers on the network.

The DCE remote procedure call (RPC) is used as the communication interface that allows the Directory Services database to respond to directory service requests. Clients use RPC to communicate with the database. DCE RPC provides the benefits of portability, security, and interoperability.

The DCE directory service is designed to participate in the X.500 worldwide directory service. It provides mechanisms that tie local users into the X.500 directory service and allows users in other parts of the world to access local names through X.500. DCE Directory Services provides for administrative domains that control the location of name partitions, levels of directory replication, and user participation in Directory Services. DCE administrative domains connect into other administrative domains through X.500 by using *global directory agents (GDAs)*. Clients that need to look up names in other administrative domains go through the GDA, which handles inter-domain requests. GDAs already exist for X.500 and the Internet Domain Naming System.

RELATED ENTRIES   Directory Services; Distributed Computing; Distributed Computing Environment, OSF; *and* X.500 Directory Services

Directory Services Naming, NetWare 4.x

The following discussion describes naming procedures in NetWare 4.x Directory Services; however, the concepts and formats are similar to other naming services. You should be somewhat familiar with NetWare Directory Services (see "Directory Services, NetWare"). While NetWare 4.x applications, utilities, and interfaces include functions that simplify object referencing, the following information is useful when moving about through the system or working at operating system level.

Keep in mind that Directory Services provides a tree structure that helps you organize network users and resources (called objects). You climb through the tree to locate users and resources in the same way you climb through a file system directory tree to locate files. For example, a user locates another user in the tree in order to forward an E-mail message. A network administrator locates user accounts in the tree to change some aspect of that account, such as the logon script or security rights.

In NetWare, references to objects are made by their directory tree names. The name specifies exactly where an object is in the directory structure, similar to a house address that specifies a street, city, and country. The default name sequence is shown here using the *type name*:

Common Name.Organizational Unit.Organization.Country

These type names are often abbreviated as shown next. A *common name* is the name of a user's account or resource such as a server or printer. Organizational Unit and Organization are *container objects* that hold other objects, in the same way a directory in a file system holds other directories or files.

CN.OU.O.C

If the user AColgan works in the Sales department, the administrator places her user account in a container called Sales. In the following example, sales is a department in the organization called CambrianCorp.

```
O=CambrianCorp
   └── OU=Sales
          └── CN=AColgan
```

This forms a path in the tree that can be written as:

CN=AColgan.OU=Sales.O=CambrianCorp

However, you can eliminate the type names and abbreviations, as shown here,

AColgan.Sales.CambrianCorp.US

unless there is a chance the system might be confused by the name if the type designators are not there. This will be discussed shortly.

This name forms a unique path constructed from *partial names*. Partial names are the names of containers and leaf objects. Each partial name is separated by a period and explicitly defined with a *type* abbreviation (CN, OU, or O), although you can eliminate these abbreviations, as just mentioned.

Eliminating the type abbreviation produces an *implied* or *typeless* naming context, because you are assuming that the operating system will recognize that AColgan is a

CN (Common Name) and CambrianCorp is an O (Organization). However, the operating system may not always recognize the context you are referring to if you don't use a type abbreviation.

The path formed by the sequence of partial names defines exactly where an object is from the root of the directory tree, much like a DOS filename path identifies exactly where the file is. However, note that NetWare Directory Services names are reversed in order from filename paths. This full path is referred to as the *distinguished name* or *complete name* of the object.

Now we get to an important concept regarding how the operating system infers contexts from the names you type. Note the following:

- The most significant partial name is always interpreted as the Organization (O)
- The least significant partial name is always interpreted as the Common Name (CN)
- All partial names between O and CN are considered Organizational Units (OUs)

You use commands such as CX (Change conteXt) to move about in the directory structure from the command line. So in the following name, TSheldon is interpreted as the CN, CambrianCorp is interpreted as O, and the two partial names between are interpreted as OUs. This command would get you directly to the CambrianCorp container.

CX TSheldon.Administration.DivWest.CambrianCorp

Consider, for example, what happens if you forgot to specify "CambrianCorp" at the end of the context. The operating system would infer that DivWest is the intended target Organization container and switch you to that container. If the DivWest container doesn't branch from the container of your current context, an error occurs.

RELATED ENTRIES   Directory Services; Directory Services, NetWare; Distributed Computing; *and* X.500 Directory Services

Disaster Recovery

Disasters are any occurrence that disturbs access to data and communications. A simple server or communication link failure is a disaster to a company that relies on that server to provide life-saving information or business transaction information. Fires, earthquakes, storms, and theft are all disasters that network managers must prepare for. There are a number of ways to protect data as summarized here:

- *Backups* Backing up data is a necessary requirement. Backups must be brought to an offsite location, but the backups must be protected from theft or loss during their transit. *Replication* of data to other sites over WAN links is another option.

- *Transactions monitoring* A transaction is an update to a record in a database. Transaction monitoring (also called online transactions processing, or OLTP, if it takes place in real time), protects data from corruption if a communication link or system fails during the writing of a transaction. When the system is brought back up, incomplete transactions are backed out. If the database is distributed and writes take place in several locations, any of the links or servers could fail. Two-phase commit procedures ensure that writes are either properly committed in all locations or back-off in all locations.

- *Disk mirroring and duplexing* Mirroring and duplexing provide protection against disk failure in servers. With mirroring, data is written to two disks at once. If one disk goes down, the other takes over until the disk is replaced. With duplexing, the disk drive adapter (channel) is duplicated as well to further protect against hardware failure.

- *Mirrored servers* In this strategy, an entire server is duplicated to protect against the failure of any component. Data is written to both systems simultaneously, and they are interconnected with fast data links to ensure synchronization. If the servers are located in different geographic areas, protection from local disasters such as fire and earthquakes is also facilitated.

- *Duplicate data centers* Some organizations running mission-critical applications duplicate their entire data center to an offsite location to provide recovery from local disasters.

Protecting Communication Links

A communication link keeps services and data at remote sites available. If those services and data are critical to operations, then backup links are required. A backup link can be a line that is always available and in use, or a line that is switched into use when another fails. The type of service used depends on data traffic requirements during the communication failure. Most carriers provide packages that include automatic line failure recovery. The types of available lines are listed here.

- *Switched voice line* A line that is established only when needed over the normal telephone network using modems.

- *Switched digital line* A digital service that sets up circuits only when needed.

- *Dedicated voice line* A dedicated line over an analog voice line that is always available.

- *Dedicated digital line* A dedicated digital line that is always available.

- *Packet-switching services* A packet-switched network provides its own redundant lines, but you might want to have two or more connections into the service.

RELATED ENTRIES   Backup and Data Archiving; Carrier Services; Disk Mirroring and Duplexing; Transaction Processing; *and* Two-Phase Commit

Disk Arrays

See Redundant Arrays of Inexpensive Disks.

Diskless Workstations

Diskless workstations are inexpensive computers without floppy disk drives or hard disk drives. They provide users with network access at a reasonable price, and they offer data security because users can't download data to floppy disks and carry it offsite. Diskless workstations are a consideration for use by temporary employees or installation in unsupervised areas.

When using diskless workstations, you'll need a network interface card that supports the use of a remote boot programmable read-only memory (PROM) chip. Most interface cards have this option, but it's a good idea to make sure. Remote boot PROMs cost about $50 and are added to cards as an option. The PROM allows the workstation to boot from a boot file located on the network server, which means that cards that use PROMs immediately connect with the network cable and server when you turn them on.

Disk Mirroring and Duplexing

Disk mirroring and duplexing provide protection against disk failures. Mirroring duplicates data to a second disk as shown in Figure D-14. You attach a second disk to the same controller and the operating system, such as Novell NetWare, writes data to both disks simultaneously. Should one disk fail, the other can continue to provide service until it is replaced.

A disk duplexing configuration consists of duplicate disk controller cards, one for each disk drive, as shown in Figure D-15. This provides the same level of protection as mirroring with the added benefit of duplicated disk channels.

RELATED ENTRIES   Disks, Partitions, and Volumes Under NetWare; Disk Storage Systems

Disks, Partitions, and Volumes Under NetWare

NetWare servers support a number of different disk configurations. All of these configurations support some form of fault tolerance in which the data is written in two places simultaneously, as discussed here:

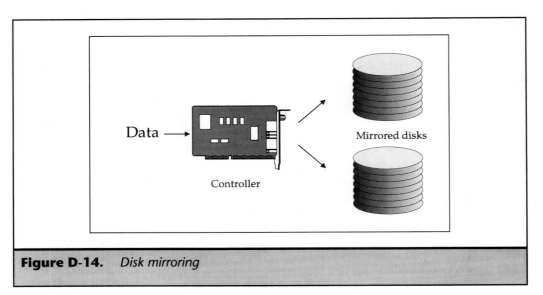

Figure D-14. *Disk mirroring*

- *Disk mirroring* A primary drive and a backup mirroring drive share the same disk controller.
- *Disk duplexing* The primary drive and the backup mirroring drive are both attached to their own controller.

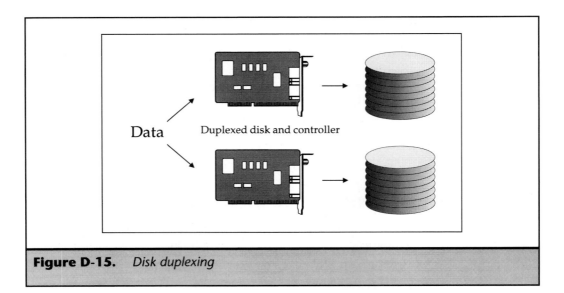

Figure D-15. *Disk duplexing*

■ *RAID systems* RAID systems are typically external subsystems that attach to a controller card installed in the server. Refer to the operator's manual for specific instructions on installing and managing RAID systems.

The section "Disk Mirroring and Duplexing" (earlier in this book) illustrates the first two configurations. Note that some disk controllers handle mirroring on their own, and they do so more efficiently than the mirroring provided by the NetWare operating system. You set up this mirroring when installing the disk controller.

Device Numbering

The drives in a NetWare server have specific numbers that identify them to the operating system. The five-digit numbering scheme is defined here:

■ The first two digits are assigned by the operating system when you select a driver for a disk controller. They identify which driver is used.

■ The third digit is the number of the controller board or host adapter in the server, but not its channel number. The first driver you load becomes the first board in the numbering scheme, so make sure you always use the same driver load order.

■ The fourth digit represents the controller number. On SCSI systems, more than one controller may be attached to the host bus adapter.

■ The fifth digit represents the actual disk attached to the controller.

You use these disk ID numbers when configuring (mirroring and duplexing) and maintaining the drives in the server. NetWare may display the number when a disk error occurs. For example, you might see the following device information associated with an error message:

Device #3 (20101)

The number in parentheses is the device number, whereas #3 is a logical number that relates to the order in which the disk drivers were loaded. If you change the load order, the logical number and the third digit of the device number change, so be aware of these changes when identifying drives.

Figure D-16 shows device numbering for a duplexed system. Figure D-17 illustrates device numbering for embedded SCSI drives when two host adapters are mounted in a server that has an existing controller (ST506, ESDI, or IDE). Figure D-18 illustrates device numbering for SCSI systems that use non-embedded controllers. In this case, each controller supports multiple drives, all of which are attached to a single host adapter.

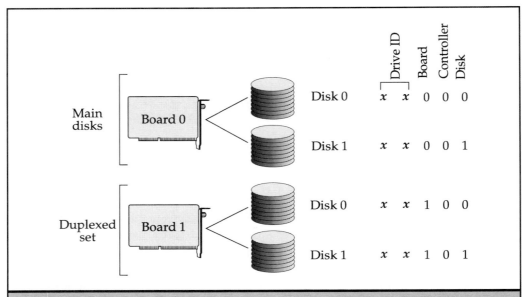

Figure D-16. *Device numbering for duplexed ESDI or IDE disk systems under NetWare*

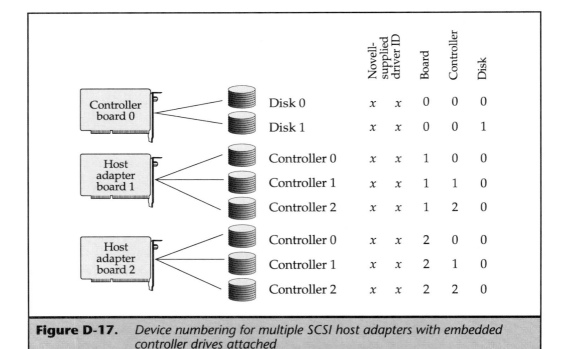

Figure D-17. *Device numbering for multiple SCSI host adapters with embedded controller drives attached*

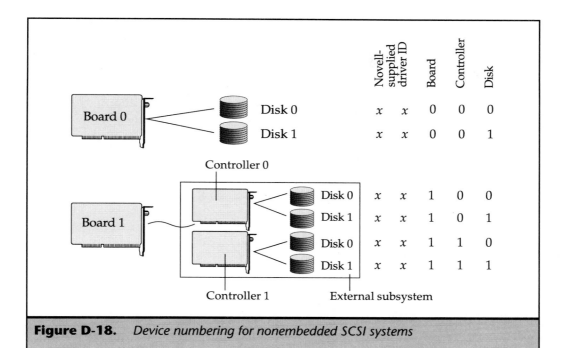

Figure D-18. *Device numbering for nonembedded SCSI systems*

Logical Device Numbering

The logical device number defines the sequential order in which disk drivers are loaded. When the first driver is loaded, the first disk attached to the controller for that driver becomes device number 0. The second disk attached to that controller becomes device number 1. When the next disk driver is loaded, the first disk attached to its corresponding controller becomes device number 2. This sequential numbering continues up to the last drive. Be careful to load drivers in the same order every time you start the system to avoid confusion. To maintain correct logical device numbers, make sure disk drivers are specified in their proper load order in the CONFIG.NCF file.

Partitions

Partitions are divisions of disks. Typically, the first disk in a server contains a small DOS partition for startup purposes, and the remainder of the disk forms the first NetWare partition. All other disks in the partition are identified by a physical partition number and a logical partition number. The physical partition number is a sequential number that identifies each partition, one after another. The logical partition number identifies mirrored or duplexed pairs.

Each partition is assigned a Hot Fix redirection area that is two percent of the partition's space. When blocks are found to be failing or defective, the NetWare operating system moves data in the blocks to the Hot Fix redirection area. If you are using an older drive, you might want to increase the redirection area size, since the disk might be more susceptible to block failure than a newer drive.

Figure D-19 shows a system with two controllers and two drives attached to each controller. The first controller and its two drives form the primary data storage area. Note that a small DOS partition exists on the first drive. The second controller and its drives form the duplexing system. Each drive has its own partition numbers. The DOS partition is physical partition 0, and the remaining partitions are numbered from 1 to 4. However, NetWare assigns logical partition numbers to mirrored drives, so partitions 1 and 3 are viewed as logical partition 1, and physical partitions 2 and 4 are viewed as logical partition 2.

These logical partition numbers are important when viewing information about mirrored disks. Logical mirrored partitions are listed in the INSTALL and MONITOR server utilities as follows:

Mirrored: Logical Partition #1
Mirrored: Logical Partition #2

However, the physical partitions that make up a mirrored set are listed as shown next. Note the device number at the end of each line that identifies the driver, controller, and disk attached to it.

In Sync -   NetWare partition 1 on Device #0 (20000)
In Sync -   NetWare partition 3 on Device #1 (20100)

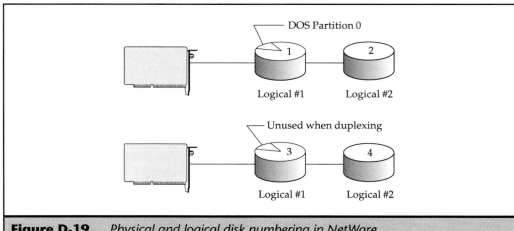

Figure D-19.   *Physical and logical disk numbering in NetWare*

Each NetWare physical partition contains its own Hot Fix redirection area. Any messages you see relating to Hot Fix redirection use physical partition numbers.

As with logical device numbers, logical partition numbers are dynamic. If you disable and then enable mirroring and duplexing, you must reboot the server, otherwise the logical numbers will change.

Volumes

Above the partition level are volumes. A volume is part of a partition. It may take up all of the partition or only part of it. A volume may *span* from one partition to part or all of another partition. The space in a volume is divided into equal blocks that can range from 4 KB to 64 KB in size. A volume used entirely for one or a few large database files benefits from large block sizes, while volumes with many small files benefit from volumes with small block sizes.

Volume Segments

Volumes can extend over physical partitions. A single disk can contain up to 8 volume segments that belong to one or more volumes. Each volume can consist of up to 32 volume segments. The first segment of a volume on a disk is segment 0, the second is segment 1, and so on.

Since segments can span drives, expanding a volume is a simple matter of adding a new segment to it. But spanned volumes should be duplexed to guard against disk failure. A failure of one disk in the spanned volume prevents access to all segments in the volume.

Volume FATs and DETs

Volumes consist of the file allocation table (FAT) and the directory entry table (DET). The FAT simply identifies every block in which a file is located. Files might be broken up into several parts and placed in noncontiguous blocks. The FAT tracks the blocks for the file. Each entry in the FAT indicates a block of the file's information and points to the next FAT entry, which indicates the next block and the next FAT entry. NetWare maintains two copies of the FAT, in case one becomes corrupted.

The DET contains directory information for the volume. Blocks that are part of the DET are designated as either directory types or file types. Directory-type entries contain subdirectory information, and file-type entries contain information such as filename, attributes, time and date stamps, and size. There are two DETs per volume to guard against corruption.

NetWare places copies of the FAT and part of the DET in cache memory to improve performance.

Name Space Support

Name space support in NetWare supports the storage of non-DOS files, such as files created on Macintosh, OS/2, UNIX, or FTAM systems, on NetWare volumes. When name space support is added to a volume, *every* DOS file-type and directory-type entry on the volume gets an additional directory entry. Each additional name space support installed adds another directory entry to the file and directory entries. Because of this, you should place name space support on separate volumes from DOS files. The most important benefit is that DOS files not needing name space support don't use extra disk space.

File Compression

By default, the File Compression field (switch) is set on when creating volumes. You can then flag files you want the system to automatically compress. In most cases, you should use file compression, but check with your application vendors to ensure that compression is compatible. You may need to store some applications on volumes where compression is not used. Note that this option allows the volume to support file compression, but you must still flag files you want to compress using SET commands. Plan on placing all files you need to compress in a single volume.

Block Suballocation

With the Block Suballocation field set on, the volume stores files more efficiently by storing files in smaller increments than the value set in the Volume Block Size field. For example, assuming block suballocation is off and a volume block size of 4 KB exists, a 6.5 KB file would still require 8 KB of disk space. With block suballocation on, that file requires only 6.5 KB of disk space. Any "leftover" free blocks are used in the future to store fragments from other files.

The combination of file compression and block suballocation maximizes the disk space on a volume.

RELATED ENTRIES   NetWare; Partitions (Disks), NetWare

Disk Storage Systems

The disk system in a server must provide superior performance in networked environments in which many users are accessing the disk. Network operating systems should use techniques that improve disk performance, such as disk caching, elevator seeking, and file allocation table caching. Disk features are described here:

- *Elevator seeking* sequences disk read and write requests so that the disk read/write head moves in a relatively smooth pattern from one read or write to the next, rather than jumping back and forth to service each read or write in the order they arrived from users.

- *File allocation table caching* moves information about the location of files on disk into memory where it is easier to look up.

- A high-speed bus such as the MCA or EISA bus provides quick transfer of information among the server and its peripherals. Superservers have proprietary single- or dual-bus architectures that improve performance considerably and handle multiple devices simultaneously.

■ The construction of a disk drive and the methods used to store information determines disk access speed. Higher-capacity drives with advanced encoding methods provide better throughput.

Several standard disk interfaces are described in the following sections.

THE ST506 INTERFACE   The ST506 interface was one of the first disk drive interfaces used in personal computers. It was originally marketed by Seagate Technologies. The ST506 interface typically uses modified frequency modulation (MFM) when writing data, and has a data transfer rate of 5 Mbits/sec. If run length limited (RLL) encoding is used, data storage and transfer rates increase. ST506 controllers were commonly used in 80286 and early 80386 systems, but they are decreasing in popularity because of their slow transfer rates. They are not recommended for servers with high traffic requirements.

THE ESDI INTERFACE   The Enhanced Small Device Interface (ESDI) is similar to the ST506 interface, but it provides 512 bytes per sector and 34 to 36 sectors per track. Its transfer rates are in the range of 10 to 15 Mbits/sec. ESDI disk systems use high-capacity drives with storage capabilities greater than 100 MB. Up to two ESDI drives can attach to an ESDI controller.

THE SCSI INTERFACE   The Small Computer System Interface (SCSI) differs radically from the ST506 interface and ESDI. Up to seven devices, such as hard drives, tape drives, and CD-ROM drives, can attach to and share the same SCSI host adapter, which takes up only one slot in the server. The adapter provides a shared bus that all peripherals use to pass data to and from the system. The bus is 8, 16, or even 32 bits wide and supports transfer rates up to 32 Mbits/sec. A new SCSI standard called SCSI-II provides even faster data throughput.

The SCSI *host adapter* provides bus services (a connection point) for intelligent devices. Intelligent devices, such as SCSI disk drives, optical disks, and backup systems, contain their own control circuitry and can work on a task while the host adapter sends commands or handles data throughput from other devices. The SCSI adapter monitors the data throughput and commands between the system and the SCSI devices. Each device handles only the requests assigned to it. Because the control circuitry is built into each SCSI device, configuration and compatibility issues are minimized. Theoretically, you can plug any SCSI device into any SCSI controller, but it's best to check compatibility and software drive requirements before doing so.

THE IDE INTERFACE   The Intelligent Drive Electronics (IDE) interface is a hybrid that combines features of the other interfaces and offers new features of its own. IDE devices were originally designed as low-cost alternatives to ESDI devices. However, like SCSI devices, IDE devices have their own control circuitry. They attach to an IDE adapter, which is inexpensive and is often built right onto the motherboard of PC systems, saving a slot. Systems that have VL-Bus slots often include IDE controllers that fit in the VL-Bus for 32-bit access.

An IDE adapter supports only two devices. Because IDE is relatively inexpensive to implement, most of the low-priced systems on the market today use it. But don't equate low price with inferior performance. When both price and performance are considered, IDE is a practical solution. The IDE interface operates at around 4 Mbits/sec, close to the SCSI rate. A typical IDE drive has an access rate of 16 ms (milliseconds). Some have built-in intelligent caches to improve performance.

RELATED ENTRIES   Redundant Arrays of Inexpensive Disks; Striping

Distance-Vector Algorithm (DVA) Routing Protocol

The Bellman-Ford algorithm is used to calculate routes for transmitting packets through networks with multiple paths to a destination. Routing decisions are based on the least number of "hops" to a destination. Tables are built by routers and exchanged with other routers, which use the routing information to construct a map of the network.

RELATED ENTRY   Routing Protocols

Distributed Computing

A distributed computing system is an evolutionary growth from centralized computer systems and client-server computer systems, as shown in Figure D-20. Distributed computing is basically client-server computing on a wide scale. Data is not located in one server, but many servers, and these servers might be at geographically dispersed areas, connected by wide area network (WAN) links. Such systems are often called enterprise networks because they join the many formerly autonomous computer systems in workgroups, departments, branches, and divisions of an organization.

Why would an organization choose to disperse its data in this way? There are a number of advantages:

■ The distributed computing model assumes that an organization has many types of data, collected at autonomous sites, but requiring access by users at many sites. With data at decentralized sites, local managers maintain control over familiar data.

■ The cost of WAN links is another motivation for decentralizing data. If a group of users at a remote site access the same data often, it makes sense to locate the data at that site, rather than provide access over slow and costly WAN links. WAN links still provide occasional access for remote users, however.

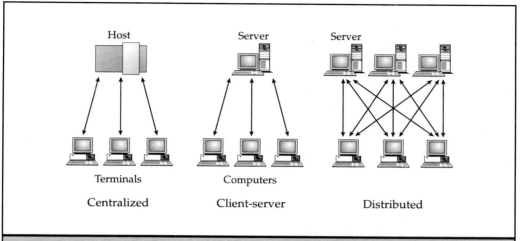

Host   Server   Server

Terminals   Computers

Centralized   Client-server   Distributed

Figure D-20. *Distributed computing has evolved from centralized and client-server computing*

- Distributing data provides protection from loss or downed systems. Data replicated to other locations improves access for users at those locations and provides redundancy.

- A distributed system takes advantage of client-server mechanisms that support distributed processing, which is the ability to involve many different computers in the completion of a processing task.

- Distributed systems have hardware advantages. Inexpensive personal computers perform their own processing and in the client-server environment, relieve the server of many tasks. Using multiple servers platforms provides flexibility in upgrades and hardware changes not possible with large centralized systems.

There are also disadvantages, summarized here. Some of these disadvantages can be overcome with improvements in processing power, faster wide area links, and improved software.

- Keeping data synchronized over distributed systems is a complex task.

- New methods are required to access heterogeneous systems and foreign data structures as formerly autonomous systems are made available on the enterprise network.

- Distributed systems require more management and supervision. The system is often built by integrating existing systems and creating chaos, rather than designing a new system from the top down.

- There is a certain feeling of security and organization that managers get from centralized systems. Managers of distributed systems may feel a loss of control and general confusion about data location, content, and management.

- Organizations with large mainframes and legacy data will have a tough time making the transition to distributed systems. Will the existing systems become part of the new system, or does it make sense to convert information to new systems?

It would appear that converting an existing system to a distributed system simply does not make sense. However, deciding to go one way or the other is no longer an option. The evolutionary trend is towards distributed systems as bandwidth increases on the local and wide area networks and as operating systems and applications integrate features for implementing distributed computing environments. The task is to make the transition as painless as possible.

The client-server model provides the architecture required to deploy distributed systems as discussed under the heading "Client-Server Computing." Figure D-21 illustrates the many ways computers in a distributed, client-server environment can access one another. The mainframe may hold legacy data, or it may serve as a centralized data warehouse (or both). It makes specific data available on staging systems that are accessed by users at local or remote sites. Staging systems and local servers reduce workloads on systems that are accessed by the entire enterprise. Users at one site can also access data on staging systems or servers at any other site. In addition, users can communicate with other users to exchange E-mail and form workgroups. For more details, refer to the "Information Warehouse" heading later in this book.

As mentioned, a distributed computing environment is similar to a client-server environment, except that there are many servers and many clients who access any one of those servers at any time. The distributed environment needs the following components:

- The network *platform* that supports a variety of multivendor products and communication protocols

- Application interfaces that let users make requests to servers using real-time connection-oriented methods, or message-passing systems that deliver responses on a more relaxed schedule

- A *directory naming service* that keeps track of resources and information and where they are located

- A *time service* to synchronize events among servers that hold related information

- A database management system (DBMS) that supports advanced features such as *partitioning* and *replication* to provide the distribution of data and ensure the availability, reliability, and protection of that data

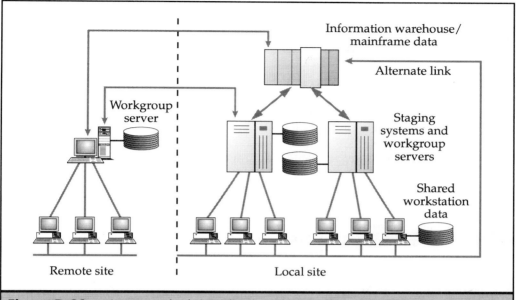

Information warehouse/
mainframe data

Alternate link

Workgroup
server

Staging
systems and
workgroup
servers

Shared
workstation
data

Remote site

Local site

Figure D-21. *Access methods in a distributed computing environment*

D

■ Security features such as authentication and authorization, as well as trust
relationships between systems so users can access multiple servers and
databases without the need to prove their identity every time they access a
remote resource

One aspect of distributed computing is the ability of a client system to search out
other computer systems on the network to process all or part of a task. The program
might be distributed to computers that are either idle, or are better suited to the task. A
distributed application is one that can run different components on different
computers attached to the network. In this respect, distributed computing is similar to
multiprocessing. In multiprocessing, a computer system such as a server has several
processors that can split up and handle different parts of the processing task.
Distributed processing can also do this, except that there is potentially much more
computing power available on the network. In addition, experts envision being able to
use the memory spaces on different computers when necessary. For example, if five
systems are sitting idle with 8 MB of memory each, 40 MB of memory is available to a
distributed application that can use it. Of course, high-speed network links are
required to make this strategy worthwhile, but faster networks using fiber-optic
interfaces are making this possible.

Distributed Databases

Server-based database management systems (DBMS) and mainframe-based information warehouses are the primary purveyors of information in the distributed environment. In the old model, users accessed their local database server, but in the new model, users access any server in the enterprise. Providing transparent access is the trick. In addition, distributed databases typically retain some level of local autonomy so that managers at the site can secure and protect the resource appropriately. See the main "Distributed Database" heading for a more complete discussion of this topic.

A number of products are available that provide interfaces for a variety of front-end applications to a variety of back-end servers, no matter what the interface, language, or communication protocol. These are discussed under "Database Connectivity APIs and Middleware."

Distributed File Systems

A distributed file system operates in a peer-to-peer mode to allow users working at workstations to act as both a client and server. Servers mount or publish directories that client machines can access. Once a server system is accessed, its directories appear to the client as if they are local drives. The three primary distributed file systems are listed here (and discussed further under the heading "Distributed File Systems" later in this book).

■ *Network File System (NFS)*   NFS was originally created by Sun Microsystems, Inc. as a file-sharing system for TCP/IP networks.

■ *Andrew File System (AFS)*   AFS is architecturally similar to NFS. AFS was developed by the Information Technology Center at Carnegie Mellon University. Its current development and marketing is in the hands of Transarc Corporation, which is made up of former ITC staff. AFS has some enhancements that NFS does not and uses a different client-caching scheme.

■ *Distributed File System (DFS)*   DFS is a version of AFS. It serves as the file system component in the Open Software Foundation's Distributed Computing Environment (DCE).

Security in Distributed Environments

Once you've distributed data, adequate security procedures such as authentication, authorization, and encryption must be used. It is assumed that some users will need to access systems at remote sites, or that database replication is necessary, and that this will occur over public data networks. Therefore, the following security measures must be considered. See "Security" later in this book for more details on these topics.

■ *Authentication* lets a user log on once, then gain access to any system at any location they are authorized to use. Authentication procedures provide a secure way for one server to trust that another server has properly identified a user.

■ *Authorization* provides a way to grant users access to remote resources based on their role or level of authority. In this way, the administrator doesn't need to know in advance each and every server that the user might access. Consequently, it is not necessary to define access rights at each location. The user simply belongs to defined groups with defined access rights, or has a "role" that authorizes various types of access.

■ *Certification* techniques provide the means by which servers can trust each other and trust the users that are accessing their resources.

■ *Cryptography* protects transmitted data from eavesdroppers.

■ *Privacy Enhanced Mail (PEM)* messages are encrypted for security reasons.

■ *Digital signatures* provide a way for users to be sure messages they receive from other users are authentic.

■ *Firewalls* are created by filtering the packets sent through a bridge or router connected to a wide area link.

Distributed Computing Applications

There are a number of applications that take advantage of distributed computing. Groupware applications, for example, let users work with the same data at the same time or take advantage of the network to easily share information. Document processing, scheduling, electronic mail, and workflow software are examples of groupware. Some applications automatically integrate data from systems attached to the network. Object linking and embedding (OLE) in Windows for Workgroups and Windows NT lets users place information in their document that is stored at other locations on the network and updated by other users. When the original information changes, the information in other users' documents changes as well. For more information, refer to "Client-Server Computing," "Distributed File Systems," "Information Warehouse," and "Transaction Processing."

Distributed Computing Environment (DCE), OSF

The Open Software Foundation (OSF) is an organization that plays a key role in the development of standards for interoperable products. The OSF Distributed Computing Environment (DCE) is a set of "enabling" software that hides the difference between multivendor products, technologies, and standards, enabling developers to create applications that work in distributed client-server environments. DCE provides an independence from operating systems and networks with an open development environment.

An enterprise-wide distributed environment typically consists of multivendor computers, operating systems, and applications, all linked to a common network platform. Figure D-22 illustrates such a *heterogeneous environment.* The trick is to make all these resources available transparently to users. Such networks can be huge in scope and subject to variations in data access speeds often dictated by wide area network connections. Synchronization of data and other problems can crop up that complicate the task of the distributed application developer. This is one area where DCE helps. In addition, users should be able to access any database on any computer with any front-end application they choose. Interoperability problems should be handled in the background and hidden from the user. One way to approach this is to build a *common infrastructure.* Developers then have a common platform to which they can build products that interoperate with products built by other vendors. OSF's goal with DCE is to create this common infrastructure.

DCE is a set of integrated services that supports the use, development, and maintenance of distributed applications. DCE makes those services available throughout the enterprise network and lets users take advantage of all the computer resources available on it.

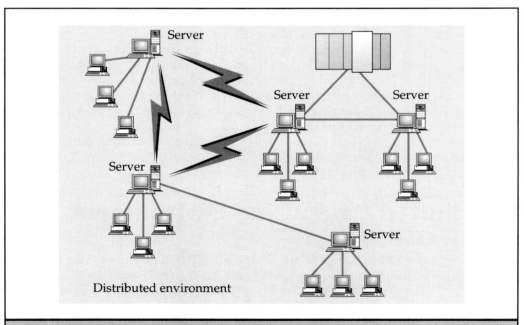

Figure D-22. *A heterogeneous environment*

- DCE is operating system-independent and network-independent. It is compatible with environments already in place in most cases.

- Major vendors such as IBM, DEC, Hewlett-Packard, and others provide products based on DCE.

- DCE provides the interoperability basis for X/Open's Common Applications Environment (CAE), a set of international open systems specifications.

DCE is driven by the movement to open systems, which is the integration and interoperability of diverse, multivendor, networked systems and products. You can contrast OSF DCE with SunSoft's Open Network Computing (ONC) environment. See "Open Network Computing, SunSoft."

A large selection of applications that support DCE should appear in the 1994-1995 time frame. DCE services are designed to port to other operating systems, including Windows NT and DEC's Virtual Memory System (VMS). It is also a part of IBM's open systems strategy. With DCE on the Multiple Virtual Storage (MVS) operating system, an IBM mainframe can be a server or client in a distributed environment.

OSF acquired its technology through a process called Request for Technology. Major hardware and software vendors submitted their technologies and OSF picked the best. A list is provided here:

- Hewlett-Packard and DEC's remote procedure call (RPC)

- DECdns directory naming services

- X.500 directory naming services from Siemens AG

- Kerberos security services from MIT with Hewlett-Packard extensions

- Andrew File System from Transarc

- LM/X PC integrated technology from Microsoft

- Concert Multi-Threads Architecture from DEC

- DECdts time services from DEC

The DCE architecture is shown in Figure D-23. It is a layered model that integrates a set of technologies described in the remainder of this section. At the bottom are the most basic services (such as operating systems) and at the top are applications. The services provided by DCE are designed to mask the complexity of multivendor network environments and let information easily flow to where it is needed.

DCE Components

The DCE services are grouped into two categories: development tools and data-sharing services. The development tools help software developers create end-user services needed for distributed computing. They include the following:

- Remote procedure calls

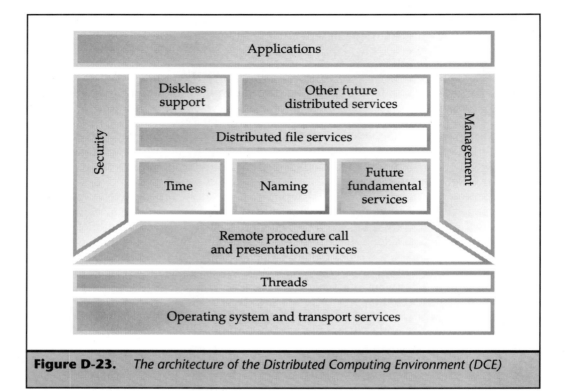

Figure D-23. *The architecture of the Distributed Computing Environment (DCE)*

- Directory services
- Time services
- Security services
- Threads services

Data-sharing services provide end users with capabilities built upon the development tools to easily access information. They include the following:

- Distributed file system
- Diskless support

DCE fits into the OSI model at layers 5 (Session), layer 6 (Presentation), and layer 7 (Application). The ISO Open System Interconnect (OSI) model defines standard protocols for multivendor interoperability. DCE allows programmers to use the standard ISO services, while shielding them from the complexity of the services.

Remote Procedure Calls (RPC)

The OSF remote procedure calls are tools for creating client-server applications that can run procedures on other computers attached to a network. OSF's RPC extends the local procedure model by supporting direct calls to procedures on remote systems, enabling programmers to develop distributed applications as easily as traditional, single-system programs. RPC presentation services mask the differences between data representation on different machines, allowing programs to work across heterogeneous systems. OSF's RPC includes the RPC facility and a compiler.

RPC lets clients interact with multiple servers, and allows servers to handle multiple clients simultaneously. A client, for example, can involve several computers on the network to help complete a processing task. RPCs help break a task down into smaller components that can run on different systems, thus taking advantage of the distributed computing environment. Threads are an important part of this capability. An operating system and application that supports threads can perform multiple processes at the same time, rather than one process after another.

Threads Service

The threads service provides portability features that support concurrent processing, allowing an application to perform many actions simultaneously. While one thread executes a remote procedure call, another thread can process user input. The thread service is suited to dealing with multiple clients in client-server-based applications.

Distributed Directory Services (DDS)

The primary directory service for DCE is DDS, which provides a single naming model throughout the distributed environment so users can identify resources such as servers, files, disks, and print queues by name, and without the need to know their location in the network. DDS has the following features:

- The X.500 global naming system is integrated into OSF's directory service
- Multiple copies of the directory database can exist on different systems to guard against system failure and ensure that name information is close to users in geographically diverse environments, thus reducing expensive WAN links. Changes are automatically propagated to all replicas of the database
- Lookup results are cached to improve performance

The services also provide security and are scalable to accommodate growing networks. Transport independence allows DDS to work over a wide range of transports in LAN and WAN environments.

DCE RPC applications can use one of three Directory Services: the OSI X.500 directory service, the TCP/IP Domain Name Service (DNS), and the RPC-based DCE Cell Directory Services (CDS). DCE also provides tools for building distributed mail applications using OSI X.400 as a delivery mechanism to other organizations. In

D

addition, the DCE distributed file system can use OSI FTAM (File Transfer and Access Method) to access different file systems.

Time Services

Time Services lets applications schedule activities and determine event sequences and durations. The distributed time services keeps track of time in networks and determines the accuracy associated with each clock used to synchronize time. The service provides fault-tolerant clock synchronization for systems in both local and wide area networks. In other words, servers with faulty clocks are identified and their time values are not used during synchronizations. To support distributed sites using the Network Time Protocol (NTP), the OSF Time Service also permits the use of time values from outside sources.

Security Service

In a distributed environment where activities span multiple hosts with multiple operating systems, authentication and authorization require an independent security service that can be trusted by many hosts. OSF's DCE Security Service integrates with the DCE distributed components and data-sharing components. It provides the network with three conventional services: authentication, authorization, and user account management. These facilities are made available through a secure means of communication that ensures both integrity and privacy.

- *Secure RPC* OSF's RPC supports secure communication in distributed environments by detecting corrupted messages.

- *Kerberos Authentication* The authentication service is based on the Kerberos system from MIT's Project Athena. Kerberos is a trusted service that validates the identity of a user or service, preventing fraudulent requests.

- *Authorization Tools* This integrated set of tools gives applications the ability to determine whether a user should have access to resources. The tools provide a simple and consistent way to manage access control information.

- *User Registry* The User Registry handles user account information in distributed, multivendor environments by providing a single, scalable system for consolidating and managing user information. The use of unique user names and passwords across the distributed environment is ensured.

Security services allows multiple hosts and operating systems to trust the authenticity of requests made across the network. The User Registry provides a single repository of user account information that prevents conflicting logons and passwords. Users can be identified by the privileges or by group membership. Like the Distributed Directory Services, the User Registry is replicated around the network to provide availability and responsiveness.

Distributed File System (DFS)

The DFS is an optional OSF's key information-sharing component that uses the services described above. It makes global file access possible over the network. It provides a uniform name space, file location transparency, and performs across long distances and with large numbers of users. Files and directories are replicated invisibly on multiple machines to protect against file server failure. DFS is derived from the Andrew File System (AFS), and it is built on the components discussed above. DFS interoperates with the Network File System (NFS) from Sun Microsystems, Inc. See "Distributed File Systems" later in this book for more information.

Diskless Support

The OSF DFS accommodates diskless workstations and provides well-defined, general-purpose protocols for diskless support.

RELATED ENTRIES   Directory Services; Distributed Computing; Distributed File Systems; Open Network Computing, SunSoft; Remote Procedure Call; *and* Security

D

Distributed Database

A distributed computing system consists of data located at multiple sites. Users should be able to access that data without regard to its location. After all, users are interested in results, not the details of the computer network. General guidelines for developing distributed database systems are listed here and were originally outlined by Chris J. Date, one of the designers of relational database systems.

- *Local autonomy* allows each site to maintain an independent nature so data and resources can be secured, protected, and managed by local authorities.

- *Noncentralization* eliminates central data sites that represent a single point of failure.

- *Continuous operation* provide services to users, even during backup.

- *Transparency* hides the location of the data from users so they don't need to be concerned where that data is or how to get to it.

- *Fragmentation* (partitioning) provides a way to split the database and store it at multiple sites.

- *Replication* provides a way to copy multiple fragments of the database to multiple sites.

- *Distributed query processing* provides a way for users to query remote sites using the best path to the site and the best resources to satisfy the query.

- *Distributed transaction processing* provides a way to ensure that writes to multiple databases are correctly written on all databases, or backed out if a failure occurs anywhere.

■ *Hardware independence* implies support for multivendor computer systems and platforms.

■ *Operating system independence* implies support for a number of operating systems.

■ *Network independence* implies support for multiple network topologies and communication protocols.

■ *DBMS independence* allows users to access any database management system from their client application. See "Database Connectivity APIs and Middleware."

Once data is distributed, transaction processing, fragmentation, and replication measures are put in place to ensure the reliability, availability, and protection of data, as described in the following sections.

Client-Server Connections

The following methods are used to provide connections between clients and servers and exchange request and response information. One of the following connection methods is used to exchange messages.

■ *Connection-oriented "circuits"* are used to establish a communication channel over a network so two systems can exchange information in real-time or maintain a continuous connection until transactions are complete.

■ *Connectionless datagram services* are used when the exchange of information is not time critical. A "circuit" is not created. Instead, information is packaged in datagrams and transmitted along a best path to the destination.

A *remote procedure call (RPC) mechanism* provides the means for an application process on one system to invoke an application process on another system. The calling party (client) makes a request to the server, then waits for a response using either connection-oriented or connectionless services. When the client gets the response, it then issues another request if necessary.

Store-and-forward messaging systems have relaxed time-constraints. A user's application sends a request to a server in an E-mail-like message. When the server receives the message, it processes the request and returns a response to the user or the user's mailbox. The user picks up the message at any time. This method assumes the server has various stored-procedures that users can run and is practical for mobile users that need to access information on company databases.

In a heterogeneous environment, making these connections is not always easy. There are a variety of communication protocols, application interfaces, and component requirements that make integration difficult. Development tools and environments for distributed computing exist. The Open Software Foundation's (OSF) Distributed Computing Environment (DCE) is one. Another is SunSoft's Open Network Computing (ONC) environment. Both are discussed elsewhere in this book.

In the database connectivity arena, so-called standard interfaces have subtle differences that prevent one vendor's client application from accessing data on another vendor's DBMS. Several vendors and standards groups are working to alleviate the problem. The SQL Access Group (SAG) is promoting ANSI and OSI standards for database connections. Microsoft is promoting its Open Database Connectivity (ODBC) which provides common interfaces for Windows applications. In addition, IBM is promoting its Distributed Relational Database Architecture.

Transaction Processing

When data is distributed over many database servers, various protection mechanisms are required to ensure that data is properly written to all databases. For example, consider a customer account balance that is updated at three separate remote databases. If a connection to any database fails during the transaction write phase, the databases will be out of synchronization. How is this situation detected and corrected? Transaction Processing (TP) monitors a procedure called two-phase commit and solves the problem to some extent.

Real-time transaction processing over distributed systems requires a *two-phase commit* procedure that ensures the integrity of data when writing the transactions to multiple databases. Each database involved must authorize the transaction before it is committed to any of the databases. If the transaction succeeds, it is committed, otherwise the transaction is rolled back. Like fault-tolerant systems, two-phase commit protects against systems that fail during the writing of a transaction, or allow an operator to abort a transaction and return the database to its previous state. A *transaction monitor* tracks the transaction as follows:

1. Write instructions are sent to each database and the transaction monitor waits for a response to ensure that all systems are ready to write. The transaction is aborted at this point if all systems don't respond.

2. Assuming all respond, the transaction monitor then instructs the databases to write, then waits for a confirmation from each system that data was written successfully.

3. If the response is not heard from all databases (due to line or system failure), the transaction monitor orders all databases to roll their writes back.

Refer to the heading "Transaction Processing" later in this book for more information on this topic.

Partitioning and Replication

Partitioning is a method of splitting a database into related blocks of information and replication is the process of copying those blocks to other locations. A master database is still maintained at one site and a partition is a portion of that database that is replicated to another site. Partitioning and replication are used for the following reasons:

- To make specific data more readily available to users at other sites
- To protect the data by duplicating it
- To provide alternate sources for the data should primary or secondary sites fail

Replication can provide an alternative to real-time two-phase commit techniques described earlier. Two-phase commit can provide immediate synchronization of databases but it has considerable overhead that significantly affects performance. In addition, a persistent problem such as WAN link errors can cause numerous transactions to abort. Replication provides a non-real-time alternative that updates databases on a periodic basis. Update schedules are set by network administrators, or take place when a server that was down (or lost its link) is restored.

Unfortunately, partitioning a relational database is not an easy procedure. The technique is more appropriate for object-oriented databases as described in the next section. The procedure for relational databases is to replicate the entire database, rather than update individual fields.

Distributed Object-Oriented Systems

Object-oriented systems provide a unique solution for storing data and creating applications in enterprise environments. Object-oriented systems have the following features:

- *Objects* are abstractions of real-world entities such as people in a customer database, invoices in an accounting system, or printers and servers in a network Directory Services database.

- An object holds data and includes a set of *procedures* that are invoked to manipulate or report on the data within the object.

- There are *classes* and *subclasses* of objects. A class is first defined, and it serves as a template for creating objects in that class. For example, an inventory for a computer warehouse would have a class called "computer."

    A subclass is a specialization of a class in a hierarchical structure. A subclass called "laptops" might be defined under the "computer" class in the warehouse inventory.

- *Inheritance* is an important aspect of the class hierarchy. Any subclass created under a class inherits the characteristics of its parent class, and can have some special characteristics of its own. Inheritance eases development by promoting reusable objects.

- Objects interact with each other by sending *messages* that invoke object procedures.

- Objects are *polymorphic* in that a message might be invoked differently by different objects. For example, invoking a print command for a customer object prints a name and address, while invoking a print command for an invoice object prints the invoice.

The information in an object is encapsulated and can only be changed by invoking the procedures that belong to the object. An external entity cannot bypass these procedures and change the internal data on its own. This creates a highly controlled environment that is easy to maintain and build applications around.

Because objects hold data in field-like entries, you could compare an object to a record in a database, but that is where the similarities end. Objects have their own internal procedures for working with the data they contain, whereas any manipulation of a relational database is handled by external procedures. This gives the object a certain amount of independence. If you move an object, the procedures needed to extract its information move with it.

More importantly for distributed systems, many different applications can access the information within an object by simply invoking its procedures. Now all you have to do is put data in objects and define the procedures for getting the data out. These procedures are then invoked by relatively simple applications that send messages to objects via a server. Creating these applications is easy because the procedures have already been defined and created as part of the objects. In addition, objects are inherently distributable because they are independent of one another, unlike a database in which large chunks of data are contained within a single file. You can "put some objects here and put some objects there." An interesting feature of this approach is that designers don't need to know in advance where the data objects will be located. They can be partitioned and replicated at any time to any location as long as a suitable mechanism is used to keep replicated data synchronized.

NetWare 4.x Directory Services is a good example of a distributed object-oriented database. It stores information about people and resources in a hierarchical tree-structured database similar to Figure D-24. The database is updated by system administrators. Typical updates include adding or deleting users, printers, servers, and other network resources. The database provides a way to document the network, and define management rights for supervisors at department levels, as well as access rights of users to resources. Users access the database to first locate, then access resources, like printers and servers, or send messages to other users on the network.

In the figure, XYZ Corporation has divisions in the US, England, and Korea. The US division has offices in Los Angeles and New York. Also shown in the illustration are the departments for the Los Angeles division. Assume a master copy of the database is stored at corporate headquarters in New York. In the directory tree, Los Angeles represents a branch that can serve as a partition point. A utility is used to define the partition, and the new partition is then replicated to a server in the Los Angeles office. Users at that office then query the local partition to locate resources instead of using wide area network (WAN) links to access the master database in New York.

If the administrator in the New York office adds an object to represent a new employee in the Los Angeles office, the master database must update the Los Angeles

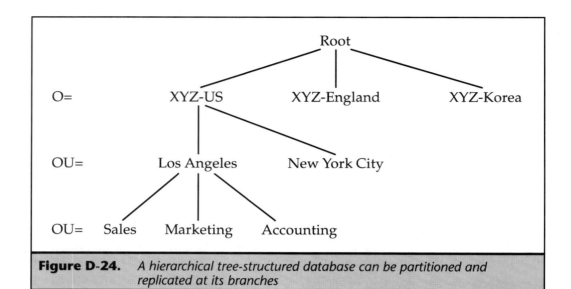

Figure D-24. *A hierarchical tree-structured database can be partitioned and replicated at its branches*

office to ensure synchronization. However, immediate updates are usually not critical, so low-speed WAN links can dial up lines that can be used to make updates between sites. It is unlikely that users in Los Angeles will need the information in the database immediately. An update during the next few minutes, or even during evening hours, would probably be sufficient.

RELATED ENTRIES Database Management System; Distributed Computing; *and* Object-Oriented Technology

Distributed File System, OSF DCE

The Distributed File System (DFS) is a version of the Andrew File System (AFS) that is included with the Open Software Foundation (OSF) Distributed Computing Environment (DCE).

RELATED ENTRIES Distributed Computing; Distributed File Systems

Distributed File Systems

Distributed file systems are designed around the client-server model. A typical network might consist of several servers that many different users can access. In addition, peer-to-peer features allow some systems to act as both clients and servers. For example, a user can "publish" a directory, which allows other clients to access it.

Once accessed, the directories appear to the client as if they are local drives. The three primary distributed files systems listed here have similar roots.

■ *Network File System (NFS)*   NFS was originally created by Sun Microsystems, Inc. as a file sharing system for TCP/IP networks. Sun estimates that over 3.1 million systems are running NFS on systems that range from mainframes to personal computers. At least 80 percent of those systems were non-Sun platforms.

■ *Andrew File System (AFS)*   AFS is architecturally similar to NFS. AFS was developed by the Information Technology Center at Carnegie Mellon University, but its current development and marketing is in the hands of Transarc Corporation, which is made up of former ITC staff. AFS has some enhancements that NFS does not.

■ *Distributed File System (DFS)*   DFS is a version of AFS. It serves as the file system component in the Open Software Foundation's Distributed Computing Environment (DCE).

A distributed file system would be simple to implement if file access were limited to one user. Unfortunately, this restriction is unreasonable in many network environments. Concurrency controls are required to allow multiple-user access to files. These take the following forms:

■ *Read-only sharing*   Any client can access a file, but not change it. This is simple to implement.

■ *Controlled writes*   In this method, multiple users can open a file, but only one user can write changes. The changes written by that user may not appear on the screens of other users who had the file open.

■ *Concurrent writes*   This method allows multiple users to both read and write a file simultaneously. It requires a tremendous amount of monitoring by the operating system to prevent overwrites and ensure that users see the latest information. Processing requirements and network traffic may make this method unacceptable in many environments, even if implemented properly.

NFS and AFS differ in the way they handle concurrent writes. When a client requests a file (or database records) from a server, the file is placed in a cache at the client's workstation. If another client requests the same file, it is also placed in a cache at that client's workstation. As both clients make changes to the file, technically, three versions of the file exist (one at each client and one at the server). There are two methods for maintaining synchronization among the versions:

■ *Stateless systems*   In stateless systems, the server does not keep information about what files its clients are caching. Therefore, clients must periodically check with the server to see if other clients have changed the file they are caching. This causes excess LAN traffic in large environments, but is usually a satisfactory method for small LANs. NFS is a stateless system.

D

■ *Callback systems* In this method, the server retains information about what its clients are doing and the files they are caching. The server uses a *callback promise* technique to inform clients when another client has changed a file. This method eliminates a lot of network traffic. AFS (and DFS in OSF DCE) are callback systems. As clients change files, other clients holding copies of the files are called back and notified of changes.

There are performance advantages to stateless operations, but AFS retains some of these advantages by making sure that it does not become flooded with callback promises. It does this by discarding callbacks after a certain amount of time. Clients check the expiration time in callback promises to ensure that they are current. Another interesting feature of the callback promise is that it provides a guarantee to a client that a file is current. In other words, if a cached file has a callback promise, the client knows the file must be current unless the server has called to indicate the file changed at the server.

Network File System (NFS)

NFS is a distributed, client-server file system. The essence of NFS is that users can share their computers with other users. Other users then connect with the shared computer and access files as if they were accessing a local hard drive. An administrator can set up access to files on a remote system so users aren't even aware that they are accessing remote files.

NFS is an open system that is publicly available and widely implemented. The original design goals of NFS were as follows:

■ Allow users to access files on other systems as if they are local files. Provide support for diskless workstations to keep network costs down.

■ Simplify remote file access for applications so that special procedures are not required to access those files.

■ Use one-at-a-time requests for service so systems can recover from a downed server or workstation.

■ Implement security features to protect files from theft and corruption.

■ Make the NFS protocols portable and simple enough that they can be implemented on many different computers, including low-end PCs.

Mainframes, minicomputers, and file servers running NFS can provide a file storage area for a variety of users. The workstation simply needs to run Transmission Control Protocol/Internet Protocol (TCP/IP) to access these systems and the files in their NFS storage spaces. NFS for the workstation is usually supplied with TCP/IP software. To a DOS user, a remote NFS file storage area appears as another disk drive letter. To a Macintosh user, a remote NFS file storage area appears as an icon.

The functions of the client and the server portions of NFS are described here:

- *Server directory sharing* A server broadcasts or advertises the directories that it is sharing. A shared directory is often called a *published* or *exported* directory. Information about shared directories and who can access them is stored in a file that is read by the operating system when it boots.

- *Client access* The process of setting up a link and accessing files on a shared directory is called *mounting*. Users access the remote file systems using the network as a communication link.

An important component of NFS is the Virtual File System (VFS), which is an interface between applications and the underlying file system. Some of the operations provided by VFS are listed here:

close	File close operation
create	File creation operation
fsync	Saves changes to a file
getattr	Accesses file attributes
link	Refers to a file with another name
lookup	Reads a directory entry
mkdir	Makes a new directory
open	File open operation
rdwr	File read and write operation
remove	Deletes a file
rename	Changes a file's name
rmdir	Removes a directory
setattr	Sets file attributes

Andrew File System (AFS)

AFS is specifically designed to provide reliable file services in large distributed environments. It creates manageable distributed environments with a structure based on cells. A cell is a collection of file servers and client systems within an autonomous area that is managed by a specific authority. It typically represents the computing resources of an organization. Users can easily share information with other users within the cell. They can also share information with users in other cells, depending on access rights granted by the authorities in those cells.

AFP servers run the following processes:

- *File server process* This process responds to client workstation requests for file services, maintains the directory structure, monitors file and directory status information, and verifies user access.

■ *Basic OverSeer (BOS) server process* This process runs in a "BOS-designated server." It monitors and manages processes running other servers and can restart server processes without human assistance.

■ *Volume server process* This process handles file system operations related to volumes, such as volume create, move, replicate, backup, and restore.

■ *Volume Location (VL) server process* This process provides location transparency for volumes, so if volumes are moved, users can access them without the knowledge that they have moved.

■ *Authentication server process* This process provides network security through authorization and mutual authentication. An "authentication server" maintains an authentication database that stores passwords and encryption keys. The system is based on Kerberos.

■ *Protection server process* This process grants users and groups access to file services based on access information in a protection database.

■ *Update server process* This process propagates updates of AFS and any configuration files to all AFS servers.

AFS also comes with a set of utilities for troubleshooting, system backup, and management of the AFS distributed file system. For example, **SCOUT** periodically probes and collects information about AFS file servers. This information is made available to managers on a formatted screen. Various thresholds are set to warn managers of impending problems, such as a disk that is about to run out of space. Another utility is **uss**, which creates user accounts based on templates with field constants. **Ubik** provides database replication and synchronization services. A replicated database is one in which information is located in several locations to make the information more available to local users. The synchronization mechanism ensures that all databases have the same information.

RELATED ENTRIES Distributed Computing; Distributed Computing Environment, OSF; Distributed Database; *and* File Systems in the Network Environment

Distributed Management

As distributed systems grow and resources spread out from their once centralized domain, problems of managing hardware, software, users, updates, configurations, and security multiply. In addition, there are synchronization problems related to making changes to interdependent systems. Differences in operating systems, hardware, or protocols complicate this.

A distributed management system needs to perform the following functions:

■ Manage users and their workstation configurations.

- Manage software distribution, updates, and licensing.
- Manage hardware monitoring, maintenance, and inventory functions.

In addition, a management system needs to provide a method for collecting data about the network and report it back to managers.

Distributed network management systems can take advantage of the network platform to spread management functions around the network, rather than centralize them in a single data center. Administrators may still run a management system from a single location, but management agents located around the network collect information and report it back to the management system. Information that was impossible to obtain in the past due to time and travel restrictions becomes available to managers. Troubleshooting and preventive maintenance is simplified. Alarms can warn of impending problems.

Some common distributed management systems are listed here:

- DEC's Enterprise Management Architecture (EMA)
- SunSoft's management system for SPARC and Intel 80x86 systems
- Novell's open management platform
- OSF's Distributed Management Environment (DME), still under development as of this writing

RELATED ENTRIES   Electronic Software Distribution and Licensing; Management Standards and Tools

Distributed Management Environment (DME)

DME is the Open Software Foundation's (OSF's) strategy for managing distributed networks based in the Distributed Computing Environment (DCE). DME is a structure that brings together system and network management in heterogeneous environments while retaining compatibility with existing solutions.

Its goal is to provide management of distributed computer networks with the following components:

- *Object Management Framework,* which includes development tools for creating object-oriented management applications. A management request broker provides communication between objects.

- *Network Management Options (NMO),* which includes industry-standard management protocols such as SNMP and CMIP. NMO defines manager-agent relationships, in which agents collect information about resources on the network and report that information to management systems.

- *Distributed Services,* which provides software licensing and distribution tools, as well as various monitoring and management tools for tracking events on the network and alerting managers of potential problems.

As of this writing, the future of DME is uncertain and readers are encouraged to contact the Open Software Foundation at (617) 621-8700 in Cambridge, Massachusetts, for more details. For example, in late 1993, OSF stopped development of the key Object Management Framework component in DME.

RELATED ENTRIES   Distributed Computing Environment, OSF; Distributed Management; Management Standards and Tools; *and* Open Software Foundation

Distributed Name Service, DEC

See DECdns.

Distributed Object Management Facility (DOMF), Hewlett-Packard

DOMF provides a communication mechanism among objects in a distributed environment. DOMF provides basic object communication and management services, forming the basis for distributed object computing. With DOMF, developers can create applications that run in multivendor environments that use different operating systems, user interfaces, and communication protocols. It provides network users and their applications with a way to access objects such as spreadsheet data or a graphic from a variety of applications, not just the application that created the object.

DOMF is Hewlett-Packard's implementation of the Object Management Group's (OMG's) Common Object Request Broker Architecture (CORBA). CORBA is defined in the OMG's Object Management Architecture (OMA). OMG is an industry consortium, including SunSoft, Hewlett-Packard, and over 300 other members. In late 1993, HP announced its Object Request Broker (ORB) Plus line of object tools and services, which are based on DOMF.

RELATED ENTRIES   Common Object Request Broker Architecture; Distributed Objects Everywhere, SunSoft; Object Management Architecture; Object-Oriented Interfaces and Operating Systems; Object-Oriented Technology; Object Request Broker; *and* Objects

Distributed Object Management Systems (DOMS)

Distributed Object Management Systems are operating systems or services that promote the use of object-oriented environments and interfaces on distributed computing platforms. The Object Management Group (OMG) Common Object Request Broker Architecture is such a system. Microsoft Cairo and the SunSoft Distributed Objects Everywhere (DOE) initiative also deal with object-oriented computing systems.

Distributed Objects Everywhere (DOE), SunSoft

D

Distributed Objects Everywhere (or Project DOE) is SunSoft's initiative to develop a fully distributed object environment for its Solaris operating system. DOE's design is based on the Object Management Group (OMG) Common Object Request Broker Architecture (CORBA). DOE allows developers to create modular applications that can work on multivendor platforms.

Hewlett-Packard, IBM, and Sun Microsystems, Inc. independently developed object-oriented interface technology, but agreed in mid-1993 to share their technologies. These object-oriented technologies are listed here:

■ *IBM's System Object Model (SOM) and Distributed System Object Model (DSOM)* These models specify an interface to enable object classes created in different environments to interoperate. SOM is implemented in the IBM WorkPlace Shell as the mechanism for providing on-screen object icons and the tools for developers to create such icons. DSOM is the network version that provides cross-platform interoperability.

■ *Hewlett-Packard's Distributed Object Management Facility (DOMF)* This mechanism provides communication among objects. It was originally developed with SunSoft.

■ Sun's Distributed Objects Everywhere (DOE) DOE provides the tools for developing applications with reusable components in the object environment. It allows cooperation while bringing the benefits of objects to distributed, enterprise computing networks.

DOE provides an object-oriented development environment with a standardized interface and inventory of objects that developers can use when creating object-oriented applications. The interface is platform-independent and allows applications on many different systems to communicate. Objects are simple to expand or replace while the existing interface structure remains the same. Key components in object applications are easy to identify and modify, allowing for easy updates. Distributed object applications are not dependent on any one programming language.

DOE defines support for the OMG Interface Definition Language (IDL), which means that any programming language supporting this interface is compatible.

DOE is equivalent to other developments in the computer industry, such as Microsoft's Object Linking and Embedding (OLE) and Apple's OpenDOC, which is based on IBM's SOM.

RELATED ENTRIES   Common Object Request Broker Architecture; Distributed Object Management Facility; Object-Oriented Interfaces and Operating Systems; *and* System Object Model

Distributed Processing

See Distributed Computing; Distributed Database; Distributed File Systems; *and* Distributed Management.

Distributed Queue Dual Bus (DQDB)

Distributed Queue Dual Bus (DQDB) is the access technology for the Metropolitan Area Network (MAN) standard, which is defined by the IEEE 802.6 committee. Since MAN is an 802.x standard like Ethernet, token ring, and token bus, it fits in well with common local area network technology, but the MAN is designed for very large and fast networks based on fiber-optic cables that span up to 50 kilometers.

DQDB has similarities to token-based networks. In a 4 Mbits/sec token ring, for example, a workstation can transmit when it has possession of a token. However, the time it takes the token to circle the network keeps transmission rates limited. To sidestep this limit, 16 Mbits/sec token ring was developed, which basically allowed more tokens on the ring. DQDB takes this concept further in its bus topology. It fills the bus with time slots into which any workstation can place a data packet at any time. Think of a train with many boxcars into which workstations can place information for transport to other locations. DQDB is a true shared-bus technology because all nodes can access the bus when they want up to the point where the network is saturated.

RELATED ENTRY   Metropolitan Area Networks

Distributed Relational Database Architecture (DRDA)

Distributed Relational Database Architecture (DRDA) is an IBM standard for accessing database information across IBM platforms that follows SQL standards. It is a key component in IBM's Information Warehouse framework, which defines large back-end servers that clients can access through smaller, workgroup-based intermediate servers. DRDA has the following capabilities:

- Defines protocols for providing interfaces between clients and back-end databases

- Provides a framework for interconnecting IBM's DB2, DBM, SQL/DS, and SQL/400 database systems

- Supports multivendor database systems

- Supports transaction (unit of work) processing over distributed databases

In DRDA, clients are called *Application Requesters (ARs)* and back-end servers are called *Application Servers (ASs)*. A protocol called the *Application Support Protocol (ASP)* interfaces the ARs with the ASs. The whole process operates on SNA networks, but OSI and TCP/IP support is planned. An additional protocol called the *Database Support Protocol (DSP)* lets an AS act as an AR to another server. In this way, servers can talk to servers and forward requests from client ARs, as shown in Figure D-25. The initial protocol supports one Structured Query Language (SQL) statement to one database, but future versions will support multiple statements to one or more databases.

DRDA is one of the foundations for building client-server computing in IBM environments. The others are Advanced Peer-to-Peer Networking (APPN) and Distributed Data Management (DDM). Through the Information Warehouse and

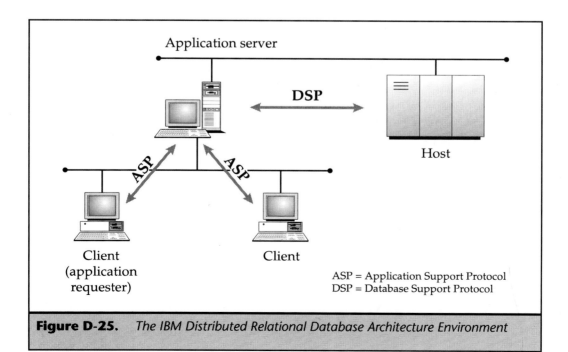

Figure D-25.   *The IBM Distributed Relational Database Architecture Environment*

DRDN, IBM plans to keep its mainframes as central components in the enterprise as the storage platforms for all types of information, including multimedia.

RELATED ENTRIES   Advanced Peer-to-Peer Networking; Database Connectivity APIs and Middleware; Distributed Database; IBM; IBM Networking Blueprint; *and* Information Warehouse

Distributed System Object Model (DSOM)

DSOM is IBM's extension to System Object Model (SOM) that allows object to communicate across platforms in distributed computing environments. SOM is an object-oriented technology that specifies an interface to enable object classes created in different environments to interoperate. SOM is implemented in the IBM WorkPlace Shell as the mechanism for providing on-screen object icons and the tools for developers to create such icons. DSOM is the network version that provides cross-platform interoperability.

While SOM and DSOM provide low-level languages to developers of object-oriented applications, a future product called VisualAge will provide object-oriented tools for creating graphical interface applications and without any knowledge of the programming language.

RELATED ENTRIES   Object Management Architecture; Object-Oriented Interfaces and Operating Systems; Object-Oriented Technology; Object Request Broker; Objects; *and* System Object Model, IBM

Document Interchange Standards

The exchange of computer information would be impossible without character formatting standards such as the American Standard Code for Information Interchange (ASCII). ASCII identifies each letter of the alphabet with a 7-bit code and provides an extended character set using 8-bit codes. Almost every computer recognizes the ASCII code set, so any files you exchange with other users can be displayed without conversion (except for custom code extensions). However, in this simple scheme, any formats you applied to the document, such as page layout, paragraph alignment, and character styles are lost. A way to preserve document formats during file exchanges across different platforms is needed.

A number of document interchange standards have been developed so users can exchange documents between applications that run under the same operating system, and between applications that run on different platforms. For example, a UNIX application and a DOS application can open and format documents if systems and documents use the same document interchange standard. Formatting—such as boldfaced headers, paragraph indentations, page layouts (margins, headers, footers), and other document information—is coded into the document, so the document appears the same when displayed on both systems. Graphic formatting information is usually included in this information as well. Microsoft's long-established rich text format (RTF) holds document formatting, but RTF is not well established except in Microsoft's own products.

Documents can be defined as having the following features:

- Documents have *content,* which is arranged on pages in a particular *layout.*

- Documents have a *structure* that defines segments of the documents, such as headers and paragraphs.

A particular document architecture provides a way to describe the above features using a language that is understood by any system that needs to open and display the document. The document should present its information in the same way, no matter what the underlying system is, so long as it recognizes the document architecture. Users should be able to edit any exchanged documents, or the sender should be able to lock a document to prevent further editing, although strictly controlling this last feature is difficult.

In an enterprise computing environment that consists of many different computing platforms, standard document formats are essential for the exchange of information among users. The primary purpose of an enterprise network is to provide a way for all users to exchange information. After building such a network, it would be ludicrous to use simple file exchange techniques that preserve only such as ASCII. Advanced document architectures that provide cross-platform document exchange are essential.

Work is underway in several areas, including object-oriented information exchange such as that implemented by Microsoft Windows Object Linking and Embedding (OLE) or Apple's Amber. These environments are strongly oriented toward the exchange of graphics and multimedia information such as sound and video. However, for complex objects that include sound and video, the person who receives the document must have an application that can "play back" the sound or video, or there must be a link back to the application that created the object. For example, a user double-clicks a sound object to hear it, and the application that can play the sound is called. This restricts the portability of the document. On a network, the application must be somewhere in the user's environment. In OLE and Amber, objects can maintain links to applications elsewhere on the network, so the user does not need to have the applications on their local system. Still, moving the document to another network poses problems if the applications are not available. See "Compound Documents" and "Object Linking and Embedding" for more details.

Electronic Data Interchange (EDI) is an electronic exchange standard under the control of the American National Standards Institute (ANSI). It has roots in the shipping industry and transportation industry. EDI defines structures for business forms such as purchase orders, invoices, and shipping notices and provides a way for organizations to exchange those forms over communication links. The exchange relationship is usually between a vendor and customer. For example, EDI provides a way for a customer's computer to place orders for goods with a vendor's computers, based on reorder levels. Deliveries are coordinated and invoices are generated. In its

D

simplest form, EDI is like inter-company electronic mail, and in some organizations, E-mail is all that has been realized of EDI. However, EDI has the potential to reduce costs and reduce workforce requirements once a proper system is installed. See "Electronic Data Interchange".

Open Document Architecture (ODA)

Open Document Architecture (ODA) is an International Organization for Standardization (ISO) standard for exchanging documents that contain a variety of information between two systems so that the receiver can view the document as it was created and revise it if necessary. This assumes that both systems conform to the ODA standard. ODA is often used when exchanging documents over X.400 mail systems or when using File Transfer Access Method (FTAM).

The components of an ODA compound document are:

- Text (ISO character sets)
- Geometric graphics based on ISO metafile computer graphics standards
- Raster graphics based on CCITT facsimile standards

ODA documents consist of *layout objects* that define a document's presentation elements such as pages, as well as running headers and footers that repeat on each page. *Logical objects* are elements added to the document layout, such as chapters, sections, paragraphs, titles, footnotes, and other formattable objects. ODA documents go through three stages that produce three different types of documents:

- The document is first created and edited to produce a *processable document,* which remains in a revisable state, even if exchanged.
- The next stage is the layout process, which defines the presentation of the document on pages. It produces a *nonrevisable formatted document* or a *formatted processable* document that can be further revised.
- The last stage is the imaging stage, which produces a document for printing or exchange.

The layout structure can be changed but the logical structure is preserved, which implies that you can change the presentation of the document, but not the original author's contents. Presentation is sometimes changed when the document is displayed on different devices or printed on different types of printers.

Standard Generalized Markup Language (SGML)

SGML is a document language that defines the structure and content of a document, but not the definitions for formatting parameters as does ODA. It goes beyond ASCII to provide ways to integrate and share information that was created in other environments. SGML is primarily used in the workflow and document management environment. It creates "smart" rather than "dumb" (ASCII) documents. SGML documents contain attributes to define components like paragraphs and headers, thus making the documents hardware and software independent. With such documents, workflow software can concentrate more on features than document conversion. Users and programmers alike can store information in documents that can be translated to perform actions or formatting on other systems when the document is used. The Dynatext document viewing software in Novell NetWare 4.x is SGML-based.

With SGML, document formats are separated from the data contained within the document. The formatting information is held in a Document Type Definition (DTD) file and style tags identify each part of the document. For example, a paragraph might have a style tag that identifies it as an indented bulleted list. Typefaces are not part of the SGML definition as they are with products such as Adobe Acrobat, as defined next.

SGML Open is an organization of vendors, including Novell, Oracle, and Intergraph, that is dedicated to advancing SGML as an interoperable standard. SGML lacks display information; however, the SGML Open group is pushing for the implementation of another ISO standard called *Document Style Semantics Specification Language (DSSSL)*, which defines an additional file with document display information.

Acrobat, Adobe Systems Inc.

Adobe Systems Inc.'s Acrobat provides portable document exchange capability that lets document recipients view a document as it was formatted. Acrobat is suitable for documentation purposes, publishing houses, and other businesses that work on documents with a lot of graphics contents using many different types of computers. Acrobat includes the following modules:

- *Portable Document Format (PDF) software,* which replaces the print driver (including PostScript drivers) in Macintosh and Windows-based computers. The application used to create the original document is not required to print exchanged documents. PDF is a document description language, similar to PostScript, that describes how a document will look when output.

- *Exchange software,* which runs on each different computer system, such as DOS, Macintosh, and UNIX systems. This software is used to view and edit documents that have been exchanged.

- *Reader software,* which lets others view and print exchanged documents, but not create them. It is sold separately at a low price.

Adobe has added SGML support to Acrobat to provide a way for users to make changes to files they have exchanged with other users.

Multipurpose Internet Mail Extension (MIME)

MIME is an Internet standard that provides a way to include different types of data, such as graphics, audio, video, and text in electronic mail messages. Formatting features allow users to specify font styles, font sizes, and page layouts in documents so they can be read and interpreted by users on other systems who don't have similar applications.

RELATED ENTRIES   Compound Documents; Electronic Data Interchange; Electronic Mail; Groupware; Imaging; *and* Workflow Software

Document Management

Document management is the storing, categorizing, and retrieval of documents, spreadsheets, graphs, and imaged (scanned) documents. Each document has an index-card-like record that holds information such as the author, document description, creation date, and type of application used. Such documents are usually targeted for archiving on less expensive tape or optical disk where they remain available for future access if necessary.

In the case of a law firm, document management tracks all the activities occurring with a document, such as the number of keystrokes, revisions, and printings, so clients can be charged for the services.

Document management systems are closely related to object-oriented operating systems such as future versions of Microsoft Windows and the IBM/Apple Taligent project. A document-oriented interface will automatically launch an application based on the information in the document.

Document management is most useful in law firms, insurance companies, financial services, advertising agencies, and other businesses that have lots of paper files or image manipulation activities.

RELATED ENTRIES   Archiving; Backup and Data Archiving; Compound Documents; Document Interchange Standards; Groupware; Hierarchical Storage Management Systems; Imaging; Storage Management System, Novell; *and* Workflow Software

Domain Name Service (DNS)

DNS is an Internet and Transmission Control Protocol/Internet Protocol (TCP/IP) service that maps network address numbers, for example, 191.31.140.115, to an easy to remember name, such as tbones.acme.com. Internet and TCP/IP utilities such as *telnet,* File Transfer Protocol (FTP) and the Simple Mail Transfer Protocol (SMTP) access DNS to locate names you've specified and resolves them into network addresses. When a name is selected, DNS translates that name to a numeric address and inserts it into a message for transport. An important feature of DNS is that address information is stored at many locations in a hierarchical structure, not at one central depository. Each site has a domain name server that maintains information about the local nodes.

Domains and DNS were introduced on the Internet as it grew in size. The structure is a hierarchical tree with branching subtrees as shown in Figure D-26, which illustrates part of the Internet. You can think of this tree in the same way you think of a hierarchical filing system in which directories hold subdirectories. There is a *top level* to the tree, sometimes called the *root level*, that is split into major divisions, called *domains*. Some of the top-level Internet domains are listed here.

GOV = Government agencies
EDU = Educational institutions
ORG = Organizations (nonprofit or noncommercial)
COM = Commercial
MIL = Military
NET = Network service providers

There are also national domains, such as CA (Canada), UK (Britain), JP (Japan), DE (Germany), and AU (Australia). Within the US (United States) domain, there are two-letter code names for each of the 50 states. These domains are used by companies or organizations that are restricted to one country, whereas an international company would use the COM domain.

Setting Up DNS

To join a domain, you contact the organization that manages it. Each site must provide a name server that contains DNS information that can be queried by other computers on the network. You can also get one of many commercial Internet service providers to run a name server for you. Then all you have to do is provide connections for the users in your domain to the service provider.

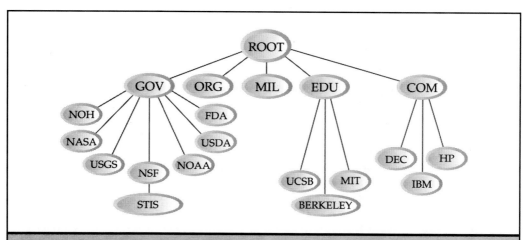

Figure D-26. *The hierarchical structure of the Internet*

When you write down DNS names, you place the host name on the left, followed by domain names up to the root. For example, to address the Science and Information Technology System (STIS) at the National Science Foundation (NSF), you would use the following address:

stis.nsf.gov

As an example, assume you are a large international company called XYZ and you wish to attach to the Internet. You contact the COM domain to request a site registration. You set up a computer to handle naming services for the users in your company's domain. This system gets connected to the nearest Internet access area. Alternatively, a small company can simply set up a link to a service provider and become part of the provider's domain. Either way, electronic mail and other transmissions will eventually find their way through the network to a destination as long as the addressing is correct.

Running Local DNS Servers

The DNS discussion above has largely talked about domains and names for the global Internet. An organization's internal naming structure can follow the same pattern, but include departmental or division domains. One or more computers are set up to manage the DNS naming. DNS is a distributed database that can reside on several different servers for protection against downed systems. There are primary and secondary DNS servers, as described here:

- *Primary DNS server* This is the main server that keeps a copy of the entire database both in memory and on disk. If the system is downed, the database is reloaded into memory.

- *Secondary DNS server* The secondary DNS server obtains a copy of the database from the primary server. An update from the primary server is required as changes occur.

There are several advantages to distributing the database in this way. First, if the network spans cities or countries and requires wide-area telecommunication links, you can keep network traffic down over these expensive links by maintaining a copy of the database at each location. Users can then search for resources and other users by querying the local copy of the database. Distributing the database also provides fault tolerance; however, each database server must be on its own power source and ideally in areas that might not suffer similar disasters such as fires, floods, or earthquakes.

The Internet community is working to implement the X.500 Directory Services standard because it has features not available in DNS. For example, X.500 provides name query services that can return information about a user or resources, such as a physical address or a phone number.

RELATED ENTRIES Directory Services; Internet; Transmission Control Protocol/Internet Protocol; *and* X.500 Directory Services

Domains

Domains define different levels of authority in a hierarchical structure. For example, in the world of government, some cities have their own management domains. Cities are within county domains, counties are within the domain of the state, and states are within the national domain. Each domain exercises its own control, but is included in larger domains. Likewise, the computing resources of an organization can be grouped into domains. Workgroups or departments form domains that may belong to larger domains. Domains are set up for management and security purposes.

NOTE: A cell and a domain are similar concepts. A cell represents a distinct group of systems managed by a central authority.

Windows NT Domains

In Windows NT Advanced Server environments, network domains exist to simplify administration and provide security in the form of authentication. As pictured in Figure D-27, a user can log on to his or her local machine and be authenticated just for that machine, or can log on to the domain and be authenticated to access the servers within the domain. The *primary domain server* authenticates the user, then lets him or her access other servers in the domain. Both the primary and secondary domain servers keep a copy of a security account manager (SAM) database that holds name and password information. The secondary server backs this information up and provides logon services should the primary server fail.

There are trust relationships between the user's computer, the primary domain server, and any other servers the user may access. Other servers "trust" that the primary domain server has properly identified the user. This eliminates the need for the user to log on to each individual server. Elaborating further, Figure D-28 illustrates how a trust relationship is set up between the primary domain servers in the accounting and sales departments to authenticate any users that need to access resources between the departments.

Lotus Notes Domains

In Lotus Notes, a domain consists of one or more Notes servers that share a common Public Name and Address Book database. The database holds information about users in each domain, such as their mail address, mail encryption information, and information about other Notes servers in the domain. The domain also provides gateway services to other products.

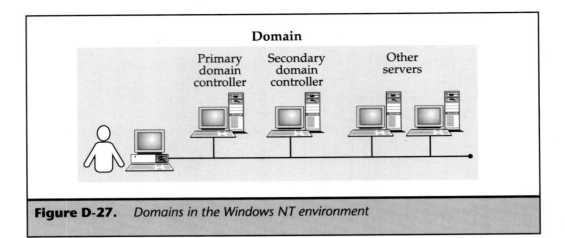

Figure D-27. *Domains in the Windows NT environment*

Routing Domains

The Internet and Open Systems Interconnection (OSI) networks are divided into autonomous regions or domains that contain hosts systems and routers and that are managed by a single authority. The systems and routers within an autonomous region can be referred to as intradomain systems (in OSI terminology) or interior systems (in Internet terminology). Any connections between autonomous systems are called interdomain connections.

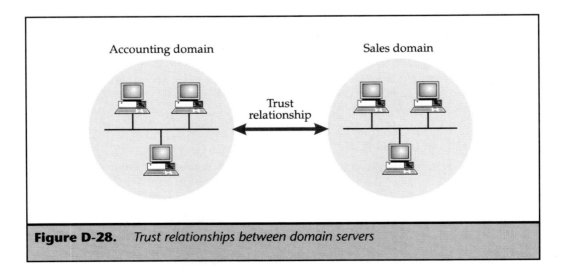

Figure D-28. *Trust relationships between domain servers*

On the Internet, interior gateway protocols (IGPs) such as Routing Information Protocol (RIP) and Open Shortest Path First (OSPF) are used to route within a domain. Exterior routing protocols are used to provide routing among domains. The Exterior Gateway Protocol (EGP) provides a way for two neighboring routers located at the edges of their respective domains to exchange messages and information.

These protocols let network administrators build networks that have hierarchical structures. Each intradomain can have its own routing tables and changes in those tables do not affect other domains, thus cutting down on network traffic and the need for every router to reconfigure its routing tables. Each domain can also have its own routing policies. For example, one domain might base routing on cost while another might base routing on speed.

RELATED ENTRIES   Domain Name Service; Lotus Notes; Routing Protocols; *and* Windows NT, Microsoft

DOS Requester, NetWare

The NetWare DOS Requester is a set of modules that allow DOS workstations to access the resources on NetWare networks. Requests for NetWare services are sent to a module called IPXODI, which adds header information and packages data for delivery over the network.

DOS Requester Modules

The following commands, typically contained in a batch file called STARTNET.BAT (located in the NWCLIENT directory), load the DOS Requester files and services. Each command is described here.

```
LSL
NE2000.COM (or other LAN driver)
IPXODI
VLM
```

Link Support Layer (LSL)

The LSL is a software driver that directs traffic between multiple communication protocols and a network interface card driver that supports Novell's Open Data-link Interface (ODI) specification, as shown in Figure D-29. Think of the LSL as an intermediary or switchboard operator that receives packets and directs them to the correct protocol stack, or sends packets from different protocols out over the same network card.

There are several possible LSL configurations. The LSL can act as an intermediary between the following:

■ A single network card running a single protocol stack

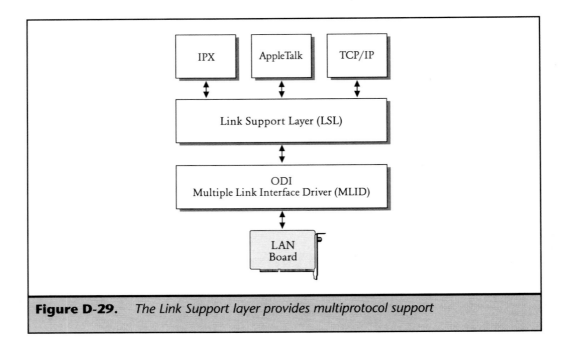

Figure D-29. *The Link Support layer provides multiprotocol support*

- A single network card and multiple protocol stacks
- Multiple interface cards and a single protocol stack
- Multiple interface cards and multiple protocol stacks

LAN Driver

The LAN driver listed in the STARTNET.BAT file depends on the network interface card selected during the installation of the workstation software. The LAN driver provides hardware-specific information about the network card installed in the system. Drivers written to the ODI Multiple Link Interface Driver (MLID) specification are not directly linked to a communication protocol stack. The MLID simply handles media access information and lets the LSL do all the protocol-specific handling.

IPXODI

As shown in Figure D-29, the LSL driver sits between the Internetwork Packet Exchange (IPX) protocol stack and the network interface card driver. IPXODI is the driver that loads an IPX protocol stack and attaches it to the LSL. IPXODI is the only protocol that is automatically installed at the server. Other stacks must be optionally installed. You need to purchase the Novell LAN WorkPlace products (DOS, Macintosh, or OS/2) to provide ODI-compatible Transmission Control Protocol/Internet Protocol (TCP/IP) protocol stacks for workstations.

Virtual Loadable Module (VLM)

VLM is an executable (EXE) file that loads the DOS Requester software. The DOS Requester has the all-important job of determining whether requests for service by the workstation should go to DOS or go out over the network to a server. VLM.EXE is only the tip of the iceberg, however. It loads the following modules, which you can see if you list the contents of the NWCLIENT directory:

- *CONN.VLM* This is a connection manager that lets a workstation connect with one or more servers simultaneously. It tracks network services and storage devices available to users on the network.

- *IPXNCP.VLM* This is the IPX packet-handling module.

- *AUTO.VLM* This module provides reconnection services.

- *TRAN.VLM* This module directs information to the correct transport protocol, such as IPX or TCP/IP.

- *NDS.VLM* This module provides access to NetWare version 4 Directory Services.

- *BIND.VLM* This module provides access to bindery-based (pre-NetWare version 4) services.

- *NWP.VLM* This multiplexer module directs information to either NetWare version 4 Directory Services, bindery-based (pre-NetWare version 4) services, or Personal NetWare, depending on which is in use. The multiplexer allows any or all of these to be mixed.

- *RSA.VLM* This module provides Rivest, Shamir, and Adleman (RSA) encryption and authentication capabilities.

- *FIO.VLM* This is the file input/output module. Control of cached or non-cached read/writes, burst mode-based read/writes, and Large Internet Packet read/writes are handled by this module.

- *GENERAL.VLM* This module provides functionality to the other modules listed here.

- *REDIR.VLM* This module provides the actual DOS redirection services.

- *PRINT.VLM* This module provides print redirection from the workstation to printers attached to the network.

- *NETX.VLM* This is an optional module that provides backward compatibility to previous versions of the NetWare shell. Some applications need the functions available in the previous shell.

RELATED ENTRIES LAN Workplace Products, Novell; NetWare; Novell; *and* Open Data-link Interface

D

Downsizing

Downsizing: An excuse to get rid of your highly paid senior employees and put in a workforce of "temps."

- Upside Magazine, Foster City, CA

Downsizing is the process in an organization of replacing minicomputers and mainframes with LAN-based servers and workstations, typically associated with a move to UNIX boxes or powerful superservers and a shift to client-server computing.

Many organizations have too much of an investment to completely move away from mainframe and minicomputer systems, or have special engineering and scientific applications that require their use, or are cost-prohibitive to redesign for network systems.

Duplexed Systems

A duplexed system provides data protection in the form of mirroring in which data is simultaneously written in two places at once. Mirroring implies that two disks are present, but attached to one disk channel (adapter card). Duplexing implies that each disk is attached to its own adapter card, which adds another level of protection. The entire server can also be duplexed so users are never without a server should one server go down. Duplexed servers are attached with high-speed interfaces (fiber) and can be placed in separate locations to protect them from local disasters.

RELATED ENTRY   Disk Mirroring and Duplexing

Duplex Transmission

See Transmission Media, Methods, and Equipment.

Dynamic Data Exchange (DDE)

DDE is an interprocess mechanism for exchanging messages between processes running in a computer. It is implemented in Microsoft Windows products.

RELATED ENTRY   NetDDE

Dynamic Routing

Dynamic routing is a process in which routers automatically adjust to changes in network topology or traffic. The opposite is static routing, in which the router manager enters the routes manually. Dynamic routing is used in all modern routers, but some amount of programming is still available for customizing routes if necessary.

RELATED ENTRY   Routing Protocols

EIA/TIA 568 Commercial Building Wiring Standard

Structured wiring or cabling is a preplanned cabling system that is designed to implement future services and growth, thus making it easy to accommodate future moves and reconfiguration. The Electronic Industries Association (EIA) and the Telecommunications Industries Association (TIA) developed a standard for telecommunication wiring for commercial buildings called the *EIA/TIA 568 Commercial Building Wiring Standard*. This standard provides a uniform wiring system and supports multivendor products and environments.

According to EIA/TIA 568 documents, the wiring standard is designed to provide the following features and functions:

■ A generic telecommunication wiring system for commercial buildings

■ Defined media, topology, termination and connection points, and administration

■ Support for multiproduct, multivendor environments

■ Direction for future design of telecommunication products for commercial enterprises

■ The ability to plan and install the telecommunication wiring for a commercial building without any prior knowledge of the products that will use the wiring

The EIA/TIA 568 specification applies to all unshielded twisted-pair (UTP) wiring schemes that work with Ethernet 10Base-T, Token Ring, PBX, ISDN, and other networks. EIA/TIA 568 has benefits for customers because it standardizes network cabling and installation, opening the market for competing products and services in the area of premises wiring, design, installation, and management.

The EIA/TIA has defined five categories of twisted-pair cable as listed here. Cabling is discussed in more detail under the heading "Cabling."

■ *Category 1* Traditional telephone cable

■ *Category 2* Cable certified for data transmissions up to 4 Mbits/sec

■ *Category 3* Cable to support token ring (4 Mbits/sec) and 10 Mbits/sec Ethernet 10Base-T networks

■ *Category 4* Cable to support 16 Mbits/sec token ring networks

■ *Category 5* Cable to support 100 Mbits/sec or greater emerging technologies such as Fast Ethernet

Wiring System Structure

The EIA/TIA 568 specification calls for a hierarchical physical star topology as pictured in Figure E-1. Cables are pulled in a star topology from the telecommunication closet to the outlet on the wall where computer devices connect

E

into the network. The TCs on each floor are joined in the equipment room, and each floor is interconnected at the main cross-connect facility. The maximum distance of the site is 3,000 meters (9,840 feet), covering 1 million square meters (about 10 million square feet) of office space, and up to 50,000 individual users.

The structured wiring architecture contains five subsystems that comprise a wiring system as follows. The entire system can be mapped as pictured in Figure E-2.

WORK AREA   The work area wiring subsystem consists of the communication outlets (wallboxes and faceplates), wiring, and connectors needed to connect the work area equipment (computers, printers, and so on) to the horizontal wiring subsystem. Typical faceplates, such as the one pictured in Figure E-3, accommodate snap-in connectors such as modular jacks for telephones or data, and modified modular jacks for low-speed data transmissions. They can also accommodate snap-in BNC connectors for coaxial cable and fiber-optic cable.

HORIZONTAL WIRING   The horizontal wiring system runs from each workstation outlet to the *telecommunication closet.* The maximum horizontal distance from the telecommunication closet to the communication outlets is 90 meters (295 feet)

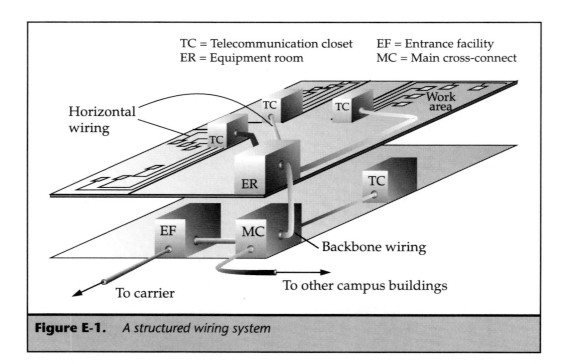

TC = Telecommunication closet   EF = Entrance facility
ER = Equipment room   MC = Main cross-connect

Figure E-1.   *A structured wiring system*

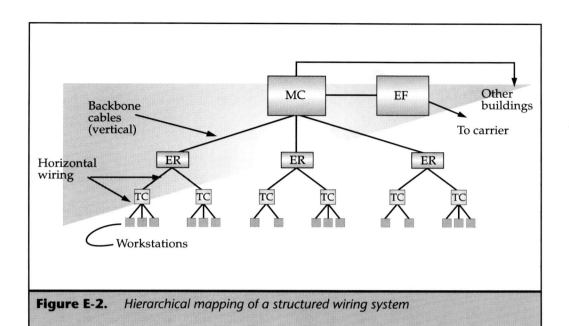

Figure E-2. *Hierarchical mapping of a structured wiring system*

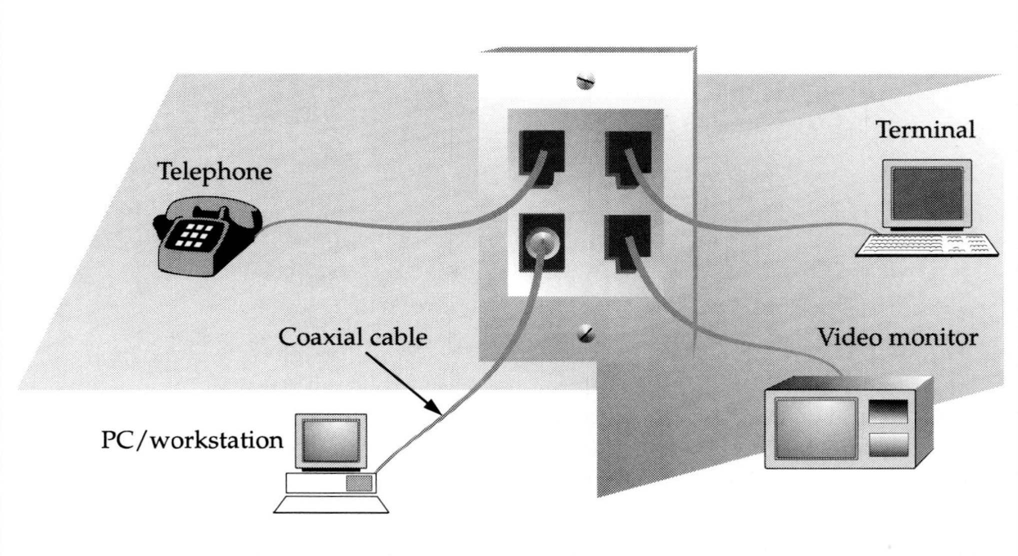

Figure E-3. *Work area faceplate in structured wiring system*

independent of media type. Four types of wire are recognized in the horizontal wiring system:

- Four-pair 100-ohm unshielded twisted-pair (UTP) cables
- Two-pair 150-ohm shielded twisted-pair (STP) cables
- 50-ohm coaxial cables
- Optical fiber cable with a core diameter of 62.5 microns

TELECOMMUNICATION CLOSET   The telecommunication closet contains the connection equipment for workstations in the immediate area and the connection to the equipment room. The telecommunication closet is a general facility that can provide horizontal wiring connections, as well as entrance facility connections. There is no limit on the number of telecommunication closets allowed.

EQUIPMENT ROOM   The equipment room provides the central connection point for all telecommunication closets in the horizontal wiring system and provides the connection for the backbone wiring. The main distinction between equipment rooms and telecommunication closets is in the equipment. The equipment room provides mechanical termination of one or more telecommunication wiring systems.

BACKBONE WIRING   The building backbone runs up through the floors of the building and interconnects the equipment rooms on each floor. The backbone cables merge into the main cross-connect, which provides the central wiring center for the entire facility. Backbone cable can be one of the types listed next, with distance limitations as pictured in Figure E-4.

- Four-pair 100-ohm UTP cables
- Two-pair 150-ohm STP cables
- 50-ohm coaxial cables
- Optical fiber cable with a core diameter of 62.5 microns

MAIN CROSS-CONNECT   The main cross-connect is the central connection point for backbone wiring and wiring that connects other buildings.

ENTRANCE FACILITIES   The entrance facility contains the telecommunication service entrance to the building, including the access through the wall. This facility may also contain campus-wide backbone connections. It also contains the *network demarcation point,* which is the interconnection to the local exchange carrier's telecommunication facilities. The demarcation point is typically 12 inches from where the carrier's facilities enter the building, but the carrier may designate otherwise.

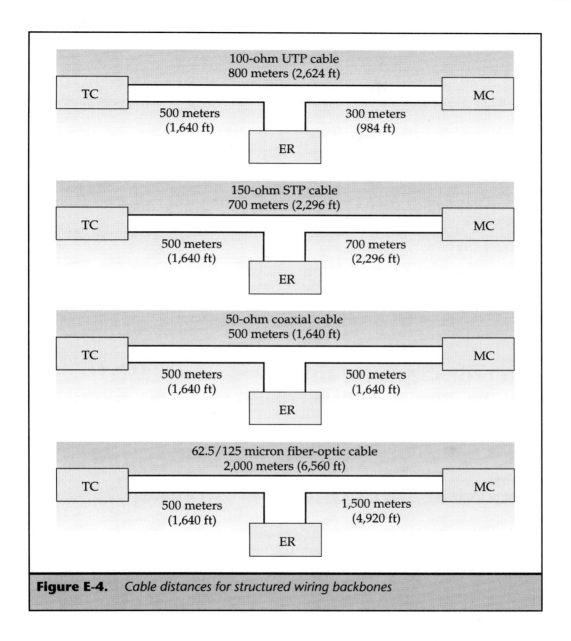

Figure E-4. *Cable distances for structured wiring backbones*

ADMINISTRATION This subsystem includes the cross-connects and inter-connects to connect the distribution subsystems. It is the point where changes in the structured wiring are managed.

There are compromises between installing the EIA/TIA 568 structured wiring system, or using a traditional cable system such as Ethernet. EIA/TIA 568 has rigid rules and is more expensive to install in large installations, but it is a standard that provides for future expansion. On the other hand, traditional Ethernet networks can be built by following the Ethernet 10Base-2 or 10Base-T standards discussed in this book under "Ethernet 10Base-2" and "Ethernet 10Base-T," respectively. The traditional methods are cost-effective in small installations or installations that already have cable installed.

 NOTE: *A similar standard, called EIA/TIA 606 (Administration Standard for the Telecommunications Infrastructure of Commercial Buildings), defines a uniform procedure for administering a wiring system, its pathways and spaces, and its grounding and bonding, including documentation and labeling procedures.*

RELATED ENTRIES   Cabling; Fiber-Optic Cable

EISA (Extended Industry Standard Architecture) Bus

See Extended Industry Standard Architecture Bus.

Electromagnetic Interference (EMI)

EMI is electronic noise that disrupts the signal on a cable and reduces its integrity. EMI is typically caused by generators of electromagnetic radiation such as motors and machines.

RELATED ENTRIES   Cabling; Power and Grounding Problems and Solutions

Electronic Data Interchange (EDI)

EDI is the electronic exchange of structured business data such as purchase orders, invoices, and shipping notices, typically between one organization and another. The relationship is usually between a vendor and customer. For example, EDI provides a way for a customer's computer to place orders for goods with a vendor's computers, based on reorder levels. The EDI system coordinates the deliveries and generates the invoices. Typical business activities EDI handles include:

Distribution
Finance and accounting
Health care
Manufacturing
Purchasing

Retail
Tax form filing
Telecommunication
Transportation and shipping

In its simplest form, EDI is like intercompany electronic mail, and, in some organizations, E-mail is all that is implemented. However, EDI has the potential to reduce costs and reduce workforce requirements once a proper system is installed. Early EDI packages used rather simple standard forms that forced companies to design their in-house documents around these generic forms. Newer EDI systems allow companies to create custom systems using simple programming or authoring tools.

The American National Standards Institute (ANSI) assigned responsibility for development of EDI standards to the Accredited Standards Committee (ASC) X.12 organization in 1979. X.12 has roots with work done in the shipping industry by the Transportation Data Coordinating Committee (TDCC) and work done in the food distribution industry by the Uniform Code Council (UCC). Some similar standards are listed here:

- Electronic Data Interchange for Administration Commerce and Transport (EDIFACT)

- International Organization for Standarization (ISO) 9735 standard, which blends EDIFACT and ANSI standards

X.12 ensures that documents are compatible among computing platforms. Documents mimic standard business forms and have American Standard Code for Information Interchange (ASCII) data in a standard data file format that is structured with records and fields. A document sent from, for example, a PC-based EDI system can be read by a mainframe-based EDI system because the text and data separators follow a standard format. The electronic documents are sent using a "store-and-forward" process similar to electronic mail systems. In this way, daily transactions can accumulate and be transferred to host systems during evening hours to reduce costs.

The X.12 standard defines a large number of EDI transaction forms that mimic most of the standard documents used in business, such as invoices and purchase orders. These forms have the following characteristics:

- A flat file structure holds multiple, variable-length records called *segments.*
- Segments consist of ASCII text and end with a carriage return terminator.
- Field data—such as "line item," "quantity," and "price"—are contained within the segments and separated by a special character code.
  Data dictionaries define each element. The segments are packaged into a single block with appropriate header and trailer information for transmission.

Traditionally, EDI has been implemented on mainframe and minicomputer systems, but several PC-based applications have recently appeared from Texas Instruments (Dallas, Texas) and Sterling Software (Columbus, Ohio). Value added network (VAN) providers (also called *clearinghouses*) such as AT&T (EasyLink), Sprint, and GE Information Services provide communication services for transmitting EDI documents. The companies can provide packaging, protocol conversion of data (to international standards), and accounting services.

RELATED ENTRY   Document Interchange Standards

Electronic Industries Association (EIA)

Founded in 1924, the EIA is a U.S. organization of electronics manufacturers. The EIA has published a number of standards related to telecommunication and computer communication and works closely with other associates such as the American National Standards Institute (ANSI) and the Consultative Committee for International Telegraph and Telephone (CCITT), now referred to as the International Telecommunications Union (ITU), its parent organization.

The primary EIA standards for telecommunication define the serial interface between modems and computers. The most popular are listed next. The Physical layer specifications define 37-pin (DB-37), 25-pin (DB-25), and 9-pin (DB-9) connectors and associated cable, as well as electrical characteristics such as the type of signal used on each pin and the timing of those signals.

- *RS-232-C*   A standard for serial connections using DB-25 or DB-9 connectors and maximum cable lengths of 50 feet.

- *RS-449*   A serial interface with DB-37 connections that defines the RS-422 and RS-423 as subsets.

- *RS-422*   Defines a balanced multipoint interface.

- *RS-423*   Defines an unbalanced digital interface.

EIA-232, which was formerly knows as RS-232, defines the serial connections between DTE and DCE devices. It is universally recognized. The EIA RS-232 standard is also the CCITT standard V.24. The CCITT V series protocols are more predominant than the EIA standards, partly because they are used in Europe where government standards dictate the type of protocol to be used.

For the most part, EIA standards have CCITT equivalents. For example, the Group 3 facsimile, which is the fax machine standard for transmissions rates up to 9.6 Kbits/sec, is the CCITT Recommendation T.4 and the EIA-465 standard.

In the area of structured cabling for networks, the EIA has recently joined with the Telecommunications Industry Association (TIA) to create the Commercial Building Telecommunications Wiring Standards (EIA/TIA 568 and 569), which defines hierarchical wiring systems in campus environment using data-grade twisted-pair wire. This standard provides a wiring structure that building designers can use to facilitate high-speed data communication equipment without the need to know in advance what that equipment will be.

RELATED ENTRIES   CCITT; Modems; *and* "V dot" Standards

Electronic Mail

Electronic mail (E-mail) is probably the most common application used on networks. Indeed, the growth of enterprise networks is often based on getting everyone in the organization connected just so they can share E-mail. Access to enterprise databases and other resources often comes as an added benefit.

The benefits of E-mail are obvious. Users can quickly communicate with one another. If a person isn't available to pick up a message immediately, the message is held in the E-mail box until it can be picked up. So-called phone tag is eliminated. E-mail also provides a quick and easy way to package information such as sales reports, graphics, and other data for transfer to another user. You simply attach the information to the message. You can even attach whole files to E-mail messages. An often overlooked advantage of E-mail is that you have time to organize your thoughts when replying to messages.

The major problem with E-mail is that it is so easy to use that people can become inundated with messages, more than they can possibly answer in a day. In addition, mail boxes require some management to dispose of messages or archive those that might be required later. Senders don't always know about your E-mail backlog and often send redundant messages.

Electronic mail and messaging systems are an increasingly important part of an enterprise network's computing strategy. The systems are designed to help users keep in contact and improve productivity. In addition, messaging systems are becoming an important tool for program development in distributed environments. A message may carry a request for service from a user to a remote database. The remote database then packages a response within a message and sends it back to the user. Of course, this is not a real-time strategy, but in distributed environments, real-time operations are not always practical.

There are many different E-mail systems in use on networks, mainframe systems, and public data networks. For example, the Internet message standard is the Simple Mail Transfer Protocol (SMTP). IBM Professional Office System (PROFS) and SNA Distributed Services (SNADS) are used in the IBM mainframe environment. VAXmail or All-In-1 are used in the DEC environment. In addition, numerous E-mail systems are available in the desktop networking environment. A single organization might have numerous E-mail systems that were implemented in the days when departments or workgroups maintained their own local area networks (LANs). As the organization was interconnected, E-mail gateway systems were often employed to translate messages among the different systems. More recently, X.400-based systems have been gaining in popularity. X.400 is a standard messaging system that provides a way to exchange messages on many different platforms.

Electronic Mail Features

An electronic mail system for an enterprise network consists of the following components:

- The user's front-end application, which provides facilities for creating, addressing, sending, receiving, and forwarding messages. Other features include the ability to attach files and other information to messages, and the ability to manage a personal address book.

- The back-end E-mail server application that forwards messages from sender to receiver. A message store holds messages until delivery, and a translation facility or gateway allows users of different E-mail systems to exchange mail.

- A directory service that maintains a database of users and services on the network. Users can access the service to locate a user and his or her E-mail address.

Additional features in some E-mail systems include the ability to secure messages with encryption, or add a digital signature to prove the authenticity of messages and prevent alterations. The ability to send and receive facsimiles is another feature included with many systems.

Electronic Mail Systems and Standards

A number of E-mail standards have existed in the mainframe and network environment. Novell's Message Handling Service (MHS) is prominent on LANs. It provides back-end server collection and routing of messages. Other standards include the Internet's SMTP and the international X.400 standard.

X.400

The Consultative Committee for International Telegraph and Telephone (CCITT) X.400 MHS standard defines an electronic system for exchanging messages among store-and-forward mail systems running on a wide variety of platforms. In International Organization for Standardization (ISO) terminology, X.400 is called the Message Oriented Text Interchange System (MOTIS). It outlines the protocols, procedures, components, terminology, and testing methods required to build interoperable E-mail systems. X.400 is based on a distributed client-server model that includes the following components:

- *The User Agent (UA)* This component runs in users' computers. It provides "message create," read, browse, and other features required in an E-mail front-end application.

- *Message Transfer Agent (MTA)* This component accepts messages from the UA, translates them if necessary, and routes them to other MTAs.

- *The Message Store (MS)* This is a storage area for messages that can't be delivered directly to a user because his or her system is off-line or not available. The user can pick the messages up from the MS at any time.

- *Access Unit (AU)* An AU provides access to the mail system for other entities, such as fax machines, teletex, and telex users.

- *The Directory System* This component provides X.500 functions for looking up user names and addresses. X.500 is providing a way to resolve some of the diversity in name and address format among E-mail systems.

Other services defined in X.400 include *distribution lists,* which are used to address groups of users; *domains* for managing local and remote message sites; and *security* features. The security features provide authentication, proof of correct delivery and receipt, detection of unauthorized users, protecting against message alteration during transit, and other features.

Internet Simple Mail Transfer Protocol (SMTP)

SMTP is the delivery standard for E-mail on the Internet. Using SMTP for E-mail, developers can employ any user interface as a front-end. An SMTP-based mail system on a PC lets users send and receive messages with users on a UNIX system or to anyone on the Internet without going through a gateway. A gateway lets users on one E-mail system send mail to users on an SMTP-based network.

Multipurpose Internet Mail Extension (MIME) is a compound document messaging standard in the Internet environment built on SMTP formats. With MIME, users can send multimedia E-mail messages that include audio, video, graphics, and text to any other user of a TCP/IP network. *Richtext* information can also be incorporated into messages. It defines the fonts, formats, and layout features of a document so the document can be easily redisplayed on many different types of systems.

The Internet Engineering Task Force (IETF) is adopting Privacy Enhanced Mail (PEM) protocols for the Internet. PEM provides for message signature and sealing, message and signature integrity verification, encryption, and decryption. E-mail senders and receivers hold private and public key pairs. The sender signs a message with the private key and the receiver checks the signature with the corresponding public key. For more information, see "Key Encryption Technology."

Novell Message Handling Service (MHS)

Novell's NetWare MHS provides message handling on local and wide area networks. Applications that have used MHS include electronic mail, workgroup scheduling, Electronic Data Interchange (EDI), and network fax. MHS provides delivery services that work in the background. Front-end user applications take advantage of its services. These applications are typically developed by non-Novell vendors. MHS is not strictly an E-mail system. It handles message flow between applications as well. Developers can use MHS to create applications that talk to other applications and exchange information. For example, queries can be made to databases on other systems using MHS.

A typical MHS installation consists of host systems that provide messaging services for a group of users. A number of hosts might support a single workgroup, department, or division of a company. Hubs are set up to route messages among host systems. Hubs handle the activities of setting up connections to destination systems and transmitting the messages that are addressed to those systems. Remote connections can include asynchronous dialup lines or dedicated lines, depending on the requirements. For example, a company might send messages among its different divisions using dedicated lines, or a company might send E-mail messages to another company on a periodic basis using dialup lines.

NetWare Global MHS is the latest version of the message handling system. It is a scalable messaging server for a range of businesses and enterprises. It consists of a set of NetWare Loadable Modules (NLMs) that combine with NetWare 3.11 or NetWare 4.x to provide a platform for messaging with store-and-forward capabilities and services such as E-mail, workflow automation, calendaring, scheduling, and fax services. MHS versions for NetWare 2.2 and DOS-based laptop and remote users are also available.

NetWare Global MHS, combined with optional protocol modules, permits interoperability between SMTP for UNIX and TCP/IP networks, SNADS for IBM AS/400s and mainframes, and CCITT (ITU) X.400 mail networks. At the front-end, or client, various electronic mail utilities are available that let users create and manage messages. FirstMail, an entry-level E-mail utility, is included with Global MHS.

Building Enterprise E-mail Systems

A typical enterprise computer system consists of a number of electronic mail systems. Clients send mail from their front-end applications to the back-end "post-offices," which are typically called message transfer agents (MTAs). Each different MTA must be tied together to provide message exchange over the enterprise. However, each mail system has its own addressing format, message format, and transport protocol. Conversion or standardization is required to successfully exchange messages. With the diversity of E-mail systems available, conversion is the current trend. Two approaches to integrating diverse electronic mail systems are discussed here and pictured in Figure E-5.

■ *Gateways* A gateway provides a way to tie together diverse E-mail systems. It basically translates messages from one E-mail standard to another and maps names among the systems. Name mapping can become complex and add management overhead. Each different E-mail system in the organization requires its own gateway between other systems, so the gateway approach is only recommended when there are only a few different systems. In addition,

E-mail systems are inconsistent in their features, so messages passing through gateways might be converted improperly.

■ *Backbone switching* In this approach, all messages are sent to a single computer or a cluster of interconnected computers that act as a "backbone." These backbone systems handle message traffic from E-mail systems, gateways, and applications. Many different E-mail systems can connect on a global scale using X.400, an internationally recognized message handling system.

The Enterprise Mail Exchange (EMX) from SoftSwitch is receiving the most attention in the industry as a backbone switching system. EMX is a multiprotocol MTA that provides full interoperability with E-mail systems using existing protocols such as IBM's SNA Distribution Service (SNADS), The Internet's Simple Mail Transfer Protocol (SMTP), Novell's Message Handling Service (MHS), and other protocols. EMX is scalable to match the requirements of individual organizations. It enables organizations to build an X.400 enterprise mail backbone network that interconnects existing electronic mail systems and allows users anywhere to exchange mail. EMX forms a logical mail backbone that extends through the entire organization over the existing network platform. EMX resides in one or more physical systems that are linked by the network.

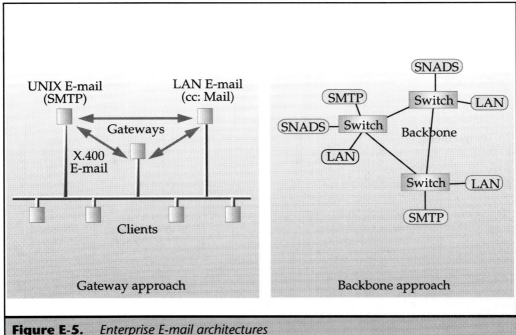

Figure E-5. *Enterprise E-mail architectures*

E-Mail API Standards

The application program interfaces (APIs) described next provide help for developers who want to integrate support for a variety of E-mail systems into their applications. They define an interface between messaging services and applications, in addition to providing services such as file attachments and addressing.

- *Messaging API (MAPI)* MAPI provides a way for Windows applications to access mail applications like Microsoft Mail, Lotus Development's cc:Mail, and Novell's Message Handling Service (MHS).

- *Vendor-Independent Messaging (VIM)* Like MAPI, VIM is a cross-platform API that allows developers to create mail-enabled applications that work on many different platforms and allows users on those different platforms to share mail. VIM was originally developed by Lotus.

- *Common Mail Calls (CMC)* CMC is an E-mail API proposed by an industry-wide group of electronic mail software developers that resolves differences between MAPI and VIM. CMC is strongly supported in the industry and could possibly emerge as an industry standard.

- *Apple Open Collaborative Environment (AOCE)* Apple Computer's AOCE technology is designed to consolidate electronic and workgroup communication, such as voice mail, electronic mail, and fax.

- *Standard Message Format (SMF)* SMF is the messaging interface found in Novell's Message Handling Service (MHS).

Mail-Enabled Applications

Electronic mail and the API discussed in the preceding section are providing a unique new class of software called *mail-enabled applications.* These applications take advantage of the store-and-forward, message-oriented nature of electronic mail systems. Groupware and workflow software, covered elsewhere in this book, are implementing mail features.

Mail-enabled applications use electronic mail communication mechanisms to transfer messages, data, and documents. Software vendors are beginning to implement the mechanisms into word processing, spreadsheet, and database applications so users can send and receive electronic mail from directly inside the application. They are especially suited for heterogeneous, distributed computing environments where users need to communicate with many different types of hardware and software systems.

RELATED ENTRIES Groupware; Messaging APIs, E-Mail; Messaging APIs, Inter-Application; *and* Workflow Software

Electronic Mail Broadcasts to a Roaming Computer (EMBARC)

EMBARC is a provider of one-way beeper and pager communication services. It competes with SkyTel and provides messaging capabilities as high as 30,000 characters, compared to the SkyTel limit of 240. EMBARC also allows users to send messages to a number of users at the same time. This is useful for updating information on several remote machines. EMBARC users can also get news from various sources, such as USA Today.

Electronic Software Distribution (ESD) and Licensing (ESL)

Software distribution and the licensing of that software is a big problem on large networks. Without an automated method for installing and updating programs, utilities, and drivers, network managers or their assistants must spend time manually updating workstations on the network. This involves travel time and expense in many cases. A typical organization may have thousands of workstations at diverse sites, some requiring more than one day's travel. Of course, the normal procedure is to hire people to do these tasks or let users upgrade their own machines. But relying on a single management package to perform automatic upgrades makes much more sense.

Electronic software distribution (ESD) and *electronic software licensing (ESL)* are now recognized as critical to the proper management of large networks. ESD provides automatic software updating, and ESL provides automatic tracking of software usage to ensure that an organization stays within its software licensing requirements.

E

Software Distribution and Management Programs

Software distribution programs ideally copy software to workstations, install the software, configure it, and provide periodic updates when necessary. Configuration involves changing system settings and the options in startup files such as AUTOEXEC.BAT and CONFIG.SYS (on DOS machines). The programs can look at system configurations and update the configurations if necessary.

Much of the work in software distribution and management programs is being handled by the Desktop Management Task Force (DMTF) and is defined in DMTF's Desktop Management Interface (DMI). Part of the DMI is an agent that collects information about network workstations and other nodes and places the information in a file called the management information format file (MIFF). The MIFF is a standard ASCII file that can contain information about hardware components of the workstation, operating system, application software, version numbers, and other information. Management programs access MIFFs throughout the network and report back with information that administrators can use to document the network, determine faults, perform diagnostics, and watch for potential problems. In addition, MIFFs provide information required to install and configure an application for a specific machine, such as its type of video, printer, and memory configuration.

Without these tools, managers are unlikely to make gathering such information a priority. Management tools make it easy to generate reports of workstations that need software updates and then automatically update those workstations over the network. Updates can be performed during off-hours to minimize network traffic. Some of the major management and software distribution products on the market are discussed here:

■ Microsoft is implementing management and software distribution developed by Software Spectrum (Garland, Texas) in its *Hermes* management product. The management software runs on Windows NT, while client software runs on DOS, Windows, and Windows NT machines. The software is DMI compliant. MIFFs collect workstation information and Hermes accesses this information to provide management reports and perform software distribution and installation. It can also perform diagnostic functions on workstations and allow managers to control a workstation from their own.

 NOTE: *Microsoft has developed a plug-and-play specification that defines hardware and software that automatically configures itself when installed. See "Plug-and-Play ISA, Microsoft."*

■ Novell's *Network Navigator Electronic Software Distribution* lets network administrators update software such as operating system updates, data files, and applications on users' machines from a central location without the assistance of a user. A scripting feature is used to build automated routines for checking configurations and updating systems. The system can provide scheduled updates and reports of those updates. Other features include scheduled virus scans, scheduled data updates, detailed audit reports, and security features.

■ IBM's *NetView Distribution Manager (NDM)* is a management product that can distribute, install, configure, and update software on network workstations.

Licensing Applications

Licensing packages are used to ensure that a company is operating within its legal boundaries for software usage. A licensing package holds keys that allow users to access software applications. Each key is a license that has been purchased from the software vendor. The licensing program delivers keys to users who request the use of an application. When the keys are gone, other users can't access applications until a key frees up, or more keys are added. Licensing programs usually include controls that prevent unauthorized users from accessing programs, or prevent users from holding a key for too long.

There are two major developments in licensing:

■ *Network License Server (NetLS)* Developed by Gradient Technologies, Inc., NetLS provides user access to software applications on the network based on the number of licenses available and currently in use. The software also provides software version tracking, inventory, and usage tracking. Tracking is important to determine who is using software and whether additional licenses are required.

■ *The Licensing Service API (LS API)* LS API is a licensing standard proposed by DEC, Lotus, Microsoft, Novell, and other vendors that defines how applications and NetLS licensing servers work together to track software usage and licensing. Microsoft has made LS API part of its Windows Open System Architecture (WOSA) strategy. The server basically grants execution privileges to applications on client machines.

Note that NetLS is the server component that distributes licenses, and LS API is a programming interface that developers use to link with a server running NetLS. Other developments in the licensing arena are listed here:

■ The Open Software Foundation (OSF) is using NetLS for the licensing management portion of the Distributed Management Environment (DME), which is linked to OSF's Distributed Computing Environment (DCE).

■ Novell's *Electronic Software Licensing for NetWare* is a NetWare Loadable Module (NLM) that uses Gradient's NetLS to monitor software usage and make applications available only when a license becomes available. The following license allocation methods are available to block application usage and keep an adequate set of licenses available for authorized users.

■ *Personal* This feature lets network managers specify which users can use a software package.

■ *Node-locked* This feature provides a way to make licenses available only at specifically designated workstations (based on node-id).

■ *Time-specific* This features provides a way to make licenses available during specific times, and for limited amounts of time.

RELATED ENTRIES Desktop Management Interface; Management Standards and Tools; *and* Windows Open System Architecture

Elevator Seeking

Elevator seeking is a disk optimizing function of an operating system that prioritizes incoming read requests based on how they can best be accessed by the read head of the disk drive, given its current location. The operation of elevator seeking is

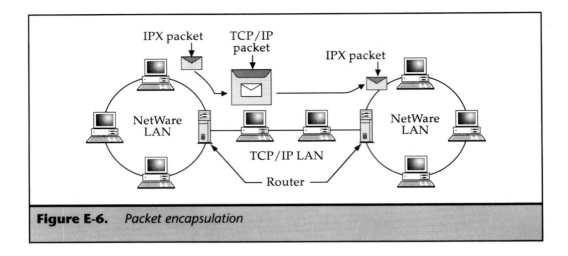

Figure E-6. *Packet encapsulation*

analogous to that of a building elevator. A building elevator doesn't make random up and down trips among floors based on which buttons were pressed first; it stops at floors on the way up or down to pick up passengers who need a ride. Elevator seeking minimizes disk head movement, thus improving access time and reducing hardware degradation. Disk writes can also benefit from elevator seeking.

RELATED ENTRY   Disk Storage Systems

E-Mail

See Electronic Mail.

Encapsulation

Encapsulation, sometimes called *tunneling,* is the insertion of one protocol's packet into another protocol's packet. The encapsulated packet "piggy-backs" a ride on the packet of the native protocol for a ride over the native protocol's network. While this adds overhead, it provides a way to send packets from one network to another over an intermediate network that uses a different protocol.

For example, in a technique called *IP tunneling,* it's possible to encapsulate NetWare Internetworking Packet Exchange (IPX) packets into Transmission Control Protocol/Internet Protocol (TCP/IP) packets and transmit them over the TCP/IP network as shown in Figure E-6. Another example is the ability to encapsulate AppleTalk packets into DECnet packets for routing over a DECnet Open Systems Interconnection (OSI) network. Routers are used to interconnect the different networks and encapsulate the packets. At the receiving end, the packet is unencapsulated and travels on to its destination.

Public data network providers such as AT&T use encapsulation to transport data packets over ATM cell switching devices with Synchronous Optical Network (SONET) interfaces. In Switched Multimegabit Data Services (SMDS), a packet structure is defined on top of a cell-switching structure. A customer's data packets are encapsulated in SMDS packets, then placed into cells to take advantage of the greater speed of cell switching.

Encapsulation also provides a way to use Fiber Distributed Data Interface (FDDI) as a backbone for a local or campus-wide network. An FDDI envelope is placed around an Ethernet frame and the whole package is sent across the FDDI backbone. When the packet reaches the bridge for the destination network, it is unpackaged and sent to the destination. Encapsulation is normally implemented in most Ethernet-to-FDDI bridges. This method assumes that nodes on the Ethernet will never need to communicate with nodes attached directly to the FDDI local area network (LAN), except for the bridge. Encapsulation makes the frames unusable until they are unpackaged at the receiving bridge. Translation is required to send Ethernet packets to workstations directly attached to the FDDI LAN.

RELATED ENTRIES   Datagrams; Networks; *and* Packets

Encina

Encina is a product from Transarc Corporation (Pittsburgh, Pennsylvania) for building and operating distributed on-line transaction processing (OLTP) applications in open systems environments. It offers a development, execution, and management environment that complies with industry standards and integrates screen managers, Remote Database Management Systems (RDBMSs), and other OLTP systems. Encina combines many of the concepts from conventional mainframe-based transaction processing systems such as IBM Customer Information Control System (CICS) with research on distributed and transactional systems done at the Massachusetts Institute of Technology and Carnegie-Mellon University in the 1980s. Encina is available in the Hewlett-Packard, IBM, and Sun Microsystems environments, and provides the OLTP functions for the Open Software Foundation's (OSF's) Distributed Computing Environment (DCE).

Transaction processing implies that a transaction, such as the updating of a bank account in a database management system, is executed immediately, as opposed to batch processing, in which a batch of transactions is stored over a period of time, then executed later. Most batch processes, such as posting to accounts, are run during evening hours. Transaction processing can occur in *real-time* when users are connected directly on-line to a computer (OLTP). OLTP results are immediately available in the database, assuming the transaction completed. The most common OLTP examples are airline reservation systems, banking transactions systems, and accounting systems such as order-entry billing. Messaging systems can also execute transactions with a non-real-time, store-and-forward approach.

E

The transaction monitoring features provided by Encina are critical in distributed database environments where transactions can involve changes on more than one database server, but must be viewed as a single *unit of work*. Those changes must be synchronized and completed fully on all servers, or else they must be backed off completely. If one server goes down during a write, any writes made on other systems during the transactions must be backed off. Encina provides the following transaction monitoring functions:

- *Initiate and terminate*   This is the process of starting a transaction by notifying all the servers involved, and terminating the transaction once it is safely completed, or has been backed out.

- *Two-phase commit*   This is the process of tracking a distributed transaction in two phases to ensure that all systems involved are ready to both write a transaction, and complete a transaction. A failure at any point during the transaction causes a complete rollback of the transaction by all involved systems.

- *Exception handling*   This is the process of handling errors as they arise.

- *Recovery*   If a transaction fails, any writes must be rolled back so all servers are in the state they were in before the transaction started.

- *Abort*   A user may need to stop a transaction in midstream. If so, any data written on any server must be rolled back.

In addition to transaction monitoring, Encina provides other management functions in modular form that can be customized to the needs of a developer or customer. Functions include transactional remote procedure call (RPC), Transactional C (a programming language), and support for communication over SNA and TCP/IP networks.

The industry is moving toward the adoption of OLTP systems for several reasons. Workstations and networking equipment are relatively inexpensive and enterprise LANs are growing. Many existing department LANs are being interconnected into enterprise networks, with the result that database servers in diverse locations are now available for access, and mainframe systems are accessible by many more users in the enterprise. Distributed databases are growing to accommodate this structure, and OLTP with two-phase commit is needed to maintain accurate information throughout the enterprise in real-time.

Encina and similar products are now available to handle these needs. Similar products include:

- Tuxedo from UNIX Systems Laboratories (Summit, New Jersey)
- IBM CICS, which uses Encina functions for its AIX/6000 implementation

RELATED ENTRIES   Connectionless Transactions; Distributed Computing; On-Line Transaction Processing; Transaction Processing; Tuxedo; *and* Two-Phase Commit

Encryption

See Security.

End System-to-Intermediate System (ES-IS) Routing

ES-IS routing is an Open Systems Interconnection (OSI) method for routing within autonomous domains. A *domain* is a set of networks administered by a single company or organization. Access into a domain is controlled by security measures put in place by the administrators of the domain. A typical network consists of a group of user computers, called *end systems,* within a department or workgroup. These subnetworks are connected to backbone networks via routers. ES-IS routing takes place only between the end systems and the routers or intermediate systems. Other types of routing are used across domains.

RELATED ENTRIES   Domains; Routing, OSI

Enterprise Management Architecture, DEC

This is Digital Equipment Corporation's management distributed architecture for enterprise networks.

RELATED ENTRY   DEC Enterprise Management Architecture

Enterprise Networks

An *enterprise,* according to Webster's dictionary, is a project that "is of some importance or that requires boldness or energy" by a "company organized for commercial purposes." With this in mind, consider that many companies are undertaking the task of interconnecting their isolated departmental or workgroup networks into an intracompany network with the potential of allowing all computer users in a company to access any data or computing resource. You could call such an internetwork a *federated system,* because it typically provides interoperability among autonomous and heterogeneous systems. However, an *enterprise network* has the eventual goal of reducing the number of communication protocols in use and to provide more interoperability among user applications, as well as improving accessibility to data from any system.

Enterprise networking is an evolutionary step beyond workgroup computing, which was concerned with integrating desktop computers into networks. Enterprise networking is both local and wide area in scope. It integrates all the systems within an organization, whether they are DOS-based computers, Apple Macintoshes, UNIX workstations, minicomputers, or mainframes. Companies have revolted against the proprietary interfaces of the so-called "big-iron" vendors such as IBM and DEC and moved to systems that provide more openness or acceptance of multivendor products. IBM and DEC are now supporting open standards. Gateways that provide users access to proprietary systems are no longer the answer. They are too restrictive, and don't scale up to the data access requirements of a connected organization.

An enterprise network should mimic a "plug-and-play" platform that an organization can use to connect any of its computing resources, as shown in Figure E-7. Departments and workgroups are links with bridges, routers, and wide area telecommunication links. No user or group is an island. Users and workstations can share information with other users and computers, even those that run different operating systems, while maintaining reasonable performance, security, and reliability. In an enterprise network, information is distributed across the entire network and users must have a quick and easy way to get to it. At the same time, sensitive information must be protected from unauthorized access.

The trick to making these "blue-sky" objectives work is to follow one of two scenarios:

■ Create a network platform with underlying standards that allows multivendor hardware and software products to work together.

■ Create operating systems and applications that support multiple standards.

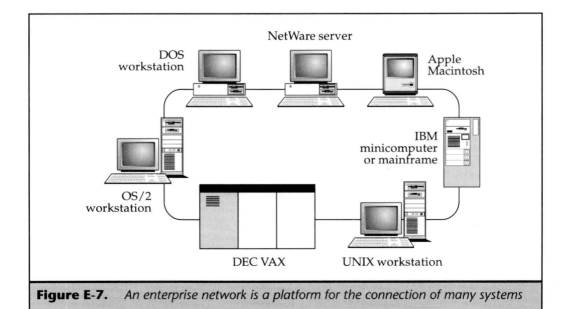

Figure E-7. *An enterprise network is a platform for the connection of many systems*

As computer processing power improves and desktop resources fall in price, it has become much simpler to implement both strategies. Rather than expecting vendors to focus on single standards or protocol architectures, it is much easier to simply support them all. Computers now have the processing power, memory requirements, and user interfaces to do this and shield the user from the underlying complexities. It is not uncommon to find a network that simultaneously transports Internetwork Packet Exchange (IPX), Transmission Control Protocol/Internet Protocol (TCP/IP), and NetBIOS protocol packets for attached DOS, UNIX, and Windows NT workstations. Servers and workstations now keep multiple protocol stacks in memory so they can communicate with a variety of systems.

However, this strategy only serves to link the subenvironment of the network (that is, the Physical, Data-Link, Network, and Transport layers relative to the Open Systems Interconnection [OSI] model). Just because a UNIX station can send TCP/IP packets to a NetWare server does not mean that it can access the resources of that server in a seamless way. Interoperability is also required at higher levels in the protocol stack. Applications are needed that let the UNIX users work with data on NetWare servers using their own UNIX applications. In contrast, a Windows users should be able to access information on a UNIX system or IBM mainframe directly from native applications such as Microsoft Excel.

Client-Server Computing and Middleware

Fortunately, this level of interoperability is emerging today with the growth of client-server computing, "middleware" products, interplatform messaging services, and vendor strategies that support other vendors' products.

Client-server computing started out by letting many clients access data on a single server. In most cases, the same or compatible operating systems and computer platforms were used. As networks grew, clients gained the ability to access data on a variety of back-end servers. The movement now is to allow any client running on any operating system to access any back-end database service. That is one of the primary catalysts for creating enterprise systems. Expanding communication is another.

Mechanisms for transmitting information between client and server systems include the following:

- A *conversational system* provides a tight interface between client and server that typically operates in real-time. A logical connection is set up between systems and a one-way or two-way conversation takes place over the connection to complete a task. This procedure is used to complete a number of tasks, not just one transaction. The tasks can follow a specific order, or even overlap.

- A *remote procedure call (RPC)* is a call that connects two computers over a synchronous connection. The connection is maintained to ensure data integrity between the two systems on a real-time basis. This type of connection is important in mission-critical applications such as banking transactions.

■ In a *message-passing system,* information and requests are sent between computers in much the same way as E-mail messages are sent between users. The message is stored and forwarded along a path to its destination. While message systems are not adequate for real-time database updating, they provide efficient read services.

The following is a list of important vendor strategies or industry consortium strategies that will lead the way to enterprise computing systems:

■ *Microsoft's Windows Open System Architecture (WOSA)* is a strategy to build middleware directly into its operating systems so that information flows more easily throughout the enterprise. WOSA includes Open Database Connectivity (ODBC), which is a standard for interfacing databases.

■ *Apple Computer's Apple Open Collaborative Environment (AOCE)* is a development environment for consolidating workgroups and workflow within an enterprise.

■ The *Open Software Foundation's (OSF's)* Distributed Computing Environment (DCE) is a set of "enabling" software that hides the difference between multivendor products, technologies, and standards by providing tools for the development and maintenance of distributed applications.

■ *SQL Access Group (SAG)* and the X/Open group are consortiums of database vendors that are enforcing Structured Query Language (SQL) standards for accessing databases across multivendor systems.

■ *Integrated Database Application Programming Interface (IDAPI)* is a Borland standard database API.

■ *Distributed Relational Database Access (DRDA)* is an IBM standard for accessing database information across IBM platforms that follows SQL standards.

■ Oracle Glue provides a way for applications that support *Dynamic Data Exchange (DDE),* such as Microsoft Excel and Visual Basic to link with Oracle and IBM DB2 servers.

■ The *Object Management Group (OMG)* is providing standards for implementing cross-platform, object-oriented environments. Common Object Request Broker Architecture (CORBA) is part of OMG's Object Management Architecture (OMA).

■ The *Common Open Software Environment (COSE)* is a consortium of vendors—including IBM, Hewlett-Packard, SunSoft, and Novell—who cooperate to deliver a common environment to the UNIX platform.

In the IBM environment, Advanced Program-to-Program Communication (APPC) and Advanced Peer-to-Peer Networking (APPN) strategies are providing a way to implement decentralized computing environments that support cooperative, peer-to-peer networking. IBM's Networking Blueprint defines support for industry standard communication protocols such as TCP/IP and the OSI protocols. APPN allows each workstation to initiate its own communication session over the network, which allows client-server computing, distributed databases, and remote procedure calls between multivendor products in traditionally centralized IBM environments.

Interoperability is also taking place at the operating system level. New operating systems like Microsoft Windows NT provide multiple protocols such as TCP/IP and NetBIOS so clients can access many back-end servers. The OSF's DCE takes this concept even further by providing an environment that any vendor can use to develop applications with built-in multivendor distributed processing capabilities, along with services such as directory services, authentication, public key encryption, and more. DCE is basically the common infrastructure on which an organization can build its enterprise system.

Messaging, Workflow, and Workgroups

Another category of software is boosting the prospects of enterprise networking. Messaging systems provide communication tools that allow network users to collaborate on projects and implement groupware and workflow software. Messaging standards such as those listed here provide different levels of interoperability for electronic mail, groupware, workflow, and workgroup applications.

- *Common Mail Calls (CMC)* This industry-supported specification will allow applications to access messaging services on a variety of supported platforms. The X.400 API Association is supporting and improving the standard.

- *Apple Open Collaboration Environment (AOCE)* Apple Computer's AOCE provides tools for creating applications in a distributed Macintosh and multivendor environment.

- *Messaging API (MAPI)* MAPI is part of Microsoft's Windows Open System Architecture (WOSA) and is a Windows-specific messaging interface.

- *Vendor-Independent Messaging (VIM)* VIM is a Lotus-defined interface that lets applications communicate with Lotus cc:Mail and Lotus Notes.

Future Trends

Current trends point to increased client-server computing in distributed computing environments. Users will require faster links to a variety of back-end services, including database management systems running on different platforms. Local area network (LAN) hardware requirements to support these trends include switched Ethernet LANs, and fast packet-switched wide area network (WAN) services such as Frame Relay, Switched Multimegabit Data Service (SMDS) and Asynchronous Transfer Mode (ATM). Traditional T1 leased lines will not provide the kind of support needed as the WAN starts to look more like the LAN, with bursty traffic and frequent access to remote resources at a variety of sites.

Graphical user interfaces that support multimedia, like Windows, will boost the requirements for new storage devices such as voice E-mail servers and video servers. Once again, switched Ethernet LANs or Fast Ethernet options can provide the bandwidth in the local environment. Switched Ethernet can provide *microsegmentation* so as few as one workstation is attached to a LAN segment by itself to communicate with voice and video servers. *Prioritization* is a method that can deliver real-time video by setting aside a number of packets in the communication link to ensure that video information has enough bandwidth to arrive on time and in order. Prioritization is available in Ethernet 100VG-AnyLAN, ATM, and other types of networks.

Vendors are now providing hubs that support a number of different LAN and media types and allow communication between those LANs. It is now possible to create "virtual LANs" that are not constrained by physical hardware. A user on a token ring segment and a user on an Ethernet segment can become part of the same workgroup. ATM switching hubs can provide the bandwidth and connectivity to link any user with any other user or device over a virtual circuit that can eliminate the need for routing devices.

In planning for future growth, it is important to evaluate the communication protocols on the enterprise network and eventually choose one or two protocols. To support future bandwidth requirements, consider an ATM hub as the master switching device in a structured wiring system, with the eventual goal of adding department and workgroup ATM hubs in the future.

RELATED ENTRIES   Asynchronous Transfer Mode; Cabling; Client-Server Computing; Distributed Computing; Groupware; Hubs; Interoperability; Structured Wiring Systems; Switched Services; *and* Workflow Software

Enterprise System Architecture, IBM

See IBM Systems Application Architecture.

Enterprise System Connections (ESCON), IBM

ESCON is a set of IBM products and services that provides a dynamically connected environment within an enterprise. ESCON provides direct channel-to-channel connections between mainframe systems over fiber-optic links at distances up to 60 kilometers (36 miles). It also provides a way for communication controllers and other devices to share a single channel to a mainframe.

RELATED ENTRIES   Cluster Controllers; IBM; *and* IBM Mainframe Environment

Error Detection and Correction

Error detection and correction is a process that occurs during the transmission of files. Errors occur during transmission due to the following causes:

- Noise caused by thermal motions of electrons in a circuit
- Attenuation of the signal caused by a resistance to current in a cable
- Distortion due to inductance and capacitance
- Loss in transmission due to leakages
- Impulses from static in the atmosphere

It is estimated that an error occurs for every 1 in 200,000 bits. Two events can happen in a communication session. The receiving device can detect an error and request a retransmission, or it can use various techniques to rebuild the information so that a retransmission is not required.

Errors are detected with simple parity-checking methods or more sophisticated cyclic redundancy checks. In the parity method, an extra bit is added to each character, and this bit is either 0 or 1 depending on whether the number of 1s in the character is even or odd. This method works well if only one bit changes but fails if two bits change since the parity would appear correct. More sophisticated methods include block-checking methods in which a checksum character is generated by the sender on the block. Basically, the value of each character is summed and the result is divided by 255, resulting in the checksum. The checksum is sent with the block. The receiver then performs the same algorithm on the block and matches its results with the checksum. If there is a discrepancy, a retransmission is required.

There is always a chance of undetected errors, but an advanced error-checking method called cyclic redundancy check (CRC) can reduce undetected errors to less than one in a million blocks. CRC uses a more sophisticated algorithm to come up with a error detection value that is 16 bits in length. CRC is used in synchronous and asynchronous transmissions.

RELATED ENTRIES   Asynchronous Communications; Flow Control Methods; Handshaking; Microcom Networking Protocol; Serial Communications; *and* Synchronous Communications

Ethernet

The Ethernet networking system was originally created by Xerox, but it was jointly developed as a standard in 1980 by Digital Equipment Corporation, Intel, and Xerox. This standard became known as DIX Ethernet in reference to the developers' names. The Institute of Electrical and Electronics Engineers (IEEE) 802.3 standard defines a similar, but slightly different network that uses an alternate frame format. (The *frame* is the structure and encoding of a transmitted bitstream across a link.) Because the IEEE

802.3 standard has been adopted by the International Organization for Standardization (ISO), it is discussed here.

Ethernet has 10 Mbits/sec throughput and uses a carrier-sensing access method in which workstations share a network cable, but only one workstation can use the cable at a time. The carrier sense multiple access with collision detection (CSMA/CD) access method is used to arbitrate access to the cable.

IEEE 802.3 committee is responsible for defining the Physical layer in the OSI protocol stack. This layer is divided into two sublayers called the Media Access Control (MAC) sublayer and the Data-Link sublayer. CSMA/CD, token ring, and token bus networks can be "plugged into" the MAC layer and the Data-Link layer serves as a bridge that can transfer packets between the networks if necessary. This is discussed in the "Data-Link Layer, OSI Model" entry earlier in this book.

The adaptations of the IEEE 802.3 standard all have transmission speeds of 10 Mbits/sec with the exception of 1Base-5, which transmits at 1 Mbit/sec but has long twisted-pair segments. Up to 8,000 workstations can be connected in a single extended local area network (LAN). Because 10Base-5, 10Base-2, and 10Base-T are the most popular topologies, only they are discussed in this book in detail, but all of the topologies are mentioned in the following list. Note that the first number in the name refers to the speed in Mbits/sec, and the last number refers to the meters per segment (multiplied by 100). *Base* stands for baseband and *Broad* stands for broadband.

- *10Base-5* Coaxial cable with maximum segment lengths of 500 meters; uses baseband transmission methods.

- *10Base-2* Coaxial cable (RG-58 A/U) with maximum segment lengths of 185 meters; uses baseband transmission methods.

- *10Base-T* Twisted-pair cable with maximum segment lengths of 100 meters.

- *1Base-5* Twisted-pair cable with maximum segment lengths of 500 meters and transmission speeds of up to 1 Mbit/sec.

- *10Broad-36* Coaxial cable (RG-59 A/U CATV type) with maximum segment lengths of 3,600 meters; uses broadband transmission methods.

- *10Base-F* Supports fiber-optic cable backbones of up to 4 kilometers with transmission at 10 Mbits/sec. The EIA/TIA has approved this cable for cross-connects between campus buildings in its Commercial Building Wiring Standard.

- *100Base-X* A new Ethernet standard that supports 100 Mbits/sec throughput and uses the existing CSMA/CD access method over hierarchical twisted-pair wiring configurations.

- *100VG-AnyLAN* A new Ethernet standard that supports 100 Mbits/sec throughput and uses a new *demand priority* access method over hierarchical twisted-pair wiring configurations.

The topology of 802.3 Ethernet networks, with the exception of those that implement the new 100VG-AnyLAN standard, is a linear bus with a CSMA/CD access method. In coaxial cable Ethernet implementations, workstations are connected in a daisy-chain fashion by attaching segments of cable between each station as shown on the left in Figure E-8. The segments form a single, large cable system called the *trunk.* The twisted-pair version of Ethernet (10Base-T) is configured as a star topology in which the cable to each station branches from a central wiring hub as shown on the right in Figure E-8.

Carrier Sense Multiple Access with Collision Detection (CSMA/CD)

Ethernet adapters transmit packets on the shared network when they have exclusive access to the cable. Collision detection refers to the method used to resolve simultaneous accesses to the cable. When a cable is not in use, two stations may attempt to access it at the same time. If both start transmitting data, a collision occurs, which can corrupt data. With the CSMA/CD protocol, a detection mechanism senses the collision, and both workstations back off for a random period of time and then try transmitting again later.

The CSMA/CD method is efficient when network traffic is light. As traffic increases, more collisions occur. Stations back off and retransmit again but if the network is still busy, this process continues and escalates, causing a performance drop and a perceived slowdown to the users. One solution is to reduce the number of workstations on each LAN segment. In microsegmentation, which requires switching hubs, as few as one workstation may occupy a segment, completely eliminating contention.

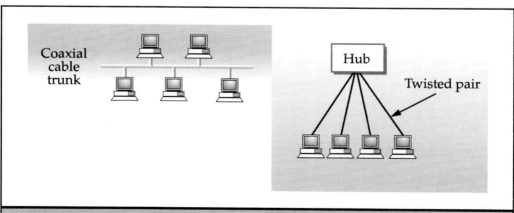

Figure E-8.   *Coaxial cable and twisted-pair Ethernet configurations*

E

The collision problem is one factor that imposes a limit on the trunk length of an Ethernet segment. The maximum distance is 2,500 meters (2.5 miles). Trunks beyond this limit are subject to signal-propagating delays that can cause a failure in the collision-detection mechanism. Stations at opposite ends of an overextended cable that attempt to access the cable at the same time may not sense the access of the other. A failure to detect multiple access causes data corruption and can lock the LAN segment.

Segmentation

Segmentation is the process of splitting an Ethernet segment into two or more segments, thus reducing the number of workstations attached to each segment and improving performance. Basically, a single segment is split and a bridge or router is attached to join the segments. The bridge or router then manages traffic between networks.

Segmentation becomes an important concern as new users join the network, especially those who require high bandwidth. Video applications require the most bandwidth. In addition, live video is time-sensitive and must be prioritized, which reduces performance for others. Users of video can share their own segments.

NetWare, Windows for Workgroups, Windows NT, and similar network operating systems have built-in routing capabilities. Each network adapter placed in a server forms a separate LAN segment. The operating system manages traffic between segments. Figure E-9 shows a server with two installed network interface cards running star and bus topology Ethernets. The choice of topology you choose depends on the layout of the office environment and the type of cabling you use.

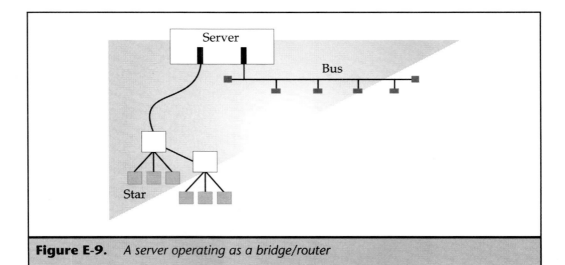

Figure E-9. *A server operating as a bridge/router*

Filtering is an important part of the segmentation scheme. Once you've divided a network to reduce traffic and improve performance, you filter packets to reduce traffic on networks where those packets don't belong. One drawback to the bridging/routing approach of interconnecting networks is that bridges and routers introduce some delay in transferring packets between networks. Switching hubs can remove this delay problem.

Ethernet Switching Hubs

Switching hubs expand on the segmentation concept by providing microsegmentation in a box. As few as one workstation can have a direct, unshared link to a server or other device, reducing contention and providing the full 10 Mbits/sec speed of the network. Networks with engineering or multimedia workstations can benefit from the high throughput provided by switching hubs.

Switching hubs are low-latency devices that implement matrix switches as shown in Figure E-10. Many switching hubs also have high-speed dedicated connections for servers, such as a Fiber Distributed Data Interface (FDDI) 100 Mbits/sec interface. The reason for this is that standard Ethernet's 10 Mbits/sec throughput is usually inadequate to handle throughput to a server. Connecting a multiprocessing superserver operating at many millions of instructions per second (MIPS) to a slow network is ludicrous. Consider the numbers. FDDI can provide 100 Mbits/sec. The switching hub in the picture provides ten ports at 10 Mbits/sec each, so the 100 Mbits/sec bandwidth of the FDDI port can adequately handle 10 workstations that are simultaneously transmitting.

Ethernet at 100 Mbits/sec

With the increasing use of multimedia, high-definition video, and real-time video—and electronic mail that incorporates these formats—there is an increasing need for higher bandwidth to the desktop. Computer-aided design (CAD) and computer-aided manufacturing (CAM) users have always had high-bandwidth requirements, and emerging applications such as imaging and document storage will require high-bandwidth as well. There are two new Ethernet standards that run at 100 Mbits/sec:

- 100VG-AnyLAN Ethernet is supported by Novell, Microsoft, Hewlett-Packard, AT&T, and 11 other vendors. It uses four-wire Category 3 cable like that used in Ethernet 10Base-T, and uses a new proprietary access method called demand priority. The IEEE 802.12 committee is responsible for its development. See "Ethernet 100VG-AnyLAN."

- 100Base-X Ethernet preserves the CSMA/CD access method and runs over unshielded twisted-pair (UTP) Category 5 data-grade cable. The IEEE 802.3 committee is now responsible for its development.

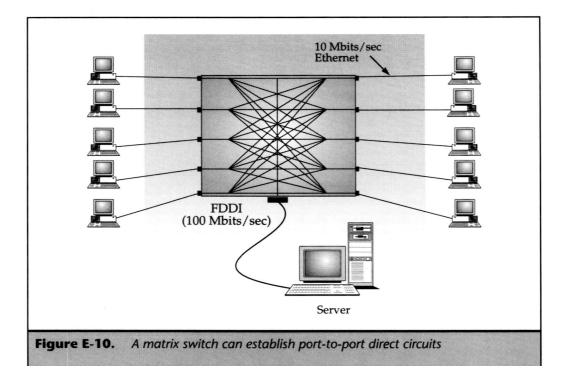

Figure E-10. *A matrix switch can establish port-to-port direct circuits*

An important consideration with 100 Mbits/sec Ethernet is the cable. Voice-grade cable is inappropriate for Fast Ethernet, and 100VG-AnyLAN requires Category 3 cable (and uses all four pairs in the cable). It is also interesting to note that 100 Mbits/sec transmission rates have been available for local area networks in the form of Fiber Distributed Data Interface (FDDI) and Copper Distributed Digital Interface (CDDI). However, these networks have not caught on for LAN connections because of high cost and lack of knowledge to implement them. Fiber cable does provide better long-term benefits in terms of increased transmission rates.

Frame Formats

An Ethernet frame represents the structure of a data packet sent over an Ethernet network. It describes the position of headers, data bits, and the payload in the packet. Understanding frame types is important if you want to connect a protocol analyzer to a network and monitor the network's traffic. You can usually troubleshoot problems on a network by looking at the contents of packets and gathering statistics about them.

There are four frame types in Ethernet:

■ *Ethernet_II* The original Ethernet frame type. It assigns a unique packet header that is used on AppleTalk Phase I networks, networks connected to DEC systems, or to computers using the TCP/IP protocol.

■ *Ethernet_802.3* The frame type commonly used in Novell NetWare networks.

■ *Ethernet_802.2* The frame type used in Novell NetWare 4.x networks by default.

■ *Ethernet_SNAP* The frame type used on AppleTalk Phase II networks.

In Figure E-11, the frame for the original Ethernet_II is shown at the top and the IEEE 802.3 frame is shown at the bottom in the figure. Important fields in the frames are described here.

■ *Preamble* This field marks the start of a frame.

■ *Start frame delimiter (SFD)* This field provides an additional field for indicating the start of the frame in IEEE 802.3 Ethernet.

■ *Destination and Source* These fields hold the origination address and where it is going.

■ *Length (LEN) of data field* This field indicates the length of the data portion of the frame.

E

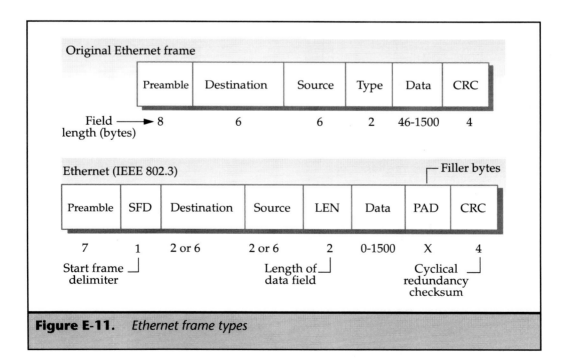

Figure E-11. *Ethernet frame types*

■ *Cyclical Redundancy Checksum (CRC)* This field holds a value calculated on the packet by the sender. The receiver performs the same calculation to see if it comes up with the same CRC value. If not, the frame is considered corrupted and is retransmitted.

RELATED ENTRIES Ethernet 10Base-2; Ethernet 10Base-5; Ethernet 10Base-T; Ethernet 100VG-AnyLAN; *and* Fast Ethernet

Ethernet 10Base-2 (Thinnet)

NOTE: See "Ethernet" for a background discussion of the Ethernet standard.

Thin coaxial Ethernet cable is physically easier to handle than thick Ethernet cable and does not require transceivers at the stations. The cable is also cheaper, but the maximum trunk length is less. Figure E-12 illustrates a thin Ethernet network, and Figure E-13 illustrates the components of the wiring system.

The components of a 10Base-2 network are described in the next sections.

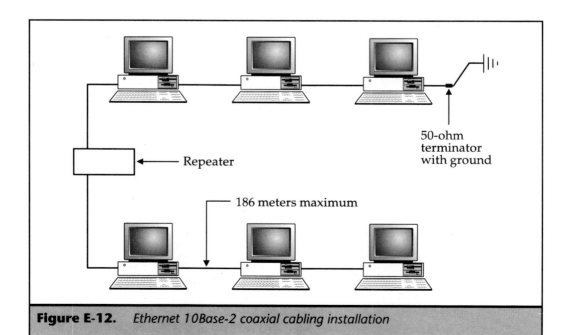

Figure E-12. *Ethernet 10Base-2 coaxial cabling installation*

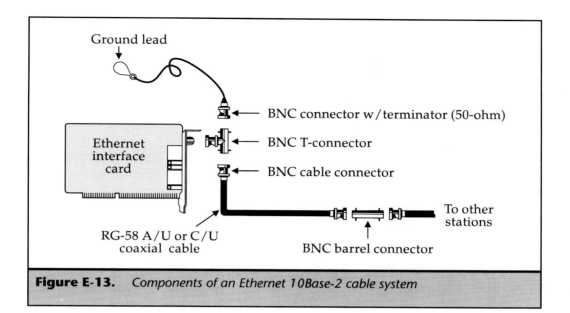

Figure E-13. *Components of an Ethernet 10Base-2 cable system*

NETWORK INTERFACE BOARD   Most Ethernet boards support either thick or thin Ethernet cabling. The board should have a BNC-type connector attached to the back and might also have a thick Ethernet connector. The trunk cable attaches to a BNC T-connector, which is then attached to a male BNC connector on the back of the board. You must use a remote-boot PROM (programmable read-only memory) if the card is installed in a diskless workstation.

REPEATER   A repeater is an optional device used to join two Ethernet trunks and to strengthen the signals between them. A message transmitted on a local area network (LAN) must pass through no more than two repeaters before either reaching its destination or passing through a LAN bridge.

THIN ETHERNET CABLE   The cabling used for thin Ethernet is a 50-ohm 0.2-inch-diameter RG-58 A/U or RG-58 C/U coaxial cable. Thin Ethernet cable is available from many vendors who have precut standard lengths ready to ship with attached connectors. Bulk cable can also be purchased, but you'll need to cut the cable and mount BNC connectors on the ends. Note that cable is available as firesafe plenum cable, nonplenum interior cable, underground-rated cable, and aerial-rated cable.

BNC CABLE CONNECTORS   BNC connectors must be attached to the ends of all cable segments. BNC cable-connector kits include a center pin, a housing, and a clamp-down sleeve. A coaxial cable stripping and crimping tool is required to mount connectors. It can be purchased at electronics stores.

BNC T-CONNECTORS A T-connector is attached to the BNC connector on the back of the Ethernet interface card. The T-connector provides two cable connections for signal-in and signal-out. You will need a T-connector for each workstation, even if it is the last station in the trunk, in which case the BNC terminator is attached to the open end of the T-connector.

BNC BARREL CONNECTORS BNC barrel connectors are used to join two cable segments together.

BNC TERMINATORS Each cable segment must be terminated at both ends with a 50-ohm BNC terminator. For each cable segment you need one terminator with a ground and one without.

You must abide by the following rules and limitations when wiring Ethernet networks with RG-58 A/U or RG-58 C/U coaxial cable:

- The maximum trunk segment length is 186 meters (607 feet).

- T-connectors are used to connect the cable to the network interface card.

- Up to five trunk segments may be joined using four repeaters. Workstations are allowed on only three of the segments. The others are used for distance.

- The maximum network trunk length is 910 meters (3,035 feet).

- You can have a maximum of 30 nodes on one trunk. Repeaters, bridges, routers, and servers count as nodes. The total number of nodes on all segments cannot exceed 1,024.

- A terminator must be placed at each end of a trunk segment, and one end must be grounded.

Combined Thick and Thin Cable

It is possible to combine thick and thin Ethernet cabling systems. For example, you might use thick Ethernet to connect two thin Ethernet segments that are far apart (beyond the reach of thin Ethernet cables). Note that a repeater can also be used to extend an Ethernet network. The maximum number of trunk segments is five.

Combination thick and thin cable segments can be created using a BNC to N-series adapter, which is available with an N-series female or N-series male adapter at one end. Combination thick and thin segments are usually between 607 and 1,640 feet long. The following equation is used to find the maximum amount of thin cable that can be used in one combination trunk segment:

$$\frac{1.640 \text{ feet} - L}{3.28} = t$$

L is the length of the trunk segment you want to build, and t is the maximum length of thin cable you can use.

Ethernet 10Base-5 (Thicknet)

 NOTE: *See "Ethernet" for a background discussion of the Ethernet standard.*

10Base-5 Ethernet is often referred to as standard Ethernet because it was the original Ethernet implementation. Figure E-14 illustrates a thick coaxial Ethernet cabling scheme. Each station on a thick Ethernet trunk is attached by using a transceiver and transceiver cable. The transceiver is not the same as the BNC T-connector used on thin Ethernet. It is a small box that provides electrical isolation of the workstation from the cable. A "heartbeat" test in the transceiver is used to determine if the station is connected properly.

 NOTE: *10Base-5 is falling into disuse as a networking system. It is mentioned here because there are a large number of existing installations you may need to expand or adapt.*

The components of a thick Ethernet network are described in the next sections.

NETWORK INTERFACE BOARD   Most Ethernet network interface boards support either thick or thin Ethernet cabling. The board should have a female DIX-type connector for the attachment of the thick Ethernet transceiver cable. If the interface card is for the server, install the best card available. If the card is for a workstation, you can scrimp a little, especially if the workstation only accesses the network occasionally. You'll need a remote-boot PROM if the card is for a diskless workstation.

REPEATER   A repeater is an optional device used to join two Ethernet trunks and to strengthen the signals between them. A repeater attaches to a transceiver on each cable trunk with a transceiver cable. A message transmitted on a local area network must pass through no more than two repeaters before either reaching its destination or passing through a LAN bridge.

TRANSCEIVER   A transceiver is a junction box on the thick Ethernet cable that workstations attach to. It has three connectors: two are the thick Ethernet in/out connectors, and the third is used to attach the workstation to the transceiver by using a transceiver cable. Transceivers attach to the network cable trunk in one of two ways. A clamping method pierces the cable, eliminating the need to cut the cable and mount connectors. Alternatively, a BNC version of the transceiver has a T-connector to which cable ends attach. You must cut the cable and attach connectors to it by using special tools.

TRANSCEIVER CABLE   A transceiver cable usually comes with a transceiver unit. A male and a female DIX-type connector are mounted on either end of the cable, along

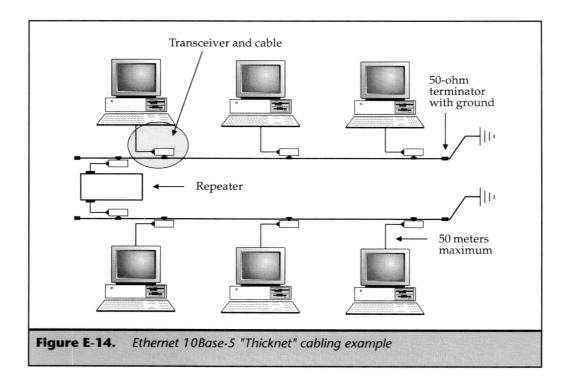

Figure E-14. *Ethernet 10Base-5 "Thicknet" cabling example*

with transceiver connectors and slide locks to lock the cable to the network interface board. The transceiver cable is usually more flexible than the trunk cable.

THICK ETHERNET TRUNK CABLE   The cabling used for thick Ethernet is a 50-ohm, 0.4-inch-diameter coaxial cable, which is stiffer than the transceiver cable. Thick Ethernet cable is available from many vendors in bulk or in precut lengths. A coaxial cable stripping and crimping tool is required to mount connectors. Note that cable is available as firesafe plenum cable, nonplenum interior cable, underground-rated cable, and aerial-rated cable.

N-SERIES MALE CONNECTORS   N-series male connectors are installed on both ends of the cable when T-connector-type transceivers are used. Preassembled cables have the connectors already mounted.

N-SERIES BARREL CONNECTORS   N-series barrel connectors are used to join two cable segments.

N-SERIES TERMINATORS   Each cable segment must be terminated at both ends with a 50-ohm, N-series terminator. For each cable segment, you need one terminator with a ground wire attached and one without a ground wire.

Specifications and limitations of the 10Base-5 standard are listed here:

- The maximum trunk segment length is 500 meters (1,640 feet).

- Transceivers are connected to the trunk segment.

- The maximum workstation-to-transceiver distance is 50 meters (164 feet).

- The minimum distance to the next transceiver is 2.5 meters (8 feet).

- Up to five trunk segments may be joined using four repeaters. Workstations are allowed on only three of the segments. The others are used for distance.

- The maximum trunk length of joined segments is 2,460 meters (8,200 feet).

- You can have a maximum of 100 workstations on one trunk. Repeaters count as workstations.

- A 50-ohm terminator must be placed at the end of each trunk segment, and one end of each segment must be grounded. To prevent loopbacks, do *not* ground a segment at both ends.

Ethernet 10Base-T (Twisted-Pair)

NOTE: See "Ethernet" for a background discussion of the Ethernet standard.

10Base-T offers most of the advantages of Ethernet without the restrictions and cost of coaxial cable. In addition, a star, or distributed, topology allows for clusters of workstations in departments or other areas.

Part of the 10Base-T specification makes it compatible with other IEEE 802.3 standards, so the transition from one medium to another is easy. You can retain existing Ethernet cards when converting from coaxial to twisted-pair cable. In addition, you can add twisted-pair trunks to existing trunks by using repeaters that support coaxial, fiber-optic, and twisted-pair Ethernet trunks. Many vendors make such products available as part of their Ethernet product line.

The 10Base-T specification includes a cable-testing feature called *link integrity testing*. With this feature, the system constantly tests the twisted-pair wiring for open wires and shorts. Monitoring is done from a central point.

A basic 10Base-T network is shown in Figure E-15. Workstations are attached to a central hub, or concentrator, that acts as a repeater. When a signal from a workstation arrives, the hub broadcasts it on all output lines. You can attach hubs to other hubs in a hierarchical configuration. Workstations are attached with an unshielded twisted-pair cable that cannot exceed 100 meters (328 feet). Cables connect to a transceiver near the workstation, and the transceiver is then connected to the workstation with a 15-wire cable that is up to 50 meters (164 feet) long.

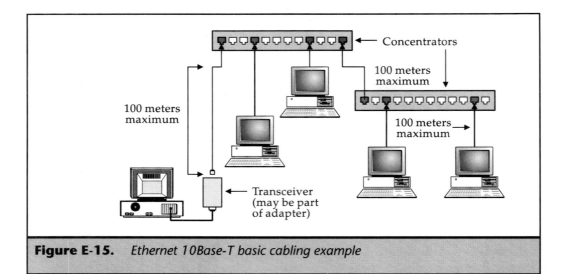

Figure E-15. *Ethernet 10Base-T basic cabling example*

10Base-T connections use Category 3 cabling, although higher grades such as Category 5 provide for future growth into faster transmission technologies such as 100 Mbits/sec Ethernet. See "Cabling" for a discussion of cabling types and techniques. In Figure E-16, a coaxial or fiber-optic backbone connects the wiring centers or closets of different departments within a building. A 10Base-T concentrator is connected to this backbone in the wiring closet. A 50-wire telephone jumper cable then connects the concentrator to a telephone punchdown block. A twisted-pair cable provides a connection between the punchdown block and the faceplate near the workstation. At the workstation, a cable is strung from the faceplate to a transceiver, which then connects to the workstation. Most 10Base-T cards today have a built-in transceiver, and the RJ-45 cable plugs directly into it.

NOTE: *Existing twisted-pair wire may be unsuitable for 10Base-T networks. Have an electrical contractor check the cable before using it.*

The components described in the following sections are typically part of a 10Base-T network. Keep in mind that a system doesn't always require all of these components.

NETWORK INTERFACE CARD   An Ethernet card with a DIX-type 15-pin connector or 10Base-T RJ-45 connector is required. Add a remote-boot PROM if you install the card in a diskless workstation.

NOTE: *Several vendors make 10Base-T "hub" cards for servers. An "octopus" cable attaches to a port on the back of the card and provides workstation connection.*

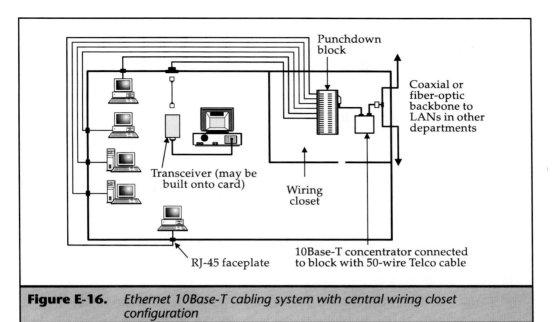

Figure E-16. *Ethernet 10Base-T cabling system with central wiring closet configuration*

HUB   The hub (also called a concentrator) often has up to 12 ports. A port for attachment to coaxial or fiber-optic backbones is usually attached to the box.

TWISTED-PAIR CABLE   10Base-T uses twisted-pair cable with RJ-45 connectors that can be up to 100 meters long. You can purchase bulk cable and connectors to make custom cables. You'll need an RJ crimp tool if you are installing the cable yourself.

TRANSCEIVER   The transceiver has an RJ-45 connector on one side and a DB-15 connector on the other. Alternatively, most cards today have a built-in transceiver.

TRANSCEIVER CABLE   The transceiver cable attaches the transceiver to the back of the network interface card.

PUNCHDOWN BLOCK CONNECTOR CABLE   If existing telephone cable is to be used, a 50-pin Telco cable that connects the concentrator directly to a telephone punchdown block simplifies the installation. Check with the concentrator vendor.

WALLPLATE   A wallplate is a connector with an RJ plug. If a phone connection is also required, dual plates can be purchased.

10Base-T Cable Specifications

The 10Base-T specifications are listed here. Note that some of these specifications are flexible, depending on the vendor. An entire connection from wallplate to hub is pictured in Figure E-17.

> *NOTE: New data-grade structured wiring for high-speed Ethernet uses four-pair cable. See "Cabling" and "EIA/TIA 568 Commercial Building Wiring Standard" for details.*

- Use Category 3, 4, or 5 unshielded twisted-pair cable.

- Use RJ-45 jacks at the end of cables. Pins 1 and 2 are "transmit" and pins 3 and 6 are "receive." Each pair is crossed over so that the transmitter at one end connects to a receiver at the other end.

- A transceiver and a 15-pin transceiver cable may be attached to each workstation. Some cards have built-in transceivers.

- The distance from a transceiver to a hub cannot exceed 100 meters (328 feet).

- A hub typically connects 12 workstations.

- Up to 12 hubs can be attached to a central hub to expand the number of network stations.

- Hubs can be attached to coaxial or fiber-optic backbones to become part of larger Ethernet networks.

- Up to 1,024 stations are possible on a network without using bridges.

RELATED ENTRIES Cabling; EIA/TIA 568 Commercial Building Wiring Standard; *and* Ethernet

Ethernet 100Base-X

See Fast Ethernet.

Ethernet 100VG-AnyLAN (Voice Grade)

> *NOTE: See "Ethernet" for a background discussion of the Ethernet standard.*

Ethernet has proved to be a versatile networking standard. The 10Base-2 standard and the newer 10Base-T twisted-pair standard are installed at thousands of sites. Ethernet is well tested and well understood. Twisted-pair wiring technology brings the cost of installation down and simplifies cabling procedures by taking advantage of structured cabling techniques. Now, high-speed Ethernet (100Base-X) standards are

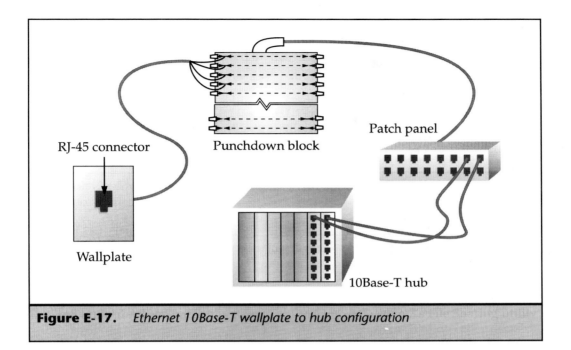

Figure E-17.   *Ethernet 10Base-T wallplate to hub configuration*

available such as 100VG-AnyLAN (voice grade) and Fast Ethernet that provide 100 Mbits/sec to the desktop. These new higher-speed standards are necessary as multimedia, real-time video, and imaging applications become available that demand higher throughput.

The 100VG-AnyLAN proposal is based on technology originally developed by AT&T and Hewlett-Packard. It is under the direction of the IEEE 802.12 committee. The standard uses four-wire twisted-pair cable like that pictured in Figure E-18. It also uses a new *demand priority* cable access method that replaces the carrier sense multiple access/collision detection (CSMA/CD) method used in existing Ethernet networks.

100VG-AnyLAN Specifications

100VG-AnyLAN uses four pairs of the Category 3 voice-grade cabling per station. The competing Ethernet 100 Mbits/sec standard (100Base-X) uses Category 5 data-grade cable, which would require recabling at many sites. 100VG-AnyLAN can take advantage of the higher-grade Category 5 cable if it is installed. If so, cable distances are boosted from 100 meters to 150 meters.

The access method of the original Ethernet is changed, but the frame stays the same. The new access method is called demand priority. With the retained frame format, bridging can occur between existing Ethernet standards and the 100VG-AnyLAN standard. According to Hewlett-Packard, the Ethernet frame format,

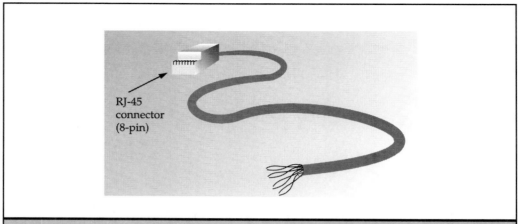

Figure E-18.   *Ethernet 100VG-AnyLAN quartet signaling uses all four wire pairs for signaling*

not CSMA/CD, is the component that defines interoperability and compatibility between different Ethernet standards.

In the demand priority scheme, the hub arbitrates when and how workstations get access to the network. A priority system can guarantee that time-sensitive applications like real-time video get the access time they need to the network. Efficiency is improved with the hub approach because contention is basically eliminated. The hub determines which station gets access.

Because 100VG-AnyLAN is similar to 10Base-T in topology, adapters and other components share many of the same features. A computer with either 10Base-T or 100VG-AnyLAN can plug into the 100VG-AnyLAN hub and operate at the speed they are designed for. The star topology and structured cabling system approach are retained, as is the frame format of existing Ethernet. In addition, 10Base-T connector types are used.

Signaling Methods

100VG-AnyLAN is rated to use the same cable as existing 10Base-T installations. Because this cable is rated as voice grade, quartet signaling is required to assure reliable 100 Mbits/sec transmissions over the line. While 10Base-T uses two pairs in the cable, one to transmit and one to receive, 100VG-AnyLAN uses all four of the wire pairs.

The quartet signaling method uses the same frequencies as 10Base-T, but transmits 25 MHz signals on each of the wire pairs in the cable. An encoding scheme called 5B6B replaces the Manchester encoding used in 10Base-T. The lower signal frequencies in 100VG-AnyLAN, split across the wires, keep radio-frequency emissions within required standards and allow use of voice-grade cable. In contrast, the 10Base-T standard transmits a 20MHz signal split over two wire pairs.

Demand Priority

Demand priority is the new access method in 100VG-AnyLAN that replaces the CSMA/CD method used in existing Ethernet standards. With demand priority, workstations can receive at the same time they transmit. This is possible through the use of the four pairs of wires in the twisted-pair bundle, and the use of quartet signaling.

Demand priority takes advantage of the structured wire design and hub-centric approach pictured in Figure E-19. This design is similar to the Ethernet 10Base-T approach; however, the hub has more control over managing access to the network. When a workstation needs to transmit, it sends a request to the hub and can request a priority level for its transmission. If the network is not busy, the workstation can start transmitting. All transmissions are directed through the hub, which provides rapid switching to the destination node.

The priority mechanism can assure that some traffic such as video, which is time-sensitive, gets priority over other types of traffic. If multiple requests for transmission arrive at the hub, the highest priority is serviced first. If two workstations request the same priority at the same time, both are serviced by alternating between the two. This transmission method is superior to CSMA/CD used in existing Ethernets. In CSMA/CD, workstations compete for access to the cable on their own, rather then under the direction of a central hub. Contention occurs when two or more workstations attempt access at the same time. Each workstation backs off and waits for a period of time before attempting access again. This reduces performance and causes more contention because workstations still need to compete for access to the cable.

An added advantage of the demand priority method is that transmissions sent through the hub are not broadcast to all other workstations, as is the case with standard Ethernet. This reduces the chances that transmissions will be monitored by eavesdroppers and ensures privacy.

RELATED ENTRIES   Cabling; EIA/TIA 568 Commercial Building Wiring Standard; *and* Ethernet

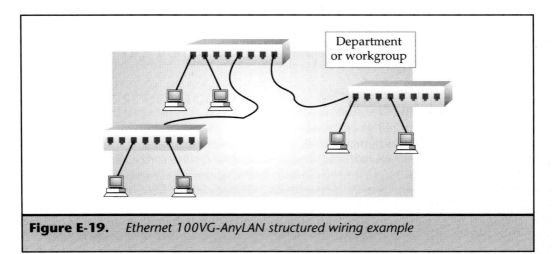

Figure E-19.   *Ethernet 100VG-AnyLAN structured wiring example*

EtherTalk

EtherTalk is an implementation of the Institute of Electrical and Electronics Engineers (IEEE) 802.3 Ethernet standard for Apple Macintosh computers. EtherTalk adapters provided by Apple include media adapters for thin coaxial cable, twisted-pair cable, and fiber-optic cable. The cards are called the Ethernet NuBus (NB) card for Macintosh IIs or the Ethernet LC card for Macintosh LCs. An external adapter is also available for non-NuBus systems. It attaches to the Small Computer System Interface (SCSI) port.

RELATED ENTRIES   Apple; AppleTalk; *and* Ethernet

Extended Industry Standard Architecture (EISA) Bus

The EISA bus was designed by a consortium of industry manufacturers in 1989 to offer support for existing ISA expansion boards as well as provide a platform for future growth. To support ISA cards, an 8 MHz clock rate is used, but the bus can provide direct memory access rates of up to 33 Mbits/sec. An EISA bus has separate input/output (I/O) and microprocessor buses, so the I/O bus can maintain a low clock rate to support ISA boards while the microprocessor bus runs at higher rates. EISA machines can provide high-speed disk I/O to multiple users.

The EISA bus is a full 32-bit bus, so its design accommodates more pins than the ISA bus can handle. The connector has a two-tier slot design that can accept both ISA and EISA cards. The top tier makes contact with ISA boards, and the lower tier makes contact with EISA boards. Although EISA buses can maintain the 8 MHz clock speed of the ISA for compatibility, they support a burst-mode data transfer method that transfers data at up to three times the speed of an ISA bus. Most servers designed for medium to large networks use the EISA bus.

RELATED ENTRIES   MicroChannel Architecture Bus; Peripheral Component Interconnect

Exterior Gateway Protocols (EGP)

The Internet and Transmission Control Protocol/Internet Protocol (TCP/IP) networks in general are divided into autonomous systems, which are collections of hosts and routers that typically use the same routing protocol and are administered by a single authority. Autonomous systems are considered domains. An autonomous system might be a collection of interconnected routers administered by a university or a company. There are two categories of protocols to handle traffic within these domains and outside the domains. While *interior routing protocols* are used within a domain, *exterior routing protocols* provide a way for two neighboring routers located at edges of their respective domains to exchange messages and information.

RELATED ENTRIES   Internet; Routing, Internet; *and* Routing Protocols

Fast Ethernet

 NOTE: See the heading "Ethernet" earlier in this book for a background discussion of the Ethernet standard.

Fast Ethernet is the Institute of Electrical and Electronics Engineers (IEEE) 100Base-X standard originally developed by Grand Junction Networks, 3Com, SynOptics, Intel, and other vendors. It modifies the existing Ethernet standard to support 100 Mbits/sec transfer rates but uses the same Carrier Sense Multiple Access/Collision Detection (CSMA/CD) access method. Electronic Industries Association/Telecommunications Industries Association (EIA/TIA) Category 5 twisted-pair data-grade wiring is required to support the high data rate. The topology is a star configuration similar to Ethernet 10Base-T with all wires leading to a central hub device.

The competing IEEE 100VG-AnyLAN standard uses EIA/TIA Category 3 twisted-pair cable, but implements a new cable access method called *demand priority.* The 100Base-X standard is handled by the existing IEEE 802.3 committee, while the 100VG-AnyLAN standard is handled by a new IEEE 802.12 committee. Some comparison points between the two standards are listed here:

- Both standards require adapter card replacement, but the 100VG-AnyLAN standard is more compatible with existing 10Base-T cable installations.

- Vendors are creating 100Base-X cards that also run 10 Mbits/sec Ethernet to help customers migrate to the new standard.

- 100Base-X requires Category 5 data-grade cable while 100VG-AnyLAN can use four-wire twisted-pair cable. Both options may force some customers to upgrade their cable.

- High-speed Ethernet is limited to 100 meters, although 150-meter lengths are possible with 100VG-AnyLAN if Category 5 data-grade cable is used.

- Both proposals can use fiber-optic cable for longer distance runs.

100Base-X is based on the fact that CSMA/CD is scalable. There is a scaled down 1 Mbit/sec version (IEEE 802.3 1Base-5) that provides longer cable distances. 100Base-X scales up the speed by shortening the cable distance. The network is easily extended by building a hierarchical cable configuration that interconnects outlying hubs (repeater devices), as shown in Figure F-1. This type of wiring fits in to new structured wiring strategies as discussed under "EIA/TIA 568 Commercial Building Wiring Standard."

The primary concern of 100Base-X developers was to preserve the CSMA/CD standard to accommodate existing Ethernet installations. By doing so, 100Base-X fits into the IEEE Media Access Control (MAC) sublayer, which can bridge different IEEE network standards such as token ring, Fiber Distributed Data Interface (FDDI), and

F

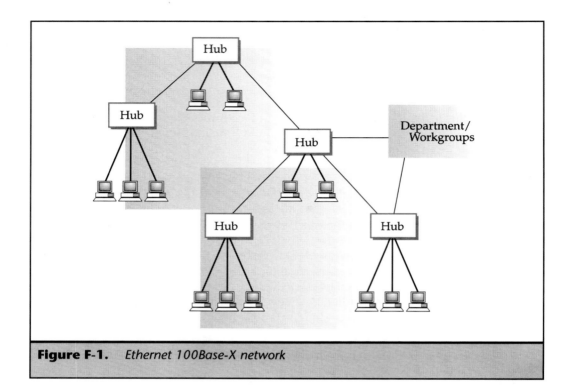

Figure F-1. *Ethernet 100Base-X network*

other Ethernet standards. A bridged network of 10 Mbits/sec Ethernet and 100Base-X would simply need to perform speed matching when exchanging packets.

There are some advantages to the competing 100VG-AnyLAN standard to be aware of when evaluating one network over the other. The demand priority access method in 100VG-AnyLAN provides a way to designate priority service for certain types of local area network (LAN) traffic, such as time-sensitive video. An added advantage of demand priority is that transmissions sent through the hub are not broadcast to all other workstations, as is the case with existing Ethernet. This reduces the chances that transmissions will be monitored by eavesdroppers and ensures privacy.

The type of cabling used to provide 100 Mbits/sec transmission is an important consideration when choosing a high-speed Ethernet design. The existing Category 3 voice-grade cable that is installed in many older buildings is not suitable for 100 Mbits/sec Ethernet networks, so rewiring is necessary for 100Base-X (the 100VG-AnyLAN standard requires four pairs, so it too may require recabling). 100Base-X takes advantage of a new American National Standards Institute (ANSI) standard called X3T9.5 (FDDI) TP-PMD, which uses two pairs of Category 5 data-grade cable. It supports fiber-optic and IBM Type-1 shielded twisted-pair (STP) cabling as well.

RELATED ENTRIES   Ethernet; Ethernet 100VG-AnyLAN

Fast Packet Switching

Fast packet switching is a common industry term that is often used to refer to two different but related types of data transmissions through mesh-type switching networks. A mesh network transfers information (in packet or cell form) through various network paths to a destination. The paths are typically telecommunication links provided by local and long distance carriers. Frame Relay and Asynchronous Transfer Mode (ATM) are normally associated with fast packet switching; however, there are basic differences between the two, as described next.

- There are variable-length packets and fixed-sized packets (called *cells*).

- Frame Relay and X.25 use variable-length packets; however, Frame Relay, as the name implies, is a relay service and X.25 is a packet service. Frame Relay does not perform the extensive error checking and acknowledgement that X.25 does, and is therefore classified as a "fast packet" technology.

- ATM transmits information in fixed-size, 53-byte cells, and is called a *cell relay* technology.

- Cell relay provides a performance improvement over frame relay and packet switching due to its fixed size cells. Variable-length frames and packets can cause congestion at switches when long frames hold up other traffic. Fixed-size cells provide predictable and manageable throughput.

- In Frame Relay and ATM, a frame or cell is immediately forwarded after the switch determines the output port. In X.25, a packet must be completely received and error-checked at each switch before it is forwarded.

The "fast" in fast packet technologies comes from the fact that error-checking, packet sequencing, and acknowledgment are not handled by the network, but by the end-stations. This allows quick relaying of information. If the network loses a packet or drops a packet due to corruption, congestion, or link errors, it is the job of the receiving station to detect the missing packet and request a retransmission. Eliminating this error checking from the network improves performance. Because most modern telecommunication facilities are built on highly reliable media such as fiber-optic cable, they are inherently reliable and do not require extensive error checking. The error checking in X.25 was implemented to accommodate unreliable telephone lines, which were prevalent when the standard was implemented and which are still prevalent in some countries.

An important feature of fast packet technology is that it is implemented at the Media Access Control (MAC) sublayer of the Data-Link layer, relative to the Open

Systems Interconnection (OSI) model. Packet switching like that implemented in X.25 takes place at the Network layer relative to the OSI model.

RELATED ENTRIES   Asynchronous Transfer Mode; Cell Relay; *and* Metropolitan Area Network

Fault Management

Fault management is the ability to locate faults, determine the cause, and make corrections. It is concerned with keeping systems available for users and involves the following:

- Continuous monitoring and the collection of statistics on workstations, traffic conditions, and usage so potential faults can be forecast and avoided
- Setting threshold conditions that can warn you with alarms of conditions on the network that may cause failures
- Setting alarms that warn of performance degradations on servers, routers, and wide area network links
- Setting alarms that warn of resource usage problems, such as a server that is almost out of disk space
- The ability to remotely control workstations and other devices
- The ability to perform some or all of the above tasks from a single management location, which may be extremely remote from some sites

Fault management requires certain procedures, personnel, and equipment to handle alarm conditions, as listed here:

- Using pager devices to warn staff members who are not at the office
- Testing equipment such as protocol analyzers
- Preparing an inventory of spare parts
- Writing procedures that unskilled users can follow if necessary
- Ensuring proper documentation of all systems

Management software and management protocols are available to handle some of these tasks, although software and equipment for centralized control of large networks is still an immature technology. Some companies outsource these tasks.

RELATED ENTRY   Management Standards and Tools

Fault Tolerance

Fault tolerance is a method for providing redundancy in hardware systems to protect against downtime should one of the redundant systems go down. In some environments, a company can lose thousands or millions of dollars when its personnel can't get at the data on a server. Implementing fault-tolerant systems protects against this loss.

DISK-LEVEL PROTECTION   The following features are implemented at the disk level in most network operating systems.

■ Most network operating systems now create multiple copies of their file allocation tables (FATs) or other data tables that keep track of the location of files. One copy of the table stored elsewhere on the disk provides a backup in case the other is corrupted.

■ The Novell NetWare operating system provides a *hot fix* feature that automatically detects bad blocks on a disk and moves data from those areas to a designated area that has not been previously used.

TRANSACTION MONITORING SYSTEMS   *Transaction monitors* can ensure that incomplete disk writes are backed off the disk. This occurs if a system or communication link failed while information is being written to the disk. In distributed environments, a transaction can involve more than one database. If these databases are at different remote locations, any of the communication links or systems may fail during the write. It is the job of the transaction monitor to track the write events and either commit or back them off.

DISK MIRRORING AND DUPLEXING   *Disk mirroring* and *duplexing* are features that write data to two disks simultaneously. The disk can share the same controller, or each disk can be attached to its controller. The latter method is called duplexing.

RAID SYSTEMS   *Redundant arrays of inexpensive disks (RAID)* are devices with multiple disks that appear as one disk to the operating system. If one disk in the array fails, the rest can still operate because a separate disk provides parity information that can supply the missing data.

FAULT-TOLERANT DUPLEXED SERVERS   Data is simultaneously written to two entirely different computer systems that are usually in separate locations to protect against natural disasters such as earthquakes and floods. High-speed, proprietary, fiber-optic connections are required between the server to keep them synchronized. See "NetWare SFT Level III" later in this book for an example of this type of system.

REDUNDANT COMMUNICATION CHANNELS   When communication between systems is critical and there is a chance the communication link could be severed, it's a good idea to create a redundant link. That link should follow a different path between systems to avoid the same problems that took out the first line (such as a backhoe or storm). Redundant backbones within a building or redundant wide area connections are part of this recommendation.

FAULT-TOLERANT COMPONENTS   Part of the communication channel includes the hubs and routers. Installing duplicate devices, along with backup power supplies, is a good investment if communication channels must stay available. Power supplies are appropriate for redundancy, as well. Switching from one power supply to another during a failure must be a clean and automatic process. Hot swapping features allow replacement of parts while a system is running.

F

MANAGEMENT SYSTEMS Centralized management systems can provide useful troubleshooting information or can monitor the network and provide problem avoidance information. These systems use standard management protocols such as the Simple Network Management Protocol (SNMP) or the Common Management Information Protocol (CMIP). "Agents" in managed systems gather statistics and system information on a regular basis, then provide this information to the management system, which can present it to an administrator in a readable form. Alarms can be set to warn of impending events (such as a disk running out of space) or traffic overload areas.

RELATED ENTRIES Disk Mirroring and Duplexing; NetWare SFT Level III; Management Standards and Tools; *and* Redundant Arrays of Inexpensive Disks

FAX Servers

Fax servers are becoming an important part of the network. They are computers with fax devices that manage incoming and outgoing faxes. Users at workstations can avoid the lines at the office fax machine by simply sending faxes from their desktop to the fax server. The fax server then sends the fax over its telephone line connections. Because the fax server is shared by many users, it reduces the need to install many individual fax devices throughout a company.

Fax servers can also provide important in-bound services. For example, an operator can monitor incoming faxes and route them to appropriate users over the local area network (LAN), or discard those that are not essential. An alternative is to assign users on the LAN an individual fax number that is linked to their E-mail address. The fax then goes into their E-mail box. This is called *inbound routing*.

Inbound routing methods may soon be standardized. the Telecommunications Industry Association (TIA), which is in charge of setting fax standards in the U.S., has been studying a set of inbound routing techniques proposed by the International Computer Facsimile Associate (ICFA). One of the techniques is to create a a unique extension for phone numbers that routes faxes to the proper destination.

Companies can also set up fax information services. Users on the network or users dialing in can select from lists of documents by pressing buttons on their phone or choosing from a menu on their computer. The information is then faxed to them by the fax server.

Developers are including fax features in their software, in the same way they have included E-mail features. For example, within applications such as Lotus Notes, you can fax the documents you are working on. There are also some developments going on in which formatted document information is transmitted from one fax to another as binary files. This eliminates the digitizing process. The system that receives the fax either prints it out or saves it as a file that can be edited. This process is basically a file transfer session handled by fax machines.

Another interesting feature offered by some vendors lets you send faxes from the road by placing them in an E-mail message. You then send the E-mail message with the enclosed fax to your company's fax server, which then unpackages it and sends the fax in the normal way to its inhouse or outbound destination. This saves you a call, assuming your company's E-mail system has a toll-free number and you call in on a regular basis to pick up mail anyway.

Other fax server features include the following:

- Fax servers can keep log files of faxing activities for later scrutiny.
- Fax servers can manage the fax address books for a company.
- Fax servers are central systems that are easier to manage.

Much of the work in simplifying both fax and E-mail technology at the workstation is being handled by Microsoft. Its Microsoft at Work strategy is designed to make office equipment more intelligent and interconnectable with desktop computers and networks. Windows and Windows applications will have menu options for working with these devices.

RELATED ENTRIES   Electronic Mail; Lotus Notes; Microsoft At Work Architecture; *and* Servers, Network

F

Federal Information Processing Standards (FIPS)

FIPS are standards developed under the U.S. government's computer standardization program. The program defines automatic data processing and telecommunication standards for government agency use. FIPS follow American National Standards Institute (ANSI) standards; government agencies must conform to FIPS standards, and vendors can choose to conform with the ANSI-defined standards for commercial use. The National Institute of Standards and Technology (NIST) is in charge of drafting specifications. Adopted standards include those for the American Standard Code for Information Interchange (ASCII) character coding scheme, data encryption, and for computer programming languages such as COBOL and FORTRAN.

Recently, the U.S. government made news by standardizing on key escrow encryption technology as a FIPS. Key escrow methods make it possible for federal law enforcement agencies to unencrypt communication by obtaining portions of the unencryption keys that are held in escrow by various agencies. Government agency telephones will use the key standards.

Another important FIPS is the Government OSI Profile (GOSIP), which requires agencies of the U.S. government to use Open Systems Interconnection (OSI) compatible computer equipment, or requires that vendors doing business with the government provide OSI functionality.

RELATED ENTRY   Government OSI Profile

Federated Database

The computing resources of many organizations consist of local area networks (LANs), minicomputers, and mainframes that exist at the department and division level as autonomous systems. These systems contain existing databases. When an enterprise computing platform is built to interconnect an organization, the diverse and heterogeneous database systems of the organization are combined into a federated system that allows many users to access data. Middleware products or environments like the Distributed Computing Environment (DCE) provide a layer of software through which users can interoperate with different systems. Because there are very few organizations that design their enterprise networks and databases from scratch, a federated system is more likely to represent real-world systems in most organizations.

While a federated system has a certain amount of interoperability to allow the integration of heterogeneous systems, some amount of autonomy is usually maintained for each system to provide security and management by local managers. In some enterprise environments, on the other hand, managers strive to achieve interoperability at all levels by reducing the number of communication protocols in use and provide access from any user application to any data on the network.

RELATED ENTRIES   Client-Sever Computing; Distributed Computing; Distributed Database; *and* Enterprise Networks

Federated Naming Services, SunSoft ONC

Within the SunSoft Open Network Computing + (ONC+) environment is the Network Information Services + (NIS+) component. This component provides naming services in client-server computing environments. NIS+ is referred to as an enterprise or organizational naming service because it provides its services within a domain (or cell) managed by a single authority.

In some cases, several different types of naming services might be used by the enterprise, such as NetWare's naming service, the OSI naming service, or the naming service in the Open Software Foundation's (OSF's) Distributed Computing Environment (DCE). *Federated naming* provides naming interoperability by supporting these and other naming systems, including naming systems that provide higher-level naming or specialized naming.

RELATED ENTRIES   Directory Services; Domains; Open Network Computing; *and* Sun Microsystems

Fiber Distributed Data Interface (FDDI)

FDDI is a fiber-optic cable standard developed by the American National Standards Institute (ANSI) X3T9.5 committee. It operates at 100 Mbits/sec and uses a dual-ring topology that supports 500 nodes over a maximum distance of 100 kilometers (60 miles). Copper-wire connections are supported, but distances are greatly reduced, as discussed later in this section. The dual counter-rotating rings offer redundancy (fault tolerance). If a link fails or the cable is cut, the ring reconfigures itself, as shown on the right in Figure F-2, so it can continue transmitting network traffic.

FDDI is an excellent medium for building backbones (see "Backbone Networks" earlier in this book), as shown in Figure F-3. Local area network (LAN) segments attach to the backbone, along with minicomputers, mainframes, and other systems. Small networks that consist of a few LAN segments will probably benefit more from a coaxial Ethernet backbone. Large networks with many LAN segments and heavy traffic produced by high-performance workstations, graphics file transfers, or other internetwork traffic will benefit from FDDI.

Stations attached directly to the FDDI cable have two point-to-point connections with adjacent stations. In the dual-ring configuration, one channel is used for transmission while the other is used as a backup. Some stations, called dual-attached stations (DASs), are attached to both of these rings. Single-attached stations (SASs) are connected through a concentrator that provides connections for multiple SASs. One of the advantages of this configuration is that a failed SAS cannot disrupt the ring. Also, most SASs are user workstations that are shut down often, which would disrupt the ring if directly attached to it.

Also notice the attachment of a router and LAN to the FDDI ring. The optical bypass provides the circuitry to keep the ring intact should the router go down. A redundant connection can be used for important devices like servers to maintain a continuous connection. Should one connection fail, the other can take over, as shown by the two DAS server connections in Figure F-3.

F

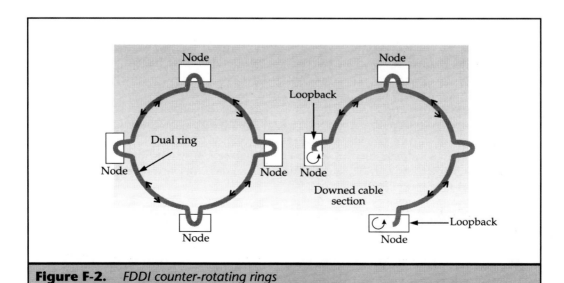

Figure F-2.   *FDDI counter-rotating rings*

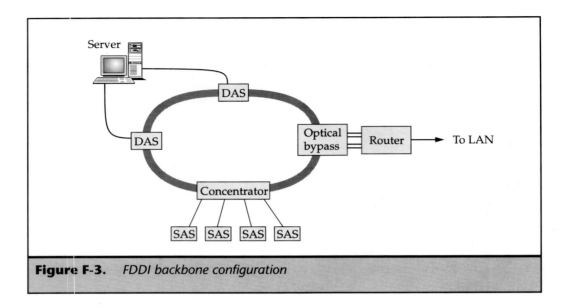

Figure F-3. *FDDI backbone configuration*

One thing to keep in mind with any shared network such as FDDI is that its bandwidth can become saturated. For example, FDDI provides 100 Mbits/sec bandwidth, but ten 10 Mbits/sec Ethernet workstations transmitting files at the same time can saturate that bandwidth. You should evaluate your backbone traffic requirements. Perhaps a high-speed switching hub will provide a better solution. With increasing use of video and multimedia, 100 Mbits/sec bandwidth may become a bottleneck. Asynchronous Transfer Mode (ATM) switching hubs may be more suitable for your network backbone requirements. For more information, see "Asynchronous Transfer Mode." Alternatively, Fast Ethernet networks may provide a more economical 100 Mbits/sec network. See "Ethernet 100VG-AnyLAN," and "Fast Ethernet."

Some of the hubs and switching devices discussed under "Hubs" have Ethernet ports for workstations and FDDI ports for servers or superservers. If a server is a multiprocessing system with a proprietary high-speed bus, it can handle much more traffic than one or more 10 Mbits/sec Ethernet segments can send it. It makes sense to use FDDI adapters in these servers. Figure F-4 illustrates how ten Ethernet workstations route their traffic to a switching hub, which forwards the combined traffic to the server over FDDI.

Some advantages of fiber-optic cable are listed here:

■ Fiber-optic cable is immune to electromagnetic interference, making it ideal in areas where interference normally causes problems.

■ Fiber-optic cable is secure. It does not emit a signal outside the cable that intruders can monitor.

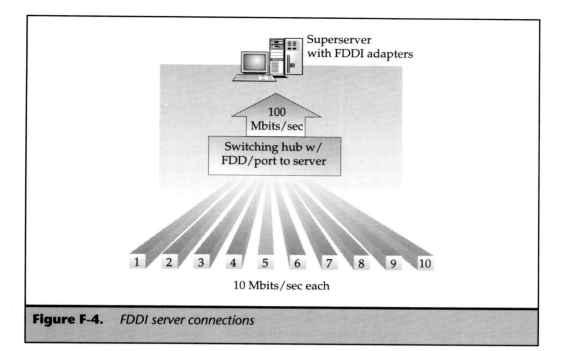

Figure F-4. *FDDI server connections*

■ Fiber-optic cable does not suffer from problems inherent in copper cable that causes data errors and the need to retransmit packets.

■ Fiber-optic networks can reach miles with few repeaters, and fiber-optic cable can replace other transmission methods, such as microwave and telecommunication links.

FDDI Access Method

FDDI uses a token-passing access method. A token frame is passed around the network from station to station; if a station needs to transmit, it acquires the token. The station then transmits data and places the token back on the ring when done. A regulation mechanism is used to prevent one station from holding the token for too long. To accommodate high-volume stations, the network administrator can prioritize the station, basically giving it a longer period of time to transmit before releasing the token. Note the features listed here:

■ Directly attached FDDI stations act like repeaters. They receive packets from their upstream neighbor and send them to their downstream neighbor. When a node sees its own address in a packet, it copies the packet into its own memory.

- Multiple frames can exist on the network. If a station relinquishes the token while its frames are still in transit, other stations can begin transmitting.

- A management mechanism called station management enables system administrators to manage and monitor FDDI networks, isolate faulty nodes, and route traffic.

Types of FDDI

The discussion so far has centered on the original FDDI standard, which is well established. But emerging multimedia and real-time video applications have special transmission requirements, based on their time-sensitive nature. Delays in the delivery of packets in a real-time video transmission can make the video appear jerky to the viewer. When some packets are delayed and others arrive on time, the delayed packets are simply dropped. The token-passing nature of FDDI and its variable-length packet structure do not provide the uniform data stream required by live video. These problems are being solved in several ways, as discussed next.

FDDI now has three transmission modes. The first two modes, asynchronous and synchronous, are available in the original FDDI standard. The third mode, circuit-based, can provide dedicated circuits. This mode is available in the new FDDI-II standard, which requires new adapter cards.

ASYNCHRONOUS SERVICES   Asynchronous ring mode is token-based. Any station can access the network by acquiring the token. This mode implies that traffic is not prioritized, so time-sensitive traffic such as video suffers. One method for solving the live video and multimedia delivery problem on existing FDDI networks is to simply buffer incoming packets until they all arrive and can be placed in order, then show the video. However, this causes a delay that may not be acceptable in live videoconferencing in which people are holding conversations but is acceptable if someone is viewing a stored video sequence.

SYNCHRONOUS SERVICES   Synchronous token-passing ring mode allows prioritization of time-sensitive traffic such as video so packets arrive on time. FDDI cards with synchronous capabilities give network managers the ability to set aside part of the bandwidth for time-sensitive traffic. Asynchronous workstations then contend for the rest. Synchronous capabilities must be added via software upgrades to most existing FDDI cards. A standard is being worked out by the ANSI committee, so the feature will be available as a standard option in most new cards.

CIRCUIT-BASED SERVICES   Circuit-based mode (FDDI-II only) can create a dedicated communication line between two stations with guaranteed bandwidth. The circuit-based services in FDDI-II are provided by assigning regular, repeating time slots in the transmission to create a dedicated communication channel between two stations. This method is called isochronous transmission.

Fiber Cable

There is single-mode and multimode fiber-optic cable. Single-mode cable passes one frequency of light, and multimode cable passes several frequencies of light. For a further discussion of these terms, refer to the main entry, "Fiber-Optic Cable." Note that a twisted-pair copper wire version of FDDI has also recently been standardized. It is discussed later in this section.

- The minimum cable type that can be used is 62.5/125 micron multimode optical fiber.

- Multimode cable can be used if the FDDI specification are adhered to. These specifications are available from any FDDI vendor. Some may prefer higher-bandwidth cables in anticipation of future requirements.

- Multimode fiber-optic cable is recommended over single-mode cable because it is more adaptable to future products.

Fiber-optic cable was once thought to be costly. However, competition has brought its price down considerably, and it is a better choice for future technologies. Refer to "Fiber-Optic Cable" for a discussion of pricing and cable types.

FDDI/OSI Relationship

The relationship of FDDI to the Open Systems Interconnection (OSI) model is shown in Figure F-5. The top level FDDI layer fits in the Media Access Control (MAC) portion of the Data-Link layer. Just above it is the IEEE 802.2 Logical Link Control layer, which can act as a bridge and transfer packets between the Ethernet and token ring network pictured. Packets for a local station are sent to higher protocol layers rather than forwarded on.

The Station Management (SMT) standard shown in the illustration manages the station and ring configuration, initialization, station insertion and removal, and diagnostics.

FDDI-II

The FDDI-II standard is designed for networks that need to transport real-time video or other information that cannot tolerate delays. FDDI-II requires that all nodes on the network FDDI-II network use FDDI-II, otherwise the network reverts to FDDI. Existing FDDI stations should be attached to their own networks.

FDDI-II uses multiplexing techniques to divide the bandwidth into dedicated circuits that can guarantee the delivery of multimedia traffic. It can create up to 16 separate circuits that operate at from 6.144 Mbits/sec each to a maximum of 99.072 Mbits/sec. The reason for this variation is that bandwidth is allocated to whatever station needs it. Each of these channels can be subdivided further to produce a total of 96 separate 64-Kbits/sec circuits.

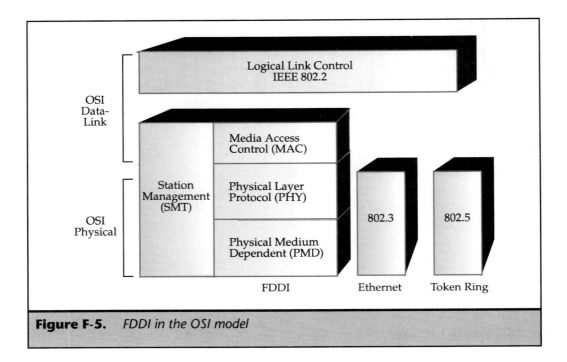

Figure F-5. *FDDI in the OSI model*

These channels can support asynchronous or isochronous traffic. Regular, timed slots in the ring are allocated for the transmission of data. Prioritized stations use the number of slots they need to deliver their data on time. If slots go unused, they are reallocated immediately to other stations that can use them.

FDDI-II will be a standard by the time you read this, but it may not become a widespread networking technology. One reason is because it is incompatible with the existing FDDI design. Another reason is that emerging Asynchronous Transfer Mode (ATM) equipment is more appealing to some as a networking technology for high-traffic and time-dependant traffic loads.

FDDI/UTP

An alternative cabling technology that follows the FDDI standard is to use unshielded twisted-pair (UTP) copper wire. It was originally proposed by IBM, DEC, Cabletron Systems, Crescendo Communications, and others. The ANSI Twisted-Pair-Physical Medium Dependent (TP-PMD) standard defines an FDDI network that runs over Category 5 data-grade cable and IBM Type 1 shielded twisted-pair (STP) cable. It provides the features of normal FDDI, except for a difference in the distance of the cable. UTP supports 100 meters (330 feet) between nodes while fiber supports 2 kilometers between nodes.

Category 5 cable is rated for high-speed data communication at 100 Mbits/sec over short distances in a configuration similar to the star-topology of Ethernet 10Base-T. Category 5 cable is part of a structured wiring specification that requires special patch panels, punchdown blocks, and wall plates. High-speed transmission is possible by tightening the specification for twisted-pair cable. For example, cable twists must be maintained right up to the taps of the wallplates and punchdown blocks.

Sites that have installed Ethernet 10Base-T with Category 5 data-grade twisted-pair cable will be ready to upgrade to the FDDI/UTP copper wire standard. But keep in mind that FDDI and 10Base-T have different cable configurations. While both support workstation attachments to concentrators, FDDI also supports workstation attachments in a station-to-station configuration that forms a dual-ring.

Workstations are connected in a star-like configuration from a concentrator device, which can provide a connection to a fiber-optic FDDI ring. The cable from the concentrators must provide a crossover of pairs 1 and 2 at some point. This can be done in the wire that runs from the concentrator to a patch panel. The patch panel organizes the cable runs to workstations through the building walls.

Network backbones that link distant local area networks will still use fiber-based FDDI. However, with copper-based FDDI on the horizon, pricing for fiber-based FDDI cards is now cheaper. Administrators should carefully evaluate the products and pricing available in the market.

RELATED ENTRIES   Cabling; Fiber-Optic Cable

Fiber-Optic Cable

Fiber-optic cable employs photons for the transmission of digital signals. A fiber-optic cable is made of pure glass, which imposes negligible resistance to the passage of the photons though it. Copper cable, on the other hand, is subject to the following problems that are not a factor for fiber-optic cable.

- Signal transmissions over long distances are subject to *attenuation,* which is a loss of signal strength or amplitude and limits the length of the cable.

- *Capacitance* is an undesirable characteristic that can distort the signal on a cable. The greater the length of a cable or thickness of the insulator, the greater the capacitance and resulting distortion.

- *Crosstalk* is a major source of noise in twisted-pair cables. It is caused by signal "leakage" from adjacent wires.

Fiber-optic cable is resistant to electromagnetic interference and generates no radiation of its own. This last point is important in locations that require security. Copper wire radiates energy that can be monitored. Taps in fiber-optic cable are detectable because the signal strength of the cable changes. Fiber-optic cable also extends to much longer distances than copper cable.

Fiber-optic cable uses light to transmit signals through a strand of glass that is so clear that, according to Michael Coden of Codenoll Technologies Corporation (a major fiber vendor), "a 3-mile-thick fiber-optic window would give you the same view as a 1/8-inch-thick glass window." The optic core of fiber-optic cable is pure silicon dioxide. It makes for good tricks. You can wrap it around yourself, then shine a light in one end and see that light on the other end.

Computer signals are sent over fiber-optic cable by converting electronic 1s and 0s to optically-coded 1s and 0s. You simply place a light-emitting diode on one end to flash light down the cable, then collect it on the other end with a simple photodetector and convert it back to electrical signals.

Cable Construction

Take a look at the fiber-optic cable in Figure F-6. The core is the transparent glass (or plastic) component of the cable. Light shines through it from one end to the other. The cladding, which is a glass sheath that surrounds the core, is a key component. Like a mirror, it reflects light back into the core. As light passes through the cable, its rays bounce off the cladding in different ways as shown in Figure F-7. The sharper the angle at which a ray bounces, the longer it takes for the ray to reach the other end of the cable. While this time difference is measured in billionths of a second, it introduces enough delay that cable distances must be restricted, depending on the diameter of the core. Dispersion is rated in nanoseconds per kilometer. Typical dispersion for multimode cable as discussed here is in the 15 to 30 nanosecond range.

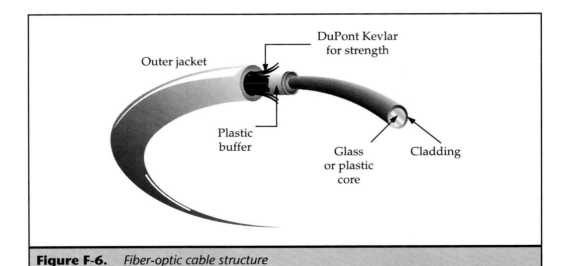

Figure F-6. *Fiber-optic cable structure*

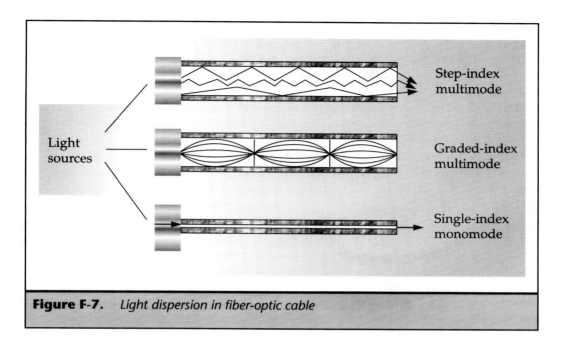

Figure F-7. *Light dispersion in fiber-optic cable*

The types of fiber-optic cable are listed here:

■ *Plastic* cable, which works only over a few meters, is inexpensive and works with inexpensive components.

■ *Plastic-coated silica* cable offers better performance than plastic cable at a little more cost.

■ *Single-index monomode fiber* cable is used to span extremely long distances. The core is small and provides high bandwidth at long distances. Lasers are used to generate the light signal for single-mode cable. This cable is the most expensive and hardest to handle, but it has the highest bandwidths and distance ratings.

■ *Step-index multimode* cable has a relatively large diameter core with high dispersion characteristics. This type of cable has a dispersion rating of 15 to 30 nanoseconds per kilometer of cable. The cable is designed for the LAN environment and light is typically generated with a light-emitting diode (LED).

■ *Graded-index multimode* cable has multiple layers of glass that contain dispersions enough to provide increases in cable distances. This cable has about 1 nanosecond of dispersion per kilometer.

Cable specifications list the core and cladding diameters as fractional numbers. For example, the minimum recommended cable type for a Fiber Distributed Data Interface

(FDDI) design is 62.5/125 micron multimode optical fiber. That means the core is 62.5 microns and the core with surrounding cladding is a total of 125 microns.

- The core specifications for step-index and graded-index multimode cables range from 50 to 1,000 microns.

- The cladding diameter for step mode cables ranges from 125 to 1,050 microns. The cladding diameter for graded multimode cable ranges from 125 to 140 microns.

- The core diameter for single-mode step cable is 4 to 10 microns, and the cladding diameter is from 75 to 125 microns.

Optical Cable Types

The following cable types are available from Optical Cable in Roanoke, Virginia, 703/265-0690. They are listed here as a representative sample of the cable types available from various manufacturers.

- A-Series simplex and duplex interconnect cables are flexible, resilient, and ideal for patch cords and jumpers. This cable is pictured in Figure F-8.

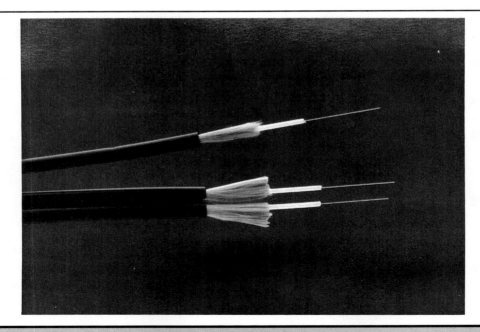

Figure F-8.   *Fiber-optic cable (Courtesy of Optical Cable Corp., Roanoke, Virginia)*

- 12-fiber standard B-series breakout cable has up to 156 fibers. It is designed for direct terminations with connectors in local area networks.

- 12-fiber standard D-series distribution cable has up to 156 fibers. It is compact in design and ideal for longer trunking distances. The cable is designed for direct termination with connectors within patch panels.

- 36-fiber DB-series subgrouping cable has up to 1,000 fibers. It is designed for high fiber count packaging with easy direct termination. Plenum-rated (firesafe) cable is also available.

- 12-fiber D-series S-type plenum cable has 12 fibers and is designed for plenum areas.

- 4-fiber standard B-series plenum breakout cable has up to 102 fibers and is designed for plenum areas.

- D-series distribution armored cable has 156 fibers and is designed to be "rodent-proof" in direct-burial environments.

- M-series aerial cable has up to 48 fibers and a stainless steel or all-dielectric messenger or self-supporting round cable for outside plant aerial installations.

F

Comparison Pricing

Codenoll Technologies Corporation of Yonkers, New York likes to dispel the myth that fiber is more expensive than copper cable. They include the following table in their *Fiber Optic LAN Handbook*, which you can get by calling 914/965-6300. The CodeNet product is an Ethernet configuration.

ISA/Ethernet Retail Price Comparison

	Category 3	Category 5	CodeNet
ISA Network card	$249	$249	$495
Cable to Hub (50m)	50	338	100
Connectors/cables	3	53	56
Labor ($45/hr)	30	40	45
Hub (per port)	365	365	115
Total ($ per port)	$697	$1,045	$811

These rates are based on the following:

- Fiber cable at $0.86 per meter, or $0.26 per foot
- Unshielded twisted pair at $0.46 per meter, or $0.14 per foot
- Shielded twisted pair at $2.05 per meter, or $0.62 per foot
- Category 5 data-grade cable at $2.31 per meter, or $0.70 per foot

RELATED ENTRY   Cabling

Fibre Channel

 NOTE: *The British spelling, fibre, is used for this standard.*

Fibre Channel is a campus-wide interconnection standard that is designed primarily to interconnect peripherals, mass storage systems such as redundant array of inexpensive disks (RAID) devices, imaging and archiving systems, mainframes, engineering workstations, and other high-speed devices together. Fibre Channel has features of a network, but it is not a network in the traditional sense. Instead, it is a high-speed channel that uses fiber-optic cable to interconnect computing devices in a relatively local environment, such as a laboratory or a campus environment as shown in Figure F-9. The speed of Fibre Channel is its most distinguishing feature: it provides bandwidth from 133 Mbits/sec to 1 Gbits/sec over a variety of cable types, including multimode fiber, coaxial cable, and shielded twisted-pair wire.

The American National Standards Institute (ANSI) X3T9 committee is developing the Fibre Channel Interconnect standard. By the time you read this, it should be ratified and added to the International Organization for Standardization (ISO) standards list as well. The Fibre Channel System Initiative (FCSI), which includes Hewlett-Packard, IBM, and Sun Microsystems, is promoting Fibre Channel. In addition, major vendors such as Emulex are developing Fibre Channel products. The primary purpose of FCSI is to develop a high-speed, open connection standard for workstations and peripherals.

To some extent, Fibre Channel is competing with emerging Asynchronous Transfer Mode (ATM) products because it can form switching environments for local area networks (LANs). ATM provides similar specifications, but provides better wide area network support. While these products at first seem similar, you should view ATM as a multiuser LAN or WAN technology and view Fibre Channel as a way to interconnect high-speed devices. Fibre Channel is a good choice for connecting two or more parallel processing computers together or for attaching mass storage devices to a superserver. However, Fibre Channel does offer switching services and can be used to build networks with a number of user workstations.

Where Fibre Channel Fits In

Existing network technologies such as Ethernet suffer from limited transmission speeds. These networks packetize data and typically send it over shared networks using connectionless methods. This strategy is not ideal for communication between high-speed workstations and peripheral devices. For example, a small research laboratory may have a few workstations operated by a scientific team that need to connect peripheral devices, superservers, minicomputers, mainframes, and supercomputers. Using LAN technology such as Ethernet is not practical in this

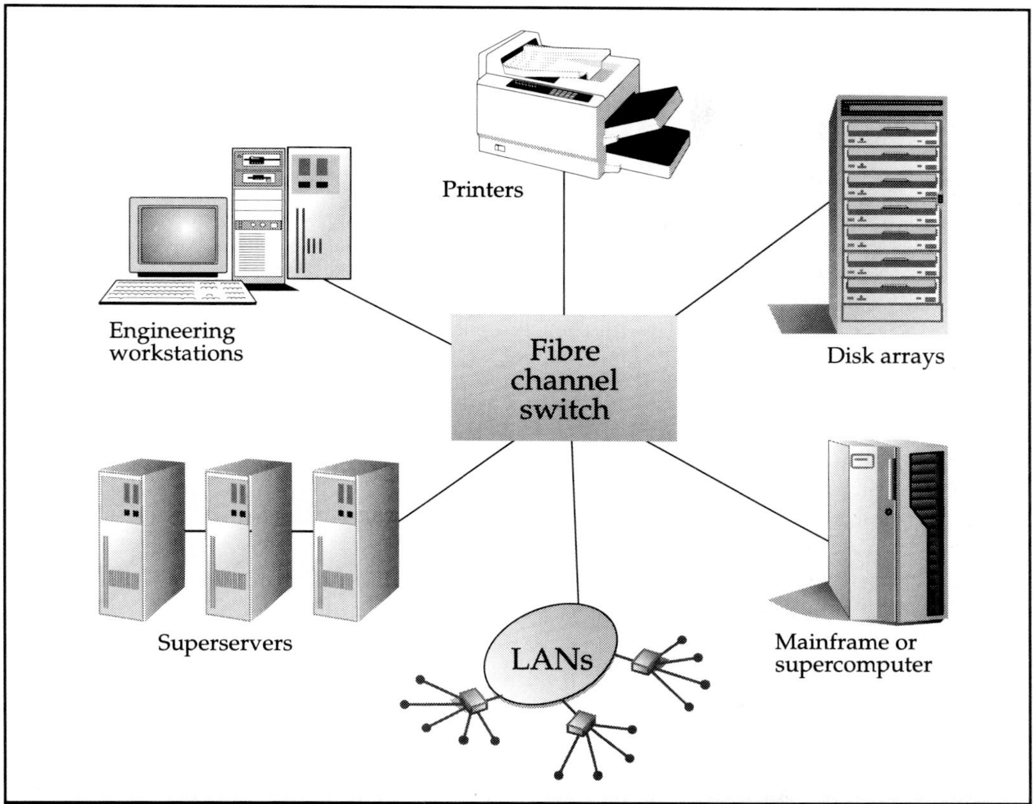

Figure F-9. *Fibre Channel configuration*

"clustered" environment because LAN throughput is far below the processing power and throughput of the computer equipment.

The Fibre Channel interface dedicates circuits for transferring data while allowing other devices to access the channel when it is free. If multiple sessions must run simultaneously, that is possible too. There are three possible connection types with Fibre Channel:

- *Point-to-point device connections* for high transfer rates over greater distances. An example would be a direct connection between a RAID disk system and a superserver. Notice that this point-to-point connection can occur over a network that other users share, but the cable is unavailable until the communication session is complete.

■ *Cluster (workgroup) connections* for high-speed workstations.

■ *Switched LAN connections* for supporting Ethernet, FDDI, and token ring networks that allow multiple, simultaneous point-to-point connections between workstations.

The Fibre Channel interface supports variable-length transmissions, which means it can transmit large blocks of data without dividing it into smaller packets. Fibre Channel also supports the interconnection of the channel and network technologies listed next. To do so, it uses encapsulation techniques in which an address header is added to the frames and transferred through the Fibre Channel switching device or network. In this respect, Fibre Channel has been called a "universal port" by one vendor.

Asynchronous Transfer Mode (ATM)
Fiber Distributed Data Interface (FDDI)
High Performance Parallel Interface (HIPPI)
Intelligent Peripheral Interface (IPI)
LANs such as Ethernet and token ring
Small Computers System Interface (SCSI)

Fibre Channel transports data coming from devices by simply reading the buffer information, packaging it, and sending it across the fabric. *Fabric* describes all the ways you can set up connections in Fibre Channel, from a single cable connecting two devices, to a switching device that uses circuit and packet switching techniques to connect many devices. Underlying data formats, packet structures, or frame types are not important in the switching scheme. Fibre Channel overcomes device restrictions, as well. Consider the SCSI interface. You can normally connect up to 8 or 16 devices to a SCSI adapter. With Fibre Channel switching, you could connect millions of devices.

As mentioned, Fibre Channel can establish dedicated, point-to-point connections between devices. These connections are like circuits, and multiple circuits can exist simultaneously with high bandwidth between the connections. The circuits are bidirectional and can provide 100 Mbytes/sec of transmission speed in both directions. When a device wishes to transmit over a switching device or network, it simply attempts to get a dedicated circuit to that device. This is very similar to making a voice telephone call. If the network is currently busy, the port tries again in a moment.

As mentioned earlier, Fibre Channel is similar to ATM and competes with it. But Fibre Channel makes a better peripheral connection technology while ATM is better in the WAN environment or for teleconferencing applications. Latency (delay) is another thing to consider. Fibre Channel uses frame sizes that are 2 Kbytes in size. Only about 1.5 percent of this frame is used for header information. On the other hand, ATM cells are 53 bytes long and 10 percent is used for header information. What this means is that Fibre Channel will transfer more data than ATM under comparable conditions.

Network administrators should consider the possibility of using Fibre Channel in local environments for high-bandwidth users and devices, and ATM as the network backbone and WAN interconnect. As both products emerge, it is expected that Fibre Channel will fall further in price than ATM.

RELATED ENTRIES   Asynchronous Transfer Mode; Connection-Oriented and Connectionless Protocols; *and* Matrix Switches

File and Directory Attributes, NetWare

Files and directories in the NetWare operating system can be flagged with the attributes listed next. When attributes are assigned to individual files in a directory, they override any rights that a user might have in the directory. For example, if a user has the right to delete files in a directory, you can override those rights for individual files by assigning the Delete Inhibit right. Users can set these rights in their personal directory if they have Modify rights in the directory.

A	*Archive Needed*	When set indicates that a file has been modified and needs backing up. It has no effect on directories.
Cc	*Can't Compress* (NetWare 4.x)	A status attribute that indicates a file cannot be compressed due to lack of disk space. It is not used for directories and you cannot assign this attribute.
C	*Compressed* (NetWare 4.x)	A status attribute that indicates a file has been compressed. It is not used for directories and you cannot assign this attribute.
CI	*Copy Inhibit*	When set prevents Macintosh users from copying the file. Not used for directories.
DI	*Delete Inhibit*	When set prevents users from deleting a file or directory.
DC	*Don't Compress* (NetWare 4.x)	When applied to a file prevents the file from being compressed. When applied to a directory prevents files in the directory from being compressed.
DM	*Don't Migrate* (NetWare 4.x)	When applied to a file prevents the file from being migrated to a secondary storage device such as an optical disk jukebox. When applied to a directory prevents files in the directory from being migrated.
X	*Execute Only*	Prevents users from copying a file thus preventing software piracy. Not applicable to directories. Once set it cannot be removed even by the ADMIN user. However, the file can be deleted then restored from a backup or the original.
H	*Hidden*	Hides a file or directory in DIR listings and prevents the file or directory from being copied or deleted.

F

IM	*Immediate Compress* (NetWare 4.x)	When applied to a file the file is compressed as soon as possible. When applied to a directory the files in the directory are compressed as soon as possible.
M	*Migrated* (NetWare 4.x)	A status attribute that indicates that a file has been migrated to a secondary storage device such as an optical disk jukebox.
P	*Purge*	When applied to a file the file is immediately purged from the system when deleted. When applied to a directory the directory and any files it holds are purged when deleted. Purged files and directories cannot be recovered by using NetWare Administrator or FILER.
RO	*Read Only*	When set prevents users from changing deleting or renaming a file. The D and R attributes are also assigned when RO is applied. Has no effect on directories.
RI	*Rename Inhibit*	When set prevents users from renaming a file or directory.
S	*Shareable*	When set allows multiple users to access the file at one time. Usually set on record-locking database files. Has no effect on directories.
SY	*System*	When set prevents users from seeing the file or directory in a DIR listing.
T	*Transactional*	When applied to a file the transaction tracking system will protect the file. Has no effect on directories.

RELATED ENTRIES   Access Rights; NetWare; Rights in Novell NetWare; *and* Security Rights

File and Directory Permissions, Windows NT

See Permissions in Windows NT.

File Server

See Servers, Network.

File Sharing

See Document Management.

File Systems, Distributed

See Distributed File Systems.

File Systems in the Network Environment

File systems store and retrieve files on physical media such as magnetic disk. Other types of media include optical disk and tape, but most operating systems require special drivers to read and write the media. This discussion concentrates on magnetic disk storage systems. A discussion of features for distributed file systems can be found under "Distributed File Systems."

A disk drive has read and write heads that move back and forth, forming tracks on the disks that spin beneath them. Data is written to and read from these tracks. You can think of a phonograph record, but the tracks don't spiral from the outside to the inside. Each track forms an individual circle, and each track is broken into sectors. There may be anywhere from 8 to over 50 sectors per track. Each sector is identified with magnetic markings by the disk controller.

Operating systems get involved above this level and leave sector and track management to the disk controller. However, an operating system transfers information to the disk system in clusters or blocks that can vary in size, depending on the operating system and the value specified when installing the operating system. The cluster/block size can be customized when installing most operating systems to take advantage of the types of files you'll store on the drive. For example, if the drive will store many small files, small cluster/block sizes are preferred. If the drive will store large files, large cluster/blocks work best. This all has to do with the efficiency of a read or write operation. If a small file is written to disk by an operating system using large clusters/blocks, much of that space will go to waste. On the other hand, if a large file is written to a disk using small clusters/blocks, the file must be broken into parts, and those parts might end up scattered around the disk, making read and write operations less efficient.

A method is needed to keep track of what files are on the disk and where they are stored. In addition, files that are fragmented because they could not fit in a contiguous clusters may be scattered throughout the disk. The operating system must track where the fragmented portions of the file are located. Several popular operating systems are discussed in the next few sections.

DOS File Allocation Table (FAT)

FAT is part of the Disk Operating System (DOS). The FAT keeps track of clusters on the disk and the files they belong to. When a file request is made, DOS checks the FAT to locate the first cluster belonging to a file. Clusters belonging to a file may become scattered on the disk, or fragmented. This is because erased files leave open spaces that are reused by DOS when storing new files. If a file can't fit in an open space, it is fragmented. Clusters contain information about where the next cluster is located.

F

The FAT is an inefficient mechanism for storing files on disks. It must be constantly updated. Since the FAT is located in a fixed place on the disk, the read/write heads must repeatedly jump back to it to make entries about changes in cluster allocations. The High Performance File System (HPFS) in the OS/2 operating system was one of Microsoft's solutions to these problems.

There are two copies of the FAT—one is a backup in case the first is corrupted. The FAT is also stored in a fixed location so the boot files can be located when the system starts.

DOS uses a filenaming format with an eight-character filename and a three-character extension. Files are stored in directories and directories can have branching subdirectories. File attributes are limited to Read Only, Hidden, System, and Archive.

High Performance File System (HPFS)

HPFS is the file system designed for OS/2, which is an enhanced form of DOS. It provides long filenames and performance enhancing features that the DOS FAT does not have. It also provides access to larger hard drives, more organizational features, and improved security features. Other features include

- HPFS preserves the FAT system used in DOS, but automatic sorting of the directory by filename was added.
- The clusters allocation method used in DOS was replaced by a simple physical sector allocation of 512 bytes, which helped to reduce unused disk space that was locked by files.
- Directory entries hold information such as the modification, creation, and access date and time.
- Directory entries in HPFS point to the FNODE, which contains a file's data or pointers that point to the location of that data.
- HPFS includes a hot fix feature that can move data in a defective sector to another area.

NT File System (NTFS)

NTFS is the file system in the Windows NT operating environment and the Windows NT Advanced Server network operating system environment. NTFS provides the following features:

- Reliability through fault-tolerant features such as recoverability (transaction tracking) and hot fixing
- A platform for adding functionality
- Support for Portable Operating System Interface (POSIX) requirements

■ Removal of limitations in FAT and HPFS file systems

NTFS provides long filenames, data protection and recovery, and security through directory and file permissions. NTFS supports large hard disks and the storage of files over multiple hard disks (this is called *spanning volumes*). For example, a company database might be so large that it spans several drives.

NTFS provides built-in security features that control file ownership and access. Files on an NTFS volume are not accessible from DOS or other operating systems. That is part of the Windows NT security system, but only when you use NTFS.

NTFS allows filenames of up to 256 characters in length. While DOS users can't access the NTFS volume, NTFS files can be copied to DOS volumes. Each NTFS file includes a DOS-readable filename that conforms to the DOS filename format. This filename is generated by NTFS from the beginning characters of the long filename.

NetWare File System

The NetWare file system is fast and efficient. It has a high capacity of up to 32 terabytes (1 million megabytes) and a single file (such as a database) can be as large as 4 gigabytes. Volumes are divisions of hard disks that can span multiple disks if necessary. Up to 32 disks can be spanned. It also supports up to 100,000 concurrent record or file locks. Information is stored in blocks and a file allocation table (FAT) keeps track of blocks. The FAT, as in DOS, keeps track of where files are located on a disk. A directory entry table (DET) holds information about file names, attributes, user rights, and other information.

The file system built into Novell's NetWare network operating system is called the NetWare Core Protocol (NCP).

The NetWare file system is similar to DOS in the way files are named and directory structures are created. The file system is fault tolerant, supporting both disk mirroring and disk duplexing. An optional product, SFT Level III, provides server duplexing. Performance-enhancing features such as those listed next are available, depending on the version:

■ *Elevator seeking*   Prioritizes incoming read requests based on the position of the read/write head.

■ *File caching*   Minimizes disk accesses by storing common information in memory.

■ *Background writes*   Separates disk writes from disk reads to improve performance.

■ *Overlapped seeks*   If mirroring is used, disk read requests can come from both disks.

■ *Turbo FAT*   The file allocation table is placed in memory where it is accessed much more quickly.

■ *File compression* On NetWare 4.x, files can be compressed to maximize disk space.

■ *Block suballocation* Maximizes disk space by using partial disk blocks for the storage of small files or fragments of files.

Distributed File Systems

There are four primary distributed file systems, as discussed next. All have similar roots.

■ *Network File System (NFS)* An *open* operating system designed by Sun Microsystems specifically for the distributed computing environment. Its specifications are readily available so it can be implemented by any vendor. In fact, many of the features in other network operating systems were derived from NFS. The file system is called Virtual File System (VFS). VFS serves as an interface between the operating system and the file system. The Sun implementations use Transmission Control Protocol/Internet Protocol (TCP/IP) protocols and provide users with transparent access to services on UNIX systems, minicomputers, mainframes, and other distributed systems. NFS has been designed to let all users on the network share a single set of files. Users establish connections to file servers on a temporary or permanent basis to access these files. Client-server computing is a strong feature of NFS.

■ *Andrew File System (AFS)* A filing system developed at Carnegie Mellon that is very similar to NFS. The same VFS interface is used to access files on an AFS system. AFS uses a feature called client caching that differentiates it from NFS, however. With client caching, information is moved to the local hard drive of a client so that the client can interact with it there. The server then informs the client when another user makes any changes to the data. In NFS, the client must periodically check with the server to see if the information it is caching from the server is changed.

■ *Distributed File System (DFS)* The file system component of the Open Software Foundation's (OSF's) Distributed Computing Environment (DCE). DFS is similar to AFS, but clients can gain control of a specific range of data from the server by accessing a token for that data. When a client has the token, no other client can change the data.

■ *File Transfer Access and Management (FTAM)* FTAM is a file transfer service that is implemented in OSI environments. It allows clients (called initiators) to exchange files with servers (called responders). FTAM is designed to help users access files on diverse systems that support OSI protocols. Users can manipulate files at the record level, which is how FTAM stores files. See the heading "File Transfer Access and Management" for more details.

For more details, see the information under the heading "Distributed File Systems" earlier in this book.

AppleTalk Filing Protocol (AFP)

The AppleTalk Filing Protocol (AFP) resides in the Presentation and Application layers of the AppleTalk protocol stack. AFP lets users communicate with AppleTalk file servers. It passes user commands down to lower-layer protocols that handle the establishment of connections and the monitoring of data flow between systems. AFP has the following features:

- AFP sets up an environment for a user that appears as if files on a remote file server are available locally.
- Access to server files is handled using the same procedures as access to local files, except that a user must initially establish a connection to the remote file server.
- AFP provides security features that can restrict user access to files.

AppleShare is based on AFP. Macintosh systems can access AppleShare servers through built-in AppleShare Client software. Macintosh System 7's File Sharing utility adds distributed file service features by allowing users to access files on other users' systems or to make files on their own systems available to other users.

File Transfer Protocol (FTP)

FTP is a program for transferring files in TCP/IP environments such as the Internet in which a user, acting as a client, downloads files from a remote server. FTP is a core component in every TCP/IP system and is implemented at the Applications level with respect to the OSI protocol model. Its operation is based on the Telnet program and TCP. FTP is available on a wide variety of computer systems and serves as a common protocol for transferring files between systems.

RELATED ENTRIES   AppleTalk Filing Protocol; Distributed File Systems; File Transfer Protocol; High Performance Filing Systems; Netware; *and* NTFS

File Transfer Access and Management (FTAM)

FTAM is an Open Systems Interconnection (OSI) standard that provides file transfer services between client (initiator) and server (responder) systems in an open environment. It also provides access to files and management of files on diverse systems. In these respects, it strives to be a universal file system. An interesting feature of FTAM is that it is implemented in all seven layers of the OSI protocol stack. Note that FTAM is a file system that fully complies with the U.S. Government OSI Protocols

(GOSIP) and, when used with X.400 mail gateways, provides the basic profiles and service requirements of GOSIP 1.0.

FTAM is designed to help users access files on diverse systems that use compatible FTAM implementations. It is similar to File Transfer Protocol (FTP) and Network File System (NFS), both of which operate in the TCP/IP environment. Users can manipulate files down to the record level, which is how FTAM stores files. In this respect, FTAM has some relational database features. For example, users can lock files or lock individual records.

FTAM is a system in which a connection-oriented information about the user and the session is maintained by a server until the session is taken down. In a stateless system, such as NFS, requests are made independently of one another in a connectionless manner. There are advantages to stateless operation. If the server crashes, the request simply goes away and the client makes another request. This simplifies recovery after the crash. In a stateful system, both systems must be aware that one or the other has crashed so they can restore the states and prevent data corruption.

Files are transferred between systems by first establishing a connection-oriented session. The FTAM client contacts the FTAM server and requests a session. Once the session is established, file transfer can take place. FTAM uses the concept of a *virtual filestore*, which provides a common view of files. The FTAM file system hides the differences between different vendor systems. FTAM specifies document types as files with straight binary information or text files in which each line is terminated with a carriage return. Data is interpreted as records and FTAM provides the virtual filestore capabilities that store record-oriented structured files.

Typical FTAM functions are:

- Transfer files to and retrieve files from FTAM servers.
- Delete files on FTAM servers.
- Read attributes of files on FTAM servers.
- List, create, and delete directories on FTAM servers.

So far, FTAM has not caught on as a useful system for transferring files between different vendor system in the LAN environment. Many of the implementations so far have failed to interoperate with one another. FTAM has worked well as a way to bring mainframe information systems into distributed environments.

RELATED ENTRIES Distributed File Systems; International Organization for Standardization; *and* Open Systems Interconnection Model

File Transfer Protocol (FTP)

FTP is a program for transferring files in Transmission Control Protocol/Internet Protocol (TCP/IP) environments such as the Internet. Typically, a user at a client computer downloads files from a remote server. FTP is a core component in every TCP/IP system and is implemented at the Applications level with respect to the OSI protocol model. Its operation is based on the Telnet program and TCP. FTP is available on a wide variety of computer systems and serves as a common protocol for transferring files between systems.

FTP features include the following:

- Support for ASCII, EBCDIC, binary, and formatted (with no translation) files
- Enables users with read and write capabilities to display, create, and delete files and directories
- Password protection
- Data compression

You use FTP to connect with another system and execute various commands for listing files and transferring files between systems. A session begins by typing the ftp command, followed by a host name. For example, you could type:

```
ftp stis.nsf.gov
```

F

or you could just type **ftp**, which puts you in a dialog session that lets you enter specific ftp commands. Once you've logged in, you see an ftp> prompt. You can then issue commands such as the following:

- **help**   Displays a list of help for commands. You can also type a command name to get specific help.
- **dir** or **ls**   Lists files in the remote system's directory.
- **cd** *directory name*   Changes directory (type the directory name after cd).
- **cdup**   Moves up a directory.
- **pwd**   Displays the current directory name.
- **get** *filename*   Copies a file from the remote system to your system.
- **put** *filename*   Sends a file from your system to the remote system.
- **bye** or **quit**   Ends the session.

Files are transferred as ASCII text files unless you choose a different transfer mode. Type **binary** before typing the command to transfer a binary file, and type **ascii** to transfer a text file. Two transfer modes are used. The stream transfer mode sends raw data while the block transfer mode sends blocks of data that are error checked.

Anonymous FTP

Anonymous FTP is an extension of FTP for accessing data in public servers on the Internet. When a site with public information sets up a system that other users can access, it creates an account with a pseudo-name called "anonymous" on the server. In most cases, a password is not required to access this account, so any user accessing the server can browse the system. The type of information on these servers usually includes public domain software and information in the form of published papers and general information. Users can search an index of anonymous FTP archives with the ARCHIE utility, which is an Internet resource discovery tool.

Trivial File Transfer Protocol (TFTP)

A separate implementation of FTP, called Trivial File Transfer Protocol (TFTP), is a stripped down version of FTP. It does not list directories or authenticate users. It only transfers files to or from a remote server.

RELATED ENTRIES   File Systems in the Network Environment; Internet

Filtering

Filtering is performed by bridges and routers on packets of information to prevent certain types of packets from passing through the bridge or router. Packets may be filtered based on their packet type—Transmission Control Protocol/Internet Protocol (TCP/IP), Internetwork Packet Exchange (IPX), or AppleTalk—or the destination address. Filtering in routers helps keep local packets from traversing an internetwork where they would add unnecessary traffic and slow performance. The barrier set up in routers is often called a *firewall*.

RELATED ENTRIES   Bridges; Routers

FINGER

FINGER is an early Internet utility that provides information about the users who are logged onto a server. It represents an early attempt at providing directory services. The user must first know what server to query, then use FINGER to display a list of users. The information listed about users by FINGER can contain messages from the users, such as a personal note, a bit of wisdom, or some directive. This information is contained in a separate file.

The WHOIS command provides more information. It creates a central database and places information about users in the database. Users then query the database to get information about users or services. However, this service is limited due to problems with maintaining the database.

Domain Name Service (DNS) is the current method for obtaining information about users and services on the Internet; however, the Internet community is experimenting with the X.500 Directory Services standard, which provides a global directory service with advanced features.

RELATED ENTRY   Domain Name Service; Internet; *and* X.500 Directory Services

Flow Control Methods

Flow control (also called *handshaking*) is an asynchronous communication protocol that is used between communicating devices to regulate the flow of a stream of data. If one station has received more information than it can hold in its buffers or process at one time, it signals the sender to pause the transmission until it can catch up. Flow control signaling can be performed in hardware (out-band signaling) or in software (in-band signaling).

Hardware flow control takes place between two systems that are directly connected together with a multiline cable. One or two of the lines are used for data transfer. Other lines are used for signaling. For example, in the request to send/clear to send (RTS/CTS) signaling method, a terminal device signals that it can send data by turning on its RTS line. The other device turns on its CTS line as a response. To control the flow, the receiver can turn off its CTS line at any time.

Software flow control assumes that devices are communicating on a single-wire channel, such as a telephone line connected with modems. In this case, XON/XOFF flow control can be used. An XON character indicates that a device can receive data. An XOFF character stops the flow of data until an XON is sent.

RELATED ENTRIES   Asynchronous Communication; Serial Communications

Forwarding

In ring network environments where a communication cable is shared by multiple stations, packets are passed around the ring from station to station until they reach their destination. Each station receives a packet and inspects the address. If the packet is not addressed to the station, the station forwards the packet to the next station.

Forwarding also takes place in bridges and routers. Packets arrive at the bridge or router, which can look at the packet address and forward it to an adjoining local area network (LAN) if the address is for that LAN. Filtering functions can be used to filter out certain packets so they are not forwarded across a bridge or router.

Fractional T1/Fractional T3

A fractional T1 line is a subchannel of a full T1 line that is sold by telephone companies and other providers at a lower price. There are 24 fractional T1 lines in a full T1 line and each has a bandwidth of 64 Kbits/sec. There are 28 T1 channels in a T3 line. Users can purchase one or more fractional lines without the need to purchase the full line and can add additional fractional lines at any time.

F

A customer's access channel into a carrier network is determined by the access rate. A T1 line channel can denote any of the following:

- Channelized T1, in which a channel is any one of the 24 T1 timeslots
- Unchannelized T1, in which all 24 T1 timeslots are considered a channel
- Fractional T1, in which a channel is a grouping of 1 to 23 timeslots

RELATED ENTRY T1/T3 Services

Frame Relay

Frame Relay is a packet-oriented communication method for connecting computer systems. It is primarily used for local area network (LAN) interconnection and wide area network (WAN) connections over public or private networks. Most of the public carriers are offering Frame Relay services as a way to set up virtual wide area connections that offer relatively high performance. Frame Relay is a user interface into a wide-area, packet-switched network that typically provides bandwidth in the range from 56 Kbits/sec to 1.544 Mbits/sec rates are emerging. Frame Relay grew out of the Integrated Services Digital Network (ISDN) interfaces and was proposed as a standard to the Consultative Committee for International Telegraph and Telephone (CCITT) in 1984. The American National Standards Institute (ANSI)-accredited T1S1 standards committee in the United States also did some of the preliminary work on Frame Relay.

Most of the major carriers such as AT&T, MCI, US Sprint, and the Regional Bell Operating Companies (RBOCs) are offering Frame Relay. Connections into a Frame Relay network require a router and a line from the customer site to a carrier's Frame Relay port of entry. This line is often a leased digital line like T1 but depends on the traffic. Figure F-10 illustrates two possible wide area connection methods, as described next.

- *Private network method* In this method, each site will need three dedicated (leased) lines and associated routers to connect with every other site, for a total of six dedicated lines and 12 routers.
- *Frame Relay method* In this public network method, each site requires only one dedicated (leased) line and associated router into the Frame Relay network. Switching among the other networks is then handled within the Frame Relay network. Packets from multiple users are multiplexed over the line to the Frame Relay network where they are sent to one or more destinations.

A permanent virtual circuit (PVC) is a predefined path through the Frame Relay network that connects two end points. The Frame Relay service provider allocates PVCs as specified by customers between designated sites. These channels remain continuously active and are guaranteed to provide a specified level of service that is negotiated with the customer. Switched virtual circuits were added to the Frame Relay standard in late 1993. Thus, Frame Relay has become a true "fast packet" switching network.

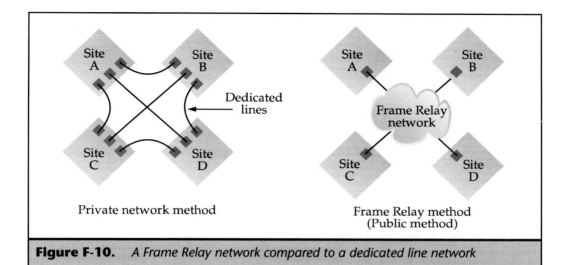

Figure F-10. *A Frame Relay network compared to a dedicated line network*

Improved Packet Switching

In the last few years, carriers have installed an abundance of fiber-optic cable in the national and global networks to make increased bandwidth available. To take advantage of this bandwidth, new communication schemes are feasible that remove the overhead inherent in older schemes. Frame Relay does this by avoiding flow-control and error handling in the network itself that cause delays. In comparison, older X.25 network technology performs extensive error checking with the assumption that unreliable telephone lines are used to transmit data.

Eliminating these features in Frame Relay does not present a problem even if errors occur. Frame Relay assumes that end-node devices are intelligent programmable machines that can perform their own error handling. End systems are not burdened by this error control because there are generally very few errors. In contrast, X.25 assumed the network would need to do this because end nodes were dumb terminals attached to host computers.

In Frame Relay, intermediate nodes (switches) simply relay frames along a predefined path. In X.25, intermediate nodes must fully receive each packet and error check it before forwarding. If there is an error, the node requests a retransmission from the sender. In this way, the sender can retransmit a packet as soon as it was lost. The state tables used in X.25 at each intermediate node to deal with management, flow control, and error checking are not necessary with Frame Relay.

If a packet is corrupted or lost due to congestion in a Frame Relay network, it is the job of the receiving system to detect the loss of the frame and request a retransmission. Frame Relay networks put all their energy into moving packets. The switch nodes in the subnetwork itself do not perform any error correction, although they can detect corrupted packets. Upon detection, the packets are discarded.

Setting Up Frame Relay Connections

To set up a Frame Relay connection, you contact a carrier such as US Sprint, MCI, AT&T, or local RBOCs. There is usually a choice of access speeds and a choice of dedicated or switched access, as described here:

- 56/64 Kbits/sec switched access provided via Switched-56 service or Integrated Services Digital Network (ISDN). Dedicated access is provided by Advanced Digital Network (ADN).

- 128 Kbits/sec access provided by two ISDN lines or two ADN lines.

- 384 Kbits/sec to 1,544 Mbits/sec connection is available through T1 lines or Fractional T1 lines.

Once you've decided on a service, you plan a link from your site to the Frame Relay service provider. Routers and Frame Relay access devices are placed at your site to establish a connection to the provider's Frame Relay port, as shown in Figure F-11.

Frame Relay ports are normally connected with PVCs. PVCs are logical links, which have specific endpoints and service characteristics. They provide logical connections over meshed topologies and provide a way for carriers to specify service characteristics and rates in advance of use. They also provide fast connections between end-points. Some of the service characteristics you define for PVCs when setting up the service with a provider are listed next.

- *Access Rate* This is the speed of the line which determines how fast data can be sent onto the network. In the U.S., common access rates are 1.544 Kbps (T1) and 56 Kbps.

- *Committed Information Rate (CIR)* The CIR is the maximum average data rate of a Frame Relay circuit. It is usually lower than the access rate; transmissions can exceed the CIR for short bursts of data.

- *Committed Burst Size (CBS)* The CBS is the maximum amount of data (in bits) that the network provider agrees to transfer under normal network conditions during a time interval.

- *Excess Burst Size (EBS)* The EBS is the maximum amount of uncommitted data (in bits) in excess of CBS that the network will attempt to deliver during a time interval. EBS data is treated as discard-eligible by the network.

Some other features provided by Frame Relay network providers are listed next.

NETWORK SERVICES The following management features and services are available on Frame Relay networks:

- *Virtual Circuit Status Messages* This service provides communication between the network and the customer. It ensures the PVCs exist and reports on deleted PVCs.

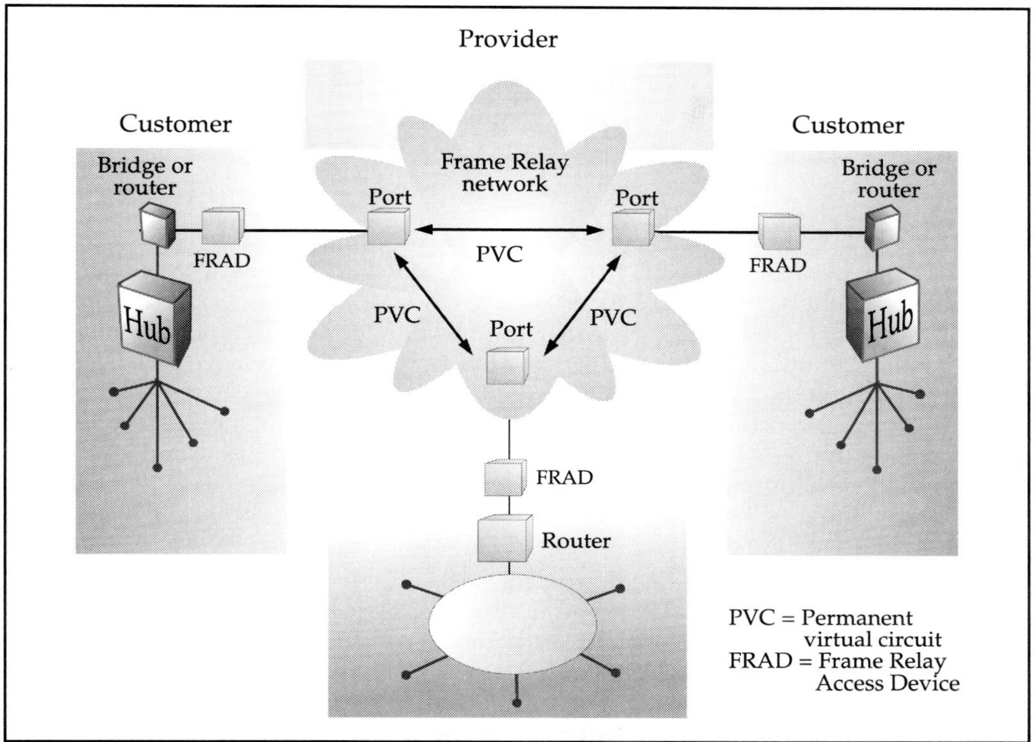

Figure F-11. *A typical Frame Relay connection*

- *Multicasting* This optional service lets one user send frames to multiple destinations.

- *Global Addressing* This optional service gives the Frame Relay network LAN-like abilities.

- *Simple Flow Control* This optional service provides the XON/XOFF flow control mechanism for devices that require flow control.

CONGESTION CONTROL When a Frame Relay network becomes congested, frames may be arbitrarily discarded (the end nodes are responsible for retransmitting them), or discarded based on customer preference. For example, customers can designate traffic that is usually not critical to the operation of the business as discard-eligible (DE). Flagging frames with DE is done either by a router or Frame Relay switch. Using DE provides a way to ensure that the most important information makes it through the network and less important information is retransmitted when the network is not so busy.

SECURITY There are several security options in Frame Relay:

- Only private lines can access the network.
- Passwords are required to access the network.
- A time-out feature logs off inactive stations.

Frame Relay Specifications

A Frame Relay network connects two LANs over a public packet-switched network. The process is quite simple—the frame from the LAN is placed in a Frame Relay frame and delivered through the network substrate (the Frame Relay mesh of connections) to the destination. Statistical multiplexing techniques efficiently interleave data from multiple sources at the customer site on a single line to the Frame Relay network. Frame Relay is a modification to High-level Data Link Control (HDLC), so it is available as an upgrade in some bridges and routers. Frame Relay is not suitable for voice and video traffic due to its variable-length frames.

Frame Structure

The frame structure for the Frame Relay packet is pictured in Figure F-12. The flags at either end delimit the frame with a special bit sequence. Following the beginning flag is the Frame Relay header, which holds address and congestion control information. This is followed by the information (payload) and the Frame Check Sequence (FCS). A checksum is calculated on an arriving frame and compared with the FCS field, which was calculated by the sender. The packet is discarded if there is a mismatch and the end-stations must resolve the missing packet. This simple error-check is all that Frame Relay switches perform.

The header contains the following information:

- *Data Link Connection Identifier (DLCI)* This information holds the identification number that identifies the logical connection that is multiplexed into the channel.

- *Discard Eligibility (DE)* This information sets priorities for frames that indicate whether a frame can be discarded if congestion occurs.

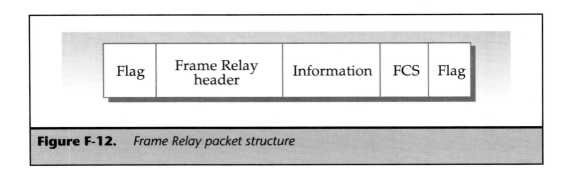

Figure F-12. *Frame Relay packet structure*

■ *Forward Explicit Congestion Notification (FECN)* This information tells the router receiving the frame that congestion was experienced on the path it took.

■ *Backward Explicit Congestion Notification (BECN)* This information is set in frames going the opposite direction of frames that encountered congestion. This information is designed to help higher-level protocols take appropriate action in providing flow control.

Frame Relay Providers

Most carriers now offer Frame Relay services, as do the Public Data Network (PDN) providers such as CompuServe. Each carrier has a specific number of places where customers can link into the network called points-of-presence. Access to this point is through the local exchange carrier (LEC) or other providers. Some of the services are listed here:

■ BT North America Inc.'s global Expresslane (800/872-7654)

■ CompuServe Frame-Net Services, (800/433-0389)

■ MCI HyperStream Frame Relay (800/933-9029)

■ US Sprint's Frame Relay service (800/877-2000)

■ Williams Telecommunications Groups Wilpak (918/588-3210)

Frame Relay Forum

The Frame Relay Forum is an association of Frame Relay users, vendors, and service providers based in Mountain View, California (415/962-2579). The organization is made up of committees that create implementation agreements for the purpose of developing Frame Relay standards. The agreements are created using information and suggestions provided by its members and others in the community. The Forum has technical material and marketing information on Frame Relay.

RELATED ENTRIES   Carrier Services; Fast Packet Switching; Packet Switching Networks; Switched Services; *and* Virtual Circuits

Frames in Communication

A frame outlines the structure for delineating data sent over a communication channel in a serial stream as shown in Figure F-13. In serial communication, data is sent as a stream from a source to a destination. The two systems maintain an active communication session with each other. The data stream is divided into frames that have a start bit, data bits, and a stop bit. The data in an asynchronous communication frame represents one character. The data in an Ethernet frame contains a whole or partial packet of information. Packets are formed in higher-level protocols at the source and fragmented to fit into the data field of one or more frames.

The frame defines how the data and control information fit into the stream of bits. In asynchronous communication, each frame is separated by a start bit and stop bit. In

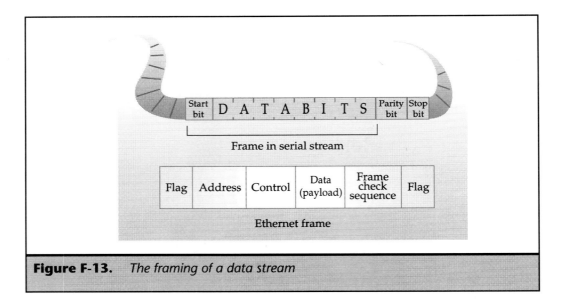

Figure F-13. *The framing of a data stream*

synchronous communication, each frame is separated in time. The fields of an Ethernet frame are described here:

- *Flag* This field contains a bit sequence (usually 01111110) that marks the beginning and end of a frame.
- *Address* This field may designate both a source and destination address.
- *Control* This field contains information to synchronize communication or indicate the size of the data in the next field.
- *Data* The field contains the data that is carried in the frame.
- *Frame Check Sequence (FCS)* This field contains error-checking values to verify that the packet has not been corrupted.

> *NOTE: An important reason for framing data transmissions is error recovery in the event of a line "glitch." Only the affected frame needs to be resent.*

The data in the frame can be variable- or fixed-length. If the frame defines variable-length data fields, its size may vary in thousands of bytes. Most LANs use variable-length frames, as does Frame Relay. Networks that use fixed frame sizes (called *cells*), such as Asynchronous Transfer Mode (ATM), have predictable delivery rates that make them useful for delivering time-sensitive information such as video. Fixed-size cells don't cause delays at switches in the network, like variable-length frames in which one can hold up other transmissions. However, frames with variable-length data fields can send more user data per transmission. The larger the data field, the fewer the frames and header information associated with the frames. For example, in Fibre Channel, an entire transmission might fit in one frame with a single header, whereas the same transmission might require many ATM cells, each with separate headers.

RELATED ENTRIES   Asynchronous Communication; Packets; Serial Communication; *and* Synchronous Communication

Frequency Division Multiplexing (FDM)
See Multiplexing.

Front-End Processor

A front-end processor (FEP) is a dedicated computer that controls communication between an IBM host computer and the terminals that communicate with it. The IBM 3725 and 3745 are front-end processors that run the Network Control Program (NCP), which communicates with programs running in physical units (PUs). FEPs connect to IBM 3270 hosts.

The primary function of the front-end processor, or communication controllers as they are commonly called, is to free up the host computer to run applications. In this way, the host is not continually interrupted by the external devices.

Communication controllers establish sessions, manage communication links, detect and correct errors, and provide concentration points for cluster controllers. The older model 3705 provides up to 352 communication lines at line speeds up to 230.4 Kbits/sec and can attach to eight hosts. Newer models, such as the IBM 3745 provide full-duplex communication lines and dual processors for standby service and backup, as well as IBM Token Ring Network support. IBM 3745 also supports IBM Systems Network Architecture (SNA) networks and public packet-switched networks (with appropriate software).

RELATED ENTRIES   Communication Controller; IBM Mainframe Environment

Front-End System

In a client-server environment, the front-end system is typically a computer on the network that a person uses to access data stored on a back-end server system.

RELATED ENTRIES   Client-Server Computing; Distributed Computing

Full-Duplex Transmissions
See Transmission Media, Methods, and Equipment.

F

Gateway

A gateway is a computer system or other device that acts as a translator between two systems that do not use the same communication protocols, data formatting structures, languages, and/or architecture. A gateway is unlike a bridge, which simply passes information between two systems without conversion. A gateway repackages information or changes its syntax to match the destination system.

Note that most gateways operate at the Application layer of the Open Systems Interconnection (OSI) protocol model, which is the top-most layer. Also note that because gateways perform protocol conversions, their performance is not spectacular.

IBM HOST GATEWAYS   An IBM host gateway connects local area network (LAN) workstations into systems that in the past did not recognize intelligent computers attached to LANs. With a gateway, workstations on the LAN appear as 3270 terminals to the IBM host. A PC's keyboard is mapped to the 3270 keyboard format. However, it's usually possible to switch between the 3270 session and a normal stand-alone computer session by pressing ALT-ESC or another appropriate key sequence. More sophisticated gateway functions allow PCs connected to the gateway to transfer files to and from the host, or to run client-server applications that let PCs access back-end database services on the host system. IBM's Advanced Peer-to-Peer Networking (APPN) provides peer-to-peer networking services in the IBM environment, so gateways are becoming less of an issue. In other words, the IBM host simply becomes part of the network.

DEC GATEWAYS   Gateways into DEC systems are used for many of the same reasons that IBM host gateways are used. Digital PATHWORKS products provide access for a variety of personal computers into DEC VMS (Virtual Memory System) systems.

LAN GATEWAYS   A LAN gateway provides a pathway for data to flow from one LAN to another with an intermediate LAN serving as the interconnection method. This intermediate LAN typically uses a different protocol, so data is converted for transport over it. A router might perform these services. For example, many routers provide both Ethernet and Fiber Distributed Data Interface (FDDI) connections. Packets moving from the Ethernet LAN to the FDDI LAN can be either translated (a gateway function) and delivered to a node on the FDDI LAN, or they can be routed to another Ethernet LAN attached to the FDDI LAN. This last option is a form of encapsulation, and the FDDI network serves as a backbone for the Ethernet LANs. There are also protocol gateways such as AppleTalk-to-TCP/IP, IPX-to-TCP/IP, and others.

ELECTRONIC MAIL GATEWAYS   Electronic mail gateways translate messages from one vendor's messaging application to another's so that users with different E-mail applications can share messages over a network. A typical E-mail gateway converts messages to the X.400 format for electronic mail messaging. X.400 is a common denominator among many E-mail systems. Most E-mail systems are able to convert their messages to X.400 and interpret X.400 messages, so the X.400 system can serve as an E-mail switching system.

INTERNET GATEWAYS   In the world of the Internet, what used to be called gateways are now called routers, and gateways now refer to systems that convert protocols, such as electronic mail relays. The Internet device that is now called a router basically joins two or more networks or is the link point between an internal and external network. This device takes packets from hosts, examines their addresses, and routes the packets to another router or to a host system. A gateway now generally refers to devices that translate between applications. For example, a gateway might translate between the OSI Virtual Terminal and the Internet Telnet terminal program.

RELATED ENTRIES   DECnet; DEC PATHWORKS; Electronic Mail; IBM Mainframe Environment; Internet; *and* Routing, Internet

Gateway-to-Gateway Protocol

This protocol is one of the first routing protocols developed for use on the Internet. It is similar to the Xerox Network System's (XNS's) Routing Information Protocol (RIP), but was found to be inadequate because it could not keep up with dynamic changes in the network. Eventually, the concept of autonomous systems (domains) was developed and Interior Gateway Protocols (IGPs) and Exterior Gateway Protocols (EGPs) were developed.

RELATED ENTRIES   Domains; Routing, Internet; *and* Routing Protocols

Global Naming Services

A naming service is similar to a phone book or directory of users and services on a network. A global naming service is one that tracks users and services on an enterprise computing system, or even a network that spans the entire globe. The Internet Standards Committees are looking into the Open Systems Interconnection (OSI) X.500 global naming service as a way to provide lookup services for everyone attached to the network.

RELATED ENTRIES   Directory Services; Directory Services, NetWare; Directory Services Naming, NetWare 4.x; Distributed Computing; Electronic Mail; *and* X.500 Directory Services

Glue, Oracle

Glue is a solution for what Oracle calls the "API gap." It provides a way to connect various front-end applications running on UNIX, Macintosh, Windows, and other systems to back-end database services. Glue provides a consistent, high-level way to use existing database application tools to access data on ORACLE V6, the ORACLE7 Cooperative Server Database, dBASE and Paradox databases, the Oracle Mail Server, the Sharp Wizard electronic organizer, as well as many native file systems.

RELATED ENTRIES   Database Connectivity APIs and Middleware; Database Management System; *and* Distributed Database

Government OSI Profile (GOSIP)

GOSIP is a set of standards, adopted by governments, that specify the use of Open Systems Interconnection (OSI) standards in the procurement of computer equipment for agencies of a government. OSI sets standards for management functions, security features, and a range of other networking functions as defined by the International Standards Organization (ISO). OSI is very broad and strives to set standards on a global level, although it is unlikely that all the standards will be followed by any one organization or vendor. The United States, the United Kingdom, Canada, Japan, France, Germany, and Australia have implemented GOSIP standards.

GOSIP is defined in the United States by the GOSIP Federal Information Processing Standard (FIPS), which was issued by the government in 1990 through the National Institute of Standards and Technology (NIST). GOSIP closely follows the OSI standards for providing interoperability among computer equipment. The U.S. government's GOSIP defines a subset of OSI. The goal is to provide an interface into a network and provide GOSIP services for some but not all of the systems in that network.

GOSIP is updated on a regular basis to keep in step with technology and changing standards. In the United States, these updates have been taking place on a yearly basis. The Advance Requirements Group, which consists of agencies of the U.S. government, relies on information provided in the Stable Implementors Agreements to guide them through the update process. The final yearly update standards are called FIPS 146. Technical specifications and guidelines for implementing and using GOSIP are outlined in the *Government Open System Interconnection Profile Users' Guide,* which can be obtained by contacting NIST in Gaithersburg, Maryland.

For the most part, the structure of GOSIP is still being defined and will continue to undergo change. It is interesting that the government is pushing OSI when Transmission Control Protocol/Internet Protocol (TCP/IP) is already prevalent. In fact, OSI and TCP/IP are competing standards. Many government contracts include TCP/IP specifications, with stipulations to include migration to GOSIP. As of this writing, NIST was considering incorporating TCP/IP products into GOSIP. However, in early 1994, some government agencies were recommending that the government drop its GOSIP standards. In many cases, agencies have already found loopholes that get around the purchase of OSI products, further weakening arguments for the use of GOSIP.

The structure of GOSIP version 2 is shown in Figure G-1. GOSIP 3 is emerging and features of GOSIP 4 are being defined. GOSIP 3 includes support for the Consultative Committee for International Telegraph and Telephone (CCITT) X.500 Directory Services standard, as well as Electronic Data Interchange (EDI), transaction processing, and Fiber Distributed Data Interface (FDDI). The Common Management Information Protocol (CMIP) is proposed as a way to manage all this.

Intergovernment GOSIP definitions may not be compatible since each country is free to define GOSIP the way it wants. For example, some countries are opting for connection-oriented transport protocols, while others are opting for connectionless protocols.

RELATED ENTRIES   International Organization for Standardization ; Open Systems Interconnection Model

Grounding Problems
See Power and Grounding Problems and Solutions.

Groups
Groups are collections of users or user accounts. You create groups to simplify the task of managing and defining rights for large numbers of users. It's also easier to send

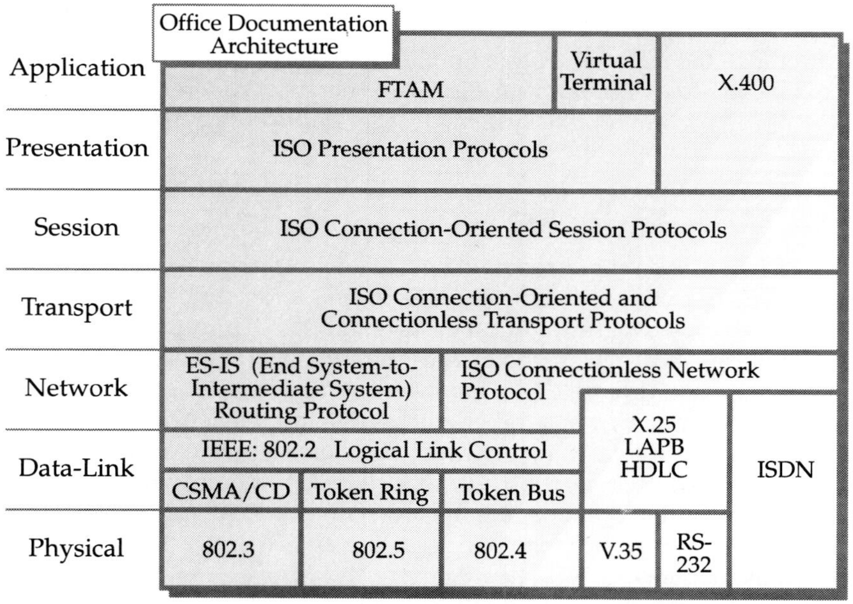

Figure G-1.   *GOSIP Version 2*

messages to groups than it is to send messages to each individual user within a group. Groups have names and can include users who work on similar projects, belong to the same department, or even belong to a club within the company. A user can belong to more than one group. For example, a user might belong to the *manager* group, the *advisory* group, and the *golf* group.

You assign directory and file access rights to groups in the same way you can assign those rights to users. However, it is much simpler to assign the rights to groups, then simply add users to the group. The user then gets all the rights and privileges of that group. Groups should be defined when planning a network and created before adding any users. Then, as you create new user accounts, you can add a user to a group. A user can be a member of more than one group. It's also easier to send messages to groups than it is to send an individual message to each member in that group.

Here are some examples of ways you could use groups:

- A word processing group with rights to run a certain word processing program and store files in its data directories.
- Electronic mail groups to simplify message addressing. For example, create a group called Managers, Employees, or Temporaries.
- A system management group that has rights in secure network directories.
- A backup group that has special access rights to backup directories.

Another interesting aspect of groups is that they provide a convenient way to change or remove the rights of a large number of users. You can delete an entire group, or you can remove users from a group. When users are removed from a group, they still retain an account on the system, but any rights they had with the group are no longer valid.

Groups in Windows NT

Windows NT includes a set of predefined groups with predefined access rights that give its members the ability to perform various tasks and activities on the system.

There are two types of groups: local groups and global groups. *Local groups* are composed of one or more users who directly access the local computer—in other words, they sit at its keyboard. *Global groups* are composed of users who access the resources of the computer from another workstation on the network. Members of the local group only have rights at the workstation where the group is defined. A typical local group is the Power User group, which includes members with some but not all of the Administrator rights for managing the local computer. A typical global group is the Network group, which includes anyone accessing an NT server from another computer on the network.

The following accounts are automatically created by NT. In most cases, one of these groups should provide an appropriate set of access rights for every type of user.

If not, you can create your own groups and assign custom access rights by using the Windows NT User Manager utility.

The Administrator Group

The Administrator group has the highest level of control and access on the NT workstation. The Administrator user account gets its access rights by being a member of the Administrator group. Initially, the group consists of the Administrator user account, the Initial User account, and, if the NT workstation is part of a Windows NT Advanced Server domain, the group called Domain Admins, which can be easily removed, if necessary.

The Administrator group has rights to perform these tasks:

- Create and manage user and group accounts on the local system.
- Assign rights to users.
- Lock and unlock the workstation.
- Format and manage hard disks.
- Create Program Manager common groups.
- Make directories and printers shareable.
- Maintain a local profile.

The Power User Group

The Power User group is one step down from the Administrator group in its abilities to access the system. Members of the Power User group are accorded the right to perform these tasks:

- Log on locally.
- Remotely access the computer assigned the Power User account.
- Change the system time.
- Shut down the system.

Members of the Power User group are like administrative assistants. One of the group's most important tasks is to create new user and group accounts and set up directory shares on the system. Power User group members can perform these tasks:

- Create and manage user and group accounts on the local system.
- Lock but not override the lock on the workstation.
- Create Program Manager common groups.
- Make directories and printers shareable.
- Maintain a local login profile.

G

The Users Group

All user accounts added after initial installation are added to the Users group. The Administrator, Guest, and Initial User accounts do not belong to the Users group. The Users group has the right to log on locally and shut down the system, and the ability to lock the workstation and keep a local profile. The group can be granted permissions to directories and files as needed.

The Guest Group

The Guest group provides limited access to the system for occasional or one-time users. Guest group members have the right to log on locally, but additional directory and file permissions can be assigned if necessary. Think of guests as temporary employees. Initially, anyone can sign in as Guest without a password; however, access to the system is extremely limited. For example, a Guest group member can start Write and save files to a floppy disk, but not to hard drives. You might want to upgrade the rights of the Guest account by creating a special document directory and granting Guest users rights to store files in the directory.

The Everyone Group

The Everyone group includes all users who use the computer. When you need to grant rights and permissions to every user of the system, grant those rights and permissions to this group. The Everyone group also includes users who access the computer over the network, although these people are also included in the Users group. You can grant the group directory and file permissions as needed. Members of the group have the right to perform these tasks:

- Log on locally.
- Remotely access the computer assigned the Power User account.
- Shut down the system.

The Backup Operators Group

The Backup Operators group has the permission to perform backup tasks, which requires the ability to read all files on the system. This includes files the owner has denied access to all users, including members of the Backup Operators group. The right to perform backup takes precedence over the file and directory permissions applied by the directory or file owner. Backup operators have the right to perform these tasks:

- Log on locally.
- Shut down the system.
- Back up files and directories.
- Restore files and directories.

Network and Interactive Groups

The Network group consists of all users who access the computer over a network connection and the Interactive group includes all local users of the computer. In other words, membership of these groups depends on who is currently accessing the system, either locally or over the network.

RELATED ENTRIES   Account, User Network; Users and Groups

Groupware

Groupware is a network software concept that defines applications used by a group of people. It is based on the assumption that because networks connect users, those users should be able to interact as well, to increase the productivity of the group as a whole. Electronic mail is a good example of groupware. It lets users communicate with one another and coordinate activities. Beyond that, groupware is a term used in many different places to define many different things.

A true groupware package allows users on many different systems to interact and collaborate on projects. Editing a file and then sending it to another user for review is not an example of groupware, but it's close. A centralized network scheduling program that looks at the schedules of a group of people, then schedules meetings that fit into time slots that all can attend is an example of groupware.

Another example of groupware is the Object Linking and Embedding (OLE) features in Windows for Workgroups. It lets different people on a network contribute elements such as graphics, text, and spreadsheet information into a master document, called a *compound document,* as shown in Figure G-2. The elements in the compound document maintain a link to a file on the workstation of the person who created the element. If that file is changed, the element linked to it in the compound document also changes. An artist, for example, could change the art in the compound document at any time by simply editing the file stored on her computer. The next time the marketing department opens the compound document, any changes made to the art file are automatically updated into the compound document.

Elaborating further, a scheduling application could set up a "meeting" that takes place over the network. Attendees sit at their workstations and collaborate on a joint project by opening documents on the screen and working on those documents together. When a document is opened, it appears on the screen of all the attendees. Any changes made in documents also appears on everybody's screens. A simultaneous conference call or videoconference session can help users coordinate their activities. In fact, desktop videoconferencing systems that run under Microsoft Windows are available that let users view other users in one window while working on documents in other windows.

Another interesting groupware concept involves the *bulletin board* and *interactive conferencing*:

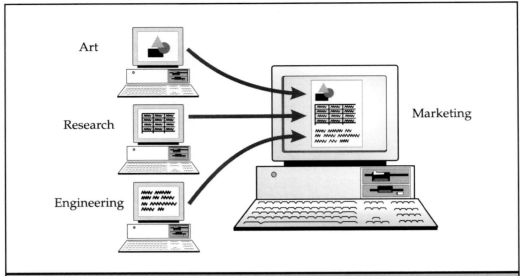

Art

Research

Engineering

Marketing

Figure G-2. *A compound document includes contributions from several members of a group that collaborate over a network*

■ A bulletin board is a place to post messages that other users see and can respond to. Company events and calendars are typically posted in the bulletin board area. Hot topics can generate a flurry of responses and counter-responses. People can just read the messages or participate with messages of their own. Of course, all the dialog can be saved to disk and printed for all to see. Instant documentation!

■ While bulletin boards are typically ongoing message sessions, an interactive conference is a scheduled event that can be compared to a brainstorming session. A company might schedule a conference in which all its employees can contribute their comments on company policies or the development of new products. Once again, people can just watch as the messages scroll by or participate. The entire session can be saved and printed for future reference. Attendees can sign-in and sign-out without disrupting the conference, and they can use a "handle" instead of their name if they prefer anonymity.

Once groupware applications are in place and users begin to take advantage of them, traditional methods of communicating fall by the wayside. Meetings seem inconvenient due to travel and inefficient use of time. In fact, meetings become events that take place over days, and in which attendees make contributions at their convenience using electronic mail. Electronic mail messages become a preferred method of communicating with others, especially if other people are hard to contact by phone. When users have the ability to attach a wide variety of information such as voice, graphics, and video to electronic messages and deliver them instantly, even express mail seems obsolete.

Some of the advantages and idealistic expectations of groupware are listed here:

■ Groupware stimulates cooperation within an organization and helps people communicate and collaborate on joint projects.

■ Groupware coordinates people and processes.

■ Groupware helps define the flow of documents and then defines the work that must be done to complete a project.

■ Groupware provides a unique way for users to share information by building it into structured, compound documents. The document becomes the central place where shared information is stored.

■ Ideally, groupware should be able to help each person in a collaborative project perform his or her specific job in a more efficient way.

■ Ideally, groupware simply defines ways of using existing applications to share information and help users collaborate, rather than being a special application from a single vendor.

Electronic Mail and Groupware

G

One of the most important components of groupware today is electronic mail. Mail messages provide the "backbone" on which any group of users can collaborate on projects and work on shared documents. In fact, electronic mail could be called "cheap" groupware because its messaging services allow people to collaborate.

Electronic messaging is a store-and-forward technology. You address a message to a user, then drop it in the user's mailbox. The recipient can read the mail at a later time. You can attach text and graphics files to messages, greatly simplifying the task of exchanging documents with other users. Consider the old approach. You placed a document in a shared directory and then called the user to tell them that the file was in the directory. If a user was at a remote location, you had to set up a modem and deal with the associated problems of agreeing on line speeds, protocols, data bits, and other factors. With electronic mail, everyone uses their own application to dial into a central mail post office where they drop messages and pick up messages.

Trends in electronic mail include the ability to place many different types of objects (a collection of information) in a message. For example, users of E-mail applications from Microsoft and other vendors can insert voice recordings or even video clips in electronic mail. Middleware products are making all this easier. Electronic mail is becoming a standard feature on the menus of most applications. Almost every Windows-based product has or will include an "Electronic Mail" option on its menu so users can send or receive mail directly from the application.

The only problem with electronic mail systems is that so many exist and so many have already been deployed. When an organization gets ready to integrate systems and users, managers are faced with the task of getting these different E-mail systems to exchange messages. For example, Joe in sales using Microsoft Mail should be able to send a message to Harry in administration using Lotus Notes. There are several ways to make this interchange happen:

- Switch the whole company over to one mail system, which is an unlikely proposition.

- Set up gateways that can translate messages from one system to another. However, you'll need a gateway for each different system. Proprietary gateways are available from E-mail software vendors, or you can use the Novell Message Handling Service (MHS) as a gateway into most of the standard products.

- Electronic mail backbones provide a common protocol environment for the exchange of E-mail. A gateway is still needed for each different type of E-mail system, but the gateways attach to the backbone. Simple Mail Transfer Protocol (SMTP) and the X.400 standard use this approach, as does Novell MHS.

- Choose message-switching systems that serve as central electronic mail routers and convert message formats among systems if necessary. Enterprise Mail Exchange (EMX) from SoftSwitch (Wayne, Pennsylvania) is such a product.

Workflow Software

Workflow software combines electronic messaging with document management and imaging. The concept is to move a document through various stages of processing by sending it to people within a group who have the equipment and skills to manipulate the document, or the authority to sign and validate it. While workflow software is not considered a true groupware application, it encourages workgroup collaboration while automating processes.

Typical environments where workflow software is beneficial include order-entry systems, in which clerks create orders and managers approve them; collaborative environments such as publishing, in which documents move from the writing stage to the editing stage to production; and the insurance industry, in which claims are processed.

These are some of the key features of workflow software:

- Documents contain routing information that serves to distribute the document to predefined users or devices.

- Documents can have simultaneous access.

- A document is viewed as "under construction" until it exits the workflow process.

- The software has a filing system, queue, and workflow manager that keep the system running.

- Authorized users sign-off at various stages, locking parts or all of the document from further editing.

■ The software provides security through authentication and digital signatures: The recipient is sure of the sender's authenticity, that the document is authentic, and that it hasn't been altered in the transmission; the sender is assured that any alterations to the document by the recipient can be detected.

Workflow systems are available from Action Technologies (Alameda, California), DEC (Maynard, Massachusetts), IBM (White Plains, New York), Lotus Development (Cambridge, Massachusetts), and others. Graphical user environments such as Windows are well suited to workflow applications in which graphics, text, and other elements from many different applications are integrated as objects into documents as they flow.

Enabling Technologies

Some standards are emerging that will provide groupware features as part of every application and make those features work across platforms. Some are mentioned here and discussed elsewhere in this book under respective entries.

STANDARD GENERALIZED MARKUP LANGUAGE (SGML) SGML defines a standard way to store information in documents. It goes beyond the ASCII (American Standard Code for Information Interchange) standard by providing ways to integrate and share information that was created in other environments. SGML documents can be viewed as "smart documents," while ASCII documents are seen as "dumb" in comparison. The files contain attributes that define each section or component, such as a paragraph, table, header, or page layout format. This information is transferrable to any other system, which simply formats the document in the same way. SGML is a primary tool for creating workflow applications that cross multivendor boundaries.

WINDOWS OPEN SYSTEM ARCHITECTURE (WOSA) WOSA is a Microsoft architecture that defines how to create applications that work across different platforms and allow the free flow of information within an enterprise. With WOSA, developers can create applications that easily access E-mail, back-end databases, and host connections. Any application running under Windows should be able to access these resources.

APPLE OPEN COLLABORATIVE ENVIRONMENT (AOCE) Apple Computer's AOCE is designed to consolidate workgroups and workflow within a network environment. The environment is implemented as a set of application program interfaces (APIs) and software modules that let applications communicate with services such as those listed here:

■ Exchange of messages between applications

■ E-mail enabled applications so users can send electronic mail from within their applications

G

- Directory naming services that store the names and locations of users and resources on the network

- Authentication services that verify login and provide global access authorization for users

- Digital signature for attaching legal electronic signatures to documents

Groupware Products

Electronic mail and document imaging is becoming an important aspect of groupware. Incoming documents (fax sheets and printouts) can be shared with all users. Optical character recognition (OCR) also provides a way to get documents, to scan documents, and to convert them to computer readable text. Several common groupware products are discussed next.

- Microsoft Windows for Workgroups is a complete workgroup environment. It is a network operating system that includes many tools and applications that help users share information and collaborate, as listed here:

  - Object Linking and Embedding (OLE) is used to create compound documents over the network.

  - A simple message system lets a number of users have "conference calls" over the network.

  - Microsoft Mail electronic mail software lets users exchange E-mail messages.

  - Microsoft Schedule+ group scheduling software lets users arrange meetings and track schedules.

- Banyan provides *Intelligent Messaging Service,* a product that lets users store, manage, and route documents and messages. It provides E-mail and workflow software.

- Digital Equipment Corporation (DEC) offers the *TeamLink* product and All-In-1 integrated office system. All-In-1 connects users to PATHWORKS (a DEC network operating system), which provides connectivity, X.400 E-mail services, file conversion, VAX Notes group conferencing software, and the TeamRoute workflow application.

- Lotus Development's *Notes* is a groupware package designed for large organizations. It provides messaging, database, and document processing functions.

- WordPerfect *Office* provides integrated E-mail, calendaring, scheduling, task management, and workflow software.

RELATED ENTRIES   Compound Documents; Document Interchange Standards; Document Management; Electronic Mail; Imaging; Messaging APIs, E-Mail; Messaging APIs, Inter-Application; *and* Workflow Software

Half-Duplex Transmission

See Transmission Media, Methods, and Equipment.

Handshaking

See Flow Control Methods.

Hermes, Microsoft

Hermes, the Greek god known as Mercury to the Romans, was a messenger of the gods and the patron of trade, communication, and travelers.

Microsoft Hermes is a network management system for the enterprise. It is a Windows NT-based set of tools for managing the inventory of personal computers, workstations, and other devices on a network. Its primary purpose is to help network administrators collect information about the systems attached to their networks, and to help them update those systems without the need to physically travel to each station or have other users do the updates. By removing the burden of upgrades and troubleshooting, network administrators can concentrate on monitoring the network for potential trouble spots. Hermes provides them with the information to do that.

Some of the features that Microsoft Hermes provides are listed here:

- An inventory feature stores hardware and software information about workstations in a file that Hermes can access.

- Software distribution features can automatically install software and updates to users' machines.

- Licensing software can track the number of software licenses available and ensure that an organization stays within its software licensing agreements. Software can be made available to users based on priority or time periods.

- Diagnostic tools can track the performance and condition of the network. Thresholds and alerts can be set to warn administrators of potential problems or overload conditions.

- An assist function lets managers, from their management workstations, view users' screens and issue commands. This feature is similar to a remote communication package and has potential in training or help-desk environments. The manager can look at specific information about the workstation to help in troubleshooting problems.

- A virtual user-defined desktop "follows" users wherever they log on. Window placement, open applications, and other desktop features can be saved so users can move to another workstation and resume their work. For example, in the user's office, the user might set up a presentation for a meeting, then move to the meeting room and retrieve the desktop settings on another computer.

H

Remote software distribution is one of Hermes' most important features. Network administrators create installation "jobs" that update operating systems, applications, utilities, and drivers, including the shell or requestor programs that connect workstations with network servers. A package of updates can be created that targets specific workstations or servers with a specific set of installs or updates. Workstations can be targeted for updates based on hardware features, software version numbers, or current status information. For example, all workstations that have a particular version of a driver can be updated with a new driver. Alternatively, that update could be based on the video card installed in the workstation. In another example, a graphical user interface like Windows could be installed on all workstations that have over 4 Mbytes of random access memory (RAM).

Hermes can read management information format files (MIFFs), defined by the Desktop Management Task Force (DMTF) in the Desktop Management Interface (DMI). A MIFF is a text file that contains information about a workstation, such as its memory availability, basic input/output system (BIOS) type, operating system version, application types and versions, available drivers, and other information. This information is obtained when the station is first turned on, or when a user first logs on. The DMI provides a standard interface to MIFFs. Vendors provide MIFF compatibility in their products. Hermes and other network management programs look at the information in MIFFs by polling stations on the network. This information is then used to determine whether software installations or updates are required, based on software or hardware version numbers or other information defined by the network administrator.

So far, Hermes is targeted to Microsoft local area network (LAN) environments and NetWare environments. With regard to its software distribution feature, Hermes is currently more suited to installing Microsoft applications than applications from other vendors. These problems are apparently being worked out as the product comes on line and third-party vendors cooperate with Microsoft. IBM is moving its NetView management system to Windows NT and Hewlett-Packard is moving its OpenView management system to Windows NT. Microsoft is enhancing Hermes with features that forward information to these platforms.

RELATED ENTRIES   Electronic Software Distribution and Licensing; Management Standards and Tools

Heterogeneous Network Environments

Heterogeneous network environments consist of computer systems from different vendors that run different operating systems and communication protocols. An organization that consolidates its computer resources is usually faced with the task of integrating its heterogeneous systems. Typically, each department or division has defined its own network needs in terms of operating systems, local area network (LAN) topology, communication protocols, applications, E-mail systems, and other components.

The goal of an enterprise network is to get these diverse resources to interconnect and interoperate (at various levels) so that network users can share files and electronic mail with other users, or access the data resources of the enterprise. In addition, an interoperable environment provides the basis for implementing groupware and workflow software applications that all users in the organization can access and participate in together or in groups.

One of the goals in developing an enterprise system is to reduce the number of protocols in use, from say four or five to two or three. Anything less than that is probably impractical until the industry develops robust local and wide area communication protocols that are universally accepted. Transmission Control Protocol/Internet Protocol (TCP/IP) is well established and viewed as a solid choice for internetworking over wide-area links, but even it has room for improvement.

Currently, multiprotocol components such as routers are required to allow different communication protocols to operate over the same network. For example, NetWare and Windows NT servers can operate with two or more protocol stacks and process or forward a number of different protocol types. For example, a NetWare server with a TCP/IP protocol stack and NetWare for Network File System (NFS) can provide file services to UNIX workstation clients. Those clients can read and store files on the NetWare server. At the same time, clients running Internetwork Packet Exchange/Sequence Packet Exchange (IPX/SPX) can access the NetWare server, which runs IPX/SPX natively.

At higher application levels, "middleware" products can hide the differences between applications and allow information exchange, messaging, and other cross-platform activities.

Another goal in uniting heterogeneous systems is to allow users to access "back-end" database systems and mainframes that were previously unavailable due to protocol and platform differences. The users' application may also present some difficulties in accessing the data, or the data may be in a format that can't be interpreted properly. A number of developments are attempting to correct these problems. For example, vendors of client-server computing products are simplifying the interface between user's front-end applications and back-end databases.

- Microsoft's Open Database Connectivity (ODBC) is a standard for interfacing Windows applications to back-end databases.

- IBM's Distributed Relation Database Access (DRDA) is a standard for accessing database information across IBM platforms that follows SQL standards.

- Oracle Glue provides a way for applications that support Dynamic Data Exchange (DDE), such as Microsoft Excel and Visual Basic, to link with Oracle and IBM DB2 servers.

Several developments are underway to create integrated development environments that hide the underlying platforms. The Open Software Foundation's (OSF's) Distributed Computing Environment (DCE) is a complete environment for

H

building applications for different platforms that work together using common industry tools, standards, and protocols. Sun Microsystems' Open Network Computing (ONC) and Apple Computer's Apple Open Collaborative Environment (AOCE) are similar environments.

RELATED ENTRIES   Distributed Computing; Distributed Database; Distributed File Systems; *and* Enterprise Networks

Hierarchical Storage Management (HSM) Systems

HSM systems automatically move little-used files or targeted files from primary magnetic disk storage to secondary optical disk or magnetic tape storage. The process is called *migration,* and because the secondary storage devices remain connected, data can be *de-migrated* back to magnetic disk if users need to view historical information or files that have been migrated. HSM systems can provide managers with file location reports, archive dates, and other information needed to manage the filing system effectively. HSM systems are designed for the following uses:

- HSM systems are practical when gigabytes of information must be available to users at any time and when it is impractical to keep those files available on magnetic disk.

- HSM systems can operate as backup and archiving systems that require little human intervention (except to move disk or tapes offsite for safe-keeping). Note that regular backups are still required to back up files that are not migrated.

- Document imaging systems require optical HSM systems. A typical imaged document (an invoice, purchase order, contract, and so on) and its associated information may require many megabytes of disk space. Optical storage can handle these requirements.

HSM can help reduce the need for large amounts of magnetic storage if the majority of files on disk are rarely accessed. It makes more sense to put those files on alternate storage and keep magnetic disks free for important files. In fact, some vendors envision using optical disks as the primary warehouse for data. All files that remain inactive for even short periods of time are migrated to keep magnetic disks free and available for important files. This is a useful strategy as multimedia, with its large file sizes, is introduced into organizations. On the other hand, magnetic disks are falling in price and some experts see the use of many such disks as a more practical solution than HSM systems.

Figure H-1 illustrates the configuration of a typical HSM system. Files are migrated from the server's magnetic online storage to the optical disk after a period of nonuse. Some files can be marked for immediate migration, or migration at a specific time. You can also de-migrate files in the same way. For example, if a file is required for end-of-month reporting, you can have that file de-migrated to magnetic disk the night before running the report. De-migration times for tape are approximately 2 to 3 minutes and de-migration times for optical disk are about 8 to 10 seconds.

After a period of time, archived files can be copied or moved from optical disk to tape to provide additional security and redundancy of data. Files moved to tape can be removed from the rewritable optical disk media to free up space, or kept online for future use, if necessary. Procedures for retiring optical media are required because some media have limitations on the numbers of times they can be erased and rewritten to.

In NetWare's HSM system, information is migrated based on volumes. Any volume can be marked for migration, typically based on the date of last access for the file. Settings are also available that initiate file migration when a volume exceeds a certain percentage of its capacity. In this last case, the oldest files are the first to migrate.

RELATED ENTRIES   Archiving; Backup and Data Archiving; High Capacity Storage System, Novell NetWare; Jukebox Optical Storage Devices; *and* Optical Libraries

High-bit-rate Digital Subscriber Line (HDSL)

HDSL permits transmission over the existing copper-based lines that provide telephone service. Transmission speeds are between 784 Kbits/sec to T1 rates of 1.544 Mbits/sec. The service is full-duplex and operates over two twisted pairs of copper cable without the need for signal repeaters, reducing installation time.

A related product, Asymmetrical Digital Subscriber Line (ADSL) works over single twisted pairs, offering a 1.544 Mbits/sec circuit in one direction and a lower-speed

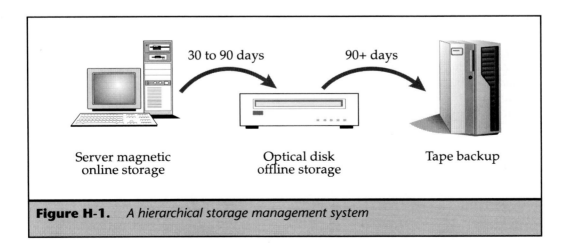

Figure H-1.   *A hierarchical storage management system*

(typically 16 Kbits/sec) data channel in the other direction. ADSL is designed for interactive video to the home using existing copper telephone lines. HDSL can offer the same services and provide a full-duplex line. Through ADSL and HDSL, telephone companies can compete with local cable companies by offering video services and access to special multimedia file servers. The file servers that will hold the digital libraries of information are still to be designed. They will require special architectures and access methods that avoid contention for services.

ADSL is a high-speed link into the fiber-optic network that the telephone companies are building, although some see HDSL and ADSL as a threat to the complete deployment of optic cable, which has more long-term benefits and higher data transfer rates. On the other hand, other experts see ADSL and HDSL and fiber-optic cable as complementary, in that ADSL and HDSL will drive the need for more fiber. A third encoding scheme, very high bit-rate digital subscriber loop (VHDSL), will provide 3 to 6 Mbits/sec service over two twisted pairs.

RELATED ENTRIES   Asymmetrical Digital Subscriber Line; Carrier Services; Channel; Circuit-Switching Services; Digital Circuits and Services; Local Loops; *and* Telecommunication

High Capacity Storage System (HCSS), Novell NetWare

The HCSS in NetWare 4.x provides a way to *migrate* files from fast magnetic storage systems to secondary storage systems as shown in Figure H-2. A secondary storage system is typically a high-capacity optical disk system, but it can also be a magnetic tape system. Files moved to secondary storage remain available to users and are *de-migrated* back to magnetic disk when accessed. The user may not even be aware that files are stored on a secondary medium, except for a slight delay in access. Autochanger devices can automatically mount any disk or tape, making gigabits of information available in the secondary storage devices.

Files that are rarely accessed or accessed periodically are candidates for migration. In fact, some optical disk vendors are advocating that all files not accessed on a regular basis are candidates for optical disk systems. They refer to optical systems as *data warehouses.* Imaged documents, historical records, and large multimedia files are also candidates for optical disk storage. As organizations implement multimedia and imaging, they will soon find the requirement for optical storage systems.

HCSS optical devices are commonly referred to as *jukeboxes.* They read and write to rewritable optical disks and use an autochanger mechanism that mounts and dismounts disks as requested. A typical jukebox may contain up to four optical drives and a device that picks disks from a bay and inserts them in the drives as needed. You can remove and lock up disks for safekeeping, or move them to other optical devices.

HCSS provides an alternative to archiving, in which files are copied to tape or other backup media and then stored. Because HCSS files are essentially always online,

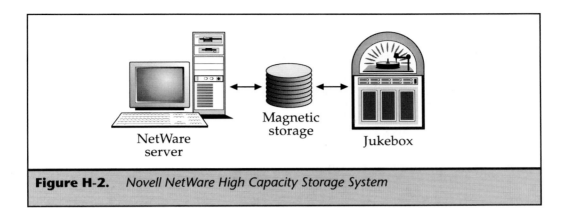

Figure H-2. *Novell NetWare High Capacity Storage System*

HCSS eliminates the bother associated with retrieving files from conventional data archives. For example, a user doesn't need to contact the archive operator who then locates the tape (or other) archive, mounts it, and restores the data. Users who need migrated files access them by searching a familiar NetWare directory structure. Access to migrated files may take a little longer, but not as long as it takes to retrieve files from conventional archives.

HCSS is designed for law firms, hospitals, insurance companies, and other organizations with documents that are rarely accessed. The benefits HCSS provides to large, geographically diverse organizations are also important. For example, an insurance agent could call up an insurance company's central archives and access old client records without an operator's intervention (assuming the agent has access rights to do so).

Structure of HCSS

The hardware of HCSS consists of the optical jukebox and the server to which it is attached. The server must have free space on its magnetic disks to cache the HCSS data. Caching is an important aspect of HCSS.

Basically, users never access files directly from optical disks. They request a file, and it is moved to the designated HCSS volume on the server's magnetic disk. The size of the HCSS volume determines the number of de-migrated files that are available to users at any one time. As new files are requested, they are de-migrated to the HCSS volume, and the least recently used files are migrated to optical disks, as shown in Figure H-3. In this respect, de-migrated files are cached on the HCSS volume in the same way that magnetic disk reads and writes are cached in memory.

The size of the HCSS volume must be at least large enough to hold the largest de-migrated file. If the volume size is small, there may not be enough room to hold all the files users request for de-migration, or the HCSS system will need to take extra time to migrate files in the volume to make room for new files. The larger the volume

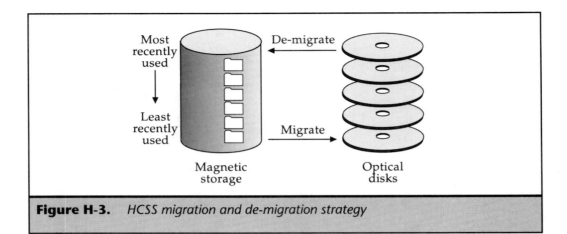

Figure H-3. *HCSS migration and de-migration strategy*

size, the better. You need to consider whether users' requests can be satisfied by files that have already been de-migrated, or whether users will always request files that must be de-migrated. In other words, what are the chances that a file needed by one user will have already been de-migrated by another user? If this is unlikely, all file requests will need to be de-migrated and there will always be an access delay. You must ensure that the HCSS volume is large enough to hold all the files that may be requested at one time.

Files stored on HCSS devices exist in directory structures that look similar to NetWare directory structures. The typical arrangement is to set up a volume on the NetWare server and in that volume store only files you need to migrate.

Note the following:

- Only one NetWare volume per server can support HCSS. You should create a specific volume for HCSS and store only HCSS files on it.

- The volume can contain any number of HCSS directories at the root level.

- You control files in the HCSS volume by setting thresholds. When an upper threshold is met (the volume is getting full), files begin migrating to the optical disk until a lower threshold is met.

- You can specify the time of day for migration in order to avoid peak hours.

- If the HCSS volume becomes full due to user requests for files, the least recently used files are moved to optical disk.

- Access rights to HCSS directories and files are controlled in the same way they are controlled for other NetWare directories.

A typical HCSS directory structure starts with a root directory called HCSS. From this directory, branch subdirectories that relate to the sides of an optical disk. For example, a law firm might have subdirectories such as CASES393, CASES493, CASES593, and so on. Users see files in these directory structures as if the files were on local magnetic disk. If they request a file, it is de-migrated into the HCSS volume. Except for a slight delay in access time, users may be unaware that the file was de-migrated from optical disk.

RELATED ENTRIES   Archiving; Backup and Data Archiving; Hierarchical Storage Management Systems; Jukebox Optical Storage Devices; *and* Optical Libraries

High-level Data Link Control (HDLC)

HDLC is a bit-oriented, Link-Layer protocol for the transmission of data over synchronous networks and is defined by the International Organization for Standardization (ISO). HDLC is a superset of IBM's Synchronous Data Link Control (SDLC) protocol. SDLC was the successful follow-up to the BISYNC communication protocol and was originally introduced with IBM Systems Network Architecture (SNA) products. Another name for the protocol is the American National Standards Institute (ANSI) standard called Advanced Data Communications Control Procedure (ADCCP), but HDLC is the widely accepted name for the protocol. There are some incompatibilities between SDLC and HDLC, depending on the vendor.

HDLC is bit-oriented, meaning that the data is monitored bit-by-bit. Transmissions consist of binary data without any special control codes. Information in the frame contains control and response commands, however. HDLC supports full-duplex transmission in which data is transmitted in two directions at the same time, resulting in higher throughput. HDLC is suitable for point-to-point and multipoint (multidrop or one-to-many) connections. Subsets of HDLC are used to provide signalling and control data links for X.25, ISDN, and Frame Relay networks.

When an HDLC session is established, one station called the *primary station* is designated to manage the flow of data. The other station (or stations) is designated as the *secondary station*. The primary station issues commands and the secondary stations issue responses. There are three possible connection methods, as shown in Figure H-4. The top two support either *point-to-point* connections between two systems, or *multipoint* connections between a primary station and two or more secondary stations.

- The normal mode is unbalanced because the secondary station can only transmit when permitted to do so by the primary station.

- The asynchronous mode is also unbalanced, but the secondary station may initiate a transmission on its own.

- The asynchronous balanced mode is designed for point-to-point connections between two computers over a duplex line. Each station can send commands and responses over its own line and receive commands and responses on the duplexed line. This is the mode used to connect stations to X.25 packet-switched networks.

H

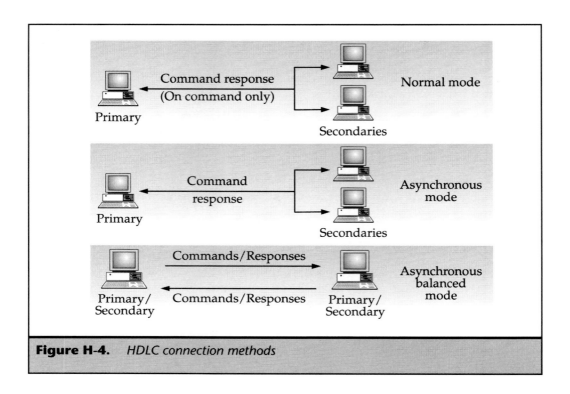

Figure H-4. *HDLC connection methods*

The HDLC frame defines the structure for delivering data and command/response messages between communicating systems. The frame is pictured in Figure H-5 and described here:

- The flag fields contain the bit sequence 01111110, which indicates the beginning and end of the HDLC frame. If any portion of the data in the frame contains more than five 1-bits, a *zero-bit insertion* technique inserts a zero bit to ensure that data is not mistaken for a flag.

- The address field generally contains the address of a secondary station. This field is normally 8 bits, but extended addressing is possible for multipoint connections that contain many different addresses. A broadcast address can also be inserted in the field to send messages to all stations in a multipoint connection.

- The control field identifies the information contained in the frame as either data, commands, or responses. Commands are sent by the primary station, and responses are sent by the secondary station. The control information can acknowledge frames, request retransmission of frames, request a suspension of transmission, as well as other commands and responses.

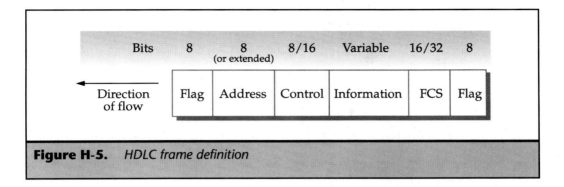

Figure H-5.   *HDLC frame definition*

A communication session starts by establishing connections between primary and secondary stations. The primary station transmits a special frame to either a single station or to multiple stations, to initiate a setup procedure. The secondary stations respond with information that is used for error and flow control during the session. When everything is set up, data transmission begins and when data transmission ends, the primary station sends a frame to initiate a disconnection of the session.

As mentioned, HDLC forms the basis for Data-Link layer control in X.25 packet-switching networks. However, the Consultative Committee for International Telegraph and Telephone (CCITT) specifies the Link Access Procedure-Balanced (LAP-B) protocol, which is a subset of HDLC. LAP-B is designed for point-to-point connections, so the address field is not necessary to identify the secondary stations. It provides the frame structure, error, and flow control mechanisms for an asynchronous balanced-mode session. Another subset of HDLC is the Link Access Procedure D-channel (LAP-D) protocol associated with Integrated Services Digital Network (ISDN). The D-channel is the signaling channel that controls the data flowing through the two B (bearer) channels. Think of the B channels as two separate phone lines and the D-channel as the line that sets up the call.

RELATED ENTRIES   Link Access Procedure; Synchronous Communications; *and* Synchronous Data Link Control

High Performance File System (HPFS)

HPFS is the file system built into Microsoft's LAN Manager, as well IBM's LAN Server and OS/2 products. In OS/2, it is simply the HPFS, but in the LAN Manager and LAN Server products, it is HPFS386, an improved version of the file system.

HPFS provides long filenames and performance-enhancing features that the file allocation table (FAT) in the DOS file system did not have. It also provides access to larger hard drives, provides more organizational features, and improves on the security features. Here is a review of other features:

■ The FAT system was preserved from the Disk Operating System (DOS), but automatic sorting of the directory by filename was added.

■ The cluster allocation was replaced by a simple physical sector allocation of 512 bytes, which helped to reduce unused disk space that was locked by files.

■ Directory entries hold information like the modification, creation, and access date and time.

■ Files of up to 16 megabytes in size can be stored in one contiguous area.

■ HPFS includes a hot fix feature that can move data in a sector that is defective to another area.

HPFS is responsible for formatting disks, as well as reading, writing, deleting, and other general file maintenance activities. Files are stored in disk blocks that are linked or chained together.

An *fnode* contains a pointer to the first block of data for a file. Fnodes are 512 bytes in size and contain file attributes, size, and access control information as well. Fnodes are located close to the physical location of the file on the disk to eliminate the disk head movement that is characteristic of the DOS file system. The HPFS file system is organized into a modified tree that organizes file information in a way that makes it very easy to locate files. When looking for a file, HPFS simply steps through the tree. Each branch of the tree points to another index node until the fnode is located.

HPFS386 adds 32-bit access to the HPFS file system and includes fault-tolerance and security features. It also operates at a more privileged level of the processor, which improves its stability and performance over the normal HPFS file system.

RELATED ENTRIES   File Systems in the Network Environment; LAN Manager, Microsoft; LAN Server; OS/2; Windows for Workgroups, Microsoft; *and* Windows NT, Microsoft

High Performance Parallel Interface (HIPPI)

HIPPI is an American National Standards Institute (ANSI) standard that is similar to but not compatible with the HSX I/O bus that connects Cray Supercomputers to graphics workstations. It grew out of work done at the Los Alamos National Laboratory (LANL) and operates at 800 Mbits/sec or 1,600 Mbits/sec. The interface is point-to-point, meaning it forms a connection between two devices. It is also simplex, meaning it transmits data in one direction; however, two simplex channels can be set up to create a duplex channel. The proposed standard is designed to allow Institute of Electrical and Electronics Engineers (IEEE) 802.2 protocols to run on top of it with the interface used to connect peripheral devices or establish connections between processors or supercomputers.

The interface specification calls for a cable that has 50 copper twisted-pair wires. Data is transferred on 32 of the wires at 25 Mbits/sec each, providing a total throughput of 800 Mbits/sec. This supports 32-bit bus operations; a 64-bit bus operating at 1,600 Mbits/sec is possible using dual cables. The actual distance of transmission on copper cables is limited to 25 meters (82.5 feet) but this expands to 2 kilometers (1.2 miles) if fiber-optic connections are used.

There are request lines and connect lines used to establish connections and parity-checking lines to ensure that data is transmitted correctly. A transmission sequence consists of bursts of data that form variable-length datagrams of 64 Kbytes to 4.3 Gbytes of data. The data dumps into frame buffers, and these buffers can continue filling while information in the buffers is processed. The proposed HIPPI standard includes a switch with 8 to 32 ports that sets up a circuit between two different end points in an environment where connections are established. Data is transferred at very high speeds, and the connections are then taken down. HIPPI is useful for direct connections to high-performance peripherals and supercomputers, but it is not useful as a local area network (LAN).

Fibre Channel is an alternative to HIPPI that provides longer cable distances and data transfer rates up to 800 Mbits/sec. Translation is possible between HIPPI and Fibre Channel so they can be used in the same environment.

RELATED ENTRY   Fibre Channel

High Performance Routing (HPR), IBM

H

HPR is an internetworking protocol designed by IBM as an upgrade to its Advanced Peer-to-Peer Networking (APPN) protocol. It was originally referred to as APPN+, but is now officially referred to as APPN HPR or simply HPR. IBM designed the protocol as a replacement for Transmission Control Protocol/Internet Protocol (TCP/IP). HPR handles routing around failed nodes and avoids the packet overhead handled by network nodes to improve performance. IBM will ship HPR in 1994 with its 6611 router and will provide further enhancements to support Asynchronous Transfer Mode (ATM) in 1995.

RELATED ENTRIES   IBM; IBM Networking Blueprint; Routing Protocols; *and* Systems Network Architecture, IBM

High-Speed Networking

High-speed networks include LANs and WANs that run above the traditional transmission speeds that were predominant prior to the 1990s. They are becoming more common and more economical; a brief description is provided here.

■ *Fast Ethernet*   100 Mbits/sec offerings that run on twisted-pair copper cable. There are two predominant standards: 100VG-AnyLAN (IEEE 802.12) which uses a new *demand priority* access method and 100Base-X (Fast Ethernet) which uses the standard CSMA/CD access method. See "Ethernet 100VG-AnyLAN" and "Fast Ethernet."

- *Isochronous Ethernet* Similar to shared-media Ethernet, but provides some circuits to support time-sensitive traffic like video. Runs at 16 Mbits/sec on twisted-pair copper cable. Expected standardization could be late 1994.

- *Fiber Distributed Data Interface (FDDI)* A shared media network that runs primarily over fiber cable, but a copper-cable version is available with limited distance. FDDI supports data, voice, and multimedia. FDDI-II is a newer version that supports dedicated circuits for multimedia traffic. FDDI Follow On LAN (FFOL) is an eventual replacement for FDDI that will operate above 2.4 Gbits/sec.

- *Fibre Channel* A switched network designed for channel connections between computers and peripheral devices. It operates above 133 Mbits/sec on coaxial or twisted-pair cable.

- *Switched Multimegabit Data Service (SMDS)* A metropolitan area switched data service offered by the local exchange carriers that provides bandwidth in the T1 (1.544 Mbits/sec) and T3 (44.7 Mbits/sec) range for customers who need LAN-like network extensions in metropolitan areas.

- *Frame Relay* A metropolitan area and wide-area packet-switching technology offered by the local exchange carriers that provides T1 (1.544 Mbits/sec) or higher transmission rates.

- *Asynchronous Transfer Mode (ATM)* A switching network that runs over copper or fiber cable and supports data, voice, and multimedia in local or wide-area environments.

RELATED ENTRIES Asynchronous Transfer Mode; Ethernet 100VG-AnyLAN (Voice Grade); Fast Ethernet; Fiber Distributed Data Interface; Fibre Channel; *and* Frame Relay

High-Speed Serial Interface (HSSI)

HSSI is a serial interface standard that was developed by Cisco Systems and T3plus Networking. It operates at speeds of up to 52 Mbits/sec at distances of up to 15 meters (50 feet). It is similar to the RS-232 and V.35 interfaces commonly used to connect computers to modems, but operates at a much higher speed.

Home Directory

Home directories are created for every user account added to a network to give those users a place to create subdirectories, store files, and install personal applications. Home directories are optional, but they provide an initial logon "location" and may be essential for users at diskless workstations. Managers can allow users to save files in shared public directories, but this doesn't give them a place for personal files, or files they need to keep secure from other users.

Some managers give users full directory and file rights in their home directories, which allows users to create new directories and grant other users rights to those directories. In this way, users control the access level for directories and determine which users on the network can access the files in the directory. Administrators may balk at giving users the ability to create directory structures and define security in them. However, most network operating systems have methods for limiting disk space usage and supervisors can still override the security imposed by users in their personal directories.

If you decide to create user directories, first create a directory called HOME or USERS, then create subdirectories for each user that branch from these directories. Operating systems like NetWare and Windows NT will optionally create user directories when you add a new user account. In environments with many users, it might be necessary to dedicate a server for user directories.

RELATED ENTRIES   Account, User Network; Groups; *and* Users and Groups

Homogeneous Network Environments

Generally, a homogeneous network is a network of components from the same vendor or compatible equipment that all run under the same operating system or network operating system. Up until the mid-1980s, IBM and DEC could claim many companies that were using their products exclusively. But as the use of personal computers and local area networks grew, many different types of systems began to populate the desktop. Today, most managers balk at proprietary systems. There are few if any companies that have homogeneous networks. This is especially true as organizations interconnect department and workgroup networks. Compare to "Heterogeneous Network Environments."

RELATED ENTRY   Heterogeneous Network Environments

Hop

A hop represents a transmission of a data packet through a router in a network of interconnected segments or subnetworks. In many networks, there are many routers connecting many segments, thus forming a number of paths that a packet can travel to get to its destination. A measure of this path is the *hop count,* or the number of routers the packet must pass through to get to its destination. This is often used as a metric by a router to determine which path it should forward a packet on. For example, a path with only three router hops is more efficient than a path with four router hops. A router uses this criterion to determine which port to forward a packet on. However, a network administrator might program the longer path in cases where the packet is not of high priority and the longer path is cheaper but not as fast.

H

The packet itself contains identification information, source and destination addresses, as well as priority information that can indicate the type of route the packet should take. In the Distance-Vector Algorithm (DVA), routing decisions are based on the least number of "hops" to a destination. Also called the Bellman-Ford algorithm, it is used to calculate routes.

The Routing Information Protocol (RIP) was one of the first routing protocols to use DVA. RIP limits the number of hops to 16 and drops packets that need to travel further. Routers pass address tables among themselves every 30 seconds and recalculate paths. This not only puts a load of traffic on the network, it requires a lot of calculations that may not be synchronized among the routers. Routers at distant locations could end up with different routing tables if they didn't receive some of the table information. Because of these problems, the more efficient link-state routing methods are used today. However, administrators can still configure path selections using hop metrics.

RELATED ENTRIES   Distance-Vector Algorithm Routing Protocol; Routing Information Protocol; *and* Routing Protocols

Horizontal Wiring System

In a structured wiring system, the horizontal wiring is the cable that runs from a telecommunication wiring closet to workstations, printers, and other network peripherals on a floor of a building, as shown in Figure H-6. In contrast, vertical wiring is the cable that stretches from the wiring closet on each floor to the main equipment room in the basement or first floor of the building.

The vertical system is usually referred to as the backbone. It may consist of fiber-optic cable that can handle the increased traffic loads imposed on it. When structured wiring is used, the horizontal wiring system is usually copper twisted-pair cable, although fiber cable can also be used to connect desktops that have high data throughput requirements. There are various grades of copper twisted-pair cable used in horizontal wiring, depending on the speed of the local area network (LAN). Newer 100 Mbits/sec LANs may require Category 3 to Category 5 data-grade cable, as discussed under "Cabling."

RELATED ENTRIES   Cabling; EIA/TIA 568 Commercial Building Wiring Standard; *and* Structured Wiring

Host

A host computer is typically defined in the centralized computer model as a large timesharing computer system that terminals communicate with and rely on for processing. It contrasts with the client-server model in which users work at computers that perform some processing of their own and access servers that provide services such as file management, security, and printer management.

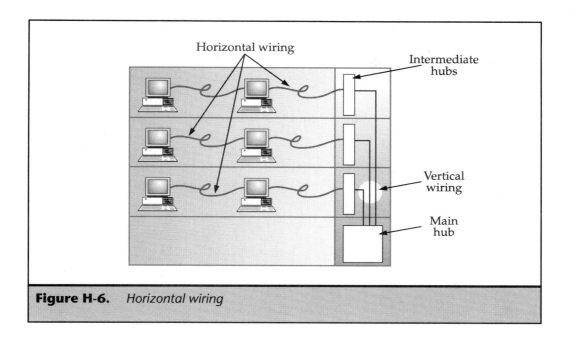

Figure H-6. *Horizontal wiring*

IBM Environment

In the IBM environment, a host system is a mainframe computer called the "host processor" such as the IBM model 3090, IBM model 4381, or IBM model 9370. These mainframes usually run the Multiple Virtual Storage (MVS) operating system, running as either XA (eXtended Architecture) or Enterprise Systems Architecture (ESA). MVS is part of IBM's Systems Application Architecture (SAA).

Devices attach to IBM host computers as shown in Figure H-7. A number of terminals or intelligent computers acting as terminals connect to a cluster controller. Terminals do not connect directly to the host. The cluster controller multiplexes the data stream from its attached terminals into a channel linked to the host. Printers may also be attached to the cluster controller. A communication controller is another device that attaches directly to a host. It connects with a remote cluster controller over a telecommunication link. The remote cluster controller multiplexes the data stream from a number of devices at that location. See "Cluster Controllers, IBM," "IBM Mainframe Environment," "Information Warehouse," and "Systems Network Architecture, IBM."

ISO Terminology

In a network environment where multiple local area networks (LANs) are connected together with a series of routers, a host is often referred to as the *end system* or *ES*. For

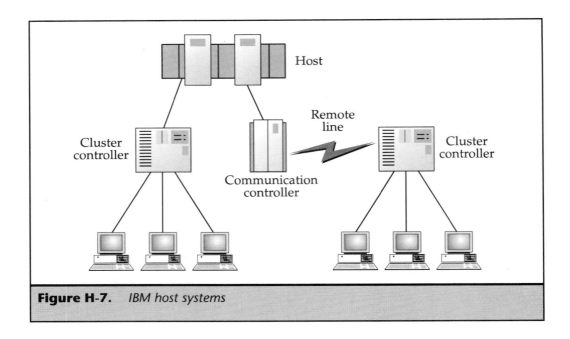

Figure H-7. *IBM host systems*

example, if the accounting department is connected to the sales department with a router, then workstations in each department are referred to as the host or end system, and the router is referred to as an *intermediate system*. There may be a number of intermediate systems that a communication message has to cross between one end system and another. See "Routing, OSI."

Hot Fix, Novell NetWare

Hot fix is a Novell NetWare feature that performs bad-block redirection on hard disk storage systems. Hot fix detects and corrects disk defects as the system runs. Data in defective sectors is moved elsewhere on the disk, and the sectors are marked as unusable. A special area of the disk called the hot fix redirection area is reserved for bad blocks. This space is not used for other types of storage so a guaranteed space is always available to redirect data from bad blocks.

Administrators need to monitor the number of bad blocks that have been redirected. If redirection starts to increase, it could be an indication of an old or failing drive. It may be necessary to increase the size of the redirection area, or replace the disk.

RELATED ENTRY   Disks, Partitions, and Volumes Under NetWare

Hub Management Interface (HMI)

Novell's Hub Management Interface (HMI) standardizes the way server-resident hub adapters are implemented and managed. A hub adapter is a card that fits into the expansion slot of a computer system that is set up as a server. It provides a jack and an octopus-type cable that has from 8 to 12 Ethernet or token ring ports. Several hub adapters can be installed in the same server and connected together.

HMI consists of a set of five extensions to NetWare Open Data-link Interface (ODI) that let vendors of hub equipment write drivers for collecting information about hubs. HMI is built around the Novell specified Hub Management Architecture (HMA). Novell also provides HubCon, a management utility for configuring hubs and viewing hub statistics. Cabletron, SynOptics, Chipcom, and other leading vendors are supporting the interface. HubCon is designed to help managers configure the hubs and gather information about their performance. HubCon can be run at the server or from a remote workstation.

RELATED ENTRY   Hubs

Hubs

There are many types of hubs, and this topic alone could fill an entire book. In its simplest form, a hub is a central location for the attachment of wires from workstations. There are passive hubs and active hubs:

■ *Passive hubs*   These are small boxes that have just a few ports for the connection of computer stations in a star configuration. A passive hub might also be a wiring panel or punchdown block. The important point is that there is no amplification of the signals. A passive hub is simply a junction box that does not require an electrical connection.

■ *Active hubs*   Active hubs usually have more ports than passive hubs and actively regenerate the signals from one device to another, as shown in Figure H-8. They require an electrical connection. Active hubs are used like repeaters to provide an extension of the cable that connects to a workstation.

Simple active hubs have a single task—to receive signals from one station and accurately retransmit them to another. Collision detection is handled by the network interface cards in individual workstations.

Hubs typically attach to other hubs, forming the hierarchy pictured on the left in Figure H-9. The physical configuration is pictured on the right. This is the configuration of a *structured wiring system* as discussed under EIA/TIA 568 Commercial Building Wiring Standard. Copper twisted-pair wire is commonly used for the horizontal wiring on each floor and fiber-optic cable is often used for the vertical risers, although these cabling types are not strictly defined. Data-grade cable can now provide transmission rates above 100 Mbits/sec for use as backbone cable. Structured wiring is

H

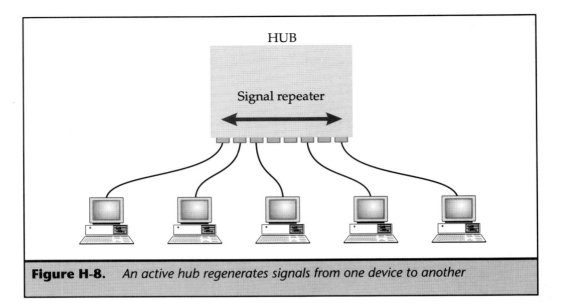

Figure H-8. *An active hub regenerates signals from one device to another*

easy to install, manage, and expand. It also supports new high-speed networks and future network technologies such as Asynchronous Transfer Mode (ATM). Hubs make structured wiring possible and provide the following benefits:

■ As the organization of a company changes, network changes are easy to implement with structured wiring systems built around hubs.

■ Networks can expand incrementally with structured wiring and hubs.

■ Hubs accommodate many different networking options, including Ethernet, token ring, FDDI, and wide area network connections such as Frame Relay, SMDS, ATM, and others.

■ Hubs provide centralized management and the automatic collection of network information.

■ Hubs provide fault-tolerant features that keep the network cable system alive.

One of the disadvantages of using copper twisted-pair wiring is the distance limitations. Hubs reduce this problem somewhat because they are repeater devices. For example, in the Ethernet 10Base-T network, a workstation can be at the end of a daisy-chain of up to four hubs.

The topology of hub networks is typically the star configuration. However, for token ring networks, the signals travel on the network in a logical loop, and in Ethernet, the signals are broadcast to all stations. While the star topology requires running a cable to each workstation from the hub, it has its advantages. Cable runs to

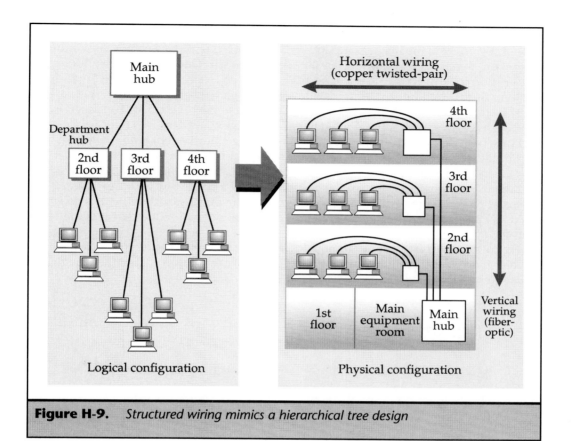

Figure H-9.   *Structured wiring mimics a hierarchical tree design*

workstations are isolated so breaks in the cable only affect one station. Managers can run diagnostics at the hub on a single cable run to determine traffic flow or isolate faults.

Hub Evolution

The original Ethernet local area networks (LANs) were created by snaking cable through buildings and connecting each workstation in a daisy-chain fashion. When all the stations were connected, you plugged each end of the cable with a terminator, and booted the network. You were lucky if the network worked the first time because loose connectors, interference from outside sources, ground loops, bent or crushed cables, or a failure to simply connect a cable to a T-connector were enough to cause disaster. The work part was trying to locate the exact location of the problem. Special tools were required that could measure the distance down a cable to a break. Hubs were designed to help solve these problems.

Hubs have evolved through several generations since the first simple repeating hubs. They are now the major components in structured wiring systems—the control centers for managing and monitoring the entire network. Through plug-in modules that support local and wide area connections, a hub can serve as the wiring center for an entire floor, a building, a campus-wide area, or a global network. These "wiring hubs" form a backbone for the entire network. Because the backbone is contained in one box, hubs are commonly called "collapsed backbone" devices.

Hubs became popular in the desktop networking environment with the growth of star-configured 10Base-T. A typical eight-port hub is pictured in Figure H-10. Administrators were expanding their networks by buying additional hubs and linking them together with connection cables. Why not build a single box with expansion slots, and then put the 10 or 12 RJ-45 connectors on an expansion module that you could just plug into a slot? The box would provide power and reduce some of the component's costs.

Figure H-11 pictures a typical multislot hub, and Figure H-12 pictures a plug-in repeater module for the hub. The pictured devices are the Chipcom (Southborough, Massachusetts) six-slot ONline System Concentrator and an eight-port 10Base-T

Figure H-10. *Chipcom's Eight-Port ONline 10Base-T Workgroup Hub*

plug-in module. The hub uses a special bus architecture that lets it support three Ethernet, four Fiber Distributed Data Interface (FDDI), or seven token ring networks.

Wiring hubs are platforms for the interconnection of many types of network communication modules. They are similar to a computer system in that they contain a power supply and a plug-in expansion bus, but they are also quite different. For example, the plug-in expansion bus is usually proprietary and extremely fast. Wellfleet Communications (Billerica, Washington) has a symmetric multiprocessing modular system that links a processor module to a link module. This pair, and others like it, connect to a set of four 256 Mbit/sec buses that handle internetwork traffic. The unit supports major LAN, WAN, and FDDI interfaces. Depending on the number of modules installed, performance ranges from 100,000 pps (packets per second) to 500,000 pps.

Wiring hubs are central connection and management points for your network. They provide management facilities that you can control from a workstation, usually with Windows graphics-based applications that show maps of the entire network and let you zoom in on individual segments to view statistics or auditing information.

Figure H-11.   *Chipcom's Six-Slot ONline System Concentrator*

H

Figure H-12. *Chipcom's ONline Ethernet 10Base-T Module*

Management consoles attach via *out-of-band* serial connections so you can manage the hub from a remote location even if the rest of the network has failed.

First-Generation Hubs

There were several attempts at building star-wired, hub-centric Ethernet networks, but the industry finally standardized on Ethernet 10Base-T networks. Structured wiring systems using twisted-pair cable began to evolve. Simple repeater devices with eight or more ports provide a connection for workstations. In some cases, existing twisted-pair cable can be used to connect workstations.

The first hubs were simple repeaters that supported a single transmission medium only. The wiring configuration they supported was appropriate for department or workgroup LANs of about 20 users. The cost of the repeaters was about $100 per port. There is generally no support for management protocols such as Simple Network Management Protocol (SNMP).

First-generation repeating hubs are still viable products in today's market because there are many small LAN sites. An interesting development is the hub adapter, which is a hub that can plug directly into the expansion slot of a server. A special cable attaches to the back of the adapter to provide the multiport connections for workstations. Multiple adapters can be installed in a server and bridged together with a cross-connect cable.

Second-Generation Hubs

Second-generation hubs are called "smart hubs" or intelligent hubs that include management features. These hubs add the ability to support multiple media types and to bridge the media. They also include features for collecting statistics about the modules in the hubs and each of the individual ports. SNMP management features began to appear in second-generation hubs.

Another feature of second-generation hubs is a backplane with multiple buses to support different media such as Ethernet, token ring, and FDDI. The bus arrangement is either one bus for each network type, or a multichannel bus that supports each network type. The backplane is typically managed by high-performance Reduced Instruction Set Computer (RISC) processors.

Still another feature to appear with second-generation hubs is the ability to create logical LAN segments within a single hub. This feature allows managers, sitting at a remote management console, to divide a LAN into smaller segments for organizational and performance reasons.

Third-Generation Hubs

Third-generation hubs are enterprise hubs, designed to support all the cabling and internetworking needs of an organization. They have intelligent features, high-speed backplanes, and are highly modular, supporting a number of plug-in modules including wide area connections and advanced management.

The devices have extremely high-speed bus designs to handle all the traffic of the enterprise, and advanced management features for monitoring and reporting on the condition of the entire network. Reliability is also an important feature—there are many redundant features to protect against failure of components such as the power supply, bus, and wide area links. Many emerging hubs use Asynchronous Transfer Mode (ATM) cell-switching backplanes that operate in the gigabit range.

In particular, third-generation hubs have features that support structured wiring systems built with data-grade twisted-pair cable. Some of the features are listed here:

- Segmented backplanes to support multiple Ethernet, token ring, and FDDI LANs

- High-speed backbones that provide internetworking features

■ Switching capabilities for microsegmenting the network into dedicated LANs for each workstation

■ Dedicated circuits between end-to-end nodes to support high-volume or time-sensitive traffic

■ Distributed management features built into each module to improve performance under heavy load conditions

Categorizing Hubs

It's possible to categorize hubs into three main groups. These groups are basically defined by the structured wiring configuration in which the stations on each floor are connected with horizontal wiring and floors are connected with vertical wiring. The three categories are the *workgroup hub*, the *intermediate hub*, and the *enterprise hub* as described in the following sections. Each has a place in the structured wiring system.

Workgroup Hubs

A workgroup hub connects a group of machines within its general vicinity. For example, it might connect eight computers in the art department. There may be several different workgroups on the same floor.

An interesting variation on the workgroup hub is the hub adapter, which is basically a concentrator box reduced to an interface card that you plug into a server. It is assumed the server is located near the workgroup, rather than a central management area. An "octopus" cable that has plug-in ports for workstations extends from the hub adapter card. Alternatively, a 50-pin Telco connector joins the card to a patch panel in a wiring closet. You can place several hub adapters in a single server and then tie them together by using wiring straps, thus creating a bridge between the ports on the cards. Novell has defined the Hub Management Architecture (HMA) and a NetWare Loadable Module (NLM) called HubCon for managing the adapters.

Intermediate Hubs

An intermediate hub is typically found in the wiring closet located on each floor. Cables branch from it to each of the workgroup hubs. The intermediate hub on each floor is connected to a vertical backbone cable that spans the conduit between floors and connects with the enterprise hub. Alternatively, the intermediate hub may have a direct fiber-optic link to the enterprise hub.

Intermediate hubs are optional, or they might form the basis for future growth into enterprise hubs. For example, an intermediate hub might gather all the connections from workstation hubs on each floor. Later, the intermediate hubs on each floor can be linked with a backbone cable as shown in Figure H-13. Still later, the intermediate hubs can connect into an enterprise hub, as discussed next, that provides better traffic control and management.

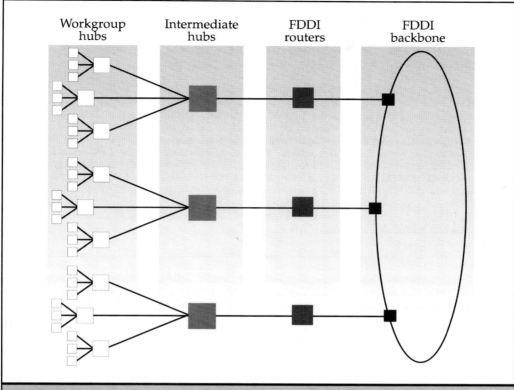

Figure H-13. *Intermediate hub connection methods*

H

Enterprise Hubs

The enterprise hub is the central connection point for all the end systems connected to workgroup hubs. Enterprise hubs either form the backbone themselves or provide connections to a backbone. They may provide bridging, routing, and wide area connection services. Advanced management modules can be located in the enterprise hub.

As mentioned, you can start with the workgroup hubs, then connect workgroups together using intermediate hubs. Later you can connect all the intermediate hubs using a backbone such as FDDI, or go all the way and install the enterprise hub. The enterprise hub provides better management, supports more traffic, and offers a better integrated approach than using an FDDI backbone.

Enterprise hubs must be designed to handle the mission-critical requirements of entire organizations and be compatible with emerging technologies such as Asynchronous Transfer Mode (ATM). Some of the features are listed here:

- Integration of many different network components in one location
- High-reliability through redundant, fault-tolerant features
- A central connection point for departmental or workgroup hubs
- High-speed connections to support the throughput generated by multiprocessing superservers. (Server modules that mount into the hub are possible.)
- The ability to dynamically reconfigure the network from a management console
- Port-switching capabilities from the management console
- Advanced management features such as fault detection and diagnosis, hot-swap components, and modular expansion to improve management and save costs

Wiring Hub Features

The features available in hubs depend on the type of hub and vendor. The features discussed next are primarily found in enterprise hubs that integrate a wide variety of network types into a central box and provide bridging, routing, and management functions. Intermediate hubs don't always require this type of functionality. A backplane to support one type of network and a connection to a corporate backbone may be sufficient. Likewise, most workgroup hubs need only be simple repeater devices that provide connections to other hubs or backbones.

Refer to Figure H-14 for the following discussions.

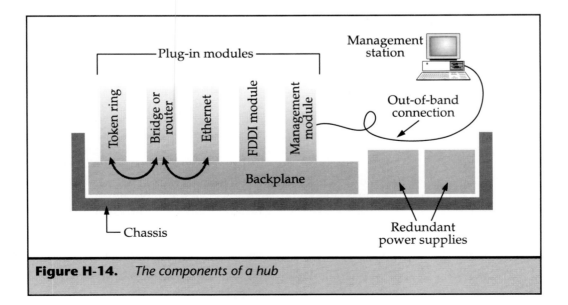

Figure H-14.   *The components of a hub*

The Chassis and Backplane

The chassis is the box surrounding the hub components. Its design and layout determines the number of expansion modules and other components you can place in the hub. The chassis layout provides the connection point for power supplies, so you'll need to be concerned with how the connection of dual power supplies is supported.

The backplane of a hub is like the motherboard of a personal computer in concept, but far superior in design. The backplane provides the bus or connection points for expansion modules, so you'll need to ensure that the backplane has enough slots for future expansion, or that you can expand the backplane in the future. Some hubs provide backplane extensions into other chassis through high-speed connections.

The bus configuration on a hub is quite different than the bus configuration on a computer motherboard, however. There is a requirement for several channels of communication so different plug-in modules can be linked. For example, two Ethernet modules need one communication channel and two token ring modules need another communication channel. How these channels are designed is the primary difference between most hubs. There are several approaches, as pictured in Figure H-15 and discussed here.

- *Standard bus* A standard bus is an EISA or MCA bus like those used in personal computers. Each module connected into the bus must use an interrupt to gain access to it. This technique is usually inadequate for enterprise networks.

- *Multiple bus* The backplane has several buses, each of which is dedicated to carrying a specific type of traffic. A typical multiple bus hub will have an Ethernet bus, a token ring bus, and an FDDI bus. Multiple modules can be connected into each bus, but only modules of the same network type.

- *Segmented bus* In this design, the bus is divided into segments and joined with common connectors. Modules plug into the connectors and can connect with other modules over the bus to form logical LAN segments. Any port on any module can become part of a customized LAN segment under the control of the network administrator working at a management console, assuming that those ports are the same type of LAN (Ethernet or token ring).

- *Multiplexed bus* A single bus is divided into multiple logical buses using multiplexing techniques. Each bus is a channel in the multiplexed stream. This technique provides many of the benefits of the segmented bus.

Most hubs include a management bus that has separate access to all the modules within the hub. Because the hub is not part of the main backplane bus, the traffic generated on that bus does not interfere with its monitoring functions. Without a separate management bus, you may be unable to monitor the network during peak traffic when it's needed most.

Segmentation is an issue in hubs. A segment is a group of stations that share the same network number and pass packets among themselves. Bridges are required to connect one segment to another. Segments with a large number of workstations can

H

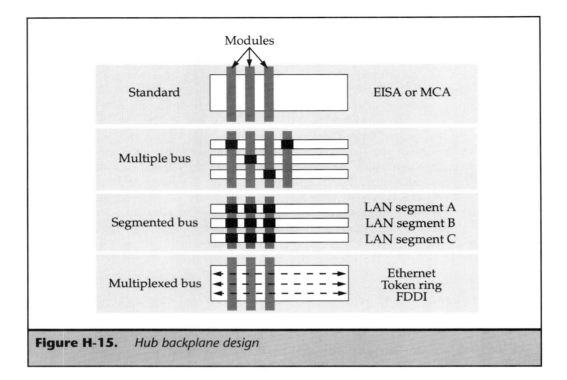

Figure H-15. *Hub backplane design*

get bogged down with traffic, so it's a good idea to divide networks into multiple segments. Each segment should have users who share the same resources and belong to the same departments or workgroups. However, a shortage of channels on a backplane will limit the number of segments you can configure. Most hubs typically have three Ethernet channels and two token ring channels, which means you'll be limited to three Ethernet segments and two token ring segments. To overcome this limitation, some vendors provide switches that let you subdivide a channel into multiple segments. Alternatively, port-switching hubs as described in the next section provide another solution. But keep in mind that bridges between segments can add a lot of expense.

As hub technology and structured wiring become the accepted method for connecting an enterprise, the need for high-speed backplanes becomes more important. High-performance RISC processors improve the performance of the backplane and provide the processing support for more nodes, integrated bridging, routing, and wide area networking.

Port-Switching Features

Port switching is a relatively new feature in hubs that provides a way to reconfigure workstation connections quickly, for example, when a user switches departments.

Consider what happens when a company reorganizes, or the company is highly workgroup-oriented. Each user needs to join a different department or workgroup and each user's workstation must be connected into an appropriate segment so he or she can access the resources located there. In particular, workgroups are often created for short periods of time. The administrator needs a quick way to join all these users, no matter what their physical location, into a segment so they can easily share common LAN traffic. When the workgroup breaks up, the workstations can be reconfigured into other segments.

In the old model, the hub modules that workstations were connected to defined LAN segments. The modules were hard-wired to repeat signals only among the attached ports. To move a user to a new LAN segment, you had to physically move the cable from one repeater module to another. Also, if a repeater module had ten ports, but a department or workgroup only had five workstations, five of the ports go unused while another module might not have enough ports.

In the new model, modules connect to a high-speed multisegment backplane as shown in Figure H-16. Each port basically has its own connection to the backplane, rather than to a hard-wired segment in the module itself. Managers configure segments at a management workstation by selecting the ports they want to be part of a segment. These segments are logically connected, rather than physically connected. Note in the figure that scattered ports form different LAN segments. The important point is that the shared backplane makes it possible to create segments that span multiport modules.

This "virtual LAN" capability supports temporary workgroups with members at diverse locations. In this strategy, there are no wasted hub ports. Each port connects to the backplane where it can be configured into any LAN segment. One limitation with

H

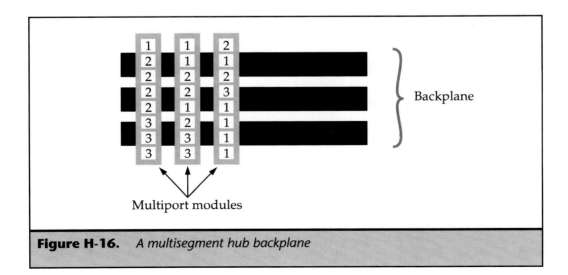

Figure H-16.   *A multisegment hub backplane*

current technology is that you can't join different network types such as Ethernet and token ring into the same segments. You'll still need a bridge for that.

 NOTE: *Don't confuse port switching with switching hubs, which are described in a moment. Port switching is a management feature used to configure workstations into logical segments. Switching hubs have banks of ports and provide a way to establish dedicated connections between any two ports.*

The number of segments you can create depends on the hub and its backplane design. Some vendors only support a few segments on the backplane, while others support over a hundred segments. Keep in mind that there might be a tendency to create many small segments that can create a bridging problem. If users in one segment need to access users or resources in another segment, you need bridging functions to connect all the segments. The number of bridges required could eventually strain the system and the budget.

Port switching is also a problem with internetworking protocols such as Internet Protocol (IP) in which stations use the network address in the Network layer for communication. If a station is moved from one logical segment to another, the network address must be manually updated.

Reliability Features

There is an increased need for reliability and fault tolerance in wiring hubs because all the wiring, concentrator units, bridges, routers, management components, and even servers are located in one place. For mission-critical applications, it's not unusual to create redundant hubs. Should one hub fail, the other immediately switches into action. Some of the redundancy features in hubs are described here:

- *Power redundancy* Most hubs support a backup power supply that either shares the power load with the main power supply or kicks in when the power fails.

- *Hot swap modules* This feature lets you change a module without downing the entire unit.

- *Management* Management features usually include remote management capabilities and SNMP support.

- *Easy reconfiguration* When workstations or users are moved among workgroups, it should be easy to reconfigure the station into the new arrangement. This can be done with software on some systems.

Some hubs use Ethernet or FDDI as the backplane instead of proprietary methods. There is potential for performance loss with Ethernet or FDDI methods because the bandwidth of the buses deteriorates as more workstations use the buses. Proprietary bus systems use hardware and software methods to boost performance, such as the use of RISC processors.

Security Features

Hubs can provide a level of security that was impractical in previous wiring methods. For example, port-switching features can control the communication links between ports and prevent a user from connecting with another station or making an internetwork connection. Filtering is provided by means of the Media Access Control (MAC) sublayer address, using methods similar to bridge filtering.

Some hubs have management features that can disconnect intruders. For example, an intruder might obtain the software address of a station using a protocol analyzer, then access various parts of the network using that address. Hub equipment with advanced security features can link a software address with the hardware address located on a network interface adapter in a workstation, then only provide service to a user when requests arrive from that workstation.

Modules

Modules are individual devices that plug into the backplane of the hub to provide connections for workstations, as well as bridging, routing, and management functions. A list of the most common types of modules follows. There is some cooperation among hub vendors and in some cases, one manufacturer will produce specialized modules that fit into another manufacturer's hubs.

- Redundant power supply hub modules are available that provide hot-swappable features so defective units can be replaced.

- Ethernet modules are available that support coaxial, twisted-pair, and fiber-optic connections to Ethernet workstations using 10Base-T or other network topologies.

- Token ring modules are available that support 12- to 24-ports and various types of shielded or unshielded twisted-pair copper wire, as well as fiber-optic cabling.

- FDDI modules are available that support enterprise backbones or high-performance workstations.

- Bridging and routing modules are available for building internetworks in the hub using multiple protocols such as Novell SPX/IPX, AppleTalk, TCP/IP, DECnet, and others.

- SNA/SDLC conversion modules are available that allow SNA SDLC devices to participate on a token ring network.

- Management modules are available that support industry standard SNMP or emerging standards like CMIP.

- Protocol monitoring devices are available in module form such as the Cabletron Novell LANtern protocol analyzer that fits into its MMAC intelligent wiring hubs.

H

Cabletron and Silicon Graphics Inc. developed a fully functional UNIX Indigo workstation as a hub for the Cabletron MMAC intelligent wiring hubs called the Distributed Network Server Module (DNSM). Users attached to Ethernet, token ring, and FDDI networks can access the computer module. It runs Cabletron's SPECTRUM, Silicon Graphic's NetVisualyzer, and other management systems. The DNSMIM can serve as a management workstation that manages the network directly from the hub.

Modules should have indicator lights that can give managers some idea of the status of each port at a glance. For example, red lights indicate a malfunctioning port. While lights can provide an indication of problems, they assume the manager is periodically walking into the equipment room to check their status. What is needed is a network management facility that can alert the manager immediately when there is a problem with the network, as discussed next.

Management Features

Management features are important. Most high-end hubs have their own microprocessor that can run programs to track data packets and errors and store this information in a management information base (MIB). A management program running at a network administrator's workstation occasionally collects the information from the MIB and formats it for presentation to the administrator. The information is useful for tracking trends, troubleshooting problems, pinpointing congestion problems, and avoiding potential future problems. Alarms can alert administrators when various thresholds are met that might pose problems. For example, alerts can warn the administrator when network traffic exceeds a level so he or she can take corrective actions, such as segmenting the LAN or moving a high-volume user to a dedicated segment.

Most vendors support the Simple Network Management Protocol (SNMP). SNMP runs on the Transmission Control Protocol/Internet Protocol (TCP/IP) protocol and uses TCP/IP as a transport for getting information from the workstation MIB to the management computer. If thresholds are met, SNMP uses TCP/IP to send warning messages (alarms) to the management computer. Other management schemes are Common Management Information Protocol (CMIP), an International Organization for Standardization (ISO) standard, and IBM NetVIEW.

Hubs are typically managed with graphical software applications that let managers control each device and network node from a single management station. The management software is usually UNIX-based, although OS/2- and Windows-based packages are available. The management features in a hub can also provide the following services:

■ Automatically disconnect problem nodes that are disrupting the network.

■ Provide a way to isolate ports for testing purposes. For example, a node might be sending excessive packets out on the network. You can isolate the node for diagnostic purposes.

- Connect and disconnect workstations based on the time or day of the week.
- Some hub vendors are providing protocol analysis tools as modules that fit into the hub.
- Offsite management of network components at remote locations.

Once you've collected information, you need to manage it. Management software can provide a number of utilities that sort through the data and display useful information in tabular form or with charts and graphs. For example, you can monitor information about how the network is being used and where traffic congestion might be occurring. Graphical user interfaces let you zoom in on specific LAN segments and display information about the nodes, bridges, or routers at those locations. You can also add or move users. Management software also provides a way to gather information about the network over a specific time period for analysis, or you can look at historical information for comparisons to current information. This can help you justify the need for new components or expansion modules.

Switching Hubs

A switching hub is a relatively new concept that takes advantage of star-wired topologies and hub designs to reduce contention on network segments. This is done through switching techniques, which should not be confused with port switching. Port switching is a management function in which a manager moves a workstation from one segment to another using a management application. Switching technology has to do with microsegmenting LANs so that there are as few as one workstation on a LAN segment, and thus no contention. The original switching hubs were designed for departmental use and are built on their own chassis. Newer switching devices are modular units that fit into hubs.

Let's look at switching further. If you have a network with 20 users that is bogged down by excess traffic, you can split the network into two segments and bridge them, thus reducing the traffic load of each segment in half. This assumes that you can keep all the users that normally talk to each other on the same segment, thus reducing the amount of traffic that needs to cross the LAN bridge. If traffic is still a problem, you can split the LAN into four segments or six segments, and so on. A switching hub performs exactly this type of segmentation. It has a number of ports, each of which is a dedicated LAN segment designed for the connection of workgroup hubs or even a single workstation. The switching hub handles interworkstation traffic via an internal matrix of switches. Switching is handled at the Media Access Control (MAC) sublayer.

The important point is that fewer workstations on each segment generate less traffic and less contention. If a station on one segment needs to communicate with a workstation or server on another segment, the switching device acts as a bridge and sets up a temporary circuit between the segments. However, this switched bridge

H

function is superior to a normal bridge in that the store and forward delay is eliminated by the direct circuit between devices.

Most switching hubs are Ethernet; if a single workstation is attached to a port, it gets 10 Mbits/sec throughput to the switching hub and the port it is communicating with. Since no other workstation shares the port, there is no contention and the workstation gets its full bandwidth. Some vendors are also working on token ring switching hubs. High-speed switching hubs are also available that implement Asynchronous Transfer Mode (ATM).

The idea of the switching hub was first pioneered by Kalpana, Inc., with its EtherSwitch. The EtherSwitch technology is being used in other vendors' products. For example, Hewlett-Packard has integrated it into its EtherTwist hubs and SynOptics Communications has included it in its LattisSwitch Series 3000 hubs.

Future Developments

Hub design is moving toward the switching concept. Major hub vendors such as SynOptics, Cabletron, and Ungermann-Bass have announced products that let users implement switching of Ethernet, token ring, and FDDI frames, with the ability to upgrade to ATM cell relay in the future. The trend is to also provide multiprotocol support, bridging, routing, wide area networking, management functions, and protocol analysis all in one box.

The bandwidth generated by all the components plugged into the hub will require the fast switching technology provided by Asynchronous Transfer Mode (ATM), which theoretically can deliver gigabit-per-second switching speeds. It is possible for any port on a hub to have a dedicated circuit to any other port through the ATM switch.

The major carriers are already incorporating ATM switching into their long distance networks. The next step for companies that require LAN-to-LAN connections over WAN links is to install ATM switches that can initially serve as backbones for the local environment and provide high-speed links to remote LANs. The next step is to incorporate ATM into intermediate hubs and eventually to workgroup hubs and desktop machines.

At least these are the plans of the major hub vendors. Almost all of them are implementing ATM switching into their enterprise hub devices. With improvements in technology and reductions in price, it seems that ATM is the networking strategy for the near future.

RELATED ENTRIES   Bridging; Cabling; EIA/TIA 568 Commercial Building Wiring Standard; Fiber-Optic Cable; Matrix Switch; Repeater; *and* Routers

IBM
(International Business Machines, Corp.)

IBM began operations in 1911 as the Computing-Tabulating-Recording Co. (CTR). In 1914, under the direction of Thomas J. Watson, CTR became International Business Machines (IBM). Over the years, IBM's primary success was in the sale of tabulating machines. In 1953, IBM announced its first computer, the model 701, and shortly after, the model 650, which became its most popular model during the 1950s. The standard-setting computer for all modern IBM systems, the System/360 was introduced in 1964. An alternative line of computers, starting with the System/3, was introduced in 1970. The AS/400 is the current model in this series. For a discussion of IBM mainframe systems, see the heading "IBM Mainframe Environment."

IBM announced the enormously successful IBM Personal Computer (PC) in 1981. The systems were originally sold through ComputerLand stores and created a whole market on their own of compatible hardware, software, and services. The personal computer market was a wild horse that IBM could not control, and compatible system manufacturers such as Compaq and mail order vendors eventually dominated the market with IBM lookalike or "clone" systems.

Due to competition in the personal computer market and falling demand for its mainframe and midrange systems, IBM fell into difficult times in the late 1980s and early 1990s. In the early 1990s, IBM broke its own company policy and began laying off people. However, this move, combined with reorganizations and other strategies, may turn IBM around. It has extensive research and marketing facilities and has begun to remove itself from the chains of the big systems. It is marketing in new areas and designing network products that work with industry-standard protocols, rather than its proprietary protocols and architectures.

During the late 1970s and 1980s, IBM pushed its Systems Network Architecture (SNA). SNA is a hierarchical networking strategy that provides a way for hardware and software products to interact with one another under the control of a program running in a central computer. Each mainframe system has its own domain of resources that it manages. Interconnection to other mainframe domains is possible so users at one terminal can open communication sessions with applications running on more than one mainframe. The traditional data link in the SNA environment includes high-speed local channels for connecting controllers directly to the mainframe, and Synchronous Data Link Control (SDLC) links. Token ring local area network (LAN) links were eventually added, and later, Ethernet links were provided.

SNA dominated the large system environment for years. Lately, IBM has recognized the new industry trend toward client-server computing. In this model, applications communicate with one another as peers and operate on multivendor hardware over networks that support a variety of protocols. Customers no longer want to commit to proprietary systems. It sees the need to move to open systems. Indeed, the U.S. Government has mandated the purchase of open systems for government agencies through its Government OSI Profile (GOSIP). IBM's large computer system architectures do not fit this new model well, and SNA is not suitable for the development of client-server applications. To counter, IBM has developed strategies that support client-server computing, application interoperability, multivendor product support, and the support of multiple communication protocols, as described next.

- *Systems Application Architecture (SAA)* A set of application, communication, and user-interface specifications for IBM mainframe operating systems such as VM (Virtual Memory), MVS (Multiple Virtual Memory), midrange operating systems such as OS/400 (for IBM AS/400 series), and OS/2 for desktop systems. SAA-compliant applications can run on any SAA platform. SAA adds the ability to allow programs to communicate with each other, rather than through the host, using APPC.

- *Advanced Program-to-Program Communication (APPC)* The marketing name for LU 6.2, which is an interprocess communication method designed to provide enterprise-wide communication between programs. APPC is part of SAA.

- *Advanced Peer-to-Peer Networking (APPN)* The underlying network communication and routing protocol that supports LU 6.2 program-to-program communications. An advanced version of APPN called High Performance Routing is expected in 1994. It provides faster performance and routing around downed routers.

- *Distributed Relational Database Architecture (DRDA)* A strategy for accessing IBM systems using Structured Query Language (SQL) standards. It defines large back-end servers that clients can access through smaller, workgroup-based intermediate servers. (See the next item in this list.)

- *The Information Warehouse (IW)* An IBM strategy for keeping its mainframe platforms alive, in order to support its existing customers and leverage its investment in large system technology to the client-server environment. The IW strategy views the mainframe as a very large server in a multivendor client-server environment.

- *The Networking Blueprint* IBM's primary announcement that it supports open systems. It goes beyond the strategies just described to provide support for other protocols such as Transmission Control Protocol/Internet Protocol (TCP/IP) and Open Systems Interconnection (OSI), as well as application interfaces such as the Open Software Foundation's (OSF's) Distributed Computing Environment (DCE). Refer to the "IBM Networking Blueprint" for a further discussion of this topic.

In the 1990s, IBM is pushing a multiprotocol approach to networking. It supports TCP/IP and OSI protocols through its Networking Blueprint. Part of that blueprint is the Multiprotocol Transport Network (MPTN), a networking protocol for its mainframe and midrange systems, as well as desktop computing environments such as OS/2. MPTN removes an application from its native networking scheme and allows it to run on other networking schemes, such as TCP/IP, OSI, or SNA. MPTN performs protocol conversions on the fly, allowing client-server applications to operate across a variety of protocols. MPTN is part of the IBM Networking Blueprint, which defines IBM's new "open" networking strategies.

RELATED ENTRIES   Advanced Peer-to-Peer Networking; Advanced Program-to-Program Communications; Cluster Controllers, IBM; Distributed Relational Database Architecture; IBM Mainframe Environment; IBM Networking Blueprint; Information Warehouse; Multiprotocol Transport Network, IBM; *and* Systems Network Architecture

IBM Cabling System

In 1984, IBM introduced a cabling system that defined cable types, cable connectors, faceplates, distribution panels and other components required to connect computers, peripherals, terminals, and mainframes into communication networks. The cable definitions specify which type of cable to use for various applications and environments, such as for voice and data, or for indoor or outdoor use. IBM Token Ring networks used the cabling system.

The wire conforms to the American Wire Gauge (AWG) standards, which indicate the diameter of a wire. The larger the AWG number, the smaller the wire. Also, due to resistance in the wire, large diameter wires do not carry signals as far, so wire with smaller AWG numbers can be extended for longer distances.

The following cable types are specified in the IBM Cabling System:

- *Type 1—A shielded twisted pair (STP)* Wire with two pairs of 22 AWG wires surrounded by a shield and casing. Type one cable is used for workstations and multistation access units (MAUs) or distribution panels.

- *Type 2—Voice and data cable* A voice/data shielded cable containing two twisted pairs of 22 AWG wires for data and four twisted pairs of 26 AWG wires for voice-added outside the shielding.

- *Type 3—Voice grade cable* Contains four solid, unshielded twisted-pair 22 or 24 AWG cables. A media filter is required for use with IBM Token Ring networks. It cannot be used with 16Mbits/sec Token Ring cards.

- *Type 4* Not defined.

- *Type 5—Fiber cable* The original Type 5 specification called for fiber-optic cable with two 100/140-micron multimode fibers. IBM now recommends cable with two 62.5/125-micron multimode fiber cables, which is the current industry standard.

- *Type 6—Data patch cable* This cable contains two 26 AWG twisted-pair stranded cables with a dual foil-and-braid shield. Distance limits are two thirds that of Type 1 cable.

- *Type 7* Not defined.

- *Type 8—Carpet cable* Specified for use under carpets. It has two shielded twisted-pair 26 AWG cables. Distance limits are one half of Type 1 cable. The cable is housed in a flat jacket.

- *Type 9—Plenum cable* This cable is rated firesafe—that is, it does not release toxic fumes when burned. It contains two shielded twisted-pair cables and has distance limits of two-thirds of Type 1 cable.

The connector for the cabling system is dual-purpose in that two of the connectors can be mated and locked together. It also shorts when disconnected so that in IBM Token Ring networks, the ring is maintained and the network is not disabled. Due to expense, many Token Ring installations now use twisted-pair wire with RJ-45 telephone-type jacks.

RELATED ENTRIES   Cabling; EIA/TIA 568 Commercial Building Wiring Standard; *and* Token Ring Network

IBM Host Connectivity

See IBM Mainframe Environment.

IBM LAN Server

IBM LAN Server is a network server system that operates on top of the OS/2 operating system. LAN Server is based on Microsoft's LAN Manager. Both were designed by Microsoft, but LAN Server is now significantly different from LAN Manager. There are still some common features, such as the ability to mirror or duplex drives, and the use of Microsoft's Network Driver Interface Standard (NDIS) interface for network cards. Both systems also use the High Performance File System/386.

LAN Server runs on top of the OS/2 operating system. Because OS/2 is the base operating system, some advantages are immediately available. First, the kernel of the OS/2 operating system runs in Ring 0 of the so-called "ringed-memory" protection scheme of Intel processors. Running in Ring 0 ensures that OS/2's kernel can never be crashed by applications that are stepping out of their memory bounds and causing errors that could possibly crash other applications. The ringed-protection scheme is hierarchical with Ring 0 in the middle. Processes running in Ring 0 can write to memory belonging to processes running in higher levels, but higher levels cannot write to memory used by lower processes.

LAN Server can be configured to run as a background task on OS/2, which means you can set it up on a nondedicated server, then use the server for other tasks. This is only practical in small network environments where file services and other LAN Manager services are kept to a minimum.

LAN Server uses the HPFS/386 file system, which is an OS/2 installable file system that provides multiuser capabilities and the ability to work with peripheral hardware. Multiple users can access and work with files in a shared filing system. HPFS/386 keeps track of file access rights, ownership, and security. LAN Server itself provides significant features that overlay the OS/2 kernel, such as networking services. Other features of LAN Server are listed here:

- It can access up to 4 Gigabytes of memory.
- It requires a minimum of 13 Mbytes of RAM.
- It supports disk mirroring and disk duplexing.
- It supports OS/2, DOS, Macintosh, and UNIX clients. An optional package is required for Macintosh support.
- It supports up to four network interface cards in the server. Networks supported include Ethernet, Token Ring, and FDDI.
- It supports the NetBIOS and NetBEUI session and transport protocols for network communication, as well as AppleTalk, IPX, and IP.
- It can be managed from an IBM NetView management console. An agent is required on the LAN Server system to track events.
- It can provide IBM SNA connections.

Domains

A domain in the LAN Server environment is a group of servers that provide similar services to a similar group of users. The concept is designed for multidepartment LANs or enterprise networks in which each department or workgroup has a set of servers that it prefers to manage on its own. A domain basically organizes the servers of the department or workgroup into a logically secure area that users or administrators in other domains cannot access unless granted rights to do so.

A single system called the *domain controller* keeps track of the structure of each domain. Systems within the domain access this information and when changes are made to the domain controller, those changes are automatically copied to the other system. If a user in another domain needs access to resources in the domain, an account is created for the user. If the network is large and has many domains with hundreds of users, this could pose a management problem.

Even though all the servers in an enterprise might share the same network cable, domains provide a way to logically separate servers into isolated groups, even if the servers are scattered throughout a large area such as a campus. Wide area connections are also supported in this scheme, so for example, the Sales domain might include sales offices in other cities.

Domains are not completely locked out to other users. The administrator of the domain can use commands like NET USE to grant any user access to the resources in the domain. There are a number of security levels available, depending on the type of access a user needs, such as Read-Only privileges or Read and Write privileges.

An aliasing feature is available in LAN Server that is not available in LAN Manager. An alias is basically a name for a network resource, such as a server or printer. Users don't need to know the location or domain of a resource to access it. They simply refer to it by name. If the network administrator decides to move the resource to another location, users still refer to it by name—they don't need to be concerned that the resource has moved elsewhere on the network.

RELATED ENTRIES   Domains; High Performance File System; *and* Peer-To-Peer Communication

IBM Mainframe Environment

NOTE: *The environment described here defines the traditional method of attaching terminals to IBM host systems in an SNA environment. New strategies for attaching mainframes, midrange systems, and PCs in peer-to-peer arrangements are discussed under "Advanced Peer-to-Peer Networking," "IBM Networking Blueprint," and "Systems Network Architecture."*

In 1964, IBM announced the IBM System/360 series of mainframe computers or *host systems*. The series was extremely popular during the 1960s. In 1970, IBM announced the IBM System/370. Both series of computers have a common architectural design that program developers can follow to create programs that use the functions of the system. These programs can be written independently of the physical configuration of a particular computer installation. This concept stimulated the growth of applications that developers could create and sell to a variety of clients. The System/370 architecture became the System/370 Extended Architecture and eventually grew into the Enterprise Systems Architecture/390 (ESA/390). The current implementation is the Enterprise System/9000 (ES/9000). An ES/9000 installation is pictured in Figure I-1.

Note that the ES/9000 series is one of IBM's first systems that does not follow the centralized control architecture. It is well suited to client-server and distributed environments. The Model 900 is the top-of-the-line model and can process at about 241 million instructions per second (MIPS), about twice as fast as the previous generation 3090s. Massively parallel versions of the ES/9000 using arrays of Reduced Instruction Set Computer (RISC) processors are planned. In such a system, multiple processors are wired together and perform processing as a single unit.

In an IBM host environment, communication takes place between terminals and host systems. A device called a *cluster controller* provides connections for a cluster of terminals and handles the input/output from the terminals to the host as shown on the left in Figure I-2. Up to 32 IBM 3278 terminals and 3268 printer devices can attach

Figure I-1. *IBM's Enterprise System/9000 System*

to the cluster controller, depending on the model used. These connections are usually made at the local site with coaxial cable over a maximum distance of 200 feet for terminals and 1000 feet for printers.

Remote terminal connections require a remote cluster controller such as the IBM 3174 R series. The remote cluster controller serves as the connection point for multiple terminals at a remote site, and more than one can be used if necessary. It connects via telecommunication link to an IBM 37xx (3745, 3720, or other) series *communication controller* at the host computer site. Communication controllers are also referred to as *front-end processors (FEP)* and attach directly to the host systems. The IBM Network Control Program (NCP) runs in the communication controller. This remote communications linking method is shown on the right in Figure I-2.

Each cluster controller can link to the communication controller at the main office through its own dedicated telecommunication link, or a communication controller can be placed at the remote site to concentrate the data from all the cluster controllers at that site. This remote communication controller is then linked with the main-office communication controller via a telecommunication link.

The Cluster Controller Connection

Cluster controllers operate with either Binary Synchronous Communications (BISYNC) or Synchronous Data-Link Control (SNA/SDLC) links. In addition, they are either directly attached to the host (channel-attached) or link-attached, which means they are attached through a communication link to a communication controller, as described above. IBM 3274 channel-attached cluster controllers with "A" model numbers are SNA devices, and those with "D" model numbers are non-SNA devices. For example, an IBM 3274 Model 41D is a channel-attached, non-SNA device.

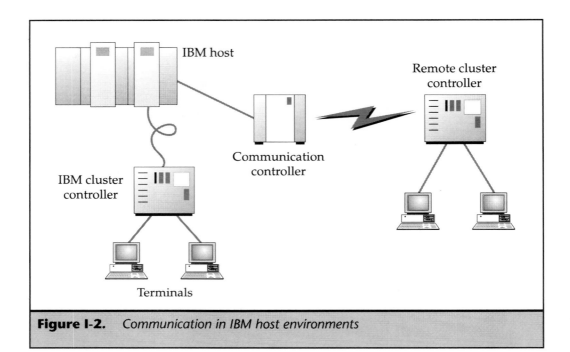

Figure I-2. *Communication in IBM host environments*

Link-attached cluster controllers have C model numbers, such as IBM 3274 Model 41C, and can be either SNA or non-SNA devices. Newer 3174 cluster controllers are discussed under "Cluster Controllers, IBM" in this book.

SNA cluster controllers are called physical unit (PU) Type 2 devices and terminals attached to the cluster controller are called logical unit (LU) Type 2 devices. A printer device attached to a PU Type 2 is either an LU Type 1 or LU Type 3, depending on the printer type.

One of the most important features of newer IBM 3174 cluster controllers in the network environment is the Token Ring attachment and Token Ring Gateway features. With a Token Ring attachment, a 3174 cluster controller can become part of a Token Ring network and provide host connections to the computers in the network. A Token Ring Gateway provides a way for one 3174 cluster controller to act as a gateway for multiple 3174 cluster controllers attached to the Token Ring network. Up to 140 Token Ring-attached devices can communicate with the host in this way.

Typically, each terminal is connected to a cluster controller with its own coaxial cable. However, if a group of terminals is located in one area, a multiplexer device is used to concentrate the data from multiple devices into a single-cable connection to the distant cluster controller, as shown in Figure I-3. The IBM 3299 terminal multiplexer provides single-wire cluster controller connections for up to eight terminals.

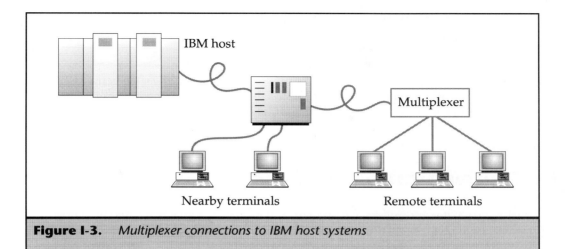

Figure I-3. *Multiplexer connections to IBM host systems*

ASCII Terminal Connections

The cluster controllers discussed in the preceding section provide connection points for standard IBM 3270 terminals. While these terminals are quite predominant, other terminals are popular, such as the DEC VT100 and Televideo 900 series American Standard Code for Information Interchange (ASCII) terminals with asynchronous (serial) connections. It is possible to communicate with IBM host systems using these ASCII terminals by attaching them to the protocol converters described here. ASCII terminal connections are made via serial interface cables.

- *IBM 3708* This protocol converter provides 10 ports, two of which provide connections to IBM hosts. The remaining ports are the connection points for the ASCII terminals. ASCII terminals attached to the 3708 appear as 3270 terminals to IBM hosts, or can also communicate with ASCII host systems.

- *IBM 3710* This protocol converter serves as both a concentrator and protocol converter for remote sites, concentrating up to 31 lines, or providing connection points for up to 56 ASCII terminals.

- *IBM 7171* This protocol converter provides up to 64 full-duplex ASCII terminal connections at a local site. The device is directly attached to the host.

Communication Controller Connection

The primary function of the communication controller, as a device separate from the host computer, is to handle all communications with external devices such as terminals and free up the host computer to run applications. In this way, the host is not continually interrupted by the external devices. IBM communication controllers are the IBM 3705, IBM 3720, IBM 3725, and IBM 3745, which are described under "Communication Controller."

Communication controllers establish sessions, manage communications links, detect and correct errors, and provide concentration points for cluster controllers. The older model 3705 provides up to 352 communications lines at line speeds up to 230.4 Kbits/sec and can attach to eight hosts. Newer models, such as the IBM 3745, provide full-duplex communication lines and dual processors for standby service and backup, as well as Token Ring network support. IBM 3745 also supports IBM SNA networks and public packet-switched networks (with appropriate software).

The Communications Process

The basic IBM system consists of terminals (or PCs running terminal emulation) attached to cluster controllers. Cluster controllers are then attached directly to host systems, or to communication controllers, which themselves attach to the host. A Token Ring network can also provide connections to the host.

Each terminal or printer is referred to as a physical unit, or PU, and each PU can have one or more "sessions" going on with the host. These sessions are called *logical units*, or *LUs*. The Virtual Telecommunications Access Method (VTAM) software runs in the mainframe. The software works in concert with the Network Control Program (NCP) that runs in the communication controller (front-end processor), which handles all the communications traffic among terminals. Users run several sessions (LUs) at once so they can, for example, run an application and check their E-mail at the same time.

RELATED ENTRIES   Cluster Controllers, IBM; Communication Controller; IBM; IBM Mainframe Environment; IBM Networking Blueprint; Information Warehouse; *and* Systems Network Architecture

IBM Networking Blueprint

The IBM Networking Blueprint is an architectural model that defines IBM's commitment to open, client-server multivendor systems. The Networking Blueprint is pictured in Figure I-4. With support for industry-standard Transmission Control Protocol/Internet Protocol (TCP/IP) and Open Systems Interconnection (OSI) protocols, as well as standard application interfaces, the model is clearly designed to entice organizations that have implemented a variety of platforms, protocols, and applications. In fact, most enterprises are faced with the task of tying together a diversity of departmental local area networks (LANs) into enterprise systems. A number of vendors and vendor consortiums are providing ways to tie these LANs together using strategies that hide the underlying network communication protocols and place the focus on application interoperability.

The Networking Blueprint accommodates applications from multiple vendors that use non-IBM communication protocols. It uses a "switching layer" approach in which

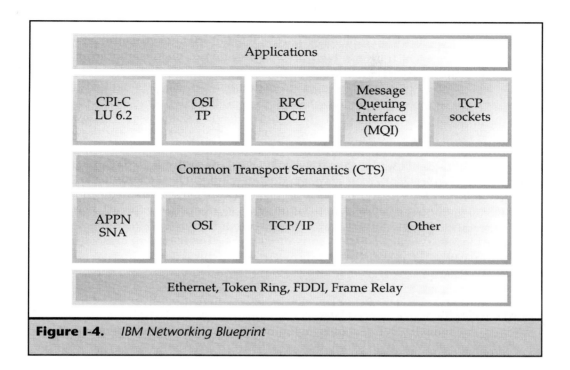

Figure I-4. *IBM Networking Blueprint*

upper applications connect with a variety of lower-level networking protocols. For example, following the Networking Blueprint, it is possible to write applications using remote procedure calls (RPCs) in the Open Software Foundation's (OSF's) Distributed Computing Environment (DCE) to run over TCP/IP protocols on fast packet wide area network (WAN) technologies like Frame Relay. The IBM Networking Blueprint defines the following application interfaces:

- *Common Programming Interface for Communications (CPI-C)*, which operates over IBM Advanced Program-to-Program Communications (APPC).
- *Remote procedure call*, which is part of the OSF DCE.
- *Message Queuing Interface (MQI)*, which is a message-based application interface that oversees the passing of messages between applications running on different platforms.

Transport protocols such as Advanced Peer-to-Peer Networking (APPN), TCP/IP, OSI protocols, and NetBIOS operate under these application interfaces. The *Common Transport Semantic (CTS)* is like a switchboard that allows any upper-level applications to use any lower-level transport protocols such as APPN, TCP/IP, and OSI. This strategy essentially makes applications independent of underlying protocols. The

Network Blueprint strategy supports current and future transmission technologies such as Frame Relay and Asynchronous Transmission Mode (ATM).

IBM's Multiprotocol Transport Network (MPTN) protocol conforms to the CTS, and IBM announced several MPTN-compatible products in 1993 collectively called *AnyNet*. MPTN decouples an application from its native networking scheme and allows it to run on other networking schemes, such as TCP/IP, OSI, or SNA. MPTN performs protocol conversions on the fly, allowing client-server applications to operate across a variety of protocols. See "Multiprotocol Transport Network, IBM" for more details.

The layered modular approach has many benefits. Managers can choose from a variety of options to fit their needs. It lets them choose from a wider array of hardware and software products since they are not tied to one protocol or interface. Developers gain from the strategy as well since they can create applications without worrying about which underlying network protocols the customer will use.

Management systems are also an important part of the Networking Blueprint. They provide a way for managers to collect information about network nodes and other components. IBM's NetView products are part of this scheme. Support is provided for Common Management Information Protocol (CMIP) and Simple Network Management Protocol (SNMP).

RELATED ENTRIES   Advanced Peer-to-Peer Networking; IBM; IBM Mainframe Environment; Information Warehouse; *and* Multiprotocol Transport Network, IBM

IBM Operating Systems

IBM runs a number of operating systems on its wide range of hardware platforms. Mainframe operating systems include VM (Virtual Machine), VSE (Virtual Storage Extended), MVS (Multiple Virtual Storage), and AIX (Advanced Interactive Executive). These operating systems will run on Enterprise Systems Architecture (ESA) systems such as the ES/9000 series. Midrange operating systems include OS/400 which runs on IBM's AS/400 computers. These systems are derived from IBM's System/3x series midrange computers.

Personal computer operating systems include PC/DOS, OS/2, and the AIX UNIX-like operating system. Microkernel-based operating systems are under development as of this writing, including IBM's Workplace OS. IBM's microkernel is based on Carnegie-Mellon University's Mach microkernel and provides basic functions such as messaging, interrupt management, thread management, and memory management. A microkernel operating system can host multiple operating system "personalities," such as UNIX, DOS, Windows and the Macintosh application program interface (API). Users simply load modules for the operating system they want to use. The IBM/Apple Taligent project is working on object-oriented operating systems, as well.

RELATED ENTRIES   Advanced Interactive Executive, IBM; IBM; IBM Mainframe Systems; Mach, Carnegie-Mellon Microkernal; Microkernel; Systems Network Architecture; Taligent; *and* Workplace OS

IBM Systems Application Architecture (SAA)

See Systems Application Architecture.

IBM Workplace OS

See IBM; Workplace OS.

IEEE Computer Society

The Institute of Electrical and Electronic Engineers (IEEE) is a United States-based society that develops, among other things, data communication standards. In particular, the IEEE 802 committees are responsible for developing local area network (LAN) drafts that are passed on to the American National Standards Institute (ANSI) for approval and standardization within the United States. The IEEE also forwards the drafts to the International Organization for Standardization (ISO). The ISO refers to the 802 specifications as the ISO 8802 standards.

The IEEE 802 committees primarily concentrate on the physical interface, which is concerned with the physical and Data-Link layers of the Open Systems Interconnection (OSI) reference model. The 802 specifications define the way network interface cards access physical media and transfer data over it. They also define the establishment, maintenance, and disconnection of connections between network devices for the purposes of transferring information. The standards also ensure that network interface products follow physical specifications for connectors and cable.

Products that follow the IEEE 802 standards include network interface cards, bridges, routers, and other components used to create twisted-pair and coaxial cable LANs. Note that most of the standards define LANs and metropolitan area networks (MANs). The 802 committees related to LAN networking are listed here:

802.1	Internetworking
802.2	Logical Link Control (LLC)
802.3	CSMA/CD LAN (Ethernet)
802.4	Token Bus LAN
802.5	Token Ring LAN
802.6	Metropolitan Area Network (MAN)
802.7	Broadband Technical Advisory Group
802.8	Fiber-Optic Technical Advisory Group
802.9	Integrated Voice/Data Networks
802.10	Network Security
802.11	Wireless Networks
802.12	Demand Priority Access LAN (100VG-AnyLAN)

The 802.1 standard defines the relationship between the IEEE standards and the ISO OSI model. For a detailed review of the remaining standards, see "IEEE 802 Standards."

RELATED ENTRY   IEEE 802 Standards

IEEE 802 Standards

The Institute of Electrical and Electronic Engineers (IEEE) 802 committees, or Project 802, defines local area network (LAN) standards. Most of the standards were established by the committees in the 1980s when personal computer networking was just beginning to emerge.

>   *NOTE: Many of the following standards are also ISO 8802 standards. For example, IEEE 802.3 is ISO 8802.3.*

802.1 INTERNETWORK DEFINITION   Defines the relationship between the IEEE 802 standards and the ISO Open Systems Interconnection (OSI) reference model. For example, this committee defines 48-bit LAN station addresses for all the 802 standards so every adapter can have a unique address. Vendors of network interface cards are registered and assigned the first three bytes of the address by the IEEE. Each vendor is then responsible for creating unique addresses for each of its products.

802.2 LOGICAL LINK CONTROL   Defines the IEEE Logical Link Control (LLC) protocol, which ensures that data is reliably transmitted through a communication link. The Data-Link layer in the OSI protocol stack is subdivided into the Media Access Control (MAC) sublayer and the LLC sublayer. In bridges, these two layers serve as a modular switching mechanism, as shown in Figure I-5. A frame arriving on an Ethernet network and destined for a token ring network is stripped of its Ethernet frame header and is packaged with a token ring header. The LLC protocol is derived from the High-level Data-Link Control (HDLC) protocol and is similar in operation. Note that LLC provides the addresses of service access points (SAPs), while the MAC sublayer provides the physical network address of a device. SAPs specify is the address of one or more application processes running in a computer or network device.

The LLC provides the following services:

■ *Connection-oriented service* in which a session is set up with a destination and taken down when data transfer is complete. Each node actively participates in the transmission, but such sessions require a setup time and monitoring overhead in both stations.

■ *Acknowledged connection-oriented services* similar to the above, in which packet transmissions are acknowledged.

■ *Unacknowledged connectionless service* in which a session is not set up. Packets are merely sent to the destination. Higher-level protocols are responsible for

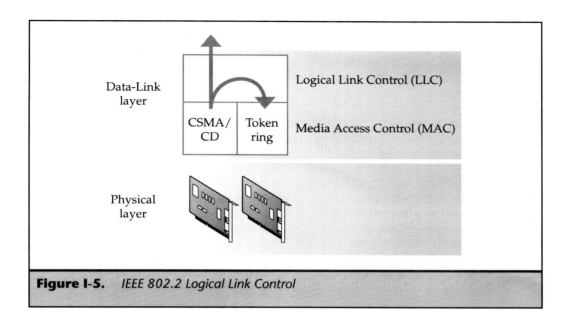

Figure I-5.   *IEEE 802.2 Logical Link Control*

requesting redelivery of packets that were lost. This is the normal service on LANs because of their high reliability.

802.3 CSMA/CD NETWORKS   The IEEE 802.3 standard (ISO 8802-3) that defines how the carrier sense multiple access with collision detection (CSMA/CD) method operates over various media. The standard defines networking on coaxial cable, twisted-pair cable, and fiber-optic media. The original transmission rate is 10 Mbits/sec, but newer implementations transmit at up to 100 Mbits/sec on data-grade twisted-pair cable. See "Ethernet."

802.4 TOKEN BUS NETWORKS   The token bus standard defines a broadband networking scheme that is used in the manufacturing industry. It is derived from the Manufacturing Automation Protocol (MAP). The network implements the token-passing method on a broadcast bus network. A token is passed from one station to the next on the network and the station holding the token can transmit. Tokens are passed in logical order based on the address of the node, but this order may not relate the physical location of the node as it does in a token ring network. The standard is not widely implemented in the LAN environment.

802.5 TOKEN RING NETWORKS   Also called the ANSI 802.1-1985, it defines the access protocols, cabling, and interface for token ring LANs. IBM made the standard popular. It uses a token-passing access method and is physically wired in a star topology but forms a logical ring. Nodes are cabled to a central access unit (concentrator) that repeats signals from one station to the next. Access units are cabled together to expand the network, which enlarges the logical ring. Fiber Distributed Data Interface (FDDI) was based on the 802.5 token ring protocol but was developed by the Accredited Standards Committee (ASC) X3T9. It is compatible with the 802.2 Logical Link Control layer, and thus other 802 networking standards.

802.6 METROPOLITAN AREA NETWORKS (MAN)   IEEE 802.6 MAN defines a high-speed protocol in which attached stations share a dual fiber-optic bus using an access method called Distributed Queue Dual Bus (DQDB). The dual bus provides fault tolerance to keep connections alive if the bus is broken. The MAN standard is designed to provide data, voice, and video services in a metropolitan area of approximately 50 kilometers at data rates of 1.5, 45, and 155 Mbits/sec. DQDB is the underlying access protocol for SMDS (Switched Multimegabit Data Service), which many of the public carriers are offering as a way to build private networks in metropolitan areas. DQDB is a cell relay network that switches fixed length 53-byte cells; therefore, it is compatible with Broadband-ISDN (B-ISDN) and Asynchronous Transfer Mode (ATM). The cells are switchable in the 802.2 Logical Link Control layer.

MAN services are connectionless, connection-oriented, and/or isochronous (real-time video). The bus has a number of fixed-length slots in which data is placed for transmission over the bus. Any station that needs to transmit simply places data in one or more slots. However, to accommodate isochronous time-sensitive data, slots at regular intervals are reserved to guarantee that data arrives on time and in order.

802.7 BROADBAND TECHNICAL ADVISORY GROUP   This committee provides technical advice to other subcommittees on broadband networking techniques.

802.8 FIBER-OPTIC TECHNICAL ADVISORY GROUP   A group that provides advice to other subcommittees on fiber-optic networks as alternatives to existing copper cable-based networks. Proposed standards are still under development at this writing.

802.9 INTEGRATED DATA AND VOICE NETWORKS   The IEEE 802.9 working group is working on the integration of voice, data, and video traffic to 802 LANs and Integrated Services Digital Networks (ISDNs). Nodes defined in the specification include telephones, computers, and video coders/decoders (codecs). The specification has been called Integrated Voice and Data, or *IVD*. The service provides a multiplexed stream that can carry data and voice information in channels connecting two stations over copper twisted-pair wire. Several different types of channels are defined including full-duplex 64 Kbits/sec nonswitched, circuit-switched, or packet-switched channels.

802.10 NETWORK SECURITY TECHNICAL ADVISORY GROUP   This group is working on the definition of a standard security model that interoperates over a variety of networks and incorporates authentication and encryption methods. Proposed standards are still under development at this writing.

802.11 WIRELESS NETWORKING   This committee is defining standards for wireless networks. It is working on the standardization of mediums such as spread-spectrum radio, narrowband radio, infrared, and transmission over power lines. The committee is also working on the standardization of wireless interfaces for network computing, in which users connect into computer systems using pen-based computers, personal digital assistants (PDAs), and other portable devices. Two approaches for wireless networks are planned. In the distributed approach, each workstation controls its access to the network. In the point coordination approach, a central hub attached to a wired network controls the transmission of wireless workstations. As of this writing, the committee was favoring the distributed approach, but the point coordination approach may be included as an option in the standard.

802.12 DEMAND PRIORITY (100VG-ANYLAN)   This committee is defining the 100 Mbits/sec Ethernet standard with Demand Priority access method proposed by Hewlett-Packard and other vendors. The specified cable is 4-wire copper twisted-pair and the Demand Priority access method uses a central hub to control access to the cable. Priorities are available to support real-time delivery of multimedia information.

RELATED ENTRIES   Connection-Oriented and Connectionless Protocols; Data-Link Layer, OSI Model; Ethernet; Logical Links; Metropolitan Area Network; Open Systems Interconnection Model; Security; Token Ring Network; *and* Wireless LAN Communication

Imaging

Imaging is the process of capturing, storing, displaying, and printing graphical information. This process includes the capturing of paper documents for archival purposes. Imaging procedures involve the use of scanners to capture the image and optical disks to store the many megabytes of information the captured images contain, as pictured in Figure I-6. In the past, imaging was largely confined to high-end systems that captured and stored a high-volume of documents, or low-end, single-user graphics workstations with low-volume requirements, typically the paste-up of bit-mapped images into page layout applications. With the advent of high-speed local area networks, distributed computing, and relatively inexpensive capture and storage equipment, imaging is becoming a popular networking application.

Imaging systems available today allow users on a network to store and call up imaged documents from centralized image storage systems. The network provides easy access to these files so users don't need to make a trip to the back-office storage area or request the files from an offsite location. For example, a branch office of an insurance company can call up imaged documents that are stored at a central office. While imaged files are many megabytes in size, collectively require gigabytes of storage, and require high bandwidth for transmission, high-speed networks and optical storage systems are reducing some of these problems and making document imaging practical.

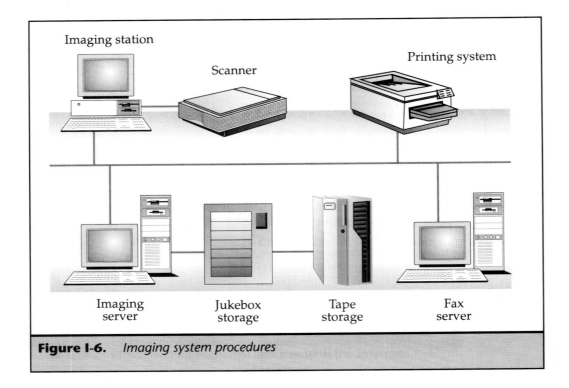

Figure I-6. *Imaging system procedures*

Imaging is part of document processing and workflow applications that manage the way documents move through an organization. But imaging systems stand on their own. They are composed of hardware and software that manage the storage and archiving of documents for insurance companies, law offices, medical facilities, and other organizations that work with large volumes of paper. A well-known securities firm that processes large volumes of paper daily is imaging all its new accounts to phase in the technology. The process starts when new applications enter the system via fax machine. The application can then be viewed by a number of users and stored for later viewing.

Document imaging has many benefits, as listed here:

- Imaging preserves the look of existing documents.
- Documents are often difficult to translate into the fields and records of a database system. Imaging solves this problem. Record-type query information is added to the imaged document to assist in later retrieval.
- Imaging can reduce the workload of data entry clerks.
- Documents are fully distributed, meaning that anyone in an organization can view them simultaneously.

Unlike paper systems, which could be lost in a fire, imaged documents provide a higher level of loss-protection because they are easily replicated to various locations. Storing documents in multiple locations also makes them more accessible by the users at those locations. Images stored on optical disk are also easier to carry to offsite, secure locations.

Imaging Hardware

The equipment required to build an imaging system is, of course, expensive. But consider that the network on which to build the imaging system is probably already in place. Also consider the savings in time and benefits of having information immediately available and the security of having information readily available should traditional systems fail. On the other hand, you need to consider how much traffic an imaging system will add to the network. These issues are discussed in this section. An imaging system consists of the components described in the following sections.

Scanner

A scanner takes a picture of a document and converts or "digitizes" it into digital information that is stored in memory and on a disk. fax machines digitize documents in this way for transmission to other fax machines. During the scanning process, light is reflected off of a document. The dark and light areas are converted to digital values that represent the level of darkness or lightness. Plain text documents with graphs or line drawing only require values for black and white, but documents with color or black-and-white photographs require higher resolutions to differentiate between the many variations between colors or black and white. Scanned images of documents to photographic quality are much larger in size than text documents that simply record black or white values.

Resolution is also dependent on the number of dots per inch (dpi) in the scan. Higher resolutions produce files that are larger in size. The resolution is usually selectable between 100 and 400 dpi. Using a lower resolution is acceptable in cases where the photographic content of a document is not as important as the text content. The photographs may look "grainy" but are still discernible in most cases. Techniques such as gray scaling and halftoning are used to retain quality in photographs. Gray-scaling requires 8 bits of storage per dot of resolution, while halftoning converts colors or scales of gray into groups of dots.

Compression

Compression can help reduce storage requirements. Assuming that a typical scanned document has an average size of 25,000 bytes and a typical high-production output would be about 1,000 documents a day, 25 Mbytes of storage would be required every day. With writeable optical disks in the 600 Mbyte range, the disk would be filled in only 24 days. An insurance company could scan as many as 1,000 documents per hour, producing 200 Mbytes of imaged files per day and filling up an optical disk in only a few days.

To get around storage limitations, compression algorithms are required. Because compression can slow things down somewhat, special compression boards are often added to the scanning system. Some scanners have built-in compression. Compression provides benefits other than reducing storage requirements. It also reduces the amount of data sent over the network when the files are saved to the imaging server or recalled at a later date. See "Compression Techniques."

Storage Systems

The optical disk is the primary storage medium for imaging systems because of its high capacity. Magnetic disks have traditionally been cost-prohibitive for archiving purposes, although falling prices are causing managers to consider using them, especially if there is a demand for fast access to archived information and imaged files. Keep in mind that the retrieval time for files from optical disk is long, in the range of 2 to 10 seconds per document.

Optical drives fall into two categories: *write once, read many* (WORM) and *rewritable*. A WORM drive is used when documents are permanently stored. This system is suitable when imaging contracts, applications, and legal forms that should not be altered. If there is a need to update a stored document, the new version is saved in another place on the disk and the old version is blocked out. If imaged files are updated often, a rewritable optical disk system is preferred. However, these systems cost more money and a disk's age must be monitored because the number of rewrites is limited.

Optical storage is available in jukebox (autochanger) systems that read and write to a number of optical disks at the same time. Hewlett-Packard and Panasonic make jukebox devices that attach to servers via Small Computer System Interface (SCSI) connectors.

Effects on LAN Traffic

As part of Novell's involvement with Kodak in the development of its imaging systems, some tests were run to see how imaging traffic affected the LAN. Documents were scanned at a rate of 4,000 pages per hour at a resolution of 400 dpi. The workstation produced a 10-percent increase in bandwidth utilization, which might be considered a lot by some, but the workstation was doing a lot of other activities associated with imaging, such as updating indices, storing data for image, and storing the image itself. Novell recommends the use of Fiber Distributed Data Interface (FDDI) LANs for organizations with high imaging requirements, although new Fast Ethernet 100 Mbits/sec LANs will also work.

Organizations that need to review documents that have been imaged and stored on optical disk can "stage" documents ahead of time. Staging is a process of copying imaged files from optical disk to magnetic disk during evening hours when the traffic generated by the moves won't disrupt normal network traffic. The documents are then available on magnetic disk for those who need them. Later, the documents are moved back to optical disk to free up space on magnetic disk.

Imaging Systems

There are a number of imaging systems available, and typical features of an imaging application are listed here:

- They work with popular networks such as Novell NetWare over common platforms such as Ethernet and token ring.

- They provide compression features or support optional hardware compression schemes.

- They provide a caching scheme that can prevent bottlenecks at the optical disk jukebox, which can take as long as 15 seconds to load a disk and access a file.

- They provide staging queues that automatically de-migrate specified documents from optical disk to magnetic disk at a specified time, then migrate the documents back to optical disk if they change.

- They provide the ability to incorporate formatted output with the image, such as text, graphics, and spreadsheets. Popular image formats are tagged image file format (TIFF), Zsoft PC Paintbrush Raster Graphics (PCX), and Group 1 through 4 fax format.

- They support document formatting standards. There are several standards that define document content across platforms, including Structured General Markup Language (SGML). Refer to "Document Management" for more details.

- They provide software to manage documents and provide an audit trail that lets managers track who is storing and accessing documents.

- They provide optional security to control who has access to documents. If the document moves from one location to another, the security list must move with it.

Kodak Desktop Document Imaging

The Kodak Desktop Document Imaging group has developed imaging equipment and standards that are currently being licensed to a number of vendors. IBM has integrated imaging into OS/2, Novell has integrated imaging into NetWare 4.x, and Lotus Development has integrated imaging into its Notes groupware application.

Kodak's Document Image Management Services (DIMS) system lets users capture, edit, and manage scanned documents which are stored as bit-mapped images. This system forms the basis of other vendors' systems.

Novell's Image Enabled NetWare

Novell's Image Enabled NetWare is a set of components that provide document imaging capabilities on NetWare networks. The primary component of the imaging systems is the *High Capacity Storage System (HCSS)*. HCSS is a standard that supports the migration and de-migration of files to and from optical storage systems such a jukebox autochanger devices. Novell is working with Kodak to bring imaging system application program interfaces (APIs) to market. Novell includes the HCSS with its

NetWare 4.x products. Two other components are designed to reduce the cost of implementing imaging application on networks and simplify the development of applications that use imaging. Here are the components of the imaging system NetWare Loadable Modules (NLM):

- *Document Management Service (DMS)* Provides a simple interface to the file system that lets managers organize information.
- *Image Management Service (IMS)* Provides a user interface to the HCSS and provides functions for capturing, storing, and retrieving imaged documents or other types of documents. It can translate between file formats and provides compression and decompression functions.
- *Mass Storage Service (MSS)* Provides the means to make hierarchical storage systems available to network users.

Imaging in Lotus Notes

Lotus Development has incorporated imaging into its Notes groupware application. Notes users can capture images with scanners and place them in documents created with word processing, spreadsheets, and graphics applications. They can also include the images in E-mail and send them to other Notes users. Lotus is working with Kodak.

Other Vendors

The following vendors make document image management software. This is not a complete list, but it gives you a starting place for acquiring more information on image management.

- Document Image Development Corp., New York, New York (800/433-4084)
- KeyFile, Nashua, New Hampshire (603/883-3800)
- Lanier Worldwide Inc., Atlanta, Georgia (800/852-2679)
- Plexus Software, Sunnyvale, California (800/999-5910)
- Science and Engineering Assoc., Albuquerque, New Mexico (800/732-1452)
- Seabreeze Engineering Assoc., Altamonte Springs, Florida (800/277-3086)
- ViewStar Corp., Emeryville, California (510/652-7827)

RELATED ENTRIES Compound Documents; Document Interchange Standards; Electronic Data Interchange; Electronic Mail; Groupware; High Capacity Storage System, Novell NetWare; Imaging; *and* Workflow Software

Industry Standard Architecture (ISA) Bus

The Industry Standard Architecture bus had its roots in the original IBM Personal Computer. It was expanded from an 8-bit to a 16-bit data path in 1984 with the introduction of the IBM PC/AT and was commonly referred to as the ISA bus.

Information Interchange Architecture (IIA)

Information Interchange Architecture (IIA) is IBM's compound document architecture standard. It provides a way to create compound documents that include text, graphics, and images that can be exchanged with other systems. It also provides a way to create documents for display-only purposes on other systems. IIA closely follows the International Organization for Standardization (ISO) Office Document Architecture (ODA) standard. ODA is concerned with the exchange of documents among multivendor systems and defines how documents are structured, edited, and layed out.

IIA documents are built on a structure that defines components such as paragraphs, tables, headings, comments, figures, indexes, and other common elements. Tags similar to the tags in Structured General Markup Language (SGML) define the structure of the document. You can think of a collection of tags as a style sheet. Files transferred to other systems will appear the same when displayed or printed as long as the system can interpret the tags sent with the file. Comparable systems include Adobe's Postscript.

Like Microsoft's Object Linking and Embedding, elements in a document can contain live links to files stored elsewhere on the system or network. For example, a document can contain a table developed by a spreadsheet application. When the file that the table is linked to is updated, the table is updated as well.

RELATED ENTRIES   Compound Documents; Document Interchange Standards; Electronic Data Interchange; Electronic Mail; Groupware; Object Linking and Embedding; *and* Workflow Software

Information Warehouse

An *information warehouse* is an entity that allows end users to quickly and easily access an organization's data in a consistent way. In the view of large system vendors like IBM and Digital, the information warehouse recasts mainframe and midrange computer systems as the central repository for current and historical data, as well as predefined data sets, reports, and catalogs of data. This strategy protects high-end system technology and customers' investments. The information warehouse provides a central point where all data is collected and made available, repackaged, or redistributed to end users.

Customers are building distributed computing environments and tying together departmental local area networks (LANs) into enterprise networks. The concept of an information warehouse positions the mainframe computer as another server attached to the network platform—but a very large one at that. Large system vendors have changed their strategy to support multivendor products and diverse network protocols so users can access data from the information warehouse using a variety of front-end systems and applications.

However, the warehouse concept is not entirely concerned with extending the life of big systems. In more practical terms, the warehouse concept is concerned with managing the vast amounts of "legacy" data that an organization accumulated over the years with various types of applications. Data is often stored in many different formats that are not easily accessible by applications other than the applications used to create and store the information. An information warehouse provides tools to make this data readily available throughout the enterprise.

The warehouse performs various "transformations" of data, such as getting *snapshots* of the way data looks at any one time, *sampling* the data for analysis, developing *forecasts* from the data, *grouping* data, and *converting* its formats and structures to fit other needs. Transformed data is then packaged and made available to users in a format that can be accessed using standard front-end tools, such as a Structured Query Language (SQL).

The warehouse might be divided into a master enterprise warehouse and several workgroup warehouses. The workgroup warehouse can perform some or all of the previous tasks for a group of users. For example, the workgroup warehouse might obtain data from enterprise warehouse, then perform its own transformations and packaging based on the workgroup's needs. This takes some of the load off the enterprise warehouse and keeps some information closer to the users who need it.

Figure I-7 illustrates an information warehouse. First, data is categorized as either relational (structured) or nonrelational, or as binary large objects (BLOBs). A BLOB consists of images, graphics, multimedia, smart documents, or database snapshots. The enterprise warehouse and the workgroup warehouses transform and package data. Users at workstations can access specially packaged data in their workgroup warehouses, or they can access the enterprise warehouse directly for special purposes. In an object linking environment such as Microsoft Windows, users can build compound documents by inserting objects like pictures that are stored at other locations on the network, such as an information warehouse. In this way, the object remains at one location, reducing storage requirements and easing management. Any changes to the object at the warehouse or its subsidiary locations are reflected in the compound document owned by the user.

IBM's Information Warehouse

IBM's information warehouse plan is defined by the Information Warehouse Framework strategy, which is designed to preserve the mainframe as a viable component for storing and retrieving data of all kinds, including multimedia objects and backups of local area network (LAN) servers. Key components of the Information Warehouse Framework include:

■ Database management systems (DBMS)

■ Interfaces for heterogeneous environments

■ Tools for transforming and packaging data

■ Management facilities

These components are designed to deliver to users data that is located on IBM's and other vendors' systems, no matter where the systems are in the enterprise. The framework defines heterogeneous environments that include IBM systems and networks, Novell networks, Apple systems and networks, UNIX systems, and others. There are three main components:

■ *Enterprise Data Element*   A DBMS that provides integrity, security, recovery, reliability, availability, and performance. This element is managed by DB2 and Information Management Systems/Enterprise Systems Architecture (IMS/ESA) software that runs on the Multiple Virtual Storage/390 (MVS/390) operating system.

■ *Data Delivery Element*   Gives users access to the data they need. IBM emphasizes that this element delivers data to users from wherever it resides in the enterprise. IBM also emphasizes that this component is capable of

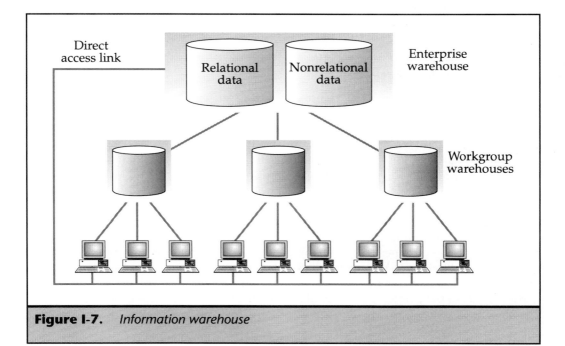

Figure I-7.   *Information warehouse*

"transforming" and "enriching" the data. IBM products for this category are Distributed Relational Database Architecture (DRDA)-compatible DB2 and various Structured Query Language (SQL) products.

- *Decision Support System* A set of tools that help users request data, then manipulate and analyze it. There are a number of applications that support this system, including IBM SAA Personal Application System/2 and Lotus 1-2-3/M.

IBM products and architectures in the Information Warehouse framework were developed by IBM Programming Systems, which is one of the largest providers of industrial-strength database technologies.

RELATED ENTRIES Database Management System; Distributed Database; Enterprise Networks; IBM; IBM Mainframe Environment; *and* IBM Networking Blueprint

Infrared Local Area Networks (LANs)

Infrared LANs are wireless networks. An infrared signal similar to the signal in a television remote control is used to send a signal between two stations. Infrared light falls below the visible light spectrum. Workstations must be within line-of-site of the infrared transmitter, which gives them some but limited mobility. Some infrared LANs operate by bouncing signals off of walls in a dispersed pattern. However, these LANs have limited distances.

RELATED ENTRIES Mobile Computing; Wireless LAN Communications

Inherited Rights

In the NetWare operating system, rights assigned to a user in a directory "flow down" to all subdirectories of that directory unless specifically changed with a filter. This flowing of rights is called *inherited rights*. In NetWare 4.x, the concept of inheritance also works in container objects of NetWare Directory Services.

If a user has Read, Write, and Create rights to a directory, that user has those same rights to its subdirectories, unless the rights are specifically changed. The rights flow down the directory structure. When a supervisor *specifically changes* rights, it means that he or she blocks the rights from being inherited in the subdirectory for all users, for a group of users, or for a single user.

The same concept applies to objects in NetWare 4.x Directory Services. If a user has trustee rights to a container object, that user has the same rights to any container and leaf objects that belong to the container object. For example, if a container holds a printer object and a user is made a trustee of the container, the user has the same trustee rights to the printer. This flow of rights continues down through every container unless the rights are blocked.

In a similar fashion, a user belonging to a container gets all the trustee rights that are assigned to a container. An example will help explain why you might want to make containers trustees. Assume that your company has a directory structure like that shown in Figure I-8. User object ACrumb in the west coast (DivWest) sales office needs to access the DOCS directory on the SYS volume of the Marantz server in the east coast (DivEast) sales office. To make ACrumb a trustee of the DOCS directory, you choose the directory and then create a trustee assignment. The trustee assignment could be any of the following:

- Grant ACrumb trustee rights to the DOCS directory.

- Grant the Sales container in the DivWest container trustee rights to the DOCS directory. Because the ACrumb object is a leaf of the Sales container, it gets the same rights by inheritance. Any other objects in the Sales container also get the trustee rights.

- Grant the DivWest container trustee rights to the DOCS directory. Now every object belonging to DivWest is granted trustee rights.

- Grant the CambrianCorp container trustee rights to the DOCS directory. Although impractical, you could make this container a trustee, which would grant every object in the directory tree trustee rights to the DOCS directory.

This demonstrates how rights flow down the tree structure. Starting at the bottom of the tree, only user object ACrumb is granted the rights. As you go up the directory tree and assign trustee rights to container objects at higher levels, the number of objects assigned the trustee rights increases. Assigning trustee rights to container objects can simplify an administrator's job, but you need to be careful. It might not be

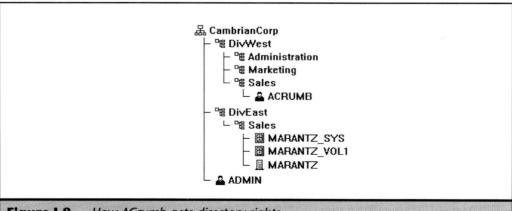

Figure I-8. *How ACrumb gets directory rights*

appropriate to grant some of the objects in the containers trustee rights. A better way to assign trustee rights is to add users to groups and then assign rights to the groups.

Inherited Rights Filters

An Inherited Rights Filter (IRF) is used to block the normal flow of rights down the directory tree. If a user has Read, Write, Create, and File Scan rights to a directory, the user also has those rights to the directory's subdirectories unless some or all of the rights are blocked with an IRF (or you make new trustee assignments in the subdirectories). For example, you could block the Write and Create rights to prevent users from creating and modifying files in a subdirectory. Every object or directory can have its own IRF, but IRFs do not block supervisor rights in the file system.

Effective Rights

The actual rights that a user has to a directory or object depend on the following, which combine to form what are called *effective rights*:

■ The object's trustee assignments to the directory or file

■ Inherited rights from parent directories

■ Rights granted to groups that the user belongs to

■ Security equivalences (discussed in the next section)

RELATED ENTRIES   Access Control; Access Rights; Account, User Network ; File and Directory Permissions, Windows NT; File and Directory Attributes, Netware; Groups; Permissions in Windows NT; Rights in Novell NetWare; *and* Users and Groups

Inverse Multiplexers

An inverse multiplexer splits a high-speed data stream from some source into two or more data streams for transmission over low-speed lines as shown in Figure I-9. The process is used to either reduce cost or take advantage of several available low-speed lines. For example, a facility that transfers data at night might use two or more available phone lines to transfer a high-speed data stream to another facility. In this way, it is not necessary to lease a dedicated line or contract for a circuit- switched, high-speed line.

RELATED ENTRY   Multiplexing

Integrated Database API (IDAPI)

Integrated Database API (IDAPI) was defined in late 1992 by Borland International, IBM, Novell, and WordPerfect as a way to simplify the connection between front-end user applications and back-end database servers. IDAPI competes with Microsoft's Open Database Connectivity (ODBC) specification. The reason such connection APIs

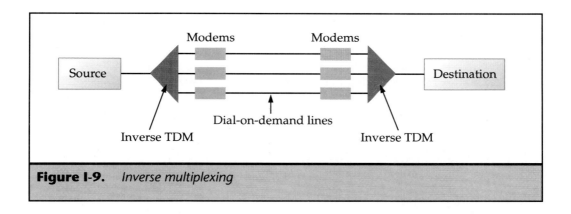

Figure I-9.   *Inverse multiplexing*

are needed is because there are so many different back-end database applications and front-end applications that need to access them. For example, common user applications such as dBase, Paradox, and Quattro need a standard way to access information stored on database management systems from vendors like Oracle, Sybase, Interbase, and others. IDAPI and ODBC provide this connection.

RELATED ENTRY   Database Connectivity APIs and Middleware

Integrated Services Digital Network (ISDN)

ISDN is often proclaimed as the public telephone and telecommunication interface of the future, although it has been slow to emerge. ISDN integrates data, voice, and video signals into a digital (as opposed to analog) telephone line. The important point is that it brings digital services all the way to the home or office. While most telephone companies have already switched to optical cable and digital transmission for intra-city and inter-city links, the "local loop" that connects many home and business users to the telephone company switching office still uses analog signaling techniques. ISDN also standardizes the services provided to subscribers on an international level, thus providing a way to create international networks.

The original ISDN standard is *narrowband ISDN*. The emerging standard called *broadband ISDN* (B-ISDN) operates in the megabit-to-gigabit range. Narrowband ISDN has a maximum rate of 2 Mbits/sec and works over copper cable. Narrowband ISDN can provide 64 or 128 Kbits/sec of digital service over wide-area links, depending on how it is configured. Compare this to typical modem rates of 28 Kbits/sec or less. ISDN provides a significant improvement over existing modem-connected lines, but it still doesn't compare to the 10 Mbits/sec rates of an Ethernet local area network (LAN). However, it's also important to realize that Ethernet LANs are shared by multiple users, so the data rate is 10 Mbits/sec only when no other users are contending for the LAN.

ISDN is now viewed as a technology that is appropriate for remote users who dial into their companies' LANs and for some LAN-to-LAN connections. ISDN can also handle fax traffic. ISDN provides an economical way to establish digital links with remote offices until traffic requirements call for more expensive dedicated lines. The ISDN interface will automatically switch among different devices attached to it, such as a bridge, phone, or fax machine. ISDN also provides a link into the access point of Frame Relay and other fast packet public networks. For example, an ISDN primary rate interface is required to access the AT&T Accunet Switched 1536 Service that lets users dial into 1.536 MBits/sec lines on AT&T's digital switched network.

ISDN Details

The first ISDN standards were issued by the Consultative Committee for International Telegraph and Telephone (CCITT) in 1984 and 1988. They define end-to-end digital connectivity and the network interfaces (NI) for users into the services. ISDN services are built on existing *telephony integrated digital networks*. It provides a way for the carriers to give customers access to this digital network from their homes and businesses. Note that end-to-end digital lines will require that voice traffic be digitized in the telephone itself before transmission and converted back to analog at the other end. Therefore, special ISDN telephones are required, or you'll need special adapters to convert existing phone signals to digital signals. Special ISDN services may not be available if converters are used.

Basic Rate Interface ISDN

The Basic Rate Interface (BRI) consists of the two 64 Kbits/sec channels for data transmission called the bearer or "B" channels, plus a 16 Kbits/sec "D" channel that provides signaling for the B channels. The D channel provides control and signaling information. For example, the D channel provides the ISDN exchange with the number of the party to call. Since signaling is done in a separate channel, call setups are much faster. The B channels are circuit-switched like a normal telephone call, meaning they are set up, then taken down when the call is complete. They can connect any two ISDN sites. This is no different than a normal voice call, but for data transmissions, ISDN provides much more flexible digital service than leased digital lines that are dedicated between two points. An ISDN line is also used to provide the connection to X.25 and Frame Relay packet-switching networks on a permanent or temporary basis.

Primary Rate Interface ISDN

The Primary Rate Interface (PRI) channels are available to ISDN subscribers who need additional throughput. They are based on the DS1 rate of 1.544 Mbits/sec and include 23 B channels and one 64 Kbits/sec D channel. The B channels can be bundled as described here.

H0 channel:	384 Kbits/sec (6 B channels)
H11 channel:	1.536 Mbits/sec (24 B channels)
H12 channel:	1.92 Mbits/sec (30 B channels)

The lines can be used as a high-speed trunk for transferring large files and other continuous data streams or be subdivided with a multiplexer to provide channels for multiple devices. By providing a range of service options, ISDN bandwidth can be configured to handle compressed video, video telephones, and teleservices.

ISDN Services

Services provided by ISDN operate at higher protocol levels than simple phone connections. Some of the services are listed here. They use the B channels for transmission and the D channel for signaling.

- *Teletex* The teletex services provide end-to-end message exchange between two devices, using standard character sets.
- *Telefax* The telefax services use CCITT Group 4 facsimile standards to provide file exchange between terminals.
- *Videotex* The videotex services provide an enhancement of the teletex service by adding text/graphic mailbox functions.

The ISDN specification identifies a series of supplementary services. These services are associated with the bearer or teleservices. The most interesting are listed here:

- *Multiple numbers* This service provides a way for a single interface (for example, a residential connection) to have multiple assigned telephone numbers.
- *Caller identification* This service displays the number of the party calling in.
- *Caller identification restriction* With this service, the caller can prevent the number from being presented to the called party.
- *Connected-line identification* This service displays the number of the party that was called.

The ISDN Physical Interface

In North America, a *network termination (NT)* device connects the customer's data or telephone equipment to the local exchange carrier's line. The NT was originally conceived as a device owned by the service provider, and that is the way ISDN is implemented outside the United States. The breakup of AT&T and the resulting judgments prevent the regional Bell operating companies (RBOCs) from owning equipment on customer sites, so in the United States, the NT is purchased and installed by the customer. Lack of understanding about this equipment is one of the main reasons why ISDN has been slow to develop in the U.S.

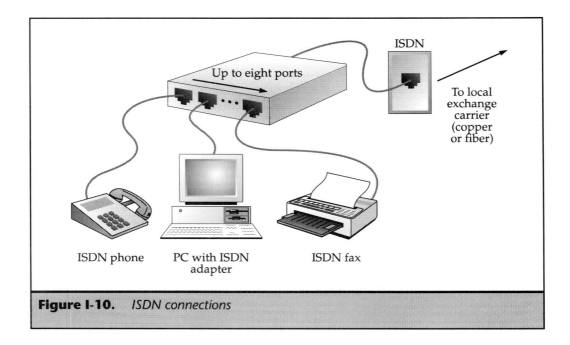

Figure I-10.   *ISDN connections*

The NT device provides a connection for terminal equipment (TE) and terminal adapter (TA) equipment to the local loop. TE devices are ISDN-compatible telephones and computers that have ISDN interfaces. TAs are devices used to connect non-ISDN-compatible equipment. They provide the ISDN interface on one side and an interface to the non-ISDN equipment on the other side.

In the U.S., the NT device has a customer side and a telephone company side (although the customer still owns the whole device). The telephone company side connects with the wire from the phone company. The customer side has a unique design that allows up to eight devices to connect with and be addressed by the NT device. Figure I-10 illustrates the NT device and the 8 possible connection points for TE and TA devices. The S-bus circuitry in the NT device allocates time for each device to access the line using a contention control scheme. Note that not all NT devices are the same. Some may have only two connectors, one for data equipment and one for a phone. Additional devices are then daisy-chained together.

Signaling Channel Interface

The D channel is separated from the B channels and provides the signaling to set up calls. This signaling operates in the Physical, Data-Link, and Network layers relative to the OSI protocol model. The protocols define message types that are exchanged between the customer equipment and the local exchange for setting up and maintaining services. The services provided by each protocol layer are described here:

■ The Physical layer sets up a circuit-switched connection that provides 64 Kbits/sec transmission. Loop-back testing and monitoring is also handled in this layer. This layer also supports a multidrop line for the connection of telephones, computers, and other equipment.

■ The Data-Link layer uses the Link Access Procedure for D Channel (LAP-D), which is similar to High-level Data Link Control (HDLC). LAP-D works across the D channel to provide control and signaling information.

It provides frame relay and frame switching services in which frames are routed through intermediate nodes. The Data-Link layer relays frames by reading address information and forwarding frames appropriately along *virtual paths* to their destination. There may be several destinations. Devices operating at this level are digital private branch exchanges (PBXs) and computer bridging devices. This level would be used to set up a private network between two sites.

■ The network layer can provide packet-switching services similar to X.25. It can also provide circuit-switching and user-to-user connections. Messages generated in this layer are transported by Data-Link layer protocols.

Teleservices such as teletex, telefax, and videotex are implemented in all seven layers relative to the OSI protocol stack.

Availability

ISDN is one of the most well-funded projects in the telecommunication industry and is supported globally. Already, Japan and Australia provide easy access to ISDN services. ISDN was slow to catch on in the U.S. due to tariff problems and implementation at the customer site. But ISDN is catching on. The service is primarily offered in large metropolitan areas at this point.

Switching to ISDN will require a conversion to ISDN phones unless you decide to keep your original connections and just use the ISDN lines for data. Adapters are available to convert existing non-ISDN equipment, but existing phones don't have the features to take advantage of some ISDN services such as caller ID.

Ordering ISDN Home Service

Bob Metcalfe, the inventor of Ethernet and publisher of *InfoWorld*, recently published a series of articles detailing his pioneering efforts to get ISDN service at his home. In his words, "ISDN will only be ready for prime time when PC people like me do not have to become ISDN experts." And that is ISDN's current state for home users. Unlike telephones, which can be purchased easily in discount stores and plugged in without much thought, ISDN requires special equipment and you need to make special arrangements with the phone company.

Most home and small business users will order the basic rate ISDN services, which consist of two B channels for transmitting either voice or data and the D channel for transmitting control information. Think of the B channels as two separate phone lines.

Because the lines are switched links and not dedicated, you can set up digital connections anywhere. This has more implications for a company that has several remote ISDN users. It can set up ISDN lines to support those users. This reduces initial costs until the organization can determine its needs for higher-rate services.

Part of the process of setting up an ISDN line is to call the phone company and tell them explicitly what you want to do with the line. They need to know whether an ISDN telephone will be attached. If multiple devices are connected to a line such as a computer and the phone, each device requires a unique number that is assigned by the phone company, much like your existing telephone number.

As mentioned, ISDN lines operate at 64 Kbits/sec, but this may not be quite the case in some areas. Calls made outside the telephone company's central office revert to 56 Kbits/sec because most existing equipment needs upgrading to support the full ISDN rate of 64 Kbits/sec.

Pricing

The setup rates can be under $100 in some areas, depending on tariff structures. Monthly fixed charges are under $50. There is a charge for the usage of each B channel that is based on the time and distance of the call. Usage charges are pennies-per-minute.

When pricing ISDN for network interconnect usage, compare its equipment costs and line setup charges with a Switched-56 line or a leased line. A Switched-56 line is a nonvoice digital channel. The channel service unit/data service unit (CSU/DSU) for the Switched-56 line can run about $900, while the equipment for ISDN costs about $400. However, Switched-56 is attractive when you consider the initial setup charges and hassles with the telephone company over simply getting an ISDN line. In some areas, Switched-56 may be the only choice.

RELATED ENTRIES   Carrier Services; Circuit-Switching Services; Switched-56 Services; *and* Telecommunications

Intelligent Hub

Hubs are central wiring concentrators that provide repeater functions in networks such as ARCNET and Ethernet 10Base-T. The hub serves as a central place to connect workstations and more easily manage the network. The first hubs were simple repeaters that supported a single transmission medium only. The wiring configuration they supported was appropriate for department or workgroup local area networks (LANs) of about 20 users. These hubs are called first-generation hubs, and they are still viable products for small LANs.

Second-generation hubs are called *intelligent hubs* because they include management features, such as the ability to detect faults, and collect information about network activities and the individual ports on the hub. The information is collected and reported back to a central management station. Simple Network Management Protocol (SNMP) management features are supported in most second-generation hubs.

Other important features of intelligent hubs are listed here:

■ They include backplanes with multiple buses to support different media such as Ethernet, token ring, and FDDI.

■ They typically use high-performance RISC processors that improve packet throughput performance.

■ They have the ability to create logical LAN segments within a single hub and bridge those segments.

■ They may have installable management modules that provide the ability to manage the hub from a remote location.

■ They may have out-of-band signaling that connects remote management stations to the hub via a separate line that remains live even if LAN communication fails.

Third-generation hubs have began to appear. These include more sophisticated management and monitoring features, faster backplanes, improved bridging and routing among segments, and the ability to microsegment the network so that a single LAN supports a single workstation. Emerging hubs provide Asynchronous Transfer Mode (ATM) switching between any ports.

RELATED ENTRY   Hubs

Interconnectivity
See Interoperability.

Interdomain Routing Protocol (IDPR)
IDPR is an OSI exterior gateway protocol similar to the Internet Border Gateway Protocol (BGP). It is designed for routing the OSI connectionless protocol packets.

RELATED ENTRY   Routing, OSI

Interexchange Carriers
Before the breakup of AT&T, long-distance calls were mostly handled by AT&T. After the breakup, long-distance calling companies began to appear such as MCI, US Sprint, and others. These services basically handle calls and other telecommunication services between Local Access and Transport Areas (LATAs). A LATA is associated with an area code and calls between LATAs are considered long distance. A local exchange carrier (LEC) has a franchise within a LATA (intraLATA) to provide services. A LEC may be a regional Bell operating company (RBOC) or an independent telephone company (ITC).

InterLATA telecommunication refers to services provided between LATAs by *interexchange carriers (IXCs)*. The services provided by the RBOCs and AT&T are regulated and prices are fixed for services. For example, tariffs that control interLATA service rates cannot be changed without approval from the federal government. IntraLATA tariffs are controlled at the local or state level. Other carriers are not subject to these tariffs but are subject to competition and so prices are relatively close. A number of IXCs are listed next.

Advanced Telecommunications Corp.
Boca Raton, Florida
800/226-8888

Allnet
Bingham Farms, Michigan
800/783-2020

AT&T
Basking Ridge, New Jersey
800/346-3288

ATC/Microtel
Atlanta, Georgia
800/749-5885

Cable & Wireless
Vienna, Virginia
800/969-9998

Consolidated Networks, Inc.
St. Louis, Missouri
314/993-9009

ITT
Tucson, Arizona
602/889-7600

MCI
McLean, Virginia
800/888-0800

US Sprint
Kansas City, Missouri
800/877-2000

Williams Telecommunications
Tulsa, Oklahoma
800/642-2299

RBOCs must provide all interexchange carriers with equal access to their LATA facilities. Users can therefore choose which interexchange carrier they want to use. That carrier then provides services between LATAs. It is estimated that there are over 1,500 businesses in the United States that provide various types of long-distance services. As of this writing, it is estimated that AT&T holds about 65% of the market.

Interior Gateway Protocols

The Internet is divided into domains, or autonomous systems. A *domain* is a collection of hosts and routers that use the same routing protocol and are administered by a single authority. In other words, a domain might be an internetwork administered by a university or other organization. Interior Gateway Protocols (IGPs) route within a domain. The Exterior Gateway Protocol (EGP) provides a way for two neighboring routers located at edges of their respective domains to exchange messages and information.

RELATED ENTRY   Routing, Internet

Intermediate System-to-Intermediate System (IS-IS)

IS-IS is an Open Systems Interconnection (OSI) routing protocol that dynamically routes packets between routers or intermediate systems. IS-IS is a link-state OSI protocol that provides routing services for Transmission Control Protocol/Internet Protocol (TCP/IP) and OSI. It determines the best path through a network for packets and updates routers as to the status of the network and its available systems.

RELATED ENTRY   Routing, OSI

International Consultative Committee for Telegraph and Telephone (CCITT)

See CCITT; International Telecommunications Union.

International Organization for Standardization (ISO)

ISO has the goal of promoting and developing standards for international exchange. ISO is responsible for the development and maintenance of the *Open Systems Interconnection (OSI) reference model,* which is described elsewhere in this book. The OSI standards promote open networking environments that let multivendor computer systems communicate with one another using protocols that have been accepted internationally by the ISO members. However, the work of the ISO is much broader than the communication and networking standards described in the OSI model. ISO is involved in the international standardization of just about every service or manufactured product.

ISO membership includes representatives from most of the major standards organizations throughout the world. Its connection within the United Nations is with the Economic and Social Council. The United States is represented by the American National Standards Institute (ANSI), and the United Kingdom is represented by the British Standards Institution (BSI). Government agencies such as the U.S. State Department are also represented in the ISO, as well as businesses, educational institutes, and research organizations. The Consultative Committee for International Telegraph and Telephone (CCITT) also has representatives within ISO.

The OSI Model

The OSI reference model defines communication protocols in seven layers. Each layer has well-defined functions, and these functions interrelate to the functions in adjoining layers. The lowest layers define the physical media, connectors, and components that provide network communication, while the highest layers define how applications access communication services. The OSI model was derived from IBM's proprietary Systems Network Architecture (SNA), which is an architectural description of the protocols, formats, and structures required to transmit packets of information in a networked environment.

Vendors use the OSI layers to design products that interoperate with other vendors' products; however, designing to the OSI model does not guarantee interoperability because there are variations in the standards. To resolve some of these problems, governments have issued OSI specifications called Government Open Systems Interconnection Profiles (GOSIPs). These profiles specify the level of OSI compatibility that hardware and software products must have. Vendors doing business with the government must provide products that comply with the profiles. In the United States, the National Institute of Standards (NIST) is responsible for GOSIP and issuing yearly updated procurement standards, which are called FIPS 146.

Layered Architecture

The OSI model is built on the concept of a layered architecture. Layered architectures provide interoperability among multivendor systems. Without open, layered, and standardized protocols, buyers would need to purchase equipment from one vendor.

Layering specifies different functions and services at levels in a "protocol stack." The OSI protocol stack is pictured in Figure I-11. Functions and standards defined for each layer are discussed in the following sections. Note that each communicating device has hardware and software that is designed around the stack. Keep in mind that the stack merely defines how to create hardware and software components that operate at each level of the stack. So if you wanted to create a network interface card that would interoperate with other vendors' cards, you would comply with protocols defined in the lower layers of the stack. Layers above the Physical layer specify the creation of software procedures, formats, and other aspects of communication. The higher you climb in the stack, the more sophisticated are the processes.

The boundary between each layer is called the interface, and the layers are connected by service access points. If a process running in an upper layer requires service from a process running in a lower layer, it passes requests through a service access point associated with the application. Communication between two systems takes place by initiating requests down through the protocol stack on one system and transferring the request at the Physical layer to the other system. The other system passes the request up through its protocol stack and responds in like manner. Each

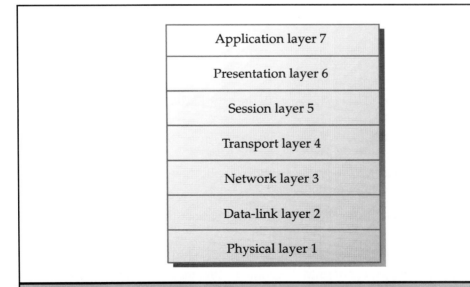

Figure I-11.   *The OSI protocol stack*

layer provides some information or service that prepares the message for transport to the other system. Examples include error checking, dividing and packaging the information, and keeping track of the session to make sure it stays alive long enough to get the message across. A summary of each layer follows.

APPLICATION LAYER   This layer defines how applications interface with the underlying communication system. Standards include:

- ISO 8649/8650/10035   *Association Control Service and Protocol* sets up, maintains, and takes down associations. Associations are relationships between application entities.

- ISO 8571   *File Transfer, Access, and Management (FTAM)* is a distributed filing system application.

- ISO 8831/8832   *Job Transfer and Manipulation* provides facilities for submitting jobs to remote systems.

- ISO 9040/9041   *Virtual Terminal Service* allows a terminal user to access a process on a remote computer.

- ISO 9066   *Reliable Transfer Service and Protocol* provides applications with connection-oriented data-exchange services.

- ISO 9072   *Remote Operation Service and Protocol (ROSE)* provides the means for an application to start an operation on a remote system.

- ISO 9579   *Remote Database Access* provides access to a remote database management system (DBMS).

- ISO 9594 (CCITT X.500)   *Directory Services* maintains a database of users and resources.

- ISO 9595/9596 (CCITT X.700)   *Common Management Information Protocol (CMIP)* defines network management services.

- ISO 9735   *Electronic Data Interchange* defines the exchange of documents between platforms.

- ISO 10021 (CCITT X.400)   *Message Handling System* defines electronic mail exchange.

- ISO 10026   *Transaction Processing* provides applications with access to transaction processing functions.

PRESENTATION LAYER   This layer provides translation functions for data formats and representation. Standards for this layer include:

- ISO 8822/8823   *Presentation Services* ensures that application data can be exchanged between communicating systems that may represent the data differently. ISO 8823 is the *Connection-Oriented Presentation Protocol*.

■ ISO 8824 *Abstract Syntax Notation One* is a language that defines application data syntax.

SESSION LAYER This layer allows dialog between stations in a connection-oriented session. Standards for this layer include:

■ ISO 8326 *Session Service and Definition* defines connection-oriented session services that establish sessions and negotiates session parameters. Operations are defined for the session-connection establishment phase, data-transfer phase, and session-connection release phase.

■ ISO 8327 *Session Service Protocol* is the protocol specification for ISO 8326.

TRANSPORT LAYER This layer provides a communication channel in which end-systems can acknowledge receipt of data or request retransmission separate from similar functions handled by the network itself. This layer includes the OSI Transport Class 0, Class 1, and Class 4, which are similar to the Internet's Transmission Control Protocol (TCP) and Novell's Sequenced Packet Exchange (SPX). Standards for this layer include:

■ ISO 8072/8073 *Transport Service Definition* defines full-duplex transport services. *Connection-Oriented Transport Protocol* provides error-free data delivery. Packets arrive in sequence with guarantees that there are no duplicates or losses. *Connectionless Mode Transport* defines a communication without setup requirements and flow control.

NETWORK LAYER This layer sets up, monitors, and takes down communication sessions. It also provides routing functions. This layer supports OSI's Connectionless Network Service (CLNS) and Connection-Oriented Network Service (CONS), which provide services similar to the Internet Protocol (IP) and Novell's Internetwork Packet Exchange (IPX). Standards for this layer include:

■ ISO 8208 *X.25 Packet Level Protocol* is an end-to-end protocol that supports CONS.

■ ISO 8348 *Network Service* defines the essential services required to route information without user intervention.

■ ISO 8880 *Protocols to Provide Network Service* provides protocol to support CONS and CLNS.

■ ISO 9542 *Connectionless End System-to-Intermediate System (ES-IS)* routing defines connectionless routing within autonomous domains.

■ ISO 10030 *Connection-Mode ES-IS* routing defines connection-oriented routing within autonomous domains.

DATA-LINK LAYER This layer frames data for bit-stream transmission in the Physical layer and ensures reliable transmission between stations. This layer typically includes IEEE 802 standards such as Ethernet Carrier Sense Multiple Access with Collision Detection (CSMA/CD), Token Bus, and Token Ring. It also includes Fiber Distributed Data Interface (FDDI). There are two sublayers: Media Access Control (MAC) and Logical Link Control (LLC). Standards for this layer include:

- ISO 4335 *High-level Data Link Control* (HDLC) provides point-to-point and multidrop connection facilities. Refer to "High-level Data Link Control."

- ISO 8802 *Local Area Networks* is a set of standards that are the same as the IEEE 802.x standards. For example, 8802.3 is the same as IEEE 802.3

PHYSICAL LAYER This layer defines hardware standards such as connectors and the structure of the bit-stream that flows between devices. Standards for this layer are too numerous to list.

RELATED ENTRIES Government OSI Profile; Layered Architecture; Open Systems Interconnection Model; *and* Standards Organizations

International Telecommunications Union

The Consultative Committee for International Telegraph and Telephone (CCITT) is a committee of a United Nations treaty organization called the International Telecommunications Union (ITU). The committee is made up of members from governments and has the task of studying, recommending, and standardizing technical and operational issues for telecommunications. The United States is involved with the CCITT through the U.S. State Department. The CCITT prepares recommendations that are voted on for approval by the ITU.

NOTE: The current trend is to refer to the CCITT standards as ITU standards.

RELATED ENTRY CCITT

Internet

The Internet is a global web of interconnected computers and computer networks. "Web" refers to the fact that the Internet is a network of networks. It integrates together local area networks (LANs) located in schools, libraries, businesses, hospitals, federal agencies, research institutes, and other entities into a single, large communication network that spans the globe. The underlying connections include the dialup telephone network, satellite and ground-based microwave links, and fiber-optic networks like those running through metropolitan areas. The actual network cannot be mapped at any one time because new computers and networks are constantly added and the electronic pathways for information are constantly changing.

While the Internet was originally conceived as a communication network for researchers, primarily military, today it is used by millions of people in business, in education, or for just plain communication. It is estimated that the Internet has over 7,500 networks with over a million host systems that support mail exchange between possibly 25 million people. These numbers are expected to double by 1995. The Internet provides electronic mail services so users can send messages to one another. It also provides information services in many forms, both public and private, that users can browse through for free, or for a charge.

The Internet could be compared to the CompuServe information service, or Prodigy or BIX (Byte Information Exchange). Users log on to access resources on a network of computer systems. But that's where the comparison ends. CompuServe and the others are private networks providing a set of services within specific boundaries. The Internet is more of a communication backbone for accessing many different services. It is a structure with ties to many public and private networks. Your access to some of these networks may be free and unrestricted, may depend on access privileges, or on how much you are willing to spend. The network itself is supported by the national and global telecommunication system, both public and private.

The Internet grew out of an earlier U.S. Department of Defense project, the Advanced Research Projects Agency Network (ARPANET), that was put into place in 1969 as a pioneering project to test packet-switching networks. ARPANET provided links between researchers and remote computer centers. In 1983, the military communication portion of ARPANET was split off into MILNET (Military Network), although cross-communication was still possible. ARPANET was officially dismantled in 1990. Its successor, Internet, continues to grow.

Internet provides connections to other networks, such as UUCP (the UNIX network), BITNET (academic and research network), and others. Internet also provides connections to global networks, such as those in Australia, Europe, Japan, and South America. In addition, other commercial information services such CompuServe now provide connections into the Internet for users.

The National Research and Education Network (NREN) is the backbone data network of the Internet, administered by the National Science Foundation. It succeeded the National Science Foundation network (NSFnet) as the major Internet network for research and education in the United States, as of the signing of the "High-Performance Computing Act of 1991," a bill sponsored by then Senator Al Gore. It calls for a high-capacity (gigabits-per-second) network and the coordination of networking efforts among federal organizations.

NREN is designed to connect K-12 schools, colleges, universities, libraries, health care industries, businesses, and manufacturers into a national public network using the Internet. The Internet provides vast quantities of timely and useful information to these institutions over existing telecommunication links. Access is obtained using standard desktop computer equipment and modems, or connection to networks that are connected to the Internet. For more information, see "Data Highways", "National Information Infrastructure", and "National Research and Education Network."

Funding for the Internet comes from many sources. The United States government funds major Internet backbones that lower-level public and private networks attach to.

For example, the National Science Foundation controls the nationwide backbone for education and research; however, it does not control the attached networks. There are also backbones for military and space-related research organizations. Coordination is handled by the Federal Networking Council (FNC).

The Internet Activities Board (IAB) coordinates the design, engineering, and management of the Internet. It has two main committees:

- *Internet Engineering Task Force (IETF)* This committee specifies protocols and recommends standards.
- *Internet Research Task Force (IRTF)* This committee researches new technologies and makes recommendations about them to the IETF.

The TCP/IP Connection

The Internet uses the Transmission Control Protocol/Internet Protocol (TCP/IP), although not exclusively. It also uses other protocols, but TCP/IP is the key to interoperability on the Internet. TCP/IP is an open communication protocol that is commonly available in many computer systems. Protocols define the rules of communication. TCP/IP was specifically designed for the interconnection of different types of computer equipment. It was first used on the ARPANET, and is now available for almost every computer operating system as either a built-in feature or as an option that you can add.

The Internet consists of thousands of interconnected communication pathways (the web) that packets can traverse. These pathways are existing network connections, dedicated telephone lines, satellite links, and a number of other possibilities. As a whole, every computer on the Internet has a potential connection to every other computer on the Internet.

One of the reasons why the Internet is so popular is because its users have such a wide variety of computers and operating systems. With TCP/IP, interconnection of these systems is possible.

Accessing the Internet

To use the services of the Internet, you first need to figure out how you are going to connect into it. Many Internet users are connected to the Internet through their company, an educational institution, or other organization. An in-house network may provide a pathway to these services. The company or organization often picks up the cost of the calls and has access to resources available on other Internet networks. For example, government agencies have access to secure Internet resources that are not available to individual home users.

If you're not so lucky to have someone else picking up the tab, you can gain Internet access through commercial providers that have their own host systems connected to the Internet, or you can connect directly to the Internet, in which case your computer becomes a host.

As for the physical components, you need a computer with a modem. If you're connecting to a service provider, you'll need a terminal emulation program. If you're connecting directly to the Internet, you'll need to run the TCP/IP protocol suite.

If you're looking to get interactive on the Internet, make sure the provider offers more than just mail services. With mail-only access, you can exchange mail with other users but that's about it. With interactive capabilities, you can access services that let you search for information, chat with other users, and transfer files. However, if Internet mail service is all you need and you already have a connection with another mail service such as CompuServe, MCI Mail, or BIX, you can simply take advantage of the Internet connections those services have for exchanging Internet mail.

USENET news is an Internet broadcast news service that distributes information, usually about the Internet, to all hosts. The USENET network includes all computers that get USENET news. If you just sign up for mail service, chances are you'll get access to this service as well.

The following table describes the different ways you can connect with the Internet. The table was put together by John S. Quarterman and Smoot Carl-Mitchel of Texas Internet Consulting and is adapted from their book, *The Internet Connection: A Guide to Connectivity and Configuration* (Addison-Wesley, 1993). The article first appeared in *ConneXtions* in October 1993. (The publication is produced by Interop Company, Mountain View, California 415/941-3399.)

Type	Mailnet	Conf	Logon Host	Dialup IP	Full
Mail:	yes	yes	yes	yes	yes
News:	yes	maybe	yes	yes	yes
FTP:	no	yes	to host (1)	yes	yes
Interactive:	no	no	yes	yes	yes
IP to:	gateway	gateway	logon host	your machine	your machine
Dialup:	yes	yes	yes	yes	yes, or dedicated
Speed:	modem	modem	modem	modem	modem or digital services
Cost:	(2)	(2), (3)	(2)	(2)	monthly

(1) This is a change from the original Quartem and Carl-Mitchel table. File transfers using FTP are sent to the logon host. You then download files from the logon host.
(2) Monthly plus connect time charges
(3) Per-message charges

Here is a description of each column in the table:

■ *Type* What you'll get from the services listed in the other columns.

- *Mailnet* Services that provide mail and news only.

- *Conf* Services such as CompuServe, BOX, and GEnie that have their own interactive services, as well as connections into the Internet.

- *Logon host* Service providers such as those listed in the next section.

- *Dialup IP* A connection directly to the Internet using Serial Line Internet Protocol (SLIP) or Point-to-Point Protocol (PPP). You'll need to run IP, TCP, and UDP on your computer.

- *Full* Implies that you have a full interactive connection to the Internet using a high-speed connection. This column also implies that you might provide a dedicated, 24-hour service so other Internet users can access your host. You'll need a domain name and an Internet number to set your system up as a host on the Internet.

The *Type* column describes the services available, such as mail, news, and FTP (used to transfer files). Some of the interactive services are described later. Interactive implies that you can interact with the Internet and use its commands—something you can't do with mail services. "IP to" indicates where and how the Internet connection is, either at a gateway, logon host, or "your machine" as described here:

- *Gateway* A service that provides you with Internet services, but you never get on the Internet yourself.

- *Logon host* A service that lets you get on the Internet and interact with it, but your machine is never actually on the Internet—the logon host is. You access the logon host with a modem. You pay the provider a monthly charge and access charges. Other Internet users don't see your machine as a host.

- *Your machine* This category implies that your machine is a host on the Internet and you can let other users access services you provide.

Dialup indicates the physical connection methods used to access the Internet. They are all dialup, except the last column, which might be a dedicated connection. The speed column merely indicates that the access rate is dependent on the modem.

Internet Service Providers

Many Internet organizations provide host services at monthly rates. Basically, the service advertises their system as your E-mail gateway. You then call into this gateway to pick up mail. Of course, many educational institutions and large companies have their own gateways, and many educational institutions make their gateways available to individual users.

You choose an Internet service provider based on its service area, the services provided (Archie, E-mail, FTP, Gopher, news, Telnet), and the cost of the services. For a complete service provider list, contact InterNIC Information Services in San Diego (800/444-4345 or 619/455-4600). Three well-known providers are listed here to give you an idea of services and costs.

- *Advanced Network & Services (ANS) Inc.* (Ann Arbor, Michigan, 914/789-5300) is a nonprofit organization formed by IBM, MCI, and Merit. Access is anywhere in the U.S. over analog, Frame Relay, or leased lines. Analog connects cost $25 per month plus hourly charges.

- *PSINET* (Reston, Virginia, 800/827-7482) provides a wide range of services, including InterFrame, a Frame Relay connection that costs $650 to access over leased lines, and analog services from various access points at hourly rates of $1.25 to $6.50, or at monthly rates of $9 to $29 month.

- *UUNET Technologies* (Falls Church, Virginia, 703/204-8001) provides analog services at $250 month or leased services from $500 to $2,000 month. Access points are anywhere in the U.S.

Internet Addressing

Every computer on the Internet has a specific name and numeric address. The name is designed to simplify access for people; the numeric address is used by communication equipment and computers. The name is not actually part of the Internet Protocol—it is a translation of the number by the Domain Naming Service. Internet names simplify the addressing of electronic mail and user access to other Internet systems.

The numeric address is a 4-byte (32-bit) numeric value that identifies both a network and a local host or node on the network. Each IP address must be unique and consist of four decimal numbers separated by periods, such as 191.255.10.3. The assignment of numeric addresses is arbitrary within a company or organization if you're just setting up an internal TCP/IP network, but if you're planning to connect a computer as a host on the Internet, you'll need to get a registered number. To do so, contact Network Solutions, Inc. (Herndon, Virginia, 703/742-4777). They can provide you with information to help with the process.

All Internet names have the two elements shown here:

local@domain

You'll use these names when addressing E-mail messages or connecting with other systems on the network. The FTP command is used to connect with other systems.

An Internet name consists of several words separated by periods as defined by the Domain Name Service (DNS). The domain name becomes part of every host address in your TCP/IP network. It combines with your organization's name and a type code that represents the type of organization you have. The most common types of codes are listed here:

.com   Commercial organization
.edu   Educational institution
.gov   Government organization

A complete Internet name for a fictitious company called Feldspar, Inc. would be FELDSPAR.COM. If the company has offices in several cities, the city could be added to the name to differentiate between the offices. For example, the following names represent the Feldspar offices in Los Angeles and San Francisco. Note that the city names are abbreviated to reduce the amount of typing required of users who type the name often.

la.feldspar.com
sf.feldspar.com

If the company wants to differentiate among its departments, abbreviations for the departments' names can be added, as follows:

la.mktg.feldspar.com
sf.acct.feldspar.com

Companies and organizations are responsible for coming up with the name. Once the name is defined, the organization registers it with the Internet. A Domain Name Service (DNS) is then assigned to host the new network. You then get an electronic mail gateway (see "Domain Name Service") and you can decide whether you want outside users to access your system as a host.

Individual users on the TCP/IP network also need a name. It's a good idea for organizations to standardize on their E-mail naming strategy from the start. For example, first initial, last name is common. Note that the case of the characters may be important on some systems or with some applications. To address an E-mail message, you tack the E-mail name onto the Internet host name in the form shown here:

username@host

where username is the identification or mailbox of the recipient and host is the computer and/or host or domain name. For example, the following is the address for Tom Jones at Feldspar, Inc.:

tjones@feldspar.com

Services Available on the Internet

Once you've obtained access to the Internet through the service provider or your own connection, you can log on and begin issuing commands and "browsing" around. Some of the commands and services are described in the following sections. Telnet is discussed first, because it's the command you use for logging in.

Telnet Logon

Telnet is the protocol or command that enables remote logon. This command is available on every system that has TCP/IP support installed. If you've connected with a service provider, the command is available on their system. Some systems have an equivalent *rlogon* command. You simply type the Telnet command, followed by the name of the host you want to log on to. If you don't type the host name, the Telnet prompt appears and you can type **help** to display information about using the command. For example, to connect with the Science and Information Technology System (SITS) at the National Science Foundation (NSF), you would type the following:

    telnet stis.nsf.gov

Once connected, you type a logon name and password. If this is the first time you've logged in and you need to get an account, type **newuser**.

When you're ready to log off the system, there are a number of commands you can type, such as **logoff**, **exit**, **quit**, and **bye**, or try pressing CTRL+D or CTRL+Z. If you're not sure, type **help**.

FTP (File Transfer Protocol)

FTP is the program you use to transfer files from one host to another. Remember that if you're logged on to a service provider's host, you can only transfer files there. You then use a local file transfer program to get the files to your machine. Features for doing this are usually built into the service provided by the host.

You can also use FTP to access *anonymous* accounts, which are host accounts that are open to the public and that provide information you can access, usually without a charge. The Internet contains a vast quantity of information available in anonymous FTP accounts. You'll find research papers, free software, debate logs, and other information. Locating information is the challenge. A service called Archie can help. It maintains dedicated databases of information available on the Internet that you can search to find information.

There is a whole set of commands you can use once you've started an FTP session. FTP is often used as a verb in the Internet literature—someone might say "FTP me the file." You can type help to get more information. Refer to "File Transfer Protocol" for more details.

Electronic Mail, Talk Services, and News

Electronic mail is probably the most active service on the Internet. There are a number of utilities you can use to create mail messages, some of which are available free on the Internet. The important component is the delivery mechanism, which is the protocol the E-mail system uses to send messages. The TCP/IP E-mail protocol is *Simple Mail Transfer Protocol (SMTP)*. As long as the protocol is SMTP, the user interface can have any look the developer chooses. An SMTP-based mail system on a PC lets users send and receive messages with users on a UNIX system or anyone on the Internet without going through a special gateway that translates messages.

If all you want to do is exchange mail with other users, you can go through a variety of service providers and bulletin board systems that perform this exchange for you. If the provider has a gateway, you don't need to worry about using an Internet-compatible mail system. For example, if you're using CompuServe, you simply write messages using the CompuServe E-mail system, then address them to an end user on the Internet.

The following networks provide Internet E-mail delivery services. Some are loose associations of connected users, while others are established, profit-making organizations.

- *UUCP mail network* A dialup UNIX network that provides mail and USENET news (UUCP means UNIX-to-UNIX CoPy protocol.)
- *FidoNet* A dialup DOS network that provides mail and Echomail, a service similar to USENET news
- *BITNET (Because It's Time Network)* A network of campus computers that is funded by the National Science Foundation
- *MCI Mail* A mail delivery service provided by MCI Corp.
- *CompuServe* Provides mail exchange services with the Internet
- *GEnie* Provides mail exchange services with the Internet

PRIVACY ENHANCED MAIL Privacy Enhanced Mail (PEM) provides confidential and authenticated E-mail. The mail is electronically signed by the sender using public key encryption methods. The receiver can then verify the signature using a public key. The Internet is adopting PEM protocols.

Information Discovery Services

The volume of information available on the Internet is staggering. Because the Internet is a loose association of many networks and many sources of information, there has been no easy way to determine the location of information. The following services have been growing in popularity and expanding the services they provide.

ARCHIE Archie, as mentioned earlier, is a service that lets you quickly locate information on anonymous FTP hosts. You access Archie through Telnet sessions, E-mail queries, or other methods. Archie tracks over 1,000 hosts worldwide. After reaching the site, you type **archie** to start the service, then type **help** to see a list of commands. To get more information on Archie access sites, use anonymous FTP to contact *quiche.cs.mcgill.ca*. Archie sites in the U.S. are listed here:

archie.ans.net (New York)
archie.rutgers.edu (New Jersey)

archie.sura.net (Maryland)
archie.unl.edu (Nebraska)

GOPHER   Gopher is a distributed document search and retrieval system developed by the University of Minnesota. It is officially defined as a "simple client/server protocol that can be used to publish and search for information held on a distributed network of hosts." Users of Gopher can view information spread out on many different hosts. Information appears in hierarchical form, or the user can request an index of matching topics. For more information, use anonymous FTP to contact *boombox.micro.umn.edu* and look in the *pub/gopher* directory.

WIDE AREA INFORMATION SERVICE (WAIS)   WAIS is a search and retrieval service that provides feedback you can use to refine future searches. WAIS has servers that maintain indexes of Internet documents. To get more information, use anonymous FTP to contact *think.com* and look in the *wais* directory for the *readme* file.

WORLD WIDE WEB   World Wide Web, or W3, provides information discovery services using hypertext links that connect one document with another. When using the service, you simply follow the links among documents. To get more information, "anonymous FTP" the host *info.cern.ch* and look in the *pub/WWW* directory for the *readme.txt* file.

Other Services
Following is a listing of other popular services available on the Internet.

CHAT SERVICES   "Chat services" are real-time communication sessions that you have with one or more Internet users at the same time. During the session, you can type messages that other participants see, or just sit back and read the messages typed by other users. Sessions take place in special forums related to special topics like politics, aviation, computers, health, finance, and many others, or you can create your own session. Two services are available:

- *talk*   An interactive one-to-one communication service
- *IRC (Internet Relay Chat)*   An interactive many-to-many communication service

USENET NEWSGROUP   Usenet is a group of systems that exchange news and encompass universities, government agencies, businesses, and home users. There is no central control. It is similar to a bulletin board or conferencing system in that there are ongoing topics or postings that anyone can view and respond to. Categories include *computers, news, science, recreation,* and, of course, *talk.*

There has been a lot of discussion as to what Usenet actually is. According to an Internet document produced by Chip Salzenberg and revised by Gene Spafford, Usenet is not an organization because there is no central authority or "central anything." It is not a democracy and it is also not fair—anyone can say whatever they want. But speech on the Usenet is not a right because the owners of the computers that support Usenet can block your speech if they wish. Usenet *is* a place where you can participate in lively discussions and express yourself freely.

For More Information

To get more information on the Internet, refer to the following publications. You can also contact the service providers discussed earlier for information, or contact the Commercial Internet Exchange (CIX) Association at 617/864-0665 or the Federation of Academic and Research Networks at 617/890-5120.

Hahn, Harley and Rick Stout. *The Internet Complete Reference*. Berkeley, California: Osborne/McGraw-Hill, 1994.

LaQuey, Tracy. *The Internet Companion, A beginner's guide to global networking*. Reading, Massachusetts: Addison-Wesley, 1993.

Lynch, Daniel C., and Rose, Marshall. *Internet System Handbook*. Greenwich, Connecticut: Addison-Wesley, 1993.

ConneXtions is a monthly publication produced by Interop Company in Mountain View, California (415/941-3399). It has excellent articles about using the Internet and Internet issues. The subscription rate is $150 per year.

RELATED ENTRIES   Anonymous File Transfer Protocol; ARPANET; DARPA; Routing, Internet; *and* Transmission Control Protocol/Internet Protocol

Internet Engineering Task Force (IETF)

IETF is responsible for standardizing the Internet protocols. IETF has standardized such applications protocols as Telnet (interactive logon) and File Transfer Protocol (FTP). IETF was created in 1989 when the Internet Activities Board (IAB) was split into two groups, one involved in long-term research and the other involved in engineering for existing needs. The Internet Research Task Force (IRTF) is the first group and the Internet Engineering Task Force (IETF) is the latter group.

The IETF group meets three times per year to discuss ongoing projects, proposals, and standards. It consists of working groups that have members with expertise in various areas, such as applications development, Open Systems Interconnection (OSI) integration, routing, security, and network management. The working groups have open membership and participation. A chair is responsible for steering the groups and helping it make decisions and come up with productive results. Specifications are reviewed and approved with the involvement of the various Internet committees, but only the IAB can formally approve a standard.

RELATED ENTRY   Internet

Internet Protocol (IP)

IP is part of the *Transmission Control Protocol/Internet Protocol (TCP/IP)* protocol suite that was developed in the mid-1970s as part of the ARPANET project funded by the U.S. Defense Advanced Research Projects Agency (DARPA). The goal of TCP/IP development was to create a set of protocols that provided interconnectivity among a variety of independent host systems. The ARPANET was a nationwide "backbone" telecommunication network that later became the NSFnet after the National Science Foundation became involved. The TCP/IP protocols are the official protocols for the Internet, which is a collection of networks that uses the NSFnet backbone. The Internet now connects computers all over the world that are used by governments, educational institutes, research institutes, companies, and home users.

TCP/IP is a packet-switching protocol. Information is broken up into packets, transmitted, then reassembled. The TCP portion of the suite is a connection-oriented protocol, while the IP portion is connectionless.

RELATED ENTRIES   Connection-Oriented and Connectionless Protocols; Datagram Delivery Protocol; Layered Architecture; Internet; *and* Transmission Control Protocol/Internet Protocol

Internetworking

See Networks.

Internetwork Packet Exchange (IPX)

Internetwork Packet Exhange (IPX) is the built-in peer-to-peer networking protocol for Novell NetWare. It was derived from the Xerox Network System (XNS) protocol, which was developed in the 1970s. NetWare is a client-server operating system that provides clients with file-sharing services, print services, security, and a variety of other optional features such as database, application, communication, fax, and electronic mail services. IPX is the primary means of providing those services. *PC Week* magazine, in its July 12, 1993 issue, indicated that there are reportedly 20 million IPX users.

IPX Packets

A *packet* is a collection of bits that contain data (the "payload") and header information (the "pilot"). Header information includes the source and destination address as well as control information to handle errors and keep packets in order. Packets are sent as framed bit-streams across a communication channel to a destination. Each packet is a separate block of information that can potentially have a different address from other packets that are traversing the network. The data in a packet might be a request for service from a client or a response from a server. Data can also be text information that is being transferred from one system to another. A typical packet can be from 512 to 6,500 bytes in size, so it may take many packets to transfer a large file over a network.

IPX is a *datagram protocol* that operates in the Network layer of the OSI protocol model. Datagram is another name for packets that are transferred in a *connectionless* communication. Connectionless implies that packets of data are sent from a source to a destination without any prior setup of the connection, and without the mutual monitoring of the packet exchange by both the source and the destination. The source simply assumes that the destination can handle any information it sends. The destination receives the packets and resequences them. If packets were lost, it requests a retransmission of the packet.

In contrast, IPX's sister protocol *Sequenced Packet Exchange (SPX)* is connection-oriented and resides in the Transport layer of the OSI protocol model. Connection-oriented means that a session is set up between two communicating systems to monitor the flow of data packets. While the SPX connection-oriented session requires more time to set up, it can guarantee the proper delivery of sensitive and timely information. Its packets are also smaller in size because full addressing information is not required. On the other hand, a connectionless session is quick and efficient, but its packets are larger in size because they require a full address to get them to their destination.

In most cases, connectionless methods are preferred on relatively error-free LANs because, over time, they are more efficient at delivering the type of data that is commonly exchanged in a network environment. That data usually comes in intermittent bursts and it would require too much overhead to set up a session for each burst. In contrast, connection-oriented sessions are preferred when using utilities such as NetWare's *Remote Console*. It uses SPX to set up a relatively permanent connection between a manager's workstation and a server for the purposes of providing continuous, real-time information about the status of a server. Because this connection remains in use, and because packets are transferred on a regular basis, connection-oriented SPX is preferred.

Using IPX

IPX is built into the NetWare operating system, so workstations merely need to install the communication protocol and run a client software package to talk to NetWare servers. IPX is not used in many non-NetWare environments, although there has been interest in using it to access the Internet.

IPX support is installed at workstations along with the workstation requester software, such as DOS Requester and OS/2 Requester. Current versions of the software include the Novell Open Data-link Interface (ODI), which provides a way to load multiple protocol stacks such as IPX and TCP/IP side-by-side. The requester software is basically a redirection utility that looks at commands issued by the user and either sends them to the local operating system or sends them out over the network to the network operating system. If requests are destined for the network, the requester software packages the requests in an IPX packet and hands it to the network interface cards, which sends the packet as a bit stream. Actually, packets can have several different destinations:

- A server on the same LAN segment
- A workstation on the same LAN segment
- A workstation or server on another LAN segment

The header information in the packet contains a LAN segment address. When the packet is broadcast on the network, a router will see this information and forward the packet to an appropriate LAN segment if that is where it is destined.

Novell NetWare supports a wide variety of data links and the transmission of IPX over them. Supported links include ARCNET, LocalTalk, Ethernet, token ring, Fiber Distributed Data Interface (FDDI), and others.

In the NetWare environment, the following protocols are intimately linked with IPX:

NETWARE CORE PROTOCOL (NCP)   NCP is the principal protocol for transmitting information between a NetWare server and its clients. NCP handles logon requests and many other types of requests to the file system and the printing system. IPX is the underlying protocol that carries the transmission. NCP is a LAN protocol that was originally designed with the assumption that servers and workstations would be relatively close. When a router gets involved and connections are made over wide area network links, NCP causes traffic congestion. It uses a request/response scheme to manage server/workstation communication. If a workstation makes a request, it must first wait for a response from the server before making another request. This required acknowledgment adds excess traffic, but several schemes to solve the problem are discussed here.

SERVICE ADVERTISING PROTOCOL (SAP)   NetWare servers and routers on NetWare networks use SAP to broadcast a message over the network every 60 seconds to indicate the types of services it can provide.

ROUTING INFORMATION PROTOCOL (RIP)   NetWare uses RIP to keep the network routers informed of the latest changes to routing paths on the network. NetWare servers can act as routers. RIP uses distance-vector algorithms (DVAs) to calculate routing paths. In DVA, routing decisions are based on the least number of "hops" to a destination. Novell's RIP also includes a field that can indicate the speed of a link, which provides another way of defining paths that packets traverse to their destinations.

RIP routing tables are exchanged with other routers every 60 seconds, and routers rebuild their routing tables based on new information. Problems can occur if a router gets behind in rebuilding its routing table, which can occur if that router is connected over a slow WAN link. In addition, exchanging the routing table can add a lot of overhead to a LAN, which causes more congestion, further delaying routing table updates. If a route fails, the delay required to rebuild routing tables can delay how quickly a new route is established.

These problems are being resolved with a new routing protocol from Novell, called NetWare Link Services Protocol (NLSP).

Wide Area Networking Support

In the past, Novell NetWare and IPX have been a poor choice for wide area networking because of some inefficiencies in both the operating system and the protocol. These inefficiencies are described in the following sections, along with the recent improvements that Novell has made to IPX to correct the problems.

BURST MODE   A requirement to acknowledge packets on IPX networks can cause the so-called "ping-pong" effect in which packets are sent and packet acknowledgments are returned. All of this activity causes significant performance loss on wide-area links. The new *burst mode* feature of IPX is designed to allow up to 128 packet transmissions before an acknowledged message. There is a potential for improving performance as much as 50 percent with burst mode. However, on multiprotocol networks, there is also a potential of holding up traffic generated by other protocols. For example, if IPX is bursting through a router, TCP/IP traffic won't be able to get through until there is a letup. Routers are available that let you prioritize some traffic so it is handled before others.

NOTE: Burst mode support is included in NetWare 4.x and available as an add on for previous versions of NetWare.

LARGE FRAME SIZE   Previously, traffic that was destined for a router was broken into 512-byte packets to prevent congestion. Novell now provides a way to send large packets of data through routers to improve internetwork packet exchange. The packet size is negotiated during setup.

NOTE: Novell provides the Large IPX (LIPX) NLM to handle large packet sizes. It comes with NetWare 4.x and is available as an add-on for previous versions of NetWare.

REDUCED SAP TRAFFIC   The Service Advertising Protocol (SAP) sends packets that inform workstations or other devices about services available on a NetWare server. However, SAP produces unnecessary traffic in cases where services are not important or workstations on the other side of a wide-area link don't care about the services. You can increase the interval between SAP broadcasts to reduce some of the overhead, or you can use Novell-provided filters that reduce SAP traffic over wide-area links.

IPX Evolution

The successor to IPX is *NetWare Link Services Protocol (NLSP)*. It provides improved internetworking capabilities by replacing SAP and RIP with a link-state routing algorithm. Link-state routing methods provide more control over the routing process, and respond faster to establish new paths if links fail. Routes can be based on the avoidance of congested areas, the speed of a line, the cost of using a line, or various priorities. NLSP is based on the Open Shortest Path First and Intermediate System-to-Intermediate System (IS-IS) algorithms.

Novell has also upgraded SPX to includes sliding windows, burst mode, and large packets. In addition, a new workstation shell is available that will search out an alternate path through the network should the current path fail.

RELATED ENTRIES   Datagram Network Services; NetWare; Novell; Routing Protocols; *and* Sequenced Packet Exchange

Internetwork Routing

Any internetwork that uses routers and contains many paths from a source to a destination requires efficient routing mechanisms to ensure that a packet of information gets to its destination in an efficient and timely manner. The Internet is such a network, as are many private networks built on Transmission Control Protocol/Internet Protocol (TCP/IP) protocols.

RELATED ENTRIES   Networks; Routers; Routing Protocols; *and* Wide Area Networks

Interoperability

Interoperability is the ability of different computer systems, networks, operating systems, and applications to work together and share information. There are different levels of interoperability. Simply because two systems are connected and sharing information does not mean that users can access that information from their applications. For example, a UNIX workstation can connect with a Novell NetWare server using the TCP/IP communication protocols. However, a user at the UNIX workstation can't access files unless compatible file protocols are in use. In this example, loading Novell's NetWare NFS product on the NetWare file server will allow the UNIX user to access files and other network resources with NetWare clients in an integrated and seamless manner.

But even this level of interoperability doesn't guarantee that the UNIX user will be able to open and edit files it accesses on the NetWare server. Translators and converters are required to allow access to incompatible file formats. In some cases, the application itself is able to read file formats created by applications that operate in other environments. Major software vendors like Microsoft are solving some of these differences by creating applications that work in many environments. For example, the Microsoft Excel spreadsheet program works in the Windows and Macintosh environments. If a Windows user transfers a file to a Macintosh, the Macintosh user can open the file and use all the formatting codes provided with the file.

The term *open systems* refers to products that are designed to work together by following accepted standards, such as the Open Systems Interconnection (OSI) model put forth by the International Organization for Standardization (ISO). The OSI model consists of seven layers that describe how systems connect and communicate with one another. The OSI model is used throughout the world as a point of reference for designing and building interoperable systems. The lower layers of the protocol stack define the networking hardware and how systems actually transmit data to one another. The upper layers define application interoperability. Most vendors create products that loosely comply with the standard, meaning that some layers are implemented as defined by OSI and others are not. Because adherence to the standard is loose, interoperability is still an issue for network administrators.

The Open Software Foundation (OSF) is doing work to support interoperability at the Presentation and Applications layers. Its Distributed Computing Environment (DCE) provides programmers with tools they can use to create interoperable applications while shielding them from the complexities of working with lower-level protocols. The resulting applications run on distributed heterogeneous network environments. The remote procedure call (RPC) tools available with OSF DCE provide both transport independence and transparency. Transport independence refers to the RPC's ability to run over any wide or local area network and transparency implies that the distributed application code acts the same way, regardless of the network on which the applications run.

Electronic mail and messaging systems are providing unique ways to solve the interoperability issue. An enterprise E-mail system can provide a way for users on diverse systems to exchange messages, files, and other information with an E-mail system serving as a gateway or switching system. Messaging systems are also implemented into applications to provide inter-application communication or non-real time message exchange between users and applications. For example, a user could send a request for a report to a database, then receive the report in his or her mail box the following day. An outgrowth of electronic mail are groupware and workflow software applications that allow users to collaborate their schedules and projects.

In the enterprise computing environment, interoperability is a major concern. Networks have joined the computing resources of formerly independent departments and divisions with the goal of allowing users throughout the network to access data on a variety of systems. Front-end applications running under Windows, Macintosh, Disk Operating System (DOS), and other environments need to access data on a variety of back-end systems. The data is in a variety of formats and is accessible by using Structured Query Language (SQL). However, there are subtle differences in each vendor's SQL, so front-end applications must either account for each of these differences, or rely on the back-end server to translate the commands sent to them. An alternative solution is "middleware." It provides a layer of interoperability between front-end and back-end applications. Middleware offerings are listed next and discussed elsewhere in this book.

■ *Microsoft Open Database Connectivity (ODBC)* ODBC provides common functions that are performed by most back-end database systems. Front-end applications are then written to ODBC and take advantage of these functions.

■ *Independent Database API (IDAPI)* IDAPI is similar to ODBC in functionality and is designed around the Call Level Interface as well.

■ *Distributed Relational Database Architecture (DRDA)* DRDA is an IBM standard for accessing database information across IBM and non-IBM platforms that follows SQL standards. It is a key component in IBM's Information Warehouse framework.

■ *Apple's Data Access Language (DAL)* Apple developed DAL to provide Macintosh users with access to a variety of back-end database products, including IBM mainframe and midrange databases. DAL is related to SQL.

■ *Oracle's Glue* Glue is an API that includes a number of commands for accessing back-end database servers. Glue reportedly requires fewer steps to access data than ODBC.

In an object-oriented system, an Object Request Broker (ORB) provides the key communication facility for distributing messages among the applications, services, and facilities of the system. You can think of the ORB as a sort of software bus, or backbone, that provides a common *messaging* interface through which many different kinds of systems can communicate. An object makes a request and sends it to the ORB. The ORB then locates an object that can service the request, formats the message, and sends it to the object. The receiving object then responds to the request and returns a response to the ORB, which formats and forwards the response to the requestor. In this model, objects simply specify a task to perform. They don't need to know the details or whereabouts of the object that can service the task. The ORB handles all the details of locating objects, formatting messages, and delivering those messages. The ORB is a common interface for all objects in the distributed environment.

STREAMS is a development and operating environment that allows the use of multiple communications protocols on a network. It is implemented in UNIX and Novell NetWare environments, among others. Applications running above the STREAMS environment can easily use any of the communication protocols it supports. STREAMS is a modular system in which protocol stacks can be added or removed as needed. It provides developers with a set of tools for implementing communication protocols as modules.

At lower levels, interoperability is providing multiple protocol support so users can access a number of different systems. For example, if TCP/IP and SPX/IPX protocol stacks are loaded in a computer, the user can access a NetWare server and a UNIX server. Novell's Open Data-link Interface (ODI) and Microsoft Network Driver

Interface Specification (NDIS) provide the ability to load multiple protocol stacks and operate those protocols over a single network interface card.

RELATED ENTRIES Compound Documents; Distributed Computing Environment, OSF; Document Interchange Standards; Electronic Mail; Groupware; Messaging API, Inter-Application; Middleware; Object Linking and Embedding; Object Request Broker; Open Systems Interconnection Model; Remote Procedure Calls; *and* Windows Open System Architecture

Interprocess Communication (IPC)

Interprocess communication (IPC) is a set of techniques used by programs and processes running in multitasking operating systems or between networked computers. There are two types of IPCs:

- *Local Procedure Calls (LPC)* LPCs are used in multitasking operating systems to allow concurrently running tasks to talk to one another. They can share memory spaces, synchronize tasks, and send messages to one another.

- *Remote Procedure Call (RPC)* The RPC is similar to the LPC, but works over networks. RPCs first appeared on Sun Microsystems and Hewlett-Packard computers running under the UNIX operating system.

One of the advantages of using IPCs is that programs can take advantage of processes handled by other programs or computers. The client-server model takes advantage of RPCs. Clients perform some tasks on their own, but rely on servers to provide back-end file services. RPCs provide the communication mechanism for the client to communicate its requests for service to the back-end server. If you think of a client-server application as a program that has been split between front-end and back-end systems, the RPC can be viewed as the component that reintegrates them over the network. RPCs are sometimes called *coupling* mechanisms.

The normal interprocess communication mechanism in UNIX is the *pipe*, and the *socket* is the interprocess communication mechanism that works across networks. It became a part of UNIX when the TCP/IP protocol stack was integrated into Berkeley UNIX in the early 1980s. This was a project funded by DARPA, as discussed under "Transmission Control Protocol/Internet Protocol."

In the OS/2 protected mode, programs can run in their own protected area of memory or communicate over networks such as IBM LAN Server or Microsoft LAN Manager. The protected mode prevents one program from corrupting the memory area used by another program. The IPC features described here are used if programs need to communicate with one another or share memory areas.

- *Shared memory* Using shared memory, processes can change values in memory that other processes can read. The memory space becomes a sort of bulletin board in which the processes can post status information and data that needs to be shared or passes among processes. The memory is always a designated area that is outside the area used to hold normal program data.

- *Queues* A queue IPC is a structured and ordered list of memory segments where processes store or retrieve data. They can be arranged in various orders, including first-in, first-out (FIFO) and last-in, first-out (LIFO).

- *Semaphores* A semaphore provides a synchronizing mechanism for processes that are accessing the same resource. No data is passed with a semaphore—it simply coordinates access to shared resources. Semaphores may contain values that are incremented or decremented to indicate whether something has been accessed and how many times.

- *Pipes* A pipe provides a way for processes to communicate with one another by exchanging messages. *Named pipes* provide a way for processes running on different computer systems to communicate over the network. *Mail slots* is a store-and-forward messaging system that doesn't require stations to synchronize with one another. Named pipes and mail slots are OS/2 extensions used in the IBM LAN Server and Microsoft LAN Manager environments only.

RELATED ENTRIES Application Program Interface; Remote Procedure Calls

Interrupts

An interrupt, or *IRQ*, is a request by a component in a computer (Intel-based system in this discussion) for service from the processor. When a component within the computer, such as a COM port or floppy disk controller, needs the attention of the CPU, it sends a request over an interrupt line. Each component has its own interrupt line, so when you install new adapters in a computer, it's important to use an interrupt line that's not already in use. If you can't find an available interrupt, you might need to disable an unnecessary component, such as the second COM port or the second parallel port. (See the following table.) When installing multiple adapters, make sure that none of the adapters use the same interrupt. Change interrupts on adapters by moving jumpers or setting dip switches as directed in the manuals that come with the adapters. When there is an interrupt conflict with the hard drive controller, the system usually fails to boot. Make a list of the interrupts used by your system, and then change the settings on your adapters to avoid conflicts.

System Component	IRQ	I/O Port Address
EGA/VGA video adapters	2	3C0 to 3CF
EGA/VGA video in color mode	2	3D0 to 3DF
COM1,COM3	4	3F0 to 3FF
COM2,COM4 (if used)	3	2F0 to 2FF
Floppy disk controller	6	3F0 to 3FF

System Component	IRQ	I/O Port Address
Parallel port LPT1	7	3B0 to 3BF
Parallel port LPT2 (if used)	5	370 to 37F
System clock	8	
Math coprocessor	13	
Hard disk controller	14	320 to 32F
Game port		200 to 20F
Bus mouse		230 to 23F

Iridium System

Iridium is Motorola's proposed global mobile telephone service. It consists of a constellation of 66 low-flying satellites that use 4,800 bits per second (bps) narrowband digital voice encoding. The World Administrative Radio Consortium (WARC) approved a spectrum allocation request for the service. Motorola had met its first round of equity financing by August of 1993. Investors include BCE Inc., Lockheed Corp., Nippon Iridium Corp., and US Sprint. Services that may be provided include mobile communication, fax, and paging from anywhere on earth. The system may come online sometime around 1996-1997.

ISDN/B-ISDN

See Integrated Services Digital Network.

IS-IS Interdomain Routing Protocol (IDRP)

IDRP is a link-state Open Systems Interconnection (OSI) protocol that specifies how routers communicate with routers in other domains.

RELATED ENTRY   Routing, OSI

Isochronous Service

An isochronous service basically guarantees a certain bandwidth within a communications channel on a data network. It is required for delivery of real-time services like voice and video in which delays in packet delivery are intolerable. Isochronous services provide synchronized real-time transmission of video and voice.

Networks that have variable-length packets cannot efficiently provide isochronous services unless a prioritization method is used to dedicate part of the bandwidth to the video traffic. ATM provides isochronous services because its cells are the same size. By dedicating every third cell in a data stream, for example, it is possible to guarantee accurate and timely delivery.

An isochronous service sets aside or preallocates bandwidth on a communication channel whether it is used or not. The bandwidth allows time-synchronized transmissions with very low delay. The services are required when a source produces signals or events that recur at known periodic intervals.

RELATED ENTRIES   Cell Relay; Fast Packet Switching; Frames in Communication; *and* Videoconferencing and Desktop Video

Jabber

Jabber is a random transmission of data on a shared network cable by a faulty transceiver at a network node. The random data can corrupt the transmission of other stations. A *jabber control* function in the device is used to inhibit further transmissions if a certain time is exceeded that corresponds to the transmitted frame size.

If a network is flooded with garbage data, a transceiver or a network card with built-in transceiver may be bad. You can use the testing tools discussed under "Testing Equipment and Technologies" or a management system to isolate the problem. Alternatively, on small networks you can remove stations or segment the network to determine which side still has the garbage data, then further segment it until you locate the source of the problem.

Jukebox Optical Storage Devices

A *jukebox* is an optical disk device that can automatically load and unload optical disks and provide as much as 500 gigabytes of near-line information. The devices are often called *optical disk libraries, robotic drives,* or *autochangers.* Jukebox devices may have up to 50 slots for disks and a picking device either traverses the slots, or the slots move to align with the picking device. The arrangement of the slots and picking devices affects performance, depending on the space between a disk and the picking device. Seek times are around 85 milliseconds and transfer rates are in the 700 Kbits/sec range.

Jukeboxes are used in high-capacity storage environments such as imaging, archiving, and hierarchical storage management (HSM). HSM is a strategy that moves little used or unused files from fast magnetic storage to optical jukebox devices in a process called *migration.* If the files are needed, they are de-migrated back to magnetic disk. After a certain period of time or nonuse, the files on optical disk might be moved to magnetic tape archives.

RELATED ENTRIES   Archiving; Backup and Data Archiving; Hierarchical Storage Management Systems; High Capacity Storage System, Novell NetWare; *and* Optical Libraries

J

Kerberos Authentication

The Kerberos authentication service was developed by the Massachusetts Institute of Technology's Project Athena as an authentication mechanism for open systems in distributed environments. It is used in the Open Software Foundation's (OSF's) Distributed Computing Environment (DCE) and by various network operating system vendors.

Kerberos was designed with distributed environments in mind where some workstations are located in unsecure areas and users may be untrusted. Kerberos has the following features:

■ Clients are authenticated when logging on. Other clients trust that the Kerberos authentication servers have properly identified the clients.

■ Users must acquire a ticket from an authentication server in order to use a service available on a target server. An *authenticator* is generated, which contains additional user information that the target server compares with a ticket to verify proper identity. This process happens in the background.

■ Tickets provide the authorization required by authenticated users to access a service.

■ Tickets are private-key encrypted and contain the identity of a client, their address, time stamps, and other information. Time stamps ensure that information crossing the network expires after a few hours to thwart intruders.

■ All sessions between clients and servers are temporary. If a client needs a new session, a new authenticator must be obtained. Tickets expire after a period of time, so clients periodically need to acquire new tickets to access a particular server.

The Kerberos system requires that each network service be modified to use Kerberos. It also requires a special server that handles the Kerberos authentication service. This system must be placed in a secure location. In addition, because network access is cut off if the Kerberos server goes down, a redundant server is recommended. While the costs are high, Kerberos provides a secure environment for organizations that need it.

RELATED ENTRIES   Key Encryption Technology; Security

Kermit

A simple file transfer protocol used to exchange files between PCs. Kermit was developed at Columbia University and named after Kermit the Frog. It provides a way to download files from mainframes to microcomputers. It has evolved into a general-purpose data transfer utility.

■ Kermit is a half-duplex communication protocol.

■ It supports 7-bit ASCII characters.

■ Data is transferred in variable-sized packets that can be up to 96 bytes long.

■ An acknowledgment is required for each transmitted packet.

■ Kermit can transfer multiple files per session.

RELATED ENTRIES   Asynchronous Communications; Transmission Media, Methods, and Equipment

Kernel

Kernel refers to the core components of most operating systems. It is the portion that manages memory, files, peripherals, and system resources. The kernel typically runs processes and provides interprocess communication among them. Some of core functions are listed below:

■ Scheduling and synchronization of events

■ Communication among processes (message passing)

■ Memory management

■ Management of processes

■ Management of input and output routines

The Mach operating system developed at Carnegie-Mellon University has a client-server architecture consisting of a relatively small kernel (microkernel) that implements minimal functions. It manages device drivers, messages, threads, and virtual memory. Other functions are modular and communicate with the kernel using interprocess communication mechanisms. Remote procedure calls (RPCs) are used to communicate with processes running on other systems.

In the DOS operating system, the kernel is considered the portion between the basic input output system (BIOS) and the application software. Commands from applications are passed though the kernel to the BIOS and then to hardware.

RELATED ENTRIES   Mach, Carnegie-Mellon Microkernel; Microkernel

K

Key Encryption Technology

Key technology provides encryption services to secure network transmissions in open environments. There are two types of key technology: private key (symmetric encryption) and public key (asymmetric encryption).

The purpose of any encryption scheme is to secure private communication. The growth of international networks, public and private E-mail systems, and radio communication requires a greater need for security. Fortunately, advances in microelectronics are making security measures easier and cheaper to implement.

Perhaps the use of protocol analyzers by technicians to monitor network traffic has enlightened managers to the fact that their data transmissions are not secure. Anyone with such a device can view selected data streams on the network.

Private-key encryption methods are called *symmetric* ciphers and public-key methods are called *asymmetric* ciphers.

- *Private-key scheme* Information is encrypted with a key that both the sender and receiver hold privately. This system assumes that both parties have already exchanged keys using some manual method and that the exchange did not compromise security.

- *Public-key scheme* Two related keys are created for each user. One is held privately and the other is placed in a public area. If someone wants to send you a message, he or she encrypts it with your public key. Upon receipt of the message, you decrypt it with your private key.

RELATED ENTRIES Data Encryption Standard; Private Key Cryptography; Public Key Cryptographic Systems; *and* Security

Knowbots

"Knowbots," as envisioned by Marvin Minsky of the Massachusetts Institute of Technology, are intelligent agents that search digital libraries of information on large networks, such as the Internet. The idea is further explored by Carl Malamud in his book *Stacks, Interoperability in Today's Computer Networks* (Englewood Cliffs, New Jersey: Prentice-Hall, 1992):

> "Perhaps the most futuristic-sounding component of the Digital Library System is the knowbot, an intelligent program that is launched onto the network. The knowbot visits different nodes looking for information of use to the knowbot's master. The knowbot performs tasks, perhaps rooting through databases or negotiating purchase terms for information, and sends messages back to its master. The master may be a person, but could well be another knowbot."

Knowbots are important because the information infrastructure is growing so large and at the same time becoming so much more available through the Internet and other networks. Knowbots can locate information without user intervention, saving time and presumably money although there will certainly be many opportunities for information services to make lots of money. Malamud and others envision systems that automatically compensate authors when online works are referenced.

RELATED ENTRY Internet

LAN

See Local Area Networks; Networks

LAN Drivers

A LAN driver is a workstation or server software module that provides an interface between a network interface card (NIC) and the redirector software running in the computer. The driver is designed for a specific NIC and is configured for a workstation or server using a setup program. The program asks you to specify the type of NIC, and then asks you to insert a disk that contains a driver module for that NIC. The driver is then integrated into the protocol stack in use for the network, such as Internetwork Packet Exchange (IPX), Transport Control Protocol/Internet Protocol (TCP/IP), NetBIOS, or other stack. Figure L-1 illustrates where the NIC driver is located in relation to the Open Systems Interconnection (OSI) protocol model.

Note that drivers reside in the lower Media Access Control (MAC) sublayer of the Data-Link layer. The upper portion, called the Logical Link Control (LLC) sublayer, can switch data among multiple network card drivers. As shown, a server might have three network interface cards (Ethernet, token ring, Fiber Distributed Data Interface [FDDI]). A driver is installed for each card and the LLC sublayer acts as a bridge by switching traffic among them.

Novell and Microsoft have developed special interface support standards that let one or more interface cards work with one or more network protocols, as shown in Figure L-2. Novell's Open Data-link Interface (ODI) and Microsoft's Network Device Interface Specification (NDIS) provide a way to:

L

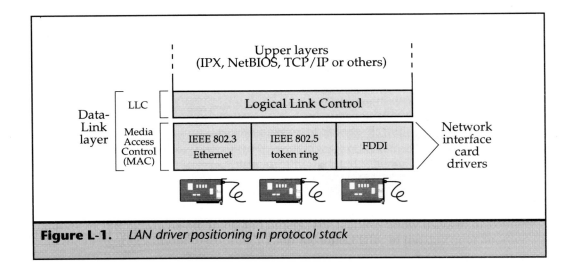

Figure L-1. *LAN driver positioning in protocol stack*

■ Transport IPX, TCP/IP, AppleTalk, and other protocols over a single network interface card and cable

■ Install multiple network interface cards in a single computer and run multiple protocol stacks to operate over those cards

RELATED ENTRIES   Client Software; DOS Requester, NetWare; LAN Workplace Products, Novell; Network Driver Interface Specification; *and* Open Data-link Interface

LAN Management
See Management Standards and Tools.

LAN Manager, Microsoft

Microsoft LAN Manager is a network management and file system that runs on top of the OS/2 operating system. Although Microsoft and IBM co-developed OS/2, Microsoft is no longer developing the operating system. IBM has made extensive enhancements to OS/2 and provides the IBM LAN Server network operating system, which is a LAN Manager-based product. Both IBM OS/2 and IBM LAN Server are now distantly related to their original products. Microsoft is phasing out LAN Manager in favor of the Windows NT Advanced Server network operating system.

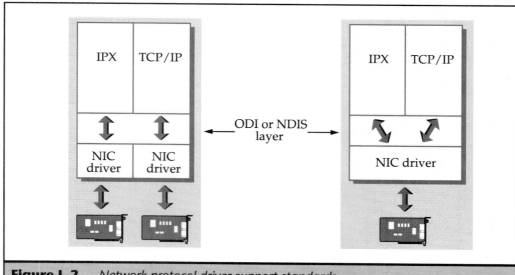

Figure L-2.   *Network protocol driver support standards*

The OS/2-LAN Manager layered architecture is illustrated in Figure L-3. OS/2 is a multitasking operating system that can run several programs as separate and protected sessions. LAN Manager runs in one of these sessions and uses an upgraded version of the OS/2 High Performance File System (HPFS) to handle multiple users. LAN Manager is intimately linked with OS/2 and so does not run on other operating systems. OS/2 is a pre-emptive multitasking operating system, meaning that it can stop one process to service a higher-priority process if necessary.

Although LAN Manager is being replaced by the Windows NT Advanced Server system, Microsoft will still support LAN Manager and provides bug fixes. According to Microsoft, customers who need to expand their networking options in the future should consider Windows NT Advanced Server. It is faster, provides full 32-bit operation, and includes Macintosh support as well as Remote Access Services (RAS) to support clients at remote locations.

RELATED ENTRIES   Mail Slots; Named Pipes; *and* Windows NT Advanced Server, Microsoft

LAN Requester

LAN requester software resides in the workstation and provides a way for applications running in the workstation to make requests for service to network servers. The LAN requester software serves as a traffic director for commands that are diverting commands for local services to the local operating system, and commands for network services to the network operating system running on a server.

RELATED ENTRIES   Client Software; DOS Requester, NetWare; LAN Workplace Products, Novell; Network Driver Interface Specification; *and* Open Data-link Interface

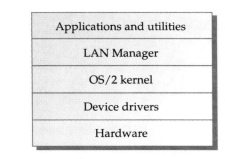

Figure L-3.   *OS/2-LAN Manager architecture*

L

LAN Server

See IBM LAN Server.

LANtastic

LANtastic is a peer-to-peer networking product developed and marketed by Artisoft (Tucson, Arizona). It was originally designed as a network that would allow small businesses to share files and resources. Today, the LANtastic network product has matured and contains many advanced features:

- Security
- Sophisticated printer functions
- Built-in electronic mail
- Disk caching
- CD-ROM sharing
- Voice capabilities
- Windows interface

The LANtastic network works in the DOS and Windows environment. Users can access multiple resources with a single logon. Management features include the ability to get a complete overview of the network to manage user rights and monitor network traffic. LANtastic also supports uninterruptible power supplies to allow proper server shutdown in the event of a power loss. Audit trails allow the LANtastic system to keep a record of all access to subdirectories and devices, such as the time and length of resource usage.

LANtastic is available in starter kits that include Ethernet adapters. The complete kits greatly simplify the installation of a network in a small office environment. Other packages include licensing for up to 500 users.

LAN Troubleshooting

See Testing Equipment and Techniques.

LAN WorkPlace Products, Novell

Novell's LAN WorkPlace products allow DOS, Windows, OS/2, and Macintosh users to directly access resources that require Transmission Control Protocol/Internet Protocol (TCP/IP) access, such as UNIX systems, Digital Equipment Corp. VAX systems, and IBM mainframes. There are four LAN WorkPlace products:

- *LAN WorkPlace for DOS* Uses Open Data-link Interface (ODI) technology to provide IPX/SPX and TCP/IP support on Ethernet, token ring, and ARCNET adapters for DOS and Windows users.

- *LAN WorkGroup* Provides NetWare clients on DOS and Windows workstations with all the features of LAN WorkPlace for DOS. However, this product is centrally installed on a server and has administrative features, such as application-use monitoring and software upgrades.

- *LAN WorkPlace for OS/2* Provides OS/2 users with direct access to Apple Macintosh computers, UNIX systems, VAXs, IBM mainframes, and other systems. Multiple concurrent sessions are possible because of OS/2's multitasking capabilities.

- *LAN WorkPlace for Macintosh* Allows Apple Macintosh users to access resources on TCP/IP networks.

With these products, NetWare users can use applications running on UNIX-based systems or other systems that use TCP/IP protocols. The TCP/IP-compatible host system can be on the same LAN segment as the user or on a different LAN segment that is connected with a multiprotocol router.

Laptop Connections

Laptop computers give users the freedom to take their computers on the road. But when users return to the office, they need a way to plug into the local area network (LAN). Most laptops are too small to have adapter interfaces, so to connect to a LAN, users can do one of the following:

- Purchase a docking station that has adapter slots and then install a network adapter card.
- Purchase an external LAN adapter.
- Connect to the LAN by using a telephone link.
- Buy a new laptop with a built-in LAN adapter.

This last choice is rather impractical, but it is an option, especially if someone else doesn't mind inheriting the old unit. The third option is practical for laptop users on the road. For the most part, the second approach is the most practical. A LAN adapter is a small device, about the size of 50 rolled up $10 bills (and that's approximately how much money you'll part with if you buy one).

NOTE: Personal Computer Memory Card International Association (PCMCIA)-compatible network adapter cards are becoming popular. These are small credit-card-sized cards that slip into an expansion memory slot on a portable computer. Many new laptops include PCMCIA slots.

L

External LAN adapters connect to the parallel port of a laptop. Most are compatible with existing LAN card standards, so you can use drivers that are included with Novell NetWare. Vendors such as Xircom Inc. (Calabasas, California), D-Link Systems (Irvine, California), and IQ Technologies (Bothell, Washington) make token ring, ARCNET, and Ethernet cards with coaxial or twisted-pair connectors.

RELATED ENTRIES   Mobile Computing; Wireless Mobile Communication

Large Internetwork Packet Exchange

When routers are present on NetWare networks running the Internetwork Packet Exchange (IPX) protocol, NetWare automatically sets the packet size to 576 bytes. This ensures that packets can cross the router. The reason for this is that NetWare cannot be sure what packet size the router can handle. NetWare v.4.x automatically supports Large Internet Packets (LIPs), which provide a way for clients and servers to negotiate an appropriate packet size without the server specifying the 576-byte limit if a router is present. However, you must be aware of the packet size that the routers on your network can handle. If any router cannot handle packets larger than 576 bytes, you must disable large packets.

Basically, the setting causes NetWare to ignore its router check during packet-size negotiation. However, you must ensure that routers can transfer larger packet sizes. If a router exists on the network that can't negotiate the larger packet size, you need to revert to the 576-byte packet size or replace the router. To revert to the 576-byte packet size at the server, set the LIP setting off using the SERVMAN utility.

RELATED ENTRIES   DOS Requester, NetWare; Internetwork Packet Exchange; NetWare; Novell; *and* Packets

Layered Architecture

Network operating systems and network communication systems are designed using a layered architecture approach. Layered architectures provide a way for vendors to design software and hardware that is interoperable with other vendors' products. Without open, standardized protocols, you would need to obtain all your networking equipment from one vendor. The single-vendor, proprietary system approach is exactly what IBM and DEC tried to push on its customers in the 1970s and early 1980s. However, the advent of desktop computers, local area networks, and client-server computing introduced heterogeneous systems into organizations and those organizations became less and less interested in the proprietary networking solutions of a single vendor.

Layering is a design approach that specifies different functions and services at levels in a "protocol stack." The Open Systems Interconnection (OSI) protocol stack pictured in Figure L-4 is commonly used for reference. It was designed as an open architecture for which any vendor could design products that would interoperate with products developed by other vendors who complied with the standard. However, OSI development has been slow, although it is internationally defined. Other standards have become more established and vendors have taken on the tasks of supporting multiple protocols.

The protocol stack defines how communication hardware and software interoperate at various levels. So if you wanted to create a network interface card that would interoperate with another vendors' cards, you would conform to the protocols defined in the lower layers of the stack. As you climb the stack, higher levels of communication and application interfacing are defined. The lower levels define the process of transmitting bit-streams of data over a physical medium. At the upper levels, layering separates the user applications from the underlying communication services.

Note the following:

■ Lower layers provide services to upper layers.

■ Each layer has a set of services.

■ Services are defined by protocols.

■ Programmers only need to be concerned with the protocols in the layer they are working with, the services provided to upper layer, and the services provided by lower layers.

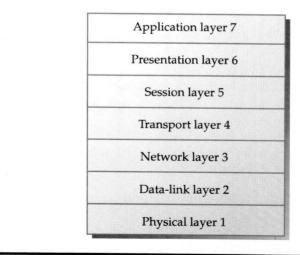

Figure L-4. *The OSI protocol stack*

When systems communicate, peer protocols at each level in the protocol stack of each system coordinate the communication process. For example, the Transport layer in one system coordinates its activities with the Transport layer in the other system. As an analogy, imagine the creation of a formal agreement between two embassies. At the top, formal negotiations take place between ambassadors, but in the background, diplomats and officers work on documents, define procedures, and perform other activities. Diplomats have rank and each rank performs some service for higher ranking diplomats. The ambassador at the highest level passes orders down to a lower-level diplomat and uses services provided by that diplomat. At the same time, the diplomat below the ambassador in rank is coordinating his or her activities with a diplomat of equal rank at the other embassy. Each diplomat follows established diplomatic procedures defined at their level of operation. For example, a diplomatic officer at a particular level may provide language translation services or technical documentation. This officer communicates with a peer at the other embassy regarding translation and documentation procedures.

In the diplomatic world, a diplomat at one embassy simply picks up the phone and calls a peer at another embassy. In the world of network communication, *entities* in each protocol layer communicate with peer entities by packaging messages and passing them down to lower-layer communication services. Eventually, the package reaches the lowest physical level, where it is framed into a stream of data bits and sent across the physical connection. As information passes down through the protocol layers, it forms a packet called the *protocol data unit (PDU)*. Entities in each layer add their own information to the PDU in the form of messages destined for peer entities in the other system. When the packet arrives at the other system, it moves up through the protocol stack and information for each entity is stripped off the packet and passed to the entity. This process is described next and illustrated in Figure L-5.

- *Entities*, like diplomats with various ranks, reside at each layer of the protocol stack and provide services to upper layers.

- Entities in one computer communicate with peer entities in the other computer. Protocols at each layer define the syntax and semantics of peer communication between the entities.

- Although entities communicate with their peers, they must utilize the services of lower layers to get those messages across. The information attached to a PDU by each entity as it passed down the protocol stack is called the *protocol control information (PCI)*. Some of the information added at each level is listed here:

Application	Destination node address information
Presentation	Code-set information added
Session	Communication session information added
Transport	Checksum header added
Network	Packet quantity/sequence information added
Data-Link	Packet checksum trailer/message end added
Physical	Convert to bit-stream and transmit

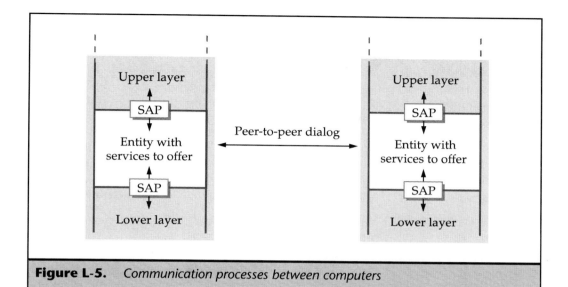

Figure L-5. *Communication processes between computers*

■ *Service Access Points (SAPs)* are the connection points that entities in adjacent layers use to communicate messages; they are like addresses, and any protocol layer may have several simultaneous SAPs active at one time.

Figure L-6 illustrates what happens as protocol data units are passed down through the layers of the protocol stack. Using the previous diplomatic analogy, assume the ambassador wants to send a message to the ambassador at the other embassy. He or she creates the letter and passes it to an assistant, who is a diplomat at the next rank down. This diplomat places the letter in an envelope and writes an instructional message on the envelope addressed to his or her peer at the other embassy. This package then goes down to the next-ranking diplomat, who repackages it and writes some instructions addressed to his or her peer at the other embassy. This process continues down the ranks until it reaches the "physical" level, where the package is delivered by a courier to the other embassy. At the other embassy, each diplomat reads the message addressed to him or her and passes the inner envelope up to the next-ranking officer.

Communication between two systems takes place by initiating requests down through the protocol stack, over the wire, and up through the protocol stack on the other system. Each layer provides a particular service to transfer the information and allow each layer to communicate with its peer layer in the other system.

RELATED ENTRIES   Open Systems Interconnection Model; Packets; Protocol Data Unit; *and* Protocols, Communication

L

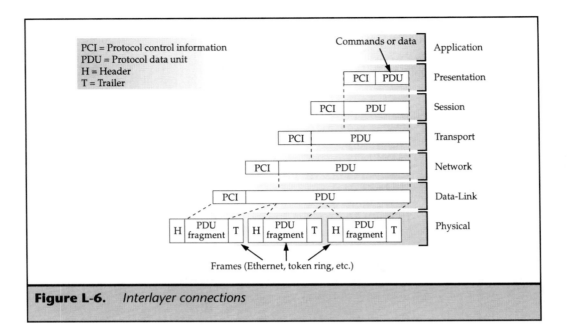

Figure L-6. *Interlayer connections*

Leaf Objects

Leaf objects are the end nodes on a directory tree structure in a directory services system such as NetWare Directory Services (NDS). A directory service provides a way to organize objects that represent real-life entities, such as users, file servers, printers, and groups. Each object holds information about the entities, such as its name, network address, or user account number. It also holds information used in documenting the object for inventory purposes, such as its physical location, serial number, human operator, phone number of the operator, and other useful information.

An example of a directory services tree is pictured in Figure L-7. This example is a screen shot from the Windows-based NetWare Administrator that comes with NetWare 4.x. The tree is organized as follows:

C = Country container
O = Organization container
OU = Organizational unit container
CN = Common Name

Container objects can hold other objects or other containers. The common name objects are *leaf* objects. They terminate the branch of the tree and no other objects can branch from them. You use containers to organize a directory tree. In the example,

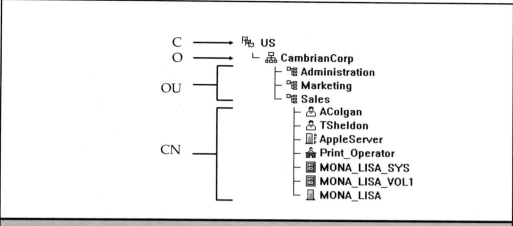

Figure L-7. *A sample NDS directory tree with the object names labeled by category*

CambrianCorp is a top-level O object that holds three OU objects (Administration, Marketing, and Sales). Each of these objects holds objects of its own, but only the Sales object is shown *expanded* in this case. The other objects are *collapsed* under the container objects for clarity.

The directory provides more than just a way to organize and document a company's resources. It also provides a way to assign security and access rights to objects. For example, the network administrator can grant a department supervisor the rights to create new users and resource objects only within a specific OU object, such as the Sales department. Users with accounts within a department are restricted to using only the resource objects in that department unless specifically granted rights to use objects elsewhere in the organization.

RELATED ENTRIES   Directory Services; Directory Services, NetWare; Global Naming Services; Name Service; *and* X.500 Directory Services

Learning Bridges

Learning bridges, also called *adaptive bridges,* "learn" which network addresses are on one side of the bridge and which are on the other. It then knows how to forward packets it receives. If there are multiple bridges, one bridge may forward a packet to another bridge, and this bridge forwards the packet onto another bridge or the final destination. When the bridge is first turned on, it broadcasts messages out on the network and waits for acknowledgment frames. From these frames it obtains the addresses of workstations attached to each of its ports and builds a table for future reference. When a packet arrives that is not listed in the table, the bridge floods the

L

network again (except the source network) to find out where this new address might be.

Most bridges now on the market are learning bridges. Before learning bridges, it was necessary for bridge installers or managers to create a table of network addresses in the bridge. Learning bridges are also called *transparent bridges* and they use the *spanning tree algorithm,* which is an IEEE 802.1 standard. It provides multivendor bridge communication and a way to create a network of bridges with no loops. Loops can cause packets to recirculate on the network and cause errors.

RELATED ENTRY   Bridging

Leased Line

A leased line is a communication circuit that is set up on a permanent basis for an organization by the phone company. Leased lines bypass the switching equipment at the local exchange carrier (LEC) and therefore do not require a setup phase before each data transmission. They are always connected. If the line is long distance (inter-LATA), then a long-distance carrier is involved, as well as the LEC at the other end of the circuit. Some alternate carriers, such as MCI, are able to provide LEC bypass facilities in various metropolitan areas. Because an organization pays a fixed rate for the lines under contract, the lines are often called *leased lines.*

The advantage of a leased line is that its quality can be verified and guaranteed. The line encompasses the local loop, which is the wire that connects a business with the LEC, and this wire is conditioned to ensure quality. Thus, it is possible to use higher data transfer rates on the line.

Leased lines are used to build *private networks,* in which an organization interconnects its remote sites using its own switching equipment and takes advantage of the privacy inherent in and dedicated bandwidth of leased lines. With leased lines and private switching equipment, an organization maintains security and control over the traffic that crosses the line. However, building and managing private networks can be expensive when compared to using the alternative *public networking* schemes like X.25 and Frame Relay. A private network requires a dedicated line between each site, with a bridge and/or router at each end, so to interconnect four sites you would need a total of six leased lines. Using a public network, only one line into the carrier's switching network is required from each site.

Leased lines can be either analog circuits or digital circuits:

- *Analog lines* require modems at each end and typically provide the same data rates as dialup lines, except that customers contract with the carrier to keep the line available for immediate use when necessary. The lines are of higher quality than dialup lines.

- *Digital circuits* are conditioned lines that can provide higher data transmission rates than analog lines—up to 45 Mbits/sec (for T3 lines) if necessary.

The standard digital line service is the *T1 channel,* which provides transmission rates of 1.544 Mbits/sec. T1 lines can carry both voice and data using multiplexer devices, so they are often used to provide voice telephone connections between an organization's remote sites. A T1 line can provide 24 channels for voice or data at 64 Kbits/sec bandwidth each. Customers who don't need the full T1 bandwidth can opt for fractional T1, which provides digital services in increments of 64 Kbits/sec. Alternatively, a T3 line can provide the equivalent of 28 T1 lines for users who need a lot of bandwidth.

While leased line usually implies a dedicated high-speed digital connection, many carriers also provide nondedicated switched digital circuits that let customers connect with different sites and make connections only when necessary. For example, a service called Switched-56 can provide redundant or backup connections to remote sites. The circuit is immediately switched into service if the primary line fails, or if additional bandwidth is required to handle heavy traffic. Switched-56 service also provides low-cost digital services for those with occasional requirements, such as end-of-month file transfers. One strategy is to combine multiple low-speed digital lines on an as-needed basis using dial-on-demand and inverse multiplexing techniques.

Network administrators who are evaluating the use of these lines need to weigh the cost of a leased line based on traffic requirements, and whether an uninterrupted connection must be maintained at all times. If traffic is light, or only required during certain times of the day, a dialup line will be less expensive and possibly more practical. Dialup lines are appropriate if electronic mail is the only information to send—a connection is established only when enough E-mail has accumulated to make the call worthwhile.

Leased lines are ordered by contacting the LEC. If the lines are long distance, you can contact the LEC, the long-distance carrier, or the LEC at the other end of the line.

RELATED ENTRIES   Carrier Services; Circuit-Switching Services; Digital Circuits and Services; Integrated Services Digital Network; Local Access and Transport Area; Public Data Networks; Switched-56 Services; Switched Services; *and* Wide Area Networks

Legacy Systems

Legacy systems are mainframe computers that have been with a company over a long period of time and through many years of software development and data accumulation. They provide established services that cannot be disrupted. Building new client-server computing systems to replace existing legacy systems is a costly endeavor, so there is a tendency to stay with the existing systems. However, current business trends and markets require rapid adaptation by companies, so the legacy systems often become the ball and chain that prevents companies from moving quickly into other markets or accessing and integrating the information they have available. This information is often on a combination of systems, including legacy systems. Some information may exist on desktops, and other information may exist at remote locations or sources outside the company.

L

Developments in distributed and enterprise computing systems are providing ways for users to access data in multivendor, multiprotocol environments. These systems use new software designs and take advantage of off-the-shelf applications to create and access data. One strategy is to keep the legacy systems in place and provide ways of getting at the data with the types of desktop applications that users prefer. Other techniques include using the system as large information warehouses.

RELATED ENTRIES   Database Connectivity APIs and Middleware; Distributed Computing; Distributed Database; *and* Information Warehouse

Licensing Server API (LS API)

The Licensing Server API (LS API) is a licensing standard proposed by Microsoft, Lotus, Novell, and many other vendors that defines how applications and NetLS licensing servers work together to track software usage and licensing. The server basically grants the applications the ability to run for a client. However, LS API will also work with other licensing server standards.

RELATED ENTRY   Electronic Software Distribution and Licensing

Line Conditioning

A conditioned line is a telephone circuit that has been treated to improve its ability to transmit data at high speeds. A T1 line is conditioned line.

RELATED ENTRIES   Digital Circuits and Services; Leased Line; *and* T1/T3 Services

Link Access Procedure (LAP)

Link Access Procedure is a Data-Link layer protocol that was originally recommended for use with X.25 packet-switching networks by the Consultative Committee for International Telegraph and Telephone (CCITT). LAP is a subset of High-level Data Link Control (HDLC). Later, the LAP-B (Balanced) protocol was recommended.

LAP-B is designed for point-to-point connections, so the address field is not necessary to identify the secondary stations. It provides the frame structure, error, and flow control mechanism for an asynchronous balanced mode data transmission session. In an X.25 packet-switched network, multiple virtual circuits exist for relaying link-by-link error and flow control and it is over a circuit that LAP-B provides a way to acknowledge that a packet has reached each link in the network.

Link Access Procedure D-channel (LAP-D) is part of the I series CCITT recommendation. It is designed for the D channel of an Integrated Services Digital Network (ISDN) connection. The D channel is the signal-carrying channel in ISDN. It coexists with the B channels, which carry voice or data. The D channel can also carry packet-switched data.

LAP-D provides a way to set up a multiplexed channel and obtain multiple logical links between two points. The frame structure is typical. It contains a flag, address information, control information, data, frame-check sequence, and ending flag. The address can identify class of service, such as voice and data, and the terminal for that service.

RELATED ENTRIES   High-level Data Link Control; Link Access Procedure; Logical Links; Synchronous Communications; *and* Synchronous Data Link Control

Link Layer

See Data-Link Layer, OSI Model; Logical Links.

Link Services Protocol, NetWare

The successor to Novell's Internetwork Packet Exchange (IPX) protocol is *NetWare Link Services Protocol (NLSP)*. It provides improved internetworking capabilities by replacing Service Advertising Protocol (SAP) and Routing Information Protocol (RIP) with a link-state routing algorithm. Link-state routing methods provide more control over the routing process, and respond faster to establish new paths if links fail. Routes can be based on the avoidance of congested areas, the speed of a line, the cost of using a line, or various priorities. NLSP is based on the Open Shortest Path First (OSPF) and Intermediate System-to-Intermediate System (IS-IS) algorithms.

RELATED ENTRIES   Internetwork Packet Exchange; Routing, NetWare; *and* Routing Protocols

Link State Routing

Link state routing provides a way to control the routing process and let routers respond faster to changes in the network, such as a broken link or the addition of a new router and network. Routes can be based on the avoidance of congested areas, the speed of a line, the cost of using a line, or various priorities. The Dijkstra algorithm is used to calculate the shortest path to a destination. The most common link state routing method is Open Shortest Path First (OSPF).

RELATED ENTRY   Routing Protocols

L

Load-Balancing Bridges

The load-balancing bridge provides a way to increase the bandwidth between two points by adding another line and balancing the traffic load between the lines. It can for example, make two long-distance circuits appear as one circuit that has the combined bandwidth of both. Load-balancing bridges are required to bridge and combine the circuits.

RELATED ENTRY   Bridging

Local Access and Transport Area (LATA)

The regional Bell operating companies (RBOCs) operate within a specific geographical area, which is divided into service areas called Local Access and Transport Areas (LATAs). LATAs were defined during the restructuring of AT&T in 1984, and there are close to 200 of them. *Independent telephone companies (ITCs)*, which are non-Bell companies, may also offer services within the LATA area. At any rate, these services are called *intra-LATA* services and encompass all the services and revenue provided within the LATA. The carrier, whether an RBOC or ITC, is referred to as the *local exchange carrier (LEC)*.

Any service provided outside the LATA is an *inter-LATA* service, and these services are provided by *interexchange carriers (IXCs)*, of which there are many, such as MCI, US Sprint, ITT, and AT&T. All LECs must provide interexchange carriers with an access point, called the *point-of-presence (POP)*, to their LATA areas.

RELATED ENTRIES   AT&T; Local Exchange Carrier; Local Loops; Regional Bell Operating Companies; *and* Wide Area Networks

Local Area Networks (LANs)

A local area network (LAN) connects computers in a workgroup, department, or building. In contrast, an internetwork is a collection of LANs within a building, group of buildings, or campus area, and a wide area network (WAN) is an internetwork that spans geographical areas and requires public or private communication links to interconnect each area.

RELATED ENTRY   Networks

Local Area Transport (LAT)

Local Area Transport (LAT) is a Digital Equipment Corporation protocol designed for the connection of terminals to host systems via LAN-attached terminal servers in DECnet environments. A terminal server is a device that connects to a network, in this case Ethernet networks, and provides a number of ports for the attachment of ASCII (American Standard Code for Information Interchange) terminals. Terminals connect to the terminal server via RS-232 cables. The LAT software allows the terminal server to effectively multiplex many terminal access requests over a single physical line.

A typical device that uses LAT is the DECserver 90TL, which provides a high-speed asynchronous connection to UNIX, ULTRIX, VMS, DOS, and multivendor network services. The device has multisession terminal connections that provide speeds up to 57.6 Kbits/sec. It supports LAT as well as Transmission Control Protocol/Internet Protocol (TCP/IP), Telnet, and Serial Line Internet Protocol (SLIP) protocols.

LAT does not conform to the Network layer relative to the Open Systems Interconnection (OSI) protocol model, so it can't be routed. The protocol designers assumed that the packets would only travel across one network. They did not design the protocol for use over wide-area networks, although some companies provide equipment for doing so. Packets don't carry enough information for routing. There is no field to indicate the logical networks the packet might need to traverse to get to a destination.

RELATED ENTRY   DECnet

Local Exchange Carrier (LEC)

A regional Bell operating company (RBOC) is a LEC that operates within a defined Local Access and Transport Area (LATA). Services outside the LATA are considered long distance and open to competition.

RELATED ENTRIES   AT&T; Local Access and Transport Area; *and* Regional Bell Operating Companies

Local Groups

Local groups are defined in the Windows NT environment. All network operating systems provide group management features to simplify the task of assigning rights and permissions to large numbers of users. You create a user account, then add that account to a group. Windows NT includes a set of predefined groups with predefined access rights that give its members the ability to perform various tasks and activities on the system.

There are two types of groups: *local groups* and *global groups*. Local groups only have rights at the workstation where the group is defined. Note that this assumes more than one person is using the local computer. A typical local group is the *Power User* group, which includes members with some but not all of the Administrator rights for managing the local computer. Global groups include users outside the current workstation. A typical global group is *Network*, which includes anyone accessing an NT server from another computer on the network.

RELATED ENTRIES   Users and Groups; Windows NT, Microsoft

L

Local Loops

A term that defines the copper telephone wire running from a customer's site to the local telephone company. It is currently the major bottleneck in telecommunication systems since lines running between telephone company offices are now high-speed optical cables.

RELATED ENTRIES   AT&T; Local Access and Transport Area; *and* Regional Bell Operating Companies

Local Procedure Calls

See Interprocess Communication.

LocalTalk

A local area network (LAN) protocol that defines AppleTalk packet transmission over a 230.4 Kbits/sec cabling system. LocalTalk was originally called AppleTalk, but Apple changed the name in 1989 to LocalTalk. Apple Computer's network architecture is now called AppleTalk, and it includes the protocols that operate over LocalTalk networks.

The original LocalTalk system was primarily designed for the attachment of a few Macintosh computers to an Apple LaserWriter printer, as shown in Figure L-8. Note that the LaserWriter attaches directly to the network. When users are ready to print, the printer automatically appears as a selectable icon on the menus of attached Macintosh workstations.

LocalTalk networks have the following features and specifications:

■ LocalTalk is a physical bus topology that is wired with twisted-pair telephone wire in a daisy-chain configuration as shown in the Figure L-8.

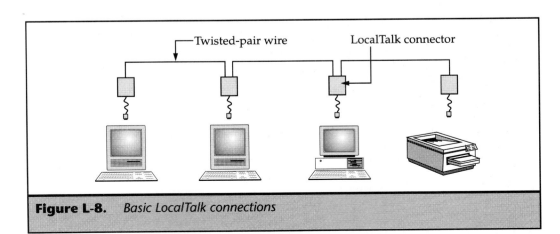

Figure L-8.   *Basic LocalTalk connections*

- The total length of the network cannot exceed 1,000 feet, but additional networks can be attached using repeaters, bridges, or routers.
- Transmission speeds are 230.4 kilobits/sec.
- Up to 32 nodes can be attached to a network segment, but performance degrades rapidly on busy networks of 20 or more nodes.
- Stations can be added to the network without bringing the whole system down.
- Every Macintosh has LocalTalk support built-in so users can immediately access attached peripherals such as printers without special software.
- File-sharing services such as AppleShare are optional, but Macintosh System 7 now includes file services so users can share files on their system with other users.
- LocalTalk easily attaches to other network segments such as EtherTalk and TokenTalk.
- Other protocols such as IPX and TCP/IP are not supported except with special third-party equipment.
- LocalTalk cards are available for non-Macintosh computers such as Intel-based systems. These computers can then access peripherals attached to the network and participate in file sharing with the proper software installed.
- Most LocalTalk cabling is preassembled and comes in shielded or unshielded twisted-pair cable. You can also build your own cable. Infrared connection methods are also available.

With LocalTalk support built-in, users only need to connect computers and peripherals together with the proper cable and connectors. Companies such as Farallon make cables and connectors that take advantage of existing telephone wire. In other words, you use the extra pair of wires in the telephone cable as the network cable, then connect each computer or peripheral to a special jack that connects at the telephone wallplate. Readers who are cabling LocalTalk networks should obtain the free catalog called Connectivity for Macintosh from Black Box (412/746-5500).

AppleShare is an optional package that provides centralized file services on a dedicated or nondedicated computer. Macintosh System 7 also includes file-sharing software as well. Without these services, LocalTalk users can only access peripheral devices attached to the network. With file-sharing services, users can share files at a central location (AppleShare) or make files available on their own system for others to access (System 7). Both systems have security features that can lock out some users or provide different levels of file access, such as the ability to change a file, or to only view it.

Setting Up the Network

The primary reason for setting up a LocalTalk network is to share expensive peripherals such as laser printers. In addition, users need to share files. Another

L

primary reason is the exchange of electronic mail. These needs are relatively simple to satisfy with LocalTalk. It is an inexpensive solution that is easy to install. Because of this, most LocalTalk networks are simply strung together with wires that are pushed up against or under carpets. This is fine in most cases, but if the network itself becomes critical to the operation of the business, it might be a better idea to secure the cabling in walls to prevent damaged or pulled cables. Professional cable installers can run a backbone cable through the walls and provide faceplates for connection into the network.

An alternative is to use existing telephone cable. There is usually an extra pair of wires in the cable that you can use to transmit data. These wires lead to a closet where the phone equipment is located as shown in Figure L-9. The leads from the wall connector attach to a punchdown block. You then attach another wire from the computer-attached leads of the punchdown block to a hub. This can be done with patch panels or 50-wire cables as discussed under "Cabling." The hub acts as a repeater so each branch of the hub is considered its own network. That means each branch can be up to the maximum length and have as many as 32 workstations. Also note that multiple devices can be attached at each branch.

Terminators are required at each end of the cable to prevent echoing of signals. Terminators are built-in to the original connector modules provided by Apple. They self-terminate if the connector is not used. Newer designs may require that you insert a terminator at the end of a cable or daisy-chain wire.

Hubs are devices that you can attach a number of LocalTalk branches to as discussed just above. The hubs are called *multiport hubs* and each port on the hub provides a connection to a separate branch of the network. Each branch is its own

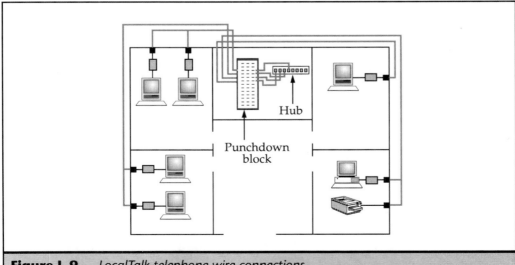

Figure L-9.   *LocalTalk telephone wire connections*

network that supports the maximum distance and workstation limits specified. The multiport hub repeats signals from one port to another.

Alternatively, you can use bridges that filter and isolate traffic so it stays on the networks where it belongs, rather than broadcasting to every network. Isolating traffic in this way helps to keep excess traffic from diminishing the performance of each individual LocalTalk branch.

Companies such as Black Box and others make a variety of equipment to expand the capabilities of LocalTalk networks. These products include the following:

- Ethernet to LocalTalk multiprotocol routers

- Equipment to access a Sun NFS host from a LocalTalk workstation

- Management software for diagnosing and documenting the LocalTalk network

RELATED ENTRIES   AppleTalk; Cabling; *and* Networks

Logical Links

A logical link is a protocol-driven communication session between two end systems in which traffic is exchanged over a real circuit or a logical circuit. A protocol stack defines communication between two systems over a media. At the bottom layer of the protocol stack are the protocols that define the many different types of connections that are available, such as local area networks (LANs), metropolitan area networks (MANs), and packet-switching public networks such as X.25 or Frame Relay. Logical links are formed between two communicating systems over physical links, which may be copper, fiber, or other media. These logical links exist just above the Physical layer in relation to the Open Systems Interconnection (OSI) protocol model. You can think of logical links as *circuits* that exist between two end systems in a network.

These links may provide any one of the following services. Note that a connection-oriented service is a logical connection, often called a virtual circuit, between two communicating nodes.

- *Connection-oriented service*   A logical circuit that requires setup but maintains a session between two end systems for the purpose of guaranteeing reliable communication.

- *Acknowledged connection-oriented services*   A logical circuit in which packet transmissions are acknowledged. This service produces more overhead, but is the most reliable.

- *Unacknowledged connectionless service*   A transmission without acknowledgments and without a prior setup phase. There is no session between end systems.

The Data-Link layer in the OSI protocol stack is subdivided into a lower Media Access Control (MAC) sublayer and an upper Logical Link Control (LLC) sublayer. When a packet is received, it is passed up from the MAC sublayer. If multiple

L

networks are attached to the device, the LLC layer may pass the packet on to another network. For example, you can install both Ethernet and token ring network adapters in a NetWare server. NetWare automatically bridges the networks attached to the adapters so that packets originating on the Ethernet can be sent to a destination on the token ring network. The LLC layer acts as a *switch* or *link relay* between the network segments; it reframes the Ethernet frame for token ring.

RELATED ENTRIES   Connection-Oriented and Connectionless Protocols; Data-Link Layer, OSI Model; Layered Architecture; Open Systems Interconnection Model; *and* Protocol Stack

Logical Units (LUs)

Logical units (LUs) are ports into an IBM Systems Network Architecture (SNA) network through which a user accesses a network resource or through which one program communicates with another.

RELATED ENTRIES   Advanced Peer-to-Peer Networking; Advanced Program-to-Program Communications; IBM Mainframe Environment; *and* Systems Network Architecture, IBM

Login Scripts

Login scripts are critical for setting up the environments of network users. A *login script* is a series of commands that execute when a user logs in. The commands placed in login scripts can map network drives for users, switch them to specific drives, display menus, and start applications. Login scripts on NetWare servers have extensive features, so they are discussed here as an example.

In most network operating systems such as Windows NT and Novell NetWare, there is one login script attached to the login account for each user. This script runs when the user logs in. In NetWare 4.x, there are three login scripts, any of which may execute when a user logs in:

- *System login script* The first type is the system login script, which executes for every user that belongs to a specific container. A container is like a department or division of a company. If the user belongs to the Sales department, for example, the login script for the Sales container object executes.

- *Profile login script* Next, there is the profile login script, which can belong to a group of users who don't necessarily belong to the same container. For example, a profile login script can execute commands specifically for managers.

- *Personal login script* Every user has his or her own personal login script. Supervisors can create the script, or users can create and modify it on their own.

NOTE: *The default login script runs if a personal login script has not been created. This is true even when system and profile login scripts execute.*

When a user logs in, the system login script executes first, followed by any profile login scripts, and finally by the personal login script.

The Default Login Script

On a new NetWare 4.x network, a simple default login script exists. Most administrators will quickly override this default script by creating new login scripts. One is listed and defined here for your convenience and as an example to help you get started with login scripts. Note that most commands in the script are MAP commands, which is typical. The numbers at the beginning of each line are not part of the script; they are identifiers for the explanation that follows.

```
1.   WRITE "Good %GREETING_TIME, %LOGIN_NAME."
2.   MAP DISPLAY OFF
3.   MAP ERRORS OFF
4.   MAP *1:SYS:
5.   MAP *1:=SYS:%LOGIN_NAME
6.   IF "%1"="ADMIN" THEN MAP *1:=SYS:SYSTEM
7.   MAP *2:=SYS:PUBLIC\OS2
8.   MAP INS S1:=SYS:PUBLIC;
         INS S2:=SYS:PUBLIC\%MACHINE\%OS\%OS_VERSION
9.   MAP DISPLAY ON
10.  MAP
```

The parameters with percent signs are login script identifiers that represent variables in the user's environment, such as the name supplied when logging in, or the version of DOS running on the system. An explanation of each line of the script follows:

1. This line displays a greeting message such as "Good morning, JJONES." The value of the identifier variable %GREETING_TIME depends on the current time, and %LOGIN_NAME is the name the user typed with the LOGIN command.

2. This line prevents MAP commands from displaying messages. It is used for esthetic reasons.

3. Line 3 prevents errors from displaying.

4. Line 4 maps the first drive to the SYS: volume. This mapping is only used if the user does not have a home directory, otherwise the next command overrides it.

5. This line maps the first drive to the user's home directory. If it doesn't exist, the mapping in line 4 is preserved.

L

6. If the user logging in is ADMIN (SUPERVISOR in NetWare 3.x), the command in line 6 maps the first drive to the SYS:SYSTEM directory.

7. The command in line 7 is only included in the script if the user logs in from an OS/2 workstation. It maps the second drive to the OS/2 utilities directory that branched from the PUBLIC directory on the SYS: volume.

8. Line 8 is a multiple command line—the semicolon separates two distinct mapping commands. It executes if users are working at a DOS or Windows workstation. The first part maps a search drive to the SYS:PUBLIC directory, and the second part maps to an appropriate DOS directory that matches the version of DOS they are running.

9. Line 9 restores the display of mapping information.

10. This line displays a list of mapped drives.

After the last command executes, the user sees a command prompt, along with the list of mapped drives.

Login Script Command Listing

Following is a brief listing of login script commands available in NetWare 4.x:

 # (EXTERNAL PROGRAM EXECUTION)   Executes external commands from within the login script. Place the command and its path after the pound sign.

ATTACH   Use ATTACH to connect with a bindery-based NetWare file server. Type the server name and user name after the command, or let the user specify the server and user name themselves when the command executes.

CLS   Clears the screen.

COMSPEC   Specifies the directory where the DOS COMMAND.COM file exists.

CONTEXT   In NetWare 4, this command displays the current context of the user in the Directory Services hierarchical tree.

DISPLAY AND FDISPLAY   Displays the contents of auxiliary text files. The files can hold text information or messages.

DOS BREAK   Specifies that DOS can be interrupted when the CTRL+BREAK or CTRL+C keys are pressed.

DRIVE   Use this command to switch to another drive. Specify the letter of the drive after the command.

EXIT   Use this command to stop the execution of remaining commands in the login script. Usually used with IF...THEN statements after a condition is evaluated as either true or false.

FIRE PHASER   Generates sounds that alert users to messages on the screen or other conditions.

GOTO   Causes branching to different parts of the login script, usually after an IF...THEN evaluation. Specifies a label after the GOTO command that matches a label in the login script.

IF...THEN   Causes execution of commands based on the truth or equality of a condition. If true, the command or commands following the IF...THEN statement and up to an END statement execute.

INCLUDE   Causes the login script to execute a set of commands in an external login script file.

LASTLOGINTIME   Displays the last time a user logged in.

MACHINE   Specifies a name for the machine the user is logging in on.

MAP   Assigns drive letters to directories, simplifying access for users.

NO_DEFAULT   In NetWare 4, use this command in system or profile login scripts to prevent the default user login script from executing.

NOSWAP   In NetWare 4, use this command to prevent LOGIN from being moved from conventional memory to high memory or onto disk when the workstation is low on memory.

PAUSE   Temporarily stops the execution of the login script.

REMARK   Use this command to include remarks in the login script itself. The remarks do not appear when the script executes. Type the remarks after the REMARK command.

SET   Use this command to create variables that can be used in batch files after the login script executes.

SET_TIME   Sets the time on the workstation to the same time as the server to which the user is logging into.

SWAP   Moves the LOGIN command into high memory to free up conventional memory so # commands can be executed.

WRITE   Displays messages and other text. Type the text after the WRITE command.

RELATED ENTRIES   NetWare; Novell

Logons and Logon Accounts

Logon (or login) is a procedure that a user follows to gain access to a privileged system, such as a file server, a database, or the actual network. The user first runs the software that connects the workstation to the network and sets up a communication channel to a network server. This process is often run automatically when the workstation is turned on. The user then types **LOGON** or **LOGIN** . The logon procedure then asks for the user's account name and password. If the user enters either of these incorrectly, the logon procedure usually allows another chance for the user to log on. After a certain number of repeated failures to supply the proper information, the logon procedure assumes the user is an intruder and locks the station from further logon attempts.

When a user successfully logs on, he or she becomes authenticated on the network and gains preassigned authorizations to use resources on the network. For example, a NetWare 4.x server can authenticate users and, through this authentication, prove the identity of the user to other servers. In this way, the user only needs to log on once, not every time a resource is accessed.

A user must have an account on a system to log on. This account has the user's logon name, access rights, and a logon script that can execute various commands when the user logs on. For example, the logon script might set various directory path mappings and display a menu specifically designed for the user. A supervisor may apply logon restrictions to the user account, as described next.

- A logon restriction may limit the time the user can log on, thus preventing the user from logging on after hours.

- A logon restriction can specify the workstation where a user logs on, preventing the user from logging on at unsupervised workstations.

- A logon restriction can require unique passwords, thus forcing the user to create a password unlike one the user recently used.

- A logon restriction can define an expiration date for the account, locking out the user after a certain period of time.

RELATED ENTRIES   Account, User Network; Authentication and Authorization; *and* Users and Groups

Lotus Notes

Lotus Notes is an enterprise-wide, client-server-based workgroup application that currently has no peers. It is designed to integrate messaging, forms generation, and document flow in large network environments. The product is expensive. Notes is often called workflow software because it can automate the flow of documents in an organization and help that organization get a better handle on projects, accounting processes, and other business related activities that involve many people. It is collaborative software that helps people work together in groups, even if they are separated geographically. While Notes might be compared to a database management system for users, it is quite different. Notes is more appropriate for unstructured data and supports multimedia data types quite well. Its messaging system allows users to interact how and when they need to, following user-defined rules. Current estimates indicate that there are over 300,000 Notes users.

Notes consists of an electronic mail messaging system that users access to create, send, and receive messages. It also includes an address book and management features for organizing received messages and managing message stores. Notes messages provide compound document features, so messages can include text, graphics, and multimedia information. Notes includes forms management features that let users store information in fields, then locate information based on those fields. The distributed document component provides a way for clients in distributed network environments to easily share documents. Other Notes features are described next:

- Notes is supported on a variety of networks, such as AppleTalk, Novell NetWare, Banyan VINES, IBM APPC, TCP/IP, and X.25.

- Users can access the Notes system through front-end applications such as word processors, databases, and spreadsheet applications.

- Microsoft Object Linking and Embedding is supported so users can build and exchange compound documents that include text, graphics, spreadsheet data, and other information that is linked to documents created by other users.

- Documents are indexed in a number of ways that let users access documents based on authors, dates, departments, or any information in the content of the document.

- Security features include the RSA encryption and authentication systems.

Lotus Notes uses the concept of domain to establish management areas and groups of users. A domain consists of one or more Notes servers that share a common Public Name and Address Book database. The database holds information about users in each domain, such as their mail address, mail encryption information, and information about other Notes servers in the domain. The domain also provides gateway services to other products.

The latest version of Notes has been specifically designed for application development in distributed enterprise-wide environments. It now includes advanced programming capabilities and forms manipulation features. Users can access these features to design custom Notes-based applications, although many organizations will use professional programmers for this task. The programming language is based on the macro language in Lotus 1-2-3.

RELATED ENTRIES   Compound Documents; Groupware; Object Linking and Embedding; *and* Workflow Software

LU 6.2

See Advanced Program-to-Program Communications.

Mach, Carnegie-Mellon Microkernel

A kernel is the core component of most operating systems. It is the portion that manages memory, resources, files, peripherals, and system security. The kernel typically runs processes and provides interprocess communication among them. The *Mach* operating system was developed at Carnegie-Mellon University. It has a client-server architecture consisting of a relatively small kernel called a *microkernel*. The microkernel architecture is designed to handle only the most critical functions of the operating system, as listed here:

- Interrupts
- Messaging
- Thread scheduling
- Virtual memory

Compare the Mach microkernel to a person who owns and manages a business. While the manager could attempt to run the entire business alone, the growth of the business will eventually depend on hiring others to handle some of the business operations. By delegating part of the workload to others and reducing his or her workload, the manager can be more efficient. Additional people are added as necessary to grow with the business.

In a similar manner, the Mach operating system uses a modular design in which additional functions are attached to the microkernel as necessary. These other functions include a file management module, a network support module, a module that runs a graphical user interface, and other modules. The modules are layered on top of the Mach microkernel.

The modules communicate using interprocess communication mechanisms. Remote procedure calls (RPCs) provide communication over a network with processes running on other systems. The Mach kernel is specifically designed for multiprocessing and improves system throughput on multiprocessor systems. Mach also supports external memory managers for applications such as transaction processing systems that must have their own control over memory.

A layered architecture lets the microkernel host a number of diverse operating systems such as UNIX System V, HP-UX, or an AIX version of UNIX, as well as DOS or OS/2 on multiple platforms such as the Motorola PowerPC RISC processor and Intel processors. Mach is the core of the Open Software Foundation's (OSF's) OSF/1 Microkernel operating system. It is also the core of IBM's new PowerPC operating system called Workplace OS. The IBM microkernel is small in size (about 40K) and handles basic tasks listed earlier.

Microkernel operating systems such as Mach give users choices as to the interfaces and features of their operating system. They fit in well with the changing computer market in which users choose a computer platform based on needs, not on a processor or operating system. Mach provides a way to run similar environments on a variety of different processors. The microkernel provides an interface between the user's choice of platforms and operating systems.

The modular approach lets users add only the functionality they need to an operating system. In older operating systems, built-in functions took up disk space and memory and went unused by some users. Microkernel architecture simplifies expansion of the operating system and makes upgrades and bug fixes easier since only modules are upgraded, not the entire operating system. In addition, it's possible to upgrade or change out modules while the core operating system runs. This is a great benefit in the server environment, where a downed server not only becomes inaccessible to users, but resets various tracking systems and statistical measures that rely on the amount of time the server is up and running.

RELATED ENTRIES   IBM Operating Systems; Microkernel; OSF/1, Open Software Foundation; Remote Procedure Call; Windows NT Microsoft; *and* Workplace OS

Mail/Message-Enabled Applications
See Message-Enabled Applications.

Mail Slots

Mail slots is a network store-and-forward messaging system extension to the OS/2 operating system. It is implemented in Microsoft LAN Manager and IBM LAN Server. It provides a way for a process on one computer to pass a message or data to a process running on another computer. A system can send a message to one other system, or broadcast a message to a number of other systems.

RELATED ENTRY   Messaging API, Inter-Application

Mainframe

A mainframe is a large system with one or more central processors. Multiple processors share the processing load or provide backup processing should one of the units fail. The systems can provide gigabytes of online data storage and archive storage. Mainframes were the primary computers in the 1960s and early 1970s and were manufactured by IBM, Burroughs, Control Data, Honeywell, Univac, and others. A distinguishing feature is that they provide centralized processing for terminals or desktop computers that emulate terminals. All the processing is performed by the mainframe system.

IBM and others still manufacture mainframes, but the role of the mainframe is changing. IBM has developed strategies for integrating mainframes into enterprise computing environments. These systems can provide intensive computing power for client-server applications or serve as a data repository as outlined in IBM's Information Warehouse strategy. IBM recognizes that organizations have a diversity of

M

systems, and it now supports multiple communication protocols and open systems as defined in its Networking Blueprint. For example, Transmission Control Protocol/Internet Protocol (TCP/IP) and Open Systems Interconnection (OSI) protocols are now supported on IBM networks, along with Advanced Peer-to-Peer Networking (APPN) and Advanced Program-to-Program Communications (APPC).

In the 1970s and 1980s, Digital Equipment established itself as a minicomputer vendor by providing efficient, cost-effective systems for departmental use. Today, most desktop computers have the memory, storage, and processing power of yesterday's minicomputers. While DEC has strengthened its line, many vendors of superservers (desktop PCs with multiple processors and vast amounts of memory) are encroaching on its turf. The new DEC Alpha AXP processors are proving to be strong contenders, however. The processors are built into single- and multiprocessor systems that run Windows NT and other industry-standard operating systems.

It is said that microcomputer systems linked by networks and running client-server applications will supplant the mainframe, but this has not yet occurred. In fact, while desktop computer systems are approaching mainframes in processing power, they still can't compare to mainframes in overall features. A mainframe can handle, in one location, huge amounts of input/output (I/O), online transaction processing, security, data integrity, availability, and management functions. In addition, there is a large installed base of mainframe applications and databases that do not currently require replacement. In fact, IBM sees an increased demand for new applications that support the Networking Blueprint and Information Warehouse strategy.

Other contenders for this market include UNIX-based Reduced Instruction Set Computer (RISC) systems. Over the last few years, these systems have gained tremendous processing power. Enhancements to the operating system and applications have also helped the systems gain ground. In addition, UNIX has supported the popular TCP/IP communication protocols, which are used on the Internet and have become popular in other environments for wide area internetworking due to efficient routing methods.

IBM Mainframe Systems

IBM's original line of mainframe computers, called the S/360, were introduced in 1964. These were largely batch processing systems in which a group of transactions were processed together, rather than one at a time. In 1970, the line was upgraded to the series S/370, and time-sharing was the major paradigm in which many users could access the computer through terminals. In the 1980s and 1990s, the series S/390 represents IBM's strategy for interactive computing.

The current processors that conform to this heritage are the IBM Enterprise System/9000 (ES/9000) series which are pictured in the section "IBM Mainframe Environment" earlier in this book. The systems come in a variety of sizes, from water-cooled systems with up to six processors to air-cooled systems with up to four processors. Input/output channels are managed with Reduced Instruction Set

Computer (RISC) processors and external devices are attached with high-speed fiber optic links.

The ES/9000 systems are part of IBM's enterprise system strategy that supports open environment and multiple protocols. IBM is already installing many of these systems as network servers and information warehouse systems. This is discussed further under "Mainframe and Minicomputer Connectivity."

RELATED ENTRIES   Alpha AXP, DEC; Client-Server Computing; DEC; Distributed Computing; IBM; IBM Mainframe Environment; IBM Networking Blueprint; Information Warehouse; Reduced Instruction Set Computer; *and* UNIX

Mainframe and Minicomputer Connectivity

Mainframe and minicomputer systems were designed over the course of the last few decades for environments in which users worked at nonintelligent terminals and relied on the central computer to perform all processing. Interoperability with systems from other vendors was usually not important. Today, intelligent multivendor desktop computers predominate and are interconnected with networks. A variety of different operating environments and communication protocols exist. The proprietary architectures and protocols of the mainframe environment are no longer in demand.

There are many strategies for providing mainframe connectivity to users, as listed here. All use the network platform as a communication channel between the user and the mainframe.

- Conform to the proprietary protocols of the vendor and access the system using traditional terminals, or desktop computers that emulate terminals. Access to the host is through a gateway.

- Use protocol emulation or conversion to access mainframe systems directly.

- Use industry-standard protocols to link users and provide application interfaces that provide translation and conversion between user and mainframe systems.

Many vendors make gateway and emulation products. For example, Novell's NetWare for Systems Applications Architecture (SAA) is a product for connecting workstations on a NetWare local area network (LAN) to an IBM Systems Network Architecture (SNA) host or an IBM AS/400 minicomputer. A stand-alone computer operating as a gateway provides the connection to the host system. Workstations attaching to the host run 3270 emulation software.

Users who want access to mainframe data from their existing applications can take advantage of the following strategies:

M

■ Develop custom client-server applications that provide access to mainframe data from specific front-end applications. This strategy can be costly and limits application portability, but is more likely to target an organization's needs.

■ Use "middleware" products that simplify the development of applications by hiding the underlying networks, communications protocols, and operating systems. These products provide a common interface through which applications can access back-end data.

■ Use *information warehouse* strategies that view mainframes as data depositories. This strategy keeps data on the mainframe where it is secure, while providing users with "snapshots" of data at intermediate workgroup servers or directly from the mainframe.

As mainframe vendors open their systems and move away from proprietary protocols, interoperability among multivendor systems improves and product development increases. Next, let's review IBM's and DEC's plan for integrating into the enterprise.

IBM Connectivity

Systems Network Architecture (SNA) has been IBM's grand plan for networking for well over a decade. But SNA is proprietary and was designed with the focus on mainframes as centralized control centers for the network. SNA was designed before intelligent desktop computers dominated the corporate landscape. IBM now supports multiprotocol open environments, including Transmission Control Protocol/Internet Protocol (TCP/IP) and Open Systems Interconnection (OSI), as well as peer-to-peer networking and client-server computing.

■ *Advanced Peer-to-Peer Networking (APPN)*, introduced in 1991, is IBM's strategy for peer-to-peer networking. APPN is well suited to creating client-server applications. High Performance Routing (HPR) is an upgrade to APPN that provides advanced features. IBM designed the protocol to compete with or replace TCP/IP. HPR handles routing around failed nodes and avoids the packet overhead handled by network nodes to improve performance.

■ The *Networking Blueprint,* introduced in 1992, is IBM's strategy for defining the programming interfaces, transport mechanisms, and media types for interoperability in the IBM environment. Its goal is to allow multiple network protocols, allow users to work with many types of equipment, and to support new media types such as video over high-bandwidth networks.

■ The *Information Warehouse (IW)* is a plan by IBM to keep the mainframe a viable platform. This strategy protects the investments of its current customers and views the mainframe as a "superserver" and data repository for enterprise-wide needs. Open systems allow users of multivendor, multiprotocol systems to access the IW.

■ *SystemView* provides a common, industry-standard interface for managing heterogeneous networks. It supports important protocols, such as TCP/IP, OSI, SNA, and others. In addition, it is based on the OSI Common Management Interface Protocol (CMIP).

Client-server application development will center around the use of the Open Software Foundation's (OSF's) Distributed Computing Environment (DEC) and the Portable UNIX Programming Interface (POSIX).

DEC Connectivity

Digital Equipment Corporation long ago created the Digital Network Architecture (DNA) to specify how its computers can interoperate. DECnet is the outcome of this architectural design. DECnet is now in its fifth phase, which DEC calls ADVANTAGE-NETWORKS. This phase integrates OSI, TCP/IP, and DECnet protocols while maintaining backward-compatibility with DECnet Phase IV. There are three main goals:

■ Multivendor connectivity through the use of OSI and TCP/IP protocols

■ Removal of addressing limitations so computer networks can support millions of nodes

■ Management of very small to very large multivendor networks using a network management entity model that is modular and extensible

ADVANTAGE-NETWORKS gives DEC's customers the ability to build a single multivendor network using open system strategies. An open system is a vendor-neutral computing environment, compliant with international and de facto standards, that permits system and network interoperability while maintaining a somewhat consistent user interface.

RELATED ENTRIES   ADVANTAGE-NETWORKS, DEC; Client-Server Computing; DEC; DECnet; IBM; IBM Mainframe Environment; Information Warehouse; *and* Middleware

Managed Object

See Management Information Base; Management Standards and Tools.

Management, Desktop Licensing and Electronic Distribution

Desktop management systems for networks are providing new features and functions that can assist network managers with the following:

M

- Licence management provides a way for an application server to track how many licenses are available for a particular application and to grant the application the ability to run for a client. The Licensing Server API (LS API) is a licensing standard proposed by Microsoft, Lotus, Novell, and many other vendors that defines how applications and NetLS licensing servers work together to track software usage and licensing.

- Electronic software distribution provides a way to automatically install new software, software updates, or drivers on users' desktops from a central management system.

RELATED ENTRY   Electronic Software Distribution and Licensing

Management Information Base (MIB)

The MIB holds the information about all the resources that are managed by a network management system. Resources on the network are represented by *managed objects* within the MIB.

A managed object is a logical representation of a real physical entity on the network that is to be managed. A managed object is stored in a *management information base (MIB)*. A managed object has a name, attributes, and properties.

Typical managed objects include hardware equipment such as bridges, routers, computers, servers, switches, multiplexers, and others. The managed object has properties that hold values, such as the address of a node, the serial number of a computer, routing table information, error counters, and more. Operations that obtain attribute values, change them, or delete them are directed to the managed object by the management system, but it is the object that performs the operation. In this respect, managed objects follow the design of any common object-oriented system in that the object itself contains both the data and the procedures for working with that data.

RELATED ENTRY   Management Standards and Tools

Management Information Format File (MIFF)

MIFF is defined by the Desktop Management Task Force (DMTF) in the Desktop Management Interface (DMI) as an ASCII text file that contains information about a workstation, such as its memory availability, basic input/output system (BIOS) type, operating system version, application types and versions, available drivers, and other information. This information is obtained when the station is first turned on, or when a user first logs on. The DMI provides a standard interface to MIFFs. Vendors provide MIFF compatibility in their products. Hermes and other network management programs look at the information in MIFFs by polling stations on the network. This information is then used to determine whether software installations or updates are required, based on software or hardware version numbers or other information defined by the network administrator.

RELATED ENTRIES   Desktop Management Interface; Desktop Management Task Force; Hermes, Microsoft; *and* Management Standards and Tools

Management Standards and Tools

The growth of local area networks (LANs) from department-level communication systems into internetworks that span buildings, campuses, metropolitan areas, and the globe has created tremendous management problems. Management is one of the biggest problems with today's networks. Some managers long for the days of centralized mainframe environments in which computing resources were located in centrally secure locations and users connected to the system with dumb terminals.

Today's network consists of data in many locations and users who want to access that data. Security is a major concern. How does the network manager support computer resources and protect data located in another city? How does the manager provide updates and bug fixes to remote users? How do you effectively manage a large distributed network without hiring additional personnel? Fortunately, products and standards exist to assist managers in these and other areas.

Management systems are designed to assist managers in collecting information about the network and its components, including the cabling system, servers, bridges, routers, gateways, and workstations. Management systems provide a way to collect information from a variety of network devices at diverse locations and display the information on a central system, where managers can manipulate and interpret it. As internetworks expand, administrators need a way to manage remote resources without actually traveling to them.

A distributed network management system spreads the management tasks out from a centralized data center to intermediate systems that gather data and handle localized events. Administration of this system can still take place at a single location, but by using distributed computing techniques, high traffic loads and large data storage requirements are removed from a single area. The distribution data can be collected at periodic intervals by the central management system.

Distributing management also provides scalability since new management systems can be added at any time in the areas of the network where they are needed most. Distributed management is also more open to multivendor systems. In the client/server model, clients run front-end end applications written for their operating systems and communicate with servers using industry-standard protocols.

Simple Network Management Protocol (SNMP) is a standard for collecting network information that got its start on the Internet. SNMP defines agents that collect information from network devices and send the information to a management information base (MIB). Applications that are SNMP compatible can use this information to report network status and other information to system administrators.

M

Another management standard is the OSI Common Management Information Protocol (CMIP). Although CMIP offers more functionality than SNMP, SNMP has raced ahead in terms of industry acceptance. Most hardware and management products advertise their SNMP compatibility. Decisions on which wiring hub or other hardware device to use are usually based on their SNMP compatibility.

These management systems have three primary components:

- *Agents* or *elements* operate within each device on the network that requires managing, such as bridges, routers, servers, and workstations. Agents collect information about a host device and make that information available to management systems.

- *The network management system* operates within a specific boundary such as a LAN and gathers information from agents within that boundary. This information is stored in a MIB. In most cases, SNMP is the protocol used to communicate between management systems and agents.

- *The system administrator* is often a host-based or UNIX-based management system that collects management information from individual management systems and compiles it for management. Common management systems discussed elsewhere in this book include *DECmcc* from DEC, *Distributed Management Environment* from the Open Software Foundation, *Hermes* from Microsoft, *OpenView Management System* from Hewlett-Packard, *SunNet Manager* from Sun Microsystems, Inc., and *NetView* or *SystemView* from IBM.

Several network management systems are discussed in the following sections and in more detail elsewhere in this book (see "Related Entries" in this heading).

Desktop Management Interface (DMI)

The DMI is a programming and reporting standard for managing desktop workstations. It was defined by the Desktop Management Task Force (DMTF), which is a consortium of industry vendors including Digital Equipment Corporation, Hewlett-Packard, Intel, Microsoft, SunConnect, SynOptics Communications, and other companies. The DMI defines how manufacturers of hardware products such as network interface cards or networking software can integrate "agents" into their products that collect information and report back to a management utility. DMI hides protocols and operating system differences.

LAN administrators can determine the following through the DMI interface:

- Basic information such as the processor type, available memory, and disk space information

- Hardware and software components installed in network systems

- How components are configured

- How well the components are working

■ Whether the components are due for an upgrade

This information can help managers quickly resolve problems and provide upgrades. The MIFF is a text file that collects information about systems and makes it available to management programs. Vendors will provide MIFFs with their DMI-compliant products.

Microsoft Hermes

Microsoft Hermes is an enterprise network management system that runs on Windows NT. One of its primary capabilities is the management of network inventory. Hermes includes tools for updating drives and software in remote workstations and other devices from a central management console. Other features provided by Hermes are listed here:

■ An inventory for storing hardware and software information

■ Automatic updates though software distribution

■ Licensing software for tracking software usage

■ Diagnostic tools to track performance and network conditions

■ Remote access utility to assist users onscreen

Hermes reads MIFFs, as defined by the Desktop Management Task Force (DMTF) in the Desktop Management Interface (DMI), as described previously. Hermes uses information in MIFFs to determine whether software installations or updates are required, based on software or hardware version numbers or other information defined by the network administrator. Both IBM and Hewlett-Packard are moving their management systems to Windows NT, and Microsoft is enhancing Hermes with features that forward information to these platforms.

NetWare Services Manager (Windows or OS/2 Versions)

NetWare Services Manager is a Windows-based network management application. It gives network administrators the tools they need to manage multivendor networks. Devices on the network are graphically displayed. Network problems are monitored and logged into a database, and supervisors are notified of them. NetWare Services Manager accepts information from other third-party devices that monitor the network, integrating network management into one application. NetWare Services Manager is made up of two components:

■ *Management workstation* This software runs under Microsoft Windows or OS/2 on a PC-compatible system.

M

■ *Management agents*   The agents reside on NetWare servers throughout the internetwork. They collect data for display on the management workstation. One agent comes with NetWare Services Manager, and additional agents can be purchased for other servers that need to be managed.

The graphical map on the management workstation lets users navigate through the network of Internetwork Packet Exchange (IPX) routers, client workstations, servers, and other objects. Multiple servers can be monitored from one location. Graphs and statistics are displayed for NetWare servers. Events are logged, and users are notified of priority events by alarms. The graphical display simplifies the management of network assets because all components of the network can be viewed and tracked. One of the biggest advantages that NetWare Services Manager provides is a reduction in downtime, because its continuous monitoring indicates problems in advance.

DEC's Enterprise Management Architecture and DECmcc

Digital's strategy for network management is designed around its Enterprise Management Architecture (EMA). EMA goes beyond normal network management, which focused on physical links such as modems, cables, and multiplexers, to the management of the systems, applications, and data that reside on the network.

Digital's architecture is open and extensive, and DEC is working with the International Organization for Standardization (ISO) and many vendors to ensure that multivendor hardware and software products can be managed with DEC's management systems. The first implementation of EMA is the DEC Management Control Center (DECmcc) family of management products.

RELATED ENTRIES   Common Management Information Protocol; Configuration Management; DEC Enterprise Management Architecture; DECmcc; Desktop Management Interface; Distributed Management; Distributed Management Environment; Electronic Software Distribution and Licensing; Hermes, Microsoft; NetView, IBM; OpenView Management System, Hewlett-Packard; Simple Network Management Protocol; SunNet Manager, Sun Microsystems; *and* SystemView, IBM

Manufacturing Automation Protocol (MAP)

MAP is an OSI protocol for manufacturing equipment that was originally developed by General Motors, starting in 1982. The standard is now under the control of the MAP/TOP Users' Group, which is administered by the Society of Manufacturing Engineers. Technical Office Protocol (TOP) is an office system communications protocol developed by Boeing Computer Services.

Both MAP and TOP use Ethernet and are usually used in conjunction. MAP defines local area networks for terminals, manufacturing devices, and robots on the manufacturing floor while TOP defines connections in the front office.

RELATED ENTRY   Technical Office Protocol

Map Command, NetWare

A *drive mapping* is a shorthand reference to a long directory name, and a *search drive mapping* is a search path to a directory that contains executable program files. Drive mappings are created to simplify switching between directories, or referencing directories. The DOS SUBST command accomplishes the same thing. Search drive mappings let you execute programs in directories other than the one you are in.

The MAP command is used to create drive maps and search drive maps. Although you can execute it at the prompt during any NetWare session to create new mappings, those mappings are not saved for your next session. MAP commands are placed in login scripts to preserve the mapping for the next login session. Occasionally, however, you'll need to execute a MAP command during a login session to create a temporary mapping, so the basics are provided here:

Using MAP

To display your current drive mappings, simply type the MAP command by itself. You'll see a list of the mapped drive letters you can switch to, followed by a list of search drive maps. A search drive is a path that the operating system follows to locate executable files in other directories.

To create a new mapping, type **MAP** followed by the letter to map and the directory to map. For example, you would type the following command to map the drive letter H to the SYS:PUBLIC directory.

```
MAP H:=SYS:PUBLIC
```

You can now switch to the PUBLIC directory by typing **H:**.

To create a search drive mapping, you need to specify a search drive number. The following command creates a search drive mapping with a path to the SYS:APPS\LOTUS directory so you can run the program files in it:

```
MAP S4:=SYS:APPS\LOTUS
```

M

To insert a search drive mapping without replacing any existing mappings, including those used for your local DOS directories, use the INS (Insert) parameter, as shown here:

```
MAP INS S4:=SYS:APPS\LOTUS
```

To view MAP help information, type the following:

```
MAP /?
```

Matrix Switch

A matrix switch has a number of incoming ports and a number of outgoing ports. An internal matrix of connections provides a way for any incoming port to connect with any outgoing port. A 4-by-4 matrix is pictured in Figure M-1, but other matrix configurations are available, such as 8 by 8 and 16 by 16. This example illustrates how a switch can provide up to four computers with a connection to a pool of four modems. Note that the switching matrix is usually implemented at the microprocessor level.

Matrix switches provide extremely fast switching between connected devices. They can become quite elaborate. Switches of this nature are becoming popular in the local area network (LAN) environment as a way to provide microsegmentation of the LAN. Each port on the switch provides a dedicated network segment for a single workstation and that segment can connect with any other segment to provide a dedicated communication link to another station or server. Ports can support a single workstation or a LAN segment with multiple workstations. A port can provide dedicated high-speed circuits between systems for applications such as multimedia, videoconferencing, and engineering systems. It can also provide switching between computers and high-speed peripheral devices such as mass-storage systems and printers.

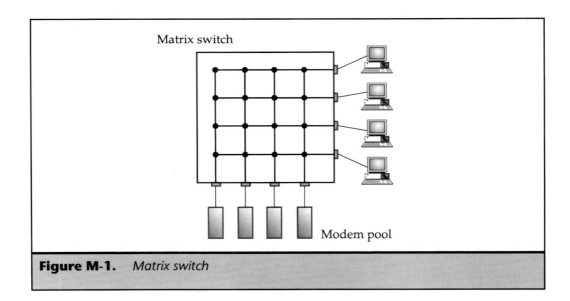

Figure M-1. *Matrix switch*

RELATED ENTRIES   Hubs; Switching Hubs

Media Access Control (MAC) Methods

In the Open Systems Interconnection (OSI) protocol stack, the Data-Link layer is just above the Physical layer. It is divided into two sublayers. The upper layer is the Logical Link Control (LLC) layer, and the lower layer is the Media Access Control (MAC) layer. The MAC layer places packets from upper protocol layers into the frame format of the destination network. It also handles some error detection, but the primary task is to implement the access control method for the destination network. The MAC layer is modular and defines a number of different ways to access shared physical media, as pictured in Figure M-2 and described next.

- *CSMA/CD (IEEE 802.3)*   This is the carrier sense multiple access/collision detection method for accessing the cable. Each station listens (carrier senses) before transmitting. If the channel is in use, the device waits before transmitting. Multiple Access (MA) indicates that many devices can be attached to and use the same cable, but not simultaneously. Collision Detection (CD) indicates that if two devices access the cable at the same time, a collision is detected and both back off and try again later.

- *Token Bus (IEEE 802.4)*   In this access method, stations must have possession of a token before they can transmit. The token is passed from station to station in numeric order, but the stations may not be physically arranged in this order.

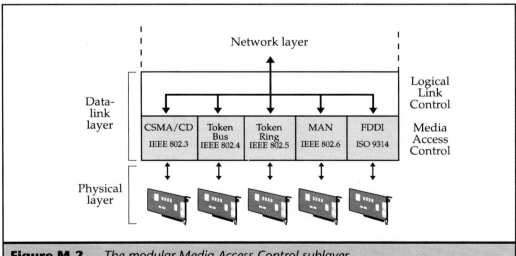

Figure M-2.   *The modular Media Access Control sublayer*

M

- *Token Ring (IEEE 802.5)* In this access method, a token travels around the network from one station to the next. In order to transmit, a station takes possession of the token. No other stations can transmit until the frame is released.

- *MAN (IEEE 802.6)* The Metropolitan Area Networks (MAN) standard uses the Distributed Queue Dual Bus (DQDB) access method. The bus transmits regularly recurring slots in which stations can place data for transmission.

- *FDDI (ISO-9314)* Fiber Distributed Data Interface (FDDI) is a 100 Mbits/sec fiber-optic network standard that has a dual-ring topology (for fault tolerance). Stations transmit when they have possession of a token.

Each of these methods provides a way to transmit data to another end station on a network. The functions of the MAC sublayer are usually implemented as firmware in the attached network interface cards. The LLC layer is responsible for transferring packets of information (protocol data units, or PDUs) from upper layers into the MAC layer, or vice versa. If multiple interface cards are installed in a system, the LLC layer is responsible for directing PDUs to the correct card, or for relaying PDUs arriving on one card to another card.

RELATED ENTRIES   Data-Link Layer, OSI Model; Layered Architecture; Logical Links; Open Systems Interconnection Model; *and* Protocol Stack

Memory Address

On Intel-based computers, a base memory address setting is required for network interface cards (NICs) to indicate the location in memory where the CPU can place data for transfer to the NIC. The base memory address is the start of a block of memory that is usually 16K or 32K in length. No two devices can use the same block of memory and the memory range of one block should not overlap another block of memory. Typical starting addresses are in upper memory blocks (above the 640K barrier on DOS machines) at C000, C800, D000, and D800.

If a computer doesn't boot or behaves erratically, especially after installing a NIC, check the interrupt (IRQ) settings and the input/output (I/O) settings to ensure that there is no conflict. Here are some tips:

- If a computer fails to boot, check for conflicts with a floppy disk or hard disk controller.

- If your system locks up when running a utility or peripheral device, there is probably an I/O port or base memory conflict.

- In some cases, an interrupt conflict between a network card and another device locks the system when you make the first network call, or results in slow or erratic performance. You might see numerous send and receive errors.

■ If a mouse is attached to a system that uses a VGA monitor, the mouse might be using IRQ 2. If a mouse is not necessary, disable its port.

Message-Enabled Applications

Messaging through electronic mail systems is becoming a critical component for supporting workgroups in network environments and application-to-application processes. Applications that fit into the groupware, workflow, and document processing categories use electronic mail links to interconnect users and assist in the flow of information. The most elementary message-enabling feature is the ability to send electronic mail from any application. Scheduling applications also take advantage of electronic mail. A scheduling application that works over the network uses E-mail to help users coordinate meetings.

Messaging integration is made possible by application program interfaces (APIs) such as Microsoft's Messaging API (MAPI), Lotus' Vendor Independent Messaging (VIM), and Novell's Message Handling Service (MHS). As pictured in Figure M-3, the APIs provide an interface between front-end applications and back-end electronic mail systems. Any user application can implement one of the APIs to gain access to the back-end messaging system.

Workflow applications such as Lotus Notes are designed to automate the flow of forms and documents through an organization. Documents move from person to person for revision or approval. Workflow applications use electronic mail to route documents to appropriate users in the workflow process. When one user completes a document, it is automatically forwarded to the next user. Time stamps and urgency tags can ensure that a document does not get held up by any single user. A set of rules

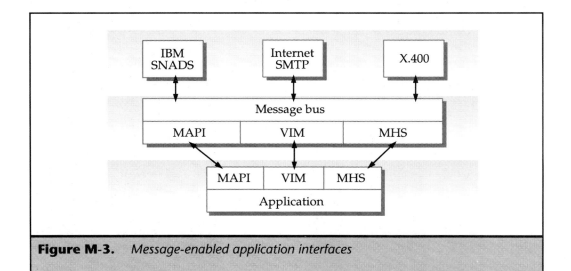

Figure M-3. *Message-enabled application interfaces*

M

defines how documents flow through the organization, based on the type of document or the point of origination.

A typical workflow application combines document imaging with electronic messaging and advanced security features such as digital signatures that can provide proof that documents are from the specified source, that they have been validated by the person indicated in the form, and that they have not been altered. Publishing is an example of a collaborative environment that can benefit from workflow software. Documents are transferred from writer to editor to production in stages using the network and its resources to store and eventually print the completed work.

A database application can also use E-mail to send and receive queries. For example, a mobile user might request a report from a corporate database by sending the database a query in an E-mail message. When the report is complete, the database places it in an E-mail message and sends it to the user's mailbox. AT&T has taken mobile messaging a step further. It envisions intelligent agents in E-mail messages that run their own programs once they enter a network. The programs are used to direct message routing and handle situations such as redirecting a message to the home system of a user that left the office early.

Message-enabled applications have their place in the enterprise network. They are appropriate when information is not time-critical. The time between a message and a response can be quite long, but this is not always a problem. The mobile user making a database query may not need the report until arriving at a motel later in the evening. The user then connects with the company's E-mail system and retrieves the requested information or report. Messaging systems are not appropriate for real-time applications in which users need the most up-to-date information on a continuing basis. These systems require connection-oriented sessions, not the connectionless sessions typical of messaging systems.

RELATED ENTRIES   Apple Open Collaborative Environment; Document Interchange Standards; Document Management; Groupware; Lotus Notes; *and* Workflow Software

Message Handling Service (MHS), Novell

NOTE: *Don't confuse the Novell Message Handling Service with the X.400 Message Handling System. See the entry "X.400 Message Handling System."*

Novell's NetWare Message Handling Service (MHS) is a system that handles message flow between applications that are located on local area networks and remote computers on wide area networks. MHS can collect, route, and deliver messages and files to other systems by using store-and-forward technology. Applications that use MHS include electronic mail, workgroup scheduling, electronic data interchange (EDI) and network fax. Think of MHS as a delivery service that works in the background, rather than an application you actually use to address messages and send them to other users. In fact, people don't access MHS directly. They use applications that take advantage of MHS's delivery services. These applications are typically developed by non-Novell vendors.

MHS is not strictly an E-mail system. It handles message flow between applications as well. Developers can use MHS to create applications that talk to other applications and exchange information. For example, queries can be made to databases on other systems using MHS.

Novell MHS does the following:

- MHS routes and transfers files between systems.

- MHS checks the routing tables on an MHS host and queues the messages for delivery.

- MHS sets up a connection to destination systems and transmits messages over the connection. The connection might be an asynchronous connection, an internetwork connection, or a gateway connection.

- MHS messages have header and body information and can also have attachments, such as files.

All MHS messages are stored and transmitted in a Standard Message Format (SMF) that many front-end applications can use. An important aspect of MHS is that it provides a form of distributed processing in which real-time, online communication is not important. The messages are delivered at the most convenient time using the store-and-forward methodology. Calls are made only when necessary, compared to real-time applications that require a dedicated phone line. The most common use for MHS is the exchange of electronic mail, but it can also be used to build systems that query databases or execute processes on other systems.

A typical MHS installation consists of the following, as pictured in Figure M-4.

- Users connect with host systems and a number of hosts are configured into workgroups. The administrator defines workgroups and how messages are routed to hosts.

- Workgroups are usually set up at corporate levels. They might include a number of hosts connected to the same LAN.

- Messages are routed through *hubs* to other hubs, usually via modem connections.

NetWare Global MHS

NetWare Global MHS is the latest version of the message handling system. It is a scalable messaging server for a range of businesses and enterprises. It consists of a set of NetWare Loadable Modules (NLMs) that combine with NetWare 3.11 or NetWare 4.x to provide a platform for messaging with store-and-forward capabilities and services such as E-mail, workflow automation, calendaring, scheduling, and fax

M

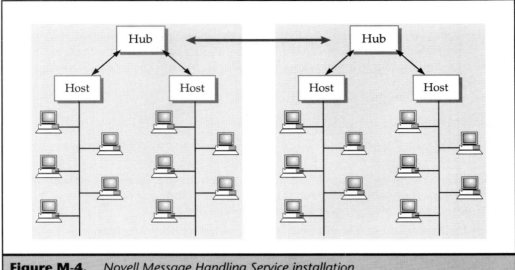

Figure M-4.   *Novell Message Handling Service installation*

services. MHS versions for NetWare 2.2 and DOS-based laptop and remote users are also available.

NetWare Global MHS combined with optional protocol modules permits interoperability between other messaging systems listed here:

- Simple Mail Transfer Protocol (SMTP) for UNIX and TCP/IP networks
- IBM SNA Distributed Services (SNADS) for IBM AS/400s and mainframes
- OSI X.400 for OSI mail networks

Novell's MHS runs as a loadable module on a NetWare server. At the front end, or client, various electronic mail utilities are available that let users create and manage messages. FirstMail, an entry-level E-mail utility, is included with MHS.

RELATED ENTRIES   Electronic Mail; Message-Enabled Applications; NetWare; Novell; *and* X.400 Message Handling System

Message Handling System

The International Organization for Standardization (ISO) message handling system is the Message Oriented Text Interchange System (MOTIS). It is based on the X.400 Message Handling System developed by the Consultative Committee for International Telegraph and Telephone (CCITT) of the International Telecommunications Union (ITU).

RELATED ENTRY   X.400 Message Handling System

Message Queuing Interface (MAI), IBM

IBM's Message Queuing Interface (MQI) is a message-based application interface that oversees the passing of messages between applications on different platforms. It is defined in the IBM Networking Blueprint.

RELATED ENTRIES   Application Program Interface; IBM Networking Blueprint; *and* Messaging API, Inter-Application

Message Transfer Agent (MTA)

In the X.400 Message Handling System developed by the Consultative Committee for International Telegraph and Telephone (CCITT) of the International Telecommunications Union (ITU), a message transfer agent (MTA) is like a post office through which messages are exchanged between systems. The MTA provides store-and-forward services. See "X.400 Message Handling System."

Microsoft's Message Transfer Agent (MTA) replaces Microsoft mail gateways. MTA links create an E-mail system around Windows for Workgroups or other Microsoft products.

Messaging API, E-mail

Messaging application program interfaces (APIs) are available to provide enterprise E-mail exchange over diverse mail systems directly from user applications. The APIs listed here provide a way for users' front-end applications to access a variety of back-end messaging systems. These APIs help developers integrate E-mail support into their applications. They define an interface between messaging services and applications, in addition to providing services such as file attachments and addressing.

■ *Messaging API (MAPI)*   A way for applications to access applications such as Microsoft Mail, Lotus Development's cc:MAIL, and Novell's Message Handling Service (MHS). MAPI defines call procedures that programmers can use to build E-mail interfaces into their applications. For example, a user could address, send, and receive an E-mail message while working in a Windows word processing program by selecting E-mail options from its menu. The user could write a note in the program and include it in an outgoing E-mail message.

■ *Vendor-Independent Messaging (VIM)*   An electronic mail API controlled by Lotus and supported by Apple, Borland, IBM, MCI, Novell, Oracle, WordPerfect, and other electronic mail developers and vendors. Like MAPI, VIM is a cross-platform API that allows developers to create mail-enabled applications that work on many different platforms and allow users on those different platforms to share mail.

M

■ *Common Mail Calls (CMC)* E-mail APIs proposed by an industry-wide group of electronic mail software developers and developed by the X.400 Application Program Interface Association (XAPIA) to resolve differences between MAPI and VIM. CMC is strongly supported in the industry and could possibly emerge as an industry standard.

■ *Apple Open Collaboration Environment (AOCE)* E-mail APIs integrated into Apple System 7. This Apple technology is designed to consolidate electronic and workgroup communications, such as voice mail, electronic mail, and fax. AOCE includes PowerTalk and PowerShare. PowerTalk provides a universal mailbox, drag-and-drop document shipping, and digital signatures and resides in Macintoshes, and PowerBook computers. PowerShare resides in AppleTalk servers. It provides PowerTalk users with store-and-forward features for electronic mail, authentication features to provide network security, and central administration functions.

■ *Standard Message Format (SMF)* The messaging interface found in Novell's Message Handling Service (MHS). Like other APIs, it allows users to send messages without leaving the applications they are working in. SMF works with NetWare Global Messaging and is therefore supported over the Simple Mail Transfer Protocol (SMTP), IBM SNA Distribution Services (SNADS), and the X.400 Message Handling System.

RELATED ENTRIES Electronic Mail; Message-Enabled Applications

Messaging API, Inter-Application

Inter-application messaging is a communication technique that is typically implemented in the client-server environment between a front-end application and a back-end server, although messaging is also implemented in peer-to-peer environments. Messaging lets applications exchange commands and information in a non-real-time, store-and-forward mode, although real-time modes can also be used. A message is formulated, then sent to the destination where it might be stored until the destination can process it. In addition, the message store may be a separate location that handles interprocess messaging. Messaging should not be confused with electronic mail systems. Although the process is similar, E-mail systems are designed for the exchange of messages among users.

A message-oriented transaction is a *connectionless transaction* that uses store-and-forward techniques. An application sends a request or command in the form of a message, then waits for a reply. There is no synchronization between two systems and the sender may broadcast messages to any number of other systems. The important point is that there is no communication "session" or connection between the client and the server. The server may respond at a much later time. Because messaging systems don't operate in real time, they are not practical for real-time mission-critical applications. However, messaging systems work well when systems are separated by wide area connections with relatively slow transfer rates. The delays caused by the wide area network (WAN) links may make real-time applications unsuitable in the first place.

In contrast, remote procedure calls (RPCs) are *connection-oriented mechanisms* for interprocess communication. A session is set up between the client and server that is maintained until the process or transaction is completed. The connection requires a setup phase and has some overhead, but provides reliable and efficient transmissions of requests and responses.

A messaging model requires queue managers at both ends of the data exchange. A message is formulated at the source and delivered to the queue associated with the destination. Message queuing is typically asynchronous—one event must complete before another event occurs. However, messages can be delivered from one source to multiple destinations. For example, messages might be distributed among multiple processors so that each can work on a task in parallel. Bidirection queues are common so that both systems can transmit messages at the same time.

Messaging systems can hide the underlying communication protocol from the applications so that an application running in an Internetwork Packet Exchange (IPX) environment can transmit messages to an application running in a Transmission Control Protocol/Internet Protocol (TCP/IP) environment. Differences in application interfaces are also minimized since the applications simply need to recognize the message formats and commands. In this respect, message passing systems are a form of "middleware." Middleware products are tools that programmers and developers use when creating applications and products to hide the complexities of underlying operating systems, communications protocols, and multivendor products. It doesn't make sense for a developer to spend a lot of time customizing applications for every possible system that the application might run on. Middleware provides all these interconnections and the developer simply makes the application interface with the middleware.

There are some notable message passing systems already installed in various network operating systems, but keep in mind that these systems are not considered middleware products since they are not designed to provide an interface for a variety of multivendor products and communication protocols. They depend on the services and communication protocols built into the operating systems.

■ Microsoft's *mail slots* is a messaging interface in the Microsoft LAN Manager and IBM Lan Server environment that is a networking extension of OS/2. Mail slots is a store-and-forward message system that allows network nodes to share data without the need to synchronize (set up a connection) with one another. In contrast, *named pipes* is a synchronized exchange between two network nodes.

■ Novell's *Message Handling Service (MHS)* is a messaging system primarily used for E-mail, but it also has the ability to transfer messages between applications. Novell has recently improved the interoperability of MHS by adding support for OSI protocols, IBM SNA, and TCP/IP.

M

■ IBM's *Message Queuing Interface (MQI)* is a message-based application interface that oversees the passing of messages between applications on different platforms. It is defined in the IBM Networking Blueprint.

A number of vendors are promoting *message-oriented middleware.* Two messaging systems are described next as an example. Several are working to integrate both SQL and non-SQL databases.

■ *Communication Integrator*   From Covia Technologies (Rosemont, Illinois). This messaging system works in IBM, DEC, UNIX, OS/2, DOS, and Windows environments. Clients use connectionless services while servers and hosts communicate through connection-oriented links. Messages can be prioritized to ensure that time-sensitive information gets through.

■ *DECmessageQ*   From Digital Equipment Corporation (Maynard, Massachusetts). This system is part of the DECnet architecture and operates in client-server and peer-to-peer environments. It supports VAX/VMS, ULTRIX, OS/2, DOS, Windows, and Macintosh. DECmessageQ operates as a message bus between many different types of front-end and back-end applications. Applications can establish a number of priority and normal message queues.

Messaging technology is important in the world of objects as well. In an object-oriented system, an Object Request Broker (ORB) provides the key communication facility for distributing messages among the applications, services, and facilities of the system. You can think of the ORB as a sort of software bus, or backbone, that provides a common *messaging* interface through which many different kinds of objects can communicate in a peer-to-peer scheme. An object makes a request and sends it to the ORB. The ORB then locates an object that can service the request, formats the message, and sends it to the object. The response is then returned through the ORB to the original requestor. In this model, objects simply specify a task to perform. They don't need to know the details or whereabouts of the object that can service the task. The ORB handles all the details of locating objects, formatting messages, and delivering those messages. The ORB is a common interface for all objects in the distributed environment.

RELATED ENTRIES   Common Object Request Broker Architecture; Connectionless and Connection-Oriented Transactions; IBM Networking Blueprint; Mail Slots; Message Handling System; Middleware; Object Request Broker; *and* Remote Procedure Call

Messaging Application Programming Interface (MAPI)

MAPI provides a way for applications to access different types of messaging systems, such as Microsoft Mail, Lotus Development's cc:MAIL, and Novell's Message

Handling Service (MHS). MAPI defines call procedures that programmers can use to build E-mail interfaces into Windows applications. For example, a user could address, send, and receive an E-mail message while working in a Windows word processing program by selecting E-mail options from its menu. The user could write a note in the program and include it in an outgoing E-mail message.

There are currently two versions of MAPI. *Simple MAPI* only works with Microsoft Mail and provides a way to access E-mail functions from a variety of Windows applications. *Extended MAPI* provides interfaces to many other mail systems, including their address books, message storage areas, and mail transport functions.

RELATED ENTRIES   Electronic Mail; Message-Enabled Applications; Middleware; *and* Windows Open System Architecture

Metropolitan Area Networks (MAN)

A Metropolitan Area Networks (MAN) is a backbone network that spans a metropolitan area and is regulated by local or state utility commissions. The telephone company, cable services, and other suppliers provide MAN services for companies that need to build networks spanning public rights-of-way in metropolitan areas. For the purposes of this book, a MAN is the IEEE 802.6 standard that defines a fiber-optic network for metropolitan areas. Telephone companies build IEEE 802.6 MANs to provide Switched Multimegabit Data Service (SMDS) to their customers. The 802.6 MAN can provide connection-oriented or connectionless services that let customers build logical networks over metropolitan areas that appear to users as local area networks. Eventually, the MAN will lead to future Broadband ISDN and Asynchronous Transfer Mode (ATM) technologies.

The MAN is basically an intra-LATA service, which confines it to local calling areas, rather than long-distance, inter-LATA areas. Still, a MAN, and the services provided by it, can span areas covering hundreds of square miles. Attachment to MANs is via bridges and routers over T1, ISDN, or similar links. Some companies may provide lines into MANs that bypass the local carriers.

The MAN is built on a dual bus architecture, meaning that two fiber cables provide transmission in opposite directions at the same time. A node attached to the dual bus can send data in either direction. The dual bus is built in a ring topology as shown in Figure M-5. Note in (A) that the two ends of the bus are not connected. If a failure occurs anywhere on the LAN, however, the bus automatically reconfigures as shown in (B). The break that was designed into the cable system is automatically joined to maintain the bus. In the case where two breaks occur, the network becomes two separate functional networks until repairs are made.

The access standard for the IEEE 802.6 MAN is the Distributed Queue Dual Bus (DQDB) technology. DQDB defines the dual bus architecture and the access method. A slot generator at the end of a bus relays fixed-size slots into which stations place data for transport on the network. The slots flow in a continuous stream such as boxcars on a track. Slots are 53 bytes in size and are compatible with the cell size implemented in

M

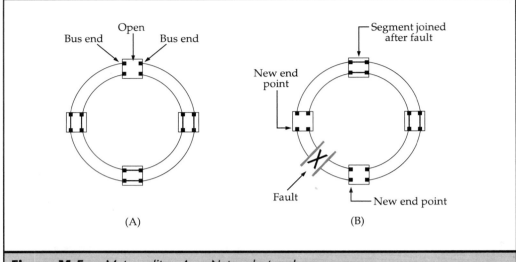

Figure M-5.   *Metropolitan Area Networks topology*

Asynchronous Transfer Mode (ATM) and future Broadband-Integrated Service Digital Network (B-ISDN) networks. Both types of networks provide scalable transmission rates that are possible on fiber-optic transmission media. All future WAN technologies will implement fixed-size cells for this reason.

Fixed-size slots provide fast packet switching and predictable delivery, unlike variable-length packet switching such as that implemented in Frame Relay and X.25 networks. Slots can be prioritized for isochronous data such as real-time video. This guarantees that a certain number of regularly recurring slots will be available so the data can be delivered in a timely way. Each isochronous data slot is marked by the slot generator as such.

The MAN can support a variety of services, such as LAN-to-LAN connections, PBX connections, direct workstation attachment, and mainframe connections. In other words, the MAN is an integrated voice and data network. It has the following additional features:

■ The MAN can provide both packet-switching and circuit-switching services.

■ The MAN can provide a *connectionless service* with frame sizes up to 9,188 bytes in length that are transported over the 53-byte slots.

■ The MAN can provide a *connection-oriented service* that transports 53-byte segments between nodes on the bus over virtual circuit connections.

■ The MAN can provide an *isochronous service* that guarantees constant transport of time-sensitive data over a logical connection.

- The DQDB layer and the physical layer are independent of one another, so that several different physical layers can be used. For example, ANSI DS3 at 44.736 Mbits/sec and SONET at 155.52 Mbits/sec are supported physical media.

- The MAN standard is compatible with other IEEE LAN standards and supports traffic following the 802.2 Logical Link Control (LLC) standard.

RELATED ENTRIES   Asynchronous Transfer Mode; Connection-Oriented and Connectionless Protocols; Fast Packet Switching; Switched Multimegabit Data Service; *and* Virtual Circuits

MicroChannel Architecture (MCA) Bus

The MCA bus was developed by IBM to help resolve the difficulties of combining fast microprocessors with the relatively slow Industry Standard Architecture (ISA) bus. Although MCA buses do not accept ISA-style boards, they provide a 32-bit interface that is faster than ISA and is a better match to 80386 and 80486 microprocessors.

The MCA bus has a single-bus design that handles both memory and input/output (I/O) transfers by using multiplexing, which allows several processes to share the bus simultaneously. Multiplexing splits the bus into several channels that can each handle different processes. This design is not as fast as multiple-bus systems, but in many cases it is adequate for server use on medium-size networks. If microprocessor-intensive applications are run at the server, a superserver might be a better choice because of its superior throughput and multiprocessor capabilities.

The MCA bus is protected by patents and licensing agreements that inhibit its growth as a standard. In addition, IBM has imposed some limitations in MCA to prevent it from competing with its minicomputer systems. Because of this, many vendors use Extended Industry Standard Architecture (EISA) or have developed proprietary bus standards.

RELATED ENTRY   Extended Industry Standard Architecture Bus

Microcom Networking Protocol (MNP)

MNP is a collection of protocols for modem data communication developed by Microcom, Inc. (Norwood, Massachusetts), a modem manufacturer. The protocols provide highly reliable data transmissions using error correction and data compression techniques. They are considered a de facto industry standard and many vendors have licensed the protocols for use in their modems. Today, the CCITT (ITU) V series standards are commonly implemented in modems because they are accepted worldwide; however, some modem vendors use both V series and MNP. The major MNP protocols are listed here—those not listed are no longer in use or are insignificant in modern communication.

- *Class 2* Full-duplex asynchronous transmission mode.

M

■ *Class 3* Full-duplex synchronous transmission producing streams of HDLC-framed data.

■ *Class 4* Provides a way to increase the frame size to improve throughput when the channel is error-free. The method is adaptive and adjusts frame size up or down based on the line quality.

■ *Class 5* Provides two times data compression, giving a 2,400 bit-per-second (bps) modem a throughput of 4,800 bps, for example. The compression technique can adapt to maximize the throughput based on the data.

■ *Class 6* Same as the CCITT (ITU) V.29 modem standard with the addition of Class 5 data compression; 9,600 baud modems using MNP Class 6 can achieve up to 19.2 Kbits/sec throughput.

■ *Class 7* Provides enhanced data compression that can reduce data by as much as 42 percent. Otherwise similar to Class 5.

■ *Class 8* Includes features of Class 7 and adds a CCITT (ITU) V.29 technique that enables half-duplex devices to operate as full-duplex devices.

■ *Class 9* Similar to CCITT (ITU) V.32 modem standard, but can triple throughput by using the Class 7 data compression technique.

Note that the CCITT (ITU) V.32 and V.42 recommendation uses the Link Access Procedure-Modems (LAP-M) for error correction, but supports MNP Class 4. Many vendors make both options available in their modems.

RELATED ENTRIES Asynchronous Communications; Bell Modem Standards; Dialup Line; Modems; Modulation Techniques; Serial Communication; Synchronous Communication; *and* "V-dot" Standards, CCITT

Microkernel

A kernel provides the core functions of an operating system. A *microkernel* is a stripped down version of a kernel that is designed to provide more portability in less memory space, and to provide a modular design that lets users install a variety of interfaces such as UNIX, DOS, Windows, Workplace OS, and Workplace UNIX. New operating systems from IBM, Microsoft, Open Software Foundation (OSF), and UNIX System Laboratories (USL) take advantage of this approach. Two notable microkernel operating systems are listed here:

■ *Mach* From Carnegie-Mellon University

■ *Nucleus* From Chorus Systems (Beaverton, Oregon), which is headquartered in France

As mentioned, a microkernel is a stripped down version of a kernel in which the layer of system services normally integrated with the kernel are separated and become optional modules that are added as required. This provides for better scalability and more efficient application development. With a microkernel design, upgrading a system is a simple matter of replacing the old module with the new module. You don't need to replace the entire operating system.

We can use a business analogy to explain the modular concept of the microkernel. Consider an overworked business manager. By delegating duties to other people, the manager can apply his or her skills to the efficient operation of the business, and concentrate on other tasks, such as starting a new branch of the business. New people are hired to support the growing business. The manager coordinates these activities, but lets each person do the job she or he was hired to do. Likewise, a microkernel operating system runs a few core tasks and manages the activities of installable modules. In this way, the microkernel is extremely efficient at what it does and is more portable, meaning that it can be designed to run on a variety of processors.

A microkernel-based operating system is layered as shown in Figure M-6 and has the following features:

- A microkernel provides a "generic" set of services such as process scheduling, interprocess communications, memory management, and device I/O handling. All other services such as file management and network support interface onto this microkernel. In contrast, a kernel is integrated and much larger.

- A microkernel is more scalable and simplifies application development. Users run only the services they need, which can help reduce disk space and memory requirements.

- Vendors can easily port the microkernel to other processor platforms, then add modular components on top to fit the requirements of those platforms (that is, file servers, engineering applications, and so on).

The microkernel interfaces with hardware components and provides an interface for installable modules. Processes interact by passing messages and run as "threads" within the microkernel. Threads provide a way to divide a single task into multiple sub-tasks, which can then execute on separate processors in a multiprocessor system. Important microkernel operating systems are listed here:

- *Windows NT*   This operating system is designed around a Microsoft-designed microkernel that closely follows the Mach design. It provides thread scheduling, interrupt and exception management, multiprocessor synchronization, and system recovery (after a power failure). It is never paged out of memory and its execution is never pre-empted by another process.

- *OSF/1 MK*   The latest version of the Open System Foundation's OSF/1 UNIX operating system uses a microkernel approach. It implements the Mach kernel and provides virtual memory management, interprocess communication, and device driver management.

M

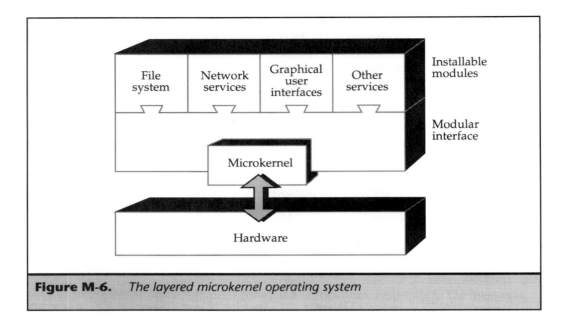

Figure M-6.   *The layered microkernel operating system*

- *UNIX SVR4*   UNIX System Laboratories, Inc. released a microkernel version of UNIX SVR4 (System V release 4). It implements the Nucleus microkernel. It provides all the features of a microkernel discussed above; however, drivers are not managed in the microkernel.

- *WorkPlace OS*   IBM's microkernel is based on the Mach microkernel. The microkernel runs on the Motorola PowerPC processor, which is a direct competitor to the Intel 80486 and Pentium processors. Users of Workplace OS can choose from a variety of interfaces that run on top of the operating system, such as DOS, OS/2, Windows, UNIX. The IBM microkernel is small in size (about 40K) and handles basic tasks such as memory management, thread management, interrupt management, and messaging.

Microkernel operating systems such as Mach and Nucleus give users choices as to the interfaces and features of their operating system. They fit in well with the changing computer market in which a variety of processors and operating systems are available. Developers also benefit. They can easily port their products from one system to another, making more applications available for end users. The modularity of the design also ensures that a rich set of optional services is available.

RELATED ENTRIES   IBM Operating Systems; Mach, Carnegie-Mellon Microkernel; OSF/1, Open Software Foundation; Remote Procedure Call; UNIX; Windows NT, Microsoft; *and* Workplace OS

Microsegmentation

Microsegmentation is a technique that reduces the number of stations on a LAN segment to improve performance. Recall that Ethernet networks use a broadcast technique in which only one station can use the cable at once. If two stations access the cable at the same time, a collision occurs, which causes delays and loss of performance. The problem increases as more stations are added to the network.

The obvious solution is to reduce the number of stations that access a network by dividing the network into two or more segments and joining them with a bridge or router. Contention for the network is then reduced to only those workstations directly attached to each segment. Bridge filtering techniques can prevent traffic for one segment from propagating into other segments. *Microsegmentation* carries this concept to extremes by limiting each local area network (LAN) segment to as few as one workstation. In this way, there is no contention for the network. The single station never waits for another station to finish transmitting. The LAN segment itself is connected to a switching hub. This hub bridges the LAN segments of stations that need to communicate, creating a direct dedicated communication channel. This channel is often called a "private LAN."

Microsegmentation requires a new breed of switching devices with enough ports to support a LAN segment for each workstation. Throughput can reach the maximum bandwidth of the network. For example, a workstation attached to an Ethernet LAN segment can achieve 10 Mbits/sec throughput, far above the throughput of a shared Ethernet LAN.

RELATED ENTRIES   Ethernet; Hubs; *and* Switching Hubs

Microsoft At Work Architecture

Microsoft At Work is an architecture that ties together computers and office equipment in a network environment that users and managers can access and control from their desktop systems. Office equipment includes devices such as fax machines, copiers, printers, handheld computers, telephone systems, network services, and PC peripherals such as built-in fax and modem cards. Over 60 companies are supporting the At Work initiative with the goal of creating an environment where any user can access information and office devices from wherever they work. Some of the vendors and their products are listed here:

■ Copiers and printers from Canon USA, Hewlett-Packard, and Xerox

■ Fax servers and adapters from Castelle, Delrina, Intel, and Ricoh

■ Telephone equipment from Rolm/Siemens, Ericsson Communications, and McCaw Cellular

M

The Microsoft At Work architecture is designed to make individual products easier to use. Office machines will interoperate with Windows-based computers, printers, and other peripherals. Some examples of office automation provided by Windows At Work are:

- Microsoft At Work lets a user operate a telephone from a graphical user interface on his or her computer using point-and-click or touch-screen techniques.

- A graphical user interface makes it much easier to set up conference calls, perform call transfers, or send and retrieve electronic messages.

- With Microsoft At Work, a user could create a document using a Windows-based word processor, then send the document to a fax machine. The transmission can be scheduled for a later time when calls are cheaper.

- The network connections supporting Microsoft At Work provide a way for a user at a copier to forward an electronic image of the documents being copied to one or more users.

Microsoft At Work takes advantage of the increasing use of digital electronics in office machines. Many fax machines, copiers, and telephones already have interfaces for connection to computer devices. Microsoft At Work will provide a common office interface that will push the development of these devices. It extends the interface of the office device into the graphical interface running in users' computers.

The components of the architecture are described here. These components serve as building blocks that are incorporated into office devices, making them compatible with one another and with PCs running Microsoft Windows.

- *Microsoft At Work Operating System*   This is a real-time, pre-emptive, multitasking operating system that is designed for use in office automation and communication equipment.

- *Communications*   This component provides network connections and Windows messaging among devices and network servers. This component includes security features and is compatible with the Windows Messaging API and the Windows Telephony API that are part of Windows Open System Architecture (WOSA).

- *Rendering*   This component provides document interchange and transmission to devices such as printers, copiers, and fax machines. The fonts and formats of the document remain intact for further editing at the destination if necessary.

- *Graphical User Interface*   This component provides user interface features such as menus, buttons, and dialog boxes on display devices such as touch screens. Office equipment will have 5×7-inch LCD touch-sensitive displays with resolutions of 320×240 dots per inch.

- *Desktop Software*   This component provides Windows-based PC applications the ability to control, access, and exchange information with any product based on

Microsoft At Work. Desktop software is the one piece of the architecture that resides in PCs.

All At Work equipment is configurable from a central location using management software. It is possible to use the existing telephone network to share information between office equipment. Microsoft At Work will provide a way for people to take advantage of features in office equipment that were previously inaccessible or inconvenient to use.

Micro-to-Mainframe Connectivity

See Mainframe and Minicomputer Connectivity.

Microwave Communication

When most people think of media, they picture copper wire or fiber-optic cable. But microwave communication does not require solid media and is the most widely used "long-haul" transmission method in the United States. Microwave transmission is used when a straight line-of-site is possible between two points, such as:

- Satellite to ground links
- Between two buildings in a metropolitan area
- Across wide open areas where it isn't practical to lay cable, such as deserts, swamps, and large lakes

A microwave transmission system consists of two directional antennas that focus beams of electromagnetic or radio-wave energy at one another in a point-to-point arrangement as shown in Figure M-7. The antennas require unobstructed (line-of-site) paths and the maximum range is about 30 miles. Antennas are often mounted on large towers to extend their range and avoid obstacles that might block the signals. Radio transceivers (transmitter/receivers) at each location transmit signals over the antennas.

Unlike a radio broadcast that sends signals from one location to many locations, microwave antennas are focussed on one point—another microwave antenna—and are thus point-to-point communication systems. Relay stations equipped with signal amplifiers are used to extend the range of microwave transmissions. A relay station consists of two antennas, each focussed on a distant antenna in a different direction. Transmission frequencies are from 2 to 25 gigahertz, with the higher bandwidths used in short-haul private networks.

Microwave is an alternative to metal or optical cable systems. Installation of a small system is often relatively simple. For example, you can establish a microwave communication link between two buildings by mounting an antenna in a window of each building and focussing the antennas together. Such systems provide considerable savings by bypassing the local exchange carrier. In campus environments, microwave systems can be more practical than burying cable.

M

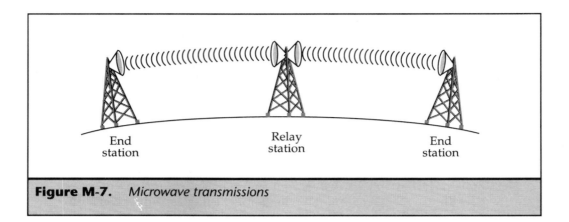

Figure M-7.   *Microwave transmissions*

RELATED ENTRIES   Satellite Telecommunication; Telecommunication

Middleware

Middleware is a category of software that hides the underlying network and its communication protocols from applications. High-level programming interfaces help developers create applications that work in a variety of environments without knowing in advance which networks and communication protocols will be used. Middleware is normally implemented in client-server environments that use different network communication protocols. It hides these protocols from client-server applications so developers can concentrate on improving the application, not developing communication interfaces.

On a broader level, middleware products provide a way to hide the differences between front-end applications and back-end applications. The layer of middleware includes translation between the application program interfaces (APIs) of common and popular applications. As an example, Microsoft's Open Database Connectivity (ODBC) standard provides common functions that are performed by most back-end database systems. Front-end applications are then written to ODBC and take advantage of these functions. ODBC hides the differences among vendor implementations of SQL. Microsoft delivers ODBC as a set of Microsoft Windows drivers that provide access to data in formats produced by Microsoft Access, Microsoft Excel, Microsoft SQL Server, FoxPro, Btrieve, dBASE, Borland Paradox, IBM DB2, DEC Rdb, and Oracle. ODBC is designed to make Windows an industry standard for client access to back-end databases.

Middleware products are appearing as organizations strive to connect their diverse computing resources into enterprise networks.

■ Users need to access services on many different back-end servers.

- The back-end servers may use a different operating system and require a different communication protocol.

- Back-end database servers have incompatible SQL command sets that make it difficult for both users and programmers to move from one system to another.

- It is no longer practical to limit users to a specific application from which they access back-end services. Users need to access services from a variety of applications.

- The new model is to let users access any back-end service with any front-end application using a variety of communication protocols in a multivendor environment.

In a multiprotocol, multivendor environment, a programmer would normally need to write the application to work with each of the protocols and systems supported. With middleware, the programmer simply writes to the middleware interface and lets it handle all the multiprotocol, multivendor issues. There are three types of middleware, *remote procedure calls* (RPCs), *conversations*, and *messaging systems*. Each does a good job of hiding the communication process and the heterogeneity of the systems on which they operate.

Remote Procedure Calls (RPC)

A remote procedure call is a request from one machine to another, over a network. RPCs that constitute middleware operate on a variety of network platforms and communication protocols. Basically, an RPC is a request by one computer directed toward another computer. It is a request/response process in which the requester waits for a response, implying that RPCs are usually real-time calls that take place over connection-oriented interfaces.

The Open Software Foundation's (OSF's) Distributed Computing Environment (DCE) is a set of "enabling" software that hides the differences between multivendor products, technologies, and standards, enabling developers to create applications that work in distributed client-server environments. DCE provides an independence from operating systems and networks with an open development environment.

The RPC implemented in DCE provides tools for creating client-server applications that can run procedures on other computers attached to a network. OSF's RPC extends the local procedure model by supporting direct calls to procedures on remote systems, enabling programmers to develop distributed applications as easily as traditional, single-system programs. RPC presentation services mask the differences between data representation on different machines, allowing programs to work across heterogeneous systems. OSF's RPC includes the RPC facility and a compiler.

RPC lets clients interact with multiple servers, and allows servers to handle multiple clients simultaneously. A client, for example, can involve several computers on the network to help complete a processing task. RPCs help break a task down into smaller components that can run on different systems, thus taking advantage of the

M

distributed computing environment. Threads are an important part of this capability. An operating system and application that supports threads can perform multiple processes at the same time, rather than one process after another. For related information, see "Distributed Computing Environment, OSF," Interprocess Communication," and "Remote Procedure Call."

Conversations

A conversation is a continuous dialog between two or more systems over a logical connection. Unlike RPC, a conversation can consist of overlapping executions in a distributed environment. For this reason, conversations are useful for updating distributed databases in which changes at multiple locations must be fully synchronized. IBM's Advanced Program-to-Program Communications (APPC) implements conversations. An OSI standard is also emerging that implements conversations. The Communications Integrator (CI) from Covia Technologies (Rosemont, Illinois) is another example of conversational middleware that operates in mainframe, midrange, and desktop environments. A number of vendors are licensing CI for their own use. See "Advanced Program-to-Program Communications" and "IBM Networking Blueprint."

Messaging Systems

Inter-application messaging lets applications exchange commands and information in a non-real-time, store-and-forward mode, although real-time modes can also be used. A message is formulated, then sent to the destination where it might be stored until the destination can process it. In addition, the message store may be a separate location that handles interprocess messaging. Messaging should not be confused with electronic mail systems. Although the process is similar, E-mail systems are designed for the exchange of messages among users.

Messaging systems are connectionless. There is no synchronization between two systems and the sender may broadcast messages to any number of other systems. Because messaging systems don't operate in real-time, they are not practical for real-time mission-critical applications. However, messaging systems work well when systems are separated by wide area connections with relatively slow transfer rates.

Novell's *Message Handling Service (MHS)* is a messaging system primarily used for E-mail, but it also has the ability to transfer messages between applications. IBM's *Message Queuing Interface (MQI)* is a message-based application interface that oversees the passing of messages between applications on different platforms. It is defined in the IBM Networking Blueprint. A number of vendors are promoting *Message-Oriented Middleware*. For related information, see "IBM Networking Blueprint" and "Messaging API, Inter-Application."

In an object-oriented environment, Object Request Brokers (ORBs) provide the key communication facility for distributing messages among the applications, services, and facilities of the system. The ORB provides a common *messaging* interface through which many different kinds of objects can communicate in a peer-to-peer fashion. For related information, see "Common Object Request Broker Architecture" and "Object Request Broker."

Trends

The latest developments on the middleware front have operating system vendors including the RPC mechanism directly into their products. Novell NetWare and Windows NT incorporate RPCs. In addition, another form of middleware that promotes workgroup activities through electronic mail and groupware services is developing in operating systems. These systems will provide common interfaces for front-end and back-end services, messaging services that let applications and users communicate, E-mail-enabled applications, directory naming services, and security features such as authentication and digital signatures. Microsoft, Apple, and the Open Software Foundation are headed in this direction. Middleware has helped solve the problems of diverse protocols in network environments. Document interchange standards are improving and object-linking standards are providing ways to share text, graphics, and multimedia objects between applications.

RELATED ENTRIES   Apple Open Collaborative Environment; Distributed Computing Environment, OSF; Open Database Connectivity, Microsoft; STREAMS; Transport Layers Interface; *and* Windows Open System Architecture

Mirroring

Mirroring is the process of duplicating stored data on a second storage device in real time so that both devices hold the same information. Mirroring is a form of fault tolerance that protects data from equipment failure. Mirroring can take place at three levels as described here and pictured in Figure M-8.

- *Mirroring*   Data is copied from on disk controller (channel) to two disk drivers. If one drive fails, the other is still operational.

- *Duplexing*   Data is duplicated over two disk channels and stored on two drives. This method extends fault tolerance to the controller.

- *Server duplexing*   This method provides the highest level of fault tolerance by duplicating the entire file server. If one server fails, the other provides continuous service to users.

Novell's *System Fault Tolerance Level III* provides server duplexing. High-bandwidth optical links are required between the systems to ensure that data is duplicated in a timely way.

M

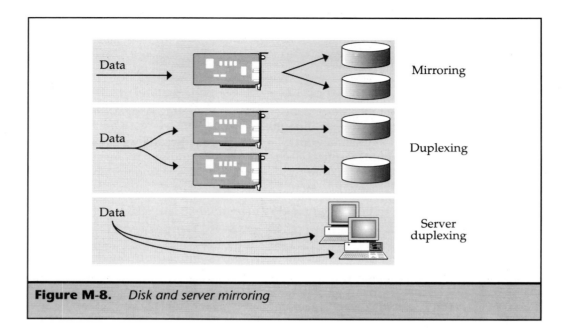

Figure M-8. *Disk and server mirroring*

RELATED ENTRIES Data Protection; Disaster Recovery; Disk Mirroring and Duplexing; Duplexed Systems; Fault Management; Fault Tolerance; NetWare SFT Level III; *and* System Fault Tolerance

Mobile Computing

Mobile computing involves the use of various radio frequency (RF) or cellular communication technologies to allow users to roam freely with their portable computer, personal digital assistants (PDAs), pagers, and other communicators. Portable computer users with modems are also part of this group, but this section will concentrate on the wireless remote user. The mobile computer user relies on electronic messaging services that let them go anywhere while keeping in touch with the office. Some vendors such as Microsoft are creating special interfaces that support mobile users. For example, as mobile users move from place to place, desktop arrangements and open documents used in the last session are restored as if the computer was never turned off.

Mobile computing is a combination of messaging technologies and wireless communication. Companies such as RAM Mobile Data are involved, not just with the communication aspect, but also with the user interface support. They want to make mobile computing easy to use. Typical users include field service technicians who need technical information, insurance representatives who are making appraisals, and sales people who need information to generate quotes. One method for obtaining information is to simply connect with the company database and make real-time queries. However, messaging can help reduce phone costs in this area as well. A mobile user might simply send an E-mail message with a database query to the database server. The server then generates a response and places that response in the user's mail box for later retrieval.

There are two primary methods for mobile data communication:

- *Packet-switched RF networks* in which customers are charged by the packet.

- *Cellular circuit-switched products* are built around the existing cellular network. Charges depend on the length of connection time.

Packet-switching wireless networks are preferable only when transmissions are short because of the way charges are incurred per packet. Circuit-switched networks are preferable for transferring large files or for other lengthy transmissions because customers are charged for the length of time they use the network.

Companies involved in packet-radio communication are Ardis (Lincolnshire, Illinois), RAM Mobile Data (Woodbridge, New Jersey), and Nextel (Lafayette, California). Ardis is a joint venture between IBM and Motorola. The signal penetration of the Ardis system was specifically designed for metropolitan areas with high building density. RAM Mobile Data is a partnership between BellSouth and RAM Broadcasting. Hardware products include those manufactured by Ericsson GE Mobile Communications such as RF-enabled modems.

Cellular Digital Packet Data (CDPD) is a contender in the wireless market. It uses the idle time on cellular systems to transmit digital data. Speeds can reach 19.2 Kbits/sec, which is about four times faster than other wireless services. CDPD is defined by a consortium of cellular carriers and computer companies, including eight of the nine Regional Bell Operating Companies (RBOCs), McCaw Cellular Data, Contel Cellular, and GTE Mobilnet.

Supporting Products

Apple, IBM, Intel, Hewlett-Packard, Novell, and others are working with wireless companies to fully support mobile users with such features as data encryption, user authentication, and location services that can find where mobile users are located.

NetWare Connect is a remote communication platform that provides a single connection point for up to 32 mobile users into NetWare networks. Users can dial in using a variety of remote control packages and access their desktop or NetWare servers. The services provide access to E-mail, faxes, and electronic software distribution in which software is automatically updated when users log on, if necessary. Connect is similar to the older NetWare Asynchronous Communication Services (NACS) package.

Network "plug-and-play" capabilities are being implemented by a number of vendors, including Microsoft, Intel, and others. The features allow users to disconnect from the network (without disrupting it) and reconnect later in the day or at another

M

location. When the user reconnects, the device is automatically reconfigured for the new location and the user's desktop environment is restored, including any open applications and work that was in progress. This eliminates the need to close files and shut down the system. Another feature is that the system will automatically check the user's E-mail when the system is reconnected.

RELATED ENTRIES   Cellular Digital Packet Data; Packet-Radio Communications; *and* Wireless Mobile Communication

Modems

Modems (**mo**dulators/**dem**odulators) are data communication equipment (DCE) devices that provide connections for computers into the public switched telephone network (PSTN). They convert (modulate) the digital signals of computers into analog signals that can be transmitted over telephone lines. A modem at the other end of the link then demodulates the signals back to digital bits.

A typical modem installation is shown in Figure M-9. Both modems must use compatible communication techniques that comply with several standards, most notably the CCITT (ITU) V series standards. Other modem standards include the Microcom Networking Protocol (MNP). The connection from the computer to the modem is typically RS-232 and the connection from the modem to the telephone wall jack is via RJ-11C. Modems for computers are available in internal or external models. An internal modem is a circuit board or adapter that fits in the slot of a computer. An external modem is a small box that rests outside of the computer and connects to its serial communications port.

When one modem "calls" another, the destination modem answers and a signal exchange takes place that establishes the parameters for a communication session. The

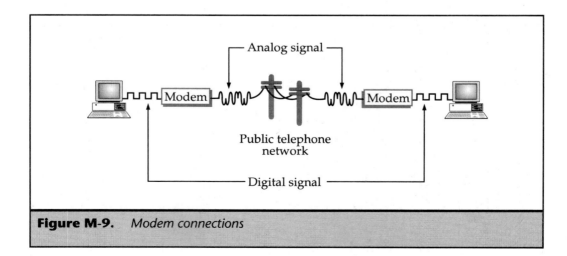

Figure M-9.   *Modem connections*

negotiation process determines the maximum signaling rate available between the two modems as well as the use of compression. The use of telephone lines imposes some restrictions on data transfer rates, as discussed next.

■ Telephone communication circuits have an approximately 3,300 Hz bandwidth restriction in the range of 300 to 3,300 Hz. This range is perfect for voice but it has imposed some limitation for data communication.

■ Because of possible poor telephone connections, it is not possible to use the entire voice bandwidth for data. Guard bands separate one line from another.

■ The bandwidth is divided into two channels to support *duplexing,* so that modems can talk and listen over separate channels. Two carrier signals are modulated within the bandwidth range to achieve this.

■ Guard bands are used to separate the two duplexed channels to prevent crosstalk and corruption.

Figure M-10 illustrates the "pipe" through which the signals travel. The guard bands separate one duplex channel from another, and the duplex channels are separated by another guard band. Once you configure all these parameters, the effective baud rate is 2,400 baud, or 1,200 baud per duplexed channel. Encoding and compression techniques are used to boost the throughput up into the 28,800 bits/sec range.

Quadrature amplitude modulation (QAM) techniques are used to attain bit rates above 2,400 bps. For example, a 9,600 bps rate is attained by encoding a 4-bit code into 16 possible phase and amplitude changes. The trellis encoding algorithm is another technique that can achieve high bit rates. It is an extension of QAM that has a higher tolerance for line noise.

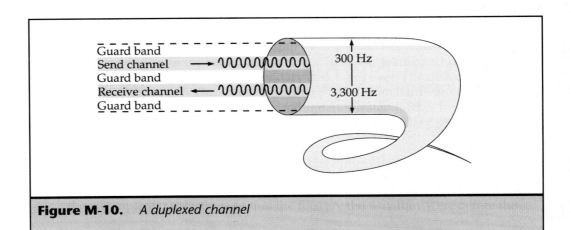

Figure M-10. *A duplexed channel*

M

High-Speed Modems

High-speed modems are generally any modems that achieve bit rates above 2,400 bps. Encoding techniques and compression are required to boost the bit rates further. The most important CCITT (ITU) standards are listed here.

V.22	1,200 bits/sec full-duplex modem standard
V.22bis	2,400 bits/sec full-duplex modem standard
V.28	Defines circuits in RS-232 interface
V.32	Asynchronous and synchronous 4,800/9,600 bits/sec standard
V.32bis	Asynchronous and synchronous standard up to 14,400 bits/sec
V.35	Defines high data-rates over combined circuits
V.42	Defines error checking standards
V.42bis	Defines modem compression using the Lempel Ziv method
V.32terbo	An emerging standard that provides 19.2 Kbits/sec rates
V.34	A standard for 28 Kbits/sec transmission rates

V.32terbo is a 19.2 Kbits/sec specification designed as an interim step between 14.4 Kbits/sec V.32bis and V.34, the 28.8 Kbits/sec emerging standard. Note the following:

■ V.32bis uses a two-dimensional trellis coding technique with 128 points in a signal constellation.

■ V.32terbo uses a two-dimensional trellis coding technique with 256 or 512 points in a signal constellation.

■ V.34 (formally called V.fast) uses a four-dimensional trellis coding technique with up to 768 points in a signal constellation.

RELATED ENTRIES   Asynchronous Communications; Bell Modem Standards; Dialup Line; Microcom Networking Protocol; Modulation Techniques; Serial Communication; Synchronous Communications; *and* "V-dot" Standards, CCITT

Modulation Techniques

Modulation is a conversion technique used to transmit digital data signals over analog transmission lines, such as the public telephone network. Modems at each end of the communication link perform the digital-to-analog and analog-to-digital conversion. An analog transmission consists of a waveform that varies in amplitude and frequency. Digital data is represented by modulating or changing the waveform. There are three types of modulation techniques as described next. They are compared with a digital signal in Figure M-11.

AMPLITUDE MODULATION (AM)   The height or amplitude of the wave is changed between two levels to match the digital data input. The signal sounds like

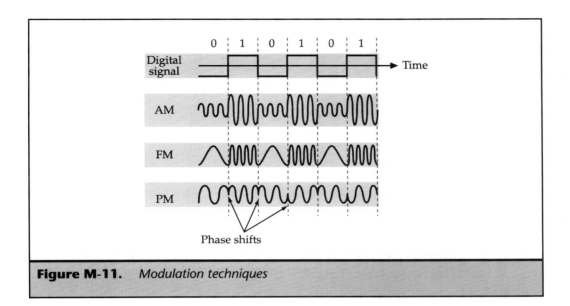

Figure M-11.   *Modulation techniques*

one tone rapidly changing in volume although it is too rapid for humans to distinguish the volume change. Basic AM modulation is not used for digital communication because the signal is prone to attenuation. However, it is used with phase modulation in some cases.

FREQUENCY MODULATION (FM)   In FM, the frequency of a signal changes depending on the binary input. The signals would sound like a continuous shifting between two audio tones. When FM is used to transmit digital signals, it is called *frequency-shift keying (FSK)* because only two frequencies are transmitted. FM is used with inexpensive, 300 and 1,200 bits-per-second modems.

PHASE MODULATION (PM)   In this method, the phase of the wave (as pictured on paper) is changed to represent a change in the binary signal. For example, if the wave is moving down, it is shifted to an upward-moving wave when the binary signal changes. The wave is basically reversed and the point of reversal represents a change in binary values. In its simplest form, PM shifts between shifted 0 degrees or shifted 180 degrees. An enhanced form of PM called *differential phase-shift keying (DPSK)* is normally used in modems. In DPSK, the binary value is determined by the degree of the phase shift from the current bit. For example, as 90-degree phase shift represents a binary 0 and a 270-degree phase shift represents a binary 1. DPSK eliminates some problems with phase change methods because the receiving modem only needs to determine the pattern of the phase change, which is easier to do.

In the preceding techniques, the bit rate corresponds to the signalling rate. *Baud* is the signal rate of a modem but a bits-per-second (bps) rating is the number of bits

M

transferred on each baud or signal change. A 300-baud modem can transmit 600 bps if each signal change represents two bits. All modems are now rated in bits per second rather than baud because of signal encoding schemes. Some alternative encoding schemes that attain high bit-rates are listed here:

- *Quadrature Amplitude Modulation (QAM)* Up to four bits are encoded in each signal change, so that a 2400 *baud* modem can attain a data rate of 9,600 bps. The CCITT (ITU) V.29 standard specifies an encoding method in which a 1,700-Hz carrier is varied in both phase and amplitude, resulting in 16 possible binary values per signal change. A four-bit binary value is represented by the position of the wave when a phase change occurs, in much the same way that time is represented by the position of hands on a clock.

- *Trellis-Coded Modulation (TCM)* This method is similar to QAM. A map of signals called a *constellation* has a set of points that relate to the phase and amplitude of a signal. Each point is associated with a bit pattern. The 14.2 Kbits/sec V.32bis standard has 128 points in its constellation, while the proposed V.32fast standard operating at 28.8 Kbits/sec has 768 points in its constellation. Using these techniques, a single point in the signalling constellation can represent a symbol. Therefore, a sending modem only needs to transmit one signal to represent a symbol. The receiving modem uses a lookup table to determine the symbol associated with the signal.

RELATED ENTRY   Modems

Motif

The Open Software Foundation (OSF) adopted the X Window System, which provides a way for different applications on a network to operate on a user's screen. The X Window System was developed at the Massachusetts Institute of Technology. Motif is a developer's toolkit that works with the X Window System and is used to define standard components on a graphical user interface such as menu bars, borders, and window backgrounds.

RELATED ENTRIES   Open Software Foundation; X Window

MOTIS (Message Oriented Text Interchange System)

See X.400 Message Handling System.

Multidrop (Multipoint) Connection

See Point-to-Point and Multipoint Connection.

Multimedia

Multimedia brings voice, video, and graphics to the network in the form of very large files that require large amounts of disk space for storage and large amounts of bandwidth during transmission. Recent trends to integrate multimedia into desktop operating systems and popular applications virtually assure the growth of multimedia. Managers will find an increasing need to accommodate multimedia by installing larger storage devices, increasing the network bandwidth, and segregating high-bandwidth users from low-bandwidth users.

When discussing network traffic generated by multimedia, it's important to distinguish between the requirements of store-and-forward and real-time multimedia. For example, a user might attach a voice recording or a video clip to an E-mail message, then send it to another user. Because a store-and-forward message that does not require immediate delivery is transmitted, a high transmission rate is not essential. Real-time video, however, must have dedicated bandwidth during the transmission and a fast transmission rate to ensure that packets arrive in a reasonable fashion. If there is not enough bandwidth, frames are dropped, producing a choppy effect that most people find irritating. Prioritization of real-time video traffic can ensure that it has enough bandwidth in the available signal to ensure quality delivery. Switched micro-segmented Ethernet, Asynchronous Transfer Mode (ATM), and new 100 Mbits/sec Fast Ethernet technologies can provide the bandwidth.

Segmentation of Ethernet LANs can reduce contention of the shared media and provide enough bandwidth to deliver video at a reasonable rate. It may be necessary to segregate video users from other users. Ethernet switching hubs provide microsegmentation of the network so that there are as few as one user per network segment. Each user gets a "private LAN" segment that no other users share. This makes the full 10 Mbits/sec bandwidth of the segment available to the user. The switching hub bridges segments that need to exchange information. However, the switch relays this information in a very fast way, rather than using the store-and-forward methods of traditional bridges.

Here are some things to keep in mind when configuring a multimedia network:

- Multimedia will "creep" into the organization. Multimedia applications are now included in Macintosh, Windows, OS/2, and other operating systems.

- Users will cut their teeth on multimedia with inexpensive sound boards, graphics packages, and multimedia E-mail. Disk requirements and bandwidth usage will rise.

- Compression must be part of any multimedia plan. It reduces disk space and bandwidth requirements. Compression can be done in software, but Intel and other vendors produce boards that perform fast compression and decompression on the spot.

M

- Multimedia and video servers are required to perform a number of tasks, such as the compression and storage of video files (training films, for example), videoconferencing management, and sequencing of multimedia events.

- Microsegmented Ethernet or 100 Mbits/sec Ethernet is appropriate for real-time video or environments with increased network traffic.

- Flicker-free video requires a delivery speed of 30 frames per second (fps). With compression, this is possible on high-speed networks, but on low-speed networks, it is necessary to drop frames. The minimum acceptable frame rate is from 10 to 15 fps.

- Video traffic should not be directed through routers. Try to keep video users within the same area or network segment.

There are a number of vendor consortiums and manufacturers that are defining multimedia specifications. The Common Open Software Environment (COSE) is developing services and tools upon which developers can create multimedia products that work across platforms and networks. COSE is a consortium of vendors including IBM, Hewlett-Packard, SunSoft, and Novell that are cooperating to deliver a common desktop environment to UNIX that can rival Microsoft Windows.

Novell, Microsoft, Apple, and IBM have their own specifications that define how to create client-server multimedia applications and hardware products. Apple's Quicktime is a multimedia operating system extension that can deliver synchronized audio and video at acceptable rates. It comes with the Macintosh System 7 operating system and does not require special hardware.

RELATED ENTRIES   Bandwidth; Common Open Software Environment; Compression Techniques; Ethernet; Microsegmentation; Switching Hubs; *and* Videoconferencing and Desktop Video

Multiplexing

To put multiplexing into perspective (at least time-division multiplexing), think of a freeway full of cars that must cross a bridge. The bridge has a single lane, so cars can only cross the bridge in single file. A traffic director motions to the car in the first lane to cross the bridge, then motions to the car in the second lane, then a car in the third and so on. The process starts all over again after the last lane. In this way, cars in every lane are equally allowed on the bridge. Multiplexing uses similar techniques to let multiple users share a single communication line to a remote facility. The line is typically a T1, T3, or Fractional T1 leased dedicated line between two points, and the data packets from each user are like cars on the bridge.

Each device that transmits over the multiplexed line is preallocated a time slot or a frequency. Even if a device is not transmitting, the slot or frequency is still allocated to it and goes unused. This causes a lot of wasted bandwidth. Using our freeway analogy, this would be like the bridge traffic director allocating an empty space in the traffic flow for each lane, even when there are no cars in the lane. Statistical multiplexing solves this problem by dynamically allocating slots to devices that need to transmit.

Multiplexing provides an economical and practical way for many users to communicate with a remote facility over a single shared line. Multiplexer devices are like the traffic directors on the bridge and the bridge is like the circuit that interconnects remote locations. It doesn't make sense to set up an individual data connection for each user to that remote facility. Telephone companies provide high-speed digital lines that provide enough bandwidth to handle both the voice and data traffic of many users. Multiplexers provide a way to utilize this bandwidth.

Bandwidth requirements must be closely evaluated. Leased lines are expensive over long distances and wasted bandwidth can quickly drain budgets. An alternative method is to use public switching networks in which each user connects over a temporary circuit or through a packet-switched network only during the time he or she needs to transmit for multiuser access. A multiplexed line is still required from the customer site to the public network, but this connection is usually only a short distance.

Multiplexing combines multiple signals onto a single line for transmission. At the receiving end, the signals are demultiplexed. A multiplexer is the device that combines and separates the signals. Separation is maintained among signals using time division multiplexing (TDM) or frequency division multiplexing (FDM), as described here and pictured in Figure M-12.

FREQUENCY DIVISION MULTIPLEXING (FDM)   FDM is a broadband analog transmission technique in which multiple signals are transmitted over a single cable simultaneously as shown in (A) in Figure M-12. Each data or voice signal is modulated onto a carrier at different frequencies. An analogy can be found in radio and TV broadcasting. Multiple stations transmit through the air or over cable at the same time. You "tune" your radio to the frequency you want to listen to. The frequency range of a channel is subdivided into narrow bands and each band then carries a different transmission signal. Guard bands separate the subdivided transmission bands to minimize interference.

TIME DIVISION MULTIPLEXING (TDM)   TDM is a baseband technology in which individual circuits (data or voice) are identified by their position in a stream of frames that have regular intervals in time as shown in (B) in Figure M-12. Analog inputs (voice) are digitized using pulse code modulation and parts of the digitized information are inserted into the time segments of the transmission. Each channel gets an interleaved time segment so that all channels equally share the medium that is used for transmission. Refer to the bridge traffic directory analogy described earlier.

INVERSE MULTIPLEXING   Inverse multiplexing is a technique of dividing a single high-speed data stream into multiple low-speed data streams for transmission over multiple low-speed connections as shown in (C) in Figure M-12. This can save some expense in leasing high-speed lines and can make better use of available lines.

STATISTICAL TIME DIVISION MULTIPLEXING (STDM)   As mentioned earlier, multiplexing doesn't make the best use of a transmission line if it preallocates time

M

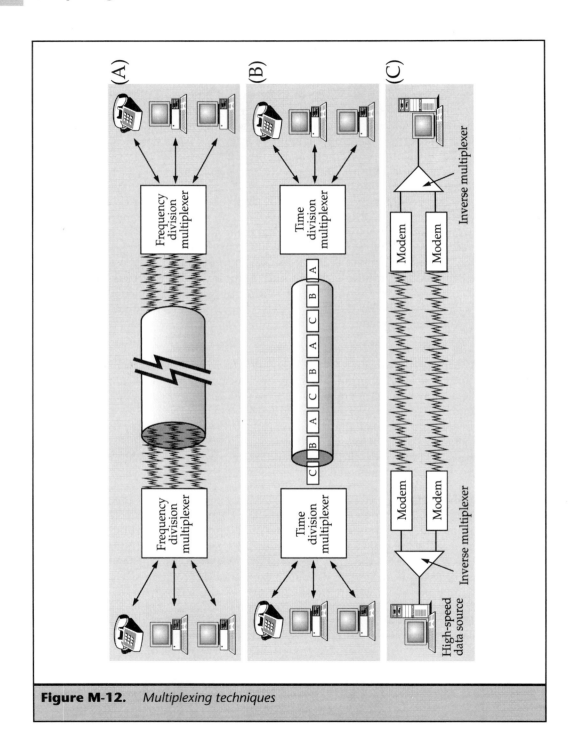

Figure M-12. *Multiplexing techniques*

slots for stations that don't always transmit. The preallocated slots go to waste. Statistical multiplexers solve this problem by dynamically allocating time slots and using the line more efficiently. Statistical multiplexers are expensive because they contain processors and use buffering techniques to efficiently use the channel. Because buffering can add delays, the processors and other circuitry must be high-performance in design to provide high transmission speeds.

There are of course, various other techniques to improve multiplexer performance. Some of these involve compression, which is practical to do on the fly with high-performance equipment.

More About TDM

A *frame* is a sequence of time segments from each input channel. For example, if there are 24 channel inputs, a frame consists of 24 segments that hold samples from each channel. A special synchronization bit follows the frame so the receiving equipment can maintain time correlation. A new frame then follows with more samples from each channel, and this process continues at very high speeds over the transmission medium.

In T1-type multiplexing, a frame consists of 24 time slots and there are 8,000 frames per second. Each time slot or segment in the frame holds 64,000 bits of information, which is obtained by sampling the analog signal 8,000 times per second and using 8 bits for each sample ($8,000 \times 8 = 64,000$, or 64 Kbits/sec). The number of bits per second supported by a transmission facility is called its channel rate or bit rate. A T1 transmission therefore has a channel rate of 1.544 Mbits/sec, which is calculated as follows:

$$24 \text{ frames} \times 64,000 \text{ bits/frame} = 1.536 \text{ Mbits/sec}$$

We add to this the synchronizing frame bit that occurs at 8,000 bits/sec (8 Kbps or 0.008 Mbps) to arrive at the final transmission rate, as follows:

$$1.536 \text{ Mbps} + 0.008 \text{ Mbps} = 1.544 \text{ Mbps}$$

Multiplexer Configurations

Multiplexers can mix both voice and data traffic and transport it over high-speed lines, as shown in Figure M-13. Analog telephone signals must be digitized by a codec (**co**der-**dec**oder) and sent to the multiplexing unit. The multiplexed signal is then transmitted over the T1 line along with data from other devices. Note that a Channel Service Unit/Data Service Unit (DSU/CSU) is attached between the T1 line and the multiplexer.

An organization can build a private network using multiplexer devices and high-speed lines such as T1 as illustrated in Figure M-14. The backbone provides both voice and data transmissions between sites. Note that telephones may have a direct

M

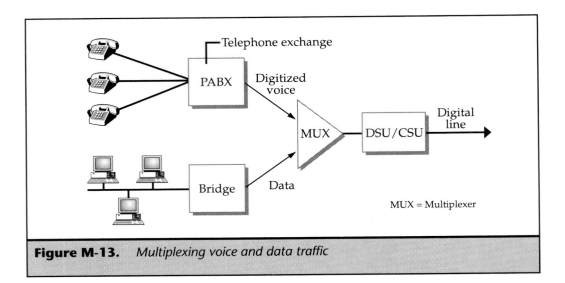

Figure M-13.   *Multiplexing voice and data traffic*

input to the multiplexer or go though a Private Automatic Branch Exchange (PABX) device. The three-way connection provides an added benefit. If one line goes down, traffic can be diverted over the other lines to reach its destination, assuming routers are used that can reconfigure the transmission routes.

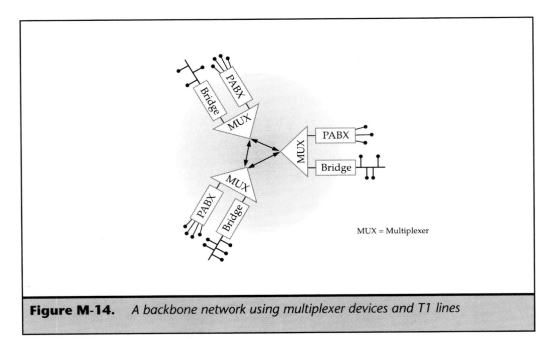

Figure M-14.   *A backbone network using multiplexer devices and T1 lines*

RELATED ENTRIES   Channel Service Unit/Data Service Unit; Dedicated Circuits; T1/T3 Services; *and* Telecommunication

Multiprocessing

A multiprocessing system is a computer that has more than one processor. Most superserver computers such as those developed by NetFrame are designed specifically for multiple processor support. Superservers include a high-performance bus, tens of megabytes of error-correcting memory, redundant array of inexpensive disk (RAID) disk systems, advanced system architectures that reduce bottlenecks, and redundant features such as multiple power supplies.

There are two types of multiprocessor system designs: *symmetrical* and *asymmetrical*. Each type has different features and benefits.

In symmetrical multiprocessor systems, system resources such as memory and disk input/output (I/O) are shared by all the microprocessors in the system. The workload is distributed evenly to available microprocessors so that one doesn't sit idle while another is overworked with a specific task. The performance of symmetrical multiprocessor systems increases for all tasks as microprocessors are added. A drawback to symmetrical multiprocessing is that operating systems that take advantage of symmetrical multiprocessing systems are harder to design, although Windows NT and other "microkernel" operating systems support symmetrical multiprocessing.

In asymmetrical multiprocessor systems, tasks and system resources are managed by different microprocessors. For example, one microprocessor handles I/O and another handles network operating system tasks. Asymmetrical multiprocessing systems do not balance workloads. A microprocessor handling one task can be overworked while another microprocessor sits idle. Symmetrical multiprocessing systems distribute the workload evenly.

The primary focus of most vendors is to increase system throughput for multiple network users on multiple local area network segments. Superserver systems support multiple network cards, increasing the number of segments possible. The high-speed bus in the server provides quick transfer of information among network segments.

RELATED ENTRIES   Mach, Carnegie-Mellon Microkernel; Multiprocessor Systems; *and* Windows NT, Microsoft

Multiprocessor Systems

A multiprocessor system contains multiple processors and is designed for high-end workstations or file server usage. While there are a number of multiprocessor systems on the market, readers should be cautious of input/output (I/O) bottlenecks that many of these systems have. While the processors can deliver "mainframe-like" power, they often implement standard bus designs such as Micro Channel and Extended Industry Standard Architecture (EISA), which can't keep up with processor performance or the demands from the network. Superserver systems that use proprietary bus designs are better able to support the I/O requirements of multiuser networks.

M

RELATED ENTRY   Multiprocessing

Multiprotocol Networks

A multiprotocol network supports multiple protocols, such as Transmission Control Protocol/Internet Protocol (TCP/IP), Internetwork Packet Exchange (IPX), AppleTalk, DECnet, and others. An organization with multivendor computing systems that run different communication protocols can attach these systems to a single network platform, rather than create a network for each different protocol. Simply put, the cable and network devices will transport data packets for any of the protocols in use by the organization. For example, TCP/IP packets traverse the network and reach their destinations unaware that IPX or other packets are using the same network to get to their destinations.

Multiprotocol routers interconnect two or more local area network (LAN) segments to create wide area connections. Most LAN-based protocols were not designed to operate over wide area network connections. Such protocols perform error checking and service advertising that produce overhead on wide area links. Because wide area links are expensive, and often much slower in response time than the LAN, costs and errors increase when these protocols are put on the LAN. Multiprotocol routers solve some of these problems by repackaging the packets into packets that efficiently cross the LAN. This is often called encapsulation.

The construction of enterprise networks has brought about the need to support multiple protocols. Previously, isolated departments and workgroups set up their own networks using the vendor equipment and communication protocols they preferred. As these systems are integrated into the enterprise network, it is necessary to provide users with the protocols they need to access company resources throughout the network. This might mean adding TCP/IP support to a NetWare IPX LAN or IPX support to a Microsoft LAN.

The ultimate goal is to create an open network on which many different products are supported. The interim solution is to support a number of different protocols, but eventually, managers will want to choose the protocol that is the most widely used and supported and shut off those protocols that are no longer important. The multiprotocol network approach provides a way to move to open systems without disrupting the current network structure. A multiprotocol network consists of the following:

■ Workstation software that lets users load more than one protocol stack so they can talk to different systems. The Novell Open Data-link Interface (ODI) and the Microsoft Network Device Interface Standard (NDIS) provide this support.

■ Network servers that support multiple protocols. This is achieved with Novell ODI and Microsoft NDIS as well.

■ Multiprotocol routers that support the transmission of many different types of protocol packets.

The following protocols are optimized for workgroups and 802.x access methods. They are generally inadequate for wide area networking:

- Microsoft Server Message Blocks (SMB) and NetBIOS
- AppleTalk
- Novell NetWare IPX

Protocols suitable for enterprise networking and wide area networking are listed here:

- IBM Advanced Peer-to-Peer Networking (APPN)
- TCP/IP
- Open Systems Interconnection (OSI)

The multiprotocol router can minimize some of the problems in using the protocols over wide areas. It can repackage "non-routable" protocols and deliver them over other networks using encapsulation techniques.

RELATED ENTRIES   Encapsulation; Enterprise Networks; Middleware; *and* Multiprotocol Router

Multiprotocol Router

A multiprotocol router is designed to handle a variety of communication protocols, not just one protocol. For example, the NetWare Multiprotocol Router supports Open Systems Interconnection (OSI), Internetwork Packet Exchange (IPX), Internet Protocol (IP), Novell NetBIOS, and AppleTalk protocols so that users can connect Ethernet, Token Ring, LocalTalk, and ARCNET networks together and route traffic from NetWare workstations, Apple Macintoshes, UNIX systems, and OSI systems.

RELATED ENTRIES   Routers; Routing Protocols

Multiprotocol Transport Network (MPTN), IBM

MPTN software provides a way to decouple applications from underlying transport protocols and remove the need for multiprotocol routers. With MPTN, an application written for one protocol can operate over a network that uses another MPTN-specified protocol. Basically, MPTN changes the transport header in a packet to fit an alternate protocol. These protocols are Transmission Control Protocol/Internet Protocol (TCP/IP), Open Systems Interconnection (OSI), and Systems Network Architecture (SNA). The advantage for customers is the ability to choose from a larger selection of applications with less concern for the underlying protocols they use.

M

MPTN is designed around the specification found in the Common Transport Semantic (CTS) layer of the IBM Network Blueprint, which is described elsewhere in this book. IBM has submitted the MPTN technology to the X/Open consortium with the intent of making it a standard way to interface with multiple transport protocols. As of this writing, MPTN implementation supports Multiple Virtual Storage (MVS) mainframe applications and OS/2 applications over SNA and the TCP/IP suite of protocols.

Figure M-15 illustrates the installation points for the MPTN software. In this case, an MPTN gateway provides a connection into an IBM SNA server for a workstation running TCP/IP. Note that MPTN acts as a switching layer for packets traversing the network.

IBM AnyNet products are multiprotocol transport services based on the MPTN architecture. *AnyNet Sockets over SNA Gateway* allows Sockets applications that use File Transfer Protocol (FTP), Network File System (NFS), or X-Windows to communicate with similar applications on IBM SNA hosts. Future products will support IBM AIX, RS/6000, and OS/400 operating systems. *AnyNet/2* is an OS/2 program for running Advanced Program-to-Program Communications (APPC) applications over TCP/IP networks. It also allows Sockets-based applications to run over SNA. IBM will also develop AnyNet products for Logical Unit (LU) 0, 1, 2, 3 protocols to provide further support for SNA applications over TCP/IP networks.

RELATED ENTRIES   Advanced Peer-to-Peer Networking; IBM; IBM Networking Blueprint; Routing, IBM; *and* Routing Protocols

Multipurpose Internet Mail Extension (MIME)

Multipurpose Internet Mail Extension (MIME) is a compound document messaging standard in the Internet environment. With MIME, users can send multimedia E-mail

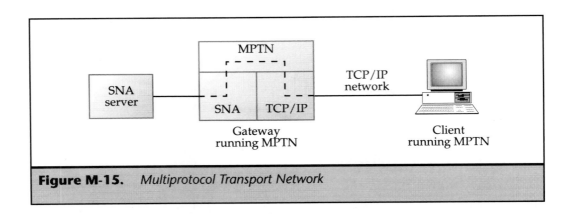

Figure M-15.   *Multiprotocol Transport Network*

messages that include audio, video, graphics, and text to any other user of a TCP/IP network. *Richtext* information can also be incorporated into messages. It defines the fonts, formats, and layout features of a document so the document can be easily redisplayed on many different types of systems.

RELATED ENTRIES   Compound Documents; Document Interchange Standards; Internet; *and* Simple Mail Transfer Protocol

Multistation Access Unit (MAU)

A MAU is a hub device in a token ring network that provides the connection point for multiple computers. It contains an internal ring that is extended to an external ring when workstations are attached, as pictured in M-16.

If a network card fails, the MAU automatically bypasses it to maintain the ring. To expand the network beyond the devices that can attach to the MAU, a cable is wired from a ring-out port on the first MAU to a ring-in port on the second MAU. Another cable is then wired from the ring-out port on the second MAU back to the ring-in port on the first MAU. This maintains the ring configuration while allowing it to grow.

RELATED ENTRY   Token Ring Network

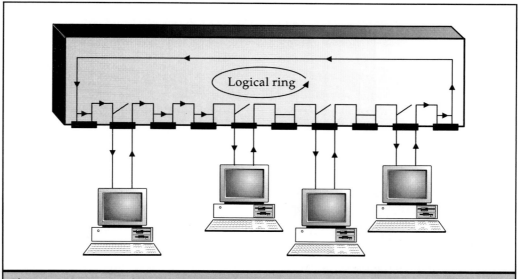

Figure M-16.   *Multistation Access Unit*

M

Name Binding Protocol, AppleTalk

The AppleTalk Name Binding Protocol provides internet-to-local translation services and uses the AppleTalk Zone Information Protocol (ZIP) to determine which networks contain nodes belonging to a zone. ZIP is an AppleTalk session-layer protocol that maintains and discovers the internetwork mapping of network number ranges.

RELATED ENTRY   AppleTalk

Named Pipes

Named pipes is a high-level interface for passing data between processes that are running on separate computers connected by a network. Named pipes is an extension of the OS/2 operating system that is implemented on Microsoft LAN Manager and IBM LAN Server network operating systems. It is the network version of interprocess communication (IPC) facilities, which provide an interface between processes running in a single, multitasking system.

Named pipes is part of a group of interprocess communication facilities in the OS/2 environment (and some other environments) that are used by concurrently running processes that need to communicate with one another. These include:

- *Shared memory*   A block of memory that two programs use to read and write common information. A set of access rules prevents the programs from writing to the same data simultaneously. The memory is used as a "holding" area for the exchange of information between programs.

- *Semaphores*   A semaphore is like a flag or signal that prevents separately running processes from simultaneously accessing input/output ports, processors, and other computer resources.

- *Messaging*   A store-and-forward messaging process in which one process exchanges a message with another process. The message might contain a request for service or data. Messaging is handled on a first-in, first-out basis. On a network, messaging may not be appropriate for applications that require immediate responses since it may take some time before the message is actually delivered, but messaging is useful for some types of database queries and the initiation of processes.

- *Pipes*   A form of interprocess communication similar to a remote procedure call that takes place between two processes in the same machine.

Compared to a pipe, a named pipe is a communication process between two remote computer systems that are attached to a network. A logical connection is set up between the two remote processes and the transfer of information takes place over the physical network. The most important aspect of named pipes is that they enable client-server applications in distributed computing environments. A process on a front-end client machine can interact with a process on a back-end server machine. For example, a client can make requests for files on a network file server or query a database on a remote database server.

The named pipes interface is better at handling network transactions than NetBIOS and can do so with a single call compared to the many operations required to perform the same actions through NetBIOS. However, the named pipes interface does not provide features of NetBIOS such as connectionless datagram services and the naming functions that allow messages to be sent to groups.

RELATED ENTRIES   Interprocess Communication; Mail Slots; Messaging API, Inter-Application; NetBIOS / NetBEUI; Pipes; Remote Procedure Call; *and* Server Message Block

Name Service

See Directory Services.

Name Space Support, Novell NetWare

The NetWare file system provides support for the file naming conventions of different operating systems through *name space* support. Normally, the NetWare file system automatically supports DOS-compatible file storage. Name space support allows files with different name lengths, legal characters, and case sensitivity to be stored on NetWare servers. Name space support is installed by loading a NetWare Loadable Module (NLM) for a particular file system.

For example, by loading name space support for the Macintosh operating system at a NetWare file server, it is possible for Macintosh users to store files on the server. A Macintosh file actually consists of two files—a *data fork* and a *resource fork*. OS/2 and UNIX (Network File System, or NFS) have different file-naming conventions (longer names). A separate name space is required to store these files on NetWare servers as well.

RELATED ENTRIES   Disks, Partitions, and Volumes Under NetWare; File Systems in the Network Environment; NetWare; *and* NetWare Volumes

National Information Infrastructure

The National Information Infrastructure (NII) is the so-called "data superhighway." The NII is a physical network of fiber-optic lines, switches, and network software that will be constructed, owned, and maintained by private information and service providers, not the U.S. government. However, the government supports it with research, education, and healthcare funding. The government is also interested in developing standards for the NII and making government information readily available. Standards and protocols for accessing data anywhere on the network are defined by the High Performance and High Speed Networking Act of 1993.

N

The information infrastructure is not necessarily a single structure like a bridge spanning a river. Instead, it is a collection of existing and planned communication structures, analogous to a set of bridges, ferries, and trams that might get you across a body of water. Users don't need to worry about which paths are taken to get from one place to another. This is handled by the service providers. Instead, users specify an address in the same way that they dial a phone number to make a long-distance call. The Internet uses an addressing scheme in which users specify a name rather than a number. For example, the following address accesses the Science and Information Technology System (STIS) at the National Science Foundation (NSF):

stis.nsf.gov

Government funding for NII may exceed 2 billion dollars a year, with a focus on providing an open structure in which anyone can access information and entertainment services. By promoting private investment, the government hopes to stimulate new and interactive applications from many sectors, including the entertainment industry. The government is also interested in aspects of security and reliability so the network can be used by federal agencies, as well as private business.

Proponents of the NII see it as a necessity for the American home, similar to the telephone system. It will provide information access to everyone. Public databases are available at locations throughout the country, such as libraries, museums, government agencies, and research facilities. The government has vast amounts of information in the Library of Congress, the Smithsonian, and other depositories that it would like to make more readily available to the public. NII will help people to access them.

The government's goal is to set up a network that stimulates electronic education and makes information available in the classroom. It can also help teachers keep in touch with parents, and help students keep in touch with their classrooms. The medical and scientific fields will also benefit from having instant access to the latest research information in databases scattered throughout the country. Increasing the available bandwidth on the network will bring big-city services to small communities. For example, a specialist in Chicago could collaborate with a doctor in a small town while viewing the images produced by a medical scanning or imaging device.

Increased bandwidth will also make other services available, including teleconferencing, enhanced electronic mail, and even entertainment services. The infrastructure will promote electronic commerce and environmentally sound telecommuting. Businesses will increasingly use Electronic Data Interchange (EDI) to exchange invoices, orders, and other accounting documents as the network expands and rates decrease. NII will make electronic mail available to everyone with a computer, and security features will ensure that only authorized recipients can read the mail.

The Physical Side

The network will be built on a combination of fiber-optic cable, copper cable, and microwave systems installed by the telephone companies, the cable television providers, and other communication service providers. The telephone companies have been busy installing fiber-optic cable for their long-distance trunks. The local loop—the connection between home and many business users and the local phone company—is still largely copper twisted-pair wire, however. There are some actions to improve this loop, including the installation of Integrated Services Digital Network (ISDN) services in some areas, or an improvement of the signaling techniques, such as the High-bit-rate Digital Subscriber Line (HDSL), which permits transmission over the existing copper-based lines at transmission speeds between 784 Kbits/sec to T1 rates of 1.544 Mbits/sec. Related products include Asymmetrical Digital Subscriber Line (ADSL) and Very High bit-rate Digital Subscriber Line (VHDSL). These offerings are discussed elsewhere in this book.

The cable television companies are ready to jump in by providing services over their existing coaxial cable systems. The companies have been upgrading their long-distance cable systems and metropolitan backbones to fiber-optic cable and plan to provide up to 500 channels.

The Internet currently serves as the model for the NII. It is a conglomeration of thousands of networks that are linked together using existing communication services, and the TCP/IP protocols are the primary method for transmitting data across the networks. The Internet was originally funded by government money and the NII plan calls for continued support.

RELATED ENTRIES   ARPANET; Defense Advanced Research Projects Agency; Internet; *and* National Research and Education Network

National Research and Education Network (NREN)

The National Research and Education Network (NREN) is the backbone data network of the Internet, administered by the National Science Foundation. It succeeded the National Science Foundation network (NSFnet) as the major Internet network for research and education in the United States, as of the signing of the "High-Performance Computing Act of 1991," a bill sponsored by then senator Al Gore. It calls for a high-capacity (gigabits-per-second) network and the coordination of networking efforts among federal organizations.

The NREN is designed to connect K-12 schools, colleges, universities, libraries, health care industries, business, and manufacturing into a national public network using the Internet. The Internet provides vast quantities of timely and useful information to these institutions over existing telecommunication links. Access is obtained using standard desktop computer equipment and modems, or connection to networks that are connected to the Internet.

RELATED ENTRIES   ARPANET; Defense Advanced Research Projects Agency; Internet; *and* National Information Infrastructure

N

NetBIOS / NetBEUI

The Network Basic Input Output System (NetBIOS) and NetBIOS Extended User Interface (NetBEUI) protocols were designed by IBM and Microsoft to support network communication in the small- to medium-sized local area network (LAN) environment. The complete protocol environment is pictured in Figure N-1 and explained here.

- *Redirector* Directs network requests to network servers and local commands to the local operating system.
- *Server Message Blocks* Provides the peer-to-peer language and formats required for computers to talk to one another.
- *NetBIOS* A Session-layer protocol in relation to the OSI protocol model. It sets up communication sessions between computers and maintains those connections.
- *NetBEUI* Provides the underlying data transport services.
- *Network Driver Interface Specification (NDIS)* A recently developed Microsoft specification that provides a way to support other protocols, such as TCP/IP, on a single interface card.

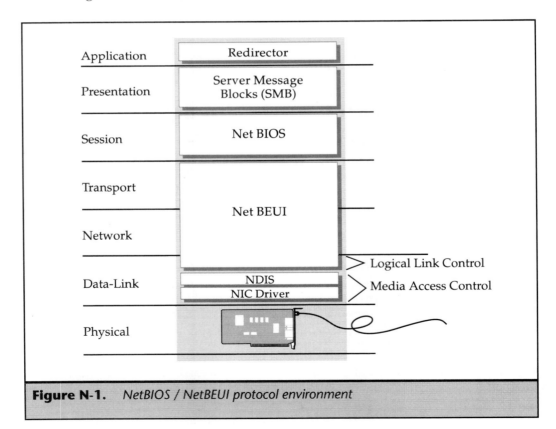

Figure N-1. *NetBIOS / NetBEUI protocol environment*

NetBIOS and NetBEUI are implemented in a number of desktop operating systems and network operating systems, including OS/2, Windows for Workgroups, Windows NT, Microsoft LAN Manager, and IBM LAN Server. Note however that Microsoft is also supporting the Transmission Control Protocol/Internet Protocol (TCP/IP) protocol stack in all its current and future network products. One reason for this is that NetBIOS is not a routable protocol and is unsuitable in the wide area network environment.

NetBEUI

NetBEUI was developed by IBM in 1985 as a network transport protocol for small- to medium-sized LANs. NetBEUI is supported by Microsoft in its networking products, including Windows for Workgroups and Windows NT. IBM and Microsoft networks can communicate due to NetBEUI and NetBIOS implementation.

NetBEUI is a Transport and Network layer protocol in relation to the OSI protocol model. It integrates with NetBIOS to provide an efficient communication system in the workgroup LAN environment. NetBEUI provides the data transport services required by NetBIOS. Think of a phone call. NetBIOS is like the person making the call and NetBEUI is like the control program that works with the underlying switching system to complete the call.

NetBIOS

NetBIOS was designed with the premise that PCs on a LAN only need to talk to other PCs on the same LAN. It is a Session layer protocol in relation to the OSI protocol model and was originally developed by Sytek Inc., for IBM to use in its broadband networks.

NetBIOS is an application program interface (API) that programmers use to create LAN applications for the IBM LAN Server, Microsoft LAN Manager, and OS/2 environments. Named pipes are a network extension to OS/2 that provides similar but more advanced features. NetBIOS and named pipes exist in the LAN environment as the protocols on which various applications are built.

NetBIOS provides the following services:

■ NetBIOS establishes unique logical names for nodes on the network, simplifying the task of referring to other systems. The name is from 1 to 15 characters long and specifically identifies a workstation to both computers and users. This name is specified when a network computer is first set up or attached to the network. Messages can be sent to groups of names.

■ NetBIOS establishes a connection-oriented session over which nodes converse with one another. The *session* takes place over a logical connection or circuit. NetBIOS sets up, maintains, and disengages a session. Workstations communicate in real-time with guaranteed delivery of data through message delivery confirmations.

N

■ NetBIOS can also provide connectionless datagram services in which messages are directed to another system without any prior setup of a connection or monitoring of the packet flow.

■ Network applications that run on NetBIOS-compliant networks use NetBIOS to locate other resources and establish connections with those resources for the exchange of data. Resources might be other applications.

■ NetBIOS broadcasts information about the location of servers and the names of those servers. This broadcasting can overload the network with excess packets, and cause problems on internetworks. Filtering in bridges and routers can solve these problems, however.

■ NetBIOS is not routable, partly because of its 15-character naming system. NetBIOS must be encapsulated (packaged) into the packets of other protocols for deliver over internetworks. The TCP/IP protocol has a procedure for encapsulating NetBIOS. Novell supports NetBIOS on its IPX networks and DEC supports NetBIOS on DECnet networks.

Servers use the broadcasting feature of NetBIOS to locate the workstations and devices in its domain (management zone). If a workstation responds to the messages, the server no longer sends it messages. If a workstation doesn't respond because it is turned off or has a defective network interface card, the server sends messages every few minutes in an attempt to get a response. Because the messages are sent everywhere on the network, including WAN links, they get expensive in terms of bandwidth usage and WAN link costs. A Remote Name Directory (RND) function can be used to turn these broadcasts into nonbroadcast datagrams that don't cross WAN links.

NetBIOS is well established and still supported in many environments, even though newer protocols such as named pipes are available. NetBIOS is also well understood and there are many applications that use it. It will be around for some time.

RELATED ENTRIES   Named Pipes; Routing Protocols; Windows for Workgroups, Microsoft; *and* Windows NT, Microsoft

NetDDE
(Network Dynamic Data Exchange)

Dynamic Data Exchange (DDE) is a method for transferring data between applications. It is used in Microsoft Windows, Microsoft Windows for Workgroups, and Microsoft Windows NT. DDE is a messaging protocol that provides dynamic exchange of data between, say a spreadsheet program and a word processor. DDE is typically used to link real-time data from stock market updates or scientific equipment like sensors into a document. DDE can also be used to create compound documents that contain a chart from a spreadsheet program, a picture from a graphics program, and elements from other types of programs. Changes to these elements are automatically reflected in the compound document. Note that the Object Linking and Embedding (OLE) protocol in Windows is built on top of DDE and provides the additional embedding services.

The network version of DDE called NetDDE has all the features of DDE, but extends them over a network. With NetDDE, applications on two or more workstations can dynamically share information. NetDDE provides linking between workstations after a DDE share is created. A DDE share is similar to sharing a file or sharing a printer, and it includes all the security-related functions that grant remote users access to information on another computer.

In Windows for Workgroups and Windows NT, the ClipBook Viewer provides the mechanism for sharing "objects" across the network. For example, an artist places an art object on his ClipBook Viewer, then shares that object. Another user accesses the artist ClipBook and copies the object to her Clipboard, and then into a document. An example of a shared ClipBook is pictured in Figure N-2. Because a link is maintained to the original file owned by the artist, any changes the artist makes to the file are also reflected in the copied image. NetDDE stores link data in the compound document that indicates the remote system and document file that contains the original object.

NetDDE and OLE dynamic links help users work on collaborative projects in which many users make contributions to a common document. This compound document is typically stored on the manager's computer and linked elements are

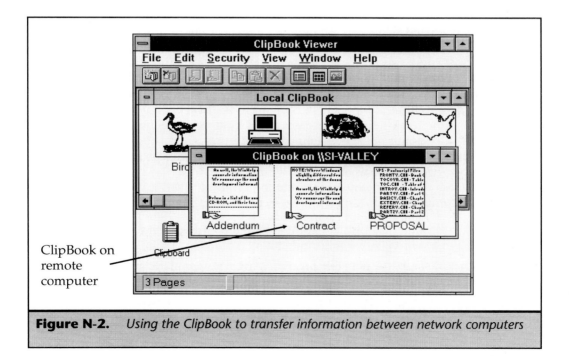

Figure N-2.   *Using the ClipBook to transfer information between network computers*

N

stored on coworkers' computers. Dynamic links ensure that any changes made to linked files are automatically updated in the manager's compound document. Groupware applications can be built around the NetDDE extensions.

RELATED ENTRIES   Object Linking and Embedding; Windows for Workgroups, Microsoft; *and* Windows NT, Microsoft

NetLS (Network License Server)

NetLS is a network licensing system developed by Gradient Technologies, Inc. that restricts access to software based on the number of licensed copies available. Licensing is used to ensure that a company is operating within its legal boundaries for software usage. The software also provides software version tracking, inventory, and usage tracking. Tracking is important to determine who is using software and whether additional licenses are required. NetLS is supported by a number of vendors of desktop management software applications

RELATED ENTRY   Electronic Software Distribution and Licensing

NetView, IBM

NetView is a network management system marketed by IBM. It is based on Hewlett-Packard's OpenView management system, but IBM has enhanced it. NetView is generally recognized as the leading network management product sold today. The original focus of NetView was the management of Systems Network Architecture (SNA) networks, but it has evolved into a general local area network (LAN) management system that supports Open Systems Interconnection (OSI) and Transmission Control Protocol/Internet Protocol (TCP/IP) protocols as well.

NetView defines three components to a managed network, as pictured in Figure N-3. NetView is the focal point that receives alerts from managed devices on the network. The entry points are agents in managed devices, such as host systems, front-end processors, controllers, and LAN components. Service points provide a gateway for non-SNA protocols and support Simple Network Management Protocol (SNMP) and Common Management Information Protocol (CMIP).

The major components of NetView are described here:

- *Command Facility*   The primary command and control center for NetView. It recommends actions to take in some cases.

- *Hardware Monitor*   Responsible for managing network alerts, including storing them for future reference.

- *Session Monitor*   Collects information about sessions on networks, such as their status, configuration, response time, failures, and error codes.

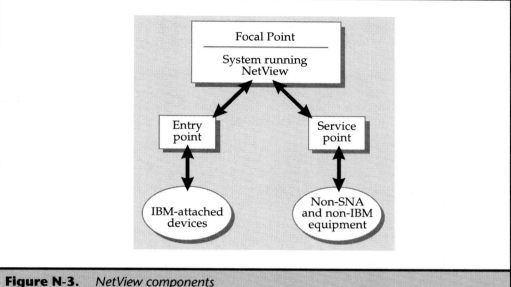

Figure N-3. *NetView components*

- *Status Monitor* Collects information about resources on an SNA network. The information is made available to the Graphical Monitor.
- *Graphical Monitor* Software that runs on OS/2 systems to provide a graphical map of the network and its resources. Users can point and click to obtain information on specific LAN segments, nodes, or devices.
- *Browse Facility* Provides a way to view information collected by NetView.

NetView can be customized by users who need to gather and display specific information about the network. Programming tools such as C, Restructured Executive External Language (REXX) and Command List (CLIST) are available to customize the system.

RELATED ENTRY Management Standards and Tools

NetWare

Novell offers a variety of network operating systems under the name NetWare, from the simple and inexpensive NetWare Lite to NetWare 4.x, an operating system designed specifically for enterprise networks. The operating system product line is briefly described here. General features of the NetWare 3.x and NetWare 4.x products are described further.

N

■ *NetWare Lite*   A peer-to-peer network operating system for two to 25 users. It runs on top of the DOS operating system and is compatible with Microsoft Windows. Users can set up a network for sharing files, applications, and printers with little networking knowledge.

■ *NetWare 2.x*   Designed for small to medium-sized businesses and workgroups within large companies. The operating system runs in dedicated or nondedicated mode on Intel 80286-, 80386-, and 80486-based computers. It provides local and remote internetworking support as well as tools for network administrators.

■ *NetWare 3.x*   A network operating system designed to support hundreds of users on a single, dedicated server. It provides many of the advanced features discussed in this section, including modular design and the ability to integrate diverse systems, including minicomputers.

■ *NetWare 4.x*   Novell's enterprise operating system that inherits all the capabilities of NetWare 3.x and adds new features of its own to create a distributed multiserver environment that provides directory services and enterprise network support.

For related information, see "NetWare 4.x Enhanced Features."

The following discussion describes the major architectural components of the NetWare operating system. Some features are not available in all versions of the software.

The NetWare operating system resides in a network server which is typically an Intel-based computer. It provides network connectivity and services to workstations. The relationship between the server and workstations is illustrated in Figure N-4. This relationship provides a communication system that distributes network services to users at workstations. The important component on the client side is the redirection software, which is typically loaded when the workstation boots. The redirecter intercepts commands for NetWare servers and sends them across the network. Non-network commands are sent to the local operating system.

The core functions provided by the NetWare server are file system management, memory management, and the scheduling of processing tasks (see "NetWare Core Protocol"). Note that the relationship between the server and the workstation is client-server-based, meaning that the workstations handle much of the processing load, freeing the server to perform its own tasks more efficiently.

The network support software links the network hardware and cabling system to the operating system. This software uses specific drivers to support the types of network cards installed in the server and in workstations.

NetWare Architecture

NetWare 3.x and 4.x are full 32-bit operating systems that use a single address space with no segmentation (a problem with DOS systems). This allows programs to operate

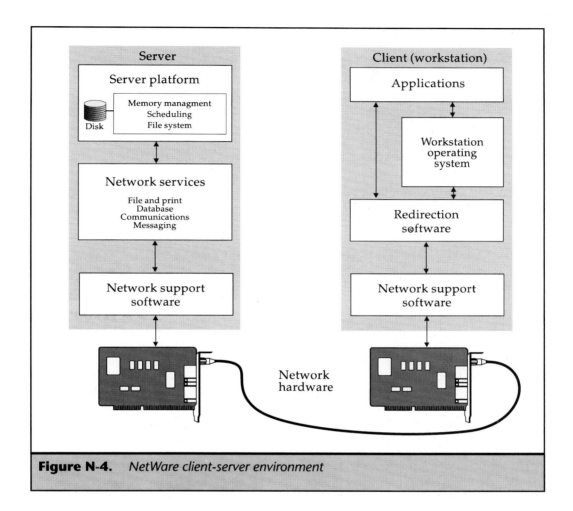

Figure N-4.   *NetWare client-server environment*

more efficiently. The operating system can handle thousands of interrupts and process thousands of client requests per second.

NetWare 3.x and 4.x are modular and expandable. Changes, upgrades, and additions to the network are possible. You can load a NetWare Loadable Module (NLM) which links into the operating system at the server to provide services like the following:

■ Support that allows for the storage of non-DOS files

■ Communication services

■ Database services

■ Messaging services

N

- Archive and backup services
- Network management services

These modules are added to the operating system as shown in Figure N-5. You can load or unload any module at any time from the server console without bringing down the server. Each module uses additional memory, so you need to make sure the server has enough memory to handle the NLMs you plan to load. Because the modules are located in the server along with the operating system, they are tightly coupled with the operating system and have instant access to services.

NetWare is an ideal platform for server applications. It solves connectivity problems by handling multiple protocols and standards concurrently at the media level, the transport level, the service protocol level, and at the file system level, as shown in Figure N-6.

Protocol Independence

One of the most important features of NetWare is its support for other operating systems. You can attach workstations that run DOS, Windows, OS/2, and UNIX. DOS, Windows, and OS/2 workstation support is bundled with NetWare, as are several management utilities that use the Windows interface. The NetWare OS/2 workstation software supplied with NetWare provides the support OS/2 workstations need to communicate with a NetWare server. NetWare allows OS/2 extended attributes and long filenames, and lets OS/2 server-based applications run on the network. Support for the Apple Macintosh, UNIX-based NFS, and OSI File Transfer Access and Management (FTAM) must be added to a NetWare network as optional products.

NetWare uses a protocol-independent structure known as the Open Data-link Interface (ODI), which provides simultaneous support for different protocols on the

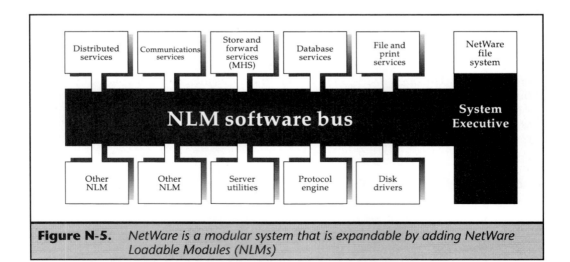

Figure N-5.   *NetWare is a modular system that is expandable by adding NetWare Loadable Modules (NLMs)*

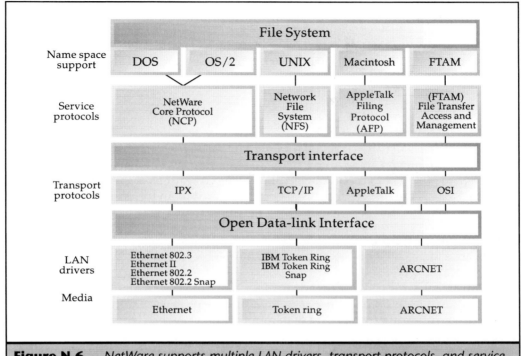

Figure N-6. *NetWare supports multiple LAN drivers, transport protocols, and service protocols*

network. The ODI interface that provides multiprotocol support at the server is shown in Figure N-6. Note that a variety of interface cards are allowed. The drivers of these cards attach themselves to the Open Data-link Interface layer. Packets are directed to the appropriate protocol stack above the ODI layer, such as IPX, TCP/IP, or AppleTalk. Near the top, service protocols provide file and system support for the various operating systems that you can install on a NetWare server.

A similar scheme is used at workstations to allow users to connect to networks that use different communication protocols, such as TCP/IP. You'll need Novell's LAN WorkPlace products or similar products from other vendors to provide TCP/IP support for workstations.

If you need to connect workstations to NetWare LANs as well as to other types of networks, such as Microsoft LAN Manager, IBM LAN Server, and 3Com 3+Share networks, you can install the Open Data-link Interface Network Support (ODINSUP) driver provided in the NetWare package. ODINSUP allows the coexistence of the ODI network driver interface and the Network Driver Interface Specification (NDIS), which is a Microsoft specification for supporting multiple drivers.

N

Name Space Support

The NetWare file system provides support for the file naming conventions of different operating systems through *name space* support, which is loaded at the server console. Name space support allows files with different name lengths, legal characters, and case sensitivity to be stored on the NetWare server. Name space support for the Macintosh is a module you load at the server.

Performance Features

One of the reasons NetWare is popular in the LAN environment is its performance. Novell long ago moved away from a network operating system that ran under DOS, and designed NetWare to access directly the advanced features of the server's CPU. NetWare 386 was the first 32-bit network operating system in the desktop computer arena. The kernel of the NetWare operating system is both multitasking and multithreaded, which means that it provides multiuser capabilities at the server and high performance during times when there are heavy loads on the system. Other performance improvements are discussed in the next sections.

Dynamic Configuration

NetWare dynamically configures itself to match current usage conditions on the network. The following features are dynamically configured:

- Memory usage
- Directory caching
- Number of volume directory entries
- Size of the open file table
- Routing buffers
- Turbo FAT indexing
- Service processes
- Active transaction tracking system (TTS) transactions

You can alter the limits and maximum values so that NetWare is not constrained. You can also adjust how quickly the operating system configures itself, and you can set the maximum amount of resources that are used.

Memory Management

NetWare supports up to 4GB (gigabytes) of RAM in the server. Memory management in NetWare 4.x is designed to have increased efficiency. NetWare v.3.11 allocated memory for different uses into five or more *pools*. This caused some applications to run out of memory because, when a process was done using the memory, the management routines did not reallocate it for other uses. NetWare 4.x manages memory as only one pool, and it is more effective at allocating memory from one operation to another.

The File System

The Universal File System in NetWare provides many performance-enhancing features:

- *Elevator seeking* This feature of the disk system prioritizes incoming read requests based on how they can best be accessed by the read head of the disk drive, given its current location. The operation of elevator seeking is analogous to that of a building elevator. A building elevator doesn't make random up and down trips among floors based on who requested service first; it stops at floors on the way up or down to pick up passengers who need a ride. Elevator seeking minimizes disk head movement, thus improving access time and reducing hardware degradation.

- *File caching* File caching minimizes the number of times the disk must be accessed. The files that are most often read are retained in the cache buffer, where they can be accessed if needed. This eliminates the need to go to disk for the information. Files in the cache are prioritized so that the least used files are flushed from the cache to make room for new files.

- *Background writes* Disk writes are handled separately from disk reads in NetWare. This separation allows the operating system to write data to disk during moments when disk requests from users have slowed. Background writes give users who need to read data from the drive the highest priority, which improves performance from their point of view.

- *Overlapped seeks* This NetWare feature is available if two or more hard disks are present and each is connected to its own controller (disk channel). NetWare accesses all the controllers simultaneously. If two disks are attached to one controller, only one of those disks is accessible at a time.

- *Turbo FAT* This feature is also known as the Index file allocation table. The turbo FAT indexes the file allocation tables of files over 2MB so that the locations of their segments are immediately available to the operating system without the need to read the FAT.

- *File compression* NetWare 4.x can increase disk space up to 63 percent with its file compression feature. NetWare manages the compression in the background. Administrators and users can flag files to indicate that they should be compressed after use or that they should never be compressed.

- *Block suballocation* This NetWare 4.x feature maximizes disk space. If there are any partially used disk blocks (usually a block is 8 KB in size), NetWare divides them into 512-byte suballocation blocks for the storage of small files or fragments of files.

N

Files up to 4GB in size are allowed, and the file system supports more than 2 million directories and files per volume and 100,000 open files. Volumes can span multiple disk drives, and the size of the volumes can be increased dynamically by adding new drives.

NetWare's salvageable file system allows recovery of deleted files. You can set a minimum amount of time that a deleted file must be kept recoverable, and you can mark files for immediate purging. You can also keep all deleted files until the volume runs out of disk space; then the oldest deleted files are removed to free space for new files. Trustee rights to files are preserved after a file has been recovered, and rights can be set to control who can salvage files. Deleted files are preserved even if a directory is deleted.

Data Protection Features

The NetWare network operating system contains several features that ensure the security and reliability of data. Security features protect data from unauthorized users and from virus attacks. NetWare supports hardware reliability features that provide redundancy to ensure that data is written correctly and is available should part of the system fail.

Security

The security features of NetWare are critical for large corporate-wide network environments. The NetWare file system and the DOS file system are quite different; a user cannot access the NetWare file system by starting the server with a DOS disk or by simply booting the disk. Of course, this doesn't prevent people from stealing or destroying a disk; you still need to keep a backup to protect yourself against such disasters, but a thief can't access the data without proper passwords and access rights.

Security is provided at several levels:

- *Login/password security*   Users type the LOGIN command to gain access to the file system. They enter their user name and then a password. No access is allowed without the password. After they are logged in, users can access computers in an internetwork based on the access rights that have been assigned to them by the network administrator.

- *Account restrictions*   Under NetWare, each user has an account that is managed by the network administrator. Restrictions can be applied to accounts to control when users can log in, the workstations they can log in at, and when their accounts expire. It's also possible to force users to change their passwords on a regular basis and to require a unique password that is not similar to one recently used.

- *Object and file security*   In NetWare 4.x, the network administrator grants users *trustee rights* to objects as well as directories, and files. These rights determine exactly how the users can access the resources of the system. Managers are typically granted rights to objects like user accounts and servers. Users are granted directory and file rights so they can access the filing system.

■ *Internetwork security* NetWare Directory Services (NDS) tracks all objects on an internetwork, including user objects and their access rights. Network administrators use NDS to create and manage user accounts, track network resources, and assign user access to network resources. Users log in once to gain access to all the network resources granted to them through the NDS system.

In addition to implementing these user security features, NetWare performs behind-the-scenes security checks. It encrypts all passwords at the server and encrypts user passwords on the cable as they are transferred to the server. This last feature prevents electronic eavesdroppers from obtaining a password by tapping the cable and then accessing the system as a normal user.

Reliability Features

The NetWare network operating system provides several important features that ensure the survivability and quick recovery of data on the server:

■ *Read-after-write verification* This feature reads every write to the disk at the time it is written to verify that it is correct. If an error occurs, the data is rewritten while it is still in the cache. An error can indicate a bad sector, which can be marked as unusable by the Hot Fix feature described shortly.

■ *Duplicate directories* NetWare duplicates the root directory structure to provide a backup in case the main directory structure is corrupted.

■ *Duplicate FAT* A duplicate of the file allocation table is maintained as a backup. If the original is lost, the disk remains accessible through the duplicate.

■ *Hot Fix* This feature detects and corrects disk defects as the system runs. Data in defective sectors is moved elsewhere on the disk, and the sectors are marked as unusable.

■ *System Fault Tolerance (SFT)* This feature allows you to provide redundancy for hardware in the system. You can install two disks and then mirror the contents of the main disk on the secondary disk (see "Disk Mirroring and Duplexing"). Should the main disk fail, the secondary disk takes over. The disk controller can also be duplicated, or duplexed, to further protect from hardware failure. SFT Level III (available optionally) takes redundancy a step further by duplexing entire servers. If the primary server goes down, the secondary server takes over without an interruption.

■ *Transaction tracking system (TTS)* The transaction tracking system protects data files from incomplete writes. This can occur when a user is editing records in a database and the server goes down. When the server is restarted, it backs out the incomplete transactions so that the files are the way they were before the

N

transaction began. Transactions must be either wholly completed or wholly abandoned under this system.

- *UPS monitoring*   NetWare monitors the status of an uninterruptible power supply (UPS) to determine if the server is running on backup power. A NetWare-compatible UPS is capable of providing this signal to NetWare. If a power failure occurs, NetWare warns users (who must be out of the blackout area or on their own UPS) and then begins to save any open information (cache data) and safely shut down the system.

Built-in Internetwork Routing

NetWare provides built-in internetwork routing services that allow you to interconnect as many network segments (token ring, Ethernet, ARCNET, and so on) as the server will hold network cards. The connected networks appear as one network to users. Creating a router is as simple as installing multiple interface cards in a NetWare server and then selecting drivers for those cards during setup or during post-setup maintenance. You can also install routing services in an external system to remove the additional workload from the server and improve its performance.

Communication Services

Novell sells a complete line of communication support packages called NetWare Communication Services that run in NetWare V.3.11 and 4 servers. These products provide LAN-to-host, LAN-to-LAN, and remote-to-LAN connectivity. NetWare Communication Services focuses on the LAN-to-host and network management requirements of organizations with large Systems Network Architecture (SNA) networks. The products include NetWare for SAA; NetWare 3270 LAN Workstation packages for DOS, the Macintosh, and Windows; and NetWare Communication Services Manager, a Windows-based management program.

Print Services

NetWare 4.x includes a print services package that lets you share up to 256 printers over the network. A print server manages print queues and the way that users access the printers. This print server can be installed in the NetWare file server or as a dedicated task on a workstation. You can attach printers to the print server or to any workstation in the network. Users access printers that are being shared through the print server.

Distributed Directory Services

Distributed directory services for NetWare are implemented as NetWare Directory Services (NDS) in NetWare 4.x. NDS is based on the X.500 Directory Services Specification. The service keeps track of all network users, servers, and resources on an internetwork. This information is kept in a database. Administrators and users can access the database to locate users and resources, without regard for their location.

NDS was designed with large internetworks in mind. It provides centralized management of the entire network directory with a common naming service. The directory database of users and resources is updated at regular intervals. The service provides gateways to other directory services, including Apple Name Binding Protocol, Sun Microsystems' Yellow Pages (NFS support), and the TCP/IP Domain Name Service.

Management Features

NetWare provides several utilities for monitoring the status of a network, and Novell sells management software packages that provide enhanced features. These are described in the following sections.

NetWare Administrator

NetWare 4.x includes the NetWare Administrator, which is a Windows-based application used to manage NetWare Directory Services objects, such as users, network resources, disk directories, and files. Figure N-7 shows a NetWare Administrator screen. A text-based version of NetWare Administrator called NETADMIN is also supplied with NetWare 4.x, but it does not provide support for managing directories and files. NetWare Administrator can be used instead of several command-line utilities. It is easier to use and provides more functionality. NetWare Administrator requires an Intel 80386 or higher system that runs Microsoft Windows.

Note the directory tree in the figure. At the top is an organization's name. Branching from that are its eastern division (DivEast) and its western division (DivWest). The DivEast branch is collapsed so that you can't see users or resources in it, but the DivWest branch is expanded. You could click any user or resource object under DivWest and then choose Details from the Object menu to make changes to the properties of that object. For example, you could select the AColgan object, which is a user account, and open it to change the user's login restrictions or rights to the file system.

Administrators use NetWare Administrator primarily to create user objects (accounts) and manage how users access the network, its resources, and its files. A browse feature lets you quickly locate similar objects. For example, you could list all users that live within a certain ZIP code area or that have rights to a certain server volume. Once you locate and select an object, you can use NetWare Administrator to change security rights, properties, and other aspects of the object. You can use NetWare Administrator to:

- Create additional objects, such as user and printer objects
- Change the login restrictions of users
- Change users' access to resources

N

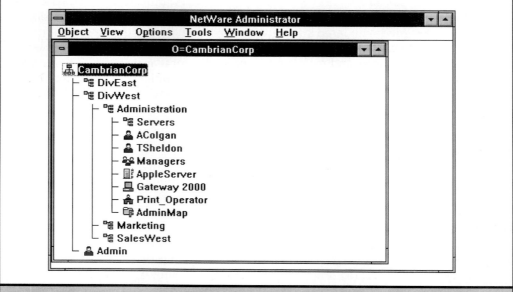

Figure N-7. *NetWare Administrator is a Windows-based object management program for NetWare*

- Change users' access to directories and files
- Change the trustees of objects (A trustee is a user who can use a given object.)
- Grant other users supervisory rights to objects on the network
- Specify groups of users and create login profiles for those users
- Create and edit system-wide and individual user login scripts
- Arrange and organize the structure of the NetWare Directory Services tree and its partitions

MONITOR

MONITOR is a NetWare Loadable Module that runs at the file server console or at a remote station if the Remote Management Facility (discussed next) is running. MONITOR lets you perform the following tasks from the console:

- Set password access for the NetWare console
- View the utilization of the server
- View the cache memory status
- View workstation connections

- See files opened by users
- Clear connections
- View the status of disk drives
- View the status of volumes
- Set verify levels for disk writes
- Activate and deactivate volumes and hard drives
- List the current LAN drivers
- List the currently loaded modules
- View the file lock status
- View memory usage

Remote Management

NetWare is bundled with the NetWare Remote Management Facility (RMF), which allows network administrators to install and upgrade NetWare, configure network services, and maintain NetWare from a remote workstation.

SERVMAN

SERVMAN is a new utility included with NetWare 4.x. It runs at the console and lets supervisors view and change the server configuration.

Those familiar with previous versions of NetWare are familiar with the SET command, which is used to make changes to the operating system. SERVMAN automates the use of this command by displaying help information for each set option and by displaying recommended settings. If a setting is changed, SERVMAN automatically updates the server startup files.

Requirements for Running NetWare

The following list defines the hardware you need to install and run NetWare version 3.11 and Netware version 4:

- An 80386 or higher system. Both the SX and DX versions of these processors are supported.

- A minimum of 5MB of memory, but 16MB is recommended as a starting point, because of the low price of memory and the benefits it offers to server performance. Servers on large networks might require more than 32MB of memory, depending on the software modules installed and the number of users who will access the server.

- A hard drive with a minimum of 30MB of storage. You need 5MB for a DOS partition and 25MB for the NetWare disk partition. If you're running NetWare for OS/2, you need a hard drive with a minimum of 120MB of storage. To

N

provide fault tolerance, you need duplicate drives and controllers or even duplicate servers if SFT Level III is used.

■ One or more network cards for each network you intend to bridge or route within the server.

RELATED ENTRIES   Client-Server Computing; Disks, Partitions, and Volumes under NetWare; DOS Requester, NetWare; Internetwork Packet Exchange; LAN Workplace Products, Novell; Large Internet Packet Exchange; NetWare 4.x Enhanced Features; NetWare Core Protocol; NetWare Loadable Module; NetWare SFT Level III; NetWare Shell; NetWare Volumes; *and* Novell

NetWare 4.x Enhanced Features

NetWare 4.x improves on the features of NetWare V.3.11 by providing Enterprise Network Support. Its most important feature is NetWare Directory Services (NDS), which enables network administrators to organize users and network resources such as servers and printers the way people naturally access them. Each user and resource, which is called an *object* in the NDS system, is tracked in a network-wide database. Administrators who need to manage the system and users who need to access resources or contact other users can quickly find objects in the NDS system, no matter where they are located in the internetwork. The database is constantly updated throughout the network so that it holds the latest information about objects. NDS makes global networks under Novell NetWare a reality by simplifying setup, tracking, and management.

NetWare Directory Services (NDS)

NDS provides important new features that simplify internetwork management. NDS organizes local and remote users and resources into a hierarchical tree structure, which makes them easy to manage.

NetWare's management utilities and procedures have changed extensively because of NDS. Although user, group, trustee, and rights concepts are similar to those in previous versions of NetWare, the methods for implementing them are somewhat different.

The Windows-based NetWare Administrator is a graphical utility supplied with NetWare that network administrators can use to create and manage user and resource objects. A text-based version of NetWare Administrator called NETADMIN is available for those who don't have a Windows or OS/2 workstation.

For related information, see "Directory Services, NetWare."

Memory Allocation and Protection

NetWare 4.x, unlike previous versions of NetWare, has one memory allocation pool. Memory is allocated among resources to optimize performance and ensure that memory is available to other NetWare Loadable Modules (NLMs) when a running

NLM closes. In previous versions of NetWare, program modules could run out of memory, because memory was not always released back to the operating system.

Memory resources are structured in NetWare 4.x to ensure that different processes running on the server do not use the same memory. A number of 4 KB memory pages are assigned to domains. NLMs are then loaded into the domains. Segments are created within domains for code and data, and a descriptor is assigned to each domain to protect the NLM running in it.

The operating system must also be protected from errant NLMs that might write to memory they do not own and consequently crash the server. To protect the operating system, privilege levels (also called protection rings) are used. There are four privilege levels, labeled 0 through 3, and the NetWare operating system runs in levels 0 and 3. If you suspect that an NLM is buggy and might crash the system, you can run it in level 3, which is a level that provides protection for the operating system. If an NLM tests successfully after a period of testing, you can move it to level 0. Novell now certifies NLMs that are safe to run in ring 0.

International Support

NetWare 4.x provides support for languages other than English. English is the default language, but you can change the language for the server and for NetWare Loadable Modules. Support files for languages are stored in subdirectories that branch from the SYS:\SYSTEM\NLS directory and SYS:\PUBLIC\NLS directory. To specify the language that the server will use, you create a file called SERVER.MSG that contains an appropriate language-specifying command. This file is stored in the DOS directory you use to start the server and where SERVER.EXE is stored. To specify the language that NLMs use, you type the LANGUAGE console command at the server. After the language is specified, utilities started by users load using that language.

Security Features

NetWare 4.x provides enhanced security features. NetWare Directory Services allows users to log in once at any server on the network and have access to services over the entire network, based on their rights. When a user logs in, the account name and password are verified and the user is authenticated onto the network. Authentication provides a secure means for users to access internetwork wide resources with only one log in. Basically, authentication guarantees that a user's password never goes beyond the login process. It is immediately converted to a different code that identifies the user and the station they are logged into during the user's current session. (For more information, see "Authentication and Authorization.")

Optical Disk Jukebox and Tape Storage Support

NetWare 4.x's High Capacity Storage System (HCSS) provides the ability to integrate libraries of optical disks or tapes into the NetWare filing system. Optical disk

N

jukeboxes use autochanger techniques to mount and dismount optical disks, based on user needs. Users see files on jukeboxes as they see any other network files. When a user requests a file that is stored on an optical disk, the file is moved from the optical disk to faster hard disk storage. Files that are no longer needed are moved back to optical storage.

Moving files from the hard disk to an optical disk is known as *migration*. Moving the files back to the hard disk is called *de-migration*. Migrated files retain their original path names so that users can access them without knowing they are from the jukebox. When a user requests a migrated file, that file is de-migrated to the faster file server disk. Administrators and supervisors can mark specific files as migratable. After a period of nonuse, files marked as migratable are moved to optical or tape storage to free up space on the hard disk volume.

The HCSS is designed for archiving seldom-used files. It is useful in image processing applications, which store graphics images of invoices, legal documents, contracts, and other documents online for quick referral, as discussed next.

Imaging System Support

Imaging systems are used to manage paper documents such as credit card applications, legal forms, insurance forms, bids, proposals, contracts, and other documents by allowing those documents to be imaged and stored on archive storage systems such as optical disks. Imaging systems are the digital equivalents of microfilm storage-and-retrieval systems that provide database-like search and retrieval. Novell is working with Eastman Kodak in the development of imaging services for NetWare. In addition, Lotus and Kodak are working on an image-enabled version of Lotus' Notes information management software.

High-speed networks provide an ideal platform for imaging systems because they make imaged documents available to a large number of users. Workstations increasingly have high-resolution displays and sufficient memory to handle imaged documents.

Consider the benefits of archiving invoice images on an optical disk jukebox. If a customer wants to see a record of past purchases, the invoices are retrieved from the archive and printed on a local printer. In a paper system, old documents are retrieved from the back-office filing system or, in some cases, requested from an offsite storage area. Optical disks store large amounts of data for quick online retrieval at a relatively low price. With WAN links, users at remote offices can retrieve document images that would normally not be available to them.

Imaging services are installed at the NetWare server as a NetWare Loadable Module. These services provide for the compression, storage, and manipulation of imaged documents, as well as the transmission of those documents over the network.

Graphical Utilities

In NetWare 4.x, new Windows- or OS/2-based text utilities can be used instead of command-line utilities. The Windows-based NetWare Administrator, for example, offers a new way to manage the network, its users, and its objects. NetWare Administrator does the work of almost all the command-line utilities, so if you run Windows (or OS/2), you can take advantage of its consolidated features.

Changes in the File System

The NetWare 4.x file system has some features not available in older versions of NetWare. These features are listed in the following sections.

Block Suballocation

In older versions of NetWare, a full block was used to store a file even if the file was much smaller than the configured block size. Block suballocation allows the last part of several files to share a disk block, thus increasing the amount of information that can be stored on a disk. Suballocation units are 512 bytes in size. Leftover fragments from other files can share these blocks.

File Compression

File compression lets you store more data on the file server hard disk by compressing the data. The compression ratio in a volume is approximately 63 percent. You can enable file compression during NetWare installation, or you can run the INSTALL utility at any time. Compression is handled in the background and has little impact on system performance. Before compressing a file, the operating system determines whether any disk sectors will be saved by doing so. Some files do not compress well. The original file is maintained on the server until a second file is successfully compressed to ensure that the file is not corrupted should the server go down.

File and Directory Attributes in NetWare 4.x

Several file and directory attributes have been added to support the High Capacity Storage System. In addition, the old Write Audit and Read Audit attributes have been removed. The new attributes are listed here:

Letter	Attribute	Description
C	Can't Compress	A status attribute that indicates that a file cannot be compressed due to lack of disk space. Not used for directories.
C	Compressed	A status attribute that indicates that a file has been compressed. Not used for directories.
Dc	Don't Compress	Prevents the compression of a file. When applied to a directory, prevents the compression of all files in the directory.

N

Dm	Don't Migrate	Prevents a file from being migrated to a secondary storage device such as an optical disk jukebox. When applied to a directory, prevents all files in the directory from being migrated.
Im	Immediate Compress	When applied to a file, the file is compressed as soon as possible. When applied to a directory, the files in the directory are compressed as soon as possible.
M	Migrated	A status attribute that indicates that a file has been migrated to a secondary storage device such as an optical disk jukebox.

RELATED ENTRIES   Disks, Partitions, and Volumes under NetWare; Internetwork Packet Exchange; LAN Workplace Products; Large Internet Packet Exchange; NetWare; NetWare Loadable Modules; NetWare SFT Level III; NetWare Shell; NetWare Volumes; *and* Novell

NetWare Core Protocol (NCP)

NetWare Core Protocol (NCP) is the principal protocol for transmitting information between a NetWare server and its clients. NCP handles login requests and many other types of requests to the file system and the printing system. Internetwork Packet Exchange (IPX) is the underlying protocol that carries NCP messages. NCP is a client-server local area network (LAN) protocol. Workstations form NCP requests and package them for transport over the network using IPX. At the server, NCP requests are received, unpackaged, and interpreted. Understanding NCP messages and viewing them with protocol analyzers can help you determine which services are most often requested of the server. From this information, you can determine whether a particular server is overloaded or having problems.

NCP provides the services that are available to users of Novell NetWare networks. These services fall into the following categories:

■ File access (opening and closing files; reading and writing data to and from files)

■ File locking

■ Security

■ Tracking of resource allocation

■ Event notification

■ NetWare Directory Services and synchronization with other servers

■ Connection and communication

■ Print services and queue management

■ Network management

The NCP is transparent to both users and stand-alone workstation applications. For example, a user can request a file from the network server, which appears as a local drive. A redirecter function in the workstation determines whether the file request is for a local drive or for the network drive, and then routes it appropriately. In this respect, the redirection software in the workstation works with the NCP to provide services to users.

NCP is a LAN protocol that was originally designed with the assumption that servers and workstations would be relatively close. When a router gets involved and connections are made over wide-area network links, NCP causes traffic congestion. It uses a request/response scheme to manage server/workstation communication. If a workstation makes a request, it must first wait for a response from the server before making another request. This required acknowledgment adds excess traffic, but several schemes to solve the problem have been developed by Novell. See "Internetwork Packet Exchange."

You can track what users are doing on the network by analyzing NCP with a protocol analyzer. Each NCP packet contains a code that identifies the type of service requested or being serviced. These codes are easily identified by most protocol analyzers, and you can use filters to see a particular type of service or traffic from one workstation. A brief description of some of the calls is listed here:

- Login and logout requests
- Directory handling requests (such as create, list, rename, delete, and others)
- File handling requests (such as open, close, create, erase, and others)
- Server requests (clear connections, down the file server, get disk information, get file server information, send messages, and others)
- Messaging services (send or receive messages)
- Printer and queue services
- File locking and unlocking services

This list only describes the general category of service requests and responses. There are hundreds of calls, each with a specific purpose and code. For example, the request "Create Directory" has a specific request type number (2222), a function code (22), and a subfunction code (10). These codes appear in packet listing during protocol analysis. For the purposes of this discussion, these codes are not important. However, they do point out how workstations communicate with servers and how you can track the activities with a protocol analyzer.

For example, you might want to track a user's activities because you suspect the user might be engaging in unauthorized activities, or you might want to track the activities of a user for auditing purposes. Novell's LANalyzer can filter out the packets produced for a single user's workstation and produce a log of every service requested by the user.

N

By following the stream of NCP requests and responses between a server and its client, you can watch users log in and log out, start applications, access files on the server, communicate with other users, and perform a number of other activities. However, for the most part, you track packet flow to isolate problems or bottlenecks in communication.

RELATED ENTRIES   Internetwork Packet Exchange; NetWare; NetWare Shell; *and* Protocol Analyzers

NetWare Disks, Partitions, and Volumes
See Disks, Partitions, and Volumes Under NetWare.

NetWare Electronic Software Distribution

Electronic software distribution provides a way for network administrators to automatically update the operating systems, drivers, applications, and network protocols on users' workstations. Novell's Network Navigator Electronic Software Distribution product line implements the NetLS and Licensing Service API (LS API) licensing systems. Network Navigator provides reports on network inventory, configuration, and update activities. It runs on IBM mainframe systems and Tandem computers, but software distributions can be downloaded to Netware, Microsoft, and Banyan servers.

RELATED ENTRY   Electronic Software Distribution and Licensing

NetWare Link Service Protocol (NLSP)

NetWare Link Service Protocol (NLSP) is a new NetWare routing protocol that provides improved internetworking capabilities and helps reduce the cost incurred when using wide area network links. NLSP reduces routing overhead and allows customers to chose from a variety of multivendor routers that support the protocol. Also in the works is an extended Internetwork Packet Exchange (IPX) protocol for wide area networking called IPXWAN. IPXWAN operates over Point-to-Point Protocol (PPP), X.25, Frame Relay, and Integrated Services Digital Network (ISDN) wide area links and is designed to provide interoperability among multivendor routers when used in wide area network installations.

NLSP is a link-state routing protocol based on Intermediate System-to-Intermediate System (IS-IS) routing maintenance protocol, which is part of the Open Systems Interconnection (OSI) protocol suite. The most common link state routing method is Open Shortest Path First (OSPF). *Link state routing* provides a way to control the routing process and let routers respond faster to changes in the network, such as a broken link or the addition of a new router and network. Routes can be based on the avoidance of congested areas, the speed of a line, the cost of using a line, or various priorities. The protocol maps out the routers within the immediate area. Changes in network configuration are more readily available and routers don't need to exchange information about the networks they service as often. The Dijkstra algorithm is used to calculate the shortest path to a destination.

RELATED ENTRIES   Internetwork Packet Exchange; Link State Routing; Open Shortest Path First Protocol; Routing, NetWare; Routing, OSI; Routing Protocols; *and* Wide Area Networks

NetWare Loadable Module (NLM)

The NetWare 3.x and 4.x operating systems are modular and expandable. You add functionality to the operating system, or make changes, upgrades, and additions by installing NetWare Loadable Modules (NLMs) at the server. Some of the services provided by NLMs are:

- Support for storing files for operating systems other than DOS
- Communication services
- Database services
- Messaging services
- Archive and backup services
- Network management services

You can load or unload any module at any time from the server console without bringing down the server. Each module uses additional memory, so you need to make sure the server has enough memory to handle the NLMs you plan to load. Because the modules are located in the server along with the operating system, they are tightly coupled with the operating system and have instant access to services.

RELATED ENTRIES   NetWare; NetWare 4.x Enhanced Features; *and* Novell

NetWare Products

The following operating system products are available from Novell and run in NetWare 3.x and NetWare 4.x servers.

NETWARE FLEX/IP   The Novell FLeX/IP product is a NetWare Loadable Module (NLM) that solves some of the basic file, print, and management problems in the NetWare UNIX environment. FLeX/IP contains three individual products, which are represented by the letters *F, L,* and *X. F* stands for File Transfer Protocol (FTP), which provides file transfer capabilities. *L* stands for Line Printer Daemon, which provides standard UNIX print utilities that make printer access more transparent between UNIX and NetWare systems. Without the *L* utilities, NetWare print sharing and UNIX

N

print sharing tend to get in each other's way on an internetwork. *X* stands for X-Windows protocol support. When the protocols are installed, a network administrator can run the NetWare console on a UNIX system and manage the NetWare network from a remote location.

NETWARE FOR SYSTEMS APPLICATION ARCHITECTURE (SAA)   NetWare for SAA gives NetWare workstations access to IBM mainframe and AS/400 host systems. The security, name services, and administration of NetWare are retained. Up to 506 display, printer, and Advanced Program-to-Program Communication (APPC) sessions are possible at once. Access to AS/400 applications is transparent to NetWare workstations. NetWare for SAA is an NLM that is installed in a NetWare file server to provide gateway services to network users. It eliminates the need for a separate gateway to the IBM systems. Alternatively, the product can run in a dedicated communication server when the NetWare Runtime application is used. NetWare Runtime is bundled with NetWare for SAA.

NETWARE FOR UNIX   NetWare for UNIX provides NetWare services on a wide variety of computer systems. It has been ported to systems manufactured by NetWare for UNIX partners such as Data General, Hewlett-Packard, IBM, MIPS/Silicon Graphics, Sequent, SunConnect, and Unisys. A host system running NetWare for UNIX can function as a NetWare file server, and provide file, print and backup services to network clients that run DOS, OS/2, Microsoft Windows, or Apple Macintosh operating systems.

NETWARE NETWORK FILING SYSTEM (NFS)   NFS is a distributed file system for UNIX environments. NetWare NFS gives UNIX users access to the NetWare environment from their systems. NetWare NFS is installed on the NetWare server, making files, printers, and other network resources shareable by UNIX users. The Transmission Control Protocol/Internet Protocol (TCP/IP) communication transport protocols are required to support NetWare NFS.

RELATED ENTRIES   Distributed File Systems; NetWare; Novell; Systems Application Architecture; Transmission Control Protocol/Internet Protocol; *and* UNIX

NetWare SFT Level III

NetWare SFT Level III is an optional Novell software product that provides true fault tolerance. It ensures that mission-critical applications are continuously available to users. An SFT III configuration consists of two servers that are connected by a high-speed data link. One server mirrors the data of the other and is immediately available should that server go down. There is no loss of service to users. SFT III is a software-only solution that works with off-the-shelf server hardware.

SFT III protects against failures that occur in random access memory (RAM), on disk, and in local area network (LAN) adapters. It allows servers to be placed in geographically different areas to protect against local disasters or power problems, but high-speed links are required to maintain tight synchronization between the duplexed systems. In addition, because the servers are mirrored, routine service and upgrades can take place on one while the other continues operation. When the upgraded server is brought back on line, its file system synchronizes with the other server.

To improve performance under SFT III, Novell recommends using dual-processor systems. One microprocessor performs all hardware-related input/output (I/O) and mirroring synchronization, and the other microprocessor handles file services and runs other server applications. You'll also need compatible high-performance Mirrored Server Links (MSLs) in each server. MSLs are typically 100 Mbits/sec Ethernet or fiber-optic links and are available from vendors such as Standard Microsystems and Thomas-Conrad.

RELATED ENTRIES   Data Protection; Disaster Recovery; Disk Mirroring and Duplexing; Duplexed Systems; Fault Management; Mirroring; Redundant Arrays of Inexpensive Disks; *and* System Fault Tolerance

NetWare Shell

NetWare is basically a client-server operating system. The NetWare shell software is a client program that enables a workstation to connect with a NetWare server. The shell, or *requester software* as it is called, intercepts requests for network services and sends them to NetWare servers. These requests can include a request to open a file or print a file on a shared printer. There are two versions of the shell. The older IPX/NET*x* shell is still in use on many local area networks (LANs), but all current versions of NetWare use the Open Data-link Interface (ODI) shell, which provides support for multiple protocol stacks and multiple network interface cards.

The requester software determines whether user or application service requests are for the local operating system or for a NetWare server. If the commands are for NetWare, it directs them across the network. Local commands are sent to the operating system in the workstation. The standard communication protocol in NetWare networks is the Internetwork Packet Exchange (IPX) protocol, but with ODI, it is possible to load Transmission Control Protocol/Internet Protocol (TCP/IP), AppleTalk, and other protocols so users can access other types of systems and networks.

IPX/NET*x* Shell

There are two major components in the IPX/NETx shell. Both are terminate-and-stay-resident (TSR) software modules that are typically loaded when the workstation is booted. IPX.COM is loaded first to initialize the network interface card and establish the basic connection between the workstation and the server. NET*x* is then loaded to provide support for a specific version of DOS. Note that the *x* in NET*x* refers to a DOS version, such as DOS version 3 or DOS version 5.

IPX.COM must be configured for each workstation based on the type of network interface card in use and the settings of the card. A file called IPX.OBJ is linked with a

N

driver specifically designed for the network interface card to create IPX.COM using a utility supplied with NetWare. Workstations with similar interface cards that have the same board settings can use the same IPX.COM file, but if any workstation uses a different brand of card, or a card with a different interrupt or I/O setting, a unique IPX.COM file must be create to match the board.

Several version of NETx.COM are supplied with the NetWare workstation software to match the versions of DOS that are available. NETx.COM must be loaded after the IPX.COM file. Once the shell software is loaded, the NetWare server is accessible as drive F, or the next available drive, depending on the number of drives in the local workstation. You switch to the drive and execute the LOGIN command to access the server.

A file called NET.CFG can be created to hold special startup parameters and configuration information for each individual workstation.

NetWare DOS Requester

The NetWare DOS Requester is a set of modules that replace the IPX/NETx shell. They are available in the latest version of NetWare. An installation utility automatically loads the modules and configures the workstation. It asks the installer to specify the type of network interface card and the settings for the card. The software is then installed in a directory called NWCLIENT. The modules are described here in the order that they load when the requester software is started.

- *Link Support Layer (LSL)* The LSL is the software driver that directs traffic between multiple protocol stacks such as IPX and TCP/IP if they are loaded.

- *LAN Driver* This is a specific driver that matches the network interface card or cards installed in the workstation. The driver might be called NE2000, for example, to indicate the Novell standard Ethernet adapter.

- *IPXODI* This is the driver that loads the IPX protocol stack. Other drivers can be specified here, such as the driver that loads the TCP/IP protocol stack.

- *VLM* This is an executable file that loads the DOS Requester support software. VLM actually loads a whole set of modules that handle network connections, Directory Services or bindery (pre-NetWare 4.x) support, encryption and authentication support, as well as file input and output support.

RELATED ENTRIES   Client-Server Computing; DOS Requester, NetWare; Internetwork Packet Exchange; LAN Workplace Products; Large Internet Packet Exchange; Network Driver Standards; Novell; *and* Open Data-link Interface

NetWare Volumes

The NetWare filing system consists of servers that have one or more volumes. The first volume on each server is always called SYS. The default names for additional volumes are VOL1, VOL2, and so on, but you can give them custom names, such as OS2VOL, MACVOL, USERS, or EMAIL, that describe what is stored on the volume and who might use it. Each volume has its own directory structure.

Volumes are mounted when the NetWare server is booted. The SYS volume is mounted automatically; other volumes are mounted by using commands in the server startup file AUTOEXEC.NCF. You can also mount or dismount volumes by using the MOUNT or DISMOUNT command at the NetWare server console. It is beneficial to leave unused or little used volumes unmounted because each volume uses anywhere from .5MB to 2MB of memory, depending on the size and type of volume (DOS name space, UNIX name space, or Macintosh name space).

You can expand volumes by adding hard disks to the system and using the NetWare INSTALL utility to integrate the disks with existing volumes, in some cases without downing the server. Volumes are divided physically into segments that can span one or more hard disks. A volume can have up to 32 volume segments that span different disks, but each disk can hold only eight volume segments. Spreading volume segments to different disks improves performance because it allows volume segments to be read or written simultaneously. The down side is that if one of the disks goes down, the entire volume will not mount. It is recommended that you always mirror segmented volumes.

The volume is the highest level in the NetWare filing system. A volume has a root directory and branching subdirectories. As mentioned, the first NetWare volume on a server is called SYS, and it contains the NetWare system and public files, unless they are moved elsewhere.

Other volumes are accessible by mapping their names to a drive letter by using the MAP command. NetWare allows up to 64 volumes per server. For example, you could map the BUDGDOCS directory on the APPS volume to drive letter R, and then switch to the volume and directory by typing the drive specification R:. For users to list or work with the files in a directory, they must have rights to that directory.

NetWare Directories

The NetWare directory system is similar to the DOS directory system. Each volume has one root directory. Directories can branch from the root, and subdirectories can branch from these directories. The NetWare installation program creates the directory structure of the SYS volume, which is shown in Figure N-8 and described in the following paragraphs.

SYS:SYSTEM   The SYSTEM directory holds NetWare executable files and other modules that are normally accessed only by supervisors.

SYS:PUBLIC   The PUBLIC directory holds the NetWare utilities that are typically accessed by all users.

N

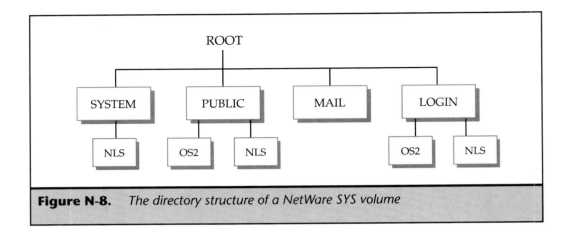

Figure N-8. *The directory structure of a NetWare SYS volume*

SYS:LOGIN The LOGIN directory contains the LOGIN commands and other files required to log users into the system. It is mapped to the first network drive at workstations before logging in.

SYS:MAIL The MAIL directory is a remnant of previous NetWare versions. NetWare used to create a subdirectory in MAIL for each user and store their login scripts in these subdirectories. Login scripts are now stored as part of user objects in the NetWare Directory Services system. However, MAIL is retained for applications that require it.

Directory Naming and Mapping

You refer to directories on NetWare volumes in the same way you refer to DOS directories: by using paths. You add the volume name to a path to refer to another volume, and you add the server name to refer to servers. For example, the full name of the SYSTEM directory on the SYS volume is SYS:SYSTEM. If this directory had a subdirectory called UTILS, its full name would be SYS:SYSTEM\UTILS. You don't need to specify the volume name if you are already working on the volume. If this directory is on a server called ACCTG, you would refer to it as ACCTG\SYS:SYSTEM\UTILS.

Users often need space on the hard drive for their personal files and programs. Most NetWare supervisors create home directories for users that branch from a parent directory called SYS:HOME or SYS:USERS. (Note that the parent directory doesn't need to be on the SYS volume.)

RELATED ENTRIES Disks, Partitions, and Volumes under NetWare; NetWare; NetWare 4.x Enhanced Features; *and* Volumes, NetWare

Network Architecture

Network architectures defines how computer equipment and other devices are linked together to form a communication system that allows users to share information and resources. There are proprietary network architectures such as IBM's Systems Network Architecture (SNA) and DEC's Digital Network Architecture (DNA) and there are open architectures like the Open Systems Interconnection (OSI) model defined by the International Organization for Standardization (ISO). Network architectures are defined in layers (see "Layered Architecture"). If the standard is open, it provides a way for vendors to design software and hardware that is interoperable with other vendor's products. However, the OSI model has remained a model, rather that a fully accepted international standard. Due to the wide variety of existing de facto standards, most vendors have simply decided to support the many different protocols that are used in the industry rather than conform to one standard.

Layering specifies different functions and services at levels in a "protocol stack." The protocols define how communication takes place, such as the flow of data between systems, error detection and correction, the formatting of data, the packaging of data, and other features. The basic structure is shown in Figure N-9.

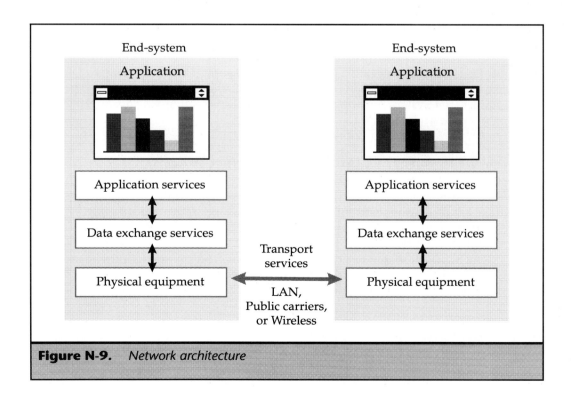

Figure N-9. *Network architecture*

N

Communication is the primary objective of any network architecture. In the past, a vendor was more concerned with making sure its own products could communicate, and while it might have opened the architecture up so other vendors could produce compatible products, making them compatible was often difficult. At any rate, protocols specify a set of rules and procedures that define how communication takes place at different levels of operation. The layers define physical connections, such as the cable type, access method, and topology, and how data is sent over the network. Further up are protocols that establish connections and maintain communication sessions between systems, and still further up are protocols that define how applications access lower-level network communication functions and interoperate with applications in other systems attached to the network.

As mentioned, the OSI model has become the model to which all other network architectures and protocols are compared. The purpose of the OSI model is to coordinate communication standards between vendors. While many vendors have continued to pursue their own standards, some, such as DEC and IBM have integrated OSI into their networking strategies along with Internet standards such as TCP/IP.

Interoperability is a major concern as LANs are connected into enterprise-wide networks. Various techniques are used to accomplish this, including the use of multiple protocols in a single system or techniques that hide protocols with a layer of "middleware." Middleware can also provide an interface that lets different applications on different platforms exchange information. Using these techniques, users can access a variety of multivendor products from their desktop applications.

RELATED ENTRIES   AppleTalk; Client-Server Computing; Digital Network Architecture; Distributed Computing Environment; Layered Architecture; Middleware; Open System Interconnection; Systems Application Architecture; *and* Systems Network Architecture

Network Control Program (NCP)

NCP is the control software that runs in an IBM Front End Processor (FEP). A FEP is a dedicated computer that controls communication between an IBM host computer and the terminals that communicate with it. The IBM 3725 and 3745 are front-end processors that run the NCP software, which communicates with programs running in physical units (PUs). FEPs connect to IBM 3270 hosts.

NCP is an application that basically acts as an input/output operating system. It manages all the data coming in from a network and going out to a network. The NCP is actually generated by the mainframe as a module that is loaded on the FEP when it starts up.

RELATED ENTRIES   Cluster Controllers, IBM; Communication Controller; IBM; IBM Mainframe Environment; IBM Networking Blueprint; Systems Network Architecture

Network Driver Interface Specification (NDIS)

The Microsoft Network Driver Interface Specification (NDIS) was designed to give network users access to a variety of protocols by detaching those protocols from network interface cards. In the design, protocols don't need to know anything about the interface card. There is no card-specific interface, only a common interface for protocols, as shown in Figure N-10. To use an NDIS card, you install the card and its driver, load all the protocols you want to use, and bind them with a command called NETBIND.

The primary purpose of NDIS is to allow the loading of multiple protocol stacks at a server or workstation so users can communicate with a variety of protocols. Before NDIS (or the comparable Novell Open Data-link Interface or ODI), it was necessary to unload one protocol stack, then load another, possibly turning off the computer if it was not possible to easily unload a protocol stack. NDIS lets multiple protocol stacks address one network interface card (NIC) and the systems on the attached network as shown on the left in Figure N-11, or lets each stack address its own NIC, as shown on the right in Figure N-11. NDIS allows a workstation to have as many as four NICs, and each NIC can support up to four protocol stacks.

For example, a user who needs to connect with both a Novell NetWare server (Internetwork Packet Exchange, or IPX) and a UNIX-based system (Transmission Control Protocol/Internet Protocol, or TCP/IP) attached to the same network simply

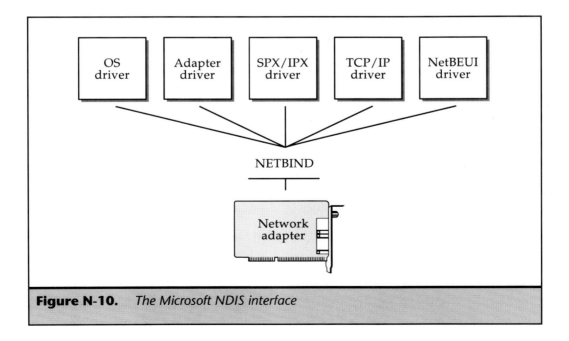

Figure N-10. *The Microsoft NDIS interface*

N

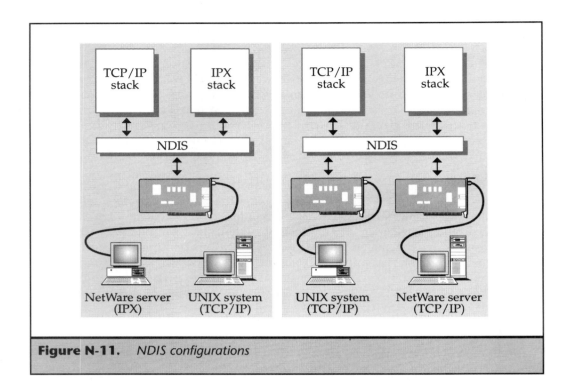

Figure N-11.   *NDIS configurations*

loads the IPX and TCP/IP protocol stacks together. NDIS arbitrates between the two protocol stacks and makes sure that incoming messages from the NetWare server are directed to the IPX stack and the TCP/IP messages are directed through the TCP/IP stack. NDIS provides either protocol with access to the network interface card and the media. If the NetWare server and UNIX system are on separate networks, the workstation needs two interface cards and must load a protocol stack for each, as shown in Figure N-11.

In the same way, a Novell NetWare server or a Microsoft Windows NT Advanced Server can run multiple protocol stacks so users at different types of workstations (DOS, UNIX, Macintosh, and so on) can access the servers.

When NDIS loads during Windows NT boot phase, it reads the contents of a file called PROTOCOL.INI. This file specifies the NICs installed in the workstation and the protocol stacks to bind to each card.

To provide support for NDIS along with ODI, Novell developed the Open Data-link Interface Network support specification, or ODINSUP (SUP is derived from "support"). It allows coexistence of the ODI and NDIS network driver interfaces so workstations can connect with any ODI systems such as an IPX server and any NDIS system, such as an NDIS LAN Manager server.

RELATED ENTRIES   Client Software; DOS Requester; LAN Drivers; NetWare Shell; *and* Open Data-link Interface

Network Driver Standards

In the past, each network operating system supplied a standard driver interface and network communication protocols. For example, Novell NetWare networks supported the Internetwork Packet Exchange (IPX) communication protocol on a wide variety of network interface cards (NICs). Today, it is necessary to connect many different types of systems running different protocols to a network. This is due to the creation of enterprise networks that tie together networks in formerly independent departments or workgroups, or the merging of companies that use different networks.

Two major network driver standards are available to allow multi-protocol support. The Microsoft *Network Driver Interface Specification (NDIS)* and the Novell *Open Data-link Interface (ODI)* provide a way to load multiple protocol stacks into the memory of a computer and support one or more network interface cards. Each of these standards is discussed under the appropriate titles.

RELATED ENTRIES   Client Software; DOS Requester; LAN Drivers; Network Driver Interface Specification; NetWare Shell; *and* Open Data-link Interface

Network Dynamic Data Exchange (NetDDE)

See NetDDE.

Network File System (NFS)

See Distributed File Systems; File Systems in the Network Environment.

Networking Blueprint

See IBM Networking Blueprint.

Network Interface Card

Network interface cards (NICs) are adapters installed in a computer that provide the connection point to a network. Each NIC is designed for a specific type of network, such as Ethernet, token ring, FDDI, ARCNET, and others. They operate at the Physical layer relative to the Open Systems Interconnection (OSI) protocol stack and provide an attachment point for a specific type of cable such as coaxial cable, twisted-pair cable, or fiber-optic cable. NICs for wireless local area networks have an antenna for communication with a base station.

N

Network interface cards are defined by Physical layer protocols. These protocols define mechanical and electrical interface specifications. The mechanical specifications define the physical connection methods for cable. The electrical specifications define the methods for transmitting bit-streams across the cable and the control signals that provide the timing of data transfers across the network. Depending on the type of network interface card, a specific cable access method is used in accordance with IEEE 802.*x* standards or other standards. The IEEE 802.*x* standards define carrier sense multiple access/collision detection (CSMA/CD), token passing, and other access methods. IEEE 802.*x* networks such as Ethernet, token ring, and FDDI use these access methods.

Circuitry on the card handles many of the network communication functions. To prepare for data transmission, a *handshaking* process takes place between two stations. This handshaking establishes communication parameters, such as the transmission speed, packet size, timeout parameters, and buffer size. Once the communication parameters are established, transmission of data packets begins. Data is converted in two ways before it is placed on the cable for transmission. First, a parallel-to-serial conversion transforms data into a bit-stream of electrical signals that are transmitted over the network. Second, data is encoded and compressed to improve transmission speed in some cases.

Network interface cards are available in two categories: those that follow the standard specification, and those that follow the specification but add enhancements to boost performance. Some of these special features are discussed later. Keep in mind that differences in hardware design among interface cards on a network can slow performance. For example, a network card with a 16-bit interface typically sends data to an 8-bit card faster than the 8-bit card can process it. To solve this bottleneck, *memory buffers* are implemented to capture and hold incoming data, preventing data overflows and allowing the 16-bit card to complete its transmission, even while the 8-bit card continues to process the information it has collected in its buffer.

Another type of bottleneck occurs between the network interface card and the memory of the computer. There are four methods for moving information from the network interface card into the computer once it has been received, as discussed next. These methods largely apply to Intel-based systems.

DIRECT MEMORY ACCESS (DMA)   When the direct memory access (DMA) method is used, a DMA controller on the PC takes control of the bus and transfers data from the network interface card's buffer directly into a designated memory location on the PC. This reduces some of the work of the CPU and increases its performance. While data is being transferred, the CPU can do some other task, but it cannot access memory.

SHARED ADAPTER MEMORY   With the shared adapter memory technique, cards have their own memory that the system processor can access directly. The memory is mapped to addresses in the upper memory blocks of a DOS system (above 640 KB). In other words, the processor thinks the memory on the card is part of its system memory and accesses it accordingly. This can lead to problems if you are not careful to ensure that the memory area allocated to the network interface card is not used by another card or process (a driver or application, for example).

NOTE: When you set up a shared-memory card, you set switches on the card or set its startup commands to specify the memory area the card will use. The adapter's manual refers to these as base memory addresses. The shared memory starts at the base memory address and extends the length of the shared memory, which may be 8 KB, 16 KB, or 32 KB. You need to ensure that no other card or process uses this memory. If so, you must change the base memory address of the network interface card or the adapter that it conflicts with.

SHARED SYSTEM MEMORY The shared system memory technique uses a shared block of memory (usually 8 KB to 32 KB in size) in the system (not on the card) that is controlled by a special processor on the network interface card. The NIC places information in a shared memory area where the system processor can access it directly. As with the shared adapter memory technique, you must ensure that the shared memory area is not used by another card or process.

BUS MASTERING With the bus mastering technique, a network adapter can transfer information directly to system memory without interrupting the system processor. Cards that use this method provide a form of enhanced DMA in which the adapter assumes control of the system bus and writes information directly to the memory of the computer without requiring permission from the processor. Bus mastering is possible on MCA and EISA machines because of their advanced bus designs. Although cards that use the bus mastering technique can increase performance by 20 to 70 percent, they are too expensive for common workstations, but are highly recommended for high-performance workstations.

Global Addressing

Global addressing ensures that every network interface card has a unique identifying node address. Token ring and Ethernet card addresses are hard-wired on the card. ARCNET addresses are switch-selectable by the end user.

The Institute of Electrical and Electronics Engineers (IEEE) committee is in charge of assigning addresses to token ring and Ethernet cards. Each manufacturer is given a unique code and a block of addresses. When installing a card, it is a good idea to determine the card address and write it down for future reference. You can also use a diagnostics utility supplied with the card to determine its address after you've installed the card in a system. You might also find the address on a label attached to the card.

Remote-Boot PROMs

Most network cards come with a socket for remote-boot programmable read-only memory (PROM). You use remote-boot PROMs on diskless workstations that can't boot on their own but instead boot from the network server. A diskless workstation is less expensive than a system with floppy disk and hard disk drives. It is also more secure because users can't download valuable data to floppy disk or upload viruses and unauthorized software.

N

What to Look For

Network interface cards are available to fit AT-class systems with 8-bit or 16-bit Industry Standard Architecture (ISA) bus slots. The 16-bit cards give better performance at a higher price. Cards are also available for Micro Channel Architecture (MCA) systems such as the IBM PS/2 line and for Extended Industry Standard Architecture (EISA) bus systems such as the Compaq DESKPRO 486 and Compaq SYSTEMPRO.

Whenever possible, use high-performance EISA-based, MCA-based, or PCI-based computers and network interface cards for servers. These interfaces provide the performance the server needs to handle network traffic and management. You can use less-expensive NICs in workstations that don't generate a lot of network traffic, such as word processing systems. However, high-performance graphics or engineering workstations will need high-performance cards.

With the increased use of graphical user interfaces such as Windows as well as multimedia and the potential for real-time video, it makes sense to install high-performance networks such as a 100 Mbits/sec Ethernet. Another strategy is to attach servers to a separate local area network. Many vendors make hubs or bridges that provide Ethernet or token ring ports for workstations and FDDI ports for servers.

RELATED ENTRIES   Access Method, Network; Extended Industry Standard Architecture Bus; IEEE 802 Standards; MicroChannel Architecture Bus; Open Systems Interconnection Model; Peripheral Component Interconnect; *and* Wireless LAN Communication

Network Layer, OSI Model

The Open Systems Interconnection (OSI) model is a standard defined by the International Organization for Standardization (ISO). It defines a layered architecture in which each layer defines protocols for various levels of communication. Each layer holds a "conversation" with its equivalent layer in the other system. Messages for the conversion are transmitted across the network by passing them down to lower layers in the protocol stack. The bottom layer, called the Physical layer, is responsible for transmitting these messages as bit-streams across the physical media. The layers immediately above the Physical layer define how data is packaged for transport over the physical network. The next layers up handle error detection and correction, the establishment of sessions, as well as methods for keeping the communication session alive. Each layer provides a higher level of functionality. Finally, the uppermost layers define how applications interface with the network. The OSI model helps developers create products that work over a large variety of platforms and operating systems.

The Network layer is the third layer of the protocol stack, just above the Physical and Data-Link layers. It is responsible for routing messages that have been assembled by higher-layer protocols and handling communication errors. It is interesting to note that the error control mechanisms provided by the Network layer are rarely used in the local area network (LAN) environment. The reason is simple. LANs are relatively error-free so connectionless datagram services are typically used to transfer data. Connectionless services trade reliable delivery (there are no acknowledgments of successful delivery) for efficiency. Consequently, the upper Transport layer is responsible for checking to make sure that all packets arrived and requesting a retransmission of any packets that didn't arrive.

The Network layer gets a workout when LANs are interconnected. In complex networks, a packet from a source system may need to traverse a maze of interconnected pathways to get to the destination. The Network layer provides the routing functions that get packets through the network along a path based on the least number of hops.

RELATED ENTRIES   Layered Architecture; Open Systems Interconnection Model; Protocol Stack; *and* Routing, OSI

Network Management
See Management Standards and Tools.

Networks

A computer network is a data communication system that links two or more computers and peripheral devices. As shown in Figure N-12, the network consists of a cable that attaches to network interface cards (NICs) in each of the devices. The logical

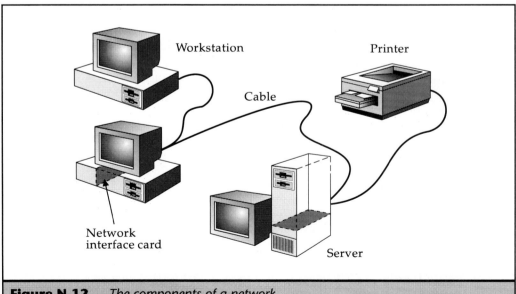

Figure N-12.   *The components of a network*

N

configuration of a network communication system is pictured in Figure N-13. In this configuration, applications use the underlying network communication software to exchange information with other applications or servers.

The basic departmental local area network (LAN) is pictured on the left in Figure N-14. On the right, several departmental LANs have been connected together to form an *internetwork*, which allows more users to communicate and share resources with one another. The internetwork in the picture is still a LAN because it occupies a local area. In fact, the term internetwork is very loosely defined. It could describe the interconnection of two LANs that use different network operating systems and communication protocols, or it could describe the interconnection of LANs that are separated by buildings or large geographic areas. This latter category constitutes a wide area network (WAN), as pictured in Figure N-15. A WAN is an internetwork that may use the public switched telephone network (PSTN) or some other public service to link networks over metropolitan, state, or national boundaries.

The range of networks is described in the following listings. A network can start small, and then grow with an organization.

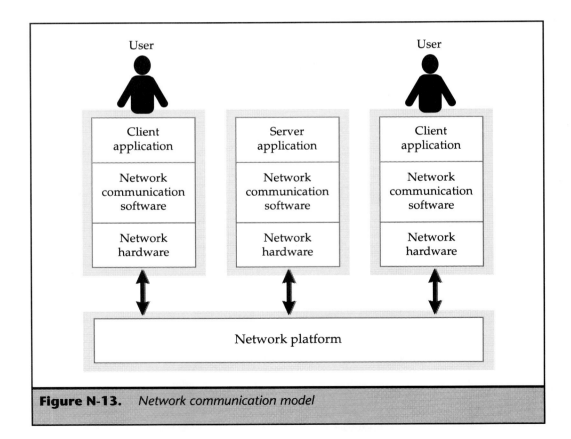

Figure N-13. *Network communication model*

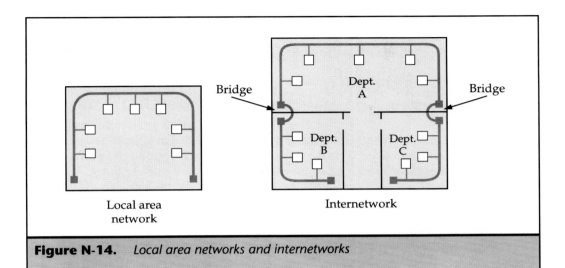

Figure N-14. *Local area networks and internetworks*

■ *Network segment* or *subnetwork*   A network segment is typically defined by hardware or a specific network address. For example, in the NetWare environment, a network segment includes all the workstations attached to a network interface card in a server. Each segment has its own network address. All computers attached to an Ethernet segment receive the same signal broadcasts.

■ *Local area network (LAN)*   A network segment with attached workstations and servers, or a collection of interconnected network segments, generally within the same area, such as a building.

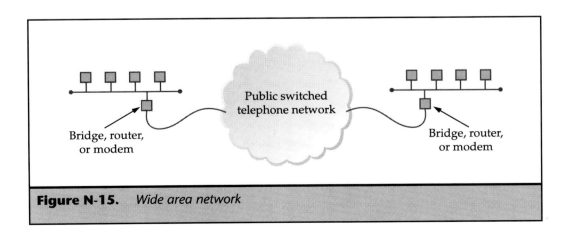

Figure N-15. *Wide area network*

N

- *Campus network* A network that extends to other buildings within a campus or industrial park area. The various segments or LANs within each building are typically connected with *backbone cables.* The organization usually owns the grounds and is free to lay cable as required.

- *Metropolitan area network (MAN)* A network that spans city or county areas and that is interconnected using MAN facilities provided by the local exchange carrier.

- *Wide area network (WAN)* and *global network* Networks that span inter-city, interstate, or international borders. Links are made with public and private telecommunications facilities, as well as microwave and satellite links.

- *Enterprise network* An enterprise network interconnects all the computer systems within an organization, regardless of operating system, communication protocols, application differences, or geographic location. It may therefore be a LAN, MAN, or WAN. The network itself is viewed as a platform onto which many different types of devices are connected. Various techniques are employed to hide the differences among systems so users can access any resources in a transparent way. For example, *middleware* products hide communication protocols and differences in applications.

The enterprise network is typically a *distributed computing system,* one in which resources and data are located throughout the organization. In this environment, directory services are required to help users locate other users, resources and data. *Security* is also an issue. Once a network connects an entire company, department and workgroup managers must be concerned with restricting access to data. Databases may be partitioned and distributed to remote locations to make data more readily available to users at those sites and to reduce costs of access over expensive WAN links. This method does require replication or synchronization techniques to ensure that databases have the same information.

For related information, see "Backbone Networks," "Distributed Computing," "Metropolitan Area Networks," "Security," and "Wide Area Networks."

Why Establish a Computer Network?

Why establish a computer network? That may seem obvious, but the reasons for doing so, as outlined in the following sections, shed light on what a network is and what it can do for an organization.

PROGRAM AND FILE SHARING Networkable versions of many popular software packages are available at considerable cost savings when compared to buying individually licensed copies. The program and its data files are stored on a file server and accessed by many network users.

NETWORK RESOURCE SHARING   Network resources include printers, plotters, and storage devices. The network provides a communication link that lets users share these devices.

DATABASE SHARING   A database management system is an ideal application for a network. A network feature called *record-locking* lets multiple users simultaneously access a file without corrupting the data. Record-locking ensures that no two users edit the same record at the same time.

ECONOMICAL EXPANSION OF THE PC BASE   Networks provide an economical way to expand the number of computers in an organization. You can attach inexpensive diskless workstations to a network that use the server's hard drive for booting and storage.

WORKGROUPS   A network provides a way to create groups of users that are not necessarily located within the same department. Workgroups facilitate new "flat" corporate structures in which people from diverse and remote departments belong to special group projects.

ELECTRONIC MAIL   *Electronic mail (E-mail)* lets users easily communicate with one another. Messages are dropped in "mailboxes" for the recipients to read at a convenient time.

GROUPWARE AND WORKFLOW SOFTWARE   *Groupware* and *workflow software* are designed specifically for networks and take advantage of E-mail systems to help users collaborate on projects, schedules, and document processing.

CENTRALIZED MANAGEMENT   A network provides a way to centralize servers and their data, along with other resources. Hardware upgrades, software backups, system maintenance, and system protection are much easier to handle when devices are located in one place.

ENHANCEMENT OF THE CORPORATE STRUCTURE   Networks can change the structure of an organization and the way it is managed. Users who work in a specific department and for a specific manager no longer need to be in the same physical area. Their offices can be located in areas where their expertise is most needed. The network ties them to their department managers and peers. This arrangement is useful for special projects in which individuals from different departments, such as research, production, and marketing, need to work closely with each other.

Network Environments

The environment of a network is defined by the network operating system and the protocols that provide communication and network services. There are two basic types of network operating systems:

N

- *Peer-to-peer*   This is an operating system that allows users to share the resources on their computers and to access shared resources on other computers. Peer-to-peer implies that all systems have the same status on the network. No system is a "slave" to another.

- *Dedicated-server*   In a dedicated-server operating system, such as Novell NetWare, one or more computers act solely as dedicated file servers and do not perform any other tasks.

Some common network operating system environments are listed next, but keep in mind that most vendors now offer a variety of operating system and communication protocol options that allow organizations to build heterogeneous networks.

- IBM peer-to-peer SNA networks running APPC/APPN protocols

- UNIX peer-to-peer operating systems running TCP/IP protocols

- Novell NetWare dedicated server operating systems running SPX/IPX communication protocols

- Windows NT and Windows for Workgroups peer-to-peer environments running NetBIOS/NetBEUI or TCP/IP communication protocols.

To understand network operating environments, it's useful to compare them to the centralized minicomputer and mainframe processing environments. In a network, clients access programs and files on central servers or peer servers, but execute those programs in their own memory. A minicomputer or mainframe system handles the processing tasks of the terminals attached to it. These terminals are often called *dumb terminals* because they have no processor or memory of their own. Each new user who logs on to the centralized system gets a share of its processing, and so performance drops.

Networks are *distributed processing systems* in which multiple servers and workstations perform processing. In other words, the entire network can be viewed as a collection of processing devices. Servers are usually the most powerful processing devices on the network. Networks and applications that split up processing between a "front-end" workstation and a "back-end" server are engaged in *client-server* relationships. The server provides tasks such as file storage and retrieval, management, printer sharing, and security.

Components of a Network

A computer network consists of both hardware and software. The hardware includes network interface cards and the cable that ties them together. The software components include server operating systems, communication protocols, and network interface card drivers.

NETWORK OPERATING SYSTEM   In a peer-to-peer network, each node on the network runs an operating system with built-in networking support that allows users to share their files and peripherals. Security and management features are also typically included. The network operating system for a dedicated network runs on stand-alone servers and workstations running client software that communicates with the server.

SERVERS   A server provides the following services to users on the network. Modular network operating systems such as Novell NetWare can provide some or all of these services in one or more servers, depending on which modular components the administrator chooses to install.

- *File server*   Provides file storage and retrieval services, including security features that control file access rights
- *E-mail server or gateway*   Provides local or enterprise-wide electronic mail services and translation between different mail systems
- *Communications server*   Provides connection services to mainframe or minicomputer systems, or to remote computer systems and networks via wide-area links
- *Database server*   A dedicated system that handles user database requests and responses
- *Archive server*   A system dedicated to backing up and archiving files on the network

CLIENT SYSTEMS (NODES OR WORKSTATIONS)   Client systems attach to the network via network interface cards. The operating system running in the workstation may include built-in software to support the cards, or it may be necessary to load client software. The client software redirects network requests from users or applications to servers. See "Client Software," "DOS Requester, NetWare," and "Network Driver Standards."

NETWORK INTERFACE CARDS (NICS)   Computer workstations attached to Ethernet, token ring, ARCNET, and other networks usually require the installation of a network interface card. There are few computers that have these interfaces built-in. The network cable attaches to the back of the NIC. See "Network Interface Card."

CABLING SYSTEM   The network cabling system is the media that connects servers and the workstations together. In the case of wireless networks that use radio or infrared, cable is not required. See "Cabling," "Wireless LAN Communication," and "Wireless Mobile Communication."

SHARED RESOURCES AND PERIPHERALS   Shared resources and peripherals include the storage devices attached to the server, optical disk drives, printers, plotters, and other equipment that is available for use by any authorized user on the network.

N

Network Connection Methods

To connect a network, you need network interface cards and cable (unless you're going wireless). There are several different types of interface cards and cabling schemes.

Types of Networks

Networks are defined by the type of cable used, the cable layout or *topology*, data transfer rates, communication protocols, and the method used by nodes to access and use the network (access methods). It's possible to build an internetwork that connects a variety of networks using bridges, routers, and gateways.

The most popular network types are Ethernet (coaxial cable or twisted-pair cable), token ring, ARCNET, and Fiber Distributed Data Interface (FDDI). The data transfer rate of a network type is usually a deciding factor. ARCNET operates at 2 Mbits/sec, token ring operates as 4 and 16 Mbits/sec, Ethernet operates at 10 or 100 Mbits/sec, and FDDI operates at 100 Mbits/sec. In the past, the cable type used by a network type was a factor, but today, most operate over inexpensive and adaptable twisted-pair cable. FDDI uses fiber-optic cable that provides a growth path to even faster network throughput.

Bridges and *routers* provide a way to join network segments of similar and dissimilar network types. Novell NetWare, Windows NT, Banyan VINES, and other server operating systems have built-in bridging and routing. Each NIC installed in the server creates a separate network segment and the operating system handles inter-network traffic.

Cable

The media used to transfer signals between network nodes is usually insulated metal cable, but fiber-optic cable and wireless communications methods such as radio and infrared provide alternatives.

- Coaxial cable, similar in construction to cable TV cable, was one of the first cable types used for networks. It provides relatively high data transfer rates (10 to 20 Mbits/sec), low cost, and some immunity to outside interference.

- Twisted-pair copper cable has been gaining in popularity due to its low price and ease of installation. New data-grade standards boost data transfer rates up to and above 100 Mbits/sec.

- Fiber-optic cable is also growing in popularity, due to its high transfer rates (100 Mbits/sec and higher), immunity to outside interference, and security (it does not emit signals and wire taps can be detected).

- Wireless methods allow mobile computing, both indoors and outdoors, depending on the method used. While transmission rates are low and line of site is necessary (infrared), wireless methods provide convenience and save cost in some cases since cabling is not required. Mobile network connections for remote users are becoming popular with packet radio and cellular techniques.

For related information, see "Cabling," "Fiber-Optic Cable," "Transmission Media, Methods, and Equipment," "Wireless LAN Communication," and "Wireless Mobile Communication."

Network Architecture

The architecture of a network is defined by its topology and the cable access method and communications protocols it uses. Before any workstation can access the cable, it must establish communication sessions with other nodes on the network. The *cable access method* of a network defines how a workstation gains access to shared media so it can transmit information. *Protocols* are the rules and procedures that systems use to communicate with one another over the network.

Topology

You can think of a network's topology as a map of its cable layout. Topology defines how you run the cable to individual workstations and plays an important part in the decision you make about cable. As illustrated in Figure N-16, a network can have a linear, ring, or star topology. You must consider the topology of a network when making decisions about which network type to install. Topology corresponds to how you will run the cable through the walls, floors, and ceilings of your building, as described here.

- *Linear topology* A linear topology consists of a single cable that extends from one computer to the next in a daisy-chain fashion. The ends of the cable are terminated with a resister. Ethernet coaxial networks use linear topologies. While easy to install, a break anywhere in the cable disables the entire network.

- *Star topology* In a star topology, all wires branch from a single location, such as a file server, or a central wiring closet. Star topologies require a cable to each workstation, but a broken cable only disconnects the workstation attached to it. Ethernet 10Base-T and token ring networks use star topologies, although internally, token ring is a ring network.

- *Ring topology* In a ring topology, the network cable connects back to itself and signals travel in a ring. Physical ring topologies are rare. Token ring and ARCNET are logical ring networks.

Cable Access Method

The cable access method describes how a workstation gains access to the cable system. When the network interface card gains access to the cable, it begins sending packets of information in a framed format as bit-streams over the network.

Linear cable systems such as Ethernet use a carrier sense multiple access/collision detection (CSMA/CD) method in which a workstation accesses the cable but backs off

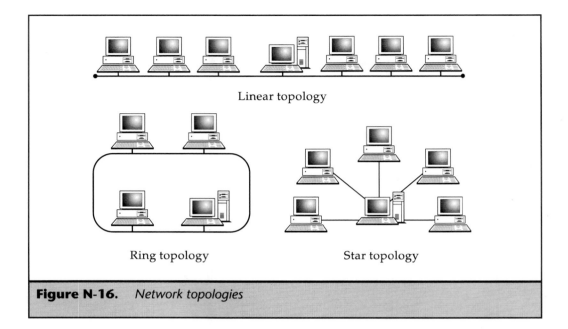

Figure N-16. *Network topologies*

if another workstation attempts to access it at the same time. A workstation broadcasts a signal and every other node on the network hears it, but only the addressed node pays attention to it. If two nodes broadcast at the same time, a collision occurs and both back off, wait for a random amount of time, and try again. Performance degrades when network traffic is heavy because of these collisions and retransmissions.

Ring networks commonly use a token passing method in which a station only transmits when it has possession of a token. Think of a *token* as a temporary ticket or pass to use the network. When a station is ready to transmit, it must wait for an available token and then take possession of the token. This prevents two machines from using the cable simultaneously.

For related information, see "Access Method, Network," "Carrier Sense Multiple Access," and "Token and Token Passing Access Methods."

Communication Protocols

Communication protocols are the rules and procedures used on a network to communicate among nodes that have access to the cable system. Protocols govern two different levels of communication. High-level protocols define how applications communicate, and lower-level protocols define how signals are transmitted over a cable. There are protocols between these levels that establish and maintain communication sessions between computers and monitor traffic for errors. Communication protocols can be compared to diplomatic protocols, in which diplomats at different ranks negotiate with peer diplomats at other embassies. When network protocols are defined and published, vendors can easily design and manufacture network products that work on multivendor systems.

For related information, see "Layered Architecture," "Open Systems," "Open Systems Interconnection Model," "Protocols, Communication," and "Protocol Stack."

Networking Devices

Network cabling systems have distance limitations due to signal loss and other electrical characteristics. You can extend the distance of a network segment by adding a *repeater,* which regenerates the electrical signal and doubles the allowable length of the cable. A repeater may not let you add more workstations to the extended network than defined in the network's specification. A repeater is often used to connect workstations in a back office or warehouse with a front office.

You can join separate network segments with a *bridge.* A bridge is a stand-alone devices, or may exist in network servers. For example, you can create a bridge in a NetWare server by installing two network cards. Bridges have the capability of keeping local traffic local and transferring only packets destined for other segments over the link. This helps reduce excess network traffic.

A *router* provides a level of interconnectivity a step above bridges. A router can read addressing information in a packet that helps it determine the best possible path that will get it to its destination when a network has many different links, or pathways.

Hubs and wiring centers are used to build structured cabling systems. A hub is a concentrator that forms the center of a star-configured wiring scheme. The hub has a bus that typically accepts plug-in Ethernet, token ring, FDDI, or other types of modules. These modules have multiple ports for network workstations. Hubs are typically installed in a department and connect all the computers in that department to one another. Department hubs are then connected to enterprise hubs forming a hierarchical wiring scheme.

For related information, see "Backbone Networks," "Bridging," "Cabling," "EIA/TIA 568 Commercial Building Wiring Standard," "Hubs," "Repeater," and "Routers."

MAN and WAN Connection Methods

Metropolitan area networks (MAN) and wide area networks (WAN) provide connections between geographically diverse sites. MANs are usually high-speed, fiber-optic networks that connect LAN segments within a metropolitan area. An alternative method is to use private networking schemes such as microwave systems. Microwave dishes are mounted on top of buildings and pointed at each other to establish an internetwork link.

WANs provide country-wide or global connections via telephone lines and satellites. Large corporations that have regional or worldwide offices use WANs to interconnect networks. Dedicated circuits are leased from long-distance carriers to provide full-time connections between systems. Alternatively, circuit-switched or

N

packet-switched connections are available that operate at lower cost and provide more flexibility as far as usage and connection points.

For related information, see "Carrier Services," "Circuit- Switching Services," "Digital Circuits and Services," "Public Data Networks," "Public Switched Data Networks," "Telecommunication," and "Wide Area Networks."

Networking in the 1990s

The current network paradigm is the multivendor, multiprotocol (heterogeneous) network, rather than the long-envisioned open systems environment in which all vendors create compatible equipment. Heterogeneous networks are built on an enterprise-wide level and connect a diverse range of systems, including department and workgroup LANs, as well as corporate mainframe and minicomputer systems. In this environment, network administrators are faced with the task of making diverse systems interoperate. This is accomplished by supporting a number of communications protocols, or using middleware products that hide protocols from users and applications.

While the physical computing resources of the network are distributed among departments and divisions of a company, responsibility and management of those resources are often by an enterprise network manager. This is because the enterprise network is designed to help the whole organization reach its goals, which include sharing of data and resources by any user anywhere within the organization. Departmental LANs can still maintain autonomy so that local managers can define security rights and protect local data from unauthorized users. However, the enterprise manager guides departments toward the common goal of company-wide integration.

The new network is built with hubs, structured wiring systems, collapsed multiprotocol backbones, and high-speed wide area connections that let users at remote sites access corporate networks with little delay. Workstations that can operate at 100 million instructions per second (MIPS) performance with hundreds of megabytes of RAM and gigabytes of disk storage space are available. Server throughput is increasing to meet the high demands of users. Ultra-high-speed servers that use multiple processors running at up to 200 MHz and providing 300 MIPS and higher are becoming common. Mainframe and minicomputer systems are now viewed as powerful servers that attach directly to the network.

Many of the lower-level communication differences have been solved by supporting multiple communication protocols in computer attached to the network. Administrators are now concerned with raising the level of interoperability to the Application layer relative to the OSI protocol model. The goal is to allow users running a variety of applications on a variety of platforms to access data throughout the enterprise network without worrying about interface, translation, and conversion issues. Middleware makes it easier for application developers to create software for these new environments. Middleware provides a standard programming layer that hides the complexity of networks and multivendor protocols from the programmer. The layers provide high-level application program interfaces (APIs).

The Distributed Computing Environment (DCE) developed by the Open Software Foundation is providing tools that help administrators integrate heterogeneous environments. Apple's Open Collaborative Environment and Microsoft's Windows Open System Architecture are strategies for building enterprise networks. Object-oriented environments such as Microsoft's Cairo are in the works with the goal of providing data access through object technologies. In an object-oriented environment, data and the methods for working on that data are combined into a single object. Objects are important because they can be used across software and hardware platforms. Users can access objects on other systems at other locations using a variety of application interfaces. This global approach lets developers more easily create applications for accessing distributed databases.

Centralized management platforms are necessary in these computing environments. They reduce the number of management utilities and packages that must be learned, and centralize management, which helps reduce the number of required administrators.

RELATED ENTRIES   Apple Open Collaborative Environment; Cairo; Distributed Computing Environment; Enterprise Networks; Middleware; Object-Oriented Environments; Object-Oriented Interfaces and Operating Systems; *and* Windows Open System Architecture

Network Service Protocol, DEC

A Transport layer protocol that manages logical network links between two nodes on DECnet networks. It controls the flow of data and handles errors. The protocol provides handshaking services so the linked nodes can have a two-way communication session. It segments information in the communication and sequences it to ensure delivery in the correct order.

RELATED ENTRIES   DEC; DECnet

Network Troubleshooting

See Testing Equipment and Techniques.

Node

A workstation, client, network user, or personal computer. Also defines servers, printers and other network connected devices.

Novell

Novell has been a major influence in the growth of the microcomputer industry. It developed Z-80-based microcomputers in the 1970s and created its first networking

N

products in the early 1980s. Novell's main product during the emerging years of the personal computer was a file-sharing device based on the Motorola 68000 processor. In 1983, when IBM announced the IBM Personal Computer XT, which has a hard disk, Novell quickly responded with a product that converted the hard disk system into a file-sharing system. A star-configured cabling system known as S-Net was used to attach workstations.

A few years later, Novell introduced NetWare/86, which provided file server capabilities. The new server operating system not only let users share files, it provided access to those files through a security system and helped manage other features of the network. As NetWare grew in popularity, its designers improved its hardware independence. Novell stopped pushing its own local area network (LAN) hardware and began providing support for products from many vendors. This was one of the most important strategies in the advancement of NetWare as an industry standard. In 1986, a new version of NetWare called Advanced NetWare provided even more support for LAN hardware by bridging different network types within the file server or an external workstation. For example, you could install both an Ethernet and token ring card in the server.

Advanced NetWare 286 was developed to take advantage of Intel 80286-based systems. It provided multitasking capabilities long before products such as OS/2 and Microsoft Windows existed. In addition, it ran in the protected mode of the 80286, which allowed it to provide advanced features not available when running only under DOS, and it did not have the 640 KB memory constraints of DOS. Many users were getting better performance when accessing files on NetWare servers than when accessing files on their local hard drive! Up to four different types of network interface cards could be installed in an Advanced NetWare 286 server.

Eventually, Novell began splitting its product line. At the low end, it offered NetWare Entry Level System (ELS), which supported a small number of users. At the high end, it introduced NetWare System Fault Tolerance (SFT). NetWare SFT provided protection from disk failures by mirroring, or duplexing, the disk system. In this arrangement, two disks record the same information, and if one fails, the other can be put into use. Novell also began offering file storage support for Apple Macintosh computers on the NetWare server.

In 1989, Novell announced NetWare 386 V.3.0, an operating system that was completely rewritten to take advantage of features built into the Intel 80386 processor. NetWare 386 is a full 32-bit operating system that was designed for large networks with massive data handling needs. It also provided enhanced security, performance, and flexibility. (Operating system changes were much easier.) In June of 1990, Novell shipped version 3.1 of the operating system, which provided enhanced performance, reliability, and system administration. Then in 1991, Novell announced NetWare V.3.11, which supports DOS, Macintosh, Windows, OS/2, and UNIX file and print services.

The current Novell operating system product line includes NetWare Lite, a DOS-based peer-to-peer operating system; NetWare V.2.2, a dedicated or nondedicated server operating system that runs on Intel 80286 and above processors; NetWare 386 V.3.11, a full 32-bit dedicated server operating system; and NetWare 4.x,

Novell's enterprise-wide network operating system. These products are described further under the NetWare heading in this book.

The Novell Product Strategy

Novell is a major force in the network industry. Surveys and estimates indicate that approximately 60 percent of existing network sites use Novell NetWare.

Novell has adopted a network operating system strategy that focuses on the *enterprise network,* which encompasses all the computing resources of an organization. Think of the network itself as a platform to which you attach any type of computer system with the goal of providing network services to any user. An interconnected network provides the communication platform, and Novell NetWare provides the software components that bind it all together. These components are either supplied with NetWare or available as optional products.

The driving force behind Novell's enterprise networking strategy is a plan to make NetWare as open as possible to integration with other systems and other vendors' products.

NTFS (New Technology File System)

NTFS is the file system in the Windows NT operating environment and the Windows NT Advanced Server network operating system environment. The goal of NTFS was to provide:

- Reliability through fault-tolerant features such as recoverability (transaction tracking) and hot fixing
- A platform for adding functionality
- Support for POSIX requirements
- Removal of limitations in FAT and HPFS file systems

NTFS provides long filenames, data protection and recovery, and security through directory and file permissions. NTFS supports large hard disks and the storage of files over multiple hard disks (called spanning volumes). For example, a large company database might be so large that it spans several drives.

NTFS provides built-in security features that control file ownership and access. Files on an NTFS volume are not accessible from DOS or other operating systems. That is part of the Windows NT security system, but only when you use NTFS.

NTFS allows filenames of up to 256 characters in length. While DOS users can't access the NTFS volume, NTFS files can be copied to DOS volumes. Each NTFS file includes a DOS-readable filename that conforms to the DOS filename format. This filename is generated by NTFS from the beginning characters of the long filename.

RELATED ENTRY   Windows NT, Microsoft

N

ObjectBroker, DEC

Digital Equipment Corporation's ObjectBroker is a layered software product that allows software developers to utilize an object-oriented approach to the linking of independently developed applications and services across mixed-vendor environments. ObjectBroker V2.5 fully implements the Common Object Request Broker Architecture (CORBA) specified by the Object Management Group. ObjectBroker simplifies the creation of client-server applications by eliminating the development of integration code at the operating system and network levels.

ObjectBroker extends the capabilities of applications that implement Microsoft's Object Linking and Embedding (OLE) or Dynamic Data Exchange (DDE) interfaces into multivendor networked environments. DEC and Microsoft have joined forces to provide an open architecture for object-based client-server development and deployment. The result is the Common Object Model (COM), which is a set of object-based distributed networking interfaces designed to allow Windows applications to access applications on other platforms. These other platforms include DEC OpenVMS environments, Macintosh systems, and several UNIX variants.

ObjectBroker features are listed next:

- Allows application processes across multiple platforms to transparently invoke, control, and interact with each other

- Provides application naming, capability registration, location, activation, and request/data dispatching through a consistent, standards-based application program interface (API) above the operating systems and network transport levels

- Encapsulates existing (legacy) applications and data, without modifying source code so existing applications can integrate into new client-server architectures

The COM initiative is an important move for Microsoft. It opens the Windows environment by allowing Windows applications to exchange information with systems that are compatible with ObjectBroker. The communication method used between the environments is based on the remote procedure call (RPC) used in the Open Software Foundation's Distributed Computing Environment. Because ObjectBroker is based on the OMG's CORBA, Microsoft gains access to CORBA without the need for ties to the OMG.

RELATED ENTRIES   Common Object Model; Common Object Request Broker Architecture; Object Linking and Embedding; *and* Object Management Group

Object Linking and Embedding (OLE)

Object Linking and Embedding (OLE) provides a way to integrate objects from diverse applications. An *object* is a block of information from a spreadsheet, a graphic from a drawing program, or an audio clip from a sound program. Each object is created and maintained by its *server* application, but through OLE, the services of the different server applications are integrated. What this means is that users don't need to switch to another application to edit an object in the current document. They simply edit the object in place (OLE 2.0) using functions that are "brought in" from the server application.

Each object has its own *data type* definitions. For example, a spreadsheet object has cells of information with formatting codes, while a graphic image consists of bit-mapped data or commands to redraw the image. OLE allows any OLE-compatible application to display objects from other applications and to set up links between the data. With OLE, documents can contain many different data types. OLE applications recognize a rich underlying set of file structures and can display objects and provide editing features even though the objects were created elsewhere.

A *compound document* is a document that contains objects created by different applications, as shown in Figure O-1. This document is a *container* that holds objects. The top window (Microsoft Word) is the compound document that contains objects from a spreadsheet program and a painting program. Users focus on the compound document, rather than each of the applications used to create the objects in the document; however, the functions of those applications are made available when necessary without the user actually switching to another application.

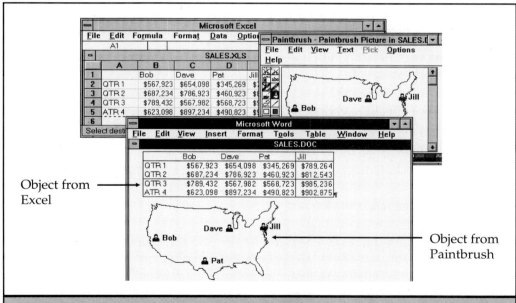

Figure O-1. *The overlapping window is a compound document that contains the objects created in the background applications*

Objects can be either embedded or linked in compound documents. Both are described separately next, but a compound document can contain both types of objects.

LINKED OBJECTS   Unlike embedded objects, a linked object doesn't actually exist within a compound document. The compound document contains a reference to the object, which exists as a separate disk file. A link is maintained to the file, so if it changes in any way, the changes are reflected in the compound document that contains a link to it. Linking has the following features:

- Linked objects exist in files outside the compound document. If the files are erased, the links are lost. If they are moved, new links must be established.

- The compound document itself is small in size since it contains only references to linked objects.

- Links can exist over networks—a compound document may exist on one computer and a linked file may exist on another computer, such as an object server.

- If a compound document is moved to another system, all linked files must move with it.

EMBEDDED OBJECTS   Unlike linked objects, an embedded object is stored directly in the compound document. An embedded object maintains an association with the application that created it. Double-clicking the object with a mouse opens the application so the object can be edited. Embedding has the following features:

- An embedded object is edited in-place so the user never needs to leave the compound document.

- Changes to an embedded object do not affect an original source file (if it exists; that is, the embedded object may be the only instance of the object).

- The object does not need to exist as a separate file.

- The object is stored with the compound document.

- Embedding simplifies document management since all the elements are stored in one file.

- An embedded object moves with the file that contains it, allowing users to easily exchange documents.

- Compound documents that contain embedded objects are large because the compound document holds all the data that makes up the object, unlike links, which reference external objects.

OLE 2.0 uses *in-place activation* for embedded objects. If a user double-clicks an object in a compound document, all interaction takes place in the compound document. The menus, toolbars, palettes, and other controls necessary to interact with the object temporarily replace the existing menus and controls of the active window.

When the user is done editing, the normal controls return and the object exists with its new changes. In the case of multimedia objects, editing is a bit of a misnomer. The user interacts with such objects by *playing* them, rather than editing, although editing may be possible as well.

Linked objects can be activated in place for operations such as playback and display, but they cannot be edited in place. Instead, a separate window opens for editing.

From the user's perspective, OLE provides a theme of common integration for all OLE-compatible applications in the Windows environments. Applications are viewed more as workspaces where users assemble objects from many different applications. OLE enables workgroup collaboration over a network by allowing users to share objects. For example, a project manager inserts linked objects created by coworkers into a compound document. Changes made to the objects by coworkers as a project progresses are reflected in the compound document.

The compound document can be viewed as the central repository for all the elements that go into the reports. It either holds those elements directly (embedded objects) or makes a reference to the files that hold the elements. In the old method of assembling documents, you wrote down the names of all the associated files that made up a document or report, then combined them after printing. In the OLE environment, you assemble all these components into the compound document and the compound document keeps track of where everything is and brings them all together when printing.

In the Windows for Workgroups and Windows NT environments, a utility called the ClipBook provides cut-and-paste features that work over a network. You place objects to share with other users on the ClipBook. Other users then open the ClipBook at their computer and paste the objects into their documents. The objects maintain a link to the file located on your computer, so if you make changes to the file, the copies in other users' documents change as well. However, if your computer is not on, users won't be able to get updates from it.

Other OLE Features

OLE implements a number of other interesting features. Version 2.0 greatly expands on the features that were available in initial releases of OLE, such as those incorporated in Windows for Workgroups V3.1 and Windows NT V3.1. Some of the version 2.0 features are discussed here.

Drag and Drop

In the Windows environment, the Clipboard was the common utility used to transfer data between applications. It was necessary to execute a Copy command at the source, then a Paste command at the destination. The drag and drop approach provides a more natural way to achieve the same results. A user first outlines the object to copy, then clicks the object, and while holding the mouse button, drags the object to the destination document.

Drag and drop removes the barriers between applications. The window frame is no longer viewed as a wall that separates applications. Users can freely drag information from one application to another, simplifying the process of creating compound documents. Drag and drop also works with resource icons such as printers and mailboxes. Dragging and dropping an object on a printer icon causes the object to print.

Property Inheritance

When an object is embedding in a compound document, it may have properties that are not consistent with the rest of the document. For example, the fonts of the embedded object may be different than the fonts used in the compound document. To make embedded objects take on the look of the compound document, OLE allows the document to "export" properties to an object. The object then inherits these properties and transforms its appearance to be more consistent with the rest of the document.

Object Type Conversion and Emulation

As mentioned previously, an object has a type characteristic that defines the format of the data and other properties of the object. These types are defined by the application that created the object. In some cases, users may prefer to convert an object to a different type so they can edit and manipulate the object with an application that has a stronger set of features.

OLE provides a mechanism through which applications can perform type conversions and/or emulation. A type conversion causes a permanent change to an object. A type emulation causes an object to take on the characteristics of an object of another type while maintaining its original name and data format. Type conversion is useful when the original application is no longer available. Type emulation provides a temporary way for a number of users to interact with a compound document using the same server application.

Searching and Spelling

Since compound documents contain objects created in a number of applications and users want to treat the compound document as a single entity, OLE provides a way to search and perform spell checks on the entire document. A tunnelling technique is used to allow string searches and spell-checks to occur inside embedded objects. This removes the need to invoke multiple applications to perform the same tasks.

OLE Implementations

Microsoft's plan is to build its workgroup applications around OLE, as can be seen in the Microsoft Office suite of products, which include Microsoft Word, Excel, PowerPoint, Mail, and Schedule+ workgroup scheduling software. These applications easily share information on the same system or among users on other systems. Windows for Workgroups uses network data exchange, and includes the Mail and Schedule+ products. The Microsoft Windows Open System Architecture (WOSA) strategy provides the structure for integrating messaging, databases, and other applications across enterprise-wide networks.

OLE is implemented in all Microsoft Windows products, including the Cairo object-oriented operating system due in 1995 and applications such as Microsoft Office. DEC and Microsoft have joined forces to provide an open architecture for object based client-server development and deployment called the Common Object Model (COM). COM is a set of object-based distributed networking interfaces designed to allow Windows OLE applications to access applications on platforms that are supported by DEC's ObjectBroker technology. These other platforms include DEC OpenVMS environments, Macintosh systems, and several UNIX variants.

However, several object models compete with OLE. These models are listed next and described elsewhere in this book.

- Sun's Distributed Objects Everywhere (DOE)
- OpenDoc, an object standard developed by Apple, IBM, Novell, and WordPerfect that is designed to work with OLE 2.0
- Hewlett-Packard's Distributed Object Management Facility (DOMF)
- Object Management Group's (OMG) Common Object Request Broker Architecture (CORBA)

DOE and DOMF are built around the CORBA environment. Also, note Hewlett-Packard, IBM, and Sun Microsystems agreed in mid-1993 to share their object technologies. While CORBA competes with Microsoft's OLE and Cairo projects, OLE is an object-sharing system in the Windows environment while CORBA is designed to provide object sharing in heterogeneous network environments that include communication across a variety of interoperable platforms. For a general description of object sharing technologies in distributed environments, see "Object Request Broker."

RELATED ENTRIES   Common Object Model; Compound Documents; Dynamic Data Exchange; NetDDE; ObjectBroker, DEC; Windows for Workgroups, Microsoft; *and* Windows NT, Microsoft

Object Management Architecture (OMA)

The initial task of the Object Management Group (OMG) was to create an architecture on which its members could standardize the development of object-oriented applications on distributed networks that contain a diversity of multivendor products and operating environments. The architecture created by OMG is comprised of four major components and pictured in Figure O-2.

- *Application objects* This level contains optional applications that can be installed and removed as necessary. Common applications include word processors, spreadsheets, and graphics programs.

O

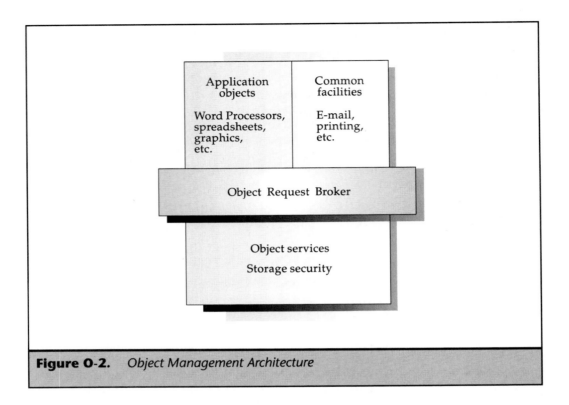

Figure O-2.   *Object Management Architecture*

- *Common facilities*   This level contains objects that are commonly used by most applications, such as E-mail systems, spelling checkers, I/O interfaces, and agents. They are separated in this way to avoid duplication of code in applications. Objects in the common facilities area can be accessed by all applications.

- *Object Request Broker (ORB)*   This is the common interface that objects use to communicate with other objects. It is defined as the Common Object Request Broker Architecture (CORBA) and discussed in this book under that heading. Also see "Object Request Broker."

- *Object services*   This level provides the essential services to implement the object technology.

A critical component is the Object Request Broker (ORB), which provides basic object communication, formatting, and management services among objects. Here are some of the advantage to using the OMA model:

- It supports modular, plug-and-play software.

- System and software installation is easier for both users and network administrators. Drivers for printers, screens, and other components reside in the Common Facilities area where they are shared by applications. Updates are immediately made available to all applications.

- Users and administrators can more easily take advantage of the distributed environment. For example, the ORB could locate objects on high-performance or idle systems to service requests, fully taking advantage of enterprise resources. This is difficult to do with traditional remote procedure calls (RPC).

- Applications development is simplified for vendors, which will ensure an adequate selection of software.

RELATED ENTRIES   Common Object Request Broker Architecture; Object Management Group; *and* Object Request Broker

Object Management Group (OMG)

The Object Management Group (OMG) is a consortium of almost 300 organizations that has developed the Object Management Architecture (OMA). OMA is a model that describes the standards the OMG wants to develop for object-oriented applications and environments. OMG members contributing major technology to the OMG are Digital Equipment Corporation, Hewlett-Packard, HyperDesk Corporation, and SunSoft. The architecture has also been adopted by the X/Open Group, which has a common goal of developing multivendor common application environments, and the Open Software Foundation (OSF), which is developing portable system software called the Distributed Computing Environment (DCE) and the Distributed Management Environment (DME). Note that OMG object standards are similar to work being done by Microsoft with its Object Linking and Embedding (OLE) 2.0 Cairo operating system. However, OMG's specifications are designed to bridge incompatible systems while Microsoft's products primarily operate in the Windows environment.

OMG is primarily concerned with developing a suite of languages, interfaces, and protocol standards that vendors can use to create applications that operate in multivendor environments. The OMG is involved in bringing about the agreement on standards so that participating members and others can create products that comply with them. OMG will then certify the compliance of products that are designed to the standard. Some of the standards are listed next.

- *Transaction processing* over distributed systems, in which updates might be written at several locations.

- *Concurrent execution* of object methods on the same system or different systems in a distributed environment.

- *Event notification* that can inform an object of events that have taken place elsewhere in the distributed system.

O

■ *Notification of changes* in object structures to ensure that object references always use appropriate versions.

■ *Internationalization,* which provides a way to handle country-specific formats.

An interesting aspect of the OMG's effort is that it builds on standards and interfaces already in place or under development by major vendors. Object-oriented technology is used because of its many benefits for the development of modular and expandable systems.

The basic architecture centers around the Object Request Broker (ORB). In this model, an object requests a service. The request is passed to the ORB, which finds a suitable "provider" object to service the request, then formats the request and passes it to the provider. The provider then sends its response to the ORB, and the ORB formats the response and forwards it to the original requester.

The first technology specification based on OMA to come out of the OMG is called the *Common Object Request Broker Architecture (CORBA).* The OMG also defined the Interface Definition Language (IDL), an interface objects present to other objects that includes the procedures for interacting with objects.

The following companies support the OMG's efforts in the development of object-oriented technologies and are implementing the technologies in their products.

■ Hewlett-Packard's distributed computing environment includes the OMG CORBA component as well as components from the Open Software Foundation's (OSF's) Distributed Computing Environment (DCE) and the OSF Motif graphical user interface.

■ Distributed Objects Everywhere (or Project DOE) is SunSoft's initiative to develop a fully distributed object environment for its Solaris operating system. DOE's design is based on CORBA.

■ The Open Software Foundation (OSF) has adopted CORBA in its Distributed Management Environment (DME) specification.

Hewlett-Packard, IBM, and Sun Microsystems independently developed object-oriented interface technology, but agreed in mid-1993 to share their technologies. The object-oriented technologies are IBM's Systems Object Model (SOM), Sun's Distributed Objects Everywhere (DOE), and HP's Distributed Object Management Facility (DOMF). By sharing and standardizing their technologies, users and developers will benefit with a more open environment. The agreement brings more competition to Microsoft's Cairo project.

RELATED ENTRIES   Common Object Request Broker Architecture; Object Management Architecture; Object-Oriented Interfaces and Operating Systems; Object-Oriented Technology; Object Request Broker; *and* Objects

Object-Oriented Database

See Distributed Database.

Object-Oriented Interfaces and Operating Systems

Object-oriented technologies are bringing about a revolution in software development, user interfaces, and database design. In an object-oriented environment, data and the methods for working on that data are combined into a single object. An object-oriented operating system consists of a set of small utilities (also called tools, accessories, or applets) that are used to write, edit, draw, chart, compile, or do a variety of other custom tasks. These utilities operate on data that is structured so that any utility added to the operating system can either manipulate the data or display it, as when creating compound documents. In the old model, files created by one application were not always accessible by other applications. Objects are also packages of information such as text, spreadsheets, graphics, sound, and video that can be created in one application and inserted in another.

Object systems are modular. When a new module is added, it reuses existing data structures so the entire operating system does not need to be recompiled. Modules simply plug into the existing structure. Imagine a building in which part of the framework is exposed to allow for future expansion. While the building might not look attractive, it is highly extensible. This topic is discussed further under "Object-Oriented Technology."

Object-oriented operating systems are becoming more and more common. Most of the major vendors such as IBM, Microsoft, Apple, Sun Microsystems, and others are moving to object-oriented systems. Some of these projects are discussed next.

TALIGENT'S PINK   Pink is the code name for Apple Computer's joint venture with IBM to develop an enterprise computing platform. It is a completely object-oriented, 32-bit operating system designed to run a variety of other operating systems (DOS, Windows, OS/2) on a variety of hardware platforms. Full delivery is not expected until 1995.

MICROSOFT CAIRO   Cairo is a distributed operating system under development by Microsoft with an expected release date of 1995. It is built on top of Windows NT and adds important new features such as an object-oriented file system, Kerberos security, and replication services, directory services, Unicode support, and an installable file-system. In recent sightings, Cairo presents itself as a graphical user interface that has some similarities to Windows. Cairo fully implements Object Linking and Embedding (OLE).

IBM'S WORKPLACE ENVIRONMENTS   IBM's Workplace operating systems use technology codeveloped with Apple Computer in its Taligent venture. The operating

O

system works on Reduced Instruction Set Computer (RISC) processors, Motorola PowerPC processors, and Intel-based systems. Workplace OS is a powerful microkernel-based operating system. It uses the same Workplace Shell graphical user interface as OS/2, but it provides a 64-bit core that will run applications designed for a number of existing operating systems, including DOS, Windows, UNIX, and of course, OS/2.

OBJECT MANAGEMENT GROUP   A major force in the move to object-oriented systems is the Object Management Group (OMG). It is a group of vendors dedicated to defining interoperability between object-oriented technologies. OMG has defined the Common Object Request Broker Architecture (CORBA), which provides a platform for building object-oriented systems that span multivendor products.

OPENDOC   The OpenDoc Alliance, which is primarily sponsored by Apple Computer, is developing the OpenDoc specification that is designed to help developers create object-sharing applications in network environments. It is a specification for creating compound documents. OpenDoc is similar to Microsoft's OLE, and it is supported by IBM, Novell, Borland, WordPerfect, and other companies that are not willing to completely rely on Microsoft's object technologies.

RELATED ENTRIES   Cairo; Common Object Model; Common Object Request Broker Architecture; Compound Documents; ObjectBroker, DEC; Object Linking and Embedding; Object Management Architecture; Object-Oriented Technology; Object Request Broker; Objects; *and* Workplace OS

Object-Oriented Technology

Object-oriented technology brings software development past procedural programming into a world of reusable programming that simplifies development of applications. Unlike old programming methods, program maintenance and debugging does not become more complicated as programs grow in size. Object technology takes place at two levels:

- At the data level, object technology can integrate the many different types of information in an organization, information that in the past has been incompatible.

- At the program development level, object technology provides modular program construction in which programs are built on a foundation of existing objects. Objects can be reused by other objects to take advantage of their procedures, eliminating the need to rewrite code every time it is needed again.

Redesigning or expanding systems is easy since it's not necessary to change or scrap the entire system. Instead, modules are discarded or changed, and new modules are added to provide enhanced functions.

An object is a self-contained package of data that includes the functions for processing the data. In an object-oriented environment, the number of objects is countless. They might include a record in a database, a file, a physical resource, and even a user (that is, the user's logon account). For developers working with object-oriented programming languages, objects are self-sufficient modules that contain data along with the structures and functions to manipulate the data.

Objects could be any of the following:

- The code to implement a process in an object-oriented operating system, such as verifying security rights
- Predefined code modules that programmers and developers use to assemble programs
- A block of data from an application such as a drawing program, spreadsheet, or multimedia tool
- Objects in a database, such as inventory items or customers

In an object-oriented database, objects might represent the actual entities you keep track of in your business, such as manufactured products, inventory, customers, and vendors. Alternatively, in an object-oriented operating system, objects are entities such as files, devices, and users, or blocks of data that form the entities of a compound document. In an object-oriented environment, you first define the basic objects, then build a system around them.

There are many potential objects, and they are categorized into hierarchical *classes* that define different types of objects. Parent classes can pass characteristics on to subclasses. Consider the class "people," which has subclasses of "male" and "female." These subclasses can have subclasses of their own, as shown in Figure O-3. Each subclass has *generalized* features inherited from its parents, along with *specialized* features of its own. Additionally, some of the inherited features are blocked because they are not appropriate for the subclass.

How does this relate to computers? Keep in mind that we are talking about a way to store many different data types and access that data with many different types of applications. By classifying data in this way, we can include the procedures for extracting, displaying, combining, and printing directly with the data in the object, then build a system upon those objects. Classifying the data simplifies the construction process as well as the revision process if necessary. For example, a block of data might include a procedure for sorting it in a specific way, which can be invoked from many different applications that use the data.

There are object classes and object instances:

- *Object class*   A class defines a group of objects. Classes have *behavior* that describes what an object can do, and *methods*, which are the programs and procedures that can operate on an object.

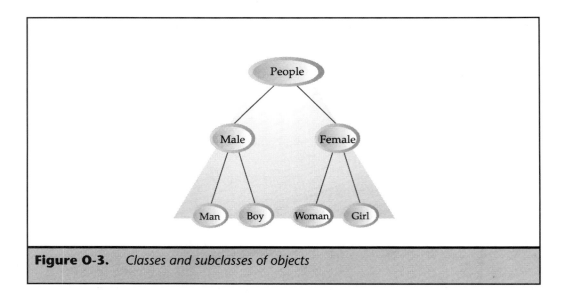

Figure O-3. *Classes and subclasses of objects*

■ *Object instance*   An object is an instance of a class that represents a real physical "thing" such as a customer or inventory part in an accounting system database.

Class inheritance is an important concept. It provides a way for a subclass to inherit the built-in specifications of its parent class. The code used in the parent class is passed down to a class that is a specialization of that class.

For example, an object-oriented database might have a class called "*client*" with subclasses called "*company*" and "*individual.*" The object called *client* is first created. It contains a structure and some procedures for manipulating the data and getting information out of it. The *company* and *individual* objects are then defined as a subclasses of *client*. As a subclass, they inherit the structure and features of the *client* object, but some of those features can be blocked, or additional features can be added. For example, the *company* subclass might have a special discount calculation that the *individual* subclass does not have. If you want a list of clients, you can ask the *client* object for the list; however, if you want to know the account balances of client, you'll need to get that information from each of the subclass objects that hold client balances.

Objects contain data and procedures and provide information when requested. Think of a box containing data that has a set of buttons you can press to run procedures on the data. *Methods* are the procedures or programs that operate on objects, causing the object to behave in a certain way based on the object's internal coding and structure. The same method can operate on different classes of objects, a concept called *polymorphism* (or *overloading*). With polymorphism, a common set of methods can operate on a wide range of classes. However, methods with the same name or call may invoke different things. For example, "next" in text data causes the cursor to jump to the next work, while "next" in spreadsheet data causes the cursor to jump to the next cell.

Objects talk to each other by sending messages. The messages essentially request procedures from objects by pushing the "buttons" on the object. In a network environment, you can envision objects attached to message buses, as shown in Figure O-4. Message passing provides an efficient way for objects to communicate in an object-oriented, distributed computing environment. Message-passing is a store-and-forward method like that used in E-mail systems. Messages pass from one computer to the next until they reach their destination.

All of this adds up to software that is easier to maintain and improve on a continuing basis without redesigning the whole system.

- Objects are reusable, making it easier to add to the system as it grows, since code in existing objects is reused to create new objects.

- Object systems are extensible—developers add modules that reuse built-in data structures without recompiling the operating system.

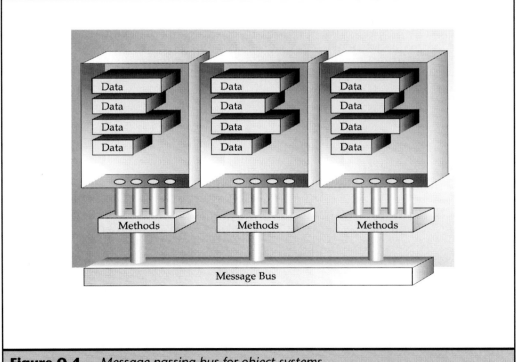

Figure O-4.   *Message passing bus for object systems*

■ It is easier to build systems because object-orientation provides a more natural approach to designing and implementing systems.

■ Objects can provide a common interface so many different applications can access data.

There are some disadvantages, including more up front design time, decreased performance, and the general immaturity of the technology. However, these disadvantages are offset as the system grows and hardware becomes more powerful. They are also offset by the fact that object systems can provide users with data on many different types of systems spread out over distributed networks.

Objects in Distributed Environments

Object technology is considered vital to implementing future distributed systems. The complexity of such systems is simplified with object models that implement messaging services such as the Object Request Broker. Objects simply request services and other objects provide those services. It is not necessary for developers to know much in advance about the systems that objects will communicate on. In fact, object technologies provide a way to design applications for local use that can expand to heterogeneous distributed environments at a later time.

Developments in this area include the following:

■ The Object Management Group's (OMG's) Common Object Request Broker Architecture (CORBA) is a specification that is designed to provide a way for objects to make and receive requests.

■ Microsoft's Object Linking and Embedding (OLE) provides a way to share data between applications on a single desktop or over a network.

■ IBM's System Object Model (SOM) and Distributed System Object Model (DSOM) provide low-level object languages.

■ OpenDoc is a development environment for sharing text, graphics, and multimedia objects developed by Apple, Borland, IBM, Novell, and WordPerfect.

RELATED ENTRIES   Cairo; Common Object Model; Common Object Request Broker Architecture; Compound Documents; ObjectBroker, DEC; Object Linking and Embedding; Object Management Architecture; Object-Oriented Interfaces and Operating Systems; Object Request Broker; Objects; *and* Workplace OS

Object Request Broker

In an object-oriented, distributed computing environment, an Object Request Broker (ORB) can provide the key communication facility for distributing messages among the applications, services, and facilities of the network. You can think of the ORB as a sort of software bus, or backbone, that provides a common *messaging* interface through which many different kinds of objects can communicate in a peer-to-peer scheme.

An object makes a request and sends it to the ORB. The ORB then locates an object that can service the request, formats the message, and sends it to the object. The receiving object then responds to the request and returns a response to the ORB, which formats and forwards the response to the requestor.

In this model, objects simply specify a task to perform. They don't need to know the details or whereabouts of the object that can service the task. The ORB handles all the details of locating objects, formatting messages, and delivering those messages. The ORB is a common interface for all objects in the distributed environment.

The ORB process is similar to a remote procedure call with the added benefit that the ORB itself is capable of locating other objects that can service requests.

Common Object Request Broker Architecture (CORBA) is the basic messaging technology specification defined by the Object Management Group (OMG) in its Object Management Architecture (OMA). CORBA has been implemented by a number of companies, including Hewlett-Packard, SunSoft (a division of Sun Microsystems), and others, as described next:

- Hewlett-Packard's distributed computing environment includes the OMG CORBA component as well as components from the Open Software Foundation (OSF) such as the Distributed Computing Environment (DCE) and the OSF Motif graphical user interface.

- Distributed Objects Everywhere (or Project DOE) is SunSoft's initiative to develop a fully distributed object environment for its Solaris operating system. DOE's design is based on CORBA.

- The Open Software Foundation has adopted CORBA in its Distributed Management Environment (DME) specification.

- The Open Software Foundation's Distributed Computing Environment (DCE) and Distributed Management Environment (DME) use the ORB concept so that objects can make requests to other objects.

RELATED ENTRIES   Common Object Request Broker Architecture; Compound Documents; Distributed Computing Environment; Distributed Objects Everywhere, SunSoft; Object Management Architecture; Object-Oriented Interfaces and Operating Systems; Objects; *and* Workplace OS

Objects

Object-oriented systems provide a unique solution for creating applications, building operating systems, and storing data. Object-oriented systems have the following features:

- In a database system, *objects* are abstractions of real-world entities such as people in a customer database, invoices in an accounting system, or printers and servers in a network directory services database.

- An object holds data and includes a set of *procedures* that are invoked to manipulate or report on the data within the object.

- There are *classes* and *subclasses* of objects. A class is first defined and it serves as a template for creating objects in that class. For example, an inventory for a computer warehouse would have a class called "computer."

- A subclass is a specialization of a class in a hierarchical structure. A subclass called "laptops" might be defined under the "computer" class in the warehouse inventory.

- *Inheritance* is an important aspect of the class hierarchy. Any subclass created under a class inherits the characteristics of its parent class, and can have some special characteristics of its own. Inheritance eases development by promoting reusable objects.

- Objects interact with each other by sending *messages* that invoke object procedures.

- Objects are *polymorphic* in that a message might be invoked differently by different objects. For example, invoking a print command for a customer object prints a name and address, while invoking print for an invoice object prints the invoice. The user executing the print command does not need to know the details about how the object prints.

The information in an object is encapsulated and can only be changed by invoking the procedures that belong to the object. An external entity cannot bypass these procedures and change the internal data on its own. This creates a highly controlled environment that is easy to maintain and build applications around.

Because objects hold data in field-like entries, you could compare an object to a record in a database, but that is where the similarities end. Objects have their own internal procedures for working with the data they contain, whereas any manipulation of a relational database is handled by external procedures. This gives the object a certain amount of independence. If you move an object, the procedures needed to extract its information move with it.

There are object-oriented programming languages, object-oriented operating systems, and object-oriented databases. Some examples are listed next.

- An object is a module in an object-oriented programming language that contains code that other objects can use to simplify program development.

- An object is a collection of information in a hierarchical naming system such as the X.500 Directory Information Base (DIB) or the Novell NetWare 4.x Directory Services (NDS). The NDS directory tree consists of containers and leaf objects.

Containers hold other contains or leaf objects and leaf objects represent real-life entities such as users, printers, servers, and data volumes.

- Compound documents are made up of objects created by other applications, such as text and graphic objects. Microsoft Window's Object Linking and Embedding (OLE) provides an example of compound document features.

RELATED ENTRIES   Compound Documents; Directory Services, NetWare; Object Linking and Embedding; *and* Object-Oriented Technology

Objects, NetWare Directory Services

The NetWare Directory Services (NDS) feature in NetWare 4.x is an X.500-compliant naming service in which user accounts and resources on the network are managed as objects. A user object holds the name, address, computer node address, login script, and other vital administrative information about a network user. Resources such as servers, printers, and volumes are also represented as objects. These objects have properties that specify who can use and change them.

Objects are stored in the NetWare Directory Database (NDB) and organized in a hierarchical tree structure. Container objects usually represent divisions or departments within an organization. Container objects hold other objects, such as user objects, server objects, and printer objects. The organization of the tree is important. Since a container object represents a division or department, an administrator can grant a manager or supervisor various rights to a container object, which then gives the person management rights to all the objects within the container.

RELATED ENTRIES   Directory Services, NetWare; X.500 Directory Services

On-Line Transaction Processing (OLTP)

A transaction is a discrete *unit of work*, typically in a database system. For example, a database transaction is a write that changes a user's account balance or updates an inventory item. On-line transaction processing takes place in real-time. The airline reservation system and bank ATM machines are examples of on-line transaction processing systems.

Most on-line transaction processing systems have traditionally been implemented on mainframe systems because of the complexity of the operation and the need for fast input/output, auditing, and management. Some systems process from 400 to 500 transactions per second or more. A management mechanism is needed to prevent overwrites of data and provides synchronization if a transaction must update data in multiple locations. Other requirements include the ability to roll back failed transactions, provide security features, and provide data recovery if necessary. This is handled by a transaction processing monitor. The monitor ensures that transactions are either fully completed, or rolled-back so the database assumes its pre-transaction state.

In a distributed environment, writes often take place on more than one database server in parallel. Such concurrent transaction processing requires a "roll-back" mechanism that can ensure the integrity of the database in case one system fails during a write. Transactions are either committed together or backed off. A transaction is backed off if one or more of the systems involved in the transaction do not respond with a commit, implying that the system may have failed or the communication failed.

Some common transaction processing (TP) monitors are listed next:

■ The IBM Customer Information Control System (CICS) is a TP monitor that runs on IBM host systems.

■ Tuxedo is a distributed TP monitor developed by AT&T and marketed by Novell's UNIX Systems Group. It runs on many different computer systems and supports a number of clients, including DOS, OS/2, DOS, and Windows.

■ Encina TP monitor is based on the Open Software Foundation's Distributed Computing Environment (DCE) software. Major vendors such as IBM and Hewlett-Packard plan to use Encina.

RELATED ENTRIES   Encina; Transaction Processing; Tuxedo, UNIX System Laboratories; *and* Two-Phase Commit

Open Collaborative Environment (OCE), Apple

Apple OCE (AOCE) is a set of services and tools that help software developers quickly create collaborative applications such as workgroup and workflow software for network environments. The environment is implemented as a set of application program interfaces (APIs) and software modules that let applications communicate with messaging services, E-mail enabled applications, and directory naming. Security features are also included.

Users will be able to operate network and communication services from inside their applications and work in collaboration with other users on projects. Group scheduling, document flow, and intergroup communication are handled by applications that are AOCE-compliant. Three types of applications are anticipated in the environment:

■ *Integrated personal communication* applications that automate electronic mail, fax, and voice messaging

■ *Workflow automation* that imitates paper routing procedures in network computing environments

■ *Team* applications that provide workgroup communication over wide areas

RELATED ENTRY   Apple Open Collaborative Environment

Open Database Connectivity (ODBC), Microsoft

Open Database Connectivity (ODBC) is a specification designed to give Microsoft Windows users access to a variety of multiple desktop databases and file formats. ODBC gives Windows users access to data stored on corporate mainframe computers as well as LAN-based database servers using database programs or other applications that run in the Windows environment.

ODBC is part of Microsoft's Windows Open System Architecture (WOSA) strategy, which is a plan for application development across different platforms in the Windows environment. WOSA includes modular application program interfaces (APIs) that provide an application created by any developer with access to network services such as E-mail, databases, and host connections. WOSA also provides a way to "plug in" back-end services created by any developer. WOSA is a so-called "middleware" strategy that is built directly into the operating system to stimulate the growth of workgroup applications that let users collaborate over networks or provide common interfaces for databases.

WOSA has its roots in Microsoft's strategy of separating printer drivers from applications. In the Windows environment, a printer driver is installed during the initial setup and can be upgraded or changed at any time with a simple procedure. Windows applications use the installed printer driver without any special configuration. They automatically interface to it and take advantage of its special features and available fonts. ODBC uses a similar strategy to provide Windows client applications with common access to back-end database systems. Without ODBC, back-end developers must write drivers for each front-end application, or front-end developers must write drivers for each back-end server system.

ODBC provides common functions that are performed by most back-end database systems. It uses Structured Query Language (SQL) to manipulate the back-end systems and provides individual interfaces to account for the differences in database managers and the way they implement SQL. Front-end applications are written to the ODBC interface and take advantage of its functions. However, this approach may only provide a set of the most common functions and may not take advantage of special features available in every back-end system. Individual implementations will require testing. ODBC is a step toward interoperability that will let users gain access to back-end data that was previous inaccessible.

Microsoft delivers ODBC as a set of drivers that run in front-end products such as Microsoft Access, Microsoft Excel, FoxPro, Btrieve, dBASE, and Paradox. Back-end system support is provided for IBM, Oracle, Paradox, and other database systems. The drivers are available for redistribution to software vendors and can be packaged with applications. The ODBC approach gives Microsoft the major advantage in supplying Windows and Windows applications as the primary client platform for accessing industry-standard database systems in enterprise environments.

O

RELATED ENTRIES   Client-Server Computing; Database Connectivity APIs and Middleware; Database Management System; Distributed Database; Enterprise Networks; Interoperability; Middleware; Structured Query Language; *and* Windows Open System Architecture

Open Data-link Interface (ODI)

NetWare uses a protocol-independent structure known as the Open Data-link Interface (ODI) to provide simultaneous support for different protocols on the network. As shown in Figure O-5, network drivers attach themselves to the ODI layer. Packets are directed to the appropriate protocol stack above the ODI layer, such as Internetwork Packet Exchange (IPX), Transmission Control Protocol/Internet Protocol (TCP/IP), or AppleTalk. Near the top, service protocols provide file and system support for the various operating systems that you can install on a NetWare server.

A similar scheme is used at workstations to allow users to connect to networks that use different communication protocols, such as UNIX-based TCP/IP. You'll need Novell's LAN WorkPlace for DOS to provide TCP/IP support for DOS and Windows workstations. In addition, Novell's LAN WorkPlace for Macintosh provides Apple Macintosh users with transparent access to a broad range of hosts, servers, and workgroups on a NetWare LAN, such as VAX minicomputers, IBM mainframes, and UNIX workstations. Similar products are available from other vendors.

If you need to connect workstations to NetWare LANs as well as to other types of networks, such as Microsoft LAN Manager, IBM LAN Server, and 3Com 3+Share

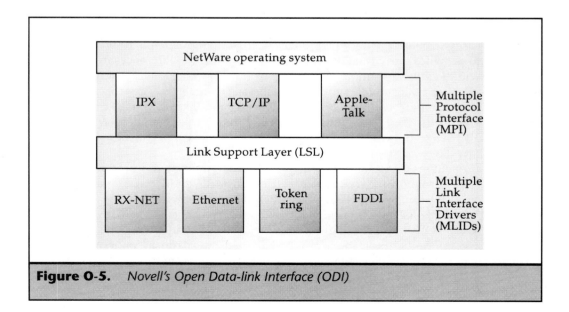

Figure O-5.   *Novell's Open Data-link Interface (ODI)*

networks, you can install the ODI network driver interface specification support (ODINSUP) driver provided in the NetWare package. ODINSUP allows the coexistence of the ODI network driver interface and the Microsoft Network Driver Interface Specification (NDIS), which is typically used by Microsoft products such as LAN Manager and Microsoft NT.

ODI provides the following benefits to those who need to interconnect with a variety of systems:

■ A single network card interfaces with different protocol stacks.

■ A logical network board is created that processes packets from different systems. Those packets can be sent on the same network cabling system attached to a single network card.

■ The workstation can use a different protocol stack without being rebooted.

■ ODI allows NetWare servers and workstations to communicate with a variety of other systems, including mainframes that use different protocol stacks.

ODI standardizes the development of network interface card drivers; vendors no longer need to worry about writing their drivers to fit a specific protocol stack. Instead, drivers are written to attach to the Link Support Layer (LSL). LSL is like a switchboard that ensures packets are directed to the proper protocol stack.

You can see the component layers of ODI in the figure. At the bottom are the interfaces for different types of network interface cards. At the top are the protocols that interface with the NetWare operating system. In between is the Link Support Layer, which directs traffic between the components.

MULTIPLE LINK INTERFACE (MLI)   The Multiple Link Interface (MLI) layer is an interface where device drivers for the network interface card are attached. The device drivers are written by vendors of network interface cards to match the Novell specification of the Link Support Layer. Drivers are referred to as Multiple Link Interface Drivers (MLIDs).

LINK SUPPORT LAYER (LSL)   The LSL provides a link for drivers at the bottom and protocols at the top. It acts as a switching board, directing network traffic from MLIDs to the proper protocol, and vice versa.

MULTIPLE PROTOCOL INTERFACE (MPI)   The Multiple Protocol Interface (MPI) provides an interface for the connection of protocol stacks, such as IPX, TCP/IP, and AppleTalk. Other protocol stacks such as OSI and SNA will be available in the future.

When a packet arrives at a network interface card, it is processed by the card's MLID and passed to the LSL. The LSL determines which protocol stack the packet should go to and hands it to the protocol. The packet passes up through the protocol stack in the normal way, where it is handled by higher-level protocols.

RELATED ENTRIES   DOS Requester, NetWare; Internetwork Packet Exchange; LAN Workplace Products, Novell; Large Internet Packet Exchange; NetWare; Network Driver Standards; *and* Novell

OPEN DECconnect Structured Wiring

A structured wiring system that follows the EIA/TIA 568 Commercial Building Wiring Standard.

RELATED ENTRIES   Cabling; Digital Equipment Corporation; *and* EIA/TIA 568 Commercial Building Wiring Standard

OpenDoc Alliance, Apple

The OpenDoc Alliance, which is primarily sponsored by Apple Computer, is defining the OpenDoc specification, which will help developers create object-sharing applications in network environments. OpenDoc is due in late 1994 or early 1995. Objects are packages of information such as text, spreadsheets, graphics, sound, and video that can be created in one application and inserted in another. It is a specification for creating compound documents (see "Compound Documents"). OpenDoc is similar in concept to Microsoft's Object Linking and Embedding (OLE), but provides more network support and compatibility with OLE objects. It is supported by IBM, Novell, Borland, WordPerfect, and other companies that are not willing to completely rely on Microsoft's implementation.

The technology refers to compound documents as *containers*, objects placed in the container as *parts*, and *part editors* to refer to the tools that manipulate parts. Parts can exist elsewhere on a network and be linked into containers. The technology is partly based on IBM's System Object Model (SOM) and Distributed System Object Model (DSOM). SOM provides the calling mechanism between objects and DSOM provides a way to distribute objects over a network.

An important feature of OpenDoc is its certification procedure, which ensures that applications work together and work on a variety of platforms including Apple System 7, DOS, OS/2, and Windows. So far, Microsoft has not provided such a procedure for its OLE. OpenDoc provides compatibility with Apple's QuickDraw, QuickTime, and Open Collaborative Environment (AOCE), and is built around the IBM/Apple/Lotus Bento object interchange architecture. It also provides compatibility with Microsoft's OLE objects.

RELATED ENTRIES   Compound Documents; Distributed System Object Model; Object Linking and Embedding; Object-Oriented Technology; Objects; *and* System Object Model, IBM

Open Document Architecture

See Document Interchange Standards.

Open Messaging Interface (OMI)

OMI was originally developed by cc:Mail, an electronic mail software developer. It was designed to help programs communicate, regardless of the networking environment. Lotus bought cc:Mail and made it compatible with Lotus and software available from IBM, Apple, and other vendors. OMI is now called Vendor Independent Messaging (VIM). VIM competes with Microsoft's Mail Application Programming Interface (MAPI), which is part of Windows Open System Architecture (WOSA).

RELATED ENTRY   Vendor Independent Messaging, Lotus

Open Network Computing (ONC), SunSoft

SunSoft's ONC technology is a set of networking protocols and distributed services that can be used to build a heterogeneous distributed computing environment. ONC and its next generation, ONC+, are designed to be independent of operating systems, computer architectures, and network transport protocols, and provide transparent access to network-based data and computing resources. They provide the building blocks for programmers to develop and implement distributed applications and simplify management of small and large networks.

More than 150 companies have developed ONC implementations on a variety of hardware platforms and operating systems. Network File System (NFS) is the best known of the ONC services. Sun Microsystems originally marketed ONC as NFS and many licensees continue to describe their products as NFS, even though they support the complete ONC platform. ONC consists of the following core protocols as illustrated in Figure O-6.

Remote Procedure Call (RPC)

RPC is a set of operating system-independent operations for executing procedures on remote systems over a network. RPC is based on the procedure call mechanism commonly used by programmers. It provides a client-server communication structure that handles low-level interprocess communication so programmers can develop distributed applications that run on heterogeneous networks.

External Data Representation (XDR)

XDR is a feature of SunSoft's Open Network Computing (ONC) environment. XDR provides an architecture-independent method of representing data, resolving differences in data byte ordering, data type size, representation, and alignment. Applications that use XDR may exchange data across heterogeneous hardware systems. SunSoft makes RPC/XDR specification and source code freely available.

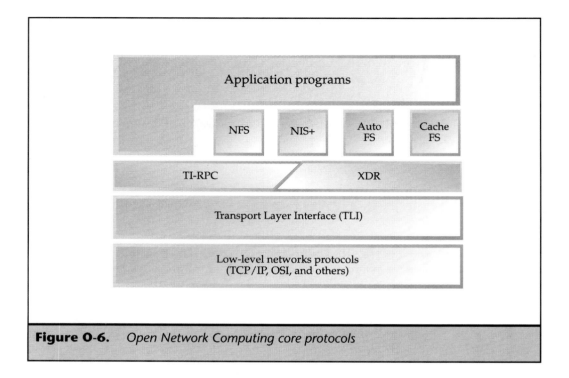

Figure O-6.   *Open Network Computing core protocols*

Transport Layer Interface (TLI)

TLI is a library that exists as a layer underneath ONC in AT&T Unix System V Release 4 that makes RPC protocol-independent, allowing RPC programs to run across multiple network transports such as TCP/IP and OSI. The enhanced RPC, written to the TLI, is known as Transport Independent RPC (TI-RPC). TI-RPC is standard in Unix System V Release 4 and is compatible with the existing ONC RPC protocol. In addition, Novell is supporting the TI-RPC technology.

Distributed Services NFS

The Network File System (NFS), introduced in 1985, is an open systems technology that allows users to share information across network-wide systems. NFS provides transparent access to remote file systems. Files stored on any system attached to the network are potentially accessible by any user. Access is based on rights granted by administrators and file owners. The modules described next are part of distributed services.

NETWORK INFORMATION SERVICE (NIS)   NIS is a network-wide data management facility. It provides an extensive database for storing system information such as hostnames, network addresses, user names, and networks. NIS was formerly known as Yellow Pages (YP).

LOCK MANAGER (LM)   LM allows a user to coordinate and control access to information by supporting file and record locking across a network. It can prevent two or more users from simultaneously modifying the same file or record and possibly destroying valuable data.

REMOTE EXECUTION (REX) SERVICE   REX is used to execute user commands or programs on remote systems. It provides access to compute capabilities not available on the local machine.

NETDISK   This module allows a diskless workstation to boot from servers that support the ONC/NETdisk protocols.

AUTOMOUNTER   Automounter automatically mounts and unmounts remote directories on an as-needed basis. This provides increased transparency and availability of NFS file systems. It supports replication of frequently read and rarely written files, such as system binaries, by allowing remote mount points to be specified with a set of servers rather than a single server.

PC-NFS DAEMON   This is a small program that runs on the ONC-based server, providing authentication and print spooling services to PCs running a DOS implementation of ONC.

ONC+ and Federated Services

ONC+ is the next phase of ONC, and Federated Services will allow ONC to coexist with other distributed computing environments such as NetWare, the Open Software Foundations' Distributed Computing Environment (DCE), and Open Systems Interconnection (OSI). New features include multithreading and a naming service. Each option is described next.

UPDATED NFS FEATURES   The new NFS includes multithreading and the addition of Kerberos authentication services (see "Kerberos Authentication" and "Authentication and Authorization"). Other planned enhancements include support of connection-oriented transport protocols such as Transmission Control Protocol (TCP), as well as write clustering and a new cache filing system to improve performance.

NIS+ NAMING SERVER   NIS+ is a replacement for NIS. It provides a hierarchical enterprise naming service for large networks. It is more scalable and secure than NIS, and easier to administer. NIS+ is interoperable with NIS clients.

TI-RPC   ONC+ will include TI-RPC discussed previously, as well as remote asynchronous call facility that permits nonblocking remote procedure calls. Other enhancements include a multithreading capability, a shared memory feature, and an improved connection management facility.

SECURITY   In addition to the Kerberos security features, RSA Data Security is supported. ONC licensees can obtain from SunSoft rights to use the RSA technology under agreement with RSA.

Federated Services

SunSoft's intentions are to allow users of its Solaris operating environment to access resources across a heterogeneous network that supports distributed services from many different vendors. These services should be able to coexist. Federated Services are extensions to the Solaris distributed computing system.

The Solaris operating environment provides standardized Federated Service Interfaces (FSI), that allow vendors to add their distributed services to Solaris in a well-integrated manner so that services become peers to the ONC+ core services within Solaris.

RELATED ENTRIES   Distributed Computing; Distributed File Systems; Enterprise Networks; Remote Procedure Call; Security; Solaris, SunSoft; Sun Microsystems, Inc.; SunOS, SunSoft; *and* Transport Layer Interface

Open Shortest Path First (OSPF) Protocol

Open Shortest Path First (OSPF) is a link-state routing algorithm that was derived from work done on the Open Systems Interconnection (OSI) Intermediate System-to-Intermediate System (IS-IS) intradomain routing protocol. Link-state routing, as compared to distance-vector routing, requires more processing power, but provides more control over the routing process and responds faster to changes. The Dijkstra algorithm is used to calculate routes, based on the following:

- Number of routers the packet must go through to get to its destination. These are called hops and the fewer hops the better in most cases.

- The speed of transmission lines between LANs. Some routes may use slow asynchronous connections while others use high-speed digital connections.

- Delays caused by traffic congestion. Variable-length frames can hold up traffic at routers. A router might send packets along a different route to avoid congestion.

- Cost of the route, which is a metric defined by an administrator, usually based on the transmission media. The cheapest route might not be the fastest, but is preferable for some types of traffic.

OSPF routing table updates only take place when necessary, rather that at regular intervals. This significantly reduces traffic and saves network bandwidth. Paths through the network are selected based on the criteria listed above. A network administrator can program paths through the network, based on the type of traffic. For example, a path that uses more hops through the network might be preferable if the lines have higher transmission rates. Alternatively, a path might be programmed for less significant traffic because the lines are low-speed and low-cost.

RELATED ENTRIES   Link State Routing; NetWare Link Service Protocol; *and* Routing Protocols

Open Software Foundation (OSF)

The Open Software Foundation is a membership organization that acquires technologies from other vendors to create computing environments. It defines what it needs, then provides those definitions, called Requests for Technology (RFT), to anyone. The only technologies that OSF actually creates are those formed by the combination of acquired technologies.

The OSF Open Systems Software Environment is a collection of open systems technologies that enables users to mix and match software and hardware from several suppliers in a virtually seamless environment. The vendor-neutral software environment consists of the following components:

- *Distributed Computing Environment (DCE)*   A platform or infrastructure that simplifies the development of products in heterogeneous environments.

- *Distributed Management Environment (DME)*   Provides tools for administration of systems and networks in distributed, mixed-vendor environments.

- *Open Software Foundation/1 (OSF/1)*   A UNIX operating system for open environments that supports symmetric multiprocessing, enhanced security features, and dynamic configuration. It is built around the Carnegie Mellon University Mach kernel.

- *OSF/Motif*   A graphical user interface that provides a common look and feel, in the spirit of Microsoft Windows and the Apple Macintosh. It is widely used on IBM systems and has associations to IBM's Common User Access (CUA).

- *OSF Architecture-Neutral Distribution Format (ANDF)*   Enables developers to produce and package one version of an application for use on different hardware architectures, creating a single market for mass-market open systems software.

OSF plays a key role in the development of standards for open systems and interoperable products. Through its Distributed Computing Environment (DCE), OSF provides developers with software that hides the differences between various technologies and products. DCE enables developers to create applications that work in distributed client-server environments. A distributed environment is pictured in Figure O-7. It is an environment in which many different servers provide services and data to clients. These systems may be in the same location, or spread out over large geographic areas.

Distributed environments are typically heterogeneous in that they consist of many different vendor products, operating systems, applications, and databases. OSF DCE simplifies the development of products in distributed client-server environments by providing a *common infrastructure* that hides underlying operating systems, communication protocols, and differences in vendor products.

Common infrastructures have been available in the past from IBM, DEC, and others, but they were proprietary. The primary objective of the OSF DCE is to provide an open environment. It defines a client-server architecture in which clients interact with back-end servers. However, in the distributed environment, servers may be at diverse locations and connected with wide area network (WAN) links. Because such networks can be huge in scope and subject to variations in data access speeds (dictated by WAN connections), synchronization of data and other problems can crop up, complicating the task of creating distributed applications. Because of the complexity in creating such applications, OSF DCE, and products like it, have become extremely important and supported by major vendors such as IBM, DEC, Hewlett-Packard, and others.

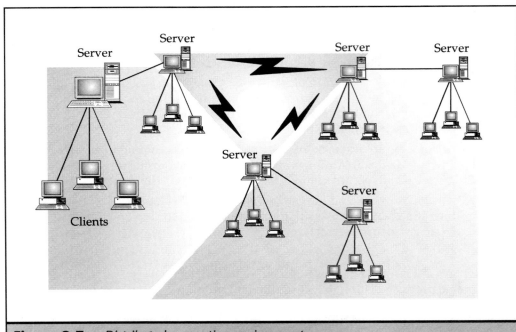

Figure O-7. *Distributed computing environment*

The vendor-neutral DCE platform provides the following core services. These services are discussed in more detail under the "Distributed Computing Environment, OSF" heading:

- Distributed directory services, derived from DEC's DECdns directory services
- A distributed file system based on the Andrew File System (AFS)
- Remote procedure call mechanisms derived from the Network Computing System developed by Apollo (now Hewlett-Packard)
- Security services such as authentication, data integrity, and data privacy provided by Kerberos, a creation of the Massachusetts Institute of Technology

Several major vendors are integrating the OSF DCE into their products. Novell will integrate DCE into NetWare as loadable modules. It is also funding DCE-related projects at several universities. IBM has added DCE client software for its OS/2 products so users can access DCE files and directory services on IBM DCE servers including OS/2 servers running DCE. Hewlett-Packard is also involved with DCE. It provides on-line transaction processing (OLTP) products, object management systems, and other products based on DEC.

RELATED ENTRIES   Directory Services; Distributed Computing; Distributed Computing Environment; Distributed Database; Distributed File Systems; Mach, Carnegie-Mellon Microkernel; Microkernel; OSF/1, Open Software Foundation; Remote Procedure Call; *and* Security

Open Systems

Open systems, in broad terms, are computer architectures, computer systems, computer software, and communication systems in which the specifications are published and available to everyone. An open system encourages the development of compatible vendor products. Customers benefit from open systems because they can choose from a wide variety of products that work with the system, and most important, are easily interconnected with other vendors' products. An open environment provides standard communication facilities and protocols, or provides a way to use a variety of protocols. The computer community is putting more pressure on vendors for open systems because there is a need to purchase equipment, under open bid, with the guarantee that equipment will work on existing open systems.

Open systems are defined by vendors, consortiums of vendors, government bodies, and worldwide standards organizations. Typically, the sponsoring vendor, consortium, or standards organization controls the specifications, but works with other vendors and users at public meetings to define the specifications. Recent trends have moved away from striving for complete openness and more towards acceptance of in-place standards. For example, the Transmission Control Protocol/Internet Protocol (TCP/IP) protocols have proved more popular than the Open Systems

Interconnection(OSI) protocols because of the momentum gained as the primary protocol in use by the Internet. Most vendors now support TCP/IP while few support the OSI protocols.

Several organizations involved in the standards process are listed next, including those that support the use and integration of in-place standards, such as the Open Software Foundation.

- The *Open Systems Interconnection (OSI)* model was developed by the International Organization for Standardization (ISO) in the early 1980s. It defines protocols and standards for the interconnection of computers and network equipment.

- The *Open Software Foundation (OSF)* is a membership organization that acquires technologies from other vendors to create computing environments. Its environments include the Distributed Computing Environment (DCE), an open platform that simplifies the development of products in heterogeneous environments. It is also involved with OSF/1, a UNIX-like environment, and OSF/Motif, a graphical user interface.

- The *Common Open Software Environment (COSE)* is a consortium of vendors including IBM, Hewlett-Packard, SunSoft, and Novell that are cooperating to deliver a common desktop environment (CDE) to UNIX that can rival Microsoft Windows.

- The *Object Management Group (OMG)* develops a suite of object-oriented languages, interfaces, and protocol standards that vendors can use to create applications that operate in multivendor environments. OMG certifies the compliance of products that are designed to the standard.

- *SQL Access Group (SAG)* SAG is a group of database management system (DBMS) vendors that have taken on the goal of creating interoperable Structured Query Language (SQL) database standards. SAG consults with the ISO and ANSI (American National Standards Institute) to bring about its goals.

- *X/Open Ltd.* A group of vendors that promotes open, multivendor environments for the creation of interoperable applications. It publishes information and provides certification services.

Computer vendors such as IBM, DEC, Hewlett-Packard, and others have recently supplemented or moved away from the proprietary architectures and systems they advocated in the 1970s and 1980s to new open environments. For example, IBM now supports its existing customer needs for Systems Application Architecture (SAA), Advanced Peer-to-Peer Networking (APPN), and other standards, as well as new customer needs for open environments by defining the Networking Blueprint, which has the following features:

- Hide the underlying networking components so customers can use applications of choice. This is accomplished through the use of the OSF DCE and OSI standards.

- Allow the use of multiple communication protocols, such as APPN, TCP/IP, and OSI.

- Use advanced bandwidth technologies for communication.

Digital Equipment Corporation supports the OSI protocols with DECnet Phase V which was announced in 1987. It provided full compliance with the OSI model and backward compatibility to Phase IV. However, in 1991, DEC announced ADVANTAGE-NETWORKS, a strategy that adds support for other protocols such as TCP/IP. In doing so, DEC backed away from its total commitment to OSI in Phase V. Most important, DEC provides support for TCP/IP and the ability to build multiprotocol backbones that can transport DECnet, TCP/IP, and OSI data. For example, users can transmit data between TCP/IP applications using OSI transport protocols, or between OSI applications using TCP protocols.

Move to Interoperability

The OSI protocols have served as the model for open systems design for the last decade, although general acceptance of the protocols has been slow. IBM and DEC now fully support OSI. Even the Internet community, which uses the TCP/IP protocols, has been working to integrate OSI protocols. However, with generally sluggish acceptance of OSI, vendors continue to design proprietary products and advocate their own networking architectures. Recently, however, TCP/IP has been one of the driving forces toward interoperability, mainly because of its ability to handle internetworking and its widespread use on the Internet.

The open systems movement has shifted from the need to develop one grand protocol model such as OSI to the acceptance of many different protocols. As companies move to integrate their departmental computers into enterprise systems, there is a requirement to integrate IPX, TCP/IP, AppleTalk, NetBIOS, and many other protocols into the emerging network platform that ties everything together. Advances in processing power, multiprotocol routers, and middleware software have made this multiprotocol support feasible.

Middleware in this case is a generic term that refers to software platforms that hide underlying systems from applications and allow applications to interface with one another. For example, a user running a Windows application on a Novell network can access a traditionally incompatible database on a UNIX computer system attached to a TCP/IP network. The middleware product handles all the communication and interfacing requirements.

The acceptance of many different protocols and the availability of equipment to handle them has brought about an expanding market in interoperable products. Network administrators and users now have more choices, and can use many more of the

O

resources available on their networks. In addition, product vendors can concentrate more on designing unique products and concentrate less on compatibility issues.

RELATED ENTRIES   Distributed Computing Environment; Enterprise Networks; Government OSI Profile; IBM Networking Blueprint; Interoperability; Middleware; Open Software Foundation; Open Systems Interconnection Model; *and* Windows Open System Architecture

Open Systems Interconnection (OSI) Model

The OSI model is a standard that was created by the International Organization for Standardization (ISO). It defines a layered model for an open systems environment in which a process running in one computer can communicate with a similar process in another computer if they implement the same OSI layer communication protocols. The OSI model is pictured in Figure O-8. During a communication session, processes running in each layer on each computer communicate with one another. The bottom layer defines the actual physical components such as connectors and cable and the electrical transmission of data bits between systems. The layers immediately above define data packaging and addressing methods. Still further up are methods for keeping communication sessions alive. Finally, the uppermost layers describe how applications use the underlying communication systems to interact with applications on other systems.

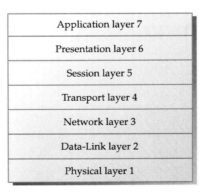

Figure O-8.   *The Open Systems Interconnection model*

The OSI model was designed to help developers create applications that are compatible across multivendor product lines, and to promote open, interoperable networking systems. While OSI hasn't caught on as planned, its model is still used to describe and define how various vendors' products communicate. A comparison of the OSI protocol stack to other protocol stacks is pictured in Figure O-9.

Protocols are loaded into a computer as software drivers. Each layer of the protocol stack defines a specific set of functions. An application at the uppermost layer interacts with the layer below when it needs to send information to another system on the network. The request is packaged in one layer and passed down to the next layer, which adds information related to functions handled at that layer, creating a new packet within a packet. This package is then passed down to the next layer and the process continues as shown in Figure O-10. Each layer adds information to the message packet and this information is read by the corresponding layer in the receiving system's protocol stack. In this way, each protocol layer communicates with its corresponding protocol layer to facilitate communication.

Each layer defines rules and procedures that communication subsystems must follow in order to communicate with peer processes on other systems. Some example processes handled by communication subsystems are listed next:

- Interaction and exchanges between applications, as well as translations between differences in syntax and data representations

- Data exchange management in either full-duplex or half-duplex modes

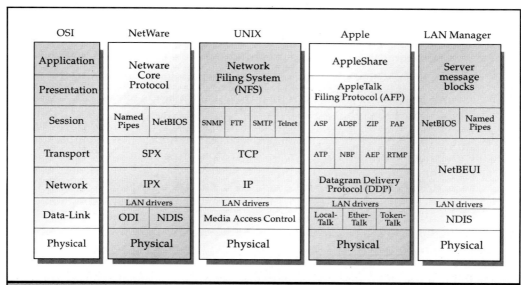

Figure O-9.   *Protocol model comparison*

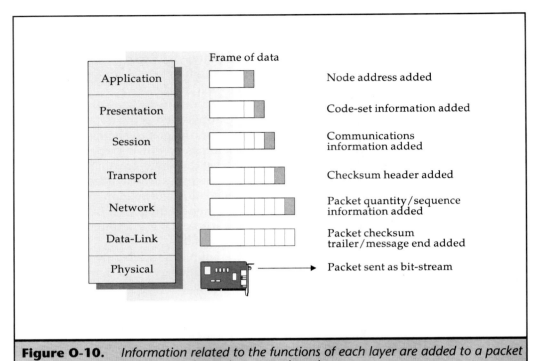

	Frame of data	
Application		Node address added
Presentation		Code-set information added
Session		Communications information added
Transport		Checksum header added
Network		Packet quantity/sequence information added
Data-Link		Packet checksum trailer/message end added
Physical		Packet sent as bit-stream

Figure O-10.   *Information related to the functions of each layer are added to a packet as it passes down the protocol stack*

- Connection-oriented session management (that is, monitoring and maintenance of a communication channel between two systems)
- Network routing and addressing procedures
- Network drivers (that is, framing of data in preparation for transmission)
- Network interface card functions (that is, the transmission of electrical, optical, or radio signals over the network media)

Product developers use protocol standards to create products that interoperate with other vendors' products. For example, the bottom layers define hardware interfacing techniques. A developer working at this level designs network hardware and software drivers following the rules defined in the layer.

In an actual communication session, each layer in the protocol stack communicates with its peer layer in the other system, but it does so by adding the information it needs to communicate to a packet that is passed down to the next lower protocol layer, as mentioned previously. This procedure is covered in more detail under "Layered Architecture."

The following sections describe network protocols. You must have the network hardware—the Physical layer—in place before any of the other layers of communication can take place, so the Physical layer is described first.

THE PHYSICAL LAYER   The Physical layer defines the physical characteristics of the interface, such as mechanical components and connectors, electrical aspects such as voltage levels representing binary values, and functional aspects such as setting up, maintaining, and taking down the physical link. Well-known Physical layer interfaces for data communication include EIA RS-232 and RS-449, the successor to RS-232. RS-449 allows longer cable distances. Well-knows local area network (LAN) systems are Ethernet, token ring, and Fiber Distributed Data Interface (FDDI).

THE DATA-LINK LAYER   The Data-Link layer defines the rules for sending and receiving information across the physical connection between two systems. This layer encodes and frames data for transmission, in addition to providing error detection and control. Because the Data-Link layer can provide error control, higher layers may not need to handle such services. However, when reliable media is used, there is a performance advantage by not handling error control in this layer, but in higher layers. Bridges operate at this level in the protocol stack. Here are common protocols occupying the Data-Link layer:

- High-level Data Link Control (HDLC) and related synchronous, bit-oriented protocols
- LAN drivers and access methods, such as Ethernet and token ring
- Fast packet wide area networks, such as Frame Relay and Asynchronous Transfer Mode (ATM)
- Microsoft's Network Driver Interface Specification (NDIS)
- Novell's Open Data-link Interface (ODI)

THE NETWORK LAYER   The Network layer defines protocols for opening and maintaining a path on the network between systems. It is concerned with data transmission and switching procedures, and hides such procedures from upper layers. Routers operate at the Network layer. The Network layer can look at packet addresses to determine routing methods. If a packet is addressed to a workstation on the local network, it is sent directly there. If it's addressed to a network on another segment, the packet is sent to a routing device, which forwards it on the network. Here are common protocols occupying the Network layer:

- Internet Protocol (IP)
- X.25 Protocol
- Novell's Internetwork Packet Exchange (IPX)
- Banyan's VINES Internet Protocol (VIP)

THE TRANSPORT LAYER   The Transport layer provides a high level of control for moving information between systems, including more sophisticated error handling, prioritization, and security features. The Transport layer provides quality service and accurate delivery by providing connection-oriented services between two end systems. It controls the sequence of packets, regulates traffic flow, and recognizes duplicate packets. The Transport layer assigns packetized information a tracking number that is checked at the destination. If data is missing from the packet, the Transport-layer protocol at the receiving end arranges with the Transport layer of the sending system to have packets retransmitted. This layer ensures that all data is received and in the proper order. A *logical circuit*, which is like a dedicated connection, can be established to provide a reliable transmission between systems. Non-OSI Transport-layer protocols that can provide connection-oriented services include the following:

- Internet Transmission Control Protocol (TCP)
- Internet User Datagram Protocol (UDP)
- Novell's Sequenced Packet Exchange (SPX)
- Banyan VINES Interprocess Communication Protocol (VIPC)
- Microsoft NetBIOS/NetBEUI

THE SESSION LAYER   The Session layer coordinates the exchange of information between systems by using conversational techniques, or dialogues. Dialogues are not always required, but some applications may require a way of knowing where to restart the transmission of data if a connection is temporarily lost, or may require a periodic dialog to indicate the end of one data set and the start of a new one.

THE PRESENTATION LAYER   Protocols at the Presentation layer are part of the operating system and application the user runs in a workstation. Information is formatted for display or printing in this layer. Codes within the data, such as tabs or special graphics sequences, are interpreted. Data encryption and the translation of other character sets are also handled in this layer.

THE APPLICATION LAYER   Applications access the underlying network services using defined procedures in this layer. The Application layer is used to define a range of applications that handle file transfers, terminal sessions, and message exchange (for example, electronic mail). OSI Application layer protocols are listed here:

- Virtual Terminal
- File Transfer Access and Management (FTAM)
- Distributed Transaction Processing (DTP)
- Message Handling System (X.400)
- Directory Services (X.500)

Figure O-11 shows how data flows through the protocol stack and over the media from one system to another. Data starts at the Application and Presentation layers, where a user works with a network application, such as an electronic mail program. Requests for services are passed through the Presentation layer to the Session layer, which begins the process of packetizing the information. A connection-oriented communication session may be opened between the two systems to provide reliable transmissions. Once the session is established, protocol layers begin exchanging information as appropriate.

RELATED ENTRIES   Connection-Oriented and Connectionless Protocols; Layered Architecture; Packets; Protocol Data Unit; Protocols, Communication; *and* Protocol Stack

OpenView Management System, Hewlett-Packard

Sun Microsystems' SunNet Manager and Hewlett-Packard's OpenView use a platform architecture approach, in which a platform is designed that handles all the core functions required for a network management system. These functions include communication protocol interfaces, data definitions, and other management features. Other products designed by the platform vendor or other vendors then plug into or

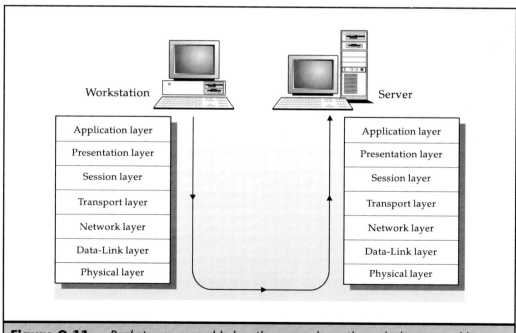

Figure O-11.   *Packets are assembled as they pass down through the protocol layers and disassembled as they pass up through the protocol layers*

interface with the platform and gain all its built-in functions such as access to a multiprotocol network, multivendor systems, and data management schemes.

RELATED ENTRY   Management Standards and Tools

Optical Fiber

See Fiber-Optic Cable.

Optical Libraries

Optical disk library systems are designed to bring data normally stored on microfiche or paper to an online device where it is quickly accessible by network users. An optical disk library can also supplement magnetic tape backup systems or serve as an intermediate storage device for data that is "migrating" to magnetic tape in a *hierarchical management system (HMS)*. In an HMS system, little-used files, or files that have been marked for migration are moved from magnetic disk to optical disk where they remain available to users. In this scheme, the optical disk is called *near-line storage*, as shown in Figure O-12. Eventually, they are moved to magnetic tape for archiving purposes. While magnetic tape offers a convenient, removable, and economical storage media, its sequential access method makes it unsuitable for online data retrieval.

Optical libraries fit in the hierarchy between high-speed magnetic disk storage and low-speed magnetic tape storage. They provide a way to extend the amount of time that computer data can stay on line. Normally, unused files might be backed up to tape or disk, but a near-line optical device can store many hundreds of megabytes of information and keep those files available to users for a much longer time. In some hierarchical systems, the files on optical disk are temporarily moved to magnetic disk when requested by a user. This provides faster file access during editing and reduces the amount of network traffic if the file is accessed by a remote user. Users are often

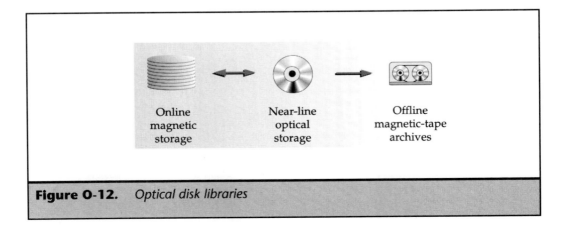

Online
magnetic
storage

Near-line
optical
storage

Offline
magnetic-tape
archives

Figure O-12.   *Optical disk libraries*

unaware that the files are from an optical disk, except for a slight delay in accessing the files while they are moved from near-line to online storage. A hierarchical management system keeps a copy of the directory for near-line files available online to users.

Online optical libraries offer many benefits and enable new types of networking services to be made available to users:

- Optical libraries provide huge amounts of data storage in an inexpensive media that fits in a small space.
- Data can remain available to users for much longer periods of time.
- Optical devices enable the use of imaging systems, in which paper documents are scanned and stored on disk for later access.
- Through imaging systems, documents are much more accessible to both local and remote users over networks.
- Optical libraries and imaging systems enable workflow applications, in which documents move from one user to another for further editing or approval.
- Optical libraries provide adequate storage for multimedia information such as voice, graphic, and video files.

An optical library such as the IBM 3995 Optical Library Dataserver Model 153 can store up to 178 gigabytes of information. The Model 153 uses IBM's new double-capacity optical drives. With 178 gigabytes of available storage, it is possible to store on line:

- The equivalent of 460,800 microfiche images
- File folders from more than 550 four-drawer file cabinets
- More than 160-million pages of computer printouts and reports
- Ten years of monthly transaction history files, at 3 gigabytes a month
- Archive data for 2,000 workstations with 160 MB hard disks

The IBM 3995 series are designed for Ethernet and token ring local area network (LAN) environments and operate with OS/2 LAN Server, IBM PC LAN, and Network File System (NFS) servers. They also can coexist on a LAN with NetWare file servers. Devices are also available for IBM AS/400 computers and in the MVS/ESA mainframe environment.

Most optical library devices use industry standard 5 1/4-inch optical media. Autochanger or jukebox-like devices provide disk stacking and storage capabilities, and provide a way to keep track of disk's contents and access those disks when necessary. For example, the IBM Model 153 holds up to 144 disks in a single library. It includes four drives per autochanger. The optical technology for the Model 153 is magneto-optical, which is a rewritable technology that allows data to be stored and erased. Erased portions of the disk can be reused.

In LAN-based imaging systems, optical libraries are typically part of a much larger system that includes imaging servers, scanners, printers, fax systems, and other related devices. The imaging system should be on a separate LAN (sub-network) to segregate its traffic from the rest of the network, primarily because imaged documents can tie up a LAN for extended times during transmission. Other users on the network who require imaged files can access this LAN when necessary, of course. Alternatively, a separate LAN could connect optical servers to the file server, so that users requesting imaged files make requests at the file server, and the file server retrieves imaged files directly from the optical server through the separate LAN. This keeps the main LAN free for normal network traffic.

Novell NetWare 4.x provides one of the first hierarchical management systems available in the LAN environment. Novell worked closely with Kodak in developing the HMS system to enable imaging and archiving of data.

RELATED ENTRIES   Archiving; Backup and Data Archiving; Hierarchical Storage Management Systems; High Capacity Storage System, Novell NetWare; *and* Jukebox Optical Storage Devices

Organization Containers

An organization container is an object in the NetWare Directory Services (NDS) feature of NetWare 4.x. It forms a branch in a hierarchical directory tree that represents departments or divisions of a company and holds other objects such as user account objects, printer objects, server objects, and even other container objects.

RELATED ENTRY   Directory Services, NetWare

OS/2

OS/2 is the cornerstone of IBM's client-server strategy for desktop computer systems. It operates as both a client and a server in a peer-to-peer environment. OS/2 can run Windows 3.1, DOS, and OS/2 applications simultaneously. This is made possible by the operating system's 32-bit pre-emptive multitasking architecture.

The OS/2 graphical user interface is called the WorkPlace Shell. It uses object-oriented icons and a drag-and-drop interface. Users can customize desktop tools and folders to help organize and simplify access to important information.

Future microkernel versions of OS/2 are planned that will run on the Motorola PowerPC processor. The microkernel will support a variety of operating system personalities, including DOS, OS/2, Windows, or UNIX. With Peer OS/2, users can communicate in peer-to-peer fashion and set up dynamic links between applications running any of these operating systems.

RELATED ENTRIES   IBM; IBM LAN Server; IBM Operating Systems; Mach, Carnegie-Mellon Microkernel; Microkernel; Microsoft LAN Manager; Object-Oriented Interfaces and Operating Systems; *and* Workplace OS

OSF/1, Open Software Foundation

OSF/1 is a UNIX operating system that provides innovative features while maintaining compatibility with current operating system implementation and standards. It provides kernel-supported symmetric multiprocessing, enhanced security, and dynamic system configuration.

The Open Software Foundation adopted many proven technologies from sources such as Carnegie Mellon University, Encore Computer Corporation, IBM, Mentat, SecureWare, and the University of California. The resulting product is an open systems platform that features:

- A Mach-based operating system kernel that is modular and expandable with reduced system maintenance through modular upgrades.

- Symmetric multiprocessing to handle parallel tasks on computer systems with multiple processors.

- Disk mirroring and logical volume management so files can span multiple storage devices, thus eliminating file size limitations.

- Enhanced security features to control access to the system and its files, and track security-related events. OSF/1 implements C2 or B1 level (as defined by the U.S. National Computer Security Center Trusted Computer Security Evaluation Criteria).

- Internationalization through the addition of Extended UNIX codes (EUC) allows commands, utilities, and applications to run regardless of code set or locale.

A path to several file system types is possible through the Virtual File System (VFS) interface. The interface enables multiple types of file systems to be used transparently. OSF/1 applications can reach through the VFS interface to the UNIX file system (UFS), a System V file system, or a Network File System (NFS) distributed file system.

OSF/1 has networking facilities that provide compatibility with current applications and the ability to take advantage of the power of multiprocessor systems. Widely used network protocols and frameworks are employed, including Transmission Control Protocol/Internet Protocol (TCP/IP) protocols.

Future developments of the OSF/1 operating system are simplified by its modular design. The long-range OSF/1 architectural strategy is to move many kernel services out of the kernel and into user space to increase system maintainability, extensibility, and flexibility. Future directions are influenced by the members of the OSF, and the OSF Research Institute.

OSF/1 is based on the Carnegie Mellon University Mach microkernel. The competing product planned by Unix System Laboratories uses the Chorus Systems, Inc. microkernel.

RELATED ENTRIES   Distributed File Systems; Mach, Carnegie-Mellon Microkernel; Microkernel; Mirroring; Multiprocessing; Open Software Foundation; Security; *and* UNIX

O

Packet Assembler-Disassembler (PAD)

A packet assembler-disassembler (PAD) is a form of multiplexer used in X.25 public packet-switched networks to convert non-packet data streams such as the start-stop bits of an asynchronous transmission into packets that can be transmitted over an X.25 packet-switched network. A PAD at the other end disassembles packets.

PADs were originally designed to provide access for multiple terminals at one location to an X.25 network. The most common PAD conforms to the CCITT X.29 specification, which defines the packetizing and depacketizing of asynchronous ASCII data.

RELATED ENTRIES   Multiplexers; X.25

Packet Burst Mode (Pipelining)

Packet burst mode or *pipelining* provides a way to transmit more than one frame of information at a time. It is especially useful for extended transmissions such as files that take place on expensive WAN links or satellite links, in which there is a propagation delay.

In Novell NetWare networks, packet burst techniques improve network communication by letting clients and servers transmit multiple packets of information without the need to reply to each packet. The replies are required by IPX to acknowledge receipt of packets, but they can significantly reduce performance on wide area networks. The new Burst Mode feature of IPX is designed to allow up to 128 packet transmissions before an acknowledge message. There is a potential for improving performance as much as 50 percent with Burst Mode. However, on multiprotocol networks, there is also a potential of holding up traffic generated by other protocols. For example, if IPX is bursting through a router, TCP/IP traffic won't be able to get through until there is a letup. Routers are available that let you prioritize some traffic so it is handled before others.

RELATED ENTRIES   NetWare; Packets

Packet-Radio Communication

Packet-radio communication is one form of transmission technology that lets mobile users communicate with their corporate networks using computing devices such as portable computer, personal digital assistants (PDAs), pagers, and other wireless communicators.

There are two primary methods for mobile communication:

- *Packet-switched RF networks*   In these networks, customers are charged by the packet.
- *Cellular circuit-switched networks*   Products are built around the existing cellular network. Charges depend on the length of connection time.

P-Q

Packet-switching wireless networks are preferable only when transmissions are short because of the way charges are incurred per packet. Circuit-switched networks are preferable for transferring large files or for other lengthy transmissions because customers are charged for the length of time they use the network.

Packet-radio breaks a transmission into small digital packets that include the source and destination address, as well as error correction information. The packets are uplinked to a satellite, then broadcast. The recipient device receives only packets that are addressed to it. Because the transmissions are two way, error detection and correction methods can be used.

Companies involved in packet-radio communication are Ardis (Lincolnshire, Illinois), RAM Mobile Data (Woodbridge, New Jersey), and Nextel (Lafayette, California). Ardis is a joint venture between IBM and Motorola. The signal penetration of the Ardis system was specifically designed for metropolitan areas with high building density. RAM Mobile Data is a partnership between BellSouth and RAM Broadcasting. Hardware products include those manufactured by Ericsson GE Mobile Communications such as RF-enabled modems.

Cellular Digital Packet Data (CDPD) is a newer contender in the wireless market that uses the idle time on cellular systems to transmit digital data. Speeds can reach 19.2 Kbits/sec, which is about four times faster than other wireless services. CDPD is defined by a consortium of cellular carriers and computer companies, including eight of the nine regional Bell operating companies (RBOCs), McCaw Cellular Data, Contel Cellular, and GTE Mobilnet.

Mobile computing is a combination of messaging technologies and wireless communication. Companies such as RAM Mobile Data are involved, not just with the communication aspect, but also with the user interface support. They want to make mobile computing easy to use. Typical users include field service technicians who need technical information, insurance representatives who are making appraisals, and sales people who need information to generate quotes. One method for obtaining information is to simply connect with the company database and make real-time queries. However, messaging can help reduce phone costs in this area as well. A mobile user might simply send an E-mail message with a database query to the database server. The server then generates a response and places that response in the user's mail box for later retrieval.

The systems can provide gateways to popular services such as AT&T Mail, MCI Mail, CompuServe, and networks such as the Internet. You can also communicate with other users. The RAM Mobile Data/Erricsson GE Mobidem wireless system buffers messages if you travel out of a transmission area, then forwards messages once you return to a transmission area. Store-and-forward capabilities hold messages until you pick them up.

RELATED ENTRIES   Cellular Digital Packet Data; Mobile Computing; *and* Wireless Mobile Communication

Packets

A packet is a package of data that is exchanged between devices over a data communication link. The data exchanged between devices may take the following form:

- Messages and commands, such as a request for service
- Control codes for managing the session, such as codes that indicate communication errors and the need for retransmission
- Data, such as the contents of a file

This is *information*, for the purposes of this discussion. Information is placed in packets by various communication subsystems of the transmitting system, then framed into a serial bit-stream and sent across the communication link. One of the main reasons for packetizing and framing information is that any errors on the communication link only affect a small, discernible part of the transmission, which is easily retransmitted. The process of creating a packet in one station and transmitting it to another station is discussed in the following paragraphs, using the Open Systems Interconnection (OSI) protocol model as a guide.

The process starts at the Application layer as shown on the left in Figure P-1. A program in system A has some information to send to system B. The information is sent down through the protocol stack, across the wire, and up through the protocol stack in system B. This information takes the form of a *protocol data unit (PDU)*. As the PDU moves through the layers of system A, each layer attaches specific information to the PDU that is relevant to the protocols in that layer. This attached information is destined for the peer layer in the receiving system. For example, the Transport layer protocol in system A adds a sequence number to the PDU. This sequence number is read by the Transport layer protocol in system B to resequence the packets.

The communication protocol defines the packet structure and the networking system in use (such as Ethernet or token ring) and defines the frame structure for bit-stream transmission. As shown in Figure P-1, each protocol layer attaches information destined for its peer layer in the other system. When the PDU reaches the Physical layer, it is transmitted as a stream of bits. On copper wire, the bit-streams take the form of voltage level changes that represent binary 1s and 0s. As shown in Figure P-2, the Data-Link layer places the PDU in one or more frames and uses a media access method (such as CSMA/CD or token) to gain access to the transmission media. The PDU might be subdivided into a number of separately addressed frames as shown in the figure. The frame format is defined by the network in use. For example, Ethernet defines frames that can hold up to 1,500 bytes of packet data.

In general, a packet is a collection of information that contains data (the "payload") and headers (the "pilot"). Headers include the source and destination address as well as control information to handle errors and keep packets flowing properly. Each packet is a separate block of information that can have a different destination address, and in some cases, different sizes. A typical packet holds 512 bytes of information, so it takes many packets to transfer a large file over a network.

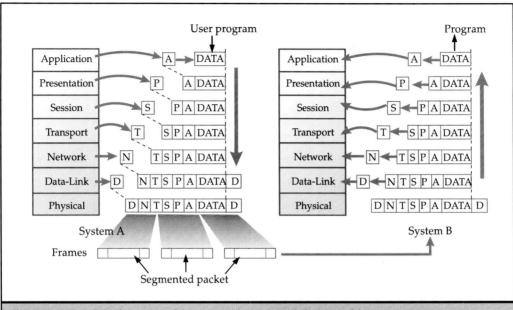

Figure P-1. *Packet assembly, transmission, and disassembly*

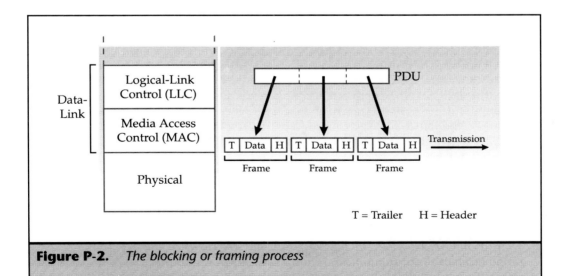

Figure P-2. *The blocking or framing process*

As packets traverse a network, the addressing information contained in them is used by bridges and routers to direct packets to their destination, or keep them off of networks where they don't belong, as described next:

- *Packet forwarding* A process performed by a network node when it forwards packets to the next appropriate mode or router in a network.

- *Packet filtering* A way of sorting and selecting packets so that only packets of a specific type or with a specific address are transmitted.

Routers direct packets along a specific path that has been predetermined as the best route to the packets' destination. Routers use algorithms to determine efficient paths in conjunction with other routers on the network. Administrators can also manually configure routers, based on the cost or speed of routes. Information can be transmitted to another system using either connection-oriented or connectionless methods. A connectionless session is more efficient for short, bursty transmissions since a session setup is not required, but the end system may need to perform more work to resequence packets that arrive out of order and check for lost packets.

RELATED ENTRIES   Connection-Oriented and Connectionless Protocols; Internetwork Packet Exchange; Layered Architecture; NetBIOS; Open Systems Interconnection Model; Protocol Data Unit; *and* Transmission Control Protocol/Internet Protocol

Packet-Switching Networks

A public data network (PDN) is a national network of interconnected access points and switches that provide simultaneous data transmission for many users between many points. There are two primary types of PDNs: the circuit-switched PDN and the packet-switched PDN.

Circuit-switching networks provide a way to set up a physical communication channel through the public network between the calling equipment and the called equipment. The telephone system is an example. When you call another person, you have a dedicated line to that person until you hang up the line. Features of circuit-switched networks include:

- A setup phase is required, which can take several seconds, although new switching equipment has reduced this time to milliseconds.

- Connections are maintained for the duration of the exchange, then taken down.

- The data transfer rate through the channel is often negotiated in advance and may not provide enough bandwidth under loads.

Circuit-switched services include Integrated Services Digital Network (ISDN), which brings digital transmission all the way to the customer's site in increments of 64

Kbits/sec, without the need for a modem. Other circuit-switched services include Switched-56 and dialup lines.

Packet-switching networks are built with a mesh of interconnections, as shown in Figure P-3. Transmissions from many users, in the form of packets, can traverse the network at the same time. Switches in the network direct packets to their destination. They typically provide connectionless services, although connection-oriented *logical circuit* services are available, as discussed shortly. A connectionless service does not set up a dedicated communication channel prior to transmission of data.

A packet-switching network is often referred to as a *cloud* because it contains many different possible physical connections and routes that a packet can traverse to get to its destination. In addition, there are multiple connections into the network on which many source devices can transmit. Because of the many possible connections and pathways, a packet-switched network is often said to provide *any-to-any* connections, as opposed to a circuit-switched network which provides a temporary dedicated connection between two systems.

The packet network is made up of *exchanges* that examine packets and forward them out a specific port that delivers them along the best route to their destination, much like a train-switching yard or a traffic circle in a downtown area. The size of packets is kept to a minimum for several reasons. If a fault on the network corrupts in-transit data, only corrupted packets require retransmission rather than the entire transmission. In addition, if packet size were unlimited, a transmission from one source might tie up a switch for a long period of time. This would be like sending data on a long train through a switching device, rather than using many individual trucks. Trucks can be held up to allow other traffic through.

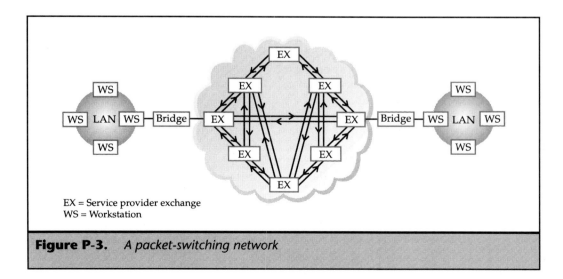

Figure P-3.   *A packet-switching network*

While packet-switching networks provide any-to-any connectionless service, it is possible to establish a *logical circuit* (also called virtual circuit) through a packet-switched network. Logical circuits provide most of the same features and benefits of a circuit-switched network, but the path through the network is predefined. Packets flow in an orderly way from the source to the destination and the delay associated with reassembling packets at the destination is eliminated. The switches along the path of the circuit maintain information about the circuit to improve performance. A circuit identifier is added to each packet to identify the circuit at the destination and distinguish it from other circuits.

The traditional packet-switching service has been X.25, but Frame Relay is growing in use as a way to build fast network connections over public switching facilities. Other services are Switched Multimegabit Data Service (SMDS) and Asynchronous Transfer Mode (ATM) services, as discussed in the following sections. All of these services require a special line from the customer site to the access point of the packet-switched network. In most cases, that line is a multiplexed switched or leased digital circuit such as a T1 line or a Switched-56 line, although switched analog lines are suitable when traffic volumes are low.

X.25   X.25 generally refers to the well-established packet-switching services that were traditionally used to connect remote terminals to host systems. X.25 defines a set of protocols for connecting to a packet-switching network. These networks use extensive error checking that was required in the days when telephone lines were not as reliable as they are today. A message is returned to the sender when a switch detects a corrupted packet, so the sender knows as soon as possible when there is a problem and it must retransmit a packet. This overhead reduces performance and is largely responsible for the growth of Frame Relay, which eliminates the error checking feature. X.25 operates in the 600 bits/sec to 64,000 bits/sec data transfer range.

FRAME RELAY   Frame Relay, as the name implies, actually switches (relays) frames and does not operate at the packet level. It is a Data-Link layer service relative to the OSI protocol stack, whereas X.25 operates in the upper Network layer where packet handling takes place. Frame Relay simply relays framed packets through the network to their destination. It performs a simple error check at each node and discards corrupted packets. End stations must detect and correct the problem. This strategy takes advantage of modern, highly reliable transmission systems. By providing only basic network transmission services, Frame Relay can transmit at T1 rates (1.544 Mbits/sec) or higher. However, Frame Relay is suitable for data only, not voice or video, largely because of its variable-length frame usage.

ASYNCHRONOUS TRANSFER MODE (ATM)   ATM is a cell relay service. A cell is a fixed size container of information that is relayed between switches in the network at the Data-Link layer. The ATM network does not provide error detection services except to throw out corrupted packets. Like Frame Relay, it relies on end nodes to detect problems and request retransmissions. ATM is purely a data transmission service and end-nodes do not rely on it for any error correction services. Because of its fixed-cell size, and the elimination of error detection, ATM can operate in the gigabit-per-second range. Fixed size cells are easily handled at switching nodes, unlike variable length frames or packets, which can cause unpredictable delays. ATM is ideal for real-time applications like video-conferencing and voice transmission, as well as data transmission. ATM is currently being implemented by the carriers and is making its way into enterprise networks.

SWITCHED MULTIMEGABIT DATA SERVICE (SMDS)   SMDS is a carrier service that uses the cell services of ATM. It was developed by Bellcore and is used by local exchange carriers in various metropolitan areas. The service is designed to provide organizations with an extension to their in-house LANs to other sites in metropolitan areas, as well as special services not available with ATM alone.

RELATED ENTRIES   Asynchronous Transfer Mode; Carrier Services; Circuit-Switching Services; Frame Relay; Switched Multimegabit Data Service; Virtual Circuits; *and* X.25

Parallel Processing

Parallel processing takes place in computers that have multiple processors. Ideally, a single task is divided into multiple parts and distributed to several processors. As each processor completes that task assigned to it, the results are joined with the results completed by other processors, as shown on the top in Figure P-4. Of course, this type of processing is difficult since programmers must devise ways to divide tasks, which are not always predictable in advance, and rejoin the results. Parallel processing is usually reserved for supercomputer systems. Massively parallel computers contain hundreds or thousands of processors and specially designed operating systems to manage them.

Multiprocessing systems, typically with four processors, are available as network servers. They operate in either asymmetric or symmetric multiprocessor modes, depending on the system and operating system. In asymmetric multiprocessing, each CPU is dedicated to a specific function, such as network interface card input/output (I/O), or file operations, as shown on the bottom in Figure P-4. In symmetric multiprocessing, any CPU can handle a task or part of a processing task as necessary. In operating systems such as Microsoft Windows NT, a process is subdivided into threads, and each thread runs on a separate processor. If one processor completes a thread, it can take on another thread. Symmetric processing is superior to asymmetric processing when it comes to handling a variety of irregular tasks.

RELATED ENTRY   Multiprocessing

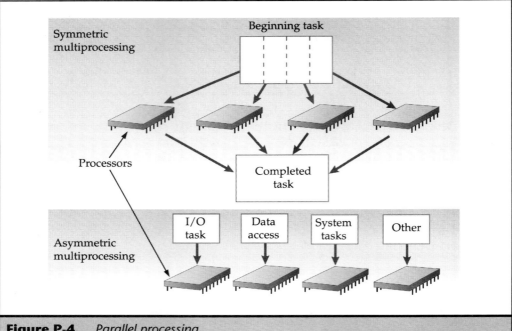

Symmetric
multiprocessing

Beginning task

Processors

Completed
task

Asymmetric
multiprocessing

I/O
task

Data
access

System
tasks

Other

Figure P-4. *Parallel processing*

Partition Management

Database partitioning is a technique for distributing data to local and remote sites in order to place data closer to the users who access it. In the case of a wide area network, it makes sense to put data close to users, rather than have them access the database over expensive or slow wide area connections. Partitioning subdivides a database so that only relevant portions of the database are copied to the remote site.

A partitioned database is typically hierarchical in structure and partitioning occurs at branches in the structure, such as departments, sales regions, or inventory types. A database partition is then copied (replicated) to another site. Because the data is replicated, synchronization is required to ensure that data in both locations remains the same. Figure P-5 illustrates the partitioning of a database to bring data closer to remote users. A link still exists between the databases so any user can access data on any other system.

Naming services provide "yellow pages"-type listings of users and resources on the network. When users needs to access a printer, they find that printer in the naming service and print to it. The printer might be located in another city. The naming service consists of a master database that is administered at one location, which partitions at remote locations. The remote partitions allow users at those sites to look up local

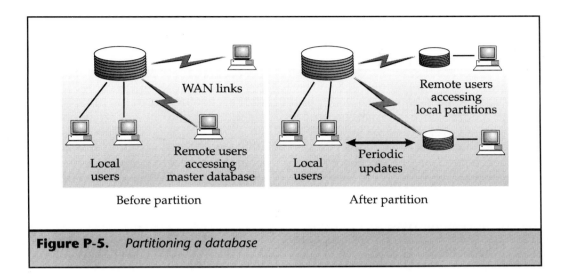

Figure P-5. *Partitioning a database*

resources locally, rather than access the master database over an expensive wide-area link. Immediate synchronization is usually not necessary in the case of a directory service. For example, if the network administrator adds a new user, it probably won't make much difference to other users if that new user doesn't appear in the directory listing for a few minutes. NetWare Directory Services is discussed later.

There are two mechanisms for synchronizing data on databases, two-phase commit and replication:

- *Two-phase commit* Is used in online transaction processing and is not necessarily applicable to partitioned databases. It can involve writes to two or more different types of databases. In a two-phase commit, all the databases involved must first acknowledge to a monitoring program that they can write the data base change, then acknowledge that they have in fact written the change. If any system fails to acknowledge, all systems abort the write. See "Transaction Processing" for more information.

- *Replication* Involves copying all or part of a database at regular intervals, or after major changes, from a remote site to the master database, or from the master database to remote sites. The method is useful when database updates are not time-critical.

NetWare Directory Services (NDS)

NetWare 4.x Directory Services (NDS) uses a distributed database called the NetWare Directory Database (NDB) to track Directory Services objects. An object holds information about users and resources such as servers, volumes, and printers. Users access the database when they want to use an object. Administrators access the database when they want to add a new object or change an existing object.

The database can reside on a network of servers, not just one server, to ensure its survival in the event a server crashes and to provide better access to the data. This is accomplished by segmenting the database into partitions and storing each partition on appropriate servers. You can copy (replicate) partitions to other servers to provide backups. Performance improves because users get directory information from local databases, not over wide-area links. The database is typically partitioned according to geographic locations. For example, the Chicago division of a national company stores the Chicago partition of the directory services database on its own server. A partition management utility is used to create, remove, join, divide, synchronize, and rebuild partitions.

Partition replicas are copies of a partition stored on the server where the partition was created, and stored on other servers where the replica is copied to provide fault tolerance. There are three types of replicas:

- *Master* The master replica is the only replica in which the structure of the directory for a partition can be changed. You can create a new partition by changing only the master replica, but objects can be created, modified, and deleted in the master and the read-write replicas. When a new NetWare server is installed, a master replica is created and stored on the server on which the new partition was created. If the master replica is lost or corrupted, another replica must be made from the backup master replica.

- *Read-Write* This replica is changeable. It synchronizes with other replicas when a change has been made. Partition information can be read from and written to this replica.

- *Read-Only* Partition information can be read from this partition, but only the read-write or master replica can write to it.

Of course, the replicas must be continuously synchronized. As changes are made to partitions, all replicas of the partition on other servers are automatically updated. These updates are made as soon as possible but not immediately since constant synchronization would introduce too much internetwork traffic and reduce network performance. The time synchronization services ensure that all servers have the latest information as soon as possible. The delay in synchronizing replicas is not critical. Delays of a few seconds in supplying information to replicas about new user objects or resources does not usually cause any problems.

Timestamps help avoid problems that might occur if an object in the database is changed at two different locations. When the two replicas are synchronized, the timestamps are compared and only the most current information is used. Timestamps are part of the Time Synchronization Services.

NetWare Directory Services forms a hierarchical tree structure in which companies are divided into divisions or departments. These divisions and departments are placed in container objects that form branches of the tree. In Figure P-6, CambrianCorp is the company name. Branches in the tree are formed by the Administration and the Sales departments. The directory tree is partitioned at these branches. In this case, the Sales department, which we'll assume is at another location is partitioned from the tree, and the partition is copied to the server in the Sales department.

Note that partitions always form at container objects (branches) in the directory tree. All objects that branch from that container are part of the partition. However, the partition does not introduce any barriers to the access of its object by users in other partitions except for those imposed by administrators. Partitions simply provide fault tolerance and quicker access to Directory Services information.

RELATED ENTRIES   Directory Services; Directory Services, NetWare; Replication; Transaction Processing; *and* Two-Phase Commit

Partitions (Disks), NetWare

See Disks, Partitions, and Volumes Under NetWare.

Passive Hub

A hub is a central location for the attachment of wires from workstations. There are passive hubs and active hubs. A passive hub is a small box that has just a few ports for the connection of computer stations in a star configuration. A passive hub might also be a wiring panel or punchdown block. The important point is that there is no amplification of the signals. A passive hub is simply a junction box that does not require an electrical connection.

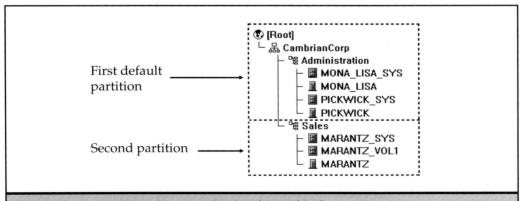

Figure P-6.   *NetWare Directory Services hierarchical tree structure*

In contrast, an active hub usually has more ports than a passive hub and actively regenerates the signals from one device to another. Active hubs require an electrical connection. They are used like repeaters to provide an extension of the cable that connects to a workstation.

RELATED ENTRY   Hubs

Patch Panel

A patch panel assists in the cabling of networks. It is typically installed in the wiring closet where network twisted-pair cable terminates. The patch panel has rows of telephone-type modular jacks. The cable installer or network administrator can easily connect, move, test, and disconnect network devices by changing the connections at the patch panel.

RELATED ENTRY   Cabling

Pathworks, DEC

A family of products that provide client-server networking environments in which DEC minicomputer systems operate as servers, and clients can be Windows, DOS, OS/2, and Macintosh computers.

RELATED ENTRY   DEC PATHWORKS

Peer-to-Peer Communication

A peer-to-peer communication session is one in which each station has similar control over the session. Workstations have their own processing power and can control their own activities. This is in contrast to the old mainframe and minicomputer model in which a central computer provided all the processing power for many different terminals. The terminals simply displayed screens of information and provided a place for users to enter commands at a keyboard. Even as intelligent computers were added to these systems, control still remained largely in the hands of the central computer.

As computers with their own processing power moved into organizations, it became apparent that there were many benefits to decentralizing the mainframe and providing cooperative processing in which a user at one computer could access and use the resources of another computer, such as its files or printer.

IBM changed its Systems Network Architecture (SNA) to support a form of peer-to-peer networking in early 1980, but the sessions were still set up and maintained by the host. IBM now embraces an arrangement in which workstations can establish their own peer-to-peer sessions. The Advanced Peer-to-Peer Networking (APPN) strategy provides cooperative computing environments in which large and small computers can communicate with one another as peers over local area networks (LANs) and wide area networks (WANs). Users at workstations, or end systems, can initiate communication on the network with other end systems without any help from the host. APPN changes the role of host systems. Many have become back-end servers that provide peer-to-peer services to network users.

Peer-to-peer networking and client-server computing are closely related. In client-server computing, workstations act as clients and access resources on other computers, which act as servers. In a true peer-to-peer arrangement, any computer on the network can make its resources available to other users. However, in the NetWare environment, this client-server relationship is limited to some extent. Workstations access resources on centralized servers that have strictly controlled environments. In a typical NetWare environment, workstations are client-to-servers and not peers with other workstations, although third-party software is available to let clients talk to one another, but in a strict NetWare environment, workstations access files either locally or from a server.

While there are many advantages to the peer-to-peer networking approach, many network managers balk at using them because they provide little management and security control. In a peer-to-peer arrangement, data is stored in many locations on the network, creating administrative problems and problems with tracking the location of data, backing it up, and making sure it is secure. Dedicated file server systems like Novell NetWare provide centralized data storage, advanced security including authentication and authorization to multiple servers, and in some cases, improved performance when superservers are used.

Despite these drawbacks, peer networking is finding its way into the organizations via workgroup users, or users who purchase packages such as Windows for Workgroups, which include peer networking features. The following network operating systems provide peer-to-peer functionality:

■ *Microsoft Windows for Workgroups* Allows users to connect with other systems and share files and peripherals. Built-in Object Linking and Embedding (OLE) lets users share objects (text, graphics, and spreadsheet data) over the network. Workgroup software such as Mail and Schedule are also included.

■ *Microsoft Windows NT* Provides all the features of Windows for Workgroups, with additional security.

■ *Novell Personal NetWare* A peer-to-peer network that lets users share files and peripherals. It works in the NetWare 3.x and 4.x dedicated server environments, allowing users to communicate directly with one another over the same network cable used to connect with servers.

■ *Artisoft LANtastic* A peer-to-peer network operating system that lets users share files and system resources over the network.

■ *IBM LAN Server and OS/2* A peer version of OS/2 that includes network DDE and a network Clipboard that lets users share objects over the network in a scheme similar to that used in Microsoft Windows for Workgroups.

RELATED ENTRIES   Advanced Peer-to-Peer Networking; Client-Server Computing; Enterprise Networks; IBM Mainframe Environment; *and* Systems Network Architecture

Peripheral Component Interconnect (PCI)

Peripheral Component Interconnect (PCI) is an Intel-developed, high-speed system bus (as opposed to a local bus) specification that provides 32-bit or 64-bit data paths at 33 MHz or 66 MHz clock rates, depending on the chip sets used. In comparison, the original IBM PC's 8-bit bus ran at 4.77 MHz and the IBM AT's 16-bit bus ran at 8 MHz. These buses were designed for 8088 and 80286 processors and cannot handle data transfer rates required for current and future high-speed technologies such as networking, graphics, and video.

The PCI bus uses burst mode to read and write data to and from adapters. Data is transferred every clock cycle, as opposed to every other clock cycle as was the case in previous designs. It can provide up to 132 Mbits/sec performance during burst mode operation. In comparison, the Extended Industry Standard Architecture (EISA) bus can burst data at 33 Mbits/sec. With the PCI 64-bit chip set, the burst mode throughput can increase to as high as 264 Mbits/sec. The slot for 64-bit PCI systems is larger than the slot for 32-bit PCI systems, but 32-bit PCI boards will fit into the 64-bit system slots, so there is some upgrade potential.

Other features of the PCI bus include the following:

■ An autoconfiguration feature assigns interrupts to installed adapter cards.

■ Intel PCI chip sets are available for Intel 80486-based PCs and Intel Pentium-based PCs. The Pentium chip set provides a 64-bit data path with speeds up to 66 MHz clock rates. The 80486 chip sets provide 32-bit data paths at 33 MHz clock rates.

■ PCI supports interface cards running either at 3.3 volts or 5 volts.

■ PCI is designed by Intel to operate with current and future generation Intel processors.

The PCI bus is not a true local bus because it is not directly connected to the processor and memory. The reason for this is that bus designs wired directly to the processor are limited in the number of devices they can support. The PCI bus can support up to ten devices; however, most systems won't have ten PCI slots. Instead, host adaptors are used that provide daisy-chain connections for devices. The SCSI-2 disk interface is a good example. One host adapter can support up to seven attached devices such as disk drives.

RELATED ENTRIES   EISA Bus; MicroChannel Architecture Bus

Permanent Virtual Circuits (PVC)

A virtual circuit is a pathway through a packet-switched, mesh-type network that appears to be a dedicated, physically connected circuit. The virtual circuit is predefined and maintained by the end systems and nodes along the circuit, but the actual pathway through the packet-switched network can change. The important point is that packets are transferred in order over a specific path and arrive at the destination without a need for resequencing.

A *switched virtual circuit (SVC)* establishes a temporary virtual circuit between individual workstations, with sessions lasting only as long as needed. Once a communication session is complete, the virtual circuit is disabled. A *permanent virtual circuit (PVC)* is a fixed circuit that is created and maintained by the end stations, even if data is not being transmitted. The permanence of the line removes the setup overhead and improves performance for periodic transmissions that require immediate connections. A PVC is used on a circuit that includes routers that must maintain a constant connection in order to transfer routing information in a dynamic network environment. Carriers assign PVCs to customers to reduce overhead and improve performance on their networks.

RELATED ENTRY   Virtual Circuits

Permissions in Windows NT

Permissions are the security rights control method in Windows NT. Permissions secure system resources such as directories, files, and printers. You grant permissions to users so they can access the resources. In other words, you select a directory, then select the users or groups that you want to access it, and finally select the specific type of access the user or group will have. For example, you could grant the Everyone group the Read (R) and Write (W) permission to a directory that holds documents. All users of the system, including network users, can then work with files in the directory since all users belong to the Everyone group.

There are two types of permissions: *individual* and *standard*. Think of the individual permissions as the basic building blocks of standard permissions. Standard permissions are simply combinations of the individual permissions that users need to perform common tasks. They are grouped together to make permission administration easier. For example, Change is a standard permission that consists of the Read (R), Write (W), Execute (X), and Delete (D) individual permissions.

Permissions also come into play when you want to share a directory on your system with other network users. The permission you apply to the shared directory determines the type of access network users have to the directory. Note that only drives formatted to use the Windows NT file system (NTFS) support directory and file permissions.

Individual Permissions for Directories and Files

As mentioned, the individual permissions are the basic building blocks for the standard permission sets. The following describes each individual permission:

READ (R)   If Read permission is given for directories, users can list files, display directory attributes, and display directory owners and their permissions. If given for a file or set of files, users can open the file and display its contents, its owner and permissions, and its attributes.

WRITE (W)   If Write permission is given for directories, users can add files and subdirectories, change directory attributes, and display directory owners and permissions. If given for files, users can display the file's owner and permissions and change the file's attributes and contents.

EXECUTE (X)   If Execute permission is given for directories, users can display each directory's attributes, change to subdirectories, and display owners and permissions. If given for files, users can run the file as well as display the file's owner, permissions, and attributes.

DELETE (D)   The Delete permission allows users to delete directories or files, whichever they've been accorded permission to delete.

CHANGE PERMISSIONS (P)   The Change Permissions permission allows users to change permissions on directories or files, whichever they've been accorded permission to change.

TAKE OWNERSHIP (O)   The Take Ownership permission allows users to assume ownership and control of a directory or file from another owner.

Standard Directory Permissions

The standard directory permissions control the access that local users and groups have to directories. The following table shows the individual permissions that each standard permission grants. Note that file permissions depend on the permissions set for each directory. The following paragraphs describe how permissions affect user access to directories.

Standard Permission	Individual Permissions in Directories	Individual Permissions for Files
No Access	None	None
All	All	All
List	R X	Not applicable
Read	R X	R X
Add	W X	W X

Add & Read	R W X	R X
Change	R W X D	R W X D
Full Control	R W X D P O	R W X D P O
Special	R W X D	Not specified

NO ACCESS   The No Access permission revokes all permissions users have to the directory or file.

LIST   For directories, the List permission allows users to switch to subdirectories, list files, and display directory attributes, owners, and permissions. It does not affect files.

READ   For directories, the Read permission allows users to switch to subdirectories, list files, and display directory attributes, owners, and permissions. For files, it allows users to run the file if it is a program, and display the file's data, owner, permissions, and attributes.

ADD   For directories, the Add permission allows users to display each directory's attributes, owners, and permissions, as well as add and change subdirectories, files, and attributes. It does not affect files.

ADD & READ   For directories, the Add & Read permission allows users to list files, display attributes, owners, and permissions, as well as create subdirectories, add files to them, and change their attributes. For files, it allows users to display each file's owner, permissions, contents, and attributes, as well as run the file if it is a program.

CHANGE   For directories, the Change permission has all the features of Add & Read and also lets users delete directories and subdirectories. For files, it allows users to display each file's owner, permissions, and contents, as well as run the file if it is a program. Users also can view and change attributes and the file's contents, as well as delete the file.

FULL CONTROL   For both directories and files, the Full Control permission allows all the permissions of Change and adds the ability to change permissions and take ownership of the directory or file.

RELATED ENTRIES   Access Rights; Users and Groups; *and* Windows NT, Microsoft

Physical Layer, OSI Model

The Open Systems Interconnection (OSI) model is a standard defined by the International Organization for Standardization (ISO). It defines a layered architecture that categorizes and defines the protocols for communication between end systems. During the communication session, processes running in each layer on each computer communicate with one another. While there are seven layers, there are three catagories.

■ The bottom layer defines the actual physical components such as connectors and cable and how data is exchanged between systems. The type of network interface and the access method are also defined here.

■ The transport layers are concerned with the reliable transmission of data between systems.

■ The application layers provide the interface between user applications and the network communication systems.

The OSI model was designed to help developers create applications that are compatible across multivendor product lines, and to promote open, interoperable networking systems. While OSI hasn't caught on as planned, its model is still used to describe and define how various vendor's products communicate. Common protocol stacks are IBM Systems Network Architecture (SNA), DEC Network Architecture (DNA), and Apple Computer's AppleTalk. Communication protocols that can be matched to layers of the stack, but are not part of any specific architectural plan, are TCP/IP (Internet/UNIX), Microsoft NetBIOS/NetBEUI, and Novell SPX/IPX. These protocol stacks are compared to the OSI stack under the "Open Systems Interconnection (OSI)" heading.

The very bottom layer of any protocol stack is the Physical layer. It defines protocols that describe the four aspects of physical interfaces: mechanical, electrical, functional, and procedural.

■ Mechanical aspects are connector specifics, circuit-to-circuit assignments, and connector latches.

■ Electrical aspects include voltage levels representing binary values and resistance.

■ Functional aspects assign functions such as control, data, and ground to particular circuits.

■ Procedural aspects define the procedures used to exchange data.

Well known Physical layer interfaces for data communication include EIA RS-232 and RS-449, the successor to RS-232. RS-449 allows longer cable distances. Well-known local area network systems are Ethernet, token ring, and Fiber Distributed Data Interface (FDDI).

RELATED ENTRIES   Layered Architecture; Open Systems Interconnection Model; *and* Protocol Stacks

Physical Unit (PU)

See Systems Network Architecture, IBM.

Ping

Ping is a protocol used in the Transmission Control Protocol (TCP) environment to test whether a node or remote device is communicating on a local area network (LAN) or wide area network (WAN). The protocol attempts to receive an echo response from a host system or a gateway. It is a useful tool for locating problems on the network related to failed connections and software problems. One datagram is sent every second over the network and any response is displayed.

RELATED ENTRY   Transmission Control Protocol/Internet Protocol

Pink, Taligent

See Taligent.

Pipes

Pipes are interprocess communication (IPC) features of the UNIX and OS/2 operating systems. They are like queues in which one process running in the multitasking operating system can store information it wants to pass to itself, to another process running in the computer, or to multiple processes running in the computer. The information is stored on a first-in, first-out basis and flows as a stream of bits that is not altered during transmission. A pipe is opened like a file and read to or written to in the manner of a file. They are unidirectional, in that one pipe is used to read and another is used to write information. Pipes exist in the Presentation layer, relative to the Open Systems Interconnection (OSI) protocol model.

Named pipes are logical structures in a server that other systems access when they need to use the resources of the server. Named pipes are a networking extension of the IPC mechanism in OS/2 and the LAN products that run on it, such as IBM LAN Server and Microsoft LAN Manager. A named pipe is a communication channel used to transfer information among programs, processes, and devices over the network. It is the basis for the communication mechanism between the client and advanced client-server applications such as Structure Query Language (SQL) servers and communication servers.

Figure P-7 illustrates the pipe process. On the left, two processes running in the same computer share information using a pipe. On the right, two processors running in separate computers share information using a named pipe. Notice that named pipes are assigned names to differentiate them from other pipes that might be available on the network.

RELATED ENTRIES   Interprocess Communication; Remote Procedure Call

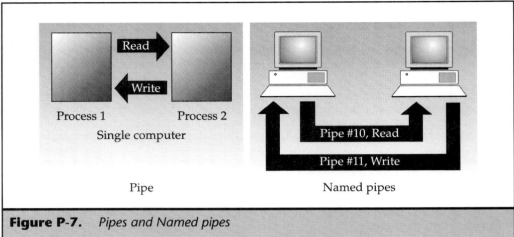

Figure P-7. *Pipes and Named pipes*

Platform

Platform has several meanings in the computer and networking world:

- A computer system based on a specific processor, such as an Intel-based platform or a Motorola-based platform

- A operating system environment, such as a NetWare platform

- An enterprise network, in which the network itself is seen as a sort-of plug-and-play platform in which a variety of networking devices can be connected

RELATED ENTRIES   Enterprise Networks; Networks

Plug-and-Play ISA, Microsoft

Plug-and-play ISA is a specification proposed by Microsoft and Intel for the Industry Standard Architecture (ISA) bus that provides automatic configuration of adapter cards. Read-only memory (ROM) chips with unique identification numbers are added to each adapter, and the adapter can arbitrate conflicts with interrupts, input/output (I/O) ports, and memory. Many types of adapters are supported, including Small Computer System Interface (SCSI) and video cards, and bus extensions such as VL-Bus and Personal Computer Memory Card International Association (PCMCIA) are addressed.

Point-to-Point and Multipoint Connection

A point-to-point connection is a communication link between two end objects or computer systems in a network of computers. The link is either dedicated (permanent) or temporary as pictured in Figure P-8. The point-to-point connection at the top is through a public network, but users at end systems view their connections as dedicated services.

In the point-to-multipoint connection pictured at the bottom of Figure P-8, multiple devices are connected to the link that branches from a single point. This is often called a *multidrop link*. The device that provides the multipoint connection is usually an intelligent controller that manages the flow of information from the multiple devices attached to it.

In an IBM environment, a multidrop connection is often used to connect multiple terminals. The terminals attach to two or more cluster controllers, which are then attached to a communication controller, which itself is attached to the host. In this case, the communication controller provides the multipoint connections for the cluster controllers.

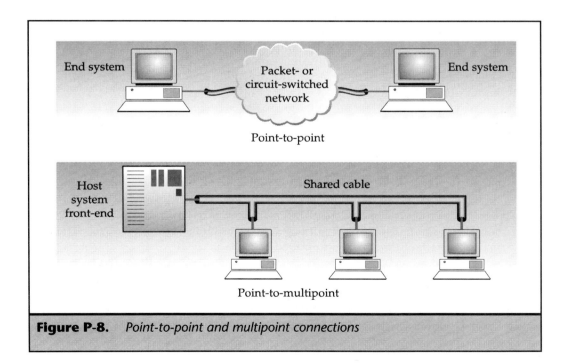

Figure P-8. *Point-to-point and multipoint connections*

Point-to-Point Protocol (PPP)

Two schemes have been adopted by the Internet community to transmit Internet Protocol (IP) datagrams over serial point-to-point lines. Serial Line Interface Protocol (SLIP) is one, and Point-to-Point Protocol (PPP) is the other. While SLIP is the original protocol, PPP is gaining in popularity because it supports a variety of protocols. Both are defined by the Internet Engineering Task Force (IETF) and both provide router-to-router, host-to-router, and host-to-host connections. Most commercial services that provide host connections into the Internet provide SLIP or PPP services. Users connect their computers to the host via modems using the protocols, which provide Transmission Control Protocol/Internet Protocol (TCP/IP) or other capabilities.

PPP is a serial communication protocol that operates over dialup or leased (dedicated) lines to provide connections into IP networks. It sets up and monitors router sessions and frames the data transmitted over the line. PPP can encapsulate different Network-layer protocols such as IP, IPX, AppleTalk, DECnet, OSI/CLNP, and MAC-layer bridging over synchronous and asynchronous point-to-point connections. PPP can turn a computer's serial port into a network adapter, meaning that it can transmit datagrams (data packets) in the same way as a network adapter by encapsulating the datagrams into the serial transmissions.

Another important feature of PPP is that it provides a way to assign an IP address automatically so that remote computers (that is, mobile users) can connect into the network at any point. Because of this last feature, PPP has been getting the most press lately, rather than SLIP. SLIP supports only IP and does not provide the automatic IP addressing scheme, but it is usually adequate for stationary remote systems that transmit only IP.

PPP is also useful for connecting remote local area networks (LANs) to form an internetwork. There are no speed limitations built into the protocol, so speeds are determined by the connecting equipment and communication lines. Still, PPP is relatively slow, so it should only be used for light traffic when creating internetwork connections.

While PPP has been primarily used on dialup or leased lines, the working group that defines PPP is working on procedures to use PPP over X.25, Frame Relay, and Integrated Services Digital Network (ISDN) networks. PPP will support bit-oriented synchronous communication or byte-oriented asynchronous communication. The physical interface requirements are described shortly.

The PPP frame, as pictured in Figure P-9 contains information that identifies the following:

- *Delimiters*   Mark the beginning and ending of the frame
- *Address*   Holds the destination address
- *Control*   Holds the sequence number to ensure proper handling
- *Protocol*   Identifies whether the frame contains IP, IPX, AppleTalk, or other

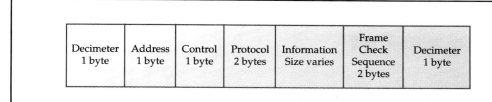

Decimeter 1 byte	Address 1 byte	Control 1 byte	Protocol 2 bytes	Information Size varies	Frame Check Sequence 2 bytes	Decimeter 1 byte

Figure P-9. *Point-to-Point protocol frame format*

- *Information* Contains the data, which can vary in length
- *Frame Check Sequence* Calculates a check sum used for error checking

The PPP protocol stack is pictured in Figure P-10 and described next.

PHYSICAL LAYER Defines transmission over asynchronous and synchronous lines using serial communication protocols such as EIA-232-E, EIA-422, EIA-423, as well as CCITT V.24 and V.35.

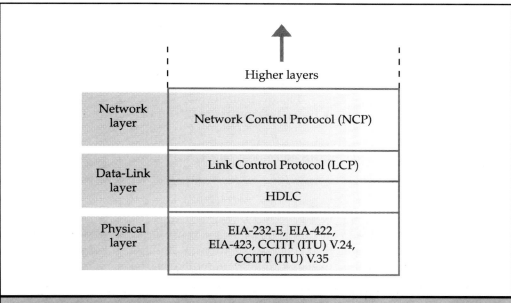

Figure P-10. *Point-to-Point protocol stack*

DATA-LINK LAYER   The Data-Link layer is based on the frame structure of High-level Data-Link Control (HDLC). The Link Control Protocol (LCP) establishes and manages links between connected stations. It specifies encapsulation methods and packet sizes, and checks to ensure links are functioning properly. LCP packets are used to setup, maintain, and terminate connections:

- *Link Configuration*   Packets are sent to establish PPP connections and determine the size of packets, control characters, compression methods, and authentication protocols (user ID and password). The receiving system responds with other LCP packets that acknowledge receipt and verify or reject configuration options. Once a connection is made, NCP packets (see "Network Layer" below) are exchanged to negotiate the type of protocol configuration and the two PPP hosts can begin exchanging datagrams.

- *Link Maintenance*   Packets provide error management control. If a host receives packets with unknown or corrupted information, the packets are returned in a Link Maintenance packet that indicates what was wrong with the packet.

- *Link Termination*   Packets are basically used to terminate a PPP link.

NETWORK LAYER   The Network layer contains a set of protocols called the Network Control Protocols (NCP), each with its own control procedures. The original NCP was the Internet Protocol Control, but others have been added, including Open Systems Interconnection (OSI), DECnet, AppleTalk, Internetwork Packet Exchange (IPX), and Banyan VINES protocols.

Many vendors are providing PPP support in their products. Most router vendors such as Cisco and Synoptics support the protocol, and Novell supports it in its NetWare MultiProtocol Router product. Some products offer additional features such as automatic recovery from a failed link and filtering for internetworks to prevent some types of traffic from crossing the line. Some vendors even support load-balancing options in which traffic is transmitted over multiple PPP links.

RELATED ENTRIES   Asynchronous Communications; Internet; Serial Communication; Serial Line Interface Protocol; *and* Synchronous Communications

Polling

Polling is an access method in which each device attached to a system such as a host or host interface is queried to determine if it has data to transmit. In an IBM mainframe environment, cluster controllers attached to a communication controller are queried by the controller to see if they have information to send to the host. Each cluster controller must wait its turn as each device is polled before it can transmit.

RELATED ENTRIES   Cluster Controllers, IBM; IBM Mainframe Environment

POSIX (Portable Operating System Interface for UNIX)

The Portable Operating System Interface for UNIX (POSIX) is a set of standards under development by the Institute of Electrical and Electronic Engineers (IEEE) and American National Standards Institute (ANSI) to promote common interface standards in the UNIX environment. The original work began in 1984 with the creation of the POSIX.1 Working Group within the IEEE's Technical Committee on Operating Systems. The International Organization for Standardization (ISO) adopted the POSIX.1 standard in 1988. A POSIX.2 standard went into draft form in 1992. A POSIX.3 standard defines testing procedures that can certify adherence to the POSIX standards.

The goal of POSIX was to create a standard operating system environment for portable operating systems and applications that can be transferred from one platform to another. Another goal was to create an information structure that POSIX-compatible applications can exchange with one another, even if those applications work on other platforms. POSIX defines a common interface, but leaves the implementation on a specific platform to the developer. With POSIX, developers can create applications that are easily moved to other platforms and that work with a variety of file structures.

The POSIX.1, 2, and 3 standards were described earlier. Other significant POSIX standards are listed here:

- *POSIX.4* Real-time programming extensions that can lock processes and synchronize events
- *POSIX.6* Security extensions
- *POSIX.7* System administration and management interface
- *POSIX.8* File access on network resources
- *POSIX.11* Transaction processing
- *POSIX.12* Protocol independent network application programming interface (API)
- *POSIX.13* Real-time application environment
- *POSIX.17* Name space support for distributed directory systems

The POSIX standards are widely accepted. Most operating system vendors embrace the standards, and they are often specified in government bids. In particular, the POSIX.7 standard is providing much-needed direction in the areas of system management by defining the management of configuration, performance, faults, accounting, and security.

IBM now supports POSIX standards on its OpenEdition Multiple Virtual Storage (MVS) platforms. OpenEdition MVS has the ability to make traditional MVS data sets accessible to POSIX applications and to make POSIX files accessible to traditional MVS applications. The POSIX data is organized within a hierarchical file system that is treated by MVS as a new kind of MVS data set.

RELATED ENTRIES American National Standards Institute; *and* International Organization for Standardization

Power and Grounding Problems and Solutions

A network that is protected against theft, data corruption, and data loss is still susceptible to uncontrolled electrical input that can damage equipment or shut it down completely. A server with reliable data is no good if you can't get to that data. Electrical power is rarely supplied as a smooth wave of steady energy. You can see this when lights flicker or when the TV goes haywire while you blend a milk shake. Electrical connections are polluted with surges and spikes (collectively called *noise*). You can think of these surges and spikes as shotgun blasts of energy. The way electronic equipment handles this transient energy is unpredictable. There are three likely scenarios:

- *Data corruption* Electrical disturbances can cause memory to change states or can disrupt the information in data packets traversing a wire. These glitches can alter a program in memory and cause it to fail. You might see general protection interrupt (GPI) errors and nonmaskable interrupt (NMI) errors. These errors, which are frequently mistaken for program bugs, are often caused by electrical noise.

- *Equipment failure* If transient energy is high, it will cause permanent damage to equipment. Small microprocessor circuitry is especially susceptible to this energy. Surge suppressors should be used to protect equipment, but if the energy is high enough, the surge suppressor can burn out. As discussed later, some surge suppressors do not provide the right kind of protection against surges.

- *Slow death* Equipment that is repeatedly subjected to low-energy surges will fail over time. The delicate circuits in a chip break down, and the equipment eventually fails for no apparent reason. Transients that cause this type of problem "sneak" through surge suppressors that are not designed to protect against them. After a period of abuse, the chips weaken and release the energy in unknown patterns throughout the chip, and the chip ultimately fails. I remember a hard drive that would become inaccessible after a few minutes of operation. I sprayed cooling Freon on its controller to reduce overheating and was able to recover important files before the controller failed completely.

As previously mentioned, the cause of these problems is often hard to determine. Equipment repair technicians can testify to the number of systems they diagnose as having no problems. As soon as the customer returns to the office, the problems reoccur. A savvy technician will often suspect that the problem stems from the power supplied to the equipment and will recommend the proper filtering and conditioning equipment. As discussed later in this chapter, improper grounding is also often a source of problems. In fact, surge suppressors are often the cause of grounding problems because it is in their design to route surges to ground. The surges then find their way back into the electrical system, where they can cause problems.

There are various tools available for checking a building's power system. For example, Ecos Electronics Corporation makes a device called Accu-Test II that you can use to check the quality of a building's electrical system wiring and grounding. Accu-Test II performs various tests to detect wiring problems. Ecos estimates that up to 90 percent of all equipment failures are the results of poor building wiring and inadequate electrical system grounding.

The electrical environment is noisy. Equipment such as air conditioners, elevators, refrigerators, and even laser printers cause transients when they are switched on and off. The electric company causes transients when it switches grids to balance the system. In fact, any device that uses electricity in a nonlinear way can cause transients that affect other devices. Common electrical line problems are listed here:

- *Noise* Often referred to as surges, spikes, or transients. Noise problems, which are illustrated in Figure P-11, cause slow or immediate damage to sensitive electronic equipment. Additional problems are caused by air conditioners, elevators, and other devices with electric motors. Most computer power supplies include built-in protection against low-level noise, but surge suppressors can protect against transients that are stronger than normal, such as those caused by lightning. In fact, cheap devices often block such surges by simply burning out and preventing any further flow of electricity.

- *Sag* When the power drops below the required level, a sag or dropout occurs, usually because the circuit is overloaded. A sag might continue for a period of time if the building is incorrectly wired or the utility company is having a problem. A long sag can cause damage to power supplies.

- *Swell* A swell is the opposite of a sag and can also cause damage to power supplies.

- *Hum* Hum is high-order harmonics caused by neutral-to-ground connection problems. Such problems indicate a defect in one of the electrical wires to ground. Hum can cause transmission errors in data communication lines. As errors occur, the communication software must check and resend incorrect packets, which causes a decrease in throughput.

Grounding Problems

In 1991, Novell Research published a report called "Power and Grounding for Distributed Computing" by David Fencl and Larry Fish of ONEAC Corporation. In

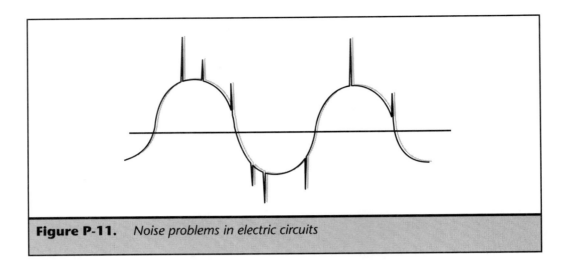

Figure P-11.   *Noise problems in electric circuits*

this report, Fencl and Fish pointed out many problems and misconceptions about established power grounding methods.

Buildings contain a low-resistance ground connection to the earth to protect people from electric shock. A good ground basically drains electrical charges into the earth. If equipment is not properly grounded and a person touches the equipment, a charge will pass through the person to the earth. Fencl and Fish point out that current grounding practices are incompatible with the requirements of digital electronics. Connecting electronic equipment to earth grounds can subject the equipment to noise that seeks the shortest path to ground. In modern buildings, the shortest path to the ground is often through electronic equipment such as computers. Put simply, noise on the AC circuit can infiltrate sensitive electronics through the grounding circuit, not just through the hot lead.

Grounding problems are especially prevalent in a network environment because the cabling system can provide a path for *ground loops*. Consider that devices on networks are usually connected to different sources of power, which are grounded. When these networks are interconnected, the cable bridges the two grounded systems together, which causes the potential for energy on the circuit to seek equilibrium by flowing from ground to ground. In doing so, it flows through the computer systems attached to the cable and causes noise problems. To solve ground-loop problems, according to Fencl and Fish, equipment on one power source must be isolated from equipment on other power sources.

On a large network, the creation of a single-point ground is usually impossible to achieve. Interconnected networks form links between close or distant points, any one of which can produce electrical problems due to poor wiring. These separate power sources might be in separate buildings or in a multistory office building that has separate power transformers on every floor or every other floor. Each transformer has its own electrical characteristics and should not be connected to equipment connected to other transformers.

Solutions

One solution to the problems of ground loops, line noise, and surges is to connect the entire network to one central power source and ground. However, this is usually impractical and defeats the purpose of a network, which is to spread computing resources to users at outlying locations. The only practical solution is to provide power conditioning and a proper ground point at the location of each network component.

Figure P-12 illustrates the Fencl and Fish method for connecting network equipment within a single building or power source area. Note that a power conditioner and an uninterruptible power supply are used at the server. The power conditioner provides dedicated transformer isolation, a clean source of power, and a solid reference ground. Similar devices should be attached to workstations if your budget allows. Note that surge suppression equipment is placed at the feed to the electrical panel. If the surge suppressors are placed on the branch circuits, they will divert surges to ground and back into the circuits of other systems through the ground connection.

There are a few things to watch out for in this installation. You should not run electrical cables in parallel with power circuits or other sources of interference such as light fixtures and motors. If you do, electrical transients can enter the network through the cable systems. Some circuits improperly divert neutral to ground intentionally to solve noise problems. They produce a repeating, low-frequency waveform on the network cable that can corrupt data. If you're having data problems or a protocol analyzer detects numerous retransmissions, have an electrical contractor check the line.

> *NOTE:* *Ensure that a single LAN segment is connected to circuits that branch from a single power source and that no point in the segment shares a ground with other power sources. An electrical contractor can perform this service.*

Figure P-13 illustrates the Fencl and Fish method for connecting an internetwork. Nonconductive fiber-optic cable is used to eliminate ground loops between the networks, which are on different power supplies. The primary reason for ensuring the separation of the power sources is that they will most likely have different ground potentials, which can cause problems in sensitive electrical equipment if they are linked together. In Figure P-13, each LAN segment is a self-contained environment in which you can more easily control grounding and noise problems. Note that internetwork devices are connected to power conditioning equipment. If fiber-optic interconnections are not possible, supplemental transient protection should be installed with the cable.

It is a good idea to buy uninterruptible power supplies and surge suppressors to protect your network equipment. These protection devices are described briefly here:

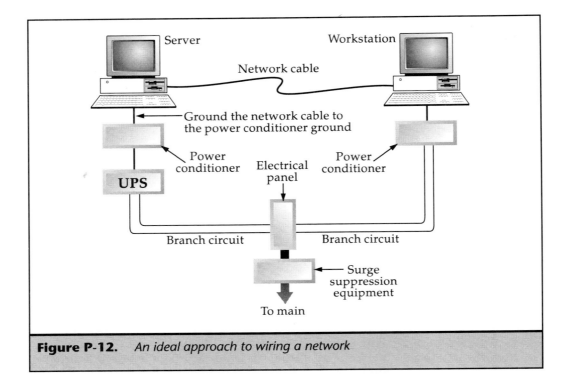

Figure P-12.   *An ideal approach to wiring a network*

- *Uninterruptible power supply*   This battery backup device, generator, or other device provides a computer with power during an outage.

- *Surge suppressor*   This device protects a system against spikes in the electrical power. Most power supplies in desktop systems can handle surges of up to 800 volts. A surge suppressor is required to protect against surges above these levels.

RELATED ENTRIES   Surge Suppressors; Uninterruptible Power Supplies

PowerOpen Association

The PowerOpen Association is a group of vendors including IBM, Apple, and Motorola that formed in early 1993 to develop hardware and software products around the PowerPC microprocessor (see "PowerPC"). The Association also promotes the PowerOpen Environment, which is an open systems user and development platform. All PowerOpen products will adhere to a common Application Binary Interface (ABI) so that applications developed for the environment will run on a range of PowerOpen-compliant systems. All members of the PowerOpen Association will get the same PowerOpen architecture, but each can enhance it as needed.

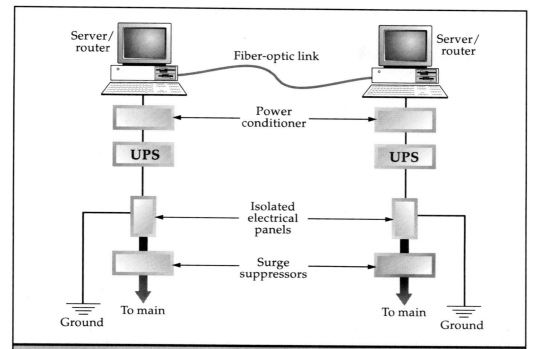

Server/
router

Fiber-optic link

Server/
router

Power
conditioner

UPS

UPS

Isolated
electrical
panels

Surge
suppressors

To main

Ground

To main

Ground

Figure P-13. *Fiber-optic cable isolates each segment of an internetwork and prevents ground loops between the different power distribution and grounding systems*

The PowerPC processor is manufactured by Motorola based on the PowerOpen architectural plan. It is designed for high-end workstation and server systems that run applications such as real-time video, multimedia, telephony, speech recognition, and graphics rendering.

PowerOpen is also the name of the UNIX-based operating system under development by the PowerOpen Association. It is designed to take full advantage of the PowerPC processor. PowerOpen is based on the Open Software Foundation's (OSF) OSF/1 kernel. Apple will provide support for the OSF Motif graphical user interface specification or the Apple Macintosh interface.

RELATED ENTRIES   Open Software Foundation; OSF/1; PowerOpen Environment; PowerPC; *and* UNIX

PowerOpen Environment

The PowerOpen Environment is an open systems environment that provides end users and software developers with an easy-to-use, standards-based, high-performance platform. The PowerOpen Environment combines hardware, based on the PowerPC microprocessor with software based on the PowerOpen Application Binary Interface (ABI). Users can choose between an OSF/Motif or Macintosh interface. The architecture of the PowerOpen Environment is pictured in Figure P-14.

The PowerOpen Environment has been adopted as an open system environment by Apple, Bull, Harris, IBM, Tadpose Technology, and THOMSON-CSF. The PowerOpen Association promotes the environment. The environment has the features listed next:

- Derived from Apple's system 7 software, IBM's AIX/6000, and IBM's POWER Architecture
- Based on the PowerOpen ABI, which is derived from AIX and conforms to industry standards such as POSIX, X/Open's XPG, and OSF's AES and Motif
- Maintains hardware bus independence
- Scalable from laptops to super computers

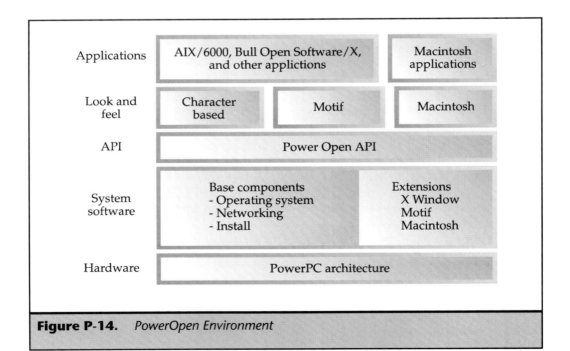

Figure P-14.   *PowerOpen Environment*

The PowerOpen Association will provide a certification program to assure PowerOpen compatibility. The Verification Test Suites (VTS) are used to certify programs. Along with the ABI, the association makes the System Information Library available, which provides technical reference information that assists system platform developers in developing an ABI-compliant operating system for PowerPC platforms.

RELATED ENTRIES   Open Software Foundation; OSF/1; PowerOpen Association; *and* PowerPC

PowerPC

The PowerPC is a microprocessor architecture developed by Motorola, in conjunction with IBM and Apple computers. It is based on IBM's Performance Optimization With Enhanced RISC (POWER) architecture. The name PowerPC reflects the refocus of the RISC architecture to the microprocessor category. The processors are suitable for portables, desktop systems, symmetrical multiprocessors, and highly parallel supercomputers. The initial product lineup called for the following processors:

- The PowerPC 601 runs at 60-80 SPECmarks and is designed for high-performance personal computers. Motorola claims the PowerPC 601 will deliver the same integer performance as an Intel Pentium and about a 30 to 40 percent floating-point improvement over Intel's Pentium processor.

- The Power PC 603 is a low-wattage microprocessor for battery-powered, hand-held mobile computing devices.

- The PowerPC 604 is a high-performance microprocessor for high-end PC workstations and servers.

- The PowerPC 620 is an ultra-high performance microprocessor, rated at 200-400 SPECmarks, and is designed for workstations, servers, and supercomputers.

The PowerPC is designed to run PowerOpen, a UNIX operating system developed by the PowerOpen Association. PowerOpen supports the Open Software Foundation's (OSF) Motif graphical user interface specification and the Apple Macintosh interface.

Applications such as real-time video, multimedia, telephony, speech recognition, and graphics rendering are particularly well suited for the PowerPC processor. Software vendors that develop products in the Windows, Macintosh, and workstation environments are developing products for the PowerPC.

IBM is developing PowerPC systems that will run Workplace OS, a microkernel operating system that will run the OS/2 workplace shell. Other platforms that will run on the PowerPC include Apple Macintosh System 7, Microsoft Windows NT, SunSoft Solaris, and the "Pink" object-oriented operating system under development by IBM and Apple.

Apple will introduce the PowerPC 601-based Macintosh early in 1994 with a version of Macintosh System 7. The ROM in the system will include an emulator so current Macintosh applications will run on the system as if they are running on a Macintosh with a Motorola 68030 or 68040 processor.

RELATED ENTRIES   Open Software Foundation; PowerOpen Association; PowerOpen Environment; *and* PowerPC

Preemptive Multitasking

Multitasking operating systems have the ability to run several programs or processes at the same time. Preemptive multitasking is a feature of the operating system that lets it interrupt a running process and allocate time to another process. Without preemptive multitasking, a process will run until it completes and not give any processing time to other tasks. In the Microsoft Windows 3.1 environment, which is multitasking, but not preemptive, an operation such as copying a file or printing cannot be interrupted until complete. Windows 3.1 is a cooperative operating system, giving each process some portion of the processors time with the hope that one of the processes won't take too much time.

Preemptive multiprocessing operating systems include Microsoft Windows NT, OS/2, Novell UnixWare, and the NeXTSTEP operating system. These operating systems monitor the allocation of processing time to each process and interrupt a process that takes too much time. Microsoft Windows will include preemptive multiprocessing and will not need to run on top of DOS.

RELATED ENTRY   Multiprocessing

Premises Distribution System (PDS)

A premises distribution system (PDS) is a preplanned network of cabling within a building or campus environment designed for the transmission of voice and data. The PDS provides a connection point for external communication and links to the public telephone network. A PDS is typically a *structured wiring system* that is designed to implement future services and growth and accommodate future moves and reconfigurations. The Electronic Industries Association (EIA) and the Telecommunications Industries Association (TIA) developed a wiring standard called the *EIA/TIA 568 Commercial Building Wiring Standard.* This standard provides a uniform wiring system and supports multivendor products and environments.

The scope of the specification covers telecommunication wiring for both horizontal wiring (telephone and computer wall outlets to the wiring equipment rooms in a building) and backbone wiring (equipment room to equipment and among buildings in a campus environment). According to EIA/TIA 568 documents, the wiring standard is designed to provide the following features and functions:

- A generic telecommunication wiring system for commercial buildings
- Support for multiproduct, multivendor environments
- Direction for future design of telecommunication products for commercial enterprises
- The ability to plan and install the telecommunication wiring for a commercial building without any prior knowledge of the products that will use the wiring

The specification lays out the topologies and distances of the wiring. The maximum distance of the site is 3,000 meters (9,840 feet), covering 1 million square meters (approximately 10 million square feet) of office space, and up to 50,000 individual users.

RELATED ENTRIES   Cabling; EIA/TIA 568 Commercial Building Wiring Standard

Presentation Layer, OSI Model

The Open Systems Interconnection (OSI) model is a standard defined by the International Organization for Standardization (ISO). It defines a layered communication architecture that categorizes the protocols required to set up a communication session between systems. A layer within the protocol stack of each machine communicates with its peer layer by attaching messages to the packets that are transferred between systems. These messages provide control information, error checking, acknowledgments, and requests. The messages are only relevant to the other peer layer.

The OSI protocol model consists of seven layers. Generally, the bottom layers are concerned with the actual transmission of bits between systems. The middle layers are concerned with the transport and reliable delivery of information between systems, and maintaining a communication session. The top layers provide the interface that applications use to access the lower network layers. When an application (such as a user's database program) needs to send a message to an application running in another computer (such as the database management system, or DBMS) running in a back-end server, it prepares a message and sends it to the lower protocol layers. Each layer adds its own information to the message and the complete packet is transmitted to the other station. The process repeats at the receiving station, except that the message is unpacked and passed up to the application.

The OSI model was designed to help developers create applications that are compatible across multivendor product lines, and to promote open, interoperable networking systems. While OSI hasn't caught on as planned, its model is still used to describe and define how various vendor's products communicate. Common protocol stacks are IBM Systems Network Architecture (SNA), DEC Network Architecture (DNA), and Apple Computer's AppleTalk. Communication protocols that can be matched to layers of the stack, but are not part of any specific architectural plan, are TCP/IP (Internet/UNIX), Microsoft NetBIOS/NetBEUI, and Novell SPX/IPX.

The Presentation layer is layer 6 in the protocol stack, just below the top-level Application layer and above the Session layer. The Presentation layer provides translation of data, defines data formatting, and provides syntax. The Presentation layer prepares incoming data for the Application layer, where the user views the data. For outgoing data, the Presentation layer translates data from the Application layer into a form that is suitable for transfer over the network. There are various encoding rules built into the Presentation layer protocols that handle all the data translations.

RELATED ENTRIES   Layered Architecture; Open Systems Interconnection Model; *and* Protocol Stack

Printer Access Protocol (PAP), AppleTalk

Printer Access Protocol (PAP) is a protocol in the AppleTalk environment that is responsible for maintaining the communication session between a workstation and a printer, or a workstation and a print service. The connection is two-way because printers need to send control information to workstations that regulate the transmission of data. For example, the printer's buffer may become full and the workstation must be signaled to stop sending data.

RELATED ENTRY   AppleTalk

Printing on NetWare Networks

Several NetWare Loadable Modules, menu-driven utilities, and command-line utilities make up the NetWare printing services. In the NetWare 4.x printer environment, which is described here, the basic printing options remain the same as in previous versions of NetWare, but the NetWare Directory Services (NDS) and Windows-based utilities offer new methods for print management.

As shown in Figure P-15, NetWare printing services use a central print server that runs on a file server. The print server manages shared printers throughout the network, including printers attached to the print server itself, printers attached to other file servers, and printers attached to workstations on the network.

Basically, the print server takes advantage of all the printer ports on the network, whether they are on the print server, file servers, or workstations. Printers with direct network connections (such as their own Ethernet port) are also supported. The printing system consists of the following components:

PRINT QUEUE   A print queue is a buffer that holds a group of print jobs from network users until they can be printed. Print queues exist in network directories. When users send a print job to a printer, NetWare sends the job to a queue appropriate for that printer. NetWare Directory Services in NetWare 4.x also allows users to search for printers in portions of the directory that they can view.

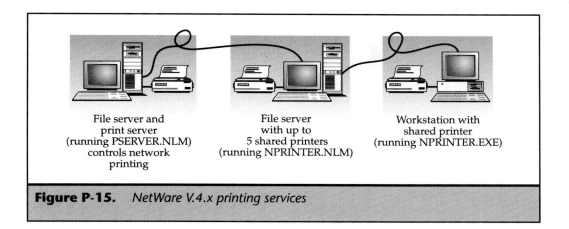

File server and
print server
(running PSERVER.NLM)
controls network
printing

File server
with up to
5 shared printers
(running NPRINTER.NLM)

Workstation with
shared printer
(running NPRINTER.EXE)

Figure P-15.   *NetWare V.4.x printing services*

PRINTERS   Each printer to share on the network must be configured and given a name. Printers can be attached directly to the print servers or to individual workstations on the network. A print server manages the flow of print jobs through print queues and to printers. Several queues might send their print jobs to a single printer, or several printers might service a single queue. First you create a printer object for each printer you want to share on the network, and then you assign it to a print server and assign queues to it.

PRINT SERVERS   The PSERVER.NLM module links queues and printers to print servers. It runs as a continuous process in the server; if unloaded, printer sharing stops. A single print server can handle up to 256 network printers, including five local printers (three parallel and two serial). Novell recommends one print queue per printer for ease of management. Each print queue can contain up to 1,000 print jobs at a time; however, the queue administrator sees only the first 255 print jobs.

RELATED ENTRIES   NetWare; NetWare 4.x Enhanced Features

Print Server

A computer on a network that manages print jobs. The print server receives print jobs from many different users and prints them in order or according to some predefined priority. A print queue holds print jobs in memory or on disk until they are ready to print. A print queue may also manage printers on the network that are attached to workstations, sending print jobs to those printers to match the requests of users. For example, a workstation may have a color printer attached. The print server knows which printers have these features and sends the job to the appropriate workstation and attached printer.

RELATED ENTRY   Networks

Privacy Enhanced Mail (PEM)

Electronic mail on the Internet is striving to reach several goals that can assure both sender and receiver of the following:

- Confidentiality in a connectionless mode
- Authentication of message origin
- Message integrity to ensure the receiver that the message has not been altered or corrupted
- Nonrepudiation, or the inability of the sender to disown a message once it is sent

The Privacy Enhanced Mail (PEM) protocol provides these services. The PEM certification system uses public-key authentication. The sender seals the message with a digital signature using his or her private key. The digital signature also provides the nonrepudiation feature. The recipient can verify the signature using the sender's public key. The sender can make the entire message confidential by encrypting it with the recipient's public key; then only the recipient can read the message. Future versions of PEM will support the Multipurpose Internet Mail Extension (MIME) as well.

RELATED ENTRIES   Authentication and Authorization; Certification Systems; Key Encryption; Multipurpose Internet Mail Extension; *and* Security

Private Key Cryptography

See Key Encryption Technology

Private Network

See Leased Line; Public Data Networks; T1/T3 Services; *and* Wide Area Networks

Project DOE (Distributed Objects Everywhere)

See Distributed Objects Everywhere, SunSoft.

Propagation Delay

A delay caused by the time it takes information to be transmitted from one place to another. In the case of satellite transmissions, the delay is often noticeable in voice and video transmissions.

Properties of Objects

In a directory naming system such as Novell's NetWare Directory Services, objects are representations of real-life entities. A directory service is a program that runs on a network to keep track of the users and resources on that network. Users consult the directory service when they want to access a resource such as a printer or send an E-mail message to another user. A directory service can be compared to a phone book.

Objects in the directory service contain properties that describe the object. The most important property is the object's name. The properties of an object are defined when the object is created, or during a subsequent change. Typical properties for *user account objects* are the following:

- The user's name, address, phone number, and fax number
- Account information, such as the balance amount
- Logon restrictions, such as the allowed time, the allowed workstations, and password requirements
- The user's identification number

Properties of a *resource object* such as a server are listed next. While this information may be used by the operating system, some is for documentation or lookup purposes.

- A description of the server, which is used for reference only
- The location of the server, which is used for reference only
- The network address of the server
- A list of users who can change the properties of the server object
- A list of server operators
- Status information about the server's operation

RELATED ENTRIES   Directory Services; NetWare

Protected Mode

A processing mode that allows multiple programs to run simultaneously, each in its own protected area. Programs request memory allocations and the allocations are protected from corruption by other programs.

Protection of Data

See Data Protection.

Protocol Analyzers

Protocol analyzers are diagnostic tools that monitor and track the activity of networks. They are available as software that runs in a computer, or a special unit that contains special boards and software. Protocol analyzers are typically portable devices that are carried to various sites by network technicians. Some of the tasks they perform are listed here:

- Display information about the types of packets traversing a network. You can monitor these packets to monitor security, determine faults, or to monitor and optimize a network.

- Query all nodes and perform point-to-point communication testing between any specified node and all other nodes on the internetwork.

- Determine the entire internetwork configuration.

- Analyze critical data from one or all nodes and report only unusual activity based on a predefined set of thresholds.

- Display performance data such as traffic volume and packets serviced.

- Provide useful information about network efficiency, network performance, possible hardware errors, noise problems, and problems with application software.

Protocol analyzers are available from a number of vendors, including Gateway Communications (EtherStat) at 800/367-6555, Triticom (LANdecoder) at 612/937-0772, and Intel (NetSight Analyst) at 800/538-3373.

RELATED ENTRY   Testing Equipment and Techniques

Protocol Converters

Protocol conversion is the process of translating electrical signals or the data formats of one communication system for transmission on another system. Several levels of conversion may be necessary. For example, a protocol converter is used between a desktop computer and an IBM mainframe system to translate characters in American Standard Code for Information Interchange (ASCII) format to Extended Binary Coded Decimal Interchange Code (EBCDIC) format. Protocol converters are available that convert asynchronous data streams into synchronous data streams so that PC serial port data can be sent to a data service unit (DSU) for connection to a digital transmission service.

In the network environment, a protocol converter can translate packets for one network, such as Internetwork Packet Exchange (IPX), for use on another network, such as Transmission Control Protocol/Internet Protocol (TCP/IP). The protocol converter is similar to a gateway device rather than a router, because all layers of the protocol stack except the topmost Application layer are involved when the packets are converted.

Encapsulation is a technique that provides a way to send packets of one protocol type over an intermediate network to another network of the same protocol. The original packet gets a piggy-back ride in a packet of the intermediate network to the destination network, so no conversion is required. For example, a TCP/IP network (such as the Internet) might interconnect two NetWare IPX networks. IPX packets from the source network are placed in TCP/IP packets for a ride over the Internet, then unpackaged at the destination network and delivered to the appropriate node on that network.

RELATED ENTRIES   Encapsulation; Gateway; Packets; *and* Protocol Stack

Protocol Data Unit

In a layered network architecture such as the Open Systems Interconnection (OSI) model, protocol data units (PDUs) are built in each layer of a transmitting system. The PDU contains information from the upper layer plus some information attached to it by the entity in the current layer. This PDU is then passed to the next lower layer. The Physical layer actually transmits PDUs as a framed stream of bits, but upper layers of the protocol stack build PDUs. The receiving system passes the packet information up through its protocol stack, extracting PDUs at each level of the protocol stack. The important point is that each layer attaches information to the PDU that is destined for its peer layer in the other system. This is how peer layers coordinate a communication session.

RELATED ENTRIES   Layered Architecture; Open Systems Interconnection Model; Packets; *and* Protocol Stack

Protocols, Communication

Communication protocols are defined within the context of a layered network architecture. Each layer specifies a protocol for handling a function or subsystem of the communication process. The most common industry-wide network protocol stacks are listed here and described elsewhere in this book:

- ISO's Open Systems Interconnection (OSI) model
- IBM's Systems Network Architecture
- DEC's DECnet
- Apple's AppleTalk
- The Internet suite, including TCP/IP

Protocols exists at each level to perform some task that accomplishes communication between systems, as long as two systems operate with similar protocols. While protocol stacks typically have about seven layers, it is convenient to group the layers into the following categories, as pictured in Figure P-16.

APPLICATION PROTOCOLS   Application protocols encompass the Application, Presentation, and Session layers, which are basically users of network communication services, and provide application-to-application interaction and data exchange. Common application protocols include those listed here, as well as remote procedure calls (RPCs), transaction processing systems, and messaging systems.

- IBM applications and Advanced Program-to-Program Communication (APPC), also called LU 6.2

- OSI Virtual Terminal, File Transfer Access and Management (FTAM), Distributed Transaction Processing (DTP), Message Handling System (X.400), and Directory Services (X.500)

- Internet and UNIX Network File System, Simple Mail Transfer Protocol (SMTP), File Transfer Protocol (FTP), TelNet, and Simple Network Management Protocol (SNMP)

- Novell NetWare Network Core Protocol (NCP), and client shells or redirectors

- Microsoft Server Message Blocks, NetBIOS, and client shells or redirectors

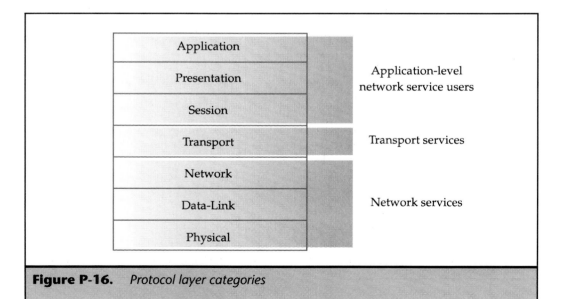

Figure P-16.   *Protocol layer categories*

■ AppleTalk AppleShare, AppleTalk Filing Protocol (AFP), and Session-level protocols such as AppleTalk Data Stream Protocol (ADSP), AppleTalk Session Protocol (ASP), Printer Access Protocol (PAP), and Zone Information Protocol (ZIP)

TRANSPORT PROTOCOLS   Transport protocols provide connection-oriented data-delivery services across networks. Basically, transport protocols provide end-to-end data exchanges in which systems maintain a session or connection with each other for the reliable sequenced exchange of data. Transport protocols include those listed here:

■ IBM Advanced Peer-to-Peer Networking (APPN)

■ OSI Connection-Oriented Transport Service (COTS) and Connectionless Transport Service (CLTS)

■ The Transmission Control Protocol (TCP) portion of the Internet and UNIX TCP/IP protocol suite

■ The SPX portion of Novell's SPX/IPX protocol suite

■ Microsoft NetBIOS and NetBEUI interfaces

■ AppleTalk Routing Table Maintenance Protocol (RTMP), AppleTalk Echo Protocol (AEP), AppleTalk Transaction Protocol (ATP), Name Binding Protocol (NBP)

NETWORK PROTOCOLS   The Network layer protocols provide link services for communicating systems. They handle addressing and routing information, error checking, and retransmission requests. They also provide the procedures for accessing a network, as specified by the particular network in use (such as Ethernet, token ring, and so on). Network protocols include the following:

■ IBM Advanced Peer-to-Peer Networking (APPN)

■ OSI Connection-Oriented Network Service (CONS) and Connectionless Network Service (CLNS)

■ The Internet Protocol (IP) of the Internet and UNIX TCP/IP protocol suite

■ The IPX portion of Novell's SPX/IPX protocol suite

■ Microsoft NetBEUI interfaces

■ AppleTalk Datagram Delivery Protocol (DDP)

Communicating systems don't need to run all levels of the above protocols within a particular protocol suite; however, systems that do implement a full suite of protocols can communicate all the way up to the application level.

In the layered architecture model, each layer in the protocol stack of a computer builds a protocol data unit (PDU) that it sends to the peer layer in the computer it is communicating with. The Physical layer actually transmits PDUs as framed bits of data to the other system, but upper layers of the protocol stack build PDUs, then pass them to lower layers for further packaging until they reach the Physical layer. The receiving system passes the packet information up through its protocol stack, extracting PDUs at each level of the protocol stack. The extracted PDU information contains information from peer protocol levels.

The dialog between protocol layers consists of messages and activities such as those listed here:

- Make requests and send data.
- Receive request and information.
- Reject requests or data.
- Acknowledge receipt.
- Handle buffering of incoming data.
- Pause and restart transmissions.
- Set transmission priorities.
- Handle error detection, correction, and retransmission.
- Maintain connection-oriented sessions.
- Packet numbering and sequencing.
- Handle addressing and routing.

Entities in the protocol layers exchange control information to accomplish the tasks listed above. Once a session is set up, data is exchanged. During the data exchange, each system occasionally transmits control information that describes the status of each system to the other. Flow control, if used, keeps data from overflowing the buffers of the receiving system. In networking environments, data is transmitted in packets by the protocol layers, then as framed bit-streams over the physical connection. Dividing information in this way is important for two reasons. First, any errors on the network only affect individual packets, which are easily retransmitted, rather than the entire transmission. Second, a long transmission can tie up relays and switches that delay other traffic. Packets subdivide the transmission and allow other traffic to get through. A cell, which is a fixed size frame of information, provides the best performance in this respect because switching is consistent and predictable.

A connectionless transmission sends packets from source to destination without first establishing a specific path through a network. If there are multiple paths to the destination, packets may take different routes and arrive out of sequence. Sequence numbers must be added to the packets so the receiving station can put them back in order in case some are delayed on the network. The sequence number can also indicate lost packets, so the receiving station can request a retransmission.

RELATED ENTRIES Acknowledgments; Advanced Peer-to-Peer Networking; Advanced Program-to-Program Communication; AppleTalk; Connection-Oriented and Connectionless Protocols; Flow Control Methods; Internet; Internetwork Packet Exchange; Layered Architecture; NetBIOS / NetBEUI; Open Systems Interconnection; Packets; Protocol Stack; Routing Protocols; *and* Transmission Control Protocol/Internet Protocol

Protocol Stack

It's impossible to discuss the interconnection of computers without referencing the underlying protocols or communication procedures that enable data exchange. Any discussion of protocols usually involves a comparison to the Open Systems Interconnection (OSI) protocol stack. The OSI protocol stack defines how vendors can create products that work with other vendors' products. However, due to lack of industry-wide acceptance, OSI serves more as a model today than an accepted standard. This is because many companies have already implemented other protocols into their products.

A *protocol* is a defined way of communicating with another system. It specifies the timing of signals and the structure of the communicated data. The lower layers in the protocol stack define the rules that vendors can follow to make their equipment interconnect with other vendors' equipment. The upper layers define how to manage different types of communication sessions and how user applications can interoperate. The higher you go in the stack, the more sophisticated the protocols.

Let's use the OSI standards to compare internetworking and interoperability among vendor operating systems and products. In the OSI model, there are seven layers in a protocol stack, each working at different levels in the hardware and software. You can examine what each layer in the stack does to see how systems communicate over local area networks (LANs). The OSI model for interconnection, or protocol stack, is illustrated in Figure P-17.

As previously mentioned, many vendors don't follow the OSI protocol stack exactly. They use other protocol stacks that closely resemble the OSI stack or combine a number of independent protocols into a suite of protocols. Figure P-18 compares some of the most popular stacks. A product that uses one protocol stack cannot directly connect and interoperate with a product that uses another protocol stack. However, using various "encapsulation" techniques and protocol conversions, it's possible to achieve certain levels of interoperability between them. Some of the major protocol stacks are described here:

■ *OSI protocol stack* The OSI protocol stack is defined by the International Organization for Standardization (ISO) to promote worldwide interoperability. It is typically used as a standard to compare other protocol stacks.

■ *NetWare SPX/IPX protocol* The NetWare Sequenced Packet Exchange/Internetwork Packet Exchange (SPX/IPX) protocol is the native protocol used by Novell NetWare. It is derived from the Xerox Network System (XNS) protocol stack.

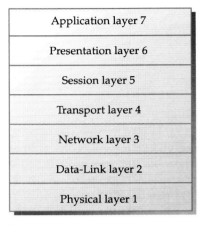

Figure P-17. *The OSI protocol stack*

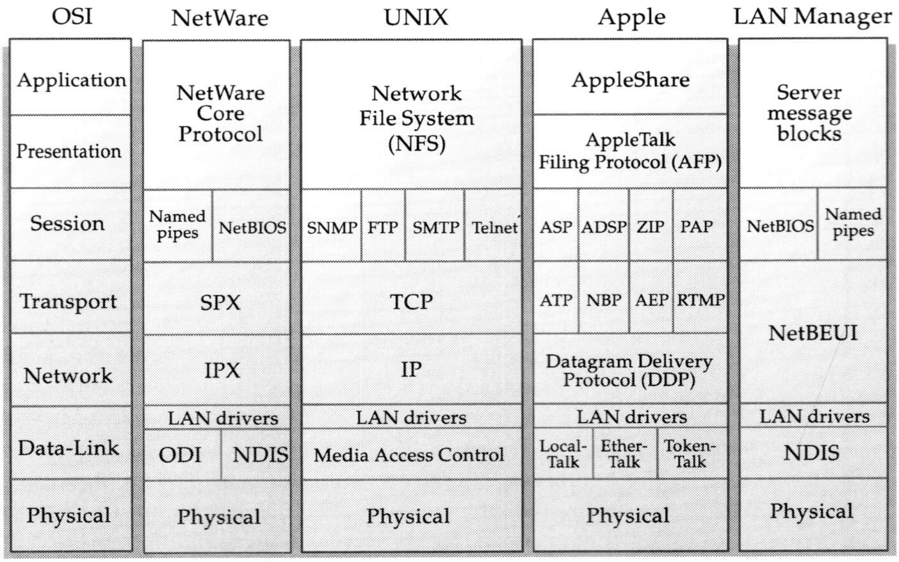

OSI	NetWare	UNIX	Apple	LAN Manager
Application	NetWare Core Protocol	Network File System (NFS)	AppleShare	Server message blocks
Presentation			AppleTalk Filing Protocol (AFP)	
Session	Named pipes / NetBIOS	SNMP / FTP / SMTP / Telnet	ASP / ADSP / ZIP / PAP	NetBIOS / Named pipes
Transport	SPX	TCP	ATP / NBP / AEP / RTMP	NetBEUI
Network	IPX	IP	Datagram Delivery Protocol (DDP)	
Data-Link	LAN drivers / ODI / NDIS	LAN drivers / Media Access Control	LAN drivers / Local-Talk / Ether-Talk / Token-Talk	LAN drivers / NDIS
Physical	Physical	Physical	Physical	Physical

Figure P-18. *Comparison of common protocols to the OSI model*

- *TCP/IP protocol suite* Transmission Control Protocol/Internet Protocol (TCP/IP) was one of the first network protocol stacks. It was originally implemented by the Department of Defense as a way to tie multivendor network products together. The IP portion provides one of the best definitions for internetwork connections available and is being used by many vendors as a way to interconnect products over local and wide areas.

- *AppleTalk protocols* The AppleTalk protocols were defined by Apple Computer as a way to interconnect Apple Macintosh systems.

- *IBM/Microsoft protocol suite* The IBM and Microsoft protocols for interconnectivity are often grouped because the two companies jointly developed products that use them, such as LAN Manager and OS/2.

RELATED ENTRIES Layered Architecture; Open Systems Interconnection Model; *and* Packets

PU 2.1

See Systems Network Architecture, IBM.

Public Data Networks (PDNs)

An organization has three choices when building networks that span wide areas over public lands. They can build private networks, use existing public networks, or use a combination of both. A private network is a bit misleading. It actually refers to a network built with public facilities, except that the customer provides all the switching equipment and sets up leased lines between sites. Private more accurately refers to the fact that the organization has full use of the lines and does not share them with others. Another way to build private networks is to use microwave installations or metropolitan area network services from providers other than the LECs. Most companies use services provided by the public data networks for wide area networks, but build private network facilities to connect local facilities, such as in a campus environment where cable is easily installed between buildings.

A public data network (PDN) is a packet-switching or circuit-switching service provided by local and long-distance telephone carriers such as MCI, US Sprint, and AT&T, or by organizations that have built networks for their own use, then made them available for others to use. Packet-switching services provided typically include X.25, Frame Relay, Switched Multimegabit Data Service (SMDS), and Asynchronous

Transfer Mode (ATM). Circuit-switching services include dialup lines, Switched 56, and Integrated Services Digital Network (ISDN).

Providers of packet- and circuit-switching services include:

- US Sprint provides circuit-switched services, X.25, Frame Relay, Internet Protocol (IP), video services, and ATM on its all-digital, fiber-optic network.

- AT&T provides a range of circuit-switched and packet-switched services. Its ACCUNET circuit-switched services such as Switched-56 have been available for years. AT&T also provides Frame Relay packet-switching services and ATM.

- CompuServe Information Services offers access points in hundreds of locations throughout the United States for X.25 and Frame Relay services.

- GE Information Services provides packet-switching and high-speed services, as well as asynchronous and synchronous services.

- Infonet Services Corp provides an array of international services.

- Tymenet Global Network has close to 5,000 global access points.

Services are available at leased-line rates (monthly charge) or at dialup rates (per-use charge). A typical PDN network forms a web of global connections between the PDN's switching equipment. Circuits consists of the PDN's own private lines or lines leased from major carriers such as AT&T.

Access to services is provided by local exchange carriers (LECs) within local access transport areas (LATAs), as pictured in Figure P-19. A dedicated private line is typically installed between the customer site and the LEC switching facility. This line is either a dialup line or a dedicated digital line. PDN service providers tap into the LEC CO at what is called a point-of-presence (POP) where they can access the customer's line. LECs must provide POP facilities as dictated by the government.

Using a PDN can reduce cost and reduce the need to lease expensive, long-distance dedicated digital lines required to build private networks. The PDN handles switching services and any problems with the network itself. It can also guarantee better data delivery at a lower price.

RELATED ENTRIES   Carrier Services; Circuit-Switching Services; *and* Packet-Switching Networks

Public Key Cryptographic Systems

See Key Encryption Technology.

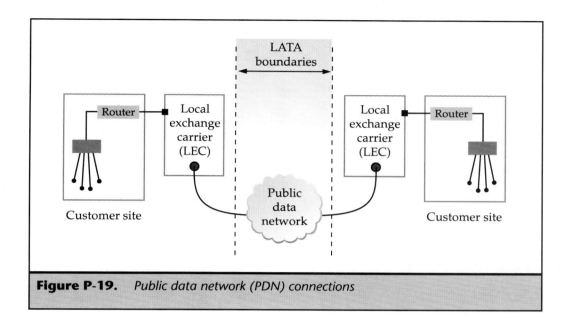

Figure P-19. *Public data network (PDN) connections*

Public Switched Data Network (PSDN)

See Public Data Networks.

Pulse-Code Modulation

Pulse-code modulation (PCM) is an analog-to-digital conversion technique. It is used to convert voice for transmission over digital facilities. It is used with Integrated Services Digital Network (ISDN), which replaces the analog lines going to most homes and office with all-digital lines. The connection of a phone therefore requires PCM techniques in order to carry the voice signal over the digital line. PCM is also used to convert voice analog data to digital data for transmission in a multiplexed voice and data stream over a T1 or other digital circuit.

A digital voice channel requires 64 Kbits/sec of transmission speed (compared to analog lines, which require a bandwidth of 4 KHz). The process involves sampling the voice signal a certain number of times-per-second to determine its amplitude. The sampled signal is then converted into binary data that represents the height of the signal.

RELATED ENTRIES   Integrated Services Digital Network; Multiplexing; *and* T1/T3 Services

Punchdown Block

A punchdown block provides the connection point and cross connections for voice and data cabling systems, as shown in Figure P-20. The cable runs from the workstation through the wall to the punchdown block. The punchdown block gathers all the signals from workstations attached to it and transfers them to the patch panel via the 50-pin Telco cable. The patch panel then distributes the connections to the hub, which serves as the repeating device and connection point between stations on the network. The patch panel also provides a way to easily move connections.

RELATED ENTRY   Cabling

Quadrature Amplitude Modulation (QAM)

See Modulation Techniques.

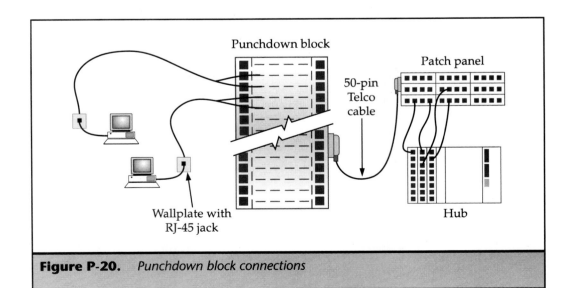

Figure P-20.   *Punchdown block connections*

Radio Networks

Radio communication enables wireless networking and mobile computing. A wireless network is one in which cables are not required to interconnect workstations. Instead, a central transmitter/receiver, or *transceiver,* is installed within an office that broadcasts signals to workstations.

Radio Networks

Wireless local area network (LAN) equipment consists of a transceiver that is connected via Ethernet cable to a server or other segment of the network. There are two radio techniques used to build wireless networks:

- *Narrow-band radio* This technique is similar to a broadcast from a radio station. You tune in to a "tight" frequency band on both the transmitter and receiver. The signal can penetrate walls and is spread over a wide area, so focusing is not required. However, narrow-band radio transmissions have problems with radio reflections (ghosting) and are regulated by the Federal Communications Commission. They must be precisely tuned to prevent interference from other frequencies.

- *Spread spectrum radio* This technique broadcasts signals over a wide range of frequencies, avoiding problems inherent in narrow-band communication. A code is used to spread the signal, and the receiving station uses the same code to retrieve it. In this way, a spread spectrum signal can operate a range of frequencies occupied by other signals. Spread spectrum radio does not interfere with conventional radio because its energy levels are too weak.

Mobile Radio Networks

There are two competing mobile radio technologies. The first is based on packet-radio techniques and links to satellite. The second is based on the use of the existing cellular telephone system. Mobile radio is becoming quite sophisticated. Service providers offer gateways to popular services like AT&T Mail, MCI Mail, CompuServe, and networks like the Internet. Operating system and software vendors like Microsoft are designing packages specifically for mobile users.

PACKET-RADIO COMMUNICATION Packet-radio breaks a transmission into small digital packets that include the source and destination address, as well as error-correction information. The packets are uplinked to a satellite, then broadcast. The recipient device receives only packets that are addressed to it. Because the transmissions are two-way, error-detection-and-correction methods can be used. Companies involved in packet-radio communication are Ardis (Lincolnshire, Illinois), RAM Mobile Data (Woodbridge, New Jersey), and Nextel (Lafayette, California).

CELLULAR DIGITAL PACKET COMMUNICATION   Cellular Digital Packet Data (CDPD) is a cellular radio network specification that allows customers to send computer data over existing cellular networks. The packet methods defined in CDPD provide efficient computer data transmission of bursty data typical of E-mail exchanges or a database query. Error detection and correction is also possible due to the two-way transmission nature of the devices. CDPD was defined by a consortium of cellular carriers and computer companies, including eight of the nine regional bell operating companies (RBOCs), IBM, McCaw Cellular Data, Contel Cellular, and GTE Mobilnet.

RELATED ENTRIES   Advanced National Radio Data Service; Cellular Digital Packet Data; Mobile Computing; Packet-Radio Communication; Wireless LAN Communication; *and* Wireless Mobile Communication

RAM Mobile Data

RAM Mobile Data and partner Ericsson GE Mobile Communications are providers of two-way wireless communication services for mobile computer users. Services cover most of the United States, with relatively low transmission speeds of 8 Kbits/sec, compared to competitor Ardis. However, the service is inexpensive and was originally designed for the consumer market.

RELATED ENTRIES   Advanced National Radio Data Service; Mobile Computing; Packet-Radio Communication; Radio Networks; Wireless LAN Communication; *and* Wireless Mobile Communication

Redirector

A *redirector* is a program running in a workstation that is attached to a network. It intercepts requests for network resources and services and redirects them over the network to file servers or peer workstations. For example, if a workstation user makes a request for local files, the redirector forwards the request to the local operating system. If the request is for files on a network server, the redirector forwards the request out over the network to the appropriate server. The request is placed in a packet with the address of the server.

On NetWare and other PC networks, redirector software is individually installed at each workstation along with the driver software for the network interface adapter installed in the computer.

RELATED ENTRIES   Client Software; DOS Requester, NetWare; LAN WorkPlace Products, Novell; *and* Network Driver Standards

Reduced Instruction Set Computer (RISC)

Microprocessors have instruction sets called *microcode* that programmers use to create low-level computer programs. The instruction sets perform various tasks, such as moving values into registers or executing instructions to add the values in registers. Microcode can be either simple or complex, depending on the microprocessor manufacturer's preference and the intended use of the chip. There are two categories:

- *Complex Instruction Set Computer (CISC)* designs include a rich set of microcode that simplifies the creation of programs that run on the processor.

- *Reduced Instruction Set Computer (RISC)* designs, as the name implies, have a reduced set of instructions that improve the efficiency of the processor, but require more complex external programming.

RISC designs are based on work performed at IBM by John Cocke. He found that about 20 percent of a computer's instructions did about 80 percent of the work. His 80/20 rule spawned the development of RISC architecture, which reduces the number of instructions to only those that are used most. The other instructions must be implemented in external software.

CISC-designed microprocessors dominated the microcomputer market in the 1980s, but RISC designs are becoming more prominent as users require more speed. In addition, modular programming techniques and advanced programming interfaces have made it easier for developing programs in general, thus hiding some of the complexities of programming associated with RISC design. RISC-based processors include the MIPS chips, the DEC Alpha, and the IBM RS family of chips. Current and future processor designs seem to favor RISC over CISC.

Redundant Arrays of Inexpensive Disks (RAID)

A RAID is a set of drives that appears as a single drive. Data is written evenly across the drives by using a technique called *striping*. Striping divides data over two or more drives, as shown by the crude example in Figure R-1. Data striping can occur at the bit level or on a sector level. A sector is a block of disk data. Striping improves throughput and provides a form of redundancy that protects against the failure of one disk in the array by encoding the scattered data to a backup drive known as the parity drive.

The disk controller is a very important piece of hardware in a RAID system because it affects performance and fault tolerance. Several controllers are often used to protect against controller failure. Small Computer System Interface (SCSI) adapters are used almost exclusively in RAID systems because of their improved read and write performance. After issuing a read or write command to one drive, a SCSI controller can disconnect from it and turn its attention to another drive. The drive continues the operation on its own.

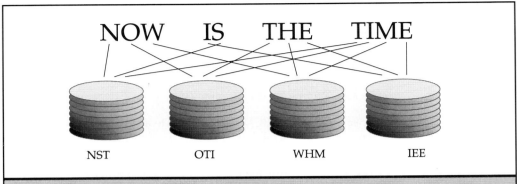

Figure R-1. *Striping techniques divides data over one or more drives*

RAID provides redundancy similar to mirroring and duplexing. The level of redundancy depends on the RAID level used, which is described under "RAID Levels" in this section. In a normal disk mirroring configuration, one backup drive is matched to one primary drive. In RAID level 3, one parity drive provides mirroring for two or more primary drives. A coding scheme is used to write information to the parity drive that represents the data written to the other drives. If one drive should fail, the parity code and the data on the remaining drives are used to come up with the missing portion of the data.

Buying a single parity drive is much cheaper than buying a backup mirroring drive for each primary drive. However, the parity drive only provides adequate protection if one drive fails at a time. If two or more primary drives fail, the parity code drive won't contain enough information to rebuild the data. However, it is unlikely that two drives would fail simultaneously, as long as the system is protected from power surges.

Many RAID systems allow *hot replacement* of disks, which means that disks can be replaced while the system is running. When a disk is replaced, the parity information is used to rebuild the data on the disk. Rebuilding occurs while the operating system continues handling other operations, so there is some loss of performance during the rebuilding operation.

RAID Levels

There are several levels of RAID. When buying systems that use RAID, you need to check their levels against your system needs.

■ *RAID level 0*   Data is striped over several drives, but there is no redundant drive. Level 0 provides RAID performance without data protection.

- *RAID level 1* Data is striped to an array of drives and each drive is mirrored to a backup drive. In a four-drive array, two are used as primary drives and two are used as mirroring drives. This level provides the performance benefits of striping and the highest level of protection by mirroring all primary drives.

- *RAID level 2* This level is not normally implemented. It provides data striping at the bit level over all drives in the array. RAID level 3 is similar, but it is implemented more widely.

- *RAID level 3* Data is striped at the bit or byte level (your choice) to all drives in the array except one, which becomes the parity drive. In a four-drive array, data is striped to three drives and parity information is written to the fourth. This level provides good read performance but relatively slow write performance because the parity drive is written to with every write operation.

- *RAID level 4* This level is similar to RAID level 3, except that data is striped in disk sector units rather than as bits or bytes. Read times are improved because each drive can retrieve an entire disk sector.

- *RAID level 5* Data is written in disk sector units to all drives in the drive array. Error-correction codes are also written to all drives. This level provides quicker writes because the parity information is spread over all the drives rather than being written to a single parity drive as is the case in RAID level 3. Disk reads are improved because each drive can retrieve an entire disk block.

Most RAID systems designed for server use on the market today use either RAID level 4 or RAID level 5. The Compaq SYSTEMPRO implements RAID level 4 but offers an upgraded software driver that implements RAID level 5, which offers better performance. Such disk arrays are expensive and you need to weigh their price against your need for continuous online data protection. You also need to weigh the price and performance of a RAID system against the standard disk mirroring and disk duplexing techniques provided in many network operating systems. An additional consideration is that RAID systems are often proprietary, which ties you to the manufacturer for future support and service.

RELATED ENTRIES Disaster Recovery; Disk Mirroring and Duplexing; Disk Storage Systems; *and* Fault Management

Regional Bell Operating Companies (RBOCs)

The *regional Bell operating companies (RBOCs)* were formed by the breakup of AT&T based on a restructuring agreement that took effect in 1984. It created 22 RBOCs. The final restructuring agreement was the United States District Court's Modification of Final Judgment (MFJ). MFJ ended the Justice Department's suit against AT&T.

The RBOCs are organized into seven regional Bell holding companies. Each RBOC operates within a specific geographical area, which is divided into service areas called *Local Access and Transport Areas (LATAs)*. LATAs were defined during the restructuring, and there are close to 200 of them. LATAs provide the boundaries between local services and long distances services.

- *Ameritech* covers the midwestern states of Illinois, Indiana, Michigan, Ohio, and Wisconsin. RBOCs include Illinois Bell, Indiana Bell, Michigan Bell, Ohio Bell, and Wisconsin Telephone.

- *Bell Atlantic* covers the mid-Atlantic states of Connecticut, Delaware, Maryland, New Jersey, Pennsylvania, West Virginia, and Virginia. RBOCs include Bell of Pennsylvania, Diamond State Telephone, New Jersey Bell, and four Chesapeake and Potomac companies (C&P of Maryland, C&P of Virginia, C&P of West Virginia, and C&P of Washington, D.C.).

- *Bell South* covers the southern states of Alabama, Florida, Georgia, Kentucky, Louisiana, Mississippi, North Carolina, South Carolina, and Tennessee. RBOCs include South Central Bell and Southern Bell.

- *Nynex* covers the northeastern states of Maine, New Hampshire, New York, Rhode Island, and Vermont. RBOCs include New England Telephone and New York Telephone.

- *Pacific Telesis* covers the western states of California and Nevada. RBOCs include Pacific Bell and Nevada Bell.

- *Southwestern Bell* covers the states of Arkansas, Kansas, Missouri, Oklahoma, and Texas. The region consists of the single RBOC called Southwestern Bell.

- *US West* covers the western states of Arizona, Colorado, Idaho, Minnesota, Montana, Nebraska, New Mexico, North Dakota, Oregon, South Dakota, Utah, Washington, and Wyoming. RBOCs include Mountain Bell, Northwestern Bell, and Pacific Northwest Bell.

Independent telephone companies (ITCs), which are non-Bell companies, may also offer services within the LATA area. All services provided within a LATA are called *intra-LATA* services. Services provided outside the LATA are called *inter-LATA* services, and are provided by *interexchange carriers (IXCs)*, of which there are many, such as MCI, US Sprint, and AT&T.

The Justice Department's MFJ defines the type of business that the RBOCs can provide. Some examples are the right to offer exchange service within LATAs, provide IXCs with access to LATAs, and the sale, but not manufacturing, of customer premises equipment. Most important, RBOCs cannot provide interexchange services, and are required to file tariffs, which are fixed prices for the services they offer.

RELATED ENTRIES   AT&T; Carriers; Carrier Services; Local Access and Transport Area; *and* Local Exchange Carrier

Remote Access Software

Remote access software provides a way for a remote workstation or mobile users to dial into a network and access the resources of that network. The link is typically via dialup lines using modems, so transmission speeds don't provide users with the same performance they would get if directly attached to the LAN. To regain performance, the amount of traffic generated between the remote user and the network must be reduced. Remote access software treats the remote users' computer like a dumb terminal and performs all computing tasks at the local area network (LAN) site. In this way, only screen and keyboard information crosses the wire. However, a dedicated computer is required to service the needs of each dial-in user, as shown in Figure R-2.

Remote access software provides the following benefits:

■ Users at remote workstations operate as if they were sitting at a workstation attached to the LAN.

■ Users can access database files in real time, with little delay in response since the files are not transferred over the line.

■ File and database access are performed at LAN speeds because all processing is handled by the local network workstation. Only keystrokes and screen displays are sent from the local PC to the remote workstation.

■ Because this method does not perform any processing at the remote workstation, a dumb terminal can often be used as the remote workstation.

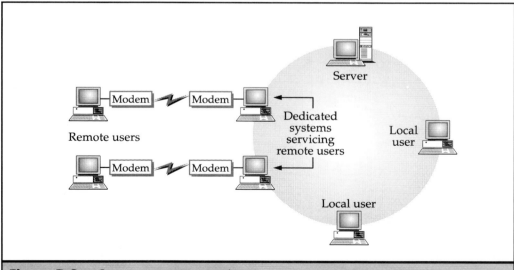

Figure R-2.   *Remote access connections*

The remote access alternative is a direct connection in which all information is passed to the user over the phone lines. If the user is working on a database or a file, all the information requested by the user is transferred to the user for processing in his or her remote systems. This is not only inefficient, but introduces security problems as well. If this method is used, the user should load and run most of the software from his or her own computer, rather than from the network. For example, the user should start Windows from his or her local disk, then access only data from the remotely connected LAN.

Some remote access products are optimized for Windows and client-server applications. For example, RemoteNB from TechSmith (Lansing, Michigan) effectively supports Windows applications by ensuring that only requests for data and responses to those requests are transmitted between the remote workstation and the LAN. Client-server requests are optimized for remote access. The LAN gateway (dedicated station attached to the LAN) intercepts and handles the network protocol overhead for the remote workstation client and keeps as much traffic as possible off the remote connection. Basically, RemoteNB works at higher layers in the protocol stack to reduce traffic.

Remote access server products are available to provide more user access to the network with fewer hardware requirements. In this scheme, a single multitasking computer runs multiple dial-in sessions so that a number of remote users can dial into the same computer over separate modems as shown in Figure R-3. For example, Novell's NetWare Access Server (NAS) runs in a dedicated communication server that provides up to 15 PC sessions. Each session running in the server acts like an Intel 8086 computer with 640K of memory. A serial port and modem are needed for each remote access connection.

Another type of remote service is electronic mail. An E-mail program can dial into a central post office system to drop off the user's mail and collect any waiting mail. These systems use phone connections efficiently. A connection is made, mail is

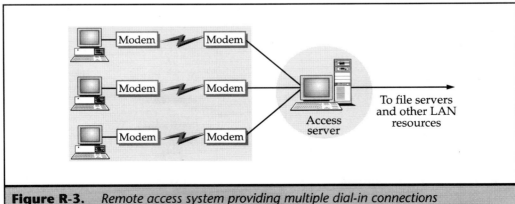

Figure R-3. *Remote access system providing multiple dial-in connections*

delivered and picked up, and the system disconnects. Electronic mail systems provide non-real-time, user-to-user communication that can be more cost effective and convenient than voice mail or conversations. The store-and-forward capabilities of E-mail provide a convenient way to send messages as well as files and other data. Users can even make database requests with an E-mail message, then call back at another time to retrieve the response, which is delivered in the form of another E-mail message.

Many vendors are gearing up for remote users by developing special add-on packages or applications that support remote users. Microsoft is developing features in Windows that automatically restore a user's work environment so the user can disconnect at one location and reconnect at another without losing his or her setup or work. Novell's NetWare Connect is a remote communication platform that lets mobile users connect to NetWare networks. It provides remote node, remote control, dial-in/dial-out services, as well as security and management features. NetWare Connect's predecessor is NetWare Asynchronous Communication Services (NACS). Future enhancements include dial-out for Macintosh and Point-to-Point Protocol support for UNIX-TCP/IP users.

While the thought of dedicating a PC or an access server to remote users may sound like an expensive proposition, the concept of remote access has its place in the network environment. When remote users require a lot of disk access, transferring data between local machines, then displaying the results on the remote system is much more economical. Network administrators need to evaluate the amount of time and phone costs generated by remote users. Remote control software can help reduce these costs.

RELATED ENTRIES Dialup Line; Mobile Computing; Modems; *and* Wide Area Networks

Remote Procedure Call (RPC)

Interprocess communications (IPC) are communication techniques used by programs and processes running in multitasking operating systems or between networked computers. There are two types of IPCs:

- *Local procedure call (LPC)* LPCs are used in multitasking operating systems to allow concurrently running tasks to talk to one another. They can share memory spaces, synchronize tasks, and send messages to one another.

- *Remote procedure call (RPC)* The RPC is similar to the LPC, but works over networks. RPCs first appeared on Sun Microsystems, Inc. and Hewlett-Packard computers running under the UNIX operating system.

With IPCs and RPCs, programs can take advantage of processes handled by other programs or computers. Client-server computing uses RPCs as a mechanism for communicating between systems, along with other techniques like messaging. Clients perform some tasks on their own, but rely on servers to provide back-end file services. RPCs provide the communication mechanism for the client to request services from back-end servers, as shown in Figure R-4. If you think of a client-server application as a program that has been split, a server can run the data-access portion because it is closest to the data, and the client can run the front-end portion of presenting the data and interacting with the user. In this arrangement, the RPC can be viewed as the component that reintegrates the split portions of the program over the network. RPCs are sometimes called *coupling* mechanisms.

By splitting a program in this way, it is not necessary to copy the entire database or major portions of it to a user's system every time the user needs to access data. Instead, the server can simply process the requests and even perform some calculations on the data, then send that finished product to the user. This process also allows more users to access similar data at the same time since database synchronization is easier if the data is managed in one location.

Distributed computing environments are collections of computers connected by a communication system—the network. It's easy to see this network as a computing platform, one in which any available computer can be a client or a server in a peer-to-peer arrangement. Individual programs might be sent to computers that are most suited for the task, while some processing tasks might be split into individual routines that are processed in parallel on several different network computers. This strategy uses idle computer resources and enhances the investment in the network. A

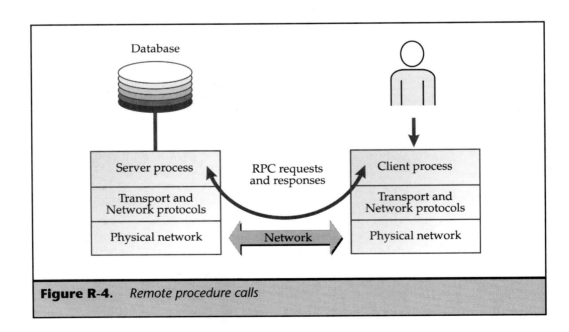

Figure R-4.   *Remote procedure calls*

typical enterprise-wide network consists of many different computer systems running different operating systems.

As enterprise networks take shape, developers must create programs that work on a wide variety of computers and network communication protocols. A movement is underway to make RPC transport independent. That means developers don't need to worry about the underlying network and the protocols used to transport data on that network. The next section describes RPCs in relation to the way they are implemented in the Open Software Foundation's (OSF's) Distributed Computing Environment (DCE). The OSF RPC is designed to operate in heterogeneous distributed computing environments.

SunSoft's Open Network Computing (ONC) Remote Procedure Call/External Data Representation (RPC/XDR) protocol is widely used. Of the 3.1 million systems running Network File System (NFS), about 2.8 million also use the ONC RPC libraries and can act as clients or servers to distributed applications. ONC RPC is supported by IBM on all its operating systems except OS/400. UNIX System Laboratories includes RPC/XDR as a standard part of UNIX System V Release 4. Novell supports the next generation ONC+ Transport Independent Remote Procedure Call (TI-RPC) technology. TI-RPC uses Tranport Layer Interface (TLI) for transport independence. TLI provides a common means of accessing connection-oriented or connectionless transport services, as discussed under "STREAMS."

Open Software Foundation (OSF) RPC

RPC tools provide a programming language and compiler to develop distributed applications with modules that run on both client and server systems as if they are local procedures. A run-time facility allows distributed applications to run on multiple, heterogeneous systems, thus making the underlying architectures and protocol transparent to the application.

The programmer creates an *interface definition* in an Interface Definition Language (IDL). IDL is a tool that programmers use to specify procedures designed to run remotely. The IDL *compiler* translates the IDL interface definition into stubs that are bound with the client and the server. The stub on the client side "stands in" for the server procedure and the stub on the server side "stands in" for the client procedure. An RPC run-time facility is located at the client and server to work in concert with the stubs to provide RPC operations.

One of the problems with using RPC in a heterogeneous environment is that different machines represent data differently. The OSF RPC gets around this problem by tagging calls with a description of the calling machine's basic data representation. When the call is received, the receiver converts the data if the tag indicates that the two machines represent data differently.

The RPC run-time facility provides the mechanisms for transferring requests from the clients to the servers and transmitting and receiving responses over the network. The DCE RPC run-time facility also interacts with other DCE services on the network, such as naming, security, and time services. The run-time facility has the following features:

- Runs on many different networks. Developers don't need to write applications for every network.

- Provides recovery from failures on the client or server side, or on the network. It supports file systems, databases, and other services that transmit variable-length data.

- Provides a name-based method for locating servers that is independent of any one directory service.

- Provides an interface to a security facility that protects RPC communication from tampering. The security service ensures the privacy of confidential information and protects the integrity of communication by providing authentication.

- Supports multithreading for concurrent or parallel processing on the network so an application can perform many actions simultaneously.

- Provides portability to and interoperability with system environments from multiple vendors.

RELATED ENTRIES   Application Program Interface; Connectionless and Connection-Oriented Transactions; Distributed Computing Environment, OSF; Enterprise Networks; Interprocess Communication; *and* Middleware

Repeater

As electrical signals are transmitted on a cable, they tend to degenerate in proportion to the length of the cable. This is called *attenuation*. A repeater is a simple add-on device that boosts a cable's signal so that you can extend the length of the network. A repeater does not normally change a signal in any way except to boost it for retransmission on the extended cable segment. Some repeaters also filter noise. A repeater is basically a "dumb" device with the following characteristics:

- A repeater regenerates network signals so that they can travel further.

- Repeaters are primarily used in linear cable systems such as Ethernet.

- Repeaters operate at the lowest level of a protocol stack: the physical level. Higher-level protocols are not used.

- Both segments connected by a repeater must use the same media access method.

- Repeaters are normally used within a single building.

- Segments connected by a repeater become part of the same network and have the same network address.

■ Every node on a network segment has its own address. Nodes on extended segments cannot have the same addresses as nodes on existing segments because they become part of the same network segment.

Repeaters pass packets at the speed of the network; about 10 Mbits/sec for Ethernet compared to a bridge, which passes about 15,000 packets per second. Routers are about five times slower than a bridge at passing packets. Distance is the usual reason for selecting a repeater (500 meters [1,650 feet] for Ethernet [thick wire] and 185 meters [610 feet] for Ethernet [thin wire]). A repeater rebuilds the packet *preamble*. The preamble allows the receiver to synchronize the bits before the packet contents are put to use.

Extending a local area network (LAN) and adding more workstations increases congestion on the LAN. A general rule is to not exceed 50 workstations per LAN segment. If congestion is high, consider splitting the LAN into two or more segments by using a bridge. Think of repeaters as connections to distant workstations, rather than as a way to add more workstations.

RELATED ENTRIES   Bridging; Networks; *and* Routers

Replication

Replication is a technique that copies all or a part of a database to another location for backup and/or to provide the latest updates to the database. Replication is only one technique for keeping distributed databases in synchronization. The other popular method is two-phase commit. Both are briefly described next for comparison.

■ *Two-phase commit* is used in online transaction processing where information is written to two or more separate databases simultaneously. A bank transaction that updates branch office databases is an example. In a two-phase commit, all the databases involved must first acknowledge to a monitoring program that they are ready to write data, then acknowledge that they have in fact made the write. If any system fails to acknowledge, all systems abort the write. See "Transaction Processing" for more information.

■ *Replication* involves copying all or part of a database at regular intervals, or after major changes, from a remote site to the master database, or from the master database to remote sites.

Not all database updates are time-critical, and this is where replication is useful. For example, a directory service contains the names of users and resources on the network. This database (or partitions of it) is copied to remote locations so users at those locations can access the data locally, rather than using a wide area network (WAN) connection to access the data at a master site. Changes to the database such as the addition of a new user are usually not critical. Remote users probably won't need this new information right away, so the remote databases are replicated at periodic intervals, or during evening hours so as not to tie up expensive WAN links.

RELATED ENTRIES   Directory Services; Directory Services, NetWare; Directory Services, Open Software Foundation; Disaster Recovery; Distributed Computing; Distributed Database; Distributed File Systems; Partition Management; *and* Transaction Processing

RG-58 Coaxial Cable

A two-conductor shielded cable similar to television coaxial cable used primarily in Ethernet networks. RG-58 is often called "thin coax." It has a 50-ohm impedance characteristic.

RELATED ENTRIES   BNC Connector; Cabling; Ethernet 10Base-2; *and* Transmission Media, Methods, and Equipment

RG-62 Coaxial Cable

A two-conductor shielded cable similar to television coaxial cable used for ARCNET network topologies. The cable has a 93-ohm impedance characteristic.

RELATED ENTRIES   ARCNET; BNC Connector; Cabling; *and* Transmission Media, Methods, and Equipment

Rights in Novell NetWare

Access rights and security are vital in a network operating system. When security is managed correctly, corruption and loss of data by unauthorized users are prevented and privacy of data is maintained. While login authentication and restrictions are the first line of defense against unauthorized users, access rights prevent logged-in users from snooping around in the file system and gaining access to sensitive information such as payroll files. Access rights also control who can use the various resources in the network.

Users granted access to files, directories, or objects are called *trustees*. NetWare access rights are grouped as shown in the following list:

■ *Directory rights* control who has access to the directories in disk volumes and the files within them.

■ *File rights* provide control on a file-by-file basis over who has access to files within directories.

■ In NetWare 4.x, *object rights* control who can create and manage user accounts objects and objects for resources like servers, volumes, and printers in the NetWare Directory Services (NDS) system.

■ In NetWare 4.x, *property rights* control who can view and change the properties of objects in the NetWare Directory Services (NDS) system.

■ In NetWare 4.x, *SMS rights* control who has access to objects within the Storage Management System (SMS) applications.

Trustee rights give users the ability to access directories and files and to manage objects:

■ A trustee of a NetWare Directory Services object can be given rights to view it in the NetWare Directory Services (NDS) tree, delete it, rename it, and if it is a container, create other objects within it. A trustee can also be given the rights to view and change the properties of the object.

■ A trustee of a directory can be given rights to view, change, delete, and create files within the directory. A trustee can also be given the rights to change the attributes, names, trustee assignments, and inherited rights filter for the directory.

■ If a user is granted the Supervisor right to an object, directory, or file, that user has unrestricted rights to the object, directory, or file.

The following section lists the directory, file, object, and property rights in Novell NetWare 4.x.

Directory Rights

■ *Supervisor*   All rights to the directory, its files, and its subdirectories. The directory Supervisor right cannot be blocked by an Inherited Rights Filter. Users with this right can grant other users rights to the directory, its files, and its subdirectories.

■ *Read*   The right to run programs in the directory and to open files in the directory and read their contents.

■ *Write*   The right to open and change the contents of existing files in the directory.

■ *Create*   The right to create new files and subdirectories in the directory.

■ *Erase*   The right to delete the directory, its files, and its subdirectories.

■ *Modify*   The right to change the attributes or names of the directory, its files, and its subdirectories, but not the right to change its contents.

■ *File Scan*   The right to see the directory and its files by using the DIR and NDIR commands.

■ *Access Control*   The right to change the trustee assignments and Inherited Rights Filter of the directory, its files, and its subdirectories.

File Rights

- *Supervisor*   All rights to the file. The file Supervisor right cannot be blocked with an Inherited Rights Filter. Users who have this right can grant other users any rights to the file and can change the file's Inherited Rights Filter.
- *Read*   The right to open and read the file.
- *Create*   The right to salvage the file after it has been deleted.
- *Write*   The right to open and write to an existing file.
- *Erase*   The right to erase the file.
- *Modify*   The right to change the attributes and name of the file, but not the right to change its contents.
- *File Scan*   The right to see the file by using the DIR and NDIR commands, including the directory structure from the file to the root directory.
- *Access Control*   The right to change the trustee assignments and Inherited Rights Filter of the file.

Object Rights, NetWare 4.x

- *Supervisor*   All access privileges to the object, including access to all the object's properties. The object Supervisor right can be blocked by an Inherited Rights Filter for the objects where the Supervisor right is granted and for individual properties of an object.
- *Browse*   The right to see the object in the directory tree. The name of the object is returned when a search is made that matches the object.
- *Create*   The right to create a new object that is subordinate to the object in the directory tree. Rights are not defined for the new object. This right is available only for container objects, because non-container objects cannot have subordinates.
- *Delete*   The right to delete the object from the directory tree. Objects that have subordinates cannot be deleted unless the subordinates are deleted first.
- *Rename*   The right to change the name of the object, in effect changing the naming property. This changes what the object is called in complete names.

Object Property Rights, NetWare 4.x

- *Supervisor*   All rights to the property. The property Supervisor right can be blocked by an object's Inherited Rights Filter.
- *Compare*   The right to compare any value to a value of the property. A compare operation can return True or False, but you cannot see the value of the property. The Read right includes the Compare right.

- *Read* The right to read the values of the property. Compare is a subset of Read. If the Read right is given, compare operations are also allowed.
- *Write* The right to add, change, or remove any values of the property. The Write right includes the Add Self and Managed rights.
- *Add Self* A trustee with the Add Self right can add or remove himself or herself as a value of the property. The trustee cannot affect any other values of the property. This right is meaningful only for properties that contain object names as values, such as group membership lists and mailing lists. The Write right includes the Add Self right.

The *Inherited Rights Filter (IRF)* controls which rights users can inherit from parent directories (or container objects in NetWare 4.x). For example, if a user has Read and Write rights in a parent directory, you can use an IRF to block the Write right in a subdirectory. You can use the IRF to remove some or all of the rights a user inherits (or can inherit) from the parent directory or object.

A *user's effective* rights to a directory or file (or object in NetWare 4) are calculated based on the following parameters:

- The user's trustee assignments to the directory, file, or object
- The user's trustee assignments to the parent directory or container object
- The user's trustee assignments in either of the previously listed parameters for groups that the user belongs to
- Security equivalence of the user
- The Inherited Rights Filter for the directory, file, or object

By default, no rights are granted except in his or her personal directory and public directory.

RELATED ENTRIES   Access Rights; NetWare; *and* Novell

Rights in Windows for Workgroups

In the Microsoft Windows for Workgroups environment, users can share files on their system with other users and access shared files on other systems. Security features are limited to restricting access to directories on two levels:

- *Read-Only* Users who have Read-Only access rights can view files in a shared directory, but they can't change or delete the files.
- *Full-Access* Users who have Full-Access rights to shared directories can change existing files, add new files, and delete files.

RELATED ENTRY   Windows for Workgroups, Microsoft

Rights (Permissions) in Windows NT

See Permissions in Windows NT; Windows NT, Microsoft.

Ring Network Topology

Ring network topology is a closed-loop topology that does not require terminators. The token ring topology forms a logical ring but has the cable layout of a star topology, with a central hub. The ring is actually maintained in the hub. When a workstation attaches to the hub, the ring extends out to the workstation through the cable and back again to the hub. If another hub is attached, the ring is maintained by running cables from the ring-out connector on the first hub to the ring-in connector on the second hub, from the ring-out connector on the second hub to the ring-in connector on the first hub.

A true ring topology network is rare. It's easier to plan and install a star configured network. Locating the point of failure is also easier on a star-configured network. The ring itself is maintained within the hub and stations that go down are simply bypassed by the hub so the rest of the network can continue to operate. The Fiber Distributed Data Interface (FDDI) and the IEEE MAN (Metropolitan Area Network) standard, use dual rings. If the cable is cut in any location, a loop-back occurs and signals reaching the break point are retransmitted in the opposite direction, thus maintaining network communication.

RELATED ENTRIES   Access Method, Network; Multistation Access Unit; Token and Token Passing Access Methods; Token Bus Network; Token Ring Network; *and* Topology

RJ-11 and RJ-45 Connections

Telephone-type jacks used in Ethernet 10-BaseT and other twisted-pair cable network systems. There are two styles:

- ■ RJ-11 is a four-wire modular connector for telephones.
- ■ RJ-45 is an eight-wire modular connector for networks and some phone systems.

RELATED ENTRIES   Cabling; Ethernet; Ethernet 10Base-T; *and* Transmission Media, Methods, and Equipment

Routers

Routers are packet switches (or Network layer relays) that operate in the Network layer of the Open Systems Interconnection (OSI) protocol model. Routers interconnect networks over local or wide areas and provide traffic control and filtering functions when more than one pathway exists between two end-points on the network, as shown in Figure R-5. Routers are critical to large internetworks and wide area networks that use telecommunication links. They direct packets along the most efficient or economical path in mesh networks that consist of redundant paths to a destination.

How Routers Work

A router examines address information in packets and sends the packet along a predetermined path to its destination. Routers maintain tables of adjacent routers and local area networks (LANs) on the network. When a router receives a packet, it looks at these tables to see if it can send the packet directly to the destination. If not, it determines the location of a router that can forward the packet to its destination.

The forwarding process does require some processing. The router must fully receive a packet, view HS address information and then forward it. Therefore, differences in router components and architecture determine throughput. Some network operating systems such as Novell NetWare support routing in the server. This is accomplished by installing two or more network interface cards. However, routing tasks can slow down a server. If so, external routers are necessary to free the server for file-related tasks only.

Routers handle either a single protocol such as Transmission Control Protocol/Internet Protocol (TCP/IP), or multiple protocols, such as Sequenced Packet Exchange/Internetwork Packet Exchange (SPX/IPX) and TCP/IP. Keep in mind that not all protocols are supported, and some protocols can't be routed. However, unroutable protocols can be carried across internetworks using *encapsulation* techniques (see "Encapsulation").

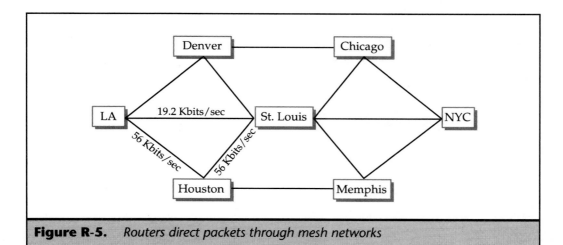

Figure R-5. *Routers direct packets through mesh networks*

Routers allow a network to be segmented into separately addressable networks. The segments are easier to manage. Each LAN segment has its own specific LAN number, and each workstation on that segment has its own address. This is the information placed in packets by the Network layer protocols.

Router Packet Processing

Routers handle packets that have the same network address. When a router receives a packet, it begins a procedure that unpackages the packet and determines where the packet should be sent. The contents of a packet and the information added by each Network protocol layer is discussed under "Packets." Here are the packet procedures a router follows:

1. The packet is error checked using the checksum value in the packet.

2. The information added by the Physical and Data-Link level protocols of the sending device are stripped off as shown in Figure R-6.

3. The information added by the Network protocols in the source computer is evaluated.

The Network layer protocol information contains the destination address, and, in the case of source routing networks like TCP/IP, a list of hops that define a

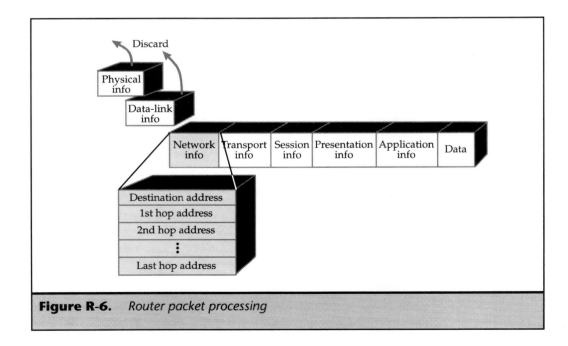

Figure R-6.   *Router packet processing*

predetermined "best path" through the network. The router may do one of several things:

- The packet might be addressed to the router itself, so the router evaluates off the remaining information in the packet.

- If a packet is for a destination on the same network, the router simply forwards it.

- If the filtering list is available, the router checks a packet's address against the list and discards the packet if necessary. This keeps packets within or out of a network for security reasons.

- If the packet contains source routing information that lists the next router along the path to the destination, the packet is forwarded to that router.

- A router maintains a table of paths through the internetwork for packets.

- If a router doesn't know a path or can't find the destination address of a packet in its routing table, it discards the packet and may return an error massage to the source.

- Some packets (such as TCP/IP) contain information about the number of hops they have made on the network. If a packet exceeds a certain hop count, it is discarded by the router with the assumption that the packet is in a loop. The router may then return an error message to the source.

Choosing the Best Path

An internetwork is usually built with fault tolerance in mind. Several paths are created among routers to provide a backup path in case a link fails. Some of these paths may use high-speed networks such as the Fiber Distributed Data Interface (FDDI) in the campus or metropolitan area or direct digital lines (T1) for wide area networks. Routers can send data over the best of these paths, depending on which is the least costly to use, the fastest, the most direct, or the one specified by an administrator.

Routing protocols (see "Routing Protocols") choose the best path through a network based on criteria such as the number of hops a packet must take through the router network to get to its destination. A best path might also be a path that goes around congested LAN segments. Traffic can be prioritized. For example, high-priority packets can be sent over a 56 Kbits/sec digital communication link, and low-priority packets can be sent over a 19.2 Kbits/sec telecommunication link. The network administrator can decide what the best paths are on a network, or in some cases, have the routers choose the best path.

A private network built with leased or dialup lines and routers is shown in Figure R-5. If Los Angeles wants to send a message to St. Louis, the router can use the 19.2 Kbits/sec direct-connect line or the 56 Kbits/sec lines that connect through Houston to St. Louis. In another situation, if New York City wants to send a message to Los Angeles, that message may go through Chicago and Denver, or through St. Louis. The router might base these decisions on the amount of congestion at Chicago or Atlanta or on the "hop count." The New York City to Los Angeles connection makes two hops if it goes through St. Louis and three hops if it goes through Chicago and Denver. Note that the mesh network has redundant links. If the Chicago to Denver line fails, messages from New York City to Los Angeles can go through St. Louis or Memphis.

Routers are also used to attach networks to backbones, as shown in Figure R-7. In this case, local traffic stays on the local LAN, while internetwork or WAN traffic traverses the FDDI fiber-optic backbone network to get to its destination. Note that the FDDI backbone is like a traffic circle in the way it moves traffic among branching nodes.

Router Specifications

If your network is small or in a single building, bridges are usually adequate. They can help segment traffic on busy local networks. Note on the right in Figure R-7 that several subnetworks are connected via bridges and this group of networks is connected to the FDDI backbone with a router.

Interconnecting more than approximately ten subnetworks with bridges can introduce excessive internetwork traffic and packet-looping problems. Use routers to interconnect different network types such as Ethernet to an FDDI backbone, or to connect with WAN links. If a network consists of multiple protocols, a multiprotocol router is required. Routers can balance loads over multiple lines, and provide path control through a complicated mesh of interconnected routers. Routers also reconfigure paths if one of the links fails.

When evaluating and buying routers, make sure all the routers in your internetwork use the same routing methods and handle the same protocols. Some routers use data compression techniques to increase the throughput of packets. To avoid problems, always try to use the same routers in all locations. Although routing methods are generally standardized, a mismatch may cause problems that result in performance degradation.

Fault-tolerance features, such as redundant power supplies and "live" module replacement, are now offered on high-end systems. Router setup is often difficult because features such as multiple protocols, redundant paths, performance, and security must be programmed into the device. A good installation program can ease this burden. Novell's MultiProtocol Router (MPR) simplifies setup somewhat by supplying default parameters for packet size, timers, and other features that are tuned to NetWare networks.

Routers are available in several price ranges. At the high end are complete wiring hubs that integrate all network ports, bridges, and routers in one unit at one location. Prices for these units start at about $20,000. They typically include 16 ports with optional support for wide area connections, such as FDDI and T1. At the middle of the price range are units priced from $10,000 to $20,000. These units usually have fewer ports, but they do offer centralized wiring schemes and management. At the low end are stand-alone router units that are placed at various internetwork locations. These units are priced under $10,000.

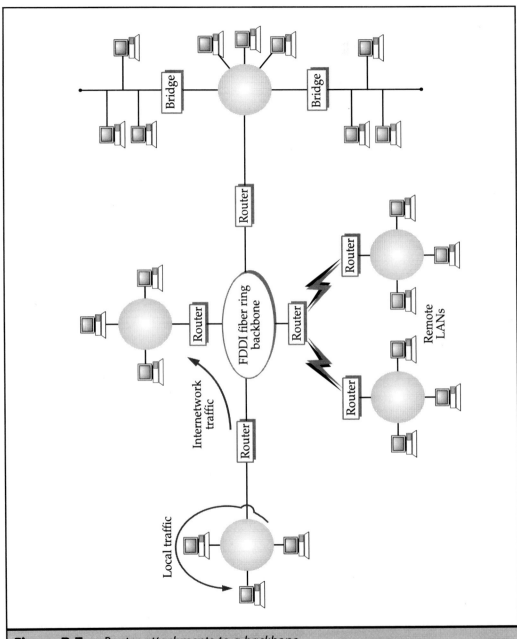

Figure R-7. *Router attachments to a backbone*

Routers can be categorized as local or remote routers. A local router has connections for LAN equipment, such as Token Ring, Ethernet, and FDDI segments. A remote router has wide area network (WAN) connections such as T1, X.25, Frame Relay, satellite, microwave, and others.

Looking at Speed

It's interesting to look at speed figures to get an idea of just how fast bridges and routers are. The number of packets per second (pps) forwarded is the usual gauge for bridge and router speed. Ethernet (10 Mbits/sec, or megabits per second) forwards about 14,880 pps on its own cable if all the packets are 64 bytes. A bridge attached to Ethernet typically filters 14,000 pps and forwards 10,000. Routers commonly forward from 8,000 to 15,000 packets per second. The store-and-forward latency of bridges and routers decreases throughput somewhat. Novell's MPR forwards packets at 3,000 to 4,000 per second.

The packet-per-second throughput of bridges and routers does not need to be higher than the capabilities of the LANs they are attached to. Also keep in mind that traffic across the bridge is less than local traffic. Although bursts from high-performance systems can saturate even the normal Ethernet wire bandwidth, the contention mechanism of the Ethernet cable access method adds enough overhead at high volumes to keep the traffic low at the bridge or router. A bridge or router that can process 5,000 64-byte packets per second is usually adequate for 10Mbits/sec once you figure in this overhead. Token ring networks have a similar saturation point. The wire itself constrains bandwidth more than a bridge does. Forwarding of Token Ring packets is handled adequately by bridges and routers that transfer from 2,000 to 3,000 packets per second. Note that high forwarding rates are less important for WAN connections because the WAN itself has a much slower throughput than a LAN. Compare 1 Mbit/sec for WANs to 10 Mbits/sec for Ethernet LANs.

Multiprotocol Routers

A multiprotocol network supports multiple protocols, such as TCP/IP, IPX, AppleTalk, DECnet, and others. Multiprotocol routers give organizations that are consolidating their network resources the ability to connect those resources to the same network platform. A multiprotocol router can run software to handle packets from each of the protocols supported on the network, depending on the capabilities of the router.

Multiprotocol networks provide a way to make a transition from many protocols to only a few. Managers can slowly switch users over to protocols the company supports, then disable the old protocols once all users have been converted.

The Novell MultiProtocol Router

The Novell MultiProtocol Router is a set of NetWare Loadable Modules that can be installed in a NetWare file server or in a separate system. It comes with a limited version of NetWare called NetWare Runtime, so that you can run the router in a system other than the NetWare file server. The software can route SPX/IPX, TCP/IP, AppleTalk, and Novell NetBIOS packets over Ethernet, Token Ring, ARCNET, and

AppleTalk LAN segments. It also supports wide area connections through X.25, 64 Kbits/sec (kilobit per second), or T1 lines. For SPX/IPX users, the NetWare Link Service Protocol (NLSP) is a link-state routing protocol that replaces the Routing Information Protocol (RIP) of SPX/IPX. For TCP/IP users, the Open Shortest Path First (OSPF) protocol is used. Both provide faster data transmissions between LAN segments.

MPR requires an 80386 or better computer system. It is bundled with NetWare Hub Services, a monitoring and management system for integrating hubs into NetWare platforms. With NetWare Hub Services, you can build router and hub connection systems. The multiprotocol router also includes WAN links for wide area network routing.

RELATED ENTRIES   Carrier Services; Hubs; Layered Architecture; Networks; Open Systems Interconnection Model; Packets; Protocols, Communication; Protocol Stack; Routing Protocols; *and* Wide Area Networks

Routing, AppleTalk

NOTE: See "Routing Protocols" for a general discussion of routing techniques.

The AppleTalk protocols were originally designed for LocalTalk, a relatively low-speed transmission medium. Support for Ethernet and Token Ring was added later. A set of separate LocalTalk LANs can be interconnected with routers, thus forming an internetwork. Support for Ethernet and Token Ring were added to AppleTalk at a later date.

To route data packets between local area network (LAN) segments, an addressing system is used that uniquely identifies each node. AppleTalk consists of older addressing techniques and newer extended addressing techniques that were introduced in 1989 with AppleTalk Phase 2. The old scheme used 8 bits for the address and allowed 254 stations per network. AppleTalk Phase 2 added support for 16 million nodes and enhanced AppleTalk for large networks.

The *Routing Table Maintenance Protocol (RTMP)* is responsible for maintaining address tables and communicating with other routers about the status of the network. This protocol is inefficient on WANs because it sends entire tables across the wide area network (WAN). RTMP sends the full routing information tables (often up to 1 Mbyte in size) every 10 seconds. With only a few devices on the network, this strategy was not a problem, but with large interconnected networks, performance problems were excessive due to this overhead.

In 1992, Apple improved RTMP by providing a routing protocol called AppleTalk Update-based Routing Protocol (AURP). While RTMP is sufficient for small LANs, it is not efficient for WAN connectivity. AURP does not replace RTMP, but complements it. The main difference between the two is that there is little or no routing traffic over the AURP link if the internetwork is stable. With AURP, routing information is transmitted only when changes actually occur on the internetwork and only the changes are sent. AURP also automated the mapping of addresses and the elimination of duplicate addresses when two AppleTalk networks are joined.

AppleTalk routes in an internetwork are selected based on the least number of hops a packet must make to reach its destination. AURP provides an improved routing mechanism and provides a way to encapsulate AppleTalk into TCP/IP or OSI packets. It is possible that Apple will replace AURP with a link- state routing algorithm such as Open Shortest Path First (OSPF) or OSI's Intermediate System-to-Intermediate System (IS-IS).

AppleTalk networks can be divided into logical groups of networks called *zones*. Each zone has a name that makes it easier for users to refer to groups of users or network equipment. The Zone Information Protocol (ZIP) works with RTMP and AURP to maintain a list of network numbers in matching zone names. This information is held in Zone Information Tables (ZITs). When an AppleTalk packet arrives at a router, the zone name in the packet is compared to the ZIT table so the router can forward the packet to the port connected to the destination network.

RELATED ENTRIES   AppleTalk; Layered Architecture; Networks; Packets; Protocols, Communication; Protocol Stack; Routing; Routing Protocols; *and* Wide Area Networks

Routing, IBM

See Advanced Peer-to-Peer Networking; High Performance Routing, IBM; Layered Architecture; Networks; Packets; Protocols; Protocol Stack; Routing; Routing Protocols; *and* Wide Area Networks.

Routing, Internet

NOTE: See "Routing Protocols" for a general discussion of routing techniques.

The Internet (TCP/IP) routing architecture is similar to the Open System Interconnection (OSI) architecture. There is a hierarchy of systems that consists of subnetworks with attached hosts (user computers, servers, and so on). These subnetworks are attached to routers that connect them to other subnetworks within an autonomous system. An *autonomous system* (also called an *interior system* or *domain*) is a collection of subnetworks and routers that generally use the same routing protocols and are under the same administrative control. Autonomous systems are pictured in Figure R-11.

Interior Gateway Protocols such as Routing Information Protocol (RIP) and Open Shortest Path First (OSPF) are used to exchange routing information within a domain. OSPF is an interior routing protocol that is very similar to the OSI IS-IS protocol. At the edges of domains are border routers that connect one domain to another. These routers use *exterior routing protocols* to exchange routing information. The Exterior

Gateway Protocol (EGP) provides a way for two neighboring routers located at edges of their respective domains to exchange messages and information. A replacement for EGP called Border Gateway Protocol (BGP) is available and provides improved features such as the ability to specify routing policies.

Interior Gateway Protocols

Interior Gateway Protocols are the protocols used within a domain for the exchange of routing information. The following routing protocols are used.

ADDRESS RESOLUTION PROTOCOL (ARP)   ARP is the neighbor discovery protocol for Internet and TCP/IP networks. It is similar to the OSI End System-to-Intermediate System (ES-IS) protocol. Both routers and host (user computers, servers, and so on) use ARP to announce themselves. A router broadcasts packets that contain an IP address. The computer or device attached to a network with the address then returns its LAN address. The information is then placed in routing tables for future use. A similar protocol, called Reverse ARP (RARP), performs the opposite task; it obtains the IP address from a known network address.

ROUTING INFORMATION PROTOCOL (RIP)   RIP uses distance-vector algorithms (DVA) to calculate routing paths. In DVA, routing decisions are based on the least number of "hops" to a destination or a cost that is calculated along with costs of paths on neighbor routers. RIP routing tables are exchanged with other routers approximately every 30 seconds and routers rebuild their routing tables based on new information. A router can get behind in rebuilding its routing table if it is connected to a low throughput WAN link. In addition, exchanging the routing table can add a lot of overhead to a network, which causes more congestion, further delaying routing table updates. If a route fails, the delay required to rebuild routing tables can delay how quickly a new route is established.

OPEN SHORTEST PATH FIRST (OSPF)   OSPF is a link-state routing algorithm that was derived from work done on the Open Systems Interconnection (OSI) Intermediate System-to-Intermediate System intradomain routing protocol. Link-state routing, as compared to distance-vector routing, requires more processing power, but provides more control over the routing process and responds faster to changes. The Dijkstra algorithm is used to calculate routes, based on the number of routers the packet must "hop," the speed of transmission lines, traffic congestion delays, and cost of routers based on a metric. OSPF routing tables are only updated when necessary and only with the significant information.

Exterior Gateway Protocol (EGP)

The Exterior Gateway Protocol (EGP) provides a way for two neighboring routers located at edges of their respective domains to exchange messages and information. The Exterior Gateway Protocol provides a way for routers to exchange routing information among themselves. Each domain has one or more routers that are picked to be EGPs.

R

Each EGP exchanges routing information with interior gateways within the same domain using an Interior Gateway Protocol so that it knows the addresses of end systems (hosts) within the local domain. EGPs connect with EGPs in other domains and exchange routing information about the end systems in the respective domains. With this information, gateways know the best way to send information to other systems outside the domain.

The primary functions of EGP are the following:

■ To perform a neighbor connection procedure in which two exterior gateways connect and decide to exchange information.

■ To periodically check with neighboring routers by sending a message and waiting for a response. This is to ensure that an exterior gateway is still available.

■ To periodically exchange routing information.

EGP routines within a router can poll neighboring routers to obtain updated information. Two tables are usually maintained, one with interior routes obtained with interior protocols such as RIP or OSPF and another with exterior routes obtained with EGP. EGP, however, has faults that the Border Gateway Protocol (BGP) attempts to solve, as described next. EGP was designed when the Internet consisted of a single backbone; it is inefficient for today's multiple backbone network. Routers are set up with static routing tables that explicitly define which routers can connect. This avoids loops and provides security, but doesn't promote a scalable network.

Interdomain Policy Routing Protocols

Several new interdomain routing protocols are being proposed for use on the Internet. As the Internet grows in size, existing exterior protocols don't provide adequate scaling capabilities. The new protocols that implement policy-based routing are more scalable (a requirement for the Internet) than EGP. Policy-based routing gives administrators more control over the network, allowing prioritization of traffic and the implementation of security features and service charges.

BORDER GATEWAY PROTOCOL (BGP) *Border Gateway Protocol (BGP)* was implemented as an interim solution to provide some limited policy features, but it does not solve the scalability requirements. Route attributes such as the cost or security of a path are also added. BGP reduces the bandwidth required to exchange routing information because the information is exchanged incrementally, rather than by sending the entire database.

INTER-DOMAIN ROUTING PROTOCOL (IDRP) *Inter-Domain Routing Protocol (IDRP)* is a policy-based routing protocol similar to the Internet Border Gateway Protocol (BGP). Policy routing provides a way to route traffic in predefined ways. IDRP is a distance-vector routing protocol, in which each router defines a path for a packet traversing the network. Note that IDRP is an OSI-based protocol.

INTERDOMAIN POLICY ROUTING (IDPR)   *Interdomain Policy Routing (IDPR)* is a link-state routing protocol that implements source routing and policy-based routing between domains. Source routing provides some useful enhancements since the packets themselves hold path information. It is necessary to initially discover the path, but subsequent packets simply place the path in their headers.

RELATED ENTRIES   Domains; Internet; Layered Architecture; Networks; Packets; Protocols, Communication; Protocol Stack; Routing; Routing Protocols; Transmission Control Protocol/Internet Protocol; *and* Wide Area Networks

Routing, NetWare

 NOTE: See "Routing Protocols" for a general discussion of routing techniques.

Novell NetWare uses the Network layer Internetwork Packet Exchange (IPX) datagram service and the Sequenced Packed Exchange (SPX) connection-oriented service to provide information exchange between communicating systems. The following protocols are used by routers to exchange information about the network topology:

- *Routing Information Protocol (RIP)*   RIP was originally developed for the Xerox Network System (XNS) and is now used by SPX/IPX and TCP/IP. RIP is a distance-vector protocol and is inefficient for wide area networks.

- *NetWare Link Service Protocol (NLSP)*   NLSP is a protocol designed by Novell to replace the RIP protocol used by SPX/IPX. It improves packet transmission between users on different LAN segments. Each router knows the topology of the network, and broadcasting of routing tables is reduced.

RELATED ENTRIES   Internetwork Packet Exchange; Layered Architecture; NetWare; Packets; Protocols, Communication; Protocol Stack; Routing; Routing Protocols; *and* Wide Area Networks

Routing, OSI

 NOTE: See "Routing Protocols" for a general discussion of routing techniques.

The Open Systems Interconnection (OSI) environment consists of administrative domains that include end systems (user computers or hosts) and routers. An administrative domain generally uses the same protocols and is managed by the same central authority. All routing within the domain is called *intradomain* routing. All routing outside of the domain that connects it with other domains is called *interdomain*

routing. Interdomain routing involves connections to "untrusted" environments, and so administrators may prefer to manually set pathways, rather than rely on a routing protocol to automatically build pathways among domains.

As pictured in Figure R-8, the OSI routing architecture is hierarchical. It consists of:

- *End System-to-Intermediate System (ES-IS)*   End systems (ESs) within a department or workgroup that communicate with each other over a network. An intermediate system is attached to this network to form a *routing domain*.

- *Intradomain Intermediate System-to-Intermediate System*   Intermediate systems are attached to other intermediate systems within the same administrative domain, forming an *intradomain* connection.

- *Interdomain Intermediate System-to-Intermediate System*   The administrative domain is linked to another administrative domain, forming an *internetwork*.

ES-IS and IS-IS are protocols used to exchange routing information. Don't confuse them with the OSI data delivery protocols called the *Connectionless Network Service (CLNS)* and the *Connection-Oriented Network Service (CONS)*. CLNS is a datagram service that operates in the Network layer and can be compared to the Internet Protocol (IP) or NetWare's Internetwork Packet Exchange (IPX). CONS provides session (connection-oriented) services and operates in the Transport layer. It can be compared to the Internet's Transmission Control Protocol (TCP) or NetWare's

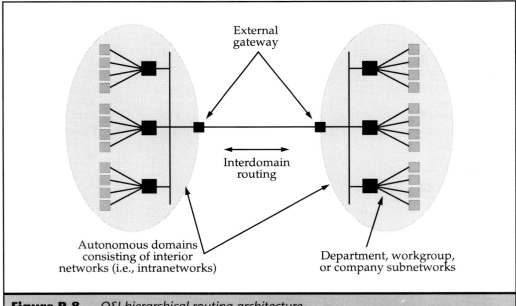

Figure R-8.   *OSI hierarchical routing architecture*

Sequence Packet Exchange (SPX). The actual protocols used to exchange routing information are ES-IS and IS-IS.

End System-to-Intermediate System (ES-IS) Protocol

End System-to-Intermediate System (ES-IS) is a *neighbor discovery* protocol that end systems use to find out the network address of other nodes on the same network. This protocol is used only between end systems and routers. The important point is that the ES only sees one "hop" between any system it needs to communicate with. To send a message to an ES in another routing domain, the ES sends packets to its local IS. This IS then handles all the routing in the intradomain or interdomain areas.

The job of the ES in the ES-IS arrangement is quite simple. It simply needs to keep track of the network addresses of other systems that it can directly communicate with. This includes other ESs on the same network, or the router that provides it with a means of sending messages to other systems.

Intermediate System-to-Intermediate System (IS-IS)

Intermediate System-to-Intermediate System (IS-IS) is a link-state routing protocol that is limited to operating within an administrative domain. The primary concern at this level in the OSI routing hierarchy is the exchange of routing information and the building of routing tables from the information that indicates the best paths through the network. It is possible to designate only one router as the router that broadcasts the routing information.

The IS-IS protocol defines an area, which is a set of physical networks and the devices attached to them. Routers that interconnect networks within an area are called Level 1 routers. Routers that interconnect one area with another area are called Level 2 routers. A *routing domain* is a collection of areas connected by Level 2 routers that is operated as a single administrative unit. Routing takes place as follows:

1. An end system (ES) sends a packet to any directly connected Level 1 router in its area.

2. The router determines where the destination address is located and sends it along the best path.

3. If the destination address is in another area, the Level 1 router sends the packet to the nearest Level 2 router.

4. The Level 2 router may forward the packet to another Level 2 router and so on until the packet reaches the destination area.

5. Level 1 routers in the destination area then handle forwarding the packet to the end system.

Interdomain IS-IS Routing

At the interdomain level of the OSI routing hierarchy, interdomain IS-IS routing facilitates communication between administrative domains. An interesting aspect of this level is that automatic route configuration and best path selection are not usually desired because of potential security problems between connected domains. There are also cost issues such as who pays for the link and authorization issues such as allowing unknown users into the network. Automatic switching of paths in this environment is not usually recommended. Network administrators will usually program routes manually.

Inter-Domain Routing Protocol (IDRP) is an OSI link-state routing protocol that routes connectionless packets in the interdomain environment. It is similar to the Internet Border Gateway Protocol (BGP) and adapts well to topology changes, such as downed lines or reconfigured connections.

IDPR is designed primarily for internetworks, and thus has little to do with intranetwork routing. It relies on dependable and stable paths to end nodes within the domains it connects. Support may be added for IP, thus providing a way to route both IP and CLNP over an interdomain with one protocol.

RELATED ENTRIES   Domains; Layered Architecture; NetWare; Open Systems Interconnection Model; Packets; Protocols, Communication; Protocol Stack; Routing; Routing Protocols; *and* Wide Area Networks

Routing Information Protocol (RIP)

Routing Information Protocol is an interior or intradomain routing protocol that uses the distance-vector routing algorithms. RIP is used in Transmission Control Protocol/Internet Protocol (TCP/IP) networks, Xerox Network System (XNS) networks, and NetWare SPX/IPX networks as the primary method for the exchange of routing information between routers. RIP is currently the most common interior gateway (router) protocol on the Internet. The Internet standard Open Shortest Path First (OSPF) supports the IP Network layer protocol and is the potential successor to RIP.

RIP-based routers perform the following tasks to keep themselves updated with the latest internetwork information:

- Request routing information from other routers to update their internal tables
- Respond to route requests from other routers
- Periodically broadcast their presence to make sure other routers are aware of the internetwork configuration
- Broadcast whenever a change in the internetwork configuration is detected

The distance-vector algorithm bases routing decisions on the least number of "hops" to a destination or the cost of the path to that destination based on preassigned values in the router and in the neighbor routers. If a packet makes more than 15 hops, its destination is considered unreachable and the packet is discarded.

RIP routing tables are exchanged with other routers approximately every 30 seconds, and routers rebuild their routing tables based on new information received from these broadcasts. Routers advertise their routes by broadcasting RIP messages that list the networks the router can reach. If a router does not broadcast within 180 seconds, its paths are considered failed.

Problems can occur if a router gets behind in rebuilding its routing table, which can occur if that router is connected over a slow wide area network (WAN) link. In addition, exchanging the routing table can add a lot of overhead to a local area network (LAN), which causes more congestion, further delaying routing table updates. If a route fails, the delay required to rebuild routing tables can delay how quickly a new route is established.

RELATED ENTRY   Routing Protocols

Routing Protocols

When two computers that are not directly connected need to communicate over several networks, as shown in Figure R-9, routers are usually necessary. Routers provide a way to develop pathways through a mesh of interconnections. In Figure R-9, note that several pathways exist between the Los Angeles and New York offices. While this mesh network provides redundant pathways to compensate for traffic loads or downed lines, there is usually one pathway that is preferred over another for cost, speed, or congestion-avoidance reasons. It is the job of the routing protocols to

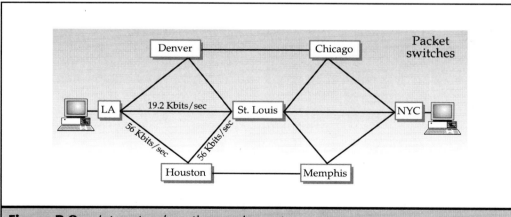

Figure R-9.   *Internetwork routing requirements*

provide routers with the information they need to create optimal pathways through mesh networks based on routing information that routers share with one another.

When a computer sends a packet out over the network, each layer in its protocol stack attaches some information to the packet. Protocols in peer layers on the destination system can read this information. The information affects some portion of the communication session. Protocols in the Network layer attach routing information. This might be the complete path through a network, or some priority value that indicates which path the packet should take. Network layer information added by the sender can only be read by Network layer protocols in routers or the destination systems. Repeaters and bridges do not have the ability to read Network layer information, and so can only repeat or relay a packet.

Routing Algorithms

A router device might have two or more ports on which it can send packets. It must have a *forwarding table* that indicates which port a particular address is located on. Early routers did not exchange information about routes on the network with other routers. Therefore, a router usually sent packets along every path, flooding the network, and sending some packets into endless loops on the network.

To avoid these problems, routers can rely on humans to program routing pathways into the device. This is called *static routing*. A better method, called *dynamic routing*, relies on the router to collect information about the network and build routing tables on its own. Routers exchange routing tables with one another, and each router merges the routing information to create new updated routing tables. Information obtained from other routers provides information about the number of hops or costs associated with pathways to destinations on the network. Over time, the routing tables in each routing device should contain roughly the same routing information.

On wide-area networks that use telecommunication links, integrated routing is essential, but must be quick to adjust to new topologies, since telecommunication links may change rapidly (for example, lines may break). A typical internetwork might consist of 2, 10, or even 50 routers, and these routers might connect with each other over dialup asynchronous links or high-speed dedicated digital links (such as T1). As packets of data travel the network, they arrive at routers and routers look inside packets, view the destination address, and send the packets to the destination along the best or most appropriate route. This route depends on the type of routing algorithm used.

There are basically two categories of routing protocols: distance-vector and link-state, as discussed in the next sections.

Distance-Vector Routing Protocols

Distance-vector routing protocols route packets based on decisions about the number of hops or the cost to the destination. This information is provided by neighboring routers. The technique generally follows the Bellman-Ford algorithm.

A router with a number of ports such as that pictured in Figure R-10 has a cost assigned to each of its ports. These costs are assigned by the network administrator as a value that represents how much it actually costs to use a line, or as a way to indicate preference for one line over another. In addition, neighboring routers inform routers of their costs to get a packet to the destination. The router adds these port costs to the cost of neighboring routers, as listed in the following examples.

Port 1 cost 10 + neighbor cost 17 = 27
Port 2 cost 20 + neighbor cost 5 = 25
Port 3 cost 30 + neighbor cost 7 = 37

In this case, the router would send the packet through port 2 because it represents the least cost to the destination. The neighboring router attached to port 2 will then calculate additional pathways through other routers if necessary.

Information about routes such as the address of the next hop is stored in tables, and routers exchange tables with other routers approximately every 30 seconds. Initially, each network knows about the routers it is directly connected to. When a router gets a table, it compares entries in the table with those in its own table. From

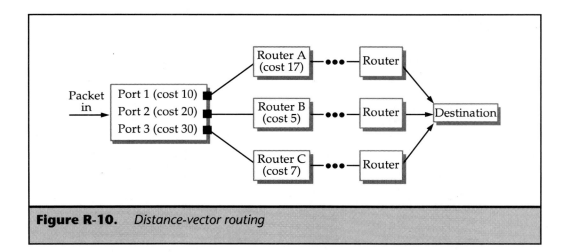

Figure R-10. *Distance-vector routing*

this information, it updates its table with new routes or deleted routes. Information in this table includes:

- Network number
- Port number
- Cost metric
- Address of next hop

The cost metric is the value that allows the router to determine which route to use when forwarding packets to the next router in the network. Common distance-vector routing protocols are the following:

- *Routing Information Protocol (RIP)* is a distance-vector routing protocol that was first implemented in the Xerox Network System (XNS) and subsequently implemented in Novell NetWare.
- *Interior Gateway Routing Protocol (IGRP)* is a distance-vector routing protocol developed by Cisco.
- *Routing Table Maintenance Protocol (RTMP)* is an Apple protocol that finds the best path between AppleTalk zones. Broadcasts occur every 10 seconds.

Distance-vector routing is not suitable for large networks that have hundreds of routers or networks that are constantly updated. On large networks, the table update process can take so long that tables in the farthest routers may fall out of synchronization with other tables. Link-state routing protocols are preferable in these situations. In addition, link-state protocols provide features that can isolate confidential packet information to specific areas for security reasons or avoid congestion areas which are common on networks with computer-aided design (CAD) or multimedia traffic. In addition, routing table information is only exchanged when necessary, not on a regular basis, thus cutting down on network traffic.

Link-State Routing Protocols

Link-state routing requires more processing power than distance-vector routing, but provides more control over the routing process and responds faster to changes. Routes can be based on the avoidance of congested areas, the speed of a line, the cost of using a line, or various priorities. The Dijkstra algorithm is used to calculate routes, based on the following:

- Number of routers the packet must go through to get to its destination. These are called hops and the fewer hops the better.
- The speed of transmission lines between LANs. Some routes use slow asynchronous connections while other are high-speed digital connections.

- Delays caused by traffic congestion. If a workstation is transmitting a large file, a router might send packets along a different route to avoid congestion.

- Cost of the route, which is a metric defined by an administrator, usually based on the transmission medium. The cheapest route might not be the fastest, but is preferable for some types of traffic.

The most common link-state routing protocol is the Open Shortest Path First (OSPF), but the OSI intermediate system-to-intermediate system (IS-IS) is similar. OSPF was originally developed by Proteon and is derived from an early version of the OSI IS-IS. OSPF is used to route IP traffic on the Internet and TCP/IP networks. IS-IS can route both IP traffic and OSI traffic.

OSPF routing table updates only take place when necessary, rather than at regular intervals. This significantly reduces traffic and saves network bandwidth. Paths through the network are selected based on the criteria listed above. A network administrator can program paths through the network, based on the type of traffic. For example, a path that uses more hops through the network might be preferable if

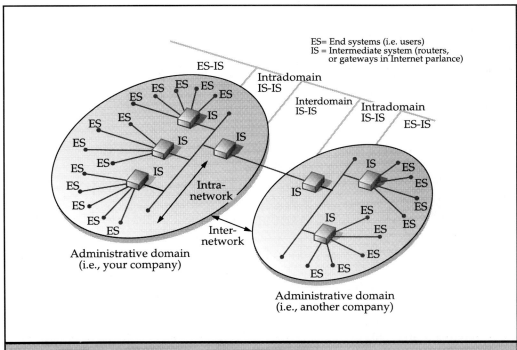

Figure R-11. *Autonomous environments*

the lines have higher transmission rates. Alternatively, a path might be programmed for less significant traffic because the lines are low-speed and low-cost.

Autonomous Environments

Internet routing (TCP/IP) and OSI routing use the concept of an Autonomous System (AS) or Administrative Domain (AD), which can simply be referred to as "domains." A domain is a collection of hosts and routers that use the same routing protocol and are administered by a single authority as pictured in Figure R-11. In other words, a domain might be an internetwork administered by a university or other organization. For example, the Internet is a set of linked autonomous systems consisting of educational institutions, government organizations, and companies.

Each of these organizations has its own *interior* networks connected to other Internet networks through *external gateways.* (Note that the Internet previously referred to routers as gateways, but now refers to them as routers.) The Internet has *Interior Gateway Protocols* and *Exterior Gateway Protocols.* OSI protocols also use the concepts of autonomous systems, but routing within a domain is called *intradomain routing.* Any routing between domains is called *interdomain routing.*

The reason for these different protocols and the division of domains is that it is not practical for all routers to keep track of every other system in the network. There are millions of addresses on the Internet! Routing information is organized in this hierarchical form so each routing device only needs to keep enough information to guide packets to the next most important router.

Interior/Intradomain Protocols

A number of Interior Gateway Protocols exist and several are commonly used on the Internet. These protocols are discussed under "Routing, AppleTalk," "Routing, Internet," and "Routing, OSI."

- *Address Resolution Protocol* is an Internet (TCP/IP) protocol that provides a way for interior routers to forward datagrams.

- *Routing Information Protocol (RIP)* is a distance-vector routing protocol.

- *Open Shortest Path First (OSPF)* is a link-state routing protocol that is superior to RIP. OSPF is the common Interior Gateway Protocol for the Internet, but the OSI IS-IS protocol is also used.

- *End System-to-Intermediate System (ES-IS)* is an OSI discovery protocol that helps end systems (i.e., users' computers) locate routers and provides a way for routers to announce their existence to end systems.

- *Intermediate System-to-Intermediate System (IS-IS)* is an OSI routing protocol that dynamically routes packets between routers within an intradomain. IS-IS is a link-state protocol.

■ *Interior Gateway Routing Protocol (IGRP)* is a distance-vector routing protocol developed by Cisco.

Exterior/Interdomain Protocols

At the edges of autonomous domains are routers (previously called gateways on the Internet). These routers exchange information with other routers using exterior protocols or Exterior Gateway Protocols (EGPs) in Internet terminology.

■ *Exterior Gateway Protocol (EGP)* is the original interdomain routing protocol for the Internet. It is being replaced by the newer Border Gateway Protocol (BGP). Routers supporting EGP must also support BGP.

■ *Border Gateway Protocol (BGP)* provides information about the reachability of neighbors. BGP reduces bandwidth requirements because routing information is exchanged incrementally, rather than by sending the routing database between routers. It also provides policy-based algorithms that give network managers more control over routing, such as the ability to prioritize some traffic.

■ *Inter-Domain Routing Protocol (IDRP)* is an OSI routing protocol that routes OSI connectionless packets (CLNP). IDRP contains policy routing features, but it probably won't replace BGP on the Internet. Support may be added for IP, thus providing a way to route both IP and CLNP over an interdomain with one protocol.

RELATED ENTRIES Carrier Services; Layered Architecture; Networks; Open Systems Interconnection Model; Packets; Protocols, Communication; Protocol Stack; Routing, AppleTalk; Routing, IBM; Routing, Internet; Routing, NetWare; Routing, OSI; Routing Information Protocol; Routing Protocols; *and* Wide Area Networks

RSA Data Security

RSA Data Security, Inc. in Redwood City, California is a company that was formed by the inventors of public key cryptography (Rivest, Shamir, and Adleman) to develop and refine the technique. The company acts as a certification authority on the Internet and can provide organizations with more information about certification, public key cryptography, and other security matters. RSA's authentication and encryption methods are widely used throughout the industry. RSA can be reached at 415/595-8782.

Products implementing RSA public key cryptography and digital signatures began to appear in 1994. For example, National Semiconductor announced a "token" card that fits into the PCMCIA slot of a portable computer. It holds the user's private key and lets him or her operate in secure mode on the computer that the card is currently plugged into. With the card, users can decode private E-mail messages, create digital signatures on outgoing documents, and authenticate themselves on other systems.

RELATED ENTRIES Digital Signatures; Key Encryption Technology; *and* Security

Satellite Telecommunication

Satellite communication systems transmit signals from earth-based transceivers (**trans**mitter/re**ceiver**) to space satellites as pictured in Figure S-1. The satellites are placed in geostationary orbits 22,300 miles above the earth. In this orbit, the satellite can synchronize with the earth's rotation and stay above one location. Ground station antennas are then aimed at the satellite and multiplexed signals containing hundreds of channels are transmitted over microwave beams to and from the satellite.

Transmissions to satellites are called *uplinks* and transmissions to ground stations are called *downlinks*. There are three frequency ranges:

- *C band*   The uplink frequencies in the C band range are in the 6 GHz range. Downlink frequencies in the C band range are in the 4 GHz range.

- *Ku band*   Uplink frequencies are in the 14 GHz range. Downlink frequencies are in the 11 GHz range.

- *Ka band*   Uplink frequencies are in the 30 GHz range and downlink frequencies are in the 20 GHz range. These frequencies are subject to attenuation caused by rain, however, earth station antennas are smaller and cheaper for the higher-frequency bandwidths.

Satellites are used for telephone, television, and data transmissions. A typical application is to provide alternate communication channels to back up primary channels in the event of a terrestrial line failure. However, a signal delay of 0.25 second occurs due to the distance the signal must travel. This delay can cause problems in some time-critical computer data transmissions. Another factor to consider is security. Signal transmissions to earth can be monitored.

Ground-based stations include the following equipment:

- Multiplexers that transmit multiple voice and data signals simultaneously

- Transceiver equipment to send and receive signals

- Radio frequency (RF) modulation and demodulation equipment

- Parabolic ground-based antennas

Antennas range in size from 3 feet to 33 feet in diameter. An antenna's size depends on the requirements for transmission. Very Small Aperture Terminals (VSAT) handle transmission rates as high as 56 Kbits/sec and are relatively inexpensive.

RELATED ENTRIES   Networks; Telecommunications; *and* Wide Area Networks

Scalable Performance Architecture (SPARC), Sun Microsystems, Inc.

Sun's SPARC processors are based on a Reduced Instruction Set Computer (RISC) architectural design that provides scalability from desktop systems to supercomputer

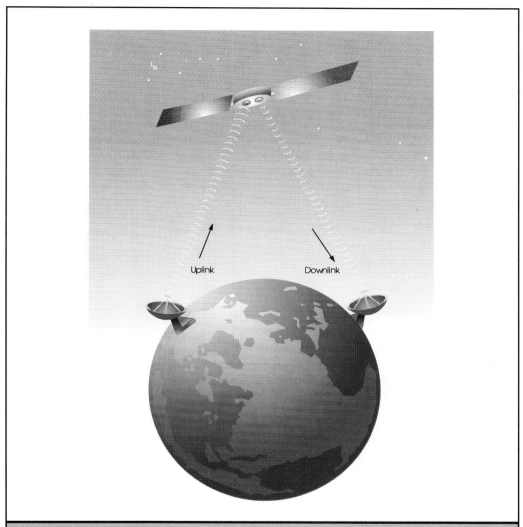

Figure S-1.   *Satellite communication links*

systems. The processors are developed in conjunction with Texas Instruments and/or Intergraph.

■ The *microSPARC* line is designed for desktop use. It is evolving into a powerful low-voltage chip for portable systems.

- The *superSPARC* line is designed for high-end desktop and server usage and has a 32-bit design with clock speeds of from 40 MHz to 90 MHz. The 50 MHz version is said to perform at 135 to 1,000 millions of instructions per second (MIPS).

- The *ultraSPARC* is a high-end 64-bit processor under development that will have clock speeds of up to 500 MHz. UltraSPARC will succeed SuperSPARC. UltraSPARC was designed in collaboration with Intergraph.

While the SPARC processor was originally designed for high-priced workstations, it has evolved in two directions to support low-cost desktop systems and high-end engineering/scientific workstation and server systems. SPARC International is a consortium of vendors that was created to promote the SPARC environment through hardware and software development.

RELATED ENTRY   Sun Microsystems, Inc.

Securing Data

See Data Protection; Security.

Security

In the distributed computing, enterprise environment, security has become an increasingly important issue. Data resources are no longer located in centralized locations where both physical and software-oriented security mechanisms can protect against unauthorized access. Lack of centralized management makes data more vulnerable to the following:

- Unauthorized monitoring of transmitted data

- The modification of information

- The masquerading of a user by an unauthorized user

- Repudiation, in which a sender of a message denies having sent the message

Key encryption techniques are used to make information confidential. A key is a software algorithm or hardware device that encrypts and locks information. Only the same key, or an associated key, can decrypt the information. For example, consider the process of sending confidential data to another user over a telephone link. Encryption techniques can be used to make the data confidential, but if a key is used to encrypt the data, how do you get the key itself to the recipient so he or she can decrypt the message? Sending the key over the line would make it available to anyone monitoring the line. You could send the key over a different line or via an express delivery service, but can you be completely sure that the key made it to the user without interception? One method is to exchange keys in advance of any transmissions. A bank might do this with its branch offices. But what if you need to transmit a confidential message on a one-time basis to a recipient you don't know? Public key encryption technology provides a solution, as discussed in the next sections.

There are a number of techniques for providing security in distributed computing environments, as listed next:

- *Authentication services* These services identify users logging onto networks and provide proof of their authenticity to other devices on the network.

- *Authorization services* These services provide authenticated users with access to services on the network through access rights.

- *Confidentiality services* These services hide data from unauthorized access and assure sender and receiver that information has not been viewed.

- *Integrity services* These services provide assurance that messages are authentic and unaltered.

- *Nonrepudiation* These services can provide proof that a message was sent by the specified sender and prevents the sender from disowning the message.

The following sections describe the services listed above in more detail and discuss several industry standards for implementing them.

Authentication and Authorization

Authentication systems in the local area network environment are typically associated with logon procedures. A password known only to a user and linked to the user's network account verifies the authenticity of the user. In extreme situations, additional techniques are required to identify users, such as the identification of biological and physical characteristics (fingerprints and voiceprints)

Card authentication systems are common. Bank automatic teller machines (ATMs) use this method. A user first inserts a card that is encoded with account information, then the user enters a password or personal identification number (PIN) to provide additional verification.

Kerberos is an MIT-developed authentication system for distributed environments. It provides a way to authenticate clients and servers without transmitting information over the network that might compromise security.

Once a user has been authenticated onto a system, authorization provides that user with access to resources. Authorization takes the form of access control lists (ACLs) that are defined by network supervisors and administrators. An ACL grants users access to directories, files, objects, and/or resources on the network.

For related information, see "Access Control," "Authentication and Authorization," and "Kerberos Authentication."

Cryptographic Services

Cryptographic systems provide a way to transmit information across an untrusted communication system without disclosing the content of the information to those that might be monitoring the line. Cryptographic systems provide confidentiality and can also provide proof that a transmission has not been viewed or altered. However, the encryption system itself must be trusted. How can you be assured that the encryption method can't be broken? Does an unauthorized person hold the key to decipher your encrypted messages? Because of these unknowns, well-tested, publicly available, and documented encryption schemes are the most popular. There are symmetrical and asymmetrical encryption schemes, as discussed next.

Private (Symmetrical) Key Schemes

In the private key system, information is transformed using an algorithm based on a private key that is held by both the sender and the receiver of the message. The transformed message is unreadable and can be transmitted over untrusted systems. The recipient can decrypt the message using the private key he or she owns. The problem is getting a copy of the key to message recipients while ensuring that the key has not been compromised. To avoid manual distribution of keys and opportunities to compromise the system, public key methods can be used in combination with private key methods.

DATA ENCRYPTION STANDARD (DES)   The Data Encryption Standard (DES) is a private key encryption scheme developed by IBM in the 1970s and adopted by the National Bureau of Standards, which is now called the National Institute of Standards and Technology (NIST). DES, as a nationally published standard, has been exposed to many years of evaluation and "attack" and is considered stable. While DES suffered from lack of public confidence, it has shown no weaknesses to date. See "Data Encryption Standard."

KEY ESCROW   Recently, the government has been interested in developing "key escrow" techniques, in which the key for decrypting communication is held in trust by the government. The method breaks keys into parts and each part is given to a separate trustee. In this way, a key is only useful when it is reassembled by bringing the trustees together and getting them to hand over their part of the key. The U.S. Attorney General would supervise access to the keys and law enforcement agencies could get keys only with court orders.

CLIPPER CHIP   The Clipper chip uses an 80-bit key to encrypt both digitized voice and data and will be installed in data communication equipment owned by the government such as computers, modems, fax machines, and phones. The Clipper data encryption chip allows federal agencies and businesses to protect themselves from hackers, intruders, and criminals. It is a 12 Mbits/sec encryption coprocessor designed by Mykotronix (Torrance, California) and manufactured by VLSI (San Jose, California).

The packaging is tamper-resistant to prevent reverse-engineering. The chip was jointly developed by the National Security Agency (NSA) and the National Institute of Standards and Technology (NIST). The Clipper chip is highly controversial. While it uses an algorithm that is classified, questions remain as to whether it has been implemented in the right way, and whether the encryption algorithm has a "back-door" decryption technique known only to the designers.

Public (Asymmetrical) Key Schemes

The public key encryption scheme solves the problem of passing keys to message recipients. In fact, it allows any user to encrypt a message to any other person without any prior exchange. It is not even necessary for either party to know the other, be part of the same organization, or connected to the same network. All that is required is that both parties have access to a common server that manages public key security.

The public key system consists of two keys. Every user holds a private key and makes a public key available in a public location. When a user wants to send a confidential message to another user, he or she encrypts the message with the recipient's public key. The recipient then decrypts the message with his or her private key. Messages encrypted with a public key can only be decrypted with a private key.

The RSA public key encryption scheme is the established public key scheme. It was developed at MIT by Rivest, Shamir, and Adleman (thus the name), and ensures that information encrypted with a public key can only be decrypted with the private key. RSA Data Security, Inc. (Redwood City, California) is a company that was formed by the inventors of public key cryptography to develop and refine the technique. The company acts as a certification authority on the Internet and can provide organizations with more information about certification, public key cryptography, and other security matters. RSA's authentication and encryption methods are widely used throughout the industry. RSA can be reached at 415/595-8782.

Certification Systems

Certificates and certification servers provide a way to authenticate clients who wish to access servers in distributed environments without the need to authenticate users every time they access a secured service. The certificate procedure was first developed at the Massachusetts Institute of Technology and is implemented in the Kerberos security system. They are now defined in the CCITT X.509 security standard.

Consider a large network in which many users need to access applications and data on many servers. In this large environment, it is unrealistic to authenticate a user every time he or she attempts to access one of the servers. Keep in mind that we must keep passwords, even those that are encrypted, off the line where they might be intercepted by an intruder to gain access to the system. Certification provides a way to authenticate users one time, when they log onto the system, and then verify to other servers that the user is who he or she claims to be. This is the basis of a "trust relationship."

The verification comes from a trusted third-party, which is called the *certification server*. The certification server, the client, and the application server use a certification process that is best described by example.

Assume you need to view secret records at your company's New York office. You work in Chicago, and your manager, who can authorize access to the secret files, works in Toledo. You call the manager and request access to the files. The manager writes an authorized certificate that includes your name, your photograph, and other information that can positively identify you at the New York office. This information is locked in a box that a security manager at the New York office has a key to open. This box is then placed in another box and locked. You have a key to unlock this box. The box-within-a-box is then shipped to you. Any attempts to open the box inappropriately are detectable, so no one along the way can tamper with the contents without you or the security manager in New York knowing about it.

When you receive the box, you use your personal key to unlock it. You now have possession of the inner locked box that contains your access certificate and a photograph that positively identifies you. The key to open this box is in New York. When you arrive in New York, the security manager opens the box with a key that only the security manager and your manager have. The security manager verifies your identity with the photograph and authorizes you to access the files. If the box had been tampered with, the security manager would simply refuse access.

This tedious process is easily handled by computer systems. The actual computer process goes like this:

1. Initially, the certification server obtains "keys" from all clients and application servers, as well as logon passwords.

2. When you log on to the system, the certification server authenticates you by requesting an ID and password.

3. To access a server, you simply switch to it, but a background process requests a certificate from the certification server. The certification server packages a certificate to access the application server in a message that is encrypted with the application server's key. This encrypted message is then encrypted again with your public key. This process secures the transmission of the access certificate to you.

4. When your system receives the certification package, it is unlocked with your personal key. Your system is now in possession of the certificate that gives you access to a server. The certificate is passed to the application server, which decrypts it with its key.

5. The user is now authenticated for the application server based on the certificate and the session information it contains.

If security is compromised during the exchange of the certificate, the certificate becomes invalid. The process uses functions that can detect tampering. The above examples assume that all the systems are owned by one organization, but certification can also control access to interorganizational resources. For example, Internet users might gain U.S. government certification to access secure networks and systems. In another example, a company might give an outside accounting or auditing firm access to some of its servers.

An important point about certification is that some authority is authenticating a user. This authority is a certification server in the above example, but it might be a third-party organization or an agency of the government. The authority is responsible for issuing certificates that can verify users. Its also necessary to validate that the certifying authority is who they say they are. In this case, notary organization can mediate between a user and an organization.

Integrity Services and Digital Signatures

Digital signatures and message authentication codes (MACs) provide a way to authenticate the source of a message and be assured that the contents of the message has not been altered during transmission. A MAC is a mechanism that calculates a unique value on the contents of a message, similar to a checksum process. The sender and receiver should be able to run the same calculation and come up with the same value, otherwise the message is corrupted. The private key of the sender and receiver is used in the calculation to ensure security.

Digital signatures are possible when using public key encryption schemes. An algorithm is used to generate a hash value from information in part of the message. This value is then encrypted using the sender's private key to produce the digital signature. The recipient verifies the message by first running the same hash algorithm. The results of the hash algorithm are compared with the decrypted digital signature. The recipient uses the sender's public key to decrypt the signature.

Because the published public key is used to verify message authentication, digital signatures are more versatile than MAC schemes, which require that two parties first exchange private keys. However, either method provides sender and receiver with the ability to know whether a message has been changed in any way. This has tremendous benefits in business and other transactions. Assume you send a message to a broker to purchase stocks. The MAC or digital signature can assure the broker that the message is in fact from you and has not been altered in any way. The broker can retain the message as proof of your transaction. The message cannot be repudiated once received since the digital signature or MAC proves its origin. What's more, the broker can't change the message content in any way since alterations would show up in a later check of the digital signature or MAC.

Privacy Enhanced Mail (PEM)

PEM is an Internet standard that is designed to provide digital signatures for electronic mail. With such strong security, electronic messaging can be used on the Internet to conduct business transactions. Both private (symmetrical) and public (asymmetrical) encryption techniques can be used to add integrity and digital signatures to messages.

RELATED ENTRIES Authentication and Authorization; Cryptography; Data Encryption Standard; Digital Signatures; Distributed File Systems; Kerberos Authentication; *and* Key Encryption Technology

Security Rights

See Access Rights; Permissions in Windows NT; *and* Rights in Novell NetWare.

Segment, Network

It is possible to define network segments in several ways. In the Ethernet environment, a network segment is a linear trunk cable that is terminated at both ends. Signals broadcast on the segment are heard by all stations attached to it. If the segment is interconnected to another segment with a bridge or router, it is possible to send packets between those segments. Network segments joined with bridges or routers form internetworks. Each segment has its own internetwork address. A segment is often called a *subnetwork.*

In the Novell NetWare environment, each network interface adapter installed in a server forms its own network segment. A cable is attached to the adapter and workstations are attached to the cable, as pictured in Figure S-2. The operating system handles the bridging and routing of traffic between these network segments.

RELATED ENTRIES Bridging; Ethernet; NetWare; Networks; Routers; *and* Routing Protocols

Semaphore

A semaphore is a communication link between two or more processes running in a multitasking operating system such as OS/2. Unlike other interprocess communication mechanisms, semaphores do not pass data from one process to another. Instead, they serve as links for conveying control information between separately running processes, or individual threads of operation performed by the same process. The semaphore exists in random access memory (RAM) as a variable to communicate information to other processes.

Semaphores also communicate information about devices that are shared by multiple processes. A typical device is a port or a print queue. When a process needs to use a port or send a print job to a queue, it first checks the semaphore for that port or queue to check its status. The semaphore may indicate the port is in use or that the queue is full. Semaphores may contain values that are incremented or decremented. In the case of a queue, the value is incremented as print jobs are placed in the queue and decremented as the jobs are printed. A queue may have a limit on the number of jobs that can exist in the queue and the semaphore can indicate the current queue status to processes wanting to use it.

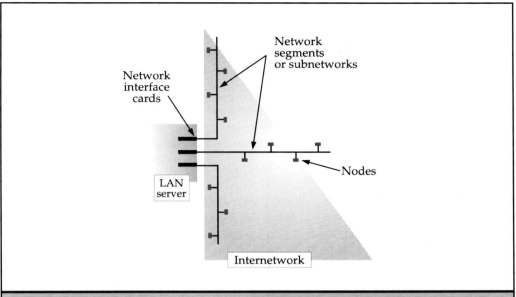

Figure S-2.   *A NetWare LAN, in which each interface card forms a LAN segment with its own internetwork address*

Sequenced Packet Exchange (SPX)

SPX is Novell's connection-oriented network communication protocol. SPX uses NetWare Internetwork Packet Exchange (IPX) to deliver messages, but SPX guarantees delivery and maintains the order of the message packet stream by maintaining a connection between communicating systems. NetWare programs that use SPX stay in contact with processes running elsewhere on the network, such as a remote printer or a server's monitoring functions.

In contrast, IPX is used to send a burst of traffic from one workstation to another or between a workstation and a server. IPX is a connectionless datagram service and a station using it simply sends packets addressed to a destination. It is the job of end stations to determine whether packets are out of sequence when received, or have been lost. IPX does not need to handle these types of error controls, and is more efficient than SPX. However, SPX is more efficient if the connection must be maintained over a period of time for the continuous transmission of a steady stream of packets.

RELATED ENTRIES   Connection-Oriented and Connectionless Protocols; Datagram Network Services; *and* Internetwork Packet Exchange

Serial Communication

Serial communication is the transmission of signals over a single channel or link, as opposed to parallel communication, which transmits multiple synchronized signals on multiple parallel lines. In serial communication, data bits are transmitted in succession, one after the other. The method is typically used to transmit a stream of bits between a computer and a peripheral like a modem. Unlike parallel signaling techniques, which can become unsynchronized over distances greater than 10 or 20 feet, serial lines can extend up to 50 feet.

A number of serial interface standards are defined in the Physical layer relative to the Open Systems Interconnection (OSI) protocol model. The interface specifications define signaling, cable types, connectors, and procedures. The Electronic Industries Association's (EIA's) RS-232 specification is one of the most popular serial interface standards, as are the Bell standards, the CCITT "V dot" standards, and proprietary high-speed interfaces such as *High-Speed Serial Interface (HSSI)*, a de facto industry standard developed by Cisco Systems that transmits at speeds of up to 52 Mbits/sec over cables of up to 50 feet in length. A comparison is shown in the following table.

Type	Pins	Maximum Cable Length	Maximum Signaling Rate
RS-232	25	50 feet	20 Kbits/sec
RS-449	37	4,000 feet	10 MBits/sec
X.21	15	N/A	1.92 MBits/sec
V.35	35	50 feet	4 MBits/sec
HSSI	50	50 feet	52 MBits/sec

NOTE: *The serial ports in many PCs are not capable of handling the transfer rates of the high-speed modem standards. To prevent data loss at high speeds, UARTs (Universal Asynchronous Receiver/Transmitter processor chips) with large buffers are required. The 16550 UART has a 16K buffer that can handle high-speed transmissions. Some serial cards have removable UARTs that can be upgraded; otherwise, you'll need to upgrade the serial card.*

RELATED ENTRIES   Asynchronous Communications; Electronic Industries Association; Modems; *and* Synchronous Communications

Serial Line Internet Protocol (SLIP)

Two schemes have been adopted by the Internet community to provide links over serial point-to-point lines into dialup routers: Serial Line Internet Protocol (SLIP) and Point-to-Point Protocol (PPP). SLIP supports the transmission of Internet Protocol (IP) datagrams encapsulated within its frames, while PPP supports IP, DECnet, Internetwork Packet Exchange (IPX), AppleTalk, and OSI CLNP (connectionless network protocol) over synchronous and asynchronous links. SLIP is the simpler of the two. PPP provides a way to assign an IP address automatically so that remote computers (for example, mobile users) can connect into the network at any point. Because of this last feature, PPP has been getting the most press lately, but SLIP is adequate for stationary remote systems that only transmit IP.

SLIP can provide connections between hosts, routers, and workstations over communication lines that support speeds up to 19.2 Kbits/sec. It supports asynchronous or synchronous transfers over dedicated or dialup lines and can transmit IP datagrams of up to 1,006 bytes in length. The same protocol is required at either side of the SLIP connection and there are no error-detection and -correction mechanisms in SLIP as this is usually handled by higher layers in the Transmission Control Protocol/Internet Protocol (TCP/IP) protocol. Since SLIP operates over point-to-point connections in which only one system is connected on either side, addressing or other identification techniques are not required. SLIP simply frames data and transmits it. Compression is not supported.

RELATED ENTRIES   Asynchronous Communications; Internet Protocol; Point-to-Point Protocol; Serial Communication; *and* Synchronous Communications

Server Message Block (SMB)

SMB is a high-level, Presentation-layer protocol that sits above NetBIOS and NetBEUI protocols on Microsoft Windows for Workgroups and Windows NT networks. The SMB protocol defines the formatting of messages to be sent across the network between communicating systems. The NetBIOS interface passes the SMB input/output (I/O) requests. Networks that implement the SMB protocol can provide peer-to-peer services and are compatible with Microsoft MS-NET and Microsoft LAN Manager.

RELATED ENTRY   NetBIOS / NetBEUI

Servers, Network

A file server provides the core functions for providing services to network users and providing management functions for network administrators. Some of the functions are listed here:

- Storage of operating system program modules, utilities, and commands
- Storage of user programs and data
- Management functions for the file system
- Management functions for security and user access
- Network monitoring and management components
- Data protection functions for reliability, such as disk mirroring, UPS monitoring, and backup

However, it may not be possible to support all users with services provided by one server. Dedicated servers that handle specific tasks such as those discussed in the following section may be necessary.

COMMUNICATION SERVERS   A communication server manages connections between nodes on a network and remote sites, or manages connections to mainframe computers. It provides communication services for users on a network who need to transfer files or access information on systems or networks at remote locations over telecommunication links. The server typically provides a limited number of outgoing or incoming sessions and may provide gateway services such as the translation between data formats, communication protocols, and cable signals. A bank of asynchronous modems attached to the server can provide dial-out or dial-in capabilities for users. Communication servers may also provide electronic mail services that automatically connect with other LANs or electronic "post offices" to pick up and deliver E-mail.

BACKUP AND ARCHIVE SERVERS   Backup and archive servers run file backup and archiving programs that can service an entire network. To accommodate these backup requirements, new tape drives and optical storage techniques are emerging that can handle gigabytes of information. Data compression and technology advancements are making this possible. Hierarchical storage systems provide methods for moving little-used data from fast-access magnetic media to high-capacity archiving devices where it can remain on line for future access if necessary.

■ An *online* storage device is a high-performance magnetic disk that stores information users access most often. *Offline* storage devices are slower, secondary units that provide backup services or archiving services.

■ *Hierarchical file systems* move little-used files or large imaged files from online storage to near-line storage systems such as optical disk where they are available on request.

■ *Tape backup systems* are the traditional backup medium while *optical disk systems* provide archiving and near-line storage requirements for imaged files.

APPLICATION SERVER   Application servers provide a central storage and access point for applications, simplifying management. It is easier for an administrator to configure user access rights and apply application updates when applications are located on one system. The application server can perform some of the application processing itself, or simply provide program access for users. In the client-server environment, both front-end and back-end systems perform processing. Applications that require intensive computing cycles benefit from high-performance servers.

DATABASE SERVERS   A database server stores structured data or object-oriented information that users access, typically following client-server database access methods. The front-end client and the back-end database split the processing load and users access data with commands that conform to Structured Query Language (SQL) standards. The database server itself is usually a high-performance machine that performs much of the processing on the data. For example, the client might request a block of sorted records that match a specific criteria. The server performs the sorting and filtering tasks, then sends the client the results. A database server is a central repository for information that many users access. In fact, most of the database architectures and query languages (SQLs) used to access the database management system on a database server have roots in the mainframe world. See "Client-Server Computing," "Database Management System," "Distributed Database," and "Structured Query Language."

ELECTRONIC MAIL SERVER   Electronic mail systems use E-mail servers that manage message traffic and mail boxes for users, along with translation facilities or gateways that allow message exchange between different types of E-mail systems. Front-end applications provide facilities for creating, addressing, sending, receiving, and forwarding messages to the E-mail server over the network. A directory service can provide user and resource location services. Additional features may include the ability to secure messages with encryption, or add digital signatures to prove the authenticity of messages and prevent undetected alterations. The ability to send and receive facsimiles is another feature included with many systems.

FAX SERVERS   Fax servers manage incoming and outgoing faxes for network users. Users can send faxes from their desktop to the fax server, which forwards them over a telephone system, or even to another user on the network. Fax servers are shared devices that provide an economical and easy way for many users to take advantage of facsimile transmissions. Fax servers can also provide inbound services that allow operators to monitor incoming faxes and route them to appropriate users over the local area network, or discard those that are not essential. An alternative is automatic inbound routing, in which users are assigned an individual fax number linked to their E-mail address. The fax then goes directly into their E-mail box.

PRINT SERVERS   A print server provides user access to printers attached to the network and manages print jobs through a print queue system. This print server can usually be installed in a file server or in a dedicated server.

DIRECTORY SERVICES SERVER   Distributed directory services provide a way for users to look up information about users and resources on the network. A directory services server keeps track of all network users, servers, and resources on an internetwork. This information is kept in a database. Administrators and users can access the database to locate users and resources, without regard for their location. A dedicated directory services server is usually only required in large network installations where databases are partitioned and frequently updated and replicated to remote sites. See "Directory Services," "Partition Management," and "Replication."

S

Service Access Point

Applications running in network attached computers rely on underlying communication subsystems to access the network and communicate with other computers on the network. The seven layer Open Systems Interconnection (OSI) protocol stack defines the communication subsystem in seven layers, each of which handles part of the communication task. The links or interfaces between each of these subsystems for a particular application process are called its service access points (SAPs). Because a computer can run several application processes simultaneously, the interfaces between each protocol layer may have more than one SAP at a time, but SAPs are linked up through the protocol stack to an application process. SAPs collectively form an address through which application processes on other network computers communicate with one another.

RELATED ENTRIES   Layered Architecture; Open Systems Interconnection Model; *and* Protocol Stack

Service Advertising Protocol (SAP)

The Service Advertising Protocol (SAP) is used by NetWare servers, print servers, gateways, and other service providers on a NetWare network to advertise their services. Workstations look at SAP messages to locate servers to attach to. A SAP broadcast normally occurs every 60 seconds and includes the name, network address, and type of service provided by a server.

SAP traffic is usually excessive on large networks and can flood a wide area network (WAN) with unnecessary traffic that drives up WAN costs. With SAP filtering, you can reduce the amount of network traffic generated by SAP, hide servers by filtering their SAP packets, and reduce or eliminate SAP traffic from rarely used servers. Network security can be improved by filtering SAP traffic, and you can prevent users from seeing servers they don't use, thus reducing network traffic. SAP filtering can also restrict traffic to local LAN segments and keep it off of remote segments that don't need to see the SAP packets.

RELATED ENTRY   Internetwork Packet Exchange

Session Layer, OSI Model

The Open Systems Interconnection (OSI) model is a standard defined by the International Organization for Standardization (ISO). It defines a layered architecture that categorizes and defines the protocols for communication between end systems. During the communication session, processes running in each layer on each computer communicate with one another. While there are several layers, we can categorize them into three broad layers:

■ The bottom layer defines the actual physical components such as connectors and cable and how data is exchanged between systems. The type of network interface and the access method are also defined here.

■ The transport layers are concerned with the reliable transmission of data between systems.

■ The application layers provide the interface between user applications and the network communication systems.

The OSI model was designed to help developers create applications that are compatible across multivendor product lines, and to promote open, interoperable networking systems. While OSI hasn't caught on as planned, its model is still used to describe and define how various vendors' products communicate. Common protocol stacks that are related to OSI include IBM's Systems Network Architecture (SNA), DEC's DEC Network Architecture (DNA), and Apple Computer's AppleTalk. Communication protocols that can be matched to layers of the stack, but are not part of any specific architectural plan, are Transmission Control Protocol/Internet Protocol (TCP/IP), Microsoft NetBIOS/NetBEUI, and Novell Sequenced Packet Exchange/Internetwork Packet Exchange (SPX/IPX) among others. These protocol stacks are compared to the OSI stack under the "Open Systems Interconnection (OSI)" heading.

The Session layer provides a way for applications to hold dialogs with one another so they can control a communication session. For example, one application might have a need to periodically stop a transmission and perform some action on the data it has received. Session-level controls are commonly used, so it makes sense to create a generic set of controls as a subsystem in the protocol stack that applications can access. The most common services provided by the Session layer are listed here:

■ Control of a full-duplex or half-duplex data exchange dialog

■ The establishment of data synchronization points, in which a block of data has a beginning and end point that can facilitate a retransmission of the block if necessary, such as when a line fails and is reestablished

■ The ability to recover from a failed line, retransmitting data that was incompletely transmitted

Note that the last two points work together. By transmitting data in definable blocks, both stations can coordinate the reestablishment of a down connection and the retransmission of blocks that were in transit during the failure.

RELATED ENTRIES   Layered Architecture; Open Systems Interconnection Model; *and* Protocol Stack

Shortest Path First Routing

Shortest path first routing (or Open Shortest Path First [OPSF]) is a router technique used to learn about pathways on a router-connected internetwork. Routers learn about paths by periodically flooding the network with *link-state* information. Link-state information describes the current links connected to a router. The link-state information also describes important information such as a value that represents the cost of a link. Other routers collect this information and build routing tables that use best paths based on the link costs or other information. Because the information is periodically broadcast over the network, routers can continually adjust their routing tables and choose the optimal shortest path for packet transmission.

RELATED ENTRY   Routing Protocols

Signals, Analog and Digital

An *analog signal* is a form of propagated energy, such as a sound wave that vibrates the air it travels through. Sound waves are measured by the frequency in cycles per second, or hertz (Hz). One hertz is one cycle per second. The majority of voice telephone service to homes currently uses analog technology.

Digital signals are transmitted over media by representing the binary digits as electrical pulses. Figure S-3 depicts the digital signal at the top and its analog equivalent underneath. The voltage of the line is varied between a high state and a low state. Thus binary 1 is transmitted by applying a positive voltage, and binary 0 is transmitted by applying a negative voltage.

As signals travel long distances, some degradation occurs. Analog signals are periodically amplified, but any distortions in the signal are also amplified. In contrast, digital transmissions can provide more reliability. Digital signals are periodically regenerated, which removes distortions.

RELATED ENTRIES   Analog Signals; Analog-to-Digital Conversion; *and* Transmission Media, Methods, and Equipment

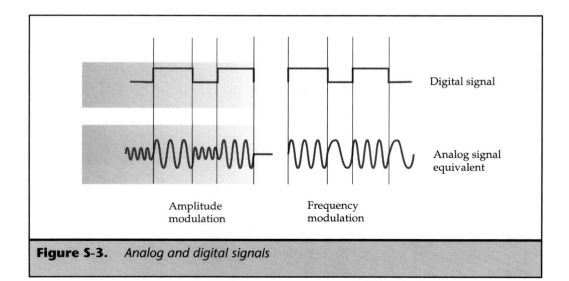

Figure S-3.   *Analog and digital signals*

Simple Mail Transfer Protocol (SMTP)

SMTP is the electronic mail transfer protocol used on the Internet, on UNIX systems, and on and Transmission Control Protocol/Internet Protocol (TCP/IP) networks. The protocol provides a store-and-forward mail capability between host computer mail systems on the network. SMTP works in conjunction with a user's mail program. It is responsible for:

- Sending mail created by users (with their mail program) to another computer
- Receiving mail from other computers on the network and passing it over to the local user's mail program

S

This relationship is pictured in Figure S-4. The SMTP protocol running in each computer provides both a client and server function. The client function takes mail messages placed in the local mailbox outgoing queue and sets up a transfer session with the destination computer. The server portion receives mail from other computers and places it in the incoming mail queue, where the user can read the mail at his or her discretion. Mailboxes hold mail until intentionally deleted, which is usually done after reading a message.

The SMTP protocol defines the control messages used by two computers to exchange electronic mail messages. Controls include verification of proper connection, identification of sender, negotiation of transmission parameters, and message transmission. The messages are composed of ASCII (American Standard Code for Information Interchange) text characters, and users create them using any SMTP-compatible mail application. The functions of the applications are not defined by SMTP because SMTP is involved only in the receipt and delivery of messages. However, mail applications that use SMTP can provide common functions such as the ability to review message contents, print messages, and forward messages to other users. "Address book" features and the ability to send messages to groups of users are other common features.

When a user is creating a mail message, another TCP/IP service is used to address the message. The Domain Naming Service is an Internet and TCP/IP service that maps network address numbers, for example 191.31.140.115, to an easy-to-remember name, such as tbones.acme.com. The name is inserted in the header of a message, along with other information, such as the names of other users to send copies to, subject, and date information. The actual transfer of mail involves a series of SMTP commands between sender and receiver. The sending system basically requests authorization to send mail and the receiving system acknowledges that it is ready to receive.

SMTP will work with other types of mail systems, assuming that an appropriate mail gateway is present to translate the messages and forward the mail to an appropriate address. The Internet community is working on a new mail standard called *Multipurpose Internet Mail Extension (MIME)*. MIME is a compound document messaging standard that lets users exchange multimedia E-mail messages with

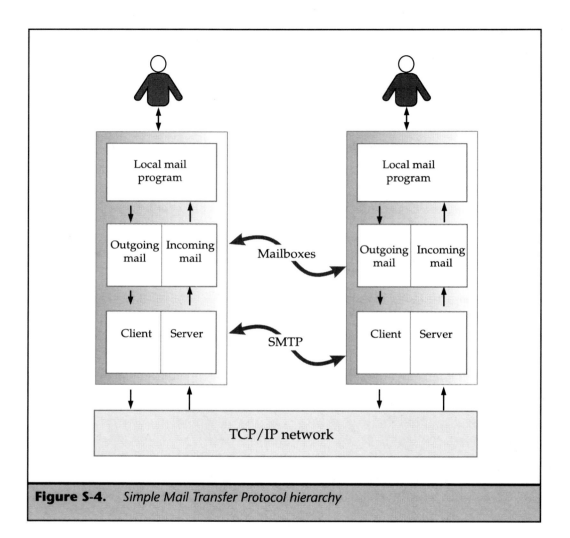

Figure S-4. *Simple Mail Transfer Protocol hierarchy*

attached audio clips, video clips, graphic images, and text. *Richtext* information can also be incorporated into messages, which define the fonts, formats, and layout features of a document so the document can be easily redisplayed on many different types of systems.

RELATED ENTRIES Document Interchange Standards; Electronic Mail; Internet; *and* Multipurpose Internet Mail Extension

Simple Network Management Protocol (SNMP)

SNMP is currently the most commonly implemented management environment protocol. It operates over the User Datagram Protocol (UDP), which is part of the Transmission Control Protocol/Internet Protocol (TCP/IP) protocol suite. The latest version supports other environments as well. Almost every network device manufacturer has implemented SNMP support. SNMP is a common communication protocol for collecting management information from devices on the network. This information is collected by agents in the devices and recorded in a management information base (MIB). The type of information that is collected reports on the features of a device, data throughput, traffic overloads, and errors. A MIB has a common format, so SNMP management utilities from a number of vendors can collect the MIB information and present it to the system administrator at the management console.

Despite its popularity, SNMP is somewhat limited in functionality. The standard was available without license when users began to demand network management facilities in the products they purchased from vendors. Other management techniques are emerging, but SNMP and vendors are adding proprietary improvements to SNMP. The Common Management Information Protocol (CMIP) is an OSI-developed management solution that is superior to SNMP in many ways, but the popularity of SNMP has held up its acceptance.

The leading SNMP network management systems are IBM's NetView 6000, Hewlett-Packard's OpenView, and SunConnect's SunNet Manager. NetView is actually an enhanced version of OpenView, so both products are very similar. IBM signed a licensing agreement with Hewlett-Packard and immediately developed an enhanced version.

SNMP Features

The key to SNMP popularity is its simplicity. It has a small command set that does a good job of collecting information from almost any network device. In an SNMP environment, most of the work is handled by the network management system. Devices that are being managed are not burdened with processing overhead that might affect their performance. A typical SNMP environment is pictured in Figure S-5, and the components in the environment are described next.

- *Managed devices* Managed devices on the network contain *agents* that collect information and provide it to the management console by way of the SNMP protocol.
- *Management console* The management console collects information from agents located in devices on the network into a management information base (MIB).

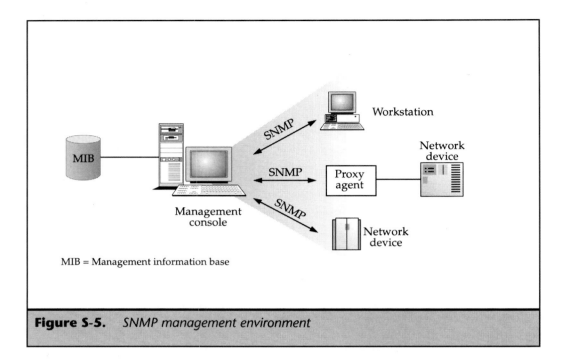

Figure S-5.   *SNMP management environment*

■ *SNMP*   This protocol queries agents in managed devices and passes
information to the management console.

■ *Proxy agent*   Some devices do not have the capability of running an agent. A
proxy agent is a device that can run an agent for such a device and provide it
with SNMP functions.

SNMP uses a request and response process in which the management console
requests information from agents in managed devices. SNMP is essentially a
connectionless transport protocol with a simple command set that accesses agents to
get values and change the status of network elements. In this respect, SNMP is
efficient and can even operate over networks that are overloaded and failing. Agents
do little work of their own, except to monitor significant events that occur within the
device. For example, the agent records errors or packet overflows. It might also record
when various thresholds have been exceeded.

The information is collected by the management console in the MIB. The MIB is
the focus of the management structure. Devices and resources on the network are
represented by *managed objects* within the MIB. A managed object is a logical
representation of a real physical entity on the network, and it has a name, as well as
attributes and properties. A *Remote Monitor (RMON)* is a remote MIB that allows
SNMP to monitor remote devices. Typical managed objects include hardware

equipment such as bridges, routers, computers, servers, switches, and multiplexers. The managed object has properties that hold values, such as the address of a node, the serial number of a computer, routing table information, and error counters.

The SNMP management console provides the user interface to the management system and its information. The management console software typically runs on a UNIX or VMS system in the X Window environment, although Microsoft Windows consoles are available. Most SNMP management systems can automatically discover the topology of the network and display that topology in graphic form. Managers can then select icons that represent components on the network to display identification and statistical information about the components. Common management console functions are listed here:

- Network topology mapping
- Event trapping with alarms
- Traffic monitoring
- Network diagnostic functions
- Report generators
- Historical record management and trend analysis

SNMP is commonly used to manage hubs and structured wiring systems. Many hubs include management modules that can run programs to track data packets and errors and store this information in a MIB. The information is useful for tracking trends, troubleshooting problems, and pinpointing congestion problems. Alarms can alert administrators when various thresholds are met that might pose problems. For example, alerts can warn the administrator when network traffic exceeds a level so he or she can take corrective actions, such as segmenting the LAN or moving a high-volume user to a dedicated segment. The management features in a hub can also provide the following services:

- Automatically disconnect problem nodes that are disrupting the network
- Provide a way to isolate ports for testing purposes
- Connect and disconnect workstations based on the time or day of the week
- Protocol analysis tools that monitor network traffic
- Offsite management of network components at remote locations

SNMP is extensible. Vendors can include features in the MIB to fit the particular devices they manufacture. Management consoles can then display information about those devices. In 1992, SNMP was improved to include support for AppleTalk, Novell Internetwork Packet Exchange (IPX), and the Open Systems Interconnection (OSI) protocols. Other improvements were made in the area of data transfer, error handling, and management features.

Common management systems supporting SNMP and discussed elsewhere in this book include *DECmcc* from DEC, *OpenView Management System* from Hewlett-Packard, *SunNet Manager* from Sun Microsystems, Inc., and *NetView* or *SystemView* from IBM.

RELATED ENTRY   Management Standards and Tools

Small Computer System Interface (SCSI)

SCSI (pronounced "scuzzy") is a peripheral interface for connecting up to seven devices, such as hard drives, tape drives, and compact disc, read-only memory (CD-ROM) drives to a single "host" adapter that plugs into desktop computers and server systems. The host adapter provides a shared bus that attached peripherals use to pass data to and from the host system. SCSI is quite popular due to its high throughput and flexible design. It is available for Industry Standard Architecture (ISA), Extended ISA (EISA), MicroChannel Architecture (MCA), and proprietary bus standards. SCSI supports high data-transfer rates and is usually the disk drive interface of choice in high-performance systems and superservers. Devices attach to the SCSI host adapter in a daisy-chain configuration in which each successive device connects to the back of the previous device.

The SCSI host adapter provides bus services (connection points) for intelligent devices. Intelligent devices are disk drives, optical disks, and tape backup systems that have their own control circuitry. In other systems, control circuitry is mounted on the adapter itself. The SCSI adapter monitors the data throughput and commands between the system and the SCSI devices. Each device handles only the requests assigned to it. Because the control circuitry is built into each SCSI device, configuration and compatibility issues are minimized. Theoretically, you can plug any SCSI device into any SCSI controller; however, this has not proved to always be the case, so it is best to check compatibility before buying.

Another important feature of SCSI is the ability of each device attached to the host adapter to logically disconnect from the adapter and perform processing on its own. In other words, the host adapter simply sends commands to devices and those devices perform disk reads and writes on their own, simultaneously. While one disk is transferring data through the host adapter, another can be seeking or writing data under the control of its own built-in circuitry.

The initial SCSI standard has a throughput rate of 1.5 and 5 Mbytes/sec. A SCSI-II standard was announced in 1991. It can accommodate a 16-bit or 32-bit bus and has transfer rates of 10 Mbytes/sec for the 16-bit bus and up to 40 Mbytes/sec for the 32-bit bus. The standard also includes an elevator-seeking algorithm in which it can reorder requests for disk blocks in the order that they are most easily accessed from the drive. A SCSI-III standard is in the works that may support such features as Fibre Channel connections with transfer rates of 133 MHz to 1.0625 GHz and a high-performance isochronous bus that can support data transfers for real-time video.

RELATED ENTRIES   Disk Storage Systems; Fibre Channel

Sockets

Sockets were originally local interprocess communication mechanisms used in the UNIX environment. They evolved into network links on Transmission Control Protocol/Internet Protocol (TCP/IP) networks. A socket is basically an end point of a communication link between two applications. Sockets that extend over a network connect two or more applications running on separate computers attached to the network. A socket is composed of two addresses, as pictured in Figure S-6:

- *Port address*   This is the address for the specific application or process running within a computer.
- *Internet Protocol (IP) address*   This is the address of the workstation on the TCP/IP network.

Sockets provide a full-duplex communication channel between one or more systems. A local port makes a connection to a remote socket. The significance of this is that the socket identifies a computer on the network and the software port within that computer for a process being run by an application. Once a channel is opened, information is sent or received, and the circuit is then dismantled. There are stream and datagram sockets, as described here:

- A *stream socket* provides an end-to-end, connection-oriented link between two sockets using the reliable TCP protocol. A stream socket provides all the features of connection-oriented links, such as reliable data transmission over circuits that deliver data in order and provide for acknowledgment of received data.

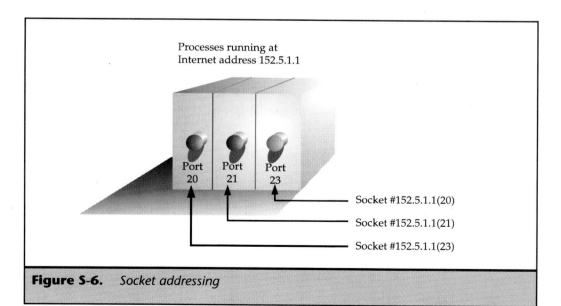

Figure S-6.   *Socket addressing*

- A *datagram socket* is a connectionless service that uses the User Datagram Protocol (UDP). Datagram services are quick and efficient, and well suited to bursty traffic patterns associated with LANs. The sending system can address datagrams to multiple sockets on multiple network computers.

The Windows Socket API is a specification that developers can use to write Windows applications that run on TCP/IP networks. Microsoft is migrating from the underpowered NetBIOS/NetBEUI protocols to TCP/IP, so this API will be important to developers who want to create interoperable applications.

RELATED ENTRIES   Transmission Control Protocol/Internet Protocol; UNIX; *and* Windows Socket API

Sockets Interface, Windows

The Windows Sockets API allows Windows applications to communicate using Transmission Control Protocol/Internet Protocol (TCP/IP) protocols by hiding the inconsistencies in PC-based TCP/IP products on the market. It is designed to ensure interoperability between any networking vendor's TCP/IP software and any Windows or Windows NT application that accesses the protocol stack.

RELATED ENTRY   Windows Socket API

Software Distribution

Software distribution can be handled automatically on computer networks with automated systems that install and update programs, utilities, and drivers on client systems. Such systems relieve network managers or their assistants from the need to individually update workstations on the network, and the time it takes to travel to workstation locations. This involved travel time and expense in many cases. *Electronic software distribution (ESD)* and *electronic software licensing (ESL)* are techniques for providing update and licensing functions on networks. ESD provides automatic software updating, and ESL provides automatic tracking of software usage to ensure that an organization stays within its software licensing requirements.

RELATED ENTRY   Electronic Software Distribution and Licensing

Solaris, SunSoft

SunSoft is a business unit of Sun Microsystems, Inc., and Solaris is SunSoft's UNIX-based operating system designed to run in several configurations on several computing platforms, including Intel x86 processors and SPARC processors.

Solaris Distributed Computing Solution

Solaris version 2.2 is comprised of SunOS 5.2 and also includes ONC+ (see "Open Network Computing, SunSoft"), OPEN LOOK, OpenWindows, and DeskSet, as described here:

- *OPEN LOOK* A graphical user interface (GUI) that incorporates pulldown menus, buttons, and drag-and-drop operations to provide a consistent operating environment for users.

- *OpenWindows* A fully compliant implementation of the X11 Windowing system. Enhancements include a customizable workspace manager, desktop integration services, and graphic libraries that support 2D and 3D graphic applications.

- *DeskSet* A set of 16 applications for task management and group productivity. DeskSet provides file management, calendaring, electronic mail (including audio and image files), and other features.

The operating system core of Solaris is SunOS. Current versions support symmetrical multiprocessing (SMP) and multithreading (MT) in the kernel. SMP allows all processors in a system to function equally in performing privileged operations (such as I/O) and increasing performance over uniprocessor or asymmetrical multiprocessing kernels. Multithreading optimizes overall throughput and application response time by allowing the system to take advantage of the inherent parallelism of many algorithms. SMP does not require that applications be rewritten, but MT applications can be written to further enhance their response and overall performance.

Solaris uses the Open Network Computing + (ONC+) networking technology, which provides distributed services. ONC+ provides the foundation for networks that tie together individuals, workgroups, and global enterprises. Users can gain access to resources anywhere on the network.

Solaris 2.2 supports Sun-4, Sun-4c, and Sun-4m system architectures with at least 16 megabytes of random access memory (RAM) and 200 megabytes of local hard disk space. A CD-ROM drive is required for installation.

Solaris 2 Desktop

Solaris 2 is SunSoft's desktop solution for Global Distributed Enterprises. Like the Solaris Distributed Computing Solution (Solaris 2.2), Solaris 2 is comprised of SunOS, Open Network Computing + (ONC+), OpenWindows, and DeskSet. It also includes ToolTalk, a network-spanning interapplication message system designed to promote cooperation among independently developed applications. The Solaris Desktop is available for SPARC and Intel 80x86 platforms.

S

Solaris 2 Workgroup and Enterprise Servers

The Solaris 2 Workgroup and Enterprise Servers are designed for departmental or workgroup use. They have all the features of the operating systems described above (except ToolTalk), plus a set of system administrator tools called AdminTools. AdminTools is a set of windows-based applications using a distributed model, allowing centralized and remote system management. The tools let administrators set up systems, set up print servers, set up client systems, add users, and manage Network Information Service (NIS) or NIS+ directory naming service databases from their own workstation.

ONC+ is Solaris' core networking technology that includes a family of heterogeneous networking protocols and distributed services that are independent of operating systems and computer architectures.

The Solaris 2 Workgroup product supports one or two SPARC CPUs, one or two Intel 80x86 CPUs, 16 to 256 megabytes of RAM, a minimum of 200 gigabytes of disk storage, up to two networking cards, and up to four each serial and parallel cards.

The Solaris 2 Enterprise product supports one to eight SPARC or Intel 80x86 CPUs, 16 to 1,024 megabytes of RAM, 200 to 256 gigbytes of disk storage, up to eight networking cards, and up to 512 terminals.

Solaris Federated Services

The Solaris operating environment provides standardized Federated Service Interfaces (FSIs) that allow vendors to add their distributed services to Solaris. The services become peers to the ONC+ core services within Solaris.

Solaris distributed computing puts resources and information at users' fingertips, independent of the resource or user location. In SunSoft's vision, users can even travel about with portable workstations, or to their homes. Users plug their portables into a phone jack and connect with the organization network. The system automatically updates the user's files on the home server and downloads electronic mail and other data to the user's system. No commands are required, just a notification to refresh.

The plug-and-play Federated Services system supports multiple autonomous distributed services such as filing, naming, and security. It assumes that heterogeneous computing is the rule, that no single distributed server predominates, and that a variety of protocols and services are used in an enterprise network.

Federated Services support file system extensions to take advantage of the innovations that have been introduced by independent software developers. The *vnode interface,* which permits integration of different filing systems into the Solaris kernel, has been enhanced with features similar to the AT&T System V Release 4 STREAMS framework. It allows integration of multiple protocol stacks so that file system modules can be stacked and unstacked. The interface will allow the integration of the Open Software Foundation's (OSF's) Distributed Computing Environment (DCE) distributed file system. All integrated file systems take advantage of the same user interface.

Naming services can also be integrated. A naming service maps network resources and gives them names so users can more easily access the resources, no matter where they are located on the network. Solaris and applications use *composite names* formed by combining names from different naming systems in the federation so the applications can access entities anywhere in the heterogeneous network environment. SunSoft is working with vendors to get naming services such as X.500, DEC CDS, and other naming services to work with the federated naming architecture.

The Solaris Federated Services support a variety of authentication technologies, including Diffie-Hellman, Kerberos, and RSA mechanisms. The system and network administrator can choose the authentication method when installing applications.

Solaris: Future Trends

Project Distributed Objects Everywhere (DOE) is SunSoft's strategy to bring open systems to the applications arena. DOE extends the Solaris model with the full range of capabilities to support an enterprise-wide distributed object environment.

DOE is based on the premise that companies are increasingly information-based, but are unable to handle the data that needs to flow throughout their operations. The failure is primarily in software, not hardware. DOE includes a broad set of features providing for the support and integration of object-based applications in a distributed computing environment. Among the capabilities and services are the following:

- A distributed, object-oriented computation model that provides object-oriented facilities across heterogeneous distributed networks
- Location independence so objects can be placed in many locations
- Scalability across computing platforms and networks
- Standard interchangeable interfaces
- Services, including security and naming
- Object Management Architecture support

RELATED ENTRIES   Distributed Computing; Enterprise Networks; Open Network Computing, SunSoft; Scalable Performance Architecture, Sun Microsystems, Inc.; Sun Microsystems, Inc.; *and* SunOS, SunSoft

Source Routing

IBM Token Ring networks use a source-routing routine that can provide bridges with information about where packets should go and how to get there. In source routing, the packets themselves hold the forwarding information. The bridge does not maintain forwarding tables; it sends packets to local area network (LAN) segments based on the packet address information.

Bridges that do source routing use a *discovery* method to determine the route a packet should take to a device. Note that although this sounds like routing, the source-routing bridge is simply a forwarding device that knows the addresses of other bridges. Best-path routing information is contained within the packet.

A workstation that needs to send a message to a workstation or server on another LAN segment sends an *explorer* packet over the network. If there are multiple bridges on the network, multiple copies of the packet appear at the destination because each bridge sends its own copy of the explorer packet to the destination. The destination workstation receives all these copies and determines the best route through the internetwork based on information stored in the packets about the paths they took. It then communicates this best-path information back to the sending station, which stores it for future use and places it in packets that it sends to the destination.

The Internet routing protocol called Inter-Domain Policy Routing (IDPR) is a link-state routing protocol that implements source routing and policy-based routing between domains. See "Routing, Internet."

RELATED ENTRY   Token Ring Network

Spanning Tree Algorithm

The spanning tree algorithm is used in bridged internetwork environments to detect and break circular traffic patterns by disabling certain links. The IEEE 801.2-D Spanning Tree Protocol (STP) inhibits loops in redundant bridges by maintaining the secondary bridge as a backup. If the first bridge should go down, the secondary bridge takes over.

- The algorithm assigns a unique *identifier* to each bridge, which is usually the bridge's Media Access Control (MAC) address.

- A *priority value* is also assigned to each bridge.

- Each port on every bridge is assigned a unique *identifier*.

- Each bridge port is then assigned a *path cost* that assigns a value to ports. The network administrator can change cost values manually to assign preferences for a particular port.

As the algorithm proceeds, a root bridge is selected from the set of bridges. The bridge with the lowest identifier is selected as the root. Once the root bridge is selected, other bridges determine which of their ports provides access to the root bridge at the least cost. This port becomes the *root port* of the bridge. If ports have the same costs, then the one with the least number of bridge-to-bridge hops is used.

The last step is to determine which bridges and bridge ports will provide a pathway through the network to the root based on the least path cost. In this process, the bridge enables ports for forwarding packets and disables other ports to prevent loops. These ports are assigned backup status in case a primary port or link fails. A switched or dedicated circuit may be attached to the backup line.

When bridges use expensive telecommunication links to span wide areas, it is not economically feasible in the minds of most network managers to attach a dedicated line to a backup port, and then not use it most of the time. Some bridge manufacturers provide load-sharing bridges that are capable of using the backup link to share the network load without causing loops. The load-sharing bridge is the most efficient form of bridge. It uses a spanning tree-type algorithm, and it uses a dual link to transfer packets, thus improving internetwork performance.

RELATED ENTRY   Bridging

SPARC

See Scalable Performance Architecture, Sun Microsystems, Inc.

Spread Spectrum Radio

Radio communication enables wireless networking and limited distance, mobile in-office computing. A wireless network is one in which cables are not required to interconnect workstations. Instead, a central transmitter/receiver, or *transceiver,* is installed within an office that broadcasts signals to workstations. One radio communication method is called *spread spectrum.*

Spread spectrum technology was first used in World War II as a way to provide jam-proof radio communication for guided torpedoes. In one technique, called *frequency hopping,* both the transmitter and the receiver jump frequencies in synchronization during the transmission so a jammer would have difficulty targeting the exact frequency on which the devices are communicating. Another spread spectrum technique, called *direct sequencing,* spreads the signal over a wide band of frequencies, rather than a specific band of frequencies. In this technique, the signal is so spread out that it appears as background white noise that is hard to detect. Both techniques are used by manufacturers and provide the very important element of security.

The direct sequencing technique broadcasts signals over a wide range of frequencies, avoiding problems inherent in narrow-band communication. A code is used to spread the signal, and the receiving station uses the same code to retrieve it. Spread spectrum broadcasts in bands where noise is prominent, but does not rise above the noise. The coding technique allows a spread spectrum signal to operate at any range of frequencies, even if other spread spectrum signals are in the same range. Spread spectrum radio signals are too weak to interfere with conventional radios and have fewer Federal Communications Commission (FCC) restrictions.

RELATED ENTRIES   Radio Networks; Wireless LAN Communication

SQL Access Group (SAG)

The Structured Query Language (SQL) Access Group (SAG) was founded in 1989 by Hewlett-Packard, DEC, Oracle, Sun, and other members (primarily database management system vendors) with the objective of promoting interoperability between SQL standards. It is a nonprofit corporation proliferating technical specifications that will enable multiple SQL-based relational databases and tools to work together. The group is not a standards organization, but a consortium of 39 leading companies intent on accelerating research underway by such standards groups as the American National Standards Institute (ANSI) and the International Organization for Standardization (ISO).

Multivendor database interoperability makes possible the sharing and exchange of data between different database software products running on different platforms, which frees customers to choose solutions that satisfy their unique business requirements.

The group has developed three technical specifications:

- *Structured Query Language*   A specification for implementing the SQL language following international specifications

- *SQL Remote Database Access*   A specification that defines communication between an SQL-based client and a remote database server

- *SQL Access Call-Level Interface (CLI)*   A set of application program interfaces (APIs) for interfacing with SQL-based products

The SQL CLI is the core of Microsoft's Open Database Connectivity (ODBC) standard, which provides a common interface between back-end databases and front-end user applications. The purpose of ODBC, from Microsoft's viewpoint, is to make Windows the most popular client platform. A number of back-end server vendors have announced ODBC drivers for their products, including IBM, DEC, and Oracle.

RELATED ENTRIES   Database Connectivity APIs and Middleware; Middleware; Open Database Connectivity, Microsoft; *and* Structured Query Language

Standard Generalized Markup Language (SGML)

SGML is a document language that defines document structures so users can exchange documents across computing platforms. SGML is primarily used in the workflow and document management environment. SGML files contain attributes that define each component in the document such as paragraphs, sections, headers, and titles.

RELATED ENTRIES   Document Interchange Standards; Groupware; *and* Workflow Software

Standard Message Format

SMF is a messaging format used in Novell's NetWare Message Handling Service (MHS). MHS is a system that handles message flow between applications that are located on local area networks and remote computers on wide area networks. MHS can collect, route, and deliver messages and files to other systems by using store-and-forward technology. Applications that use MHS include electronic mail, workgroup scheduling, electronic data interchange (EDI), and network fax.

Vendors are providing connectivity to the base and network operating systems through standards such as Novell's NetWare Global Messaging and Standard Message Format (SMF), Microsoft's Messaging Applications Programming Interface (MAPI), Apple Computer's Apple Open Collaborative Environment (AOCE), and Lotus's Vendor Independent Messaging (VIM).

RELATED ENTRIES   Electronic Mail; Message-Enabled Applications; Message Handling Service, Novell; *and* Messaging API, E-mail

Standards Organizations

Standards organizations define the physical and operational characteristics of networking and communication equipment, operating systems, and software. Vendors following these standards can create products that work with other vendors' products and services. Standards are recommendations that vendors can choose to follow, and most do. However, vendors often make changes to established standards to fit their own needs, and so there is always a need to use caution when combining equipment from different vendors.

A *de facto* standard is a standard that has become popular without the guidance of any standards organization. A de facto standard typically evolves from a product or service created by a single vendor. The product becomes popular and other vendors create products that work with or compete with it.

The following organizations are responsible for setting standards within the United States and internationally. They are listed here and discussed elsewhere in this book.

- American National Standards Institute (ANSI)
- Common Open Software Environment (COSE)
- Consultative Committee for International Telegraph and Telephone (CCITT)
- Corporation for Open Systems (COS)
- Electronic Industries Association (EIA)
- Institute of Electrical and Electronic Engineers (IEEE)
- International Organization for Standardization (ISO)
- Object Management Group (OMG)

■ Open Software Foundation (OSF)

■ SQL Access Group (SAG)

Stateless and Call-Back Filing Systems

In a distributed client-server environment, several users may access the same file or block of data at the same time. A mechanism is required to keep information caches in the memory of a computer up-to-date with any changes that have been made by other users on the network.

In a *stateless* environment such as a Network File System (NFS), servers do not hold information in memory for clients that interact with them. Each request for service is handled independently, so that one request must completely finish before another can take place. Stateless operations can cause problems, however. A workstation can place a file (or set of records) from the server in its own cache, but another client might change the file at the server in the mean time. Since the server doesn't keep track of which clients are caching the file, the clients must periodically check in with the server to see if the file has changed. Checking the server adds overhead and excess network traffic. To reduce overhead and traffic, it is possible to increase the check interval, but this also increases the potential that data will become unsynchronized.

In contrast, the Andrew File System (AFS) is a *call-back* operating system. It is implemented in the Open Software Foundation (OSF) Distributed Computing Environment (DCE) as the Distributed File System (DFS). AFS provides a *call-back promise* in which the server informs clients when files they are caching change at the server, as when another client accessing the same file saves that file back onto the server. AFS makes sure that it does not become flooded with call-back promises by occasionally discarding old callback promises. Clients check the expiration time in callback promises to ensure that they are current.

Another interesting feature of the call-back promise is that it provides a guarantee to a client that a file is current. In other words, if a cached file has a call-back promise, the client knows the file must be current unless the server has called to indicate the file changed at the server.

RELATED ENTRY   Distributed File Systems

Static Routing

An internetwork typically consists of subnetworks connected with bridges or routers. Large internetworks typically have many different paths that packets can take to reach a destination. Routers are the switches that direct packets over one path or another, based on stored information that indicates the best path to a destination.

Static routing implies that the paths must be manually programmed into the router by a network administrator. If a path fails, the administrator must reprogram the router so packets follow other paths. In mission-critical environments, this is usually unacceptable, so dynamic routers are used that automatically locate and determine the best paths through the internetwork and dynamically recalculate paths when lines fail.

RELATED ENTRIES   Routers; Routing Protocols

Storage Management System, Novell

Novell's Storage Management System (SMS) is a set of specifications for backing up information on networks. Novell hopes SMS will become an industry standard. Its most important feature, support for multiple operating systems, may make this possible. Many major system manufacturers are already supporting the standard, and backup device vendors are including SMS support within their packages. Currently, SMS is the only reliable way to back up data on NetWare 4.x servers. It also ensures that current backups, as well as backup systems, will be compatible with future backup strategies.

S

Novell had many goals for the SMS during its development:

■ Centralize and simplify the backup of NetWare data, no matter where it is on the network.

■ Support the backup of many different file types (other operating systems).

■ Make it easy for vendors to integrate their hardware or applications into the SMS, even as NetWare versions change.

■ Continue to support old hardware devices as the SMS changes, and provide access to old backups way into the future. For example, you could access a 10-year-old backup even if the SMS software has changed over time.

Backup on networks is much more complex than backup on a single computer using one operating system. Networks consist of a diversity of operating systems and file types. In addition, files have special attributes (compression, migration, and so on) and rights information. Novell's SMS is designed to handle this diversity.

The volume of information to back up on a network is also an issue. The SMS will eventually work with a whole range of archiving devices, from single tape backup systems to optical jukeboxes that hold gigabytes of information. In this way, users can back up without worrying about backup device limitations. Because the SMS is modular, hardware vendors simply write drivers and modules so their equipment fits into the system.

How the SMS Is Implemented

A basic SMS configuration consists of an archive server called the *Storage Management Engine (SME)* that provides backup services and one or more *target service agents (TSAs)* that run on client systems and provide backup services for specific operating systems. TSAs are executable programs that are specifically written for client operating systems such as DOS, UNIX, or Macintosh.

In the latest incarnation of SMS, a Storage Management Data Requester (SMDR) sits between the SMEs, the TSAs, and the backup devices. The SMDR is like a switchboard, routing requests and information between all the devices. The advantage of the SMDR is that multiple SMEs that handle different environments can become part of the backup strategy.

The arrangement is typically client-server based, in which the TSAs are clients and the archiving device is a NetWare Loadable Module running in a server, as shown in Figure S-7. However, archiving devices can also be located on other systems, such as DOS workstations, Macintosh systems, or UNIX systems. Novell's SMS runs as a server process, but other vendors' systems may run in workstations.

The archive server consists of the Storage Device Interface (SDI). Think of SDI as a plug-and-play interface. Backup device vendors create modules that plug into the interface and allow the hardware to participate in an SMS backup system. The SMS itself doesn't really care about the type of hardware attached. That is all handled by the vendor's interface module, which is attached to the SDI. The SMS simply sends streams of data from TSAs to the device through the SDI interface. This modular design is what makes the SMS so viable for future growth.

All data in the SMS is stored using a special System-Independent Data Format (SIDF). Workstations running TSA software provide the data in SIDF, which the SMS sends to the SDI for storage on whatever archive device is attached. Because SIDF is standardized, it's possible to restore data to other devices and operating systems, as long as they accept SIDF data. The TSA software is responsible for providing the SIDF data. In this way, each TSA is designed to work with the idiosyncrasies—such as the file formats, attributes, resource forks (Macintosh), and other information—specific to the operating system it runs on.

Because TSAs simply provide SIDF data to SMS backup devices, they can change over time as the operating systems or platforms they run on change. This strategy is

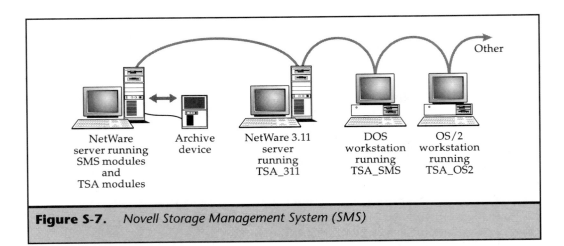

Figure S-7.   *Novell Storage Management System (SMS)*

similar to Novell's workstation shell technology, in which each new shell version supports change in the operating system.

The SBACKUP Utility

You run the SBACKUP utility at the SMS archive server. During the backup, data is sent to the archive device from the selected target device. Each backup session has a name and creates a "Backup Session Log" and a "Backup Error Log," which are stored in a continuously updated "Backup and Restore Log" file on the archive server. These files are also stored on the backup medium, in case the originals are lost. They are re-created during a restore.

With SBACKUP, you can perform the following types of backups:

- *Full backup*   Backup of all files
- *Incremental backup*   Backup of files modified since the last full or incremental backup
- *Differential backup*   Backup of files modified since the last full backup
- *Custom backup*   Backup of files you specify

The "archive needed" attribute for files is cleared in the full and incremental backup, but not for the differential backup. In a custom backup, you can specify how SBACKUP should handle the attribute.

RELATED ENTRIES   Backup and Data Archiving; NetWare; *and* Novell

STREAMS

STREAMS is a development and operating environment that allows the use of multiple communication protocols on a network. Applications running above the STREAMS environment can easily use any of the protocols it supports. STREAMS is a modular system in which protocol stacks can be added or removed as needed. It provides developers with a set of tools for implementing communication protocols as modules. To better understand STREAMS, it is necessary to start with the concept of sockets.

A socket is an interprocess communication mechanism developed in the UNIX and Transmission Control Protocol/Internet Protocol (TCP/IP) environment to provide links for the transfer of messages and data between applications. A socket that extends over networks can connect two or more applications running on separate computers attached to the network. A socket is composed of an Internet address, which is the address of the computer, and a port address, which is the address of an application process running in that computer, as pictured in Figure S-8. Multiple port addresses can exist within a computer for each running process or application.

There are stream sockets and datagram sockets. A *stream socket* is connection-oriented and uses the TCP protocol to provide reliable, acknowledged, and

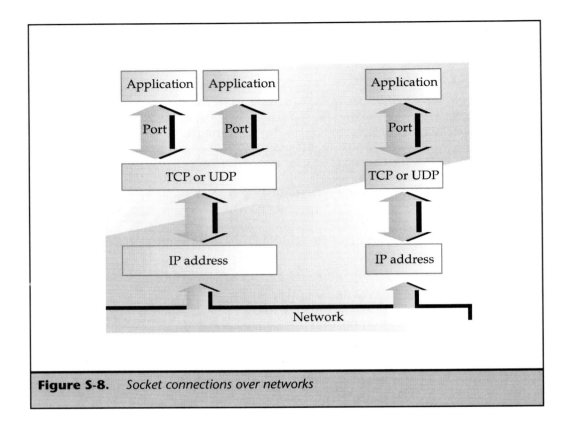

Figure S-8. *Socket connections over networks*

sequenced data transfer between two applications. A *datagram socket* is a connectionless service that uses User Datagram Protocol (UDP) and provides data transfer between multiple sockets.

As shown in the Figure S-8, the port address of the socket interfaces with the Transport-layer protocols such as TCP or UDP. It is here that a switching layer is added so that applications can use other Transport-layer protocols, such as the Open Systems Interconnection (OSI) protocols. This switching layer is implemented in STREAMS.

STREAMS is an important part of the UNIX operating system. It provides a way for an application running in upper layers to access a device driver running in lower layers. In the network environment, STREAMS provides an interface between applications and device drivers for network adapters. The function provided by STREAMS is the ability to add and remove modules to and from the stream. Thus, if encryption is required, an encrypting module is pushed into the stream without the need to recompile the operating system.

The top of the stream is called the *stream head* and it is the point where applications interface with the modules in the stream. Data and control information is transferred between the stream and the application with messages. As pictured in Figure S-9, data is placed in a stream at the stream head, and it passes downstream to the network controller. Modules can be inserted into the stream, such as TCP/IP and OSI network protocols.

The types of messages that programmers can use to interface with the stream are defined by a transport provider interface. The Transport Layer Interface (TLI) is a library of calls and run-time modules originally defined by AT&T that simplifies the task of programmers. The programmer simply writes applications using the calls in the TLI library instead of writing the applications to use a specific network transport protocol. Since protocol-specific code is not designed into the program, the protocols can be updated or changed without affecting the program.

The functions provided by TLI allow applications to request connection-oriented or connectionless transport services from the lower-level transport protocols. The application does not need to know the details of network communication. It simply makes a request. Many other standard functions are also available in the TLI layer for applications to use.

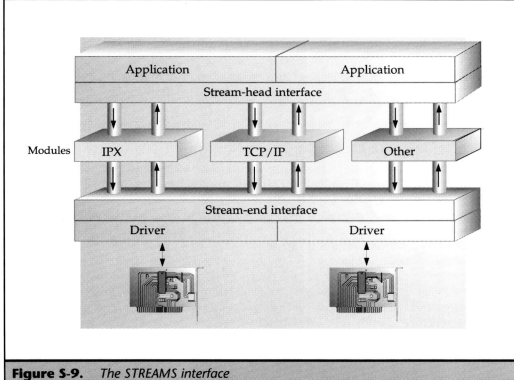

Figure S-9. *The STREAMS interface*

In SunSoft's Open Network Computing (ONC) environment, TLI exists as a layer that allows remote procedure call (RPC) programs to run across multiple network transports such as TCP/IP and OSI. The enhanced RPC, written to the TLI, is known as Transport Independent RPC (TI-RPC). TI-RPC is standard in UNIX System V Release 4 and is compatible with the existing ONC RPC protocol. Novell is supporting the TI-RPC technology.

RELATED ENTRIES   Connection-Oriented and Connectionless Protocols; Datagram Network Services; Open Network Computing, SunSoft; Remote Procedure Call; Sockets; Transmission Control Protocol/Internet Protocol; *and* UNIX

Striping

See Redundant Arrays of Inexpensive Disks.

Structured Query Language (SQL)

SQL, pronounced "see-quel," was originally developed by IBM as a database query language in the mid-1970s to operate on the VM/370 and MVS/370 operating systems. It was later commercialized by Oracle Corporation, after which many other companies jumped on the bandwagon. The original intent of using SQL as a database query tool was never realized because it was too impractical to expect normal users to learn and use it. It went through several repackaging phases in an attempt to make the language easier to use. Today, SQL is viewed as an interface to access data on many different types of database systems, including mainframes, midrange systems, UNIX systems, and network servers.

In the 1980s, the process of standardizing the language was initiated by the International Organization for Standardization (ISO), the American National Standards Institute (ANSI), and X/Open. This standardization is still not complete, even with the help of the SQL Access Group (SAG), which is dedicated to promoting SQL standardization, or at least interoperability among the different SQL standards. ANSI is responsible for SQL'89, a 1989 attempt at standardization, and SQL'92, a 1992 attempt. Because these standards failed to unite the industry, SAG developed its own standards and ANSI is working on a new standard called SQL3, which includes object-oriented technology. The SAG standards are partly based on ANSI standards, and partly the work of X/Open.

In the client-server environment, the user's front-end application interfaces to a database management system (DBMS) "engine" running on a back-end server. The interface between the front and the back end is a specific application program interface (API) provided by the DBMS vendor. SQL is supposed to provide a standard interface to back-end data, but subtle differences in each vendor's implementation prevent this reality.

SQL interfaces are implemented in two ways:

- *Embedded APIs* In the embedded API method, SQL statements to access the database are embedded into a programming language such as C or COBOL.

- *Call-level APIs* In the call-level method, procedures or functions external to the program are called to access the database.

The current trend is to provide so-called "middleware" products between the clients and servers to allow users to access any back-end server using a variety of front-end applications. They hide the differences between access languages and database APIs. Two members of SAG have taken advantage of this strategy and work done by SAG. Microsoft introduced its Open Database Connectivity (ODBC) standard and Borland developed its Integrated Database Application Programming Interface (IDAPI). In addition, IBM developed the Distributed Relational Database Architecture (DRDA) SQL standard. All implement the call-level APIs.

RELATED ENTRIES Database Connectivity APIs and Middleware; Database Management System; Distributed Database; *and* SQL Access Group

Structured Wiring

Structured wiring or cabling is a preplanned cabling system that is designed with growth and reconfiguration in mind. The Electronic Industries Association (EIA) and the Telecommunications Industries Association (TIA) developed a standard telecommunication wiring for commercial buildings called the EIA/TIA 568 Commercial Building Wiring Standard. This standard provides a uniform wiring system and supports multivendor products and environments.

Structured wiring forms an infrastructure with pathways for critical parts of a network. The system includes cables, communication connectors, jacks, plugs, adapters, baluns, patch panel systems, and electronic components. Ideally, it provides a way to transmit data, video, voice, and other information. Structured wiring systems are standards-based. Distances, topologies, and physical specifications are already defined and future cable requirements are accommodated; thus, a building can be wired without any prior knowledge of the data communication equipment that will use it. The cable plant is easy to manage and faults are easy to isolate.

RELATED ENTRIES Cabling; EIA/TIA 568 Commercial Building Wiring Standard

Subnetworks

An internetwork is a composite of local area networks (LANs) and wide area networks (WANs) that are interconnected with bridges and routers. Each network in this arrangement is called a subnetwork. A subnetwork is usually confined to a departmental area or a workgroup of users. An enterprise network is typically constructed from a number of preexisting department and workgroup networks, some of which may use different communication protocols and operating system environments. As pictured on the left in Figure S-10, a backbone cable may connect all the subnetworks. A mesh of dedicated or switched links can connect networks over wide areas, as shown on the right.

The significance of subnetworks is important. Each has its own subnetwork address and communication protocols that differ from other subnetworks. Traffic is usually isolated within a subnetwork. The bridge or router device that joins subnetworks into internetworks is called an intermediate system (IS) in International Organization for Standardization (ISO) terms. The workstations, servers, and other devices at the ends of subnetworks are called end systems (ESs). Thus, there are End System-to-Intermediate System (ES-IS) routing protocols (computer-to-router) and Intermediate System-to-Intermediate System (IS-IS) routing protocols (router-to-router). Similarly, on the Internet there are Interior Gateway Protocols that handle routing within a managed set of systems and Exterior Gateway Protocols that handle routing between management domains. See "Domains" and "Routing, Internet."

Routers may need to handle multiple protocols in an enterprise environment. Thus, multiprotocol routers are required that run software for interpreting and forwarding different types of packets. Encapsulation may be required to transfer some packets over other networks. For example, a NetBIOS packet can be encapsulated into an IP packet for transport over a Transmission Control Protocol/Internet Protocol (TCP/IP) network such as the Internet.

RELATED ENTRIES   Domains; Networks; *and* Segment, Network

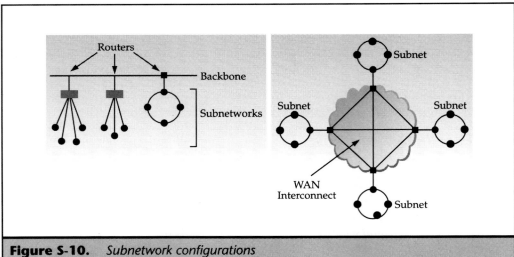

Figure S-10.   *Subnetwork configurations*

SunLink Network

The SunSelect (Billerica, Massachusetts) division of Sun Microsystems, Inc. is responsible for SunLink products, which provide communication links in local area network and multivendor product environments. The SunLink File Transfer Access and Management (FTAM) suite of products allows Solaris 2.x operating systems to work in Open Systems Interconnection (OSI) environments.

NetWare SunLink software is an optimized version of NetWare for UNIX 3.11 that runs on the Solaris operating system. Without any changes to existing NetWare client environments, NetWare SunLink enables users to share files, applications, printers, and other networking services on a SPARC and Solaris network. Other features include:

- Transparent file storage and retrieval from a NetWare client to a SPARC and Solaris environment
- A gateway between NetWare and NFS files for access to enterprise-wide information
- Access for NetWare clients to access printers on SPARC and Solaris networks
- Support for Ethernet and Token Ring networks
- IPX and TCP/IP routing

RELATED ENTRIES   Distributed Computing; Distributed Objects Everywhere, SunSoft; Enterprise Networks; NetWare; Networks; Open Network Computing, SunSoft; Scalable Performance Architecture, Sun Microsystems, Inc.; Security; Solaris, SunSoft; *and* Sun Microsystems, Inc.

Sun Microsystems, Inc.

Sun Microsystems, Inc. has a number of subdivisions and spin-off companies. The name Sun is an acronym for Stanford University Network, and the company is based in Mountain View, California. Its earliest products were UNIX-based engineering workstations with Motorola processors. By 1990, Sun had largely replaced its product line with SPARC microprocessor-based systems. SPARC systems are used in scientific, engineering, financial, and other commercial environments.

Sun's Open Network Computing (ONC) initiative provides open protocols and services such as development and management tools to support heterogeneous computing environments. The ONC environment has been widely adopted. Sun recently joined the Common Open Software Environment (COSE) group along with Hewlett-Packard, IBM, and others to create operating system environments based on OSF/Motif (OSF is the Open Software Foundation).

Sun Microsystems Computer Corporation

Sun Microsystems, Inc. codeveloped the Scalable Performance Architecture (SPARC) microprocessors with Texas Instruments and the newer UltraSPARC processors with Intergraph Corp. SPARC processors come in a variety of models that run in workstations developed by the Sun Microsystems Computer Corp. The workstations are available in desktop models and multiprocessing systems. Graphic and imaging workstations are also available.

The SPARCstation 10 line can support from two to eight processors in a multiprocessor design that runs the Solaris 2.x operating system developed by the SunSoft division. Solaris 2.x supports symmetrical multiprocessing (SMP). The SPARCserver line is designed for network file server applications and includes supports for up to 20 50-MHz SuperSPARC processors.

SunSelect

The SunSelect division of Sun Microsystems, Inc. has the goal of integrating PCs into multivendor environments, including UNIX systems, mainframes, and minicomputers. The product line includes the following:

- *PC-NFS*   PC-NFS is a distributed file system for client-server environments. It supports data exchange across many operating systems and is highly portable. PC-NFS enables PCs to participate in networks based on Transmission Control Protocol/Internet Protocol (TCP/IP) and Open Network Computing (ONC) standards while working in familiar Microsoft Windows and MS-DOS environments.

- *SunPC*   SunPC is a high-performance PC-emulation product that enables SPARC workstation users to access popular PC applications directly from the SPARC workstation.

- *NetWare SunLink*   This product integrates NetWare LANs with SPARC and Solaris environments.

- *SelectMail*   This product integrates Microsoft Windows and MS-DOS users with enterprise electronic mail systems.

Other products include Windows Application Binary Interface (WABI), which lets Microsoft Windows-based products run on UNIX workstations. Sun is also working with Intergraph to port the Windows NT operating systems to the SPARC processor.

SunSoft

A division of Sun Microsystems, Inc. that is responsible for Open Network Computing (ONC), which provides distributed file system, security, and naming services. The SunSoft division is responsible for development of the Solaris operating system and SunOS, a UNIX operating system, as described here:

- *SunOS*   An operating system that incorporates UNIX System V Release 4 with SunSoft's Open Network Computing (ONC) distributed computing environment.

- *Solaris*   A distributed computing operating system that is based on SunOS, and implementation of UNIX System V Release 4, but contains Sun-specific improvements. Solaris offers multitasking, multiprocessing power and fully integrated open networking in a single package with a graphical user interface. Solaris runs on Intel x86 and SPARC processors, with future versions planned for the PowerPC processor, a development of IBM, Apple, and Motorola.

- *Open Network Computing (ONC) Environment*   A standard environment for implementing distributed computing.

- *ToolTalk*   A network-spanning interapplication message system that promotes cooperation among independently developed applications. The goal of ToolTalk is to provide universal plug-and-play capabilities in distributed network environments.

RELATED ENTRIES   Distributed Computing; Enterprise Networks; Open Network Computing, SunSoft; Solaris, SunSoft; *and* SunOS, SunSoft

SunNet Manager, Sun Microsystems, Inc.

Sun Microsystems' SunNet Manager is a network management system that uses a platform architecture approach. In this approach, a platform is designed that handles all the core functions required for a network management system such as communication protocol interfaces, data definitions, and other management features. Other products then plug into or interface with the platform and gain all its built-in functions. These include access to a multiprotocol network, multivendor systems, and data management schemes.

SunNet Manager is a management application development platform that provides an Open Systems Interconnection (OSI) management-agent model and support for third-party products through Sun's Open Network Computing (ONC) strategy, as well as Simple Network Management Protocol (SNMP) and other protocols. The product runs on Transmission Control Protocol/Internet Protocol (TCP/IP) communication protocols. The OPEN LOOK graphical user interface gives managers a view of the network and the ability to easily manage systems and events.

RELATED ENTRIES   Distributed Computing; Enterprise Networks; Management Standards and Tools; Open Network Computing, SunSoft; Simple Network Management Protocol; *and* Sun Microsystems, Inc.

SunOS, SunSoft

SunSoft is a Sun Microsystems, Inc. business unit, and its SunOS is a software environment that incorporates UNIX System V Release 4 (SVR4). The software includes Open Network Computing (ONC) and is the foundation for the Solaris operating environment.

While the foundation of SunOS 5.0 is UNIX System V, Release 4 (SVR4), the following extensions have been added by SunSoft:

- Symmetrical multiprocessing with multithreads
- Real-time extensions
- Increased security
- Improved system administration

SunOS 5.0 supports symmetrical multiprocessing with a multithreaded kernel. Multiple threads can execute concurrently in the operating system and several processors can execute concurrently within the same kernel component such as the file system, or a device driver. The SunOS 5.0 kernel also provides application-level multithreading so separate applications can run on multiple processors concurrently.

Other features include:

- Security enhancements, such as the ability to increase security levels from low to medium to high, and the ability to age passwords and control logons
- Authentication, using Kerberos services
- The framework for an object-oriented management system
- Network Information Service + (NIS+), a distributed name service for networks that provides a hierarchical name space to simplify administration
- Internationalization for global operation

RELATED ENTRIES   Distributed Computing; Distributed Objects Everywhere, SunSoft; Enterprise Networks; Open Network Computing, SunSoft; Security; *and* Sun Microsystems, Inc.

Supervisor

A supervisor is a person who is responsible for administering and maintaining a network. The term has particular meaning on NetWare networks. The supervisor has all access rights to all volumes, directories, and files and is the first person to log onto a server after installation. The supervisor then immediately changes the password so that no other user can access the server and gain the unlimited access rights of the supervisor.

In NetWare 4.x, a system administrator has full control over an entire enterprise network. This administrator is typically the person who installs the first server and defines the NetWare Directory Services (NDS) structure for the organization. Other servers may be added and become part of the initial structure. The administrator can create users that have supervisor-like control over specific areas of the network, such as departments or the servers in those departments.

RELATED ENTRIES   Administrators, NetWare 4.x; Directory Services, NetWare

Surge Suppressors

The primary job of a surge suppressor is to protect systems against spikes. An uninterruptible power supply (UPS) is required to protect against sags and power outages. Most power supplies in desktop systems can handle surges of up to 800 volts. You'll need a surge suppressor to protect against surges above these levels. Most off-the-shelf surge suppressors divert surges to the ground line, and these surges might resurrect themselves in other computer systems, depending on the electrical wiring of a building. Look for surge suppressors that use coils and electrolytic capacitors to absorb excess energy rather than diverting it to ground. Ground-line diversion is used primarily to prevent the surge suppressor itself from burning out. Currently, most surge suppressors use this technique, but more products are becoming available that avoid it.

Spike protection ratings should be as high as 6,000 volts. Units are often equipped with electromagnetic interference (EMI) and radio-frequency interference (RFI) noise filtration circuitry. However, most desktop systems already include this type of filtering in their power supplies, so you should view ads that stress EMI/RFI noise filtration with skepticism.

Be leery of surge-suppression devices that use transient voltage surge suppressor (TVSS) technology. They might protect against large transients, such as lightning bolts, but fail to recognize transients below a certain level that can still be destructive to electronic equipment. In addition, they pass transients to the ground, where they can find their way back into other equipment. The problem is exacerbated if networks have multiple ground connections.

RELATED ENTRY   Power and Grounding Problems and Solutions

Switched-56 Services

Switched-56 is a digital communication technology for transporting data over switched synchronous lines at 56 Kbits/sec or switched asynchronous lines at 57.6 Kbits/sec, although compression can provide four times the bandwidth. The channels are dialup, so customers can use the service only when needed, or establish a link to handle traffic overflow from another line. Customers are finding Switched-56 useful for videoconferencing, LAN-to-LAN connections, Group 4 facsimile interconnections, and as a high-speed service for telecommuters. Switched-56 and Integrated Services Digital Network (ISDN) fall into similar circuit-oriented service categories. But while ISDN offers two 64 Kbits/sec channels (one can handle data while the other handles a voice call), Switched-56 provides only one 56 Kbits/sec channel and is typically more readily available.

Switched-56 customers find the service a reasonable option that is a step above dial-up analog lines but far less expensive than leased lines such as T1 or Fractional T1. It can also supplement these lines. There is an initial setup fee for Switched-56 lines and this is higher than setting up an analog telephone line. Charges, however, are about the same as a normal dialup telephone call. Pacific Bell recently announced that it would waive setup charges (approximately $500, plus a monthly service charge) for customers that kept their lines longer than two years.

Switched-56 lines are digital and do not require a modem. Instead, a channel service unit/data service unit (CSU/DSU) device is required to connect a router attached to a LAN to the Switched-56 phone line installed by the phone company. A typical Switched-56 connection between two LANs is pictured in Figure S-11 and requires a CSU/DSU at each end of the connection. The interface between the router and CSU/DSU is typically a V.35 serial cable. Once set up, the lines operate like dial-out lines. The lines also have a telephone number that you can dial from a remote site.

Switched-56 is useful in low-traffic LAN environments where traffic occurs in bursts or E-mail is delivered to other sites on a periodic basis. Switched-56 is growing in popularity at sites that previously used dialup 9,600 bits per second (bps) modems to handle these tasks. It is also used to provide backup support for faster digital lines such as T1. For example, in the event that traffic exceeds the carrying capacity of a T1 line, the Switched-56 line is automatically dialed to handle the overload, as discussed next.

With the proper customer premises equipment (CPE), Switched-56 can provide dial-on demand connections to provide bandwidth as required. The CPEs have a number of ports, each of which attaches to a Switched-56 line as shown in Figure S-12. Inverse-multiplexing is used to spread the customer's signal out over multiple lines. A similar device recombines the signals at the destination. The devices set up lines

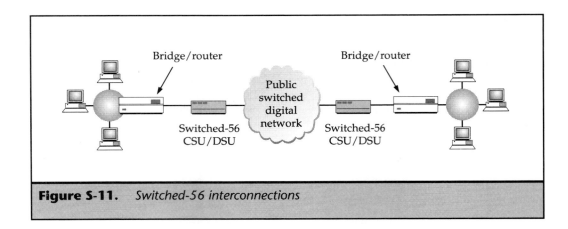

Figure S-11.   *Switched-56 interconnections*

automatically as needed and take them down as traffic requirements diminish. This is an ideal arrangement for LAN environments where traffic patterns increase during certain times of the day and customers don't want to lease dedicated lines that might go partially unused.

The carriers are touting Switched-56 services as products for transmitting voice, data, and video at low cost. They are providing the services using a variety of different names. For example, Pacific Bell calls its services Switched Digital Service Integrated System (SDS-56). Rates also vary. Pacific Bell charges a one-time installation fee, a monthly service fee, and usage charges based on a per-channel basis. As mentioned earlier, the company will waive these charges if the lines are kept for over 2 years.

RELATED ENTRIES   Carrier Services; Channel Service Unit/Data Service Unit; Circuit-Switching Services; *and* Wide Area Networks

Switched Multimegabit Data Service (SMDS)

Switched Multimegabit Data Service (SMDS) is a local exchange carrier (LEC) service that provides a way to extend local area networks in a city-wide area. SMDS was developed by Bellcore and is offered as a service by LECs in many metropolitan areas. Note that SMDS uses the same fixed-size cell relay technology as Asynchronous Transfer Mode (ATM) and carriers are offering SMDS as a service that runs on top of them.

As a switching technology, SMDS has advantages over building private networks with dedicated digital lines such as T1. Customers set up one line (of appropriate

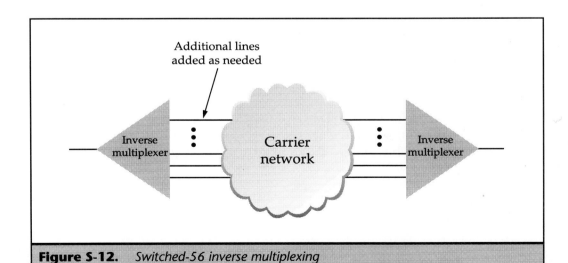

Figure S-12.   *Switched-56 inverse multiplexing*

bandwidth) into the LEC's SMDS network, rather than set up lines between all the sites that need interconnection. It is a connectionless, cell-based transport service that can provide any-to-any connections between a variety of sites without a call setup or tear-down procedure. This provide the ability to extend LAN-type communication techniques over metropolitan areas. Once information reaches the SMDS switching network, it is directed to any number of sites.

The switching technology of SMDS can provide customers with connection options that accommodate changing business needs. The cost of the service is typically based on a flat monthly fee, but it is ideal for customers that need to switch connections among many sites. Because the local exchange carriers are the primary providers of SMDS, there is usually no competition for the service in some areas. However, customers might want to weigh the use of SMDS against other switching services such as Frame Relay.

SMDS is one of the "fast-packet" technologies that leaves error-checking and flow control procedures up to the end nodes. If a packet is missing, the receiving node requests a retransmission. The network itself is not burdened with this type of error checking. While this places more work on end systems, it takes advantage of the fact that modern transmission facilities have few errors. The three fast packet technologies are defined here:

- ■ SMDS is a fixed-length cell technology that is available in metropolitan areas. Switched or dedicated circuits provide the connection from the customer site into the SMDS network. Transmission speeds range from one Mbit/sec to 16 Mbits/sec or higher in the future.

- ■ Frame Relay is a variable-length packet technology that is widely available to handle local to global connections. It provides speeds of 56 Kbits/sec to 1.544 Mbits/sec.

- ■ ATM is an emerging high-bandwidth technology that provides superior fixed-length cell relay technology on a global scale.

Figure S-13 shows the basic configuration of a customer connection to the telephone company's SMDS network.

SMDS is compatible with the IEEE 802.6 Metropolitan Area Network (MAN) standard, as well as Broadband ISDN (B-ISDN). SMDS does provide management and billing services not specified in the MAN standard, however. It uses the Distributed Queue Dual Bus (DQDB) as the interface and access method for the network. The SMDS network is a dual bus design that forms an unclosed ring. Physically, it takes on the form of a star-configured network like token ring in which all cables are connected at a central location. If the bus is spliced, the formerly unclosed portion is automatically joined to maintain the ring. DQDB fills the bus with time slots into which any connected device or site can place data for transport. Think of a train full of boxcars into which data is placed for transport to other locations.

DQDB provides a true multi-access bus technology because all nodes can access the bus when they want until the network is saturated. Up to 512 nodes are allowed

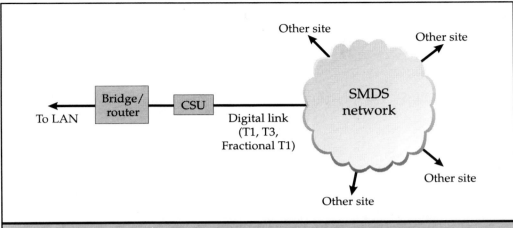

Figure S-13. *Switched Multimegabit Data Service connection scheme*

on the bus, which can extend up to 160 km and operate at 150 Mbits/sec. Slot access can be controlled to prevent some nodes from using too many slots. The slot size is 53 bytes, with 5 bytes used for header information and 48 bytes used for data. A transmitting node can transmit packets of up to 9,188 bytes. These are split up into smaller 48-byte chunks to fit into the SMDS slots and reassembled at the receiving end. Header information completes the slot data.

Many carriers are gearing up for ATM, and are either installing SMDS as a stepping-stone to ATM, or are providing mostly ATM services. MCI and GTE are deploying SMDS, but AT&T is pushing ATM. SMDS differs from ATM with the addition of many "service" enhancements. For example, SMDS provides usage-based billing and some interesting network management features. It builds packets on top of the cell structure, taking advantage of both packet features and fast cell switching. Packet features include the ability to address special groups or screen packets. Customers can build a logical private network through the SMDS network if necessary.

Some industry analysts feel that SMDS will fail to become popular due to Frame Relay and ATM technology. Carriers have been slow to adopt SMDS, and it is not available in every metropolitan area. Currently, equipment for Frame Relay connections is approximately one sixth the cost of comparable SMDS equipment.

The SMDS Interest Group (SIG) is an association of local and telecommunication carriers, SMDS product vendors, service providers, and end users based in Mountain View, California (415/962-2590). The SIG consists of user groups and *working groups* that promote SMDS and work on specifications that improve the standard and promote compatibility. There is a technical working group that is developing new specifications such as support for protocols including Transmission Control Protocol/Internet Protocol (TCP/IP), Systems Network Architecture (SNA),

Internetwork Packet Exchange (IPX), AppleTalk, DECnet, and others. The technical working group is also working on a Frame Relay encapsulation method. An *intercarrier working group* is made up of carriers that define the interconnection and management of intercarrier SMDS. A public relations group and a user group organize seminars, educational sessions, and generally make information about SMDS available.

RELATED ENTRIES Asynchronous Transfer Mode; Carriers; Carrier Services; Frame Relay; Local Exchange Carrier; Packet-Switching Networks; Switched Services; *and* T1/T3 Services

Switched Services

A switched service is a telecommunication offering that provides customers with more flexible wide area networks options than building private networks with dedicated leased digital lines. In a private network, as shown on the left in Figure S-14, a customer installs their own switching equipment, then leases dedicated lines from local exchange carriers and/or long distance carriers to interconnect all the remote sites. Customers get full, private use of the lines. Customers using public switching services have two service options as described next. There are circuit-switching services and packet-switching services:

■ *Circuit-switched services* provide high-quality digital circuits between two points on a temporary basis, giving customers who don't need full-time dedicated services an economical option for obtaining high-speed private digital lines only when required.

■ *Packet-switching services* provide any-to-any connections for simultaneous transmitters over a mesh-type packet-switched network. A packet-switched network is compared to a private network in Figure S-14.

Keep in mind that customers still need switched or dedicated lines to access the packet-switched network, but the distance of the access line is usually short and keeps cost down. In addition, only one line is needed to connect into the network, instead of a dedicated line to every site.

To overcome some of the problems of dedicated lines and provide more economical service to its customers, the carriers provide either circuit-switching or packet-switching services. These services offer three important features:

■ Switching services can provide any-to-any connectivity. Customers can change the end points of the link to accommodate changing business needs, such as an office move or the addition of a new customer.

■ Switching services can provide bandwidth-on-demand. During peak traffic, more bandwidth is made available. The customer is typically charged a different rate for any bandwidth used over the contracted rate.

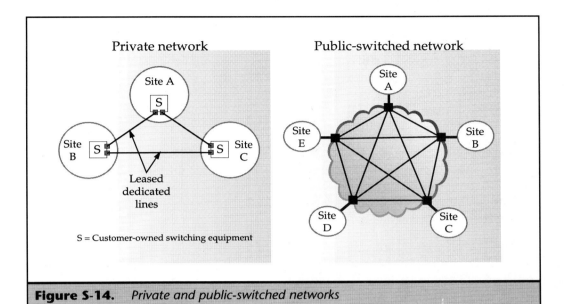

Figure S-14. *Private and public-switched networks*

■ Charges are based on actual customer usage, as opposed to leased lines in which customers pay a flat rate, even if the line goes unused part of the time.

The two types of switching services, circuit switching and packet switching, are discussed in the following sections.

Circuit-Switched Services

Circuit-switching networks provide a way to set up a physical communication channel between the calling equipment to the called equipment. Features of this type of line include a fixed data rate in which both ends must operate at the same rate. A setup phase is required, but digital switching equipment now used by carriers such as AT&T reduces setup time to milliseconds. Integrated Services Digital Network (ISDN) brings digital transmission all the way to the customer's site at up to 64 Kbits/sec, without the need for a modem. Other circuit-switched services include Switched-56 and dialup lines.

Switched digital circuits are available from many carriers including the regional Bell operating companies (RBOCs) such as Ameritech and Bell Atlantic, as well as interexchange carriers (IXCs) like US Sprint, MCI, and AT&T. These services accommodate internetworks, as well as imaging and video traffic. They are also used for fax connections and backup lines. Switched T1 is a relatively new service based on the T1 technology first introduced by AT&T in 1962.

Switched-56

Switched-56 service has recently grown in popularity as an economical link for video teleconferencing, LAN-to-LAN connections, Group 4 facsimile interconnections, and as a high-speed service for telecommuters. Traditionally, its fast setup and switching feature has been used as a backup line to handle overflow traffic from other connections, such as T1 lines. Rates are usually cheaper than permanent leased lines, but special connection equipment is necessary. See "Switched-56 Services."

Integrated Services Digital Network (ISDN)

ISDN provides all-digital services on the local loop between the home or business user. ISDN has three channels, two that provide 64 Kbits/sec and a third used for signaling that provides 16 Kbits/sec. See "Integrated Service Digital Network" for more details.

AT&T Switched Digital Services

AT&T offers a set of circuit-switched digital services. Many of these services have been available for some years.

- ACCUNET Switched-56, 64, 384, and 1,536 Kbits/sec Services. The 384 and 1536 services are accessed only with ISDN links.

- Software Defined Data Network (SDDN) is a service that provides 56, 64, and 384 Kbits/sec rates with volume discounted pricing and a private numbering plan. It also has vertical ISDN features such as calling-party screening.

- Switched Digital International (SDI) is offered at 56 and 64 Kbits/sec in 20 countries. Video teleconferencing and Group 4 facsimile interconnections are commonly used on these lines.

- Global Business Video Services provides multipoint video teleconferencing.

The following table illustrates AT&T's pricing structure:

Service	Monthly Charge	Price of Transmitting a 1 MB File
Private Line	$1,550	N/A
Voiceband Data 2.4 Kbits/sec	$459	$19.05
Voiceband Data 19.2 Kbits/sec	$92	$2.38
ACCUNET Switched-56	$86	$0.75
ACCUNET Switched-64	$54	$0.66

Dedicated lines are fixed in cost; costs for switched lines are based on usage. Figure S-15 shows AT&T's estimate of the crossover point between a Switched-56 Kbits/sec line and a dedicated 56 Kbits/sec line.

MCI Communications Virtual Private Data Services

MCI Communications Corp. provides switched T1 and T3 services through its Virtual Private Data Services. Prices depend on distance and connection time. Switched T1 starts at $2.50 for the first 30 seconds and 20 cents for each additional 6 seconds for distances of less than 55 miles. The rate nearly doubles for distances over 1,910 miles. Switched T3 begins at $37.50 for the first 30 seconds and $3.00 for each additional 6 seconds for circuits under 55 miles. This rate also almost doubles for distances over 1,910 miles.

Packet-Switched Services

Packet-switched networks transmit addressed packets of data from one location to another through a network in which there is no single circuit, but a mesh of many circuits. Users on a local area network connected to a packet-switched network can simultaneously send packets to many different destinations on the packet-switched network. The service is connectionless, meaning that it is not necessary to set up a circuit, although logical circuits can be set up through the network that provides connection-oriented services such as packet acknowledgement and flow control.

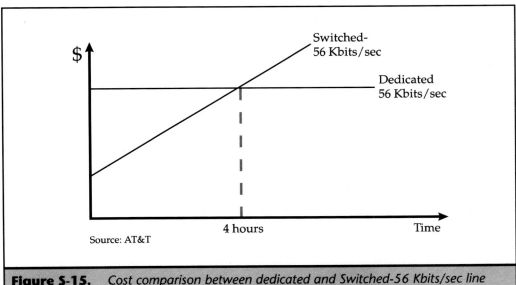

Figure S-15. *Cost comparison between dedicated and Switched-56 Kbits/sec line*

Virtual circuits provide all the benefits of dedicated lines or circuit switching over a packet-switched network.

A *packet-switching public data network (PSPDN)* is often pictured as a cloud due to the many possible connections, as shown on the right in Figure S-14. This type of network provides *any-to-any* connections, as opposed to a circuit-switched network, which provides a temporary dedicated connection between two systems. The PSPDN is made up of *exchanges* that examine packets and forward them out a specific port that delivers them along the best route to their destination, much like a train switching yard or a traffic circle in a downtown area. Packets are limited in length to prevent extremely long packets from tying up the exchange and preventing other packets from getting through.

Packet-switching networks such as Asynchronous Transfer Mode (ATM) are emerging that offer megabit-per-second transfer rates. The "fast-packet" services are providing new ways to communicate over wide areas. See "Packet-Switching Networks."

RELATED ENTRIES   Cell Relay; Circuit-Switching Services; Frame Relay; Packet-Switching Networks; Switched Multimegabit Data Service; *and* X.25

Switched Virtual Circuit

A virtual circuit is a pathway through a mesh-type, packet-switched network that appears to be a dedicated circuit. A *switched virtual circuit (SVC)* is a connection between end stations with sessions lasting only as long as needed. The connection is disabled when the session ends. A *permanent virtual circuit (PVC)*, is a fixed circuit that is assigned and maintained by the network. The line is always set up, eliminating the time required to set it up and take it down. A PVC is typically established between routers that must maintain a constant connection in order to transfer routing information in a dynamic network environment.

RELATED ENTRY   Virtual Circuits

Switching Hubs

A switching hub is a device that can reduce contention on shared network topologies by reducing the number of nodes on a segment using microsegmentation techniques. On a microsegmented network, a local area network (LAN) segment may have a few as one node. The switching hub then handles all the connections between nodes on different LAN segments that need to communicate. Switching techniques should not be confused with port switching, which is a management function that managers use to move workstations from one logical segment to another using a management program rather than physically moving cables at a hub. With switching technology LANs can be segmented, and the switch handles traffic between segments much like a bridge, but without the slow throughput of a bridge. The original switching hubs were designed for departmental use and are built on their own chassis. Newer switching hubs are modular units that fit into enterprise hubs.

If you have a network with 20 users that is bogged down by excess traffic, you can split the network into two segments and bridge them, thus cutting the traffic load and reducing contention on each new LAN segment. This assumes that you can keep all the users or devices that normally talk to each other on the same segment, thus reducing the amount of intersegment traffic. If traffic is still a problem, you can split the LAN into four segments, six segments, and so on. A switching hub performs exactly this type of segmentation. It has a number of ports, each of which is a dedicated LAN segment.

The switching hub handles intersegment traffic via an internal matrix switch. All switching is handled at the Media Access Control (MAC) layer. When a packet arrives at the switch, its destination address is quickly noted and a connection is set up to the appropriate end segment. Subsequent packets are relayed through the switch without the need to store-and forward packets, as is necessary with bridges.

Most switching hubs are Ethernet, so a single workstation attached by itself to a port would get 10 Mbits/sec throughput to the switching hub. Since no other workstation shares the port, there are no contentions and the workstation gets the segments full bandwidth. Some vendors are also working on token ring switching hubs. High-speed switching hubs are also available with Asynchronous Transfer Mode (ATM) switching backplanes.

The idea of the switching hub was first pioneered by Kalpana, Inc., with its EtherSwitch. The EtherSwitch technology is being used in other vendors' products. For example, Hewlett-Packard has integrated it into its EtherTwist hubs and SynOptics Communications has included it in its LattisSwitch Series 3000 hubs.

Symmetrical Multiprocessing

See Multiprocessing.

Synchronous Communication

When devices exchange data, there is a flow of information between the two, called a *bit-stream*. In any data transmission, the sender and receiver must have a way to extract the individual characters or blocks (frames) that are transmitted in the bit-stream. Imagine standing at the end of a data pipe. Characters arrive in a continuous stream of bits, so you need a way to separate one block of bits from another. In asynchronous communication, each character is separated by a flag so you know exactly where a character begins and ends. The sender places the flag between the characters. In synchronous communication, both the sender and receiver are synchronized with a clock, so, for example, every second you reach down and grab a block of bits.

The important point is that in synchronous communication, the sender and receiver must synchronize their clocks so the receiver knows exactly where new characters begin. To maintain clock synchronization over long periods, a special bit-transition pattern is embedded in the digital signal that assists in maintaining the timing between sender and receiver. One method of embedding timing information is called *bipolar encoding* as pictured in Figure S-16. In this method, the bit-stream pictured at the top is meshed with the clock pulse pictured in the middle to produce the transmission signal shown at the bottom. Note that changes in the value of the bit stream, combined with the clock signal, creates a clock signal that is either a positive or a negative value, depending on the bit value.

Synchronous communication is either character-oriented or bit-oriented. Character-oriented transmissions are used to send blocks of characters such as those found in American Standard Code for Information Interchange (ASCII) files. Each block must have a starting flag similar to asynchronous communication so the receiving system can initially synchronize with the bit-stream and locate the beginning of the characters. Two or more control characters known as *synchronous idle (SYN)* characters are inserted at the beginning of the bit-stream by the sender. These characters are used to synchronize a block of information. Once correct synchronization has been established between sender and receiver, the receiver places the block it receives as characters in a memory buffer.

Bit-oriented synchronous communication is used primarily for the transmission of binary data. It is not tied to any particular character set and the frame contents doesn't need to include multiples of eight bits. A unique 8-bit pattern (01111110) is used as a flag to start the frame.

RELATED ENTRY   Synchronous Data Link Control

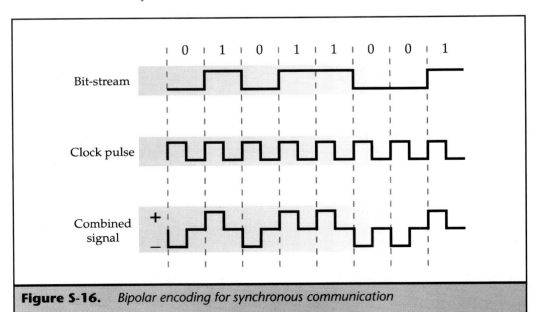

Figure S-16.   *Bipolar encoding for synchronous communication*

Synchronous Data Link Control (SDLC)

SDLC is an IBM-defined Data Link Control protocol developed in the 1970s for communication over wide-area links to IBM host systems in Systems Network Architecture (SNA) environments. SDLC is based on synchronous, bit-oriented operations as compared to byte-oriented protocols such as Bisync. IBM submitted SDLC to standards committees, which produced the following standards, although SDLC remains the primary serial link protocol for SNA.

■ ANSI created the Advanced Data Communication Control Procedure (ADCCP) from SDLC.

■ ISO created the High-level Data Link Control (HDLC).

■ The CCITT modified HDLC to create Link Access Procedure (LAP) and Link Access Procedure, Balanced (LAP-B).

In SDLC, a primary station controls the operation of other secondary stations. Secondary stations are polled to see if they have data to send. If a secondary station has data, it transmits when recognized by the primary station. The primary station is responsible for establishing and maintaining links. There are four basic connection methods:

■ *Point-to-Point* A primary station is directly connected to a secondary station.

■ *Multipoint* A primary station is connected to multiple secondary stations.

■ *Loop* A primary station is connected to multiple secondary stations in a loop configuration in which messages are passed from one station to the next.

■ *Hub Go-Ahead* A little-used loop configuration using daisy-chained cables is connected from a primary station to secondary station and leading back to the primary station.

SDLC uses a typical frame format in which information is bounded by flags to separate each frame. An *address field* contains the address of the secondary station, a *control field* that specifies the type of frame, and a *Frame Check Sequence (FCS)* contains error checking values.

A typical SDLC configuration consists of multiple 3270 dumb terminals at a remote site connected to a cluster controller such as an IBM model 3x74. The cluster controller then connects with the host system over a 56-Kbits/sec leased line. Companies such as Cisco have improved this connection scheme. Cisco routers can pass native SDLC traffic through point-to-point serial links and can multiplex other protocol traffic with SDLC over these links. An encapsulation scheme is available to transport SDLC frames in Internet Protocol (IP) datagrams for transport over non-SDLC networks. This type of arrangement provides routing rather than bridging using routing protocols such as Cisco's Interior Gateway Routing Protocol (IGRP).

RELATED ENTRY High-level Data Link Control

Synchronous Optical Network (SONET)

SONET is a Physical layer standard for fiber-optic transmissions that was first proposed by Bellcore in the mid-1980s. It was standardized by the American National Standards Institute (ANSI) and recommended worldwide by the Consultative Committee for International Telegraph and Telephone (CCITT). Think of SONET as a physical network for a global communication system in the same way you think of an Ethernet twisted-pair LAN as the communication system for your organization's network. It is a potentially global network, built on fiber-optic cable with standardized data rates, and is recognized worldwide. SONET removes the boundaries between the telephone companies of the world.

SONET defines the transmission of synchronous and isochronous (time-sensitive data such as real-time video) information. With SONET, carriers can provide customers with a way to build fast networks initially on a metropolitan scale and eventually on a global scale, since SONET provides a way for the carriers worldwide to interconnect their communication equipment. International digital signaling rates have been in disagreement, which has blocked the development of global transmission systems. For example, DS1 defines 1.544 Mbits/sec in the US, while the European counterpart, E1, defines 2.048 Mbits/sec. SONET defines the digital hierarchy in Table S-1.

While SONET defines the fiber-optic network for transporting signals, wide area network (WAN) technologies such as Switched Multimegabit Data Services (SMDS) and Asynchronous Transfer Mode (ATM) operate on top of it. These are cell relay technologies, not variable-length frame technologies; therefore, they scale easily up to the transmission rates possible on the SONET networks. See "Cell Relay" for more information.

SONET defines the following:

■ Transmission rates, optical interfaces, operation, and maintenance.

OC Level	Line Rate
OC-1	51.8 Mbits/sec
OC-3	155.5 Mbits/sec
OC-9	466.5 Mbits/sec
OC-12	622.0 Mbits/sec
OC-18	933.1 Mbits/sec
OC-24	1.24 Gbits/sec
OC-36	1.86 Gbits/sec
OC-48	2.48 Gbits/sec

Table S-1.   *SONET Interface Rates*

■ A hierarchy of optical signal rates as listed in Table S-1 that is consistent throughout the world.

■ Multiplexed channels over synchronous circuits. Such a structure provides a way to know exactly where the frames are located for a particular channel and extract those frames without demultiplexing the entire multiplexed signal. The advantage for customers is that many different types of channels (low-speed and high-speed) can be routed through the network.

■ Fiber-optic transmission standards that allow interconnection of different vendor and carrier systems.

A SONET system consists of cable runs between SONET multiplexing devices. SONET defines fiber-optic cable and light-generating specifications, as well as multiplexing of data and frame generation. The SONET signal carries data and control information in a synchronous stream. The control information is embedded in the signal and is referred to as the *overhead*. The overhead portion of the SONET signal contains the following components:

■ The *section* overhead portion handles frame generation and error monitoring. All devices on the line use these features.

■ The *line* overhead portion provides a way to monitor the status of the line.

■ The *path* overhead portion provides control signaling and error-monitoring data between the end points (path termination equipment) on the network.

The SONET specification also defines how low-speed signals like T1/E1 and T3/E3 are inserted into the synchronous transmissions. SONET provides services beyond the current T3 45 Mbits/sec barrier. The basic optical transmission rate of 51.8 Mbits/sec accommodates one T3 line or 28 T1 lines. At the high-end, the OC-48 optical carrier can accommodate up to 1,344 T1 lines or 48 T3 lines. Initially, the OC-3 rate will provide customer-to-carrier services, but higher-rate services will grow in use through the 1990s.

Optical cable provides enormous bandwidth, which will bring pricing for wide area networks down to affordable ranges. Many companies will be able set up networks that give remote users the same access speed to data as local users, increasing their ability to communicate and compete. Copper wire does not provide the scalability of fiber-optic cable because much more wire is needed to deliver the same bandwidth.

RELATED ENTRIES   Asynchronous Transfer Mode; Carriers; Cell Relay; Fiber-Optic Cable; Telecommunication; *and* Wide Area Networks

System Fault Tolerance (SFT)

This feature allows you to provide redundancy for hardware in a system. Fault tolerance is the more general term. System Fault Tolerance (SFT) is used by Novell when describing the fault-tolerant features built into its NetWare operating systems. SFT allows you to install two disks and then mirror the contents of the main disk on the secondary disk (see "Disk Mirroring and Duplexing"). If the main disk fails, the secondary disk takes over. The disk controller can also be duplicated, or duplexed, to further protect from hardware failure. SFT Level III (available optionally) takes redundancy a step further by duplexing entire servers. If the primary server goes down, the secondary server takes over without an interruption.

RELATED ENTRY   Fault Tolerance

System Object Model (SOM), IBM

IBM's System Object Model is an object-oriented technology that aims to improve existing procedural programming projects with object-oriented techniques. It is a language-neutral technology that allows classes written in different languages to work together assuming they support SOM bindings. Distributed SOM (DSOM) is an extension of SOM that operates over distributed networks. It allows systems to share objects using an object request broker and manages the communication between objects. The products work on Transmission Control Protocol/Internet Protocol (TCP/IP) networks and NetWare Internetwork Packet Exchange (IPX) networks.

In 1993, IBM, Sun Microsystems, Inc., and Hewlett-Packard decided to share the object technologies in an effort to compete against the object technology in Microsoft's Cairo project. Sun's object technology is Distributed Objects Everywhere (DOE) and Hewlett-Packard's object technology is Distributed Object Management Facility (DOMF). SOM is also part of OpenDOC, which is a specification designed to help developers create object-sharing applications in network environments. OpenDOC is defined by the OpenDOC Alliance, which is primarily sponsored by Apple Computer and supported by IBM, Novell, Borland, WordPerfect, and other companies that are not willing to completely rely on Microsoft's Object Linking and Embedding for their object technologies.

IBM is working to make SOM and DSOM into industry standards. They are working with several standardization committees and encouraging language vendors to use the technologies. IBM has produced a SOM library for the Workplace Shell of OS/2 2.0. In addition, IBM's VisualAge is an object-oriented development tool for manipulating SOM and DSOM objects. VisualAge can be used to create applications that run across multiple platforms without the developer needing to get too involved in programming details. The applications can be implemented with graphical interfaces and get involved with network resource sharing and back-end database access to IBM legacy systems. Records can be mapped into objects.

RELATED ENTRIES   Compound Documents; Distributed Object Management Facility; Distributed Objects Everywhere, SunSoft; Distributed System Object Model; Object Linking and Embedding; Object-Oriented Technology; *and* Objects

Systems Application Architecture (SAA)

IBM Systems Application Architecture (SAA) is a set of application, communication, and user-interface specifications for IBM mainframe operating systems such as Virtual Memory (VM), Multiple Virtual Memory (MVS), midrange operating systems like OS/400 (for IBM AS/400 series), and OS/2 for desktop systems. SAA defined *common applications*, which are applications that can run on any SAA platform. Thus, applications written to SAA can run on a wider range of systems. There are three main components in the architecture:

- *Common Programming Interface (CPI)*   Provides a common environment across the SAA platforms for executing programs. The APIs within CPI provide database, communication, presentation, and other services. CPI-C (Communication) is part of the IBM Networking Blueprint.

- *Common User Access (CUA)*   Defines how information is presented to the user using an interface that is common over different platforms.

- *Common Communication Support (CCS)*   Defines the interconnection of SAA systems and the protocols used for communications and data exchange.

Some industry analysts see SAA as a failed strategy because it only linked IBM systems and did not produce enough products to make it a significant standard. The Networking Blueprint is IBM's newest vision that encompasses support for multiple application interfaces, networking protocols (TCP/IP, OSI, SNA, and NetBIOS), and transmission methods such as fast-packet Frame Relay and Asynchronous Transfer Mode (ATM).

RELATED ENTRIES   IBM; IBM Networking Blueprint

Systems Network Architecture (SNA), IBM

Systems Network Architecture (SNA), first introduced in 1974, is IBM's scheme for connecting its 3270 family of products. SNA includes a suite of networking protocols.

Included in this architecture are mainframe computer systems (hosts), midrange computer systems, 3270 terminals and desktop computers, and a strategy that lets these systems communicate with host systems, or with each other in a peer-to-peer arrangement.

A brief history will help distinguish how centralized, hierarchical SNA fits into today's peer-to-peer, client-server paradigm. SNA was designed in the days when large numbers of nonprogrammable terminals connected to IBM host systems. SNA provided static routing between interconnected hosts so that a user working at one of the terminals could access any of the interconnected hosts. Prior to this arrangement, a user had to log on to a separate terminal for each host. At about the same time, the Transmission Control Protocol/Internet Protocol (TCP/IP) protocol was under development with the objective of interconnecting computers of many sizes, including personal computers, not just host systems. This is the main difference between SNA and TCP/IP. The latter was specifically designed for the predominant peer-to-peer environment we have today.

Because SNA was designed for centralized IBM-only mainframe computing environments, it is not suitable for today's peer-to-peer, client-server, multivendor, multiprotocol environments. These environments were typically created at the department level as each manager designed and built his or her local area network (LAN). As enterprise networks are built to interconnect these LANs, the multitude of vendor products and protocols must be dealt with. IBM's SNA strategy began to crumble as its customers added LANs and wanted to integrate them into the SNA environment.

To provide program-to-program communications, IBM introduced Advanced Program-to-Program Communications (APPC), and to counter the TCP/IP threat, IBM introduced Advanced Peer-to-Peer Networking (APPN). APPN provides decentralized network computing on an enterprise scale while maintaining the viability of host systems. Large and small systems interoperate as peers over APPN networks. IBM's newest strategy is to continue supporting APPN while embracing industry-standard protocols such as TCP/IP and the Open Systems Interconnection (OSI) protocols. This is outlined by the *Networking Blueprint* and implemented in products that conform to it. An example is *Multiprotocol Transport Network (MPTN)*, which decouples applications from underlying network protocols, allowing applications written to work with one specific protocol to use other protocols.

With this in mind, a description of SNA follows. You might want to refer to "Advanced Peer-to-Peer Networking"—often called the "new SNA"—for a further discussion.

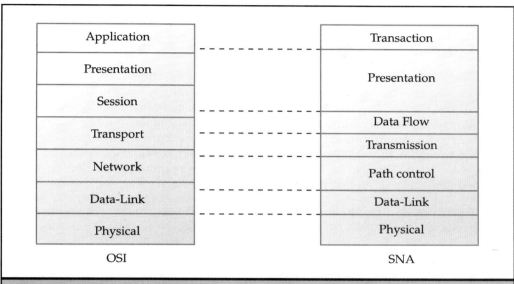

Figure S-17.   *SNA and OSI protocol stack comparison*

SNA

The SNA protocol stack is compared to the OSI protocol stack in Figure S-17. It is interesting to note that the ISO used IBM's SNA protocol stack as a starting model for its OSI stack.

■ The *Physical* layer allows many different types of physical connections.

■ The *Data-Link* layer defines Synchronous Data Link Control (SDLC) and LAN protocols such as Token Ring.

■ The *Path Control* controls routing and can subdivide datagrams and reassemble them to accommodate the transmission facilities.

■ The *Transmission* layer provides connection-oriented services that can set up a link between two end points to monitor data flow and guarantee delivery.

■ The *Data-Flow* layer monitors the flow of data and handles "conversations" between end-points to prevent data overflow.

■ The *Presentation* layer performs data conversions and application interfacing

■ The *Transaction* layer provides the interface into networking services for applications.

As discussed under the heading "IBM Mainframe Environment," an IBM SNA network consists of host systems, terminals (or PCs running emulation software) and printers, cluster controllers, communication controllers, and other components. The terminals and printers are connected to cluster controllers, which in turn connect to the host or to a communication controller if they are remote from the host. These hardware components and the software that runs in them are called *nodes*, and they are interconnected with *data links*. Nodes are end points or junctions in the network as described here:

■ Type 2 nodes are basically peripheral nodes, such as midrange computers, personal computers, terminals, and printers.

■ Type 4 nodes are communication controllers, which provide remote terminal links into host systems. Communication controllers relieve mainframe systems from the constant interruptions that come from terminals. They transmit and receive information, detect and correct errors, and concentrate the connections of many terminals.

■ Type 5 nodes are host computer systems that control and manage the network.

The media that interconnect nodes are copper wire, fiber-optic cable, or microwave. Data links are governed by the Synchronous Data Link Control (SDLC) protocol, Binary Synchronous Communications (BISYNC) protocol, Token Ring, X.25, and more recently, Ethernet, Frame Relay, and Fiber Distributed Data Interface (FDDI). In addition, a channel link is a direct connection between hosts, or hosts and their front-end processors. These links can be "slow" copper cables, or high-speed, fiber-optic cables that can extend many kilometers.

The nodes and links discussed here are physical entities. When a user runs an application, he or she does so through *sessions*. A session is a communication channel to *network addressable units*. The SNA network consists of logical and physical units:

■ *Logical units (LUs)* LUs are ports into the network through which a user accesses a network resource. LUs are considered sessions and have the following types:

  Type 1   A session that provides interactive batch transfers
  Type 2   IBM 3270 display terminal
  Type 3   IBM 3270 printer session
  Type 6.2   A program-to-program communication session
  Type 7   IBM midrange computer sessions over 525x terminals

■ *Physical units (PUs)* The PU resides in the node that communicates with the host. PUs manage and control the communication link. There are currently three PU types:

Type 2 Implemented in cluster controllers
Type 4 Implemented in front-end processors
Type 5 Implemented in host communication software

There are two main software components in the SNA network:

■ *System Services Control Point (SSCP)* This software runs in the host and manages all the resources within the host's domain. The host system actually runs the Virtual Telecommunications Access Method (VTAM) software, which contains the SSCP.

■ *Network Control Program (NCP)* This software runs in the communication controller (front-end processor). It relieves the host of communication processes such as routing, session management, buffering of incoming and outgoing data, error detection and correction in communications, and other tasks.

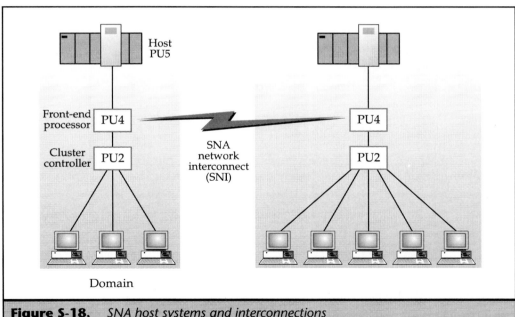

Figure S-18. *SNA host systems and interconnections*

The different components of an SNA network are pictured in Figure S-18. An SNA Network Interconnect (SNI) feature provides a way to connect two separate host systems, which are located in separate areas, called *subareas* or *domains*. SNI merges and maps the network resource names and addresses on the joined systems and provides alias names to avoid conflicts. SNI is sometimes used for Electronic Data Exchange (EDI) applications between suppliers and manufacturers, or when two companies merge.

As internal networks proliferated in the 1980s, organizations became more and more interested in peer-to-peer models for interconnecting desktop computer systems. This model differs from the central control model of SNA. In response, IBM introduced Advanced Program-to-Program Communications (APPC) and LU 6.2. APPC provided the programming interface and protocols to implement LU 6.2, which provided a communication session between two separate applications. From there, IBM developed Advanced Peer-to-Peer Networking (APPN), a peer-to-peer routing protocol.

To manage the SNA environment, IBM introduced NetView in 1986. It provides monitoring and control features for managing nodes on the network.

RELATED ENTRIES   Advanced Peer-to-Peer Networking; Distributed Relational Database Architecture; IBM; IBM Mainframe Environment; IBM Networking Blueprint; Information Warehouse; *and* Multiprotocol Transport Network, IBM

SystemView, IBM

SystemView is an enterprise-wide network management system that recognizes and manages systems in heterogeneous environments. It was one of IBM's first products to recognize industry-standard protocols such as Transmission Control Protocol/Internet Protocol (TCP/IP) and Open Systems Interconnection (OSI), not just its own Systems Network Architecture (SNA) protocols.

- SystemView is built on the Systems Application Architecture (SAA) environment.
- It uses the OSI Common Management Information Protocol (CMIP).
- Information about managed resources on the network is stored in an object database.

While SystemView is an IBM product that focuses on the management of IBM equipment, it includes OSI standards that make it a viable option for managing the enterprise network.

RELATED ENTRIES   IBM; IBM Networking Blueprint; *and* Management Standards and Tools

T1/T3 Services

The T-carrier services deliver digital data and voice transmission over local or wide areas at rates as high as 45 Mbits/sec. The circuits are traditionally dedicated, but switched services are also available for customers that need high-bandwidth on a periodic basis. Customers can build their own private networks with T1 or T3 lines, as pictured on the left in Figure T-1. The customer leases a dedicated line from the phone company between each site, then installs onsite switching equipment that manages packet traffic among those sites. This is called a private network because the customer's equipment directs the traffic to each of the leased-line sites.

In contrast, packet-switched technologies such as Frame Relay, Switched Multimegabit Data Transfer Service (SMDS), and Asynchronous Transfer Mode (ATM) provide any-to-any connections over mesh topologies as shown on the right in Figure T-1. A packet is a self-contained, addressed package of data that is forwarded through relays in the packet-switched mesh network to its destination. A predefined connection between two points is not always necessary. Customers can build virtual networks using packet-switched services and avoid the use of expensive long-distance T1 lines. T1 or other digital services are still required in most cases to connect into the packet-switched services, but the trunk distance is much shorter and customers get the benefits of the switched network. However, some customers will still need the dedicated and private line services that T1/T3 provide, especially if a lot of traffic exists between two points.

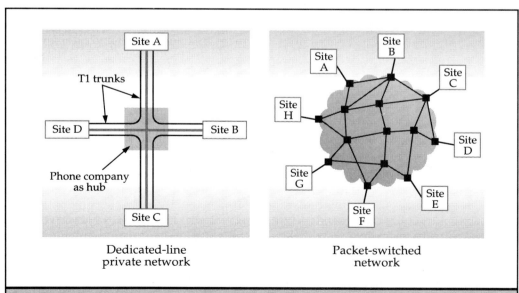

Dedicated-line
private network

Packet-switched
network

Figure T-1.   *Dedicated or switched connection facilities*

With T1, the local telephone company serves as a hub for each network within a certain geographic area. Networks at different company sites within the area serviced by the phone company (usually a metropolitan area) are connected to the hub provided by the phone company. Local telephone companies operate within Local Access and Transport Areas (LATAs), which are equivalent to the geographic area covered by a telephone area code. If the T1 line needs to connect sites located in other LATAs, it is necessary to involve the local phone company, the remote phone company, and an interexchange carrier that can provide long-distance connections.

T-carrier circuits are typically leased on a month-to-month basis and include an initial setup charge. The distance of the lines determines their cost, especially if they cross inter-LATA boundaries and involve two or more phone companies. T1 is usually priced per mile plus a monthly service charge. Prices range from about $3,000 a month for short distances to over $20,000 a month for a connection across the continental United States. A typical use for T1 is real-time access to a company's database by outlying offices. T-carrier services provide the following transmission rates:

- *T1* is the most common digital leased-line service. It provides a bandwidth of 1.544 Mbits/sec.

- *Fractional T1* is an offering that lets customers lease less than the full T1 line. It provides 24 channels of 64 Kbits/sec bandwidth, of which customers can choose the number of those lines that fit their needs. This yields 1.536 Mbits/sec. An additional 64 Kbits/sec is required for overhead, giving a total of 1.544 Mbits/sec.

- *T2* is not offered to the public. It is an internal carrier specification that is equivalent to four T1 lines (6.3 Mbits/sec).

- *T3* is equivalent to 28 T1 circuits and provides a total bandwidth of 44.736 Mbits/sec. This service was initially employed to transmit between microwave stations.

- *Fractional T3* is an offering that lets customers lease less than the full T3 line, depending on their needs.

A digital signal hierarchy is used in the United States as shown in the following table. The T1 services fits into this hierarchy, with a T1 signal equal to the DS-1 signal rate. Note that European signal rates are different than those in the United States. The basic European carrier is E-1, which has a data rate of 2.048 Mbits/sec. Synchronous Optical Network (SONET) will standardize a new signal hierarchy throughout the world with the goal of allowing global interconnection of the phone systems. See "Synchronous Optical Networks."

Service Class	Digital Signal
DS-0	64 Kbits/sec
DS-1	1.544 Mbits/sec

DS-2	6.312 Mbits/sec
DS-3	45 Mbits/sec
DS-4	274 Mbits/sec

The fractional services provide a low-end entry point for customers who initially have low-bandwidth requirements, but anticipate higher-bandwidth requirements in the future. T1 bandwidth of 1.544 Mbits/sec can be divided into twenty-four 64-Kbits/sec channels, each carrying one voice or data transmission. A T1 connection is still installed, but adding additional channels is a simple matter of calling the phone company.

A T1 line is basically a conditioned telephone line, meaning that signal regenerators are placed at closer intervals on the line between the customer and the phone company to reduce line noise. A T1 connection starts with two twisted-wire pairs at the customer site. These wires lead to the conditioned lines established by the phone company. To connect a local area network (LAN) to a T1 line, you need the following equipment.

- *Channel service unit (CSU)* The CSU is the first point of contact for the T1 wires. It diagnoses and prepares the signals on the line for the LAN, and it keeps the line alive if there are problems with the LAN connection equipment.

- *Data service unit (DSU)* The DSU connects to the CSU. It converts LAN signals to T1 signaling formats.

- *Multiplexer* A multiplexer provides a way to load multiple channels of voice or data into the digital line.

- *Bridge or router* The bridge or router provides the connection point between your LAN and the T1 line.

Both voice and data can be multiplexed into the 24 channels of the T1 line. In this configuration, a company can lease a T1 line to transport data and provide channels for frequent voice calls between its company sites. Digitized voice is sampled 8,000 times per second and each sample is represented by an 8-bit value, thus requiring a bandwidth of 64 Kbits/sec per voice call. A typical configuration is pictured in Figure T-2.

The customer interface to the digital facilities of the telephone company is the channel service unit/data service unit (CSU/DSU). It generates digital signals that can be transmitted over the T1 trunk. The local exchange carrier (LEC) is involved if the connections are within a LATA, but inter-LATA connections complicate matters. You need to contact the local and remote LEC, as well as the interexchange carrier (IXC), then the remote LEC. Also, the local loops in each LATA at either side of the long-distance connection are separately billable.

T1 grew out of a need for more bandwidth than that provided by X.25 packet-switched networks or 56 Kbits/sec digital data service (DDS). The ability to multiplex voice on the same line and reduce telephone calling charges also caused a

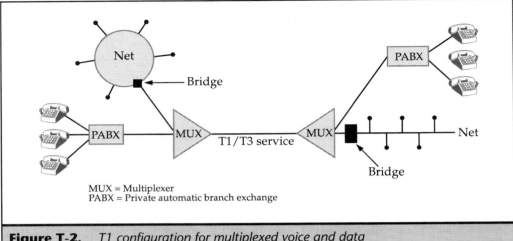

MUX = Multiplexer
PABX = Private automatic branch exchange

Figure T-2.   *T1 configuration for multiplexed voice and data*

dramatic increase in the use of the lines. However, leased dedicated lines have limitations. The first is that they are dedicated and require a high initial setup fee. In addition, bandwidth is fixed, which doesn't accommodate the burst traffic of LANs. Customers may find themselves paying for bandwidth that often goes unused, except during peak traffic hours, and then there isn't enough bandwidth. They are also an expensive way to build private networks over large geographic areas especially when compared to services like Frame Relay.

In today's business environment, companies need to change their wide area network connections as markets change, as workgroups form and disband, or as mergers take place. Fast packet-switching services such as Frame Relay, Switched Multimegabit Data Service (SMDS), and Asynchronous Transfer Mode (ATM) can solve these problems. They provide bandwidth on demand and the ability to switch connections. In addition, they can mimic dedicated circuits through "virtual circuit" capabilities, if necessary. But, keep in mind that dedicated services like T1 are still needed to connect the customer site to the access point of service.

New technologies are boosting the transmission rate in the local loop, which is the connection between customer sites and the local phone company. Integrated Services Digital Network (ISDN) services are now installed in many areas and provide switched digital links in to carrier services. Improvements in signaling techniques are underway. For example, High-bit-rate Digital Subscriber Line (HDSL) permits transmission over the existing copper-based lines at rates of 784 Kbits/sec to T1 rates of 1.544 Mbits/sec. Related products include Asymmetrical Digital Subscriber Line (ADSL) and Very High bit-rate Digital Subscriber Line (VHDSL). These offerings are discussed elsewhere in this book.

RELATED ENTRIES   Carrier Services; Channel Service Unit/Data Service Unit; Circuit-Switching Services; Multiplexing; Networks; Packet-Switching Networks; *and* Wide Area Networks

Taligent

Taligent is an independent company formed by IBM and Apple Computer to develop and market object-oriented operating systems and products. The code name for the operating system product under development is "Pink." Pink is implemented in IBM's Workplace OS operating systems and Apple's new operating system products that run on Macintosh computers and other platforms. The Pink operating system will compete with other object-oriented operating systems such as Microsoft's Cairo. In the meantime, Taligent is concentrating on object-oriented development tools.

Pink is a completely object-oriented operating system due in the 1994-1995 time frame. One of Taligent's goals with Pink is to have it run applications that are already written, including those that run under DOS, Windows, Macintosh, and UNIX. But the real power of object-oriented operating systems is the reusable modular approach to coding new applications. Users will be able to purchase core modules for applications, then add additional feature modules as needed. Pink's common interface lets users replace modules supplied with software such as a spelling checker, draw utility, or charting module with modules produced by other vendors that have more features or a preferred operating method. Microsoft's Object Linking and Embedding implements similar features in the Windows environment.

But Pink goes beyond the ability to add modules at the application level. The operating system level is also modular so users can add network functionality at a later date, or change to a different file system. Users can even run multiple file systems if necessary. Pink will run on systems built around the Motorola PowerPC processors, the Motorola 68060-based Macintoshes, and the Intel Pentium-based systems. IBM is implementing parts of Taligent's work in its Workplace OS operating system. Hewlett-Packard is also working with Taligent, and will implement some of its object-oriented technology in upcoming object-oriented applications.

RELATED ENTRIES   Cairo; Common Object Model; Common Object Request Broker Architecture; Compound Documents; ObjectBroker; Object Linking and Embedding; Object Management Architecture; Object-Oriented Technology; Object Request Broker; Objects; *and* Workplace OS

TeamLinks, DEC

TeamLinks is a distributed groupware product designed for the Microsoft Windows environment that operates on DEC's PATHWORKS networks. It integrates personal productivity tools such as word processors, spreadsheets, and other applications with electronic mail, workflow automation, document routing, conferencing, reference libraries, database access, document management, and other tools to facilitate the flow of information throughout the workgroup.

RELATED ENTRIES   Client/Server Computing; DEC PATHWORKS; *and* Digital Equipment Corporation

Technical Office Protocol (TOP)

TOP (Technical Office Protocol) is an Open Systems Interconnection (OSI) protocol that defines local area network specifications and protocols for office system communication. It was originally developed by Boeing Computer Services, but is now associated with Manufacturing Automation Protocol (MAP). MAP is a networking standard for manufacturing equipment such as plant equipment, robots, computers, terminals, and other programmable equipment. The standard is now under the control of the MAP/TOP Users' Group, which is administered by the Society of Manufacturing Engineers.

Both MAP and TOP use Ethernet and are usually used in conjunction. MAP defines local area networks for terminals, manufacturing devices, and robots on the manufacturing floor, while TOP defines connections in the front office.

RELATED ENTRIES   Manufacturing Automation Protocol; Open Systems Interconnection Model

Telecommunication

Telecommunication is derived from the Greek tele (distant) and communicare (sharing). In modern terms, telecommunication is the electronic transmission of sound, data, facsimiles, pictures, voice, video, and other information between connected systems using either analog or digital signaling techniques. In the United States, the telecommunication industry is regulated by the federal government. Regulation began in 1866 with the signing of the Post Roads Act, which gave the U.S. Postmaster General control over the telegraph industry. The Federal Communications Commission (FCC) now controls both interstate and international telecommunication. The FCC was formed with the Communications Act of 1934.

American Telephone and Telegraph (AT&T) played an important part in the formation of the U.S. telecommunication system, so much so that several antitrust suits were brought against it over the course of many years. In 1913, AT&T was forced to divest itself from Western Union and allow independent carriers to use its long-distance networks. Various actions were taken through the years to break up AT&T, and, by 1984, AT&T was forced by the Justice Department to break up into several regional holding companies called the regional Bell operating companies (RBOCs), in addition to the research division called Bellcore. Today, most local telecommunication involves one of the RBOCs, and long-distance communication involves a local and remote RBOC, along with a long-distance carrier such as AT&T, MCI, or US Sprint. See "Regional Bell Operating Companies."

A public telecommunication network (often called the *public switched telephone network* or PSTN) consists of *transmission components* and *switching components*:

- Transmission components (links) define the actual media used to transmit data and the encoding, multiplexing, and transport techniques.

- Switching components (nodes) includes transmitters and receivers for voice and data routing using circuit switching or packet switching techniques.

The service areas and facilities of the telephone network are pictured in Figure T-3. *Customer premises equipment* includes the telephones, switches, cables, and other hardware at the customer's site. This equipment connects via a *local loop* to the *local exchange carrier (LEC) central office (CO)*. The local loop is typically two- or four-wire copper cable and represents one of the biggest investments of the telephone company. The LEC operates within a *Local Access and Transport Area (LATA)*. LATAs are subdivisions of the seven regions in which the RBOCs operate. For example, the Los Angeles basin is one of 11 LATAs within Pacific Bell's operating area. A LATA typically contains many interconnected *central office* switching facilities that provide localized service. Note that non-RBOC independent phone companies may operate within a LATA to provide competing services.

Any traffic outside a LATA is considered long distance and is handled by interexchange carriers (IXCs) such as AT&T, MCI, and US Sprint. The LECs are required by law to provide a point-of-presence (an interface) for the IXCs. Communication facilities employed by the IXCs include fiber-optic cable, ground-based microwave towers, and satellite-based microwave systems.

The bandwidth of a voice conversation on the analog telephone system is 3 KHz. In the 1970s and 1980s, the carriers began offering digital services such as T1 to accommodate both voice and data traffic. To accommodate voice on these lines, digitizing techniques are used that convert the 3 KHz voice signal into a 64 Kbits/sec digital data signal. A 1.544 Mbits/sec T1 line can accommodate 24 of these 64 Kbits/sec voice channels, although some of the channels are typically used for data. T1 makes sense for a company that makes a lot of voice calls and data connections to branch offices. Multiplexing techniques are used to combine the voice and data signals into a single line for transmission through the telephone network.

Transmission Methods

Transmitting digital computer information over analog telephone lines requires a modem, which converts digital signals to analog signals. The synchronization mechanisms discussed next are used by the sending and receiving stations to ensure that signals are interpreted properly.

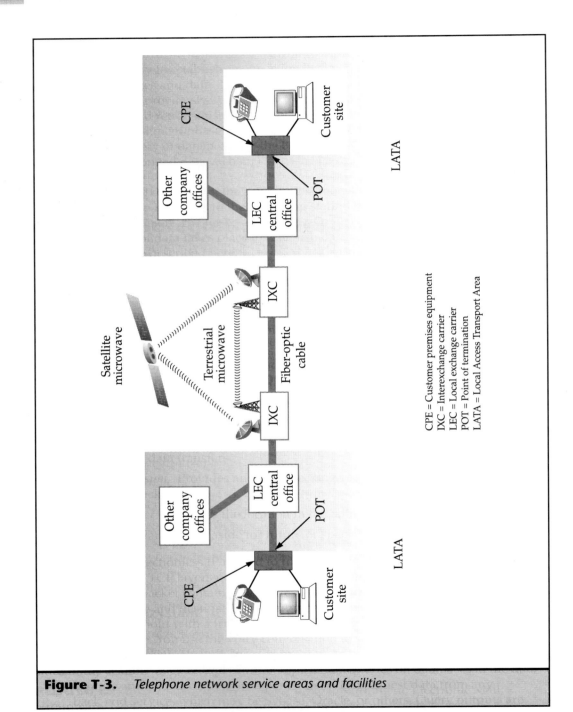

Figure T-3. *Telephone network service areas and facilities*

- *Synchronous transmission* Information is transferred in blocks (frames) of bits that are synchronized with clock signals. Special characters are used to begin the synchronization and periodically check its accuracy. See "Synchronous Communication."

- *Asynchronous transmission* Information is sent one character at a time as a set of bits. Each character is separated by a "start-of-character" bit and "stop" bit. A parity bit is used for error detection and correction. Modems typically use asynchronous methods. See "Asynchronous Communications" and "Modems."

As mentioned, modems convert digital signals for transmission over analog telephone equipment. Modems attach to data terminal equipment (DTE) devices such as desktop computers. There are Bell, Electronic Industries Association (EIA), and International Telecommunications Union (ITU) standards that govern modem design and operating parameters to ensure that two modems can communicate with one another. Some manufacturers use proprietary designs to enhance performance, but you'll usually need the same type of modem on both sides of the communication session.

International standards provide for a maximum rate of 2,400 bits/sec; however, most modems today support various data-compression techniques that can enhance transmission rates as much as 200 percent. Such speeds make inexpensive telephone lines a viable option when compared to digital lines, either dedicated or leased.

Signals follow unidirectional one-way paths or bidirectional two-way paths as described here:

- *Simplex circuit* A one-way transmission, such as a radio broadcast
- *Half-duplex circuit* A two-way transmission, but only in one direction at a time
- *Full-duplex circuit* A two-way simultaneous transmission such as the telephone system

Available Services

A range of connection methods is available for building data networks. The services described here are offered by local exchange carriers, interexchange carriers, and value added carriers (VACs).

- *Dialup telephone connections* A temporary connection over analog telephone lines between a user and a network or between two networks. Modems are required at both ends. Under current standards, transmission rates can go as high as 28.8 Kbits/sec when compression is used.

- *Dedicated analog circuits* This circuit is similar to the dialup line, except that it is always connected (does not require dialing and setup) and the carrier may provide a better grade of service (such as error-free lines).

- *Dedicated digital circuits*   A digital line that is always connected, such as T1, T3, or Fractional T1. The lines are typically leased on a monthly basis and set up between two fixed points.

- *Switched digital circuits*   A digital line that can be switched to provide connections to any site, and only when needed. Customers only pay for what they use. While this option provides more flexibility than the previous method, only two points are connected during the call. These circuits are available from many different carriers. AT&T's ACCUNET services are an example.

- *Packet-switching networks*   Packet-switching is a way to provide any-to-any connections. Network packets from many users are transferred into the packet-switching network where they can be delivered to any remote site attached to the network. X.25 services were common during the 1980s, but the requirements of remote data access, multimedia, and videoconferencing are driving the need for *fast packet services* such as Switched Multimegabit Data Service (SMDS), Frame Relay, and Asynchronous Transfer Mode (ATM).

The transmission of graphics and video images over telecommunication links is becoming a reality because compression technologies are decreasing the size of the information, and the carriers are providing faster transmission services to accommodate it. If a system is available to deliver the information at an affordable rate, the services will be used.

One of the roadblocks to faster transmission services has been the *local loop* between users and the phone company, which is still largely copper-wire analog lines. To provide T1 services on the local loop, signal repeaters must be added every 606 meters (2,000 feet). Integrated Services Digital Network (ISDN) is offered in some areas to provide digital connections to the home. The ISDN line consists of two 64 Kbits/sec voice or data lines and one 16 Kbits/sec signaling line. Even higher digital throughput is planned with the services listed next.

- *Asymmetric Digital Subscriber Line (ADSL)* uses existing lines to provide speeds as high as 1.544 Mbits/sec (T1) in one direction. ADSL is related to Integrated Services Digital Network (ISDN).

- *High-bit-rate Digital Subscriber Line (HDSL)* supports two-way communication and it permits T1 transmission over 12,000 feet.

- *Very High bit-rate Digital Subscriber Line (VHDSL)*, can provide 3 to 6 Mbits/sec service over two twisted pairs.

These techniques open the possibility for services such as video on demand, interactive information, telecommuting, and tele-education.

Other Developments

Other developments underway in the telecommunication market support remote and mobile users. Fiber-based metropolitan area networks are under construction in many areas by companies that compete with the local exchange carriers. In addition, the cable television companies are developing network services to take advantage of the coaxial cable installed in over 60 percent of homes in the United States.

PACKET-RADIO COMMUNICATION   Packet-radio breaks a transmission into small digital packets and transmits them to a mobile user at speeds up to 9,600 bits/sec. The recipient device receives only packets that are addressed to it. Companies involved in packet-radio communication are Ardis (Lincolnshire, Illinois), RAM Mobile Data (Woodbridge, New Jersey), and Nextel (Lafayette, California). See "Wireless LAN Communication."

CELLULAR DIGITAL PACKET COMMUNICATION   Cellular communicators are mobile computing devices that provide two-way transmissions between users and their home office or network. The devices provide E-mail capabilities, and the ability to transmit and receive files and other information. Cellular Digital Packet Data (CDPD) is a cellular radio network specification defined by a consortium of cellular carriers and computer companies. It allows customers to send computer data over cellular networks. See "Wireless LAN Communication."

FIBER-OPTIC METROPOLITAN AREA NETWORKS (MAN)   A metropolitan area network provides customers with transmission right-of-ways through public areas within a city. A MAN is typically associated with the IEEE 802.6 MAN standard, which defines a fiber-optic network built with a dual bus and transmission rates of T1 (1.544 Mbits/sec) to T3 (45 Mbits/sec). The range of the network is 160 kilometers (96 miles). MANs are being built by the telephone carriers to be compatible with services such as Switched Multimegabit Data Service (SMDS). In metropolitan areas, the FCC also allows noncarrier companies to build fiber-based networks that compete with the carriers. These companies are providing competitive rates and superior services in many cases. Customers can connect into any of these networks to build their own private networks within the metropolitan area.

CABLE COMPANY NETWORKS   Cable companies have traditionally relied on coaxial copper cable all the way to their subscribers. However, the requirements of boosting this signal in large metropolitan area networks has limited the bandwidth of the system. The cable franchises now want to install fiber-optic cable as backbones to reduce signal attenuation and the need for amplifiers. Doing so will allow the cable companies to significantly boost their bandwidth and provide more than double the current number of channels. In fact, the cable companies are planning to install enough fiber cable capacity that they can sell lines to other service providers.

    While the cable companies may be better prepared to supply coaxial links to home users than the phone companies, they do not have the switching services that the

T

phone companies have to create connections between customer sites for building networks or setting up video conferencing. In addition, the phone companies were allowed by the FCC to provide video programming over their networks, although they may not own or license programs in the areas they service. There is also talk of removing some of the restrictions placed on the RBOCs, such as a prohibition on providing long-distance services.

The telephone companies are starting to run cable within a few hundred feet of homes in anticipation of future services. While fiber all the way to the home is not planned, existing twisted-pair cable will be used to carry voice signals off the fiber, and coaxial cables will carry video signals. With increased bandwidth, there will be a move away from existing hierarchical structures in which programs are broadcast to many, and a move to two-way communication in which users can interact with other users or service providers.

RELATED ENTRIES   Asynchronous Communication; AT&T; Carrier Services; Local Access and Transport Area; Regional Bell Operating Companies; Signals, Analog and Digital; Synchronous Communication; *and* Transmission Media, Methods, and Equipment

Telenet

The first U.S. commercial packet-switched network. Now called Sprint Net. Not to be confused with Telnet, the login command for Transmission Control Protocol/Internet Protocol (TCP/IP) network systems such as the Internet.

Telnet

Telnet is the login and terminal emulation program for Transmission Control Protocol/Internet Protocol (TCP/IP) networks such as the Internet. It was originally developed for ARPANET but is now mainly used in Internet sessions. Its primary function is to allow users to log into remote host systems. Originally, Telnet was a simple terminal program that sent all user input to the remote host for processing. Newer versions perform more processing locally, thus providing better response and reducing the amount of information transferred over the link to the remote host.

Telnet is a client-server process in which the user invokes the Telnet application on the local system and sets up a link to a Telnet process running on a remote host. The user issues requests at the keyboard that are passed to the Telnet client running in his or her system. Telnet then transmits the requests to the Telnet server on the remote host. Through this process, users can initiate programs on the remote host and run those programs from their own systems as if they were attached directly to the remote host. Most processes run on the remote host. It receives requests from the user's system and processes them in its workspace, thus reducing traffic over the link.

RELATED ENTRY   Internet

Terminal

A terminal is typically a "dumb" user device attached to centralized host systems such as IBM mainframes. The terminal accepts keyboard input from a user and sends that input to a host system. The host system processes the user's keystrokes and commands, then returns output to display on the terminal screen. Personal computers can run programs called *terminal emulators* that allow them to mimic a dumb terminal.

In the IBM environment, a terminal is a device that end users use to communicate with a host. The device may be a monitor/keyboard device, or a printing device. It is connected with coaxial cable to a cluster controller, which is either connected directly to the host or connected through a communication controller to the host. Up to 32 terminals may be attached to a single cluster controller, depending on the model of cluster controller. Each terminal has a separate cable attached to the cluster controller or, to save cable, is attached to a nearby multiplexer device that is attached to a distant cluster controller with one cable.

In the IBM Systems Network Architecture (SNA) environment, cluster controllers are called Physical Unit (PU) Type 2 devices and terminals attached to the cluster controller are called Logical Unit (LU) 2 devices. A printer device attached to a PU Type 2 is either an LU Type 1 or LU Type 3, depending on the printer type.

There are two categories of IBM 3270 terminal devices. Type A devices provide support for extended attributes such as color, highlighting, reverse video, and special character sets. Type B devices are older models without these special attributes.

It is also possible to attach ASCII terminals such as IBM's 3100 series, DEC's VT-52 and VT100 series, Televideo's 900 series, and others to an IBM host by cable-connecting them to IBM 3708, 3710, or 7171 protocol converters, as described under "IBM Mainframe Environment." All ASCII terminals use RS-232-C (or RS-422-A) interfaces, rather than coaxial cable connections.

It's possible to connect with and run host applications using personal computers. One method is to add a special adapter card and 3270-emulation-software combination. The adapter provides a coaxial cable connector so the personal computer can be attached to a cluster controller, and the software makes the terminal emulate an IBM terminal. In emulation mode, the PC can have multiple concurrent sessions with the mainframe.

RELATED ENTRIES   IBM; IBM Mainframe Environment; Mainframe; Multiplexing; *and* Systems Network Architecture

Terminal Servers

Terminal servers are used to connect large numbers of terminals to IBM host systems or minicomputer systems over a local area network (LAN). The terminals are attached to the terminal server via RS-232 serial interfaces and the terminal server is connected to an Ethernet or token ring network. The network then serves as the link between the host system and the terminals. A terminal server is basically an asynchronous multiplexer that connects not only terminals, but computers, modems, printers, and other peripherals to the host system. The terminal server has a number of serial ports and the appropriate network interface.

Terminal servers are not gateways because the attached terminal devices are using a communication protocol that is compatible with the host. When a personal computer is attached to a host through a terminal server, it runs a terminal emulation program that lets it mimic the communication protocols of a terminal. Note however that the terminal server does encapsulate data from terminals for transport over the network to the host system.

Terminator

A terminator is a resister that reflects cable signals. On coaxial cable bus networks two terminators are installed, one at each end of the cable. One terminator, but not both, requires a ground connection. Terminators must have specific resistance value, depending on the network:

Network Type	Value
Ethernet RG-58A/U (Thinnet)	50 ohms
Ethernet RG-59/U (Thicknet)	75 ohms
ARCNET RG-62/U	93 ohms

RELATED ENTRIES   ARCNET; Cabling; Ethernet; Networks; Topology; *and* Transmission Media, Methods, and Equipment

Testing Equipment and Techniques

The primary tools for network testing include cable testers and protocol analysis products. Cable testers are used to test or certify the physical cable plant, while protocol analyzers operate higher up in the protocol stack. A protocol analyzer can look at packets and determine which stations are generating traffic, monitor where errors are occurring, and watch for unusual events on the network such as peaks in traffic or resource usage.

Network Cable Testers

A common source of problems on a network is the cable. There are a number of devices you can use to test cable. Some are quite affordable and should be part of any network manager's toolkit. More expensive equipment can be rented, or you can rely on the services of consultants and professional cable installers. However, a new breed of cable testers is now available that includes a whole range of testing features, including protocol analysis, for several thousand dollars. Most are the size of portable phones. Some cable testing is performed simply to test existing cable or to certify that a cable installation follows customer, vendor, or industry standards for signal-to-noise ratios, performance, and integrity. Cable testers should test for the following:

- *Continuity* testing can determine whether a cable, either on the roll, or installed, will conduct electricity correctly from one end to the other. Cable testing devices include the components for measuring at one end of the cable if it is already installed.

- Cable testers should test for *electrical noise.* Noise below 150 KHz is from electrical transmission lines and fluorescent lights. Noise above 150 KHz is from electrical equipment such as computers and copiers. *Impulse noise* occurs spontaneously and lasts only a short time, so measurements must be taken over time to determine if external sources are causing a continuous impulse problem on the cable plant.

- *Crosstalk* is noise emanating from the digital signals transmitted through adjacent wire pairs. Most testing devices can measure crosstalk by injecting a signal in a wire pair and measuring the energy induced by the signal in adjacent pairs. These tests are not useful for cable on a spool, only for installed cable. Maintaining wire twists all the way up to the connector can reduce crosstalk.

- *Attenuation* is measured by sending a signal through a cable and measuring the signal at the other end of the cable. Attenuation is a natural characteristic of cable, but uncharacteristic attenuation may indicate excessive bends or partial breaks in the cable.

- *Capacitance* measurements can indicate whether a cable has been stretched or has kinks. Cable has a capacitance value that is measured in pico Farads (pF) per foot. A test of cable, either on the spool or installed, will indicate damage.

If you don't have a specific cable-testing device, a simple voltage meter can serve as a tool for testing continuity. You set the meter to its ohm or resistance setting and measure through the center wire and then through the ground, or use an alligator clip to form a loop-back at one end of the cable. If the cable is already installed, you can still measure continuity. For coaxial cable, place a terminating resistor at one end of the cable, then touch the ground with one lead and the center wire with the other. For twisted-pair cable, use an alligator clip to connect the wire pair at one end, then test the other end.

Cable Tracers

You trace a cable to determine its path in a wall or ceiling, or its source and destination. A cable tracer is useful if you need to determine the destination of one wire in a bundle of wires. A tone generator is attached to one end of the cable and an amplifier is then used to listen for the tone at the other end, which is typically a punchdown block for twisted-pair cable. The amplifier indicates when it is near the wire that is producing the signal.

A popular product is the Microtest Tracer. With it, you can locate any coaxial, twisted-pair, or other type of wire hidden inside a floor, wall, or ceiling. The Tracer's sending unit is connected to the wire or cable, and then its pocket-size receiving unit is run over the areas where you suspect the wire runs. When the Tracer's receiving unit passes over the wire, an alarm sounds; the alarm grows stronger as you get closer to the wire.

Time Domain Reflectometers (TDRs)

A TDR determines the locations of breaks and shorts in cables. It sends a high-frequency pulse down the length of the cable and then measures the time it takes for the reflection of the signal to return. Reflections occur at shorts and breaks, and the time and amplitude of the reflection indicates the distance to the problem. In addition, the polarity indicates whether the problem is a short or an open connection. TDRs are now available for under $1,000 from vendors such as Black Box. Note that optical TDRs are also available for testing fiber-optic cable installations.

The Microtest Cable Scanner (approximately $1,500) is a stand-alone, hand-held TDR. It has a 32-character display that reports fault problems in plain English, such as "Short at 306 ft." The Cable Scanner can print a hard copy to any serial printer and save test results in memory for later review. You can test Ethernet, ARCNET, and token ring networks that use coaxial or twisted-pair cable. The Cable Scanner also provides real-time monitoring of a local area network's activity to help determine when a bridge or repeater might need to be added. You can attach the Cable Scanner to an oscilloscope to analyze waveforms. The Tracer product described earlier is included with the Cable Scanner.

Protocol Analyzers

As a general rule, as a network grows, its performance drops. Of course, you can spend more money to upgrade the network. The practical alternative is to tweak settings and look for bottlenecks. You need to be on the lookout for improperly configured devices or overworked servers. You should also watch for excess wide area network (WAN) traffic. Cable testers and local area network (LAN) analysis products can help you determine the source of problems. If you have a LAN with over 50 nodes, such products are easily justified, especially if the nodes are scattered over a large area. They let you analyze the network from your office and locate potential problem areas. Many of the tasks you can do with a protocol analyzer are listed here:

- Determine which network stations are the most active on the network. If a workstation is using too much of a LAN segment's bandwidth, you might want to move it to another LAN segment.

- Locate workstations that are generating errors. It might be necessary to replace the network adapter in the workstation.

- Filter and view specific types of packets, such as routing information packets. You can use this information to adjust the broadcast frequency of servers and routers to reduce network traffic.

■ Filter packets by their protocol type (IPX, TCP/IP, AppleTalk, and so forth) to determine the type of network traffic crossing a LAN segment.

■ Get short-term and long-term trends about the network's performance. The more you learn about peak usage, the more you can predict network loads and configure the network appropriately.

■ Set alarms that alert you when unusual network events occur, such as a surge in a particular type of packet or an increase in errors.

■ Load test the network by sending out diagnostic packets. Tests can help you check the network cabling, monitor transmission delays, or test node adapters.

Of course, this is only a small sampling of protocol analyzer activities. Products differ in their capabilities, so you should check with the manufacturer and read product evaluations in trade journals. Protocol analysis products are available from Gateway Communications at 800/367-6555, Triticom at 612/937-0772, and Intel at 800/538-3373.

The LANalyzer

In the NetWare environment, a product called LANalyzer for Windows is available to help managers monitor network operations and analyze packet traffic on Ethernet and Token Ring networks that use IPX, TCP/IP, and AppleTalk protocols. LANalyzer is discussed here as a typical protocol analyzer. It runs as software on a management station.

You use LANalyzer for daily or periodic monitoring of the network. Periodic monitoring can produce long-term trends that help you observe changes in network traffic. These trends might point out potential problems or identify users who are requesting excessive network services. With LANalyzer, you can correct or adjust the hardware and settings of a network before problems occur. You can also pinpoint the source of problems causing slow network response, failed connections, and excess network traffic.

The LANalyzer window is shown in Figure T-4. It consists of the Dashboard and several fields that display current and long-term statistics about the network.

■ The Dashboard shows real-time information about the network, such as the number of packets sent per second, the utilization of the network, and the number of errors per second. Two needles appear if you specify that you want to filter out certain types of packets.

NOTE: *Utilization in this case is the bandwidth, or packet-carrying capacity, of the network.*

■ The Station Monitor window shows a table of active stations and their current statistics.

■ The lower portion of the window shows an alarm and a message window, which alerts you to unusual events on the network.

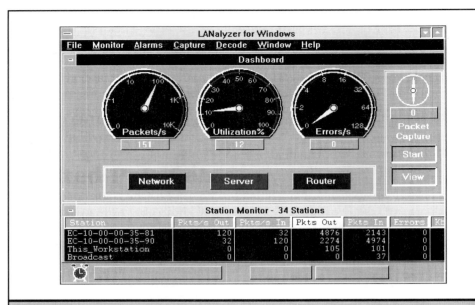

Figure T-4.   *The LANalyzer main window*

- The Packet Capture field is used to capture a series of packets for analysis.

Figure T-5 shows a typical packet capture window. In this case, a word-processed document file is transferred to the server. The summary window shows a list of packets transmitted. You can click on any packet to view detailed information about it, which appears in the middle decode window. At the bottom is a hexadecimal window that shows the contents of the packet. LANalyzer has a filtering feature that lets you specify a particular workstation for analysis, and/or the types of packets you want to view. You can also filter on a specific protocol, such as NetWare IPX, AppleTalk, or TCP/IP.

LANalyzer also has graphing capabilities. A graph can show real-time events or display historical data for trend analysis. You can also print station monitor data, packet capture data, and graphs, or import the data into a spreadsheet for custom analysis.

RELATED ENTRIES   Cabling; Packets; Protocols, Communication; *and* Transmission Media, Methods, and Equipment

Threads

Threads are parts of processes that execute in multitasking operating systems. A multitasking operating system can run several programs or processes at once. Every process has a certain amount of work that needs to be done, and this work can be split

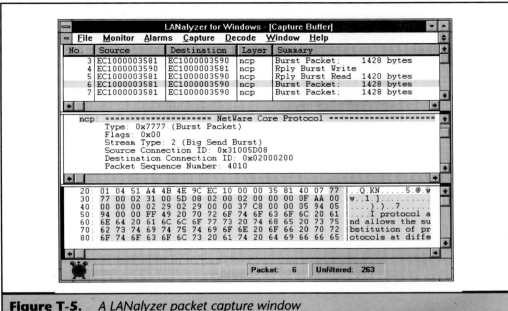

Figure T-5. *A LANalyzer packet capture window*

into one or more parts or units that execute as threads. If the system has only one processor, then each thread is executed in turn, one after the other. A single thread does not dominate the processor, but instead is given a small amount of time to complete some or all of its tasks. Users have the illusion that several programs are running at the same time.

Multiprocessor systems can help improve the performance of multitasking operating systems. Each thread can run on a separate processor at the same time. Processes run faster because multiple processors work together to complete tasks. Threads are useful because they eliminate the need for the operating system to constantly load and unload information to and from memory. The information required for each thread is kept in memory. This reduces overhead, not only in memory space, but in the time it takes to create the information in memory. Each thread may interact with a different part of the system, such as disk systems, network input/output (I/O), or the user. Threads are scheduled for execution because some may need to wait for events to occur or the completion of a task by another thread.

Microsoft Windows NT and NetWare are multiprocessing and multithreaded operating systems. The thread scheduler for NetWare 4.x has been improved to enhance performance further. Microkernel operating systems such as Carnegie-Mellon University's Mach also take advantage of multiprocessing and multiprocessor systems by using threads. Mach, as the core for new UNIX systems, will provide multithreading capabilities.

RELATED ENTRIES   Mach, Carnegie-Mellon Microkernel; Multiprocessing; Multiprocessor Systems; *and* Windows NT, Microsoft

Throughput

Throughput is a measurement of the data transfer rate for a computer or a data communication system such as a bridge, router, gateway, or wide area network connection. Throughput is typically an overall measure of a system and its components to handle requests or transfer data. For example, the throughput of a server depends on its processor type, the type of network interface card, the size of the data transfer bus, the speed of the disk, memory buffer size, as well as the efficiency of the software to manage the components. In a communication system, the measure is usually based on the number of bits or packets that can be processed per second, which depends on the bandwidth of the network and the speed of the switching components such as routers or hubs. The throughput between two end systems on a network depends on the computers, the network interface cards, and the network that connects them.

Time Division Multiplexing

Time division multiplexing provides a way to merge signals from several sources such as telephones, computers, and video equipment into a single channel for communication over telephone lines, microwave systems, or satellite systems. The channel is divided into time slots and each transmitting device is assigned one of the time slots for its transmissions. The time slots are assigned in such a way that each transmitting device gets an equal share, although some devices, such as video conferencing systems, may require more slots to ensure that data arrives on time. You can imagine a train of boxcars in which each transmitting device gets every fifth boxcar, for example. At the receiving end, the data stream is demultiplexed and the signals from each device are recombined and sent to the destination node on the network or voice telephone.

RELATED ENTRY   Multiplexing

Time Domain Reflectometer (TDR)

A time domain reflectometer is a device used to test the physical components of a communication network. It sends a signal through a cable that can locate shorts and opens in a cable and detect impedance mismatches caused by cable defects such as crimps and bends. A pulse is sent through the cable and reflected at the opposite end. A measure of the reflection time can indicate distances to the end of the cable, or distances to known problems. Changes in polarity can indicate shorts.

RELATED ENTRY   Testing Equipment and Techniques

Time Synchronization Services

A time service provides a way for systems in a distributed computing environment to synchronize their clocks so that transaction events and other database updates can be timed and executed correctly. Two examples are given here.

TIME SERVICES IN NOVELL NETWARE 4   NetWare Directory Services must ensure that servers are time-synchronized to facilitate accurate updates to directory information throughout the internetwork. Time synchronization helps establish and maintain the order of events. There are two time synchronization schemes. The first uses a *single-reference time server* for geographically close networks. The time server is the sole source of time on the network. Any time changes are set on this server, and then others synchronize with it. The other method is used for geographically distant networks and includes the following time servers:

- *Primary server used on geographically diverse networks*   Synchronizes time with other primary time servers or a reference time server, and provides the correct time to secondary time servers. If there are multiple primary servers on a network, they "vote" on what the common network time should be.

- *Reference server*   A reference server gets its time from an external source (such as a radio clock) and is a contact to what the outside world says the time should be. A reference server does not use or change its internal time clock. A reference server helps primary time servers set a common time by using a "voting" procedure. Eventually all time servers are set to the time indicated by the reference server's outside time source.

- *Secondary server*   All other servers on the network can be secondary time servers. They merely get the time from single reference, primary, or reference time servers and do not participate in the establishment of a common time over the network.

The cost of long-distance wide area network (WAN) links determines the type of time server to use. Secondary servers should get their time from a local primary or reference server rather than using a WAN link to access a distant time server. Multiple primary time servers are used on internetworks that span large geographic areas.

TIME SERVICES IN OSF'S DISTRIBUTED COMPUTING ENVIRONMENT (DCE)
OSF Time Services is a component of DCE that lets applications schedule activities and determine event sequences and durations. The services keep track of time in networks and determine the accuracy associated with each clock used to synchronize time. The service provides fault-tolerant clock synchronization for systems in both local and wide area networks. In other words, servers with faulty clocks are identified and their time values are not used during synchronizations. To support distributed sites using the Network Time Protocol (NTP), OSF Time Services also permits the use of time values from outside sources.

RELATED ENTRIES   Distributed Computing Environment; NetWare Directory Services

Token and Token Passing Access Methods

A token is a special packet on token ring, token bus, and Fiber Distributed Data Interface (FDDI) networks that controls access to the network. A node that takes control of the token packet holds the right to communicate on the network. Unlike contention-based networks (such as Ethernet), workstations do not attempt to simultaneously access the network. Only the station that obtains an available token transmits. On Ethernet networks, "collisions" occur when two or more workstations attempt to access the cable. They must back off and try again later, which reduces performance, especially as the number of workstations attached to a network segment increases.

In token ring networks, a station takes possession of a token and changes one bit, converting the token to a start-of-frame sequence (SFS). A field exists in the token in which workstations can indicate the type of priority required for the transmission. The priority setting is basically a request to other stations for future use of the token. The other stations compare a workstation's request for priority with their own priority levels. If the workstation's priority is higher, the other stations will grant the workstation access to the token for an extended period.

RELATED ENTRIES Access Method, Network; Fiber Distributed Data Interface; *and* Token Ring Network

Token Bus Network

A token bus network is similar to a token ring network in that a station must have possession of a token before it can transmit on the network. However, the topology and token passing method are different. The Institute of Electrical and Electronics Engineers (IIEEE) 802.4 committee has defined token bus standards as broadband networks as opposed to Ethernet's baseband transmission technique. Token bus networks are constructed with 75 ohm CATV coaxial cable using a bus topology. The broadband characteristics of the 802.4 standard supports transmission over several different channels simultaneously. Broadband cable has longer distance capabilities and transmission rates as high as 10 Mbits/sec. It is sometimes implemented in networks for manufacturing floors using the manufacturers automation protocol.

The token is passed from one station to another following the numeric sequence of the station addresses. Thus, the token follows a logical ring rather than a physical ring. The last station in numeric order passes the token back to the first station. The token does not follow the physical ordering of workstation attachment to the cable. Station 1 might be at one end of the cable; station 2 might be at the other end with station 3 in the middle.

The topology of the network can include groups of workstations connected by long trunk cables. These workstations branch from hubs in a star configuration, so the network has both a bus and star topology. ARCNET is a token bus network, but it does not conform to the IEEE 802.4 standards. Refer to "ARCNET" for illustrations of token bus topologies. Token bus topology is well suited to groups of users that are separated by some distance. While token bus is used in some manufacturing environments, Ethernet and token ring standards have become more prominent in the office environment.

Token Ring Network

Token ring is the Institute of Electrical and Electronics Engineers (IEEE) 802.5 standard for a token-passing ring network that can be configured in a star topology. IBM made the standard possible by marketing the first 4 Mbits/sec Token Ring network in the mid-1980s. While the network physically appears as a star configuration, internally, signals travel around the network from one station to the next. Therefore, cabling configurations and the addition or removal of equipment must ensure that the logical ring is maintained.

Workstations connect to central hubs called *multistation access units (MAUs)*. Multiple hubs are connected together to create large multistation networks. The hub itself contains a "collapsed ring," as shown in Figure T-6. If a workstation fails, the MAU immediately bypasses the station to maintain the ring of the network. Note that unconnected stations are bypassed.

The installation of additional MAUs is pictured in Figure T-7. A ring-in and ring-out receptacle is provided on each MAU for connection to other MAUs. The ring formation is maintained when MAUs are connected in this way. Because the cable contains multiple wire pairs, a cut in the cable causes the ring to revert back on itself,

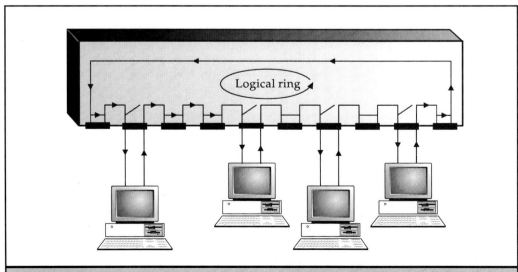

Figure T-6. *The multistation access unit contains a collapsed ring with bypass switching*

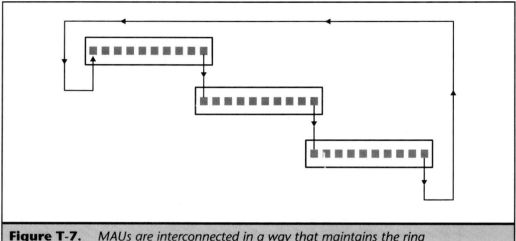

Figure T-7. *MAUs are interconnected in a way that maintains the ring*

as shown in Figure T-8. Signals simply reroute in the opposite direction, creating a loop-back cable configuration. Repeaters are also available to extend the distance of a Token Ring network. Figure T-9 shows how a Token Ring network might be configured in a large office or multistory building. The main ring connects all the MAUs in a circular formation.

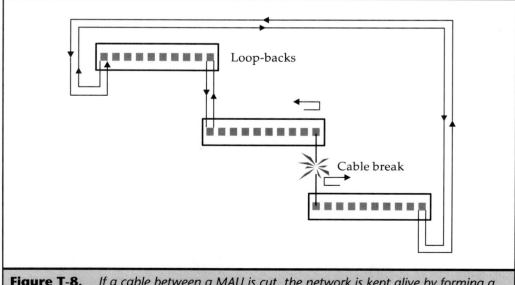

Figure T-8. *If a cable between a MAU is cut, the network is kept alive by forming a loop-back ring using a redundant set of wires in the cable*

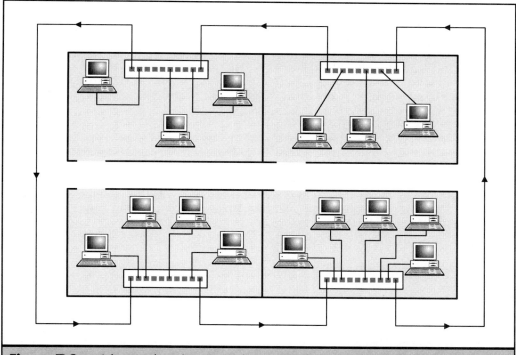

Figure T-9. *A large token ring network consists of a ring that spans the entire organization*

   IBM Token Ring cards are available in a 4 Mbits/sec version and a 16 Mbits/sec version. The faster version has an increased frame length that requires fewer transmissions for the same amount of data. Token Ring networks that follow the IEEE 802.5 standard and use connection methods that expand on the IBM design are now available from several manufacturers. Unshielded twisted-pair cable and MAUs with 16 ports are common. In addition, two- and four-port hubs are available from some vendors. These hubs branch from an eight-port MAU and provide for the connection of two or more workstations in a cluster. Non-IBM vendors also make sophisticated MAU devices that contain additional ports, fault detection features, and management features. Token Ring connections are also available on minicomputer and mainframe systems.

   IBM Token Ring specifications allow for the following cable types:

- *Type 1*   A shielded cable containing two twisted-pair 22 AWG wires.
- *Type 2*   A voice/data shielded cable containing two twisted-pair 22 AWG wires for data with four twisted pairs of 26 AWG wires added outside the shield for voice.

■ *Type 3* Contains four solid, unshielded twisted-pair 22 or 24 AWG cables. A media filter is required for use with Token Ring networks.

■ *Type 5* Fiber-optic (100/140 micron) cable (two strands).

■ *Type 6* Flexible, shielded twisted-pair patch cables of 26 AWG wire. Distance is limited to two-thirds that of Type 1. A patch cable connects a PC to another device or a wall plug.

■ *Type 8* Shielded twisted-pair 26 AWG cable for use under carpets. Distance limits are half of Type 1.

■ *Type 9* Shielded twisted-pair 26 AWG plenum firesafe cable. Distance is limited to two-thirds that of Type 1.

Although Type 1 shielded cable is the most commonly used cable, Type 3 is also used. Type 3 cannot be used with 16 Mbits/sec Token Ring cards, but a specification to implement it is in the works. The components of a standard Token Ring network that uses Type 1 cable are described in the following sections.

TOKEN RING ADAPTERS Token Ring cards are available in a 4 Mbits/sec model and a 16 Mbits/sec model. If a 16 Mbits/sec card is used on a 4 Mbits/sec network, it reverts to 4 Mbits/sec operation. Be sure to run 16 Mbits/sec cards on their own network. Token Ring cards for diskless workstations will require a remote-boot chip.

MULTISTATION ACCESS UNITS (MAUS) A MAU connects eight or more workstations using network adapter cables. Up to 12 MAU devices can be interconnected. MAUs are available from a number of vendors with numerous ports and diagnostics features.

TOKEN RING ADAPTER CABLES Token ring cables typically have a nine-pin connector on one end to attach to the network interface card and a special *Type A* data connector that plugs into the MAU. Adapter cables are usually only 8 feet in length, but patch cables are available to extend them in increments of up to 150 feet. Telephone-type cable and adapters are also available from some vendors.

PATCH CABLES Patch cables extend the distance of a workstation from a MAU device, or they cable two or more MAU devices together. In the IBM system, they should be Type 6 cable of any length up to 150 feet, and when used, they halve the potential workstation-to-MAU distance.

CONNECTORS Type 1 cable uses IBM cabling system Type A data connectors, which are hermaphroditic. You can directly connect one Type A connector to another by flipping it over.

MEDIA FILTERS When Type 3 telephone twisted-pair cable is used, a media filter is required at the workstation. It converts cable connectors and reduces line noise.

PATCH PANELS   A patch panel is useful for organizing cable between the MAU and a telephone punchdown block. A standard telephone connector is used to connect the patch panel to the punchdown block. Another method is to wire the MAU directly to the punchdown block.

The maximum number of stations on one ring is 260 for shielded cable and 72 for unshielded telephone twisted-pair cable. The maximum distance from a workstation to a MAU when you use Type 1 cable is 101 meters (330 feet). This assumes that the cable is one continuous segment. If cable segments are joined by using patch cable, the maximum workstation-to-MAU distance is 45 meters (150 feet).

If multiple MAUs are used, they should be stacked together and cabled locally. Calculating the maximum distance of a Token Ring network can be complicated because of its ring nature. The total length of the LAN may vary as each station logs in. For example, if a station connected to a MAU with an 8-foot patch cable logs in, 16 feet are added to the total ring distance. This is because the signal travels from the MAU out to the workstation, then back again to the MAU and on to the next workstation.

Anyone who intends to cable IBM Token Ring networks over large areas should refer to IBM publications on the subject. These are available from IBM dealers. If other vendors are used, refer to their specification sheets or catalogs. Black Box, Andrews, Star-Tek, and Nevada-Western are vendors of non-IBM Token Ring products who have excellent catalogs and planning guides.

Token Ring Frames

The two token ring frame types are pictured in Figure T-10. The top frame is for the token and the bottom frame is used to transfer data or control information. The fields of these frames are described in the following sections.

- *Start delimiter*   Signifies the beginning of data. It has a unique code to differentiate it from data.

- *Access control*   Contains information about the priority of the frame and a need to reserve future tokens, which other stations will grant if they have a lower priority.

- *Frame control*   Defines the type of frame, either Media Access Control (MAC) information, or information for an end station. If the frame is a MAC frame, all stations on the ring read the information. If the frame contains information, it is only read by the destination station.

- *Destination address*   Contains the address of the station that is to receive the frame. The frame can be addressed to all stations on the ring.

- *Source address*   Contains the address of the station that sent the frame.

- *Data*   Contains the data "payload." If the frame is a MAC frame, this field may contain additional control information.

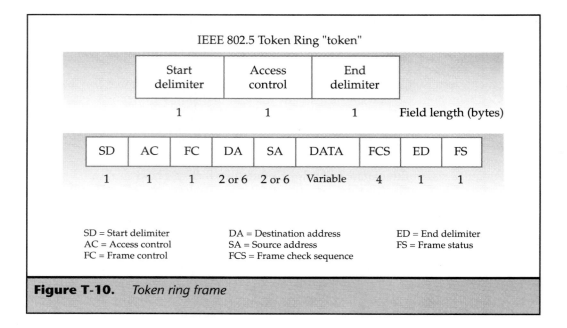

Figure T-10. *Token ring frame*

- *Frame check sequence* Contains error checking information to ensure the integrity of the frame to the recipient.

- *End delimiter* Indicates the end of the frame.

- *Frame status* Provides indications of whether one or more stations on the ring recognized the frame, whether the frame was copied, or whether the destination station is not available.

In token ring networks, a station takes possession of a token and changes one bit, converting the token to a start-of-frame sequence (SFS). A field exists in the token in which workstations can indicate the type of priority required for the transmission. The priority setting is basically a request to other stations for future use of the token. The other stations compare the workstation's request for priority with their own priority levels. If the workstation's priority is higher than theirs, they grant the workstation access to the token for an extended period. Other workstations can override the priorities, if necessary.

Workstations attached to the ring transfer packets to their downstream neighbors. Thus, each workstation acts a repeater. When a new station is attached to the network, it goes through an initialization sequence to become part of the ring. This sequence checks for duplicate addresses and informs downstream neighbors of its existence.

The role of an *active monitor* is assigned to one of the workstations on the network, usually the first workstation recognized when the LAN comes up. The active monitor watches over the network and looks for problems, such as errors in the delivery of frames, or the need to bypass a workstation at a MAU because it has failed. The active monitor basically makes sure the network runs efficiently and without errors. If the active monitor should fail, other workstations are available to take its place and basically bid for the job by transmitting "claim tokens."

RELATED ENTRIES   Network; Token and Token Passing Access Methods; *and* Topology

Topology

Network topologies describe the physical layout of networks. There are two categories of topological designs, depending on whether the network is a local area network (LAN), or internetwork connection with routers and wide area network (WAN) connections. The two categories are discussed separately in the following sections.

Local Area Network Topologies

LAN topologies are basically the subnetwork divisions of internetworks. They consist of the following designs, which are pictured in Figure T-11.

- *Bus*   A single trunk cable connects each workstation in a daisy-chain topology. Signals are broadcast to all stations, but packets are received only by the station to which they are addressed. IEEE 802.3 Ethernet is the primary bus standard.

- *Star*   Workstations attach to hubs and signals are broadcast to all stations or passed from station to station.

- *Star-configured ring*   A ring network in which signals are passed from one station to another in a circle. The physical topology is a star in which workstations branch from concentrators or hubs. IEEE 802.5 Token Ring is the primary standard.

- *Star/bus configuration*   A network that has groups of star-configured workstations connected with long linear bus trunks.

If all your workstations are in a row—such as in a classroom or down a hallway in an office building, a bus topology is easy to install and manage. However, breaks in the cable can bring down the whole network. Ethernet 10BASE-T is a star/bus topology that connects workstations to central concentrator boxes. A break in a cable only affects the workstation attached to the cable segment. A broadcast method is used that transmits signals to all workstations, but stations only listen to broadcast meant for them. A new demand priority access method puts the hub in charge of cable access and reduces contention problems.

Star topologies provide protection from cable breaks. The whole LAN segment won't go down if a cable to a workstation is cut. It is also easy to diagnose connection problems since each workstation is individually connected to the hub. Most star-configured networks use inexpensive twisted-pair cable and all wiring leads are located in one place for diagnostics and testing.

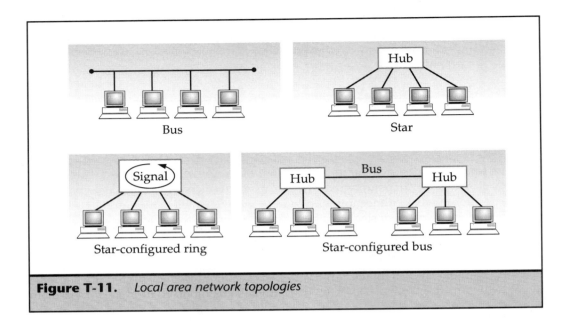

Figure T-11. *Local area network topologies*

The following table lists the various forms of network topologies and the maximum length of segments in each.

Network Topology	Maximum Segment Length
Thick Ethernet (10BASE-5)	500 meters (1,640 feet)
Thin Ethernet (10BASE-2)	185 meters (607 feet)
Twisted-pair Ethernet (10BASE-T)	100 meters (330 feet)
Fiber-optic cable	2 kilometers (6,562 feet)
Twisted-pair Token Ring	100 meters (330 feet) from MAU
Coaxial ARCNET (star)	609 meters (2,000 feet)
Coaxial ARCNET (bus)	305 meters (1,000 feet)
Twisted-pair ARCNET (star)	122 meters (400 feet)
Twisted-pair ARCNET (bus)	122 meters (400 feet)

Internetwork Topologies

An internetwork consists of department or workstation LANs that are interconnected with bridges and routers. A backbone cable is often used in the local environment, such as a building, but public services like those offered by the telephone company are used to build metropolitan or wide area networks. The three main topologies are pictured in Figure T-12 and discussed here.

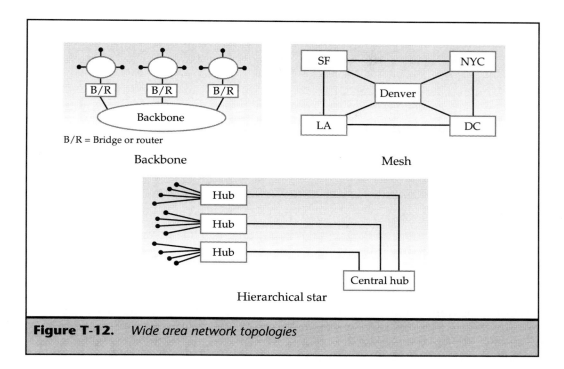

Figure T-12. *Wide area network topologies*

- *Backbone network* Typically found in office or campus environments in which departments or buildings are interconnected over the backbone cables. Bridges or routers manage traffic flow between attached subnetworks and the backbone.

- *Mesh network* Routers are interconnected with other routers. The topology may be configured locally, but is often found in metropolitan or wide area networks that connect remote offices over telecommunication links. Routers are used to select the best or most efficient paths from source to destination through the mesh. Link failures are bypassed using other pathways in the mesh.

- *Interlinked star* This is the new topological paradigm for structured wiring systems in buildings and campus environments. Departmental star-configured hubs are wired to a central hub that handles inter-hub traffic.

RELATED ENTRIES ARCNET; Cabling; Ethernet; Networks; Token Ring Network; *and* Wide Area Networks

Transaction Processing

A transaction is a discrete unit of work that is typically part of a business transaction. An *online transaction processing (OLTP)* system operates in real-time to collect and process transaction-related data and post changes to shared databases and other files. In online transaction processing, transactions are executed immediately, as opposed to batch processing, in which a batch of transactions is stored over a period of time, then executed later. Most batch processes, such as posting to accounts, are run during evening hours. The results of an OLTP are immediately available in the database, assuming that transactions complete. The most common examples of OLTPs are airline reservation systems and banking transactions systems.

Database management systems execute transactions using statements in languages such as Structured Query Language (SQL). IBM has defined the following types of transactions:

- One statement at a time executed against one database

- A *unit of work,* which includes multiple statements executed on one database

- A *distributed unit of work* that involves multiple statements executed on multiple databases with one statement per database at a time

- A *distributed request* that involves multiple statements executed on multiple databases, with multiple statements per database at a time

Executing transactions in single-user, single-database environments is simple because there are no contention problems or need for synchronization between databases. Maintaining the integrity of multiple databases in distributed environments is another matter. Contention problems occur when multiple users attempt to change the same block of data simultaneously. In addition, writes to multiple databases must be synchronized, and there must be an assurance that the writes were indeed made to all the databases. A monitoring program is required to ensure database integrity. There are four requirements, collectively called "ACID," for transaction processing in distributed environments:

- *Atomicity* Defines individual units of work. If a transaction is distributed, all the subtransactions that affect data at separate sites must execute together as a single transaction, either to completion, or rolled back if incomplete. To keep data at multiple sites consistent, a two-phase commit procedure is used as described in a moment.

- *Consistency* Consistency is basically a requirement that databases move from one state to another in coordination. The transaction monitor must verify that all affected data is consistent.

- *Isolation* Transactions must execute in isolation until completed without influence from other transactions.

- *Durability* This property has to do with the final commitment of a transaction. Once a transaction is verified to be accurate on all affected systems, it is committed and cannot be rolled back.

Two-Phase Commit

A feature of transaction processing is the ability to roll back a transaction that cannot be completed (for example, because of insufficient funds or lack of credit), or that was not completed because of a power failure or failed communication link. A transaction must be either fully completed or rolled back so the database returns to its pre-transaction state. A *transaction monitor* is the program that monitors this process. As a user steps through a transaction, changes are made to a database. If the user needs to abort the transaction, the transaction monitor makes sure that all affected databases revert to their pre-transaction states.

Transaction processing in distributed environments introduces many complexities. Users may need to access multiple databases at diverse locations and make changes to multiple databases at the same time. The changes must be coordinated. For example, if bank account balances are kept at multiple branches and a teller makes a change to a customer account, the changes must be made in all locations at the same time. If a link to any of the branch office computers fails during the transaction, the transaction monitor must know this and inform the other branches that the transaction is incomplete and requires a rollback. Two-phase commit accomplishes this task.

Two-phase commit separates the writing of data into two phases each ending with a verification of completeness. In the following steps, assume that no faults occur during the transaction:

1. The database systems involved in the transaction hold the data to commit to the database in memory.
2. The transaction monitor sends a "pre-commit" command to the database systems.
3. The database systems reply that they are ready to commit.
4. On hearing back from every database system, the transaction monitor sends a "commit" command.
5. The database systems reply that they successfully committed the data.
6. The transaction monitor completes the transaction when it receives a response from all database systems that data was successfully committed.

If the transaction monitor fails to hear a response from every database system in steps 3 and 5, the transaction monitor alerts the systems to roll back their transactions.

Common Transaction Processing Systems

The following products are transaction monitors that are available to work in various distributed environments:

- *Encina* from Transarc Corporation (Pittsburgh, Pennsylvania) is an online transaction monitor that can ensure the integrity of data across multiple platforms and databases by providing transaction initiation and termination, two-phase commit, exception handling, recovery, and abort operations. Encina is available in the Hewlett-Packard, IBM, and Sun Microsystems environments.

- *Tuxedo* from UNIX Systems Laboratories (Summit, New Jersey) can be used to coordinate updates across a network. Tuxedo runs processes concurrently on several systems, which distributes the work load and ensures that processing can continue if one system goes down.

- IBM *Customer Information Control System (CICS)* is one of the most widely used transaction processing systems. It supports distributed environments and includes a transaction manager and transaction monitor. CICS uses Encina functions for its AIX/6000 implementation.

RELATED ENTRIES   Connectionless and Connection-Oriented Transactions; Encina; *and* Tuxedo

Transceiver, Ethernet

A transceiver provides a physical and electrical connection to the standard (Thicknet) 802.3 Ethernet cable. Transceivers are often tapping devices, which means the device will clamp onto the cable without cutting it, and can be added to or removed at any time.

Transfer Rates

See Data Transfer Rates.

Transmission Control Protocol/Internet Protocol (TCP/IP)

The development goals for the TCP/IP protocol suite were to allow communication among a variety of independent, multivendor systems. In 1983, TCP/IP protocols became the official transport mechanism for the Department of Defense Internet, which evolved into a system of interconnected networks spanning the globe. It has strong internetworking capabilities and is undergoing a surge of popularity primarily because its development is open and supported by the U.S. government. The protocols are well tested and documented.

NOTE: *The historical information presented here is derived from accounts by Vinton Cerf, coinventor of the TCP/IP protocol suite, and Daniel C. Lynch, president and founder of Interop Company. The accounts appear in the **Internet System Handbook** (Greenwich, Connecticut: Addison-Wesley, 1993).*

In the late 1960s and early 1970s, the Internet began to take shape in the form of a wide-area network called ARPANET. ARPANET was funded by the U.S. Defense Advanced Research Projects Agency (DARPA). It consisted of computers that, starting in 1969, had been set up and connected using an experimental packet-switching system. At first, the systems used a client-server relationship but it was decided that a host-to-host protocol was preferred. This protocol was called the *Network Control Protocol (NCP)*.

By 1972, demonstrations were taking place in which many terminals were connected to a variety of hosts over various telecommunication links. As the experiment continued, there was an increased need to simplify the process of interconnecting many different types of computers. Each computer vendor used different hardware and software techniques to interconnect its systems. The goal was to develop an interconnection method that could support many different types of computers over many different types of transmission methods, including low-speed, high-speed, and wireless connections.

Development on the *Transmission Control Protocol (TCP)* protocol suite was started in 1973 by Bob Kahn, then from DARPA, and Vinton Cerf, then at Stanford University. By 1978, it was largely completed and by then called the *Transmission Control Protocol/Internet Protocol (TCP/IP)* because of requirements to split the TCP protocol into a sequenced, connection-oriented protocol (TCP) and a best-effort, end-to-end connectionless protocol (IP).

At one point in the late 1970s, there was an effort to integrate the TCP/IP protocol suite into the Open Systems Interconnection (OSI) protocols but this effort failed. DARPA had funded UC Berkeley to integrate TCP/IP into its UNIX version. The integrated product became a commercial success and helped seal TCP/IP as the internetworking standard of choice in the United States.

In 1975, the ARPANET became an operating entity rather than an experiment, and so it was transferred over a 6-month period to the Department of Defense (DOD) Defense Communications Agency (DCA). The DCA then began administering the network. In 1985, the National Science Foundation (NSF) started funding the efforts with a vision of creating a backbone that could interconnect many universities and research institutes. This backbone was created and called the NSFnet, replacing the ARPANET and becoming the backbone for the Internet.

In the meantime, the TCP/IP protocol suite has continued to evolve. One of the most important aspects of TCP/IP's development was the program of testing and certification carried out by the government to ensure that developers met published TCP/IP standards, which are published and available to the public free of licensing arrangements. This ensured that developers didn't alter the standard to fit their own needs, and possibly cause confusion in the rest of the TCP/IP community. Today, the use of TCP/IP protocols virtually assures interconnection, and in some cases, interoperability, among systems that use it for communication.

The TCP Protocol

The original TCP protocol was developed as a way to interconnect networks using many different types of transmission methods. To accommodate these media, the concept of a gateway (later called a router) was created in which packets from one network were encapsulated into a package that contained the address of another gateway. The packet might be repackaged and addressed to several gateways before reaching its final destination, as shown in Figure T-13. This encapsulation method was used for several reasons, but the most important was that the designers did not want the owners of the various networks to alter their intranetworking schemes to accommodate internetworking. It was assumed that every network would implement its own communication techniques.

The TCP protocol sets up a two-way (duplex) connection between two systems using the *sockets* interface. A socket is one end of a communication that specifies the address of the computer and a "port" within that computer that a running application is using to communicate. You might think of this arrangement as you would a telephone within a building—the building has an address and the telephone number is like a port within that building that connects you with a specific person. Likewise, a socket is a connection to an application or process running within a computer.

TCP communication sessions are connection-oriented and have the features described next.

- *Flow control* provides a way for two systems to actively cooperate in the transmission of packets to prevent overflows and lost packets.

- *Acknowledgment* of packet receipt lets the sender know the recipient has received packets.

- End-to-end *sequencing* ensures that packets arrive in order so the destination doesn't need to organize them.

- A *checksumming* feature is used to ensure the integrity of packets.

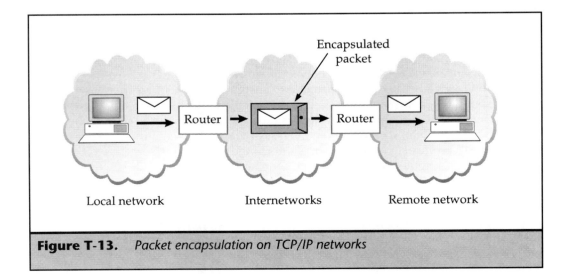

Figure T-13. *Packet encapsulation on TCP/IP networks*

■ *Retransmission* of corrupt or lost packets can be handled in a timely and efficient manner.

Connection-oriented sessions require a setup phase, a take-down phase, and a lot of monitoring and possibly more excess traffic from overhead than is necessary for some data transmissions. During the development of TCP, Denny Cohen at USC recommended splitting the TCP protocol to accommodate "timeliness rather than accuracy." He argued that all the flow control and error-checking features just described as well as the overhead of setting up a connection-oriented session were not always necessary. What was needed was a way to quickly get data to another system, then let that system handle all the error checking and sequencing on its own. Thus, TCP became the TCP and Internet Protocol (IP). The *User Datagram Protocol (UDP)* was also created to provide a way for applications to access the connectionless features of IP. Both TCP and UDP use IP. All are briefly described here, then covered in more detail further on.

■ TCP provides reliable data transport from one node to another using connection-oriented techniques.

■ UDP provides datagram services for applications. UDP's primary role is to add the port address of an application process to an IP packet.

■ IP is a connectionless service that provides basic datagram delivery services.

The IP and TCP protocols are discussed in more detail in the following sections. IP is discussed first because TCP uses it to transport information over networks. There are two other protocols not discussed here, but used on TCP/IP networks:

■ *Internet Control Message Protocol (ICMP)*   Provides a way to report errors on the network. The ICMP packets are transported using the IP protocol and provide information about errors produced by datagrams or provide a way to query about conditions at remote locations.

■ *Internet Group Message Protocol (IGMP)*   Provides a way to send messages to a group of users using the IP protocol. This capability is called multicasting.

Internet Protocol (IP)

IP is a connectionless communication protocol that by itself provides a datagram service. Datagrams are self-contained packets of information that are forwarded by routers based on their address and the routing table information contained in the routers. Datagrams can be addressed to single nodes or multiple nodes. There is no flow control, acknowledgment of receipt, error checking, and sequencing. Datagrams may traverse different paths to the destination and thus arrive out of sequence. The receiving station is responsible for resequencing and determining if packets are lost. IP handles congestion by simply discarding packets. Resequencing and error handling are taken care of by upper layer protocols, not by IP. Thus, IP is fast and efficient and well suited to modern networks and telecommunication systems that already provide relatively reliable service.

IP works on a number of local and wide area networks. When IP runs in the LAN environment on an Ethernet network, for example, the data field in the Ethernet frame holds the IP packet and a specific field in the frame indicates that IP information is enclosed. IP uses an addressing scheme that works independently of the network addressing scheme. For example, every Ethernet adapter has a factory-assigned hardware address. IP does not use this address, but instead uses an assigned address for each node, as described next.

IP Addressing

Every node on a TCP/IP network requires a 4-byte (32-bit) numeric address that identifies both a network and a local host or node on the network. This address is written as four numbers separated by dots, for example, 191.31.140.115. In most cases, the network administrator sets up these addresses when installing new workstations; however, in some cases it is possible for a workstation to query a server for a dynamically assigned address when it boots up.

The assignment of addresses is arbitrary within a company or organization, but if the company plans to connect with the Internet anytime in the near future, it is necessary to obtain registered addresses from the Defense Data Network (DDN) Network Information Center (NIC), which is managed by Network Solutions in Chantilly, Virginia. With the growing popularity of the Internet, it is recommended that all organizations obtain registered addresses to avoid address conflicts in the future.

There are three classes of Internet addresses, Class A, Class B, and Class C:

- *Class A* Supports 16 million hosts (attached computers), but only 127 assignable network numbers exist.
- *Class B* Supports 65,000 hosts and 16,000 networks.
- *Class C* Supports 254 hosts and 2 million network numbers.

Because the Internet address is a combination of host and network numbers, multiple hosts can share the host portion of the number but each host has its own unique number. For example, in class C numbers, the first set of digits is the host number and the last three sets of digits are the network number.

IP addressing supports millions of addresses, but lately, the potential for shortages has emerged. With the surge in popularity of the Internet, a shortage of assignable addresses is eminent.

It is estimated that the Internet will run out of addresses by 1995. A new protocol, called Simple Internet Protocol (SIP) will remedy this situation. SIP will use 64-bit addresses rather than IP's 32-bit addressing, doubling the number of potential addresses. SIP will be backward compatible with IP.

The IP Datagram Structure

The IP datagram contains addresses, routing information, and other header information for delivering a package of data from a source to a destination. The fields of the IP datagram are described in the following list. Note that the identification, flags, and fragment offset fields have to do with the fragmentation of packets into two or more datagrams for delivery over subnetworks that are incapable of handling large datagrams.

- *Version* Describes the IP protocol version and allows for the transition from one protocol version to another.
- *Length* Specifies the length of the header.
- *Type of service (TOS)* Used to indicate the type or "quality" of service required for the datagram. Routers that handle the datagram read this field and provide priority service if necessary. Originally, this field specified packet priorities for military emergencies or crisis events. The definition of TOS is changing to indicate a need to either minimize delay, minimize monetary cost, maximize throughput, or maximize reliability, according to recent discussion within the Internet Engineering Task Force (IETF).
- *Total length* Specifies the total length of the datagram, which has a maximum length of 65,536 bytes.
- *Identification* Provides information to link fragmented datagrams uniquely so the destination can reassemble them into full packets.
- *Flags* There are two flag bits. The first indicates that a packet should not be fragmented and thus must be sent across subnetworks that can handle its current size. The second flag bit indicates that a datagram is the last of a fragmented packet.
- *Fragment offset* For fragmented datagrams, this field indicates the original position of the data in the packet and is used during reassembly.
- *Time-to-live* The time in seconds that a datagram can be in transit. The datagram is considered lost or in a loop and is discarded if this time is exceeded.
- *Protocol* Identifies the protocol type of the datagram, thus allowing non-TCP/IP protocols.
- *Header checksum* Provides an error-checking value to ensure the integrity of a delivered packet.
- *Source/destination address* The addresses of the datagram source and the destination for the datagram.
- *Options* This field has options that provide a way to record a path through a network or dictate a path (source routing).

T

Transmission Control Protocol (TCP)

TCP provides a way to establish a connection between end systems for the reliable delivery of messages and data. The TCP connection has all the connection-oriented features discussed previously, such as flow control, acknowledgment, sequencing, checksumming, and retransmission. When an application uses TCP, there is a connection establishment phase, but once the connection is made, it provides reliable and efficient delivery of data between the end systems. Connection-oriented sessions are useful for prolonged data exchanges or when a relatively permanent connection is necessary.

To set up a TCP connection, the activating station sends a message to another station. That station responds to the activating station that it is ready to establish a communication session. The first station then responds to confirm the connections and an initial transfer of data takes place to establish data transfer controls. The fields of the TCP packet are described here:

- *Source/destination port*   Contains the port number for the applications process using TCP services.

- *Sequence number*   Provides the information needed by the receiver to order packets and know if packets are missing.

- *Acknowledgment number*   Provides an indication of bytes received back to the sender so it can retransmit lost packets if necessary.

- *Length or offset*   Specifies the length of the header.

- *Codes*   This field contains codes that indicate urgently needed data or that this packet is the end of data.

- *Sliding window*   Provides a way to increase packet size, thus improving efficiency in data transfers.

- *Header checksum*   Provides an error-checking value to ensure the integrity of a delivered packet.

- *Urgent pointer*   Indicates the location in the data where urgent data is located.

- *Options*   A variable set aside for future or special options.

Note that connectionless IP is used to transport data between nodes on the network while the TCP layers running in the end systems provide the reliability functions. The IP packet contains the address of end nodes while the TCP packet contains the source and destination port number. An analogy to this would be a conversation you hold with a friend while transferring information to that friend over another phone line. You use the voice conversation to set up parameters for the data communication session, then discuss the progress of the exchange as it takes place, and finally acknowledge receipt of the complete data set.

Application Protocols

The following applications have been built on top of the TCP/IP protocol suite and are available in most TCP/IP installations, including the Internet. These applications are discussed elsewhere in this book.

■ *Network File System (NFS)* A filing system for UNIX hosts that is shareable and distributed. It was originally developed by Sun Microsystems.

■ *Simple Network Management Protocol (SNMP)* A network management protocol that collects information about the network and reports it to administrators.

■ *File Transfer Protocol (FTP)* Enables file transfers between workstations and a UNIX host or Novell NetWare NFS.

■ *Simple Mail Transfer Protocol (SMTP)* A protocol that enables electronic messaging.

■ *Telnet* DEC VT100 and VT330 terminal emulation.

RELATED ENTRIES Advanced Research Projects Agency Network; Connection-Oriented and Connectionless Protocols; DARPA (Defense Advanced Research Projects Agency); Datagram Network Services; Domain Name Service; Encapsulation; Internet; Routing Internet; Routing Protocols; *and* Sockets

Transmission Media, Methods, and Equipment

Transmission media support the propagation of acoustic, electromagnetic, and light wave signals. The media are typically metal wires or fiber-optic cable that constrains the signals within the media itself. Radio transmissions are provided by line-of-sight microwave and satellite communication. The type of media used, its shielding, and even the number of twists in copper wire pairs determine the data transfer rate possible on the wire.

Transmission lines can be "balanced" or "unbalanced." A balanced line is typically a twisted-pair or twinax cable that contains two conductors. An unbalanced line is typically a coaxial cable. In a balanced line, both wires are connected to the generator (sender) and receiver and each of the wires has an equal current, but the currents are in opposite directions. In an unbalanced line, current flows through the signal conductor and returns on the ground.

Cable Types

The common cable types used for network communication systems are described in the following sections and pictured in Figure T-14.

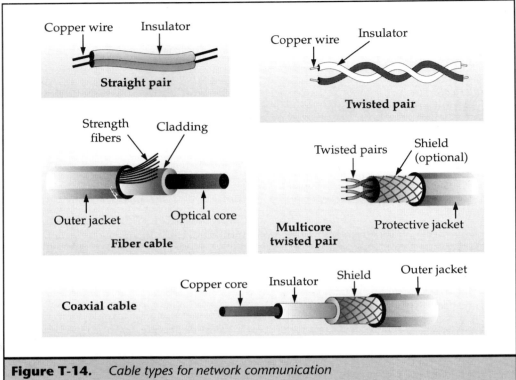

Figure T-14. *Cable types for network communication*

STRAIGHT CABLE Straight-pair cable consists of copper wires surrounded by an insulator. The wire comes in bundles or as flat "ribbon" cables and is used to connect various peripheral devices over short distances and at low bit rates. Serial cables used to connect modems or serial printers use this type of wire. Crosstalk can occur between side-by-side wires, but this is reduced by twisting the cable, as described next.

TWISTED PAIRS Twisted-pair cable consists of copper-core wires surrounded by an insulator. Two wires are twisted together to form a pair, and the pair forms a balanced circuit. The twisting prevents interference problems. Twisted-pair cable is commonly used in the voice telephone systems and computer networks. High data rates (100 Mbits/sec) are possible by using a high grade of cable (Category 5) and ensuring that twists are maintained all the way up to connection points. The cable is available with multiple twisted pairs and shielding if necessary.

COAXIAL CABLE Coaxial cable consists of a solid copper core surrounded by an insulator, a combination shield and ground wire, and an outer protective jacket. High bit-rates are possible with coaxial cable, but newer transmission techniques for twisted-pair cable equal or surpass coaxial cable rates. However, the specified cable distance for coaxial cable is still greater than twisted-pair cable.

FIBER CABLE   Fiber-optic cable consists of a center glass core through which light waves propagate. This core is surrounded by a glass cladding that basically reflects the inner light of the core back into the core. A thick plastic outer jacket surrounds this assembly along with special fibers to add strength. Fiber-optic cable is available with a metal core for strength if the cable will be hung over distances. Fiber cable transmits photons through clear glass. It is not susceptible to signal interference and does not radiate a signal that could be monitored. Fiber cable also extends over much longer distances than copper cable. See "Fiber-Optic Cable."

OPEN SPACE TRANSMISSIONS   This type of transmission is accomplished with infrared and radio waves. See "Microwave Communication," "Satellite Telecommunication," "Wireless LAN Communication," and "Wireless Mobile Communication."

Transmission Methods

A signal is generated by electricity, radio waves, or light as a way to transmit coded information. The two methods used to transmit signals over a medium are analog signaling and digital signaling:

- Analog signals are *continuously* variable voltages or waves that can represent an infinite number of values within the range of the device that is producing, measuring, recording, or transmitting the signals. For example, an analog signal is a replica of the waveform produced by a microphone in a telephone handset.

- Digital signals are transmitted by changing the voltage level on a channel between a high and a low state. The primary task is to represent coded information as the binary digits 0 and 1 in the transmitted signal.

Analog Transmissions

An analog signal is a form of propagated energy, such as a sound wave that vibrates the air it travels through. A sound wave that varies in pitch and loudness can be mapped out on paper as shown in Figure T-15.

A microphone or a telephone headset contains a transducer device that converts analog sound waves into corresponding electrical signals. At the receiving end of a telephone or audio system, a speaker vibrates to the amplitude (loudness) and pitch of the electrical signal. Pitch refers to the frequency of vibration of the sound wave. Frequency is usually measured in cycles per second (CPS) or hertz (Hz). One hertz is one CPS. A kilohertz (KHz) is 1,000 hertz, a megahertz (MHz) is 1,000 KHz, and a gigahertz (GHz) is 1,000 MHz. The range of human hearing is between the range of 20Hz to 20,000Hz and this is the range of operation for high-fidelity sound equipment.

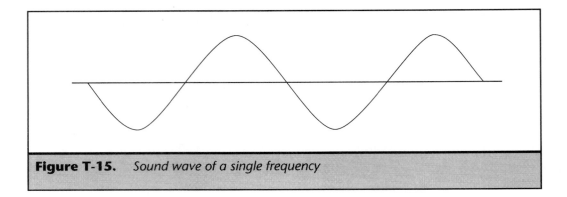

Figure T-15. *Sound wave of a single frequency*

Analog waveforms may be simple or complex. A simple waveform produced by a single piano note consists of a single frequency. A complex waveform—like that of the human voice or the sound of an orchestra—consists of a combination of many different frequencies, as shown in Figure T-16.

The telephone system uses analog-switched lines to provide voice communication. In general, data communication over analog lines has several problems that limit its usefulness. A modulation process is required to convert digital signals to analog signals and the bits-per-second transmission rate is limited due to the narrow bandwidth of the voice line. Also, analog signals must be amplified over long distances periodically, and any distortion in the signals is amplified as well. The increasing need to transmit larger amounts of information for applications such as imaging and video requires higher bandwidth than analog services can provide.

Digital Transmissions

Voice, video, data, and other "information" can be efficiently transmitted by encoding it as binary values, and transmitting the values as electrical pulses. The voltage of the

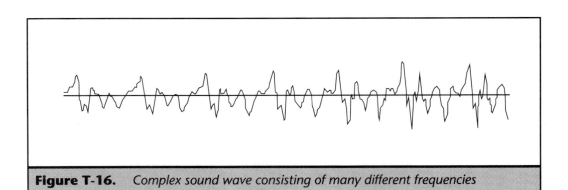

Figure T-16. *Complex sound wave consisting of many different frequencies*

line is varied between a high state and a low state. Thus, binary 1 is transmitted by applying a positive voltage and binary 0 is transmitted by applying a negative voltage. Digital services are more reliable than analog services, especially over long distances. If the signal needs boosting, the digital signals are simply regenerated, as pictured in Figure T-17. In contrast, analog signals are periodically amplified over distances, which also amplifies any distortion on the line.

Analog-to-digital conversion, or digitizing, is the process of converting real-world, continuous waveforms into digital information that can be processed and stored in a computer. The analog-to-digital conversion process (often called pulse code modulation, or PCM) consists of sampling a signal at regular intervals and capturing its amplitude and frequency as a binary value. The accuracy of the value a depends on the number of bits used to hold the value. If a wave is sampled 1,000 times per second (1 KHz), 1,000 separate digital values are captured for storage or transmission. When voice is converted for transmission over a digital line, it is sampled 8,000 times per second and each sample is converted to an 8-bit binary value. Thus, a digitized voice channel requires 64,000 bits per second of bandwidth.

Transmission Modes

Data is transmitted as either bit-oriented or character-oriented (also called byte-oriented) information. In a bit-oriented transmission, the bits represent a continuous stream of data (such as graphic data) and have no significant meaning to the sender or receiver except for a special flag bit pattern that represents the beginning of a frame. In the common character-oriented protocol, sequences of 8 bits represent control codes and alphanumeric characters. Character-oriented protocols involve several transmission modes, as discussed next.

■ *Simplex circuit* A one-way transmission, like a radio broadcast, in which the receiver cannot respond. In data communication, simplex circuits are used in master-slave configurations in which one device controls another and there is no need for the slave to respond. Simplex circuits are typically not used when human interaction is required at the slave station.

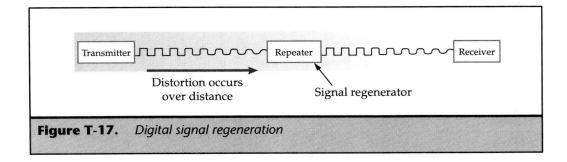

Figure T-17. *Digital signal regeneration*

- *Half-duplex circuit*   A two-way transmission, but only in one direction at a time. The best example is citizen band (CB) radio, in which only one operator can talk at a time. When one operator is finished talking, he or she says "over" so the other operator can talk. Likewise, half-duplex circuits use a signaling system to indicate when one device is finished sending or receiving so the other device can access the line. Half-duplex transmissions are possible with a single, dual-wire cable such as twisted pair.

- *Full-duplex circuit*   A two-way simultaneous transmission. On digital networks, two pairs of wires are necessary to complete the circuit. Analog circuits connected by modems require only one wire pair. The circuit bandwidth is divided into two frequencies, which allows simultaneous data flow in both directions.

When a terminal is connected in half-duplex mode, characters typed at the terminal are displayed and transmitted. However, a terminal in full-duplex mode displays the character after it is "echoed" back from the receiving system, thus providing a form of error checking. Problems can occur if the communicating systems are not using the same mode. For example, if a terminal is in half-duplex mode, it immediately displays the character typed. If the receiving system, or host, is in full-duplex mode, it returns a character to the terminal, causing two characters to appear for each character typed at the terminal. If the terminal is in full-duplex mode and the host is in half-duplex mode, the terminal does not display any characters because its full-duplex mode waits for an echo from the host, which doesn't echo because it is in half-duplex mode.

Data Communication Equipment (DCE)

There is a wide range of data communication equipment, all dubbed DCE in the DTE/DCE relationship (see "Data Communication Equipment"). A DCE sits between Data Terminal Equipment (DTE) and a transmission circuit or channel. It provides a connection for the DTE into a communication network and back again. In addition, it usually terminates a circuit and provides clocking for the circuit. Several types of transmission devices are discussed next.

MODEMS   Modems (*modulator/demodulators*) convert digital signals to analog signals and transmit the signals over voice telephone networks. The digital electric pulses representing binary 0 and 1 are converted to analog waveforms at one end of the transmission, and converted back to digital at the receiving end by another modem. The modem is controlled with commands sent from a data communication package and handles the dialing and answering of the phone. It also controls the transmission speed, which ranges from 300 bits/sec to 9,600 bits/sec. If compression is used, top speeds up to 28,800 bits/sec are possible with the latest standards, although higher rates are under development.

CHANNEL SERVICE UNIT (CSU)   This device is used to connect to digital communication lines (such as T1). It is inexpensive and provides a termination for the digital signal. The CSU provides various loop-back tests on the line and keeps the line connected if the other communication equipment attached to it fails. A CSU is usually combined with a DSU.

DATA SERVICE UNIT (DSU)   This device is sometimes called a digital service unit. It is the hardware component you need to transmit digital data over the digital channel. The device converts signals from bridges, routers, and multiplexers into the bipolar digital signals used on the digital lines.

REPEATERS AND LINE DRIVERS   Signal distortion occurs over long distances that can make a digital signal unrecognizable. To overcome this problem and increase transmission distances, repeaters are introduced into the line to read distorted pulses and regenerate them. In the phone system, repeaters are required every 1,818 meters (6,000 feet). A serial connection from a computer to a peripheral device requires a line driver at approximately 15 meters (50 feet). Some line drivers can extend this distance limitation to 5,000 feet.

BRIDGES   A bridge connects two similar or dissimilar packet-oriented local area networks. It operates at the Open Systems Interconnection (OSI) reference model's Data-Link level. The bridge can forward packets to other local area networks or filter packets to reduce internetwork traffic.

ROUTERS   Routers interconnect local area networks (LANs) with other LANs to backbones, or to wide area networks. A router is like a bridge, but provides advanced features. It can learn the destination of nodes and the routes to get there, then choose the best route on which to forward a packet.

Transmission Services

Transmission services are provided by the carriers or other provides such as companies that have built metropolitan area networks. These services are covered extensively under "Carrier Services."

RELATED ENTRIES   Asynchronous Communication; Bandwidth; Cabling; Carrier Services; Data Transfer Rates; Networks; Synchronous Communication; *and* Wide Area Networks

Transport Layer, OSI Model

The Open Systems Interconnection (OSI) model is a standard defined by the International Organization for Standardization (ISO). It defines a layered architecture that categorizes and defines the protocols for communication between end-systems. During the communication session, processes running in each layer on each computer communicate with one another. There are seven layers that can be categorized into three general layers.

- The bottom layer defines the actual physical components such as connectors and cable and how data is exchanged between systems. The type of network interface and the access method are also defined here.
- The transport layers are concerned with the reliable transmission of data between systems.
- The application layers provide the interface between user applications and the network communication systems.

The OSI model was designed to help developers create applications that are compatible across multivendor product lines, and to promote open, interoperable networking systems.

The Transport layer is layer 4 in the OSI protocol stack. It resides above the Physical, Data-Link, and Network layers and just below the Session layer. It provides a messaging service for the Session layer and hides the underlying network from the upper layers.

The Transport layer provides reliable end-to-end data transport. Error checking and other reliability features are handled by the protocols in the Transport layer if they are not handled by the underlying network. This is the case for Frame Relay and Asynchronous Transfer Mode (ATM) networks, which don't perform error checks when delivering packets. Instead, error checking is assumed to be handled by Transport layer protocols, which examine information in the packet to make sure they were delivered error-free.

The Transport layer can provide connection-oriented or connectionless services. In a connection-oriented session, a circuit is established through which packets flow to the destination. In this arrangement, packets arrive in order and don't require a full address or other information because the circuit guarantees their deliver to the proper destination. This type of arrangement is used for long transmissions, or connections in which one system will access the resources of another for an extended period. A connectionless session does not establish circuits or provide reliable data delivery. Packets are fully addressed and sent out over the network. Each packet can conceivably follow a different path and even arrive out of order. The Transport layer protocols at the destination can put the packets back in order and request a retransmission of missing or defective packets.

RELATED ENTRIES   Layered Architecture; Open Systems Interconnection Model; *and* Protocol Stacks

Transport Layer Interface (TLI)

The Transport Layer Interface (TLI) is a library of calls and run-time modules that runs on top of the STREAMS environment. STREAMS and TLI were originally defined by AT&T for use in the UNIX environment.

RELATED ENTRY   STREAMS

Transport Protocols
See Protocols, Communication.

Trivial File Transfer Protocol (TFTP)
See File Transfer Protocol.

Troubleshooting
See Testing Equipment and Techniques.

Trustees

In the NetWare environment, a trustee is a user who has been assigned some right to use a resource or access the file system. The rights assigned to the trustee are called the trustee assignments. In NetWare 4.x, trustee assignments can also include rights to manage objects in NetWare Directory Services.

RELATED ENTRIES   Access Rights; Administrators, Novell NetWare; File and Directory Rights, NetWare; Rights in Novell NetWare; *and* Users and Groups

Tunneling
See Encapsulation.

Tuxedo, UNIX System Laboratories

Tuxedo is a client-server "middleware" product that mediates between the client and the server to ensure that transactions are handled properly. Tuxedo is a transaction processing (TP) monitor that manages the transactions performed by online transaction processing (OLTP) systems (see "Transaction Processing"). Clients make requests of servers using Structured Query Language (SQL) calls or other types of requests. The TP monitor makes sure that updates are handled correctly to ensure the integrity of data. This is especially important in the distributed environment in which a transaction might make changes to databases in multiple locations. The TP monitor uses a two-phase commit to ensure that all databases have received and committed the data properly. Otherwise, the database is returned to its pre-transaction state.

Transaction monitors have historically been associated with large mainframe systems, but Tuxedo is designed to run on less expensive UNIX-based systems. AT&T originally developed Tuxedo as an OLTP for its own use. While Tuxedo itself must run on a UNIX system, it works with DOS, OS/2, Windows, and UNIX clients. It also uses common communication protocols such as Transmission Control Protocol/Internet Protocol (TCP/IP) and Network Basic Input Output System (NetBIOS), and can provide distributed processing support in these environments. For example, it can route a request for service from a client to a specific server based on the type of request. The basic feature of Tuxedo is its OLTP system, but Tuxedo also works to integrate relational, flat-file, and hierarchical database systems.

RELATED ENTRIES   Connectionless and Connection-Oriented Transactions; Transaction Processing

Twisted-Pair Cable

Twisted-pair cable consists of two insulated copper wires that are twisted around each other. The twists provide protection from the crosstalk produced by nearby cables. Twisted-pair cable is available in the following categories:

- *Category 1*   Voice-grade twisted telephone wire not suitable for data transmission.
- *Category 2*   Rated for data transmission up to 4 Mbits/sec.
- *Category 3*   Rated for data transmission up to 10 Mbits/sec. Usually used for Ethernet 10Base-T networks.
- *Category 4*   Rated for use with 16 Mbits/sec token ring networks.
- *Category 5*   Rated for use for new networks that transmit at up to 100 Mbits/sec to 150 Mbits/sec. Such networks include Fast Ethernet, 100BaseVG, and Copper Distributed Digital Interface (CDDI). CDDI is the copper-wire version of the Fiber Distributed Digital Interface (FDDI).

RELATED ENTRY   Cabling

Two-Phase Commit

Two-phase commit is a strategy that ensures the integrity of data when writing transactions that involve distributed databases in multiple locations. Each database involved must authorize the transaction before it actually commits. If the transaction succeeds, it is committed; otherwise the transaction is rolled back.

Like fault-tolerant systems, two-phase commit protects against systems that fail during the writing of a transaction. It also allows an operator to abort a transaction and return the database to its previous state. When a transaction involves data stored in multiple locations, it is necessary to ensure that all systems have properly written the transaction changes before committing the transaction as complete. If one of the systems fails, the other systems must know of the failure so they can roll the transaction back.

RELATED ENTRY   Transaction Processing

Unified Network Management Architecture (UNMA), AT&T

AT&T's Unified Network Management Architecture (UNMA) is a model for an enterprise network management system that conforms to OSI protocols. It defines a system that operates in distributed computing environments and over local exchange carrier facilities and interexchange carrier facilities. The architecture consist of five levels:

- *Network Elements* The LANs, communication equipment, PBXs, and other components at customer sites and carrier facilities.
- *Element Management System (EMS)* Management system that handles various components of the network.
- *Network Management Integration Laye*r The management system that ties the EMS together.
- *Network Management Protocol* A set of standards for managing the configuration, performance, accounting, security, operation, and other features of the network.
- *Unified User Interface* Graphical user interface that simplifies network management.

AT&T's Accumaster Integrator is built on the UNMA architecture. The product initially lacked Simple Network Management Protocol (SNMP) support and AT&T is now touting the NCR StarSENTRY network management system.

RELATED ENTRIES Accumaster Integrator; AT&T; *and* Management Standards and Tools

Uninterruptible Power Supply (UPS)

An uninterruptible power supply (UPS) provides electrical power to computers or other devices during a power outage. A UPS can be one of the following:

- A battery system
- A rotary UPS that uses the inertia of a large flywheel to carry the computer system through brief outages
- Internal combustion motors that run AC generators

UPS devices come in two forms: online and standby. A *standby* device kicks in only when the power goes down. It must therefore contain special circuitry that can switch to backup power in less than 5 milliseconds. An *online* device constantly provides the source of power to the computer. Because of this, it doesn't need to kick in. If the outside source of power dies, the batteries within the unit continue to supply the computer with power. Although online units are the best choice, they are more expensive than standby units. But because online units supply all the power to a computer, that power is always clean and smooth.

When purchasing a battery backup system, you need to know the following about the devices:

■ The amount of time the UPS battery supplies power

■ Whether the UPS provides a warning system to the server when the UPS is operating on standby power

■ Whether the UPS includes power conditioning features that can clip incoming transient noise

■ The life span of the battery and how it degrades over time

■ Whether the device warns you when the batteries can no longer provide backup power

■ Whether the batteries are replaceable

You also need to know the power requirements of the devices you'll hook to the UPS. For a server installation, this might include the CPU (and any added devices), the monitor, external routers, concentrator units, and wiring centers. You can find out the power requirements of these devices by looking at the backs of the equipment. Labels on the equipment list the power drawn by the units. UPSs are rated in volts-amperes (VA), which is the line voltage multiplied by the current (amperes). You'll need to add up the power requirements of the equipment you plan to attach to the UPS, then purchase a UPS that can handle the load. Start by obtaining the amp rating on the back of a device and multiply it by the voltage (usually 120 volts), then add the values for each device and select an appropriate UPS.

A UPS attached to a file server usually requires an additional cable that alerts the file server when the UPS is running on standby power. The server will then proceed with shutdown procedures. One end of the monitor cable should have either a stereo phone plug (for plugging into the stand-alone UPS monitor board or the SS keycard in a non-PS/2 file server) or a 4-pin mouse plug (for plugging into the mouse port of an IBM PS/2 file server). The other end of the monitor cable should have the type of connector required by your particular UPS.

Some vendors have developed advanced features for their power protection equipment. American Power Conversion's Smart-UPS series provides network managers with diagnostics information via a software control program called PowerChute. The software is installed on the server and communicates with the UPS over a cable. Managers can then track power quality, UPS operating temperature, line frequency, UPS output voltage, maximum and minimum line power, battery strength, line voltage, and UPS load. American Power Conversion can be reached in West Kingston, Rhode Island at 401/789-5735.

RELATED ENTRIES   Data Protection; Fault Management; Fault Tolerance; Power
Grounding Problems and Solutions; *and* Surge Suppressors

Unit of Work

See Transaction Processing.

UNIX

The UNIX operating system was developed at AT&T Bell Laboratories by Ken
Thompson and Dennis Ritchie in 1969 and the early 1970s. It is a multiuser system that
supports networking and distributed file systems such as Sun Microsystems' Network
File System (NFS) or the Open Software Foundation's (OSF) implementation of the
Andrew File System (AFS). The operating system has a number of variations that were
implemented after AT&T made the operating system available on an open basis to
universities and colleges for use in research projects and computer science programs.
The current release is UNIX System V Release 4.2 (SVR4.2), which includes the
Berkeley Software Division enhancements and other enhancements.

Some of the major developments in the UNIX environment are listed here:

- In the early 1980s, the *Portable Operating System Interface for UNIX (POSIX)*
  standard was defined by the Institute of Electrical and Electronics Engineers
  (IEEE) and the American National Standards Institute (ANSI) to create an
  industry-standard UNIX-like system and a set of application program interfaces
  for developing portable applications. Various working groups within the IEEE
  are still defining the standard. The original specifications were adopted by the
  International Organization for Standardization (ISO) in 1988.

- The *X/Open* group was founded in 1984 by Bull, Nixdorf, Philips, Siemens, and
  other companies to promote open UNIX standards by testing for conformity
  among products.

- The *Open Software Foundation* was formed in 1988 by IBM, DEC,
  Hewlett-Packard, Nixdorf, Siemens, and hundreds of other members to develop
  the OSF/1 UNIX distributed operating system as well as the Distributed
  Computing Environment (DCE).

- *UNIX International* was formed in 1988 by AT&T's UNIX System Laboratory
  (USL), Control Data, Data General, Informix, Intel, Motorola, NCR, Olivetti,
  Texas Instruments, and hundreds of other companies to promote open UNIX
  through publicly available documentation. After fulfilling goals, the
  organization disbanded in late 1993.

- *The Common Open Software Environment (COSE)* was founded in 1993 by IBM,
  Hewlett-Packard, SunSoft, Novell, and others, with the goal of cooperating to

U

deliver a common desktop environment (graphical user interface) for UNIX that can rival Microsoft Windows.

■ In 1991, Novell and AT&T's UNIX System Laboratories (USL) joined forces to create Univell, a company with goals of developing UnixWare, a desktop UNIX system with built-in Novell NetWare support. In 1993, Novell purchased USL and formed the UNIX Systems Group (USG) to manage UnixWare. Univel will eventually become nonexistent.

With the purchase of USL, Novell gained control of UNIX SVR4 to the dismay of other UNIX vendors. However, in an attempt to consolidate the industry on a common UNIX operating system, Novell gave the UNIX trademark to the X/Open organization. X/Open will grant the UNIX trademark to UNIX implementations that are compatible with a set of specifications defined by the COSE group. This set of specifications, called the *COSE Spec 1170 APIs*, defines programming interfaces that promote the portability of applications between operating systems.

One of the main advantages of UNIX is its widespread use as a development platform and desktop operating system. As mentioned earlier, AT&T made the code available in the academic environment, spurring its proliferation onto many platforms and the development of unique applications. Most of this work was done at the University of California at Berkeley, which produced versions called the Berkeley Software Distributions (BSDs). UC Berkeley is responsible for adding the Transmission Control Protocol/Internet Protocol (TCP/IP) networking protocols and porting UNIX to the DEC VAX. A number of UNIX variations exist, including XENIX from Microsoft, ULTRIX from DEC, and Advanced Interactive Executive (AIX) from IBM.

The operating system initially became popular in the engineering, computer-aided design, and scientific environments, where it was implemented on powerful workstations. It eventually found its way into business, medical, and many other environments. Another contributing factor to UNIX's popularity is that it is written in the C programming language. Thus, UNIX is highly portable and contains system components written in a common, well-known programming language that are easily recompiled to work on a variety of systems.

The major growth and development of UNIX today are taking place on smaller systems such as those based on Intel x86 processors and low-priced workstations based on the Reduced Instruction Set Computer (RISC) chip. The number of UNIX versions has stalled its industry-wide acceptance, but the growing use of Windows NT has provided incentive for UNIX vendors to create compatible products and common graphical user interfaces to promote the UNIX environment.

UNIX Kernel and File System

UNIX consists of a small kernel that runs processes, such as user applications and services. The UNIX kernel is a solid core that changes little from system to system, while processes are added at the user's discretion. This design approach makes it easy for the user to add new services or remove unnecessary services. It also makes upgrades easier since the entire operating system does not need to be recompiled. Users interact with the operating system through a *shell*, which is also a process that accepts user input and performs various tasks. Because the shell is a replaceable process, there are many variations, such as the Bourne shell, the C shell, and the Korn shell.

The file system is hierarchical. There is a root directory and branching subdirectories, and each directory can have its own set of subdirectories. Files are stored in directories (or subdirectories) and the full name of a file includes the complete pathname of the directory tree, although it's not necessary to specify the full path if the file's directory is the current context. Devices such as displays and printers have device names that are handled in the same way as files. For example, a user could direct the output of a process or file listing to the display or a printer by using the display or printer name in a command. A piping feature provides a way to direct the output of one command, such as a sort, into another command.

UNIX in the Network Environment

UNIX and the TCP/IP protocols are closely linked. Most UNIX implementations now include TCP/IP and support for Ethernet, which greatly simplifies networking in the environment. In addition, Sun Microsystems' Network File System (NFS) is the common distributed file-sharing system included with UNIX although OSF is implementing the Andrew File System (AFS), which is superior in many ways. Thus, UNIX provides in one package the ability to install a powerful operating system on a computer that lets users share files and run programs on other users' computers, through one of the most common and powerful networking protocols in the industry.

TCP/IP is an extremely useful and common internetworking protocol. It was developed by the Department of Defense as a way to connect many dissimilar systems. TCP/IP has several applications to facilitate file transfers and access between systems, such as Telnet and File Transfer Protocol (FTP). Telnet is a remote terminal program that lets a user control a program on a host system. FTP provides a way to transfer files between systems. NFS lets users access files on remote systems as if the remote systems were part of their own system. No extra commands or procedures are required to list files, view their contents, create new files, or copy files to the local hard drive. The remote file system is "mapped" so that it appears as a local drive.

UNIX Implementations

The following products represent implementations of the UNIX operating system as an example.

ULTRIX, DEC   Ultrix is Digital Equipment Corporation's native implementation of the UNIX operating system for Virtual Address Extension (VAX), MicroVAX, VAXstation, and RISC-based DECstation systems. TCP/IP and NFS are bundled with the Ultrix operating system. Other features include the following:

■ A Yellow Pages (YP) feature that provides centralized file management.

- A backup and restore system that managers can activate from remote systems.
- Diskless workstation support.
- POSIX-compatible file and record locking.
- Remote procedure call (RPC) based on Apollo's NCS V1.5.
- X/OPEN Transport Interface Library on UDP and TCP transports.
- Simple Network Management Protocol (SNMP) model agent.
- Bundled LAT and LAT/Telnet Gateway support. The latter product allows access to a TCP/IP network from a DECnet network that uses the LAT protocol.

NOVELL UNIXWARE   UnixWare includes features from UNIX System V, NetWare, and DR DOS, and is designed to provide an integration platform for corporate computing that will allow DOS, Microsoft Windows, NetWare, and UNIX systems to interoperate. Features include the following:

- A graphical user interface
- Support for thousands of available UNIX applications
- A fault-tolerant, journaling file system

Novell's UnixWare Application Server is a multiuser version of UnixWare that provides distributed access to UNIX, DOS, and Microsoft Windows applications. Users can log in under multiple session using either NetWare Internetwork Packet Exchange/Sequenced Packet Exchange (IPX/SPX) or TCP/IP. UnixWare consists of two configurations: a client version and a server version. Both configurations are described next.

- *UnixWare Personal Edition* adds a UNIX desktop environment to the NetWare network. It includes a graphical desktop manager that supports Motif and the Open Look interface.
- *UnixWare Application Server* is an application platform that integrates full NetWare IPX/SPX and TCP/IP protocols with UNIX System V Release 4.2. UnixWare Application Server enables DOS, UNIX, and other PC operating system clients to take full advantage of UNIX-based client-server applications, while simultaneously maintaining access to NetWare services and LAN resources. It can optionally serve as a traditional TCP/IP network server and support NFS as well as the standard Internet utilities. In addition, it provides support for multiple X terminals for running the graphical desktop.

The Univell UnixWare product line competes with Open Desktop from SCO and Solaris 2.0 from SunSoft. All of these products are UNIX-based operating systems for Intel processors, and they run hundreds of existing applications. The UnixWare products include the integration of NetWare features. UnixWare also competes with Microsoft NT and OS/2, which are non-UNIX products but designed as a multitasking client-server operating system that will compete against UNIX. However, Microsoft NT is a relatively new product without the range of applications that UNIX has.

RELATED ENTRIES   Common Open Software Environment; Digital Equipment Corporation; Distributed File Systems; Kernel; Novell; Open Software Foundation; OSF/1; POSIX; Transmission Control Protocol/Internet Protocol; *and* X/Open

UNIX International

UNIX International was a not-for-profit international organization with an open membership that was dedicated to the evolution of the UNIX System V operating system and related software. UNIX International was formed in 1988 by AT&T and Sun Microsystems, as well as NCR, Unisys, and hundreds of other members. It originally formed to counter the Open Software Foundation but was disbanded in 1993 because its members felt that such an organization was no longer needed.

RELATED ENTRIES   UNIX

UNIX System Laboratories (USL)
See UNIX.

UNIX-to-UNIX Copy Program (UUCP)

UUCP is a UNIX application that provides file copying services between two UNIX systems over a single connection. Many UNIX electronic mail applications use UUCP.

Unshielded Twisted Pair (UTP)
See Cabling; Transmission Media, Methods, and Equipment.

USENET

USENET news is an Internet broadcast news service that distributes information, usually about the Internet, to all hosts. The USENET network includes all computers that get USENET news. If you sign up for an Internet mail service, chances are you'll get access to this service. It provides a way for users everywhere on the Internet to read and post news. The environment is uncensored and the USENET community works hard to keep it that way.

RELATED ENTRY   Internet

User Agent

In X.400 electronic-mail systems, the User Agent is the component that packages the data, creates headers, and addresses and forwards messages.

RELATED ENTRY   X.400 Message Handling System

User Datagram Protocol

The *User Datagram Protocol* (UDP) is part of the TCP/IP protocol suite. It was created to provide a way for applications to access the connectionless features of IP. Both TCP and UDP use IP. UDP was designed to allow applications to create datagrams and address them to the ports for accessing applications or processes. UDP's primary role is to add the port address of an application process to an IP packet.

RELATED ENTRIES   Internet; Internet Protocols; *and* Transmission Control Protocol/Internet Protocol

Users and Groups

Network operating systems provide security by requiring that all users log on by typing their user account name and a password. Once the user is verified or authenticated (see "Authentication and Authorization"), the user can access the network based on the rights they have been granted throughout the network. Some network operating systems require users to log on every time they access a resource at a different location on the network. The latest trend is to incorporate user authentication features that verify the authenticity of a user one time for all resources on a network. Trust relationships are established so that one server "trusts" that another server has properly authenticated a user.

User accounts hold information about the user, including any restriction they have on a network. For example, a user might be restricted to logging on at a specific workstation or during a specific time. Groups are collections of users that network administrators create to simplify user management. It is far easier to include users in a group, then assign network access rights to the group, than it is to assign those rights individually to each user. Groups also simplify messaging. For example, it's easier to send an electronic mail message to a group called Managers than to each person in that group individually. Managers should create groups for users, projects, and management purposes when planning and setting up the network, then add user accounts to groups as users are added to the network.

User Accounts in NetWare

Users can gain access to the network as soon as the network administrator or a supervisor has created a user object for them using management utilities like SYSCON or the NetWare 4.x NETADMIN utility. After creating a user account, rights to the file system and network resources are assigned to the account. Alternatively, the account is added to a group and thus attains all the rights and privileges of the group. The restrictions of a user account are discussed in the following sections.

ACCOUNT BALANCE RESTRICTIONS   You can restrict a user's access to the system and its resources by specifying a credit limit. A credit limit is a balance in an account that depletes as time and resources are used. Once depleted, the user can't log into the system until given more credit.

EXPIRATION RESTRICTIONS   You can set an expiration date and time for a user account. The account is closed at the time specified. You might use this restriction for temporary employees.

PASSWORD RESTRICTIONS   The administrator or a supervisor can specify the length and uniqueness of login passwords. You can force users to change their passwords at regular intervals and to use passwords that they haven't used recently.

DISK SPACE RESTRICTIONS   Disk space restrictions prevent users from using too much of the server's disk space by loading unnecessary programs or files.

CONNECTION RESTRICTIONS   Connection restrictions can limit the number of stations a user can log into simultaneously.

TIME RESTRICTIONS   Time restrictions specify the hours, in half-hour blocks, that users can log into the system.

STATION RESTRICTIONS   Station restrictions prevent a user from logging in at any station other than the specified workstation. This prevents users from logging in at unsupervised workstations where their activities cannot be monitored. In NetWare, these restrictions can be assigned individually to each account, or assigned as default settings that are applied when new accounts are created.

RELATED ENTRIES   Access Control; Access Rights; Account, User Network; File and Directory Rights, NetWare; Groups; Home Directory; Permissions in Windows NT; *and* Workgroups

U

Value-Added Carrier (VAC)

A VAC (also called a public data network) is a one-stop service provider of long-distance telecommunication services for customers who want to build national and international private or virtual networks. The VAC provides all the data links that the customer requires; the customer pays one bill. Connections are typically packet-switching networks. A VAC may have initially established the network services it provides to customers for its own use. It may even lease some of the underlying connections from carriers such as AT&T, but often creates its own private lines using fiber-optic, microwave, and satellite links. The VAC may also perform some data processing and protocol conversion for its customers. A connection into a VAC's network is typically through an analog phone line or digital line. Services provided typically include X.25, Frame Relay, and even Asynchronous Transfer Mode (ATM). Major VACs are listed here:

- *CompuServe Information Services* offers access points in hundreds of locations throughout the United States for X.25 and Frame Relay services.
- *GE Information Services* provides packet-switching and high-speed services, as well as asynchronous and synchronous services.
- *Infonet Services Corp.* provides an array of international services.
- *Tymenet Global Network* has close to 5,000 global access points.

Using a PDN saves you the trouble of contracting for the lines and setting up your own switching equipment. The providers handle any problems with the network itself and can guarantee data delivery through a vast mesh of switched lines.

RELATED ENTRIES   Packet-Switching Networks; Public Data Networks; Public Switched Data Network; Switched Services; *and* Wide Area Networks

VAX, Digital Equipment Corporation (DEC)

The VAX line of computer systems was first introduced in 1977. The first system, the VAX 11/780, competed with IBM systems and provided an upgrade path for DEC's existing customers. The VAX 11/780 had a compatibility mode in which it could run software written for DEC's PDP-11 minicomputer systems. It also had a compatible bus so DEC customers could use some of their existing peripherals.

The Virtual Memory System (VMS) was announced with the VAX line. VMS is an operating system designed to take advantage of the 32-bit architecture of the VAX system. VMS provides a true multitasking/multiuser environment. Also announced with the VAX was DECnet, a networking system that provided a way to interconnect various computer systems using parallel cables. In 1980, Digital, Intel, and Xerox introduced Ethernet, which became the underlying communication system for a new generation of DECnet products and connectivity.

RELATED ENTRY   Digital Equipment Corporation

"V dot" Standards, CCITT (ITU)

The Consultative Committee for International Telegraph and Telephone and (CCITT) is a committee of a United Nations treaty organization called the International Telecommunications Union (ITU). The ITU, made up of members of different nations, has the task of studying, recommending, and standardizing technical and operational issues for telecommunication. The CCITT modem standards, called the "V dot" standards, are accepted worldwide for modem communication. These standards are based on some original standards developed by AT&T, and contain features made popular in the Microcom Networking Protocol (MNP). The most important CCITT standards are listed in the following table and some are discussed further in the section that follows.

Standard	Description
V.22	1,200 bits/sec full-duplex modem standard
V.22bis	2,400 bits/sec full-duplex modem standard
V.24	Defines circuits in RS-232 interface
V.32	Asynchronous and synchronous 4,800/9,600 bits/sec standard
V.32bis	Asynchronous and synchronous standard up to 14,400 bits/sec
V.35	Defines high data-rates over combined circuits
V.42	Defines error-checking standards
V.42bis	Defines modem compression using the Lempel Ziv method
V.terbo	An emerging standard that provides 19.2 Kbits/sec rates
V.34	A proposed standard for 28 Kbits/sec transmission rates

V.24   V.24 is the same standard as the Electronic Industries Association (EIA) RS-232C standard. They define the methods for interfacing data terminal equipment (DTEs) such as terminals and computers to data communication equipment (DCEs) such as modems.

V.35   This standard defines the interface for connecting DTE to high-speed synchronous modems. The physical definition specifies a 34-pin connector and clock signals that synchronize modems.

V.32 STANDARDS   The following standards use trellis encoding techniques to represent signals. Trellis encoding is a way of representing data bits in the phase amplitude changes of a signal. These signal changes map into a constellation of points and the points represent more complex symbols.

V

- V.32 is a two-wire duplex modem standard that provides 2,400 bits per second (bits/sec) throughput using quadrature amplitude modulation techniques and 9,600 bits/sec throughput using trellis encoding.

- V.32*bis* uses a two-dimensional trellis encoding technique with 128 points in a signal constellation. It provides transmission rates from 4,800 to 14,400 bits/sec.

- V.32*terbo* uses a two-dimensional trellis encoding technique with 256 or 512 points in a signal constellation. It provides transmission rates of up to 19,200 bits/sec and is designed as an interim step between 14,400 bits/sec V.32*bis* and V.34, the emerging 28,800 bits/sec standard.

V.42 The error-checking standard defined by V.42 is designed to reduce data errors caused by noisy phone lines. The cyclical redundancy checking (CRC) method verifies the integrity of transmitted data. A CRC value is calculated on a block of data and sent with the block. When the receiving system receives the block, it calculates its own CRC value and compares it to the CRC value from the sender. Discrepancies in CRC values initiate retransmissions of data. V.42 actually packetizes blocks of data, reducing the need for start and stop bits and the amount of information that is transmitted. This increases throughput by about 20 percent.

V.42BIS This is the data compression standard that provides a four-to-one data compression ratio. If data has already been compressed by a utility such as PKZIP, the V.42bis compression standard should not be used since it will simply add a lot of unneeded overhead to the transmission. However, on uncompressed data, the standard can double the throughput of a 2,400 bits/sec modem to 4,800 bits/sec.

V.34 (FORMERLY KNOWN AS V.*FAST*) V.34 is a proposed standard that is due for completion in mid-1994. It uses a four-dimensional trellis encoding technique with up to 768 points in a signal constellation. It provides transmission rates up to 28,800 bits/sec. With compression, throughput can reach 100,000 bits/sec. However, most serial ports in personal computers and Macintosh systems cannot handle throughput at these rates, so some vendors are working on transmission through parallel ports or the use of enhanced serial ports.

RELATED ENTRIES Asynchronous Communications; Bell Modem Standards; Dialup Line; Microcom Networking Protocol; Modems; Modulation Techniques; Serial Communication; *and* Synchronous Communications

Vendor Independent Messaging (VIM), Lotus

VIM is an electronic mail application program interface (API) controlled by Lotus and supported by Apple, Borland, IBM, MCI, Novell, Oracle, WordPerfect, and other electronic mail developers and vendors. It was originally called Open Messaging

Interface (OMI) by cc:Mail, its developer. Lotus purchased cc:Mail, updated OMI by adding compatibility, and changed its name to VIM. Vendors use electronic mail APIs to add connectivity to network operating systems. Competing standards include Novell's NetWare Global Messaging and Standard Message Format (SMF), Microsoft's Messaging Applications Programming Interface (MAPI), Apple Computer's Open Collaborative Environment (AOCE), and Lotus's Vendor Independent Messaging (VIM).

VIM is a cross-platform API that allows developers to create mail-enabled applications that work on many different platforms and allows users on those different platforms to share mail. VIM gives developers and users access to message transport facilities that operate over a variety of protocols. The interface allows any VIM-enabled application such as E-mail programs and groupware to work with a VIM-compatible operating system.

Information is exchanged between applications using store-and-forward methods, so the attached mail system must have this feature. Information to exchange is viewed as an object that can contain any combination of text, data (spreadsheet), graphics, voice, and video. Users can send basic messages from within their applications, or they can send complex documents such as spreadsheet files or graphic files. VIM also includes services for creating, reading, and sending messages, as well as the ability to keep an address book.

An important feature of VIM is its ability to link with other messaging APIs, including Apple's AOCE, Microsoft's MAPI, and the Standard Message Format (SMF) implemented in Novell's Message Handling Service (MHS).

RELATED ENTRIES   Document Interchange Standards; Electronic Mail; Groupware; Lotus Notes; Message-Enabled Applications; Messaging API, E-mail; *and* Workflow Software

Vertical Wiring

In a structured wiring system, the vertical wiring is the cable that stretches from the wiring closet on each floor to the main equipment room in the basement or first floor of the building. In contrast, the horizontal wiring is the cable that runs from a telecommunication wiring closet to each of the workstations on a floor of a building.

RELATED ENTRIES   Cabling; EIA/TIA 568 Commercial Building Wiring Standard

Very Small Aperture Terminals (VSATs)

See Satellite Telecommunication.

Videoconferencing and Desktop Video

Video applications are becoming more prominent in the network environment. Desktop applications are implementing multimedia and video in new ways to help network users communicate and share information. Videoconferencing provides a way for people at remote locations to meet without traveling. In the network environment, videoconferencing can go beyond letting people look at each other. The video screen can have multiple windows that focus on computer-based applications, allowing users to see drawings, charts, spreadsheets, and other collaborative information, while viewing and listening to one another. These videoconferencing systems integrate computer-based information with live video and transport it over the local or wide area network connections.

There are four methods for delivering video in the network environment:

- Prerecorded video, such as educational segments, computer-based training, and video mail clips, that is stored on a video server can be delivered over the network to a user at any time upon request.

- Prerecorded video such as company bulletins, announcements, meeting highlights, and other newsworthy information is *broadcast* to many users at scheduled times, or when a group of users requests it.

- Live video is broadcast in a one-way format to many users over the network with little interaction.

- Videoconferencing techniques involve broadcasting live, two-way interactive video among many users. This option is time-sensitive and requires a delivery system that transmits high volumes of data on time.

These four applications can be categorized into local delivery systems and videoconferencing systems. In the local environment, managers need to make sure that video transmissions do not tie up network bandwidth. Shared local area network (LAN) systems such as Ethernet are not designed to deliver video, but it is possible to provide adequate non-real-time video performance if microsegmentation techniques and switching hubs are used that place as few as one user on each LAN segment. This reduces contention on the LAN and can provide each user with the full 10 Mbits/sec bandwidth of the Ethernet network.

Local Video Delivery Systems

Video (multimedia systems) in the LAN environment typically consists of multimedia servers that store video, audio, and graphic files. Compression software or special compression boards help reduce the size of these files. End-user systems run software to request and display video from the server, such as training or help clips. A full video recording and playback system uses video cameras, microphones, and speakers at end-user systems as pictured in Figure V-1. Lotus Development's Video Notes is an E-mail system designed with video in mind.

In the LAN environment, the difference between prerecorded video and live video is significant. Delivery delays are not a factor for viewers of prerecorded video. When a user makes a request to view video files or video E-mail clips, the files or clips are

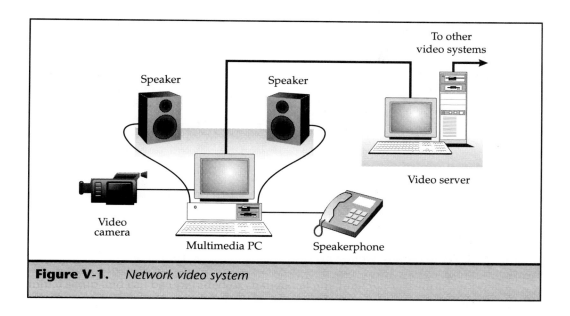

Figure V-1. *Network video system*

first delivered and assembled, then played back. Delayed or lost packet problems are resolved with the users having little knowledge that such problems exist.

In contrast, live videoconferencing requires enough bandwidth to deliver video to all users on time and without losing packets. If packets are lost or dropped due to insufficient bandwidth and congestion, the video will appear "jerky." Some frame dropping is acceptable, as long as it is done in a controlled way. Frame dropping techniques are often used to deliver video on computers or networks with insufficient bandwidth. Anything below 10 frames per second (fps) appears as a series of still pictures while 15 fps is acceptable but has a noticeably unnatural appearance. Frames rates higher than 15 fps deliver adequate video.

High-speed networks such as Fast Ethernet or Fiber Distributed Data Interface (FDDI) are often implemented for desktop videoconferencing in the LAN environment. Asynchronous Transfer Mode (ATM) is an emerging network standard that can accommodate live video. Its high data transfer rates and fixed-size cells provide predictable data delivery services that are ideal for real-time video. With compression and microsegmentation switching techniques, 10 Mbits/sec Ethernet LANs can deliver relatively high-quality video. New 100 Mbits/sec Fast Ethernet standards are designed to support video.

Videoconferencing

Videoconferencing provides a way for users at remote locations to "hold meetings" over computer networks in the local area or over carrier-based services in the wide area. A video camera, speakerphone, and computer are typically required at each site.

While some vendors make complete integrated videoconferencing systems, you can build systems by installing special PC boards in computers that provide video and audio inputs. Videoconferencing software manages the equipment and session, and typically provides a way to display pictures and charts for everyone to view. The software is interactive, allowing attendees to make changes that others can see. A typical videoconferencing system, such as the PictureTel Live PCS 100, uses a Windows graphical user interface so that users can see images captured by video cameras in one window and computer graphics pulled up from files or generated by applications in another window. Some high-end systems include multiple monitors for viewing camera images and computer-generated images.

The current industry videoconferencing standard is defined by the CCITT and collectively called Px64. This standard is referred to as Px64 because it defines compression in multiples of 64 Kbits/sec. H.320 is the latest specification within Px64. It defines multipoint videoconferencing (simultaneous conferencing at multiple locations) and associated requirements such as encryption, remote camera control, and audio/video compression. The standards define the functions for codecs (**co**der/**dec**oders), which are responsible for video compression and decompression. They also provide some compatibility between television display formats in other countries.

Other features and functions defined by the H.320 family of standards include:

- Voice and high-fidelity audio compression at up to 16 Kbits/sec
- Frame formats for transmitting compressed information
- Procedures for establishing communication sessions between conferencing locations and the exchange of control information between codecs
- The creation of a multipoint conference (three or more conferencing systems) using a multipoint control unit (MCU)
- Encryption techniques to ensure privacy

H.320 codecs are being manufactured by leading chip producers such as Texas Instruments and AT&T. The standard has stimulated the market for videoconferencing products. The AT&T Personal Video System is a desktop PC-based video system that lets users see each other and share information using a Microsoft Windows interface. The system operates at 10 to 15 frames per second over transmission lines of 112 to 128 Kbits/sec. A multipoint control unit is available that allows up to 24 sites to connect into a videoconference.

Carriers are also involved since videoconference connections are made through their facilities. US Sprint, for example, offers a one-stop service for making videoconference connections, no matter what codec, local exchange carrier, or interexchange carrier is involved.

RELATED ENTRIES   Asynchronous Transfer Mode; Carrier Services; Compression Techniques; Fast Ethernet; Fiber Distributed Data Interface; Multimedia; *and* Security

VINES, Banyan

See Banyan VINES.

Virtual Circuits

A virtual circuit is link between two or more end stations on a packet-switched mesh network. It provides a temporary or dedicated connection-oriented session between two end points. The defining characteristic is a predefined path through a network that has many paths. Defining a path ahead of time improves performance and reduces the header requirements of frames and packets, which increases throughput. Technically, the underlying physical paths through the packet-switching network may change to avoid congestion or downed lines, but the two end stations maintain a connection and update the path specification as necessary. Figure V-2 illustrates virtual circuits between LAN users and remote sites. Notice how the virtual circuit for user A spans the LAN connection, the mulitplexed link between the bridge/routers, and the packet-switched network, and the links through the packet-switched network.

There are permanent and switched virtual circuits, as described next:

■ A *permanent virtual circuit (PVC)* is a connection between end stations that is defined in advance and requires little if any setup time. In public-switched carrier services such as Asynchronous Transfer Mode (ATM) or Frame Relay, customers negotiate the end points of PVCs in advance with the carrier and contact the carrier if they need to reconfigure the end points of a PVC.

■ A *switched virtual circuit (SVC)* is a temporary connection between end stations. Connections last only as long as necessary and are disconnected when the session is complete. The virtual circuit must be set up just prior to data transfer. Some packet-switching services provided by the carriers allow customers to dynamically define an SVC as required.

SVCs and PVCs are typically discussed in terms of the public data network, although organization with in-house switching networks built around technology such as ATM can define PVCs in advance to reduce network overhead. In terms of carrier services, customers are typically charged an initial setup cost for a PVC, then charged on a monthly basis or on a per-packet basis. While SVCs are comparable to dialup phone calls, PVCs are comparable to dedicated leased telephone lines between two points.

In the ATM environment, logical connections between end stations are called *virtual channels (VCs). A virtual path (VP)* is a defined path that one or more VCs follow through a mesh network to reach the same destination, although each VC may connect with a different end system or application process at that destination. Think of a VP as a cable that contains a bundle of wires as pictured in Figure V-3. In this analogy, the cable connects two points and the individual circuits within the cable connect end systems. The advantage is that connections sharing the same path through the network are grouped together and use the same management functions. If

V

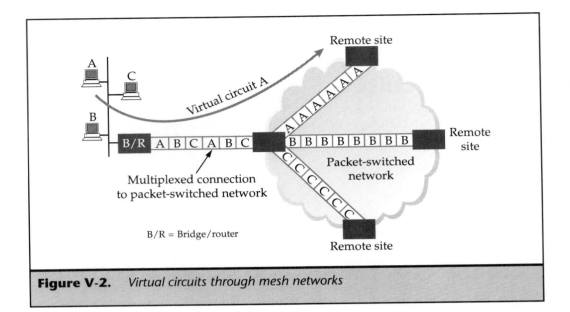

Figure V-2. *Virtual circuits through mesh networks*

a VP is already set up, adding new VCs is easy since the work of defining paths through the network is already done. In addition, if the network needs to change a path to avoid congestion or downed lines, all the VCs set up for a VP are directed along the new path.

PVCs are the traditional connection method in the Frame Relay environment, although SVC support was added to the specification in late 1993. PVCs have specific service characteristics. You define PVCs and the service characteristics listed here when setting up the service with a provider. The service characteristics of the link are *committed burst size, committed information rate, excess burst size,* and *frame size.* They are defined at subscription time.

- *Committed burst size (CBS)* is the maximum amount of data (in bits) that the network provider agrees to transfer under normal network conditions during a time interval.

- *Committed information rate (CIR)* is the rate at which the network provider agrees to transfer CBS committed data during normal network conditions on a PVC.

- *Excess burst size (EBS)* is the maximum allowed amount of uncommitted data (in bits) in excess of CBS that the network will attempt to deliver during a time interval. EBS data is treated as discard-eligible by the network during congestion periods.

- *Frame size* is the size of the frame in which customer data is transferred through the packet-switched network.

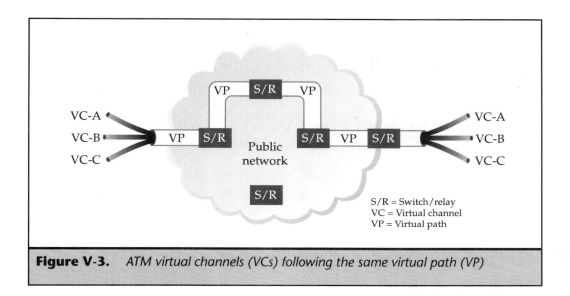

Figure V-3.   *ATM virtual channels (VCs) following the same virtual path (VP)*

RELATED ENTRIES   Carrier Services; Connection-Oriented and Connectionless Protocols; Packet-Switching Networks; *and* Wide Area Networks

Virtual Data Networks

The carrier community is deploying the technology that organizations need to create *virtual data networks* among remote sites in the campus environment, metropolitan area, wide area, or on a global scale. A virtual data network provides a way to fully interconnect all systems at all sites in the organization at much lower costs than leasing dedicated lines and building private networks. The goal is to provide LAN-like speeds over wide area networks.

Packet-switched services such as Frame Relay and Switched Multimegabit Data Service (SMDS) are providing virtual data network capabilities and replacing the need for dedicated lines. The services provide bandwidth on demand with millisecond switching capabilities. Customers only pay for the services they use. Services are provided by long-distance carriers such as AT&T, MCI, and US Sprint, as well as value-added carriers (VACs) such as CompuServe, Infonet, and Tymenet. Circuit-switched services such as Switched-56, Switched 384K (AT&T), Switched T1, and Switched T3 are now common with the carriers as well.

With reduced costs, smaller sites can now be included in the larger corporate data network. In addition, personnel requirements are not as high because the carrier services handle the switching elements. With packet-switched services, a single "data pipe" delivers the data from the customer site to the carrier, and the carrier then delivers it to other sites. However, network managers should consider the loss of control inherent in assigning more network management to a public carrier, although those carriers can provide adequate management information about the services.

RELATED ENTRIES   Carrier Services; Circuit-Switching Services; *and* Packet-Switching Networks

Virtual File System (VFS)

The Virtual File System (VFS) was created by Sun Microsystems, Inc. when defining the Network File System (NFS), a distributed file system for network environments. VFS is an interface that allows a number of different file system implementations to be used with the operating system.

RELATED ENTRY   Distributed File Systems

Virtually Integrated Technical Architecture Lifecycle (VITAL)

VITAL is Apple's blueprint for integrating desktop computers into enterprise system environments. Its guidelines define the creation of consistently built, shared, and reusable software modules, called *services*. Users invoke these services from the desktop. The strategy encompasses multivendor personal computing devices, not just Apple computer systems. VITAL sees users as the focus of software services, rather than end points of a computing system. The key goals are to provide easy user access to information on platform-independent devices that can accommodate rapid changes in technology and integrate existing technology.

VITAL divides enterprise systems into four interrelated logical environments tied together by a systems infrastructure, as shown in Figure V-4 and described in the following list. Keep the client-server model in mind, which places data in back-end server systems and presents it to clients at front-end workstations. The system is distributed, meaning that data is on many different servers—clients access data without needing to know where those servers are located. Also note that back-end services are typically provided by SQL-compliant database systems. VITAL defines back-end data storage in terms of "warehousing." A warehouse server stores large amounts of information, but users don't access it directly. Instead, the warehouse moves data requested by users to local access servers (LASs) as shown in Figure V-5. You can think of LASs as "retail outlets" for warehouse information. This optimizes the warehouse servers for access from many LASs.

- *Desktop integration environment* Provides the human interface, application support, navigation, and interconnection to the enterprise network through desktop services called *objects*. Objects perform routing, communication, and enterprise computing functions under the management of an integration services manager.

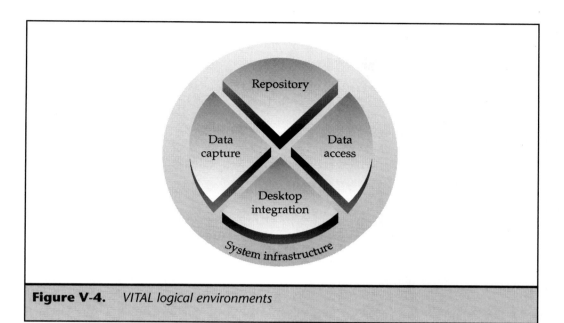

Figure V-4. *VITAL logical environments*

■ *Data capture environment* Concerned with all aspects of collecting and storing information. It uses an update-oriented transaction system and manages the release of cross-functional shared data to the data access environment.

■ *Data access environment* Manages the acquisition, warehousing, and distribution of shared data to local access databases that are used by individual applications and their users.

■ *Repository environment* Provides an encyclopedia of metadata, which is data about the components in the total environment. Consistency in the environment is maintained by the repository services.

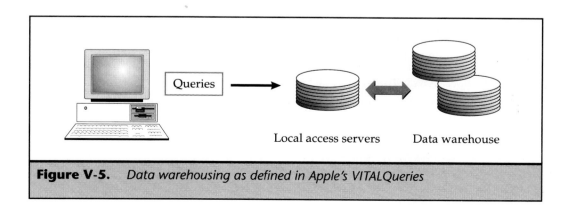

Figure V-5. *Data warehousing as defined in Apple's VITALQueries*

■ *Systems infrastructure environment* This environment encompasses the utility software, hardware, network, organization, security, standards, and disciplines on which the other components are built.

There are several reasons for separating data capture from data access. First, it ensures consistent data that will be cross-functional among transaction systems. It also reduces interdependencies and streamlines transaction processing. Transaction systems perform two primary functions. First, they retrieve, modify, and reinsert small amounts of data. Second, they manage record contention, which ensures that no user overwrites information written by another. VITAL separates these two environments so the tasks can be performed on many platforms.

The Desktop Integration Environment

The desktop integration environment provides user support. It sees the user as both a data producer and data consumer. The activities performed by users are part of a seamless desktop environment that frees the user from the need to worry about where data is located, its structure, and its integrity. The environment provides a consistent interface that lets users quickly reach data anywhere in the enterprise, then prepare, capture, view, analyze, synthesize, report, and distribute it. These functions are provided by *integration services.*

Integration services fall into three logical groups, each of which is listed next.

SYSTEMS INFRASTRUCTURE AND COLLABORATIVE SERVICES

■ Authentication, authorization, and encryption/decryption services

■ Software-license management

■ Version control and synchronization

■ Metadata synchronization

■ Time synchronization

■ Directory interface

■ Mail and messaging services

■ File transfer services

■ Printer services

■ Network connection services

INFORMATION CONSUMPTION SERVICES

■ Data synchronization, which ensures that local databases on individual computers are synchronized with copies on database servers.

■ Query submittal service lets users submit data queries on databases in the data capture and data access environments. Users can request data from any back-end service, which may be Sybase, Oracle, or others. Query outputs are provided in whatever format is used at the desktop.

- External data delivery makes information available to users from many different sources either on demand or on a regularly scheduled basis. This service can integrate data from many sources and present it in formats designed by users.

- Multimedia access services provide a richer form of content information by handling the compression/decompression, format translation, and retrieval of rich data forms such as sound and video.

DATA PRODUCTION SERVICES

- Forms processing provides electronic forms display and input services. It can locate forms and their associated editing specifications from a server and display it for the user.

- Transaction submittal services provide the operations for submitting an insert/update transaction to servers that provides transaction processing capabilities. It provides seamless and consistent record-locking, contention management, priority detection, and update-commitment control for online transaction processing (OLTP) transactions.

The Data Capture and Access Environments

Both the data capture and data access environments are based on the principle that client-server computing is the preferred method of interaction with the host. The desktop computer provides a graphic view of information. Where possible, data is validated at the desktop, relieving host computers from these services. The data capture process moves information captured by users to the data warehouses and the data access services provide that data to users. Data in shared warehouses is consistent in format, definition, structure, and value across the systems that use it.

DATA CAPTURE SERVICES

- *Access and write routines*   For accessing and writing to isolated files
- *Data capture services*   For capturing data to storage devices
- *Validation services*   Ensures that the form of data is consistent
- *Deliver transactions*   Ensures receipt of data
- *Create and send snapshot*   For data extraction and query routines
- *Initiate event processing*   For job scheduling routines
- *Transaction management*   Provides monitoring of transactions

DATA ACCESS SERVICES

- *Manage access to collections*   Assists users in finding data and scheduling requests for it
- *Place order for collection*   Places data requests with the warehouse network

- *Provide direct warehouse access*   Provides a set of stored procedures, typically standard queries
- *Manage warehouse inventory*   Optimally services user requests at the lowest possible system cost
- *Receive data and build collections*   Verifies that extracts are correct
- *Fulfill order for collection*   Helps to deliver data to local access databases

The Repository Environment

The repository environment deals with the management and administration of metadata and control services to support the data capture, data access, and desktop integration environments. A robust repository environment is crucial to developing a consistent view of information across systems, geography, and disparate hardware platforms.

The objective of the repository environment is to maintain a single source of metadata references to all users, developers, applications, services, and databases. It also presents a consistent view of data when the data is partitioned and distributed both in form and in management. Finally, the environment provides extensive version management for metadata.

The *Repository* provides the basic access control, routing, and synchronization data required for distributing shared data from the shared data warehouse network to information consumers. It contains a data dictionary of reference metadata that identifies and defines such things as:

- Queries and other procedures
- Database structure definitions and descriptions
- Standard validation criteria
- Data warehouse specifications that define collections, extractions, and transactions
- Authorization and authentication rules and profiles

The repository environment provides a way for Apple to work with its business partners. While Apple does not expect to develop its own repository product, Apple is working to integrate VITAL services with technologies found in the IBM, Digital, Tandem, and UNIX environments.

RELATED ENTRIES   Apple Computer; Apple Open Collaborative Environment; *and* AppleTalk

Virtual Memory System (VMS)

VMS is the proprietary operating system of Digital Equipment Corporation's VAX computer systems. VMS was first announced in 1977, along with the announcement of

DEC's VAX 11/780. VMS is an operating system that takes advantage of the 32-bit architecture of the VAX system and provides true multitasking and multiuser capabilities.

Virtual Telecommunication Access Method (VTAM)

VTAM is an IBM Systems Network Architecture (SNA) application that provides users with access to network resources and information.

RELATED ENTRIES   IBM; Systems Network Architecture, IBM

Virtual Terminal (VT)

Virtual Terminal (VT) is an International Organization for Standardization (ISO) protocol that provides remote terminal emulation similar to the Internet's Telnet protocol. Users at remote terminals can run applications on remote computers as if they were sitting at that computer.

Volumes, NetWare

See Disks, Partitions, and Volumes Under NetWare; NetWare Volumes.

Volume Spanning

With volume spanning, the size of a volume is not limited by the storage capabilities of a disk drive. Volumes can span multiple drives and provide many megabytes of storage. This is essential for some database files.

In the NetWare environment, volumes are the primary unit of storage. You can divide a single disk into two or more volumes, or you can span a volume over several disks. Spanning a volume over several disks provides some performance enhancements; it is possible with one controller and multiple drives or with several controllers and multiple drives. Volumes can be increased in size by simply adding another drive and making part of that drive available as a volume attachment. It is not necessary to reformat the original volume, because NetWare simply adds the new volume attachment to it.

Although spanning can improve performance, it can also be risky unless precautions are taken. If one drive in a spanned volume fails, NetWare cannot use the entire volume. Fault-tolerance features such as disk mirroring and duplexing should be used in this configuration.

RELATED ENTRIES   Disks, Partitions, and Volumes Under NetWare; NetWare Volumes

V

WHOIS ("Who Is")

WHOIS is an Internet database of people, host systems, networks, and domains that is maintained by the Defense Data Network (DDN) Network Information Center (NIC). The information in the database is limited to users and host systems that have registered their systems on the Internet with the NIC. You can search the database to determine users' E-mail addresses. The procedure is to log onto the WHOIS database at *nic.ddn.mil*, then make a query using the WHOIS command. Type **HELP** at the prompt to get more information.

RELATED ENTRY   Internet

Wide Area Networks (WAN)

A WAN is a communication system that interconnects geographically remote computer systems. It links the computers outside of an organization's properties (buildings or campus area) and crosses public areas that are regulated by local, national, or international authorities. Typically, the public telephone network forms the links between remote sites, but an organization can install its own WAN links by installing microwave, satellite, or other communication technologies. The range of networks is described next:

- *Local area network (LAN)*   A network confined to a single department, workgroup, or building.

- *Campus network*   Interconnects LANs in different buildings of a campus or industrial park area. The transmission facilities and the property they cross are usually privately owned.

- *Metropolitan area network (MAN)*   A network that spans public right-of-ways in metropolitan areas and is built by a local exchange carrier, a cable company, or other provider that makes services available to the public. The networks are typically built with microwave systems and/or fiber-optic cable.

- *Wide area network (WAN)*   A WAN is a network with potentially global proportions. If public facilities are used, a WAN involves local exchange carriers (LECs), long-distance interexchange carriers (IXCs), and carriers at the remote sites.

An *enterprise-wide network* is a wide area network that interconnects the computing resources of an organization over local or wide areas, regardless of operating systems, communication protocols, or platforms. It usually is managed by a central authority.

Private Network

Organizations can build private networks or public networks. A *private network* consists of switching and communications equipment owned by an organization that is interconnected with leased lines or privately owned communication lines (such as microwave systems). Private lines help the organization maintain security and control over the traffic that crosses the line, and contracted levels of service from the provider guarantee line quality and availability. Private networks built with leased T1 (1.544 Mbits/sec) or T3 (45 Mbits/sec) are feasible under some conditions, depending on budgets, transmission requirements, and distance between sites, as described next:

- The cost of leased lines increases with distance, so they may only be feasible within certain geographic areas.

- Four or more hours of WAN traffic per day between two sites may justify a leased private line, but distance costs may affect this calculation.

- Private networks built with leased lines are feasible when interconnecting a few sites, but are inappropriate for interconnecting many different sites that have relatively low levels of traffic.

- Voice calls and data transmissions can be multiplexed into the same leased line, so organizations can often justify such lines if a lot of voice and data traffic exists between sites.

A private network connecting four separate sites might look like Figure W-1. The sites may be located within the same geographic local access and transport area (LATA) in which the leased lines are supplied by the local exchange carrier (LEC). If they cross LATA boundaries, the LEC at the local and remote sites is involved, along with an interexchange carrier (IXC).

W

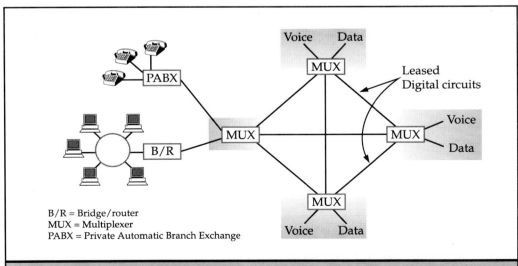

B/R = Bridge/router
MUX = Multiplexer
PABX = Private Automatic Branch Exchange

Figure W-1. *Private network connecting four remote sites*

Public Facilities

A *public data network (PDN)* is operated by a carrier or by a value-added carrier (VAC). Switching is done in the carrier's network. Public networks are best for linking many remote sites and for linking sites when there is not enough traffic between any two sites to justify dedicated leased lines. Also, public packet-switched networks are best if the distance between customer sites is far enough that distance costs make leased lines prohibitive. A PDN provides either packet-switching or circuit-switching services, as described next.

Circuit-Switching Services

- Circuit-switching services provide a fixed path between two points that is set up prior to information exchange.
- Circuit-switching services provide dedicated circuits with a known and guaranteed bandwidth.
- There is some delay required when setting up the circuit.
- The bandwidth is typically fixed and doesn't accommodate bursts in traffic.
- Data transmission begins only after the circuit is established. Both end systems must be available to set up a link, as in a voice phone connection.
- Downed lines can halt all transmission, or require user intervention to route around the problem.

Packet-Switching Services

- Packets of information are routed through a mesh network based on destination address information in the packet header.
- Packets travel through shared ports, where slight delays may occur, especially if packets are variable in length.
- There is no delay associated with setting up a circuit, but logical, connection-oriented circuits can be defined in advance.
- Variable bandwidth capabilities support bursts in traffic.
- The source can transmit at any time. It is not necessary to set up a session in advance.
- The network automatically routes around downed lines or nodes. In the public networks, there are many "alternate" routes that can handle traffic from failed paths.

A decision about which method to use, either circuit-switching or packet-switching, is based on the amount of delay that can be tolerated between the sender and the receiver. In a message-oriented system that delivers E-mail and data files, delays of seconds, minutes, or even hours is acceptable, and packet-switching systems provide the most economical service. For real-time applications such as online transaction processing and other interactive requirements, circuit-switched systems are essential, and the type of circuit depends on the amount of traffic and the number of locations that must be connected. If only one user is involved, a high-speed dialup line is acceptable, but if multiple users require access to a central location at the same time and on an ongoing basis, it may be necessary to build a private network, or use circuit-switched facilities that provide near-instantaneous connections between sites.

VACs such as CompuServe Information Services, GE Information Services, Infonet Services Corp., and Tymenet Global Network provide one-stop WAN services and billing for their customers. Typically, a VAC has a national network it has established for its own use by building its own communication facilities or leasing lines at considerable discount from other carriers. The VAC may also perform some data processing and protocol conversion for its customers. Using a PDN saves you the trouble of contracting for the lines and setting up your own switching equipment. A PDN handles any problems with the network itself and can guarantee data delivery through a vast mesh of switched lines.

The topology of a wide area connection is pictured in Figure W-2. A local access and transport area (LATA) is a geographic area usually associated with a telephone area code. A local exchange carrier (LEC), which is one of the regional Bell operating companies (RBOCs), operates within LATA areas. Other non-Bell carriers may also

W

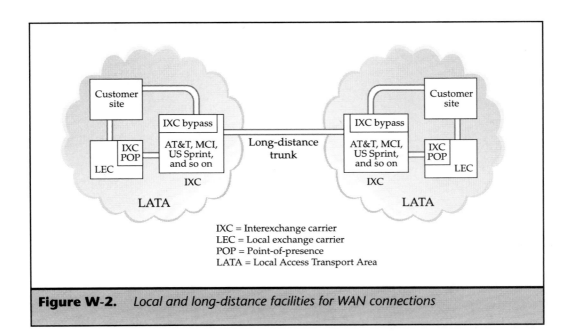

IXC = Interexchange carrier
LEC = Local exchange carrier
POP = Point-of-presence
LATA = Local Access Transport Area

Figure W-2. *Local and long-distance facilities for WAN connections*

operate within a LATA. A LEC is required to provide a point-of-presence (POP) facility for long-distance interexchange carriers (IXCs) such as AT&T, MCI, and US Sprint so customers can choose the IXC of their choice. Some long-distance carriers provide bypass facilities so customers can connect directly into their long-distance services, rather than go through the LEC. MCI, for example, recently announced plans to build alternate long-distance access facilities that bypass the LECs in 20 major US cities. This should provide considerable savings for customers.

The physical equipment for WAN connections is pictured in Figure W-3. A bridge or router funnels WAN traffic from the local network over the wide area connection. Attached to the bridge or router is a modem for analog lines or channel service unit/data service unit (CSU/DSU) for digital lines. In (A), modems connect two LANs over analog telephone lines. In (B), a CSU/DSU connects two remote lines over a digital line. In (C), multiple sites are interconnected over separate T1 digital lines. In (D), a single connection into a public Frame Relay network provides connections to multiple remote sites using the carrier's switching facilities and Frame Relay packet services. Note that in (C) and (D), a voice/data multiplexer can also be used to transmit both voice and data over the same lines.

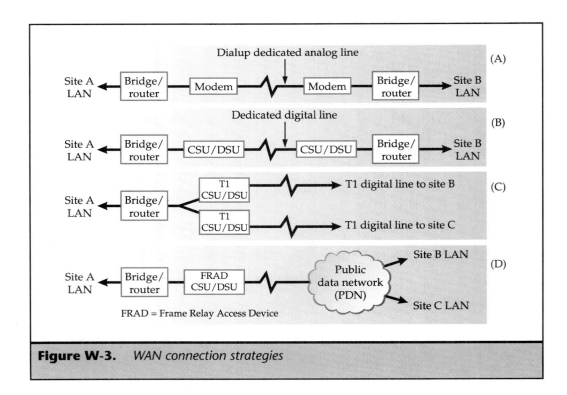

Figure W-3. *WAN connection strategies*

Carrier Services for WAN Connections

Carrier services consist of dialup phone lines, dedicated lines, and circuit-switched or packet-switched services. Transmission rates for dialup analog lines range from 1,200 to 28,800 bits/sec (under existing standards). Dedicated switched digital services range from 56 Kbits/sec to 45 Mbits/sec, with cell relay services like Asynchronous Transfer Mode (ATM) currently providing services at T3 rates of 45 Mbits/sec. Typical applications are listed here:

■ Electronic-mail transfers require transmission rates of 2,400 to 9,600 bits/sec.

■ Remote control programs need transmission rates of 9,600 to 56,000 bits/sec.

■ Remote interaction with LAN-based application requires speeds of 9,600 to 384,000 bits/sec.

To get an approximation of the type of throughput needed, you can multiply these rates by the number of users who need to access a link simultaneously.

Dialup Analog Services

Dialup lines use modems that can provide transmission rates as high as 28,000 bits/sec over switched lines (using new ITU/CCITT V.34 modem standards). Because the lines are switched, charges are incurred only during connection time.

Dialup services are ideal for occasional links. They can provide links for transferring electronic mail between company sites or allowing home or mobile users the ability to dial into the company database. In the case of a remote-control connection, a user dials into the company network and takes control of a computer attached to the LAN. The LAN-attached computer performs the processing, but sends screen output to the remote user and accepts keyboard input from the remote user. This technique minimizes the amount of traffic transferred through the remote link.

Private Lines

Digital lines are available from the carriers in various forms and are typically leased on a monthly basis. There is an initial setup charge, and the rates depend on distance. If the line connects sites in two separate LATAs, the local exchange carrier (LEC) in each local access and transport area (LATA) is involved, along with the long-distance carrier. As mentioned previously, this situation may be changing as long-distance carriers like MCI move to provide customers with direct links to long-distance connections, instead of going through the LECs.

AT&T and the RBOCs offer Dataphone Digital Service (DDS) in data rates that range from 2,400 to 56,000 bits/sec. The AT&T offerings are used to create inter-LATA dedicated lines, and the RBOC offerings are used to created dedicated lines within a LATA area.

Moving up the scale, T1, Fractional T1, and T3 provide data transfer rates in the megabit range. A T1 line is rated at 1.544 Mbits/sec. Fractional T1 is for those who don't need a full T1 line, but anticipate such a need in the future. It provides 24 channels at 64 Kbits/sec each. A customer can start with a number of Fractional T1 lines and grow into a full T1 line as necessary. The carrier sets up a full T1 line, but only makes the contracted bandwidth available until more is needed. A T3 line is equivalent to 28 T1 lines.

Dedicated digital lines are often used to carry voice, video, and data. A digitized voice conversation requires 64 Kbits/sec bandwidth, so many T1 customers use digitizing and multiplexing techniques to merge both voice and data onto the same digital lines. In this way, a customer can lease a full T1 line, and use some of the channels for voice calls between company sites. The remaining bandwidth is used for data. A multiplexer is required to merge the signals from voice, video, and data sources for transfer as a single stream of data over the T1 line. A de-multiplexer at the other end then separates each individual channel.

Not all leased lines are dedicated. An organization may temporarily lease a high-speed line for occasional use, such as end-of-month file transfers or weekly videoconferences. Such services are usually reserved in advance with the carriers. However, the switched digital services discussed next have reduced the need for these types of lines.

Circuit-Switching Services

Basically, a circuit-switched service is not much different than a voice telephone call. A dedicated channel is set up between two points for the duration of the call. It provides a specific amount of bandwidth during the call. Users pay for only the time they are connected, and they may call many different sites. These services are often referred to as *dial-on-demand* services. A call setup delay is often associated with these services; however, new switching equipment has reduced the setup time to microseconds. In many cases, a short setup time is not a problem.

Circuit-switched lines are often used as backup lines for higher-speed dedicated lines in the following cases:

- In the case where a leased dedicated line fails, one or more circuit-switched lines are connected to handle traffic between sites until the dedicated lines are reconnected.

- In the case where a dedicated line becomes saturated with traffic, circuit-switched lines are connected to handle excess traffic loads. This strategy provides an economical way for network managers to link sites without the need to acquire an excessive amount of dedicated service.

A technique that combines circuit-switched lines with inverse multiplexers provides bandwidth on demand. In this technique, additional links are added as bandwidth increases. Inverse multiplexers at each end divide and recombine signals over multiple low-speed lines.

A common switched service is *Switched-56,* which operates at 56 Kbits/sec and requires a special Switched-56 CSU/DSU at each site. Switched-56 services were originally intended to provide an alternate backup route for higher-speed leased lines such as T1. If a leased line failed, a Switched-56 line would quickly establish an alternate connection. Switched-56 can still be used in this way, but it is also used to handle peaks in traffic, fax transmissions, backup sessions, bulk E-mail transfers, and LAN-to-LAN connections. Rates are calculated by the minute in most cases.

For higher data rates, carriers such as AT&T offer services such as Switched 384K and Switched T1. The customer is required to install the primary Integrated Services Digital Network (ISDN) service, as discussed in the next section.

Integrated Services Digital Network (ISDN)

ISDN is a service that provides all-digital services on the *local loop,* which is the cable that runs between the home or business user and the local exchange carrier's switching office. This loop is still largely copper twisted-pair wire supporting analog transmissions. ISDN is offered in selected areas, and it is used in the same way as dialup services. While it provides high-speed digital circuit-switched services between a customer and the telephone company, it also provides a range of integrated voice and data services on which many other offerings are built. For example, AT&T offers two services, Switched 384K and Switched T1, that require users to set up an ISDN interface between their site and the telephone company. In addition, Frame Relay is an outgrowth of ISDN, as discussed in a moment.

Basic ISDN, which is called the *Basic Rate Interface (BRI),* has three channels: two provide 64 Kbits/sec, and a third provides 16 Kbits/sec signaling. The ISDN *Primary Rate Interface* provides extended services for those who need it. It consists of 23 voice or data channels at 64 Kbits/sec each, and one signaling channel at 64 Kbits/sec. In either interface, the signaling channel provides the important function of setting up calls. This provides microsecond call setup speeds and out-of-band signaling, which keeps the data channels free for data-only transmissions.

Packet-Switching Services

A packet-switching network provides a mesh of connections through which data packets travel to reach their destination. Data from the source system is separated and placed into packets of a predefined size. There are two types of services for delivering packets:

- A *connectionless service,* in which each packet is an independent entity that follows its own course through the network, depending on the best path available or the decisions made by switches along the way. Because packets may follow different paths, they may arrive at the destination out of order, and require resequencing by the destination system.

- A *circuit-oriented service,* in which a logical connection or path is established through the network. The path is predefined, which improves performance and packet overhead. Since the packets follow a predefined path, they arrive in order and resequencing is not required.

X.25 is a protocol that defines connections to a packet-switched public data network (PSPDN). Physical network connections and data-link connections are defined in the protocol. X.25 networks operate at speeds up to 64 Kbits/sec. They perform extensive error checking at every node to ensure data delivery over unreliable telephone lines. In developed countries, lines are now extremely reliable, so faster services that eliminate nodal error checking are growing in popularity. Frame Relay is such a service.

Frame Relay Services

Frame Relay is an innovation that emerged from the ISDN specification. It is a circuit-oriented service, although it is often discussed as a fast packet service. Frame Relay streamlines packet-switching techniques by eliminating the network-layer processing associated with X.25. Frame Relay networks typically deliver 1.544 Mbits/sec of data throughput, although higher rates are being implemented.

The overhead in X.25 is extensive compared to Frame Relay. For example, in X.25, every node along a packet's path must completely receive a packet and perform an error check on the packet before sending it on. Frame Relay nodes simply look at the packet header destination information and immediately forward the packet, in some cases even before it is completely received. Frame Relay does not require the state tables used in X.25 at each intermediate node to deal with management, flow control, and error checking. End nodes must detect missing frames and request a retransmission.

Gaining Access to Switched Services

The problem with any switched service is gaining access to the carrier facility that provides the service. The any-to-any connections from local LAN users to remote LAN users are not provided at the customer site for public networks, but in the carrier's switching equipment. Customers must lease dedicated lines such as T1 or T3 with enough capacity to carry multiplexed local data traffic to the carrier's switching facility, or use switched lines such as Switched-56 or the ISDN interfaces to reach the facility.

At first, leasing a dedicated line to reach the carrier facility may appear to defeat the purpose of using switched facilities, but keep in mind that the distance to the carrier's network is usually relatively short. The switched facilities then provide any-to-any connections over long distances at rates that are far less expensive than building private networks over long distances.

The problem and expense of current WAN services is the requirement that customers route traffic through local exchange carrier (LEC) facilities in their area, where it is picked up by the long-distance carriers at the point-of-presence (POP) facility. As mentioned earlier, MCI and other long-distance carriers plan to alleviate this situation by building bypass facilities in major metropolitan areas.

Other Trends

The current national and international phone systems are incapable of handling emerging multimegabit data transfer requirements for high-bandwidth computing and multimedia. It's worthwhile to look at some of the technologies and services that will support future global data, voice, and video networks. The amount of data traffic on networks will increase as the power and speed of computing systems improve. As demand grows, the data network will become as prevalent and transparent as the voice network. Synchronous Optical Network (SONET) is a transport network that enables this. It defines a multiplexing standard for fiber-optic cable transmission with data rates that range from 51 Mbits/sec to 2,488 Mbits/sec.

Asynchronous Transfer Mode (ATM) carries data on SONET networks. It multiplexes cells (fixed-size packets) of data from many sources on the physical network (SONET). ATM provides virtual communication paths through the SONET network. A connection-oriented virtual circuit between two points can reach speeds from 45 Mbits/sec to 622 Mbits/sec, although 45 Mbits/sec is the current carrier limit. ATM switching is useful at the LAN level in wiring hubs. Is is also useful as a switching technology for international and global telecommunication networks.

Above ATM is Broadband-Integrated Services Digital Network (B-ISDN). ATM is the engine for B-ISDN. B-ISDN is a successor to ISDN, which defined how to provide circuit-switching communication to homes and offices in increments of 64 Kbits/sec. B-ISDN uses ATM technology and the SONET physical network to deliver data transfer speeds from 155 Mbits/sec to 622 Mbits/sec along with a variety of customer services. Another offering is Switched Multimegabit Data Service (SMDS), which was developed by Bellcore, a research division of the regional Bell operating companies. SMDS is designed to provide public and private data networks within metropolitan areas.

RELATED ENTRIES   AT&T; Circuit-Switching Services; Leased Line; Local Access and Transport Area; Networks; Packet-Switching Networks; Public Data Networks; Public Switched Data Network; Regional Bell Operating Companies; T1/T3 Services; *and* Telecommunication

Windows for Workgroups, Microsoft

Microsoft Windows for Workgroups is a peer-to-peer networking version of the popular Windows operating system. It makes it easy for people to connect their computers, share information, and work together. You can send electronic mail (E-mail) to your associates, schedule group meetings, share files and printers, manage calendars, and work together on group projects.

With Windows for Workgroups, any 80386 or later model system can act as a *server* and share its resources (files and printers) with other users on the network. Any other system connected to the network and running Windows for Workgroups can use those shared resources as a *client*. You can run the program on a system that is already attached to an existing network, or you can build a new network by adding network interface cards (NICs) and tying them together with network cable. A similar product called Workgroup Connection for MS-DOS contains all the software you need to connect an MS-DOS-based PC as a client to a Windows for Workgroups server.

Bill Gates, chairman and CEO of Microsoft, has said that "the integration of networking and workgroup features into Windows is an enormous and innovative step. Whether a company is small or large, people need to work together in groups, share information, quickly involve one another in decisions, and coordinate schedules and business activities. These everyday activities will be supported by the services built into Windows for Workgroups, and by existing and new applications that take advantage of the operating system's workgroup extensions. Windows for Workgroups makes group computing easier."

Windows for Workgroups provides developers with the features and tools they need to write Windows-based applications that take advantage of workgroup capabilities. This ensures that many network-compatible applications will be available. Applications can easily be extended to support the electronic mail functionality in Windows for Workgroups. For example, spreadsheets, word processing documents, or even voice-annotated messages can be sent to other users by attaching them to mail messages. Applications are being enhanced to take advantage of networking features. For example, Microsoft Excel and Microsoft Word for Windows upgrades automate common workgroup activities, such as document assembly and schedule tracking, forms routing and notification, information sharing, and application-specific workgroup tasks.

Companies with an existing network can use Windows for Workgroups as a client to bring new services and capabilities to their local area network (LAN) users, such as workgroup-enabled applications, scheduling, and network dynamic data exchange (DDE). The product is compatible with other Microsoft products such as Windows NT. It is also compatible with Novell NetWare networks and includes Sequenced Packet Exchange/Internetwork Packet Exchange (SPX/IPX) communication protocol support. Users can simultaneously access Microsoft and NetWare networks. MIS managers and users can install and configure Windows for Workgroups in a single drag-and-drop action for both of these popular networks. This saves time and trouble and reduces desktop support issues. In addition, Windows for Workgroups also works on other networks, such as Banyan VINES.

Windows for Workgroups Features

Windows for Workgroups provides several network applications and utilities so you can begin working with other users once your network is installed. Of course, Windows for Workgroups also includes all of the desktop accessories and utilities included with the Windows 3.1 product. Here are some basic advantages of connecting computers into a Windows for Workgroups network:

- Quick and easy file transfers among computers on the network
- Centralized file storage and backup
- Support for Object Linking and Embedding (OLE) over the network, which provides automatic updating of information in linked documents
- Electronic mail and messaging
- Peripheral sharing of printers, hard drives, CD-ROM drives, and other devices
- Workgroup applications

Windows for Workgroups contains a handy Chat utility so you can type messages to other users and read their responses. It also includes several network utilities so you can monitor the way your system is being used by other network users and change your network configuration. The following features and utilities are also part of the Windows for Workgroups package.

MICROSOFT MAIL   Mail is an electronic mail service that lets users read, compose, forward, and reply to electronic mail messages, as well as manage messages they receive. You can attach an entire document to a mail message. The version of Microsoft Mail that ships with Windows for Workgroups is compatible with only one workgroup. If you need to connect with other workgroup post offices on the network or to other E-mail systems, you'll need the additional support provided by the Microsoft Mail and Schedule+ Extensions for Windows for Workgroups.

SCHEDULE+   Schedule+ is a full-featured graphical scheduling application that allows people to schedule group meetings and manage their daily calendars and task lists electronically. You can set up group meetings and view the schedules of other users. It is an excellent tool for people who are working together on group projects that must meet various deadlines.

NETWORK DDE   Network DDE provides a way for users to create compound documents that share data across the network. You can insert information in your documents from documents owned by other users, even if those documents reside on other network computers. Network DDE ensures that changes made to the original documents are made in the documents where the information is pasted. For example, a group leader could create a compound document that contains information from the accounting department, graphics from the art department, and text from the marketing department. Each department can change its portion of the compound document as necessary. Every time the group leader opens the compound document to view or change its contents, any changes made by the departments are automatically made in the group leader's document.

SECURITY   Windows for Workgroups offers security features that can lock out unauthorized users from using shared resources on the network. Users can share files and printers with other users on two levels. Other users on the system can either be given full access to a directory, or granted permission to read files but not modify them in any way. Access is granted by giving users specific passwords related to the level of security they should have. If more sophisticated security is required, Microsoft Windows NT or Novell NetWare is recommended.

Windows for Workgroups Packaging

Windows for Workgroups has everything that even nontechnical users need to install the product quickly and easily. Several software-only configurations provide an upgrade for Windows 3.0, Windows 3.1, and MS-DOS. Other configurations include software, network cards, and cables as listed here:

- Starter kits include all the software, network cards, and cables needed to connect two PCs in a complete Windows-based network. A starter kit is recommended for users with no existing network. The kit includes a 15-minute videotape that walks you through a step-by-step installation process. To expand the network, you purchase a user kit.

- User kits contain all hardware and software needed to connect an additional PC to the network.

- Software-only packages are available for users who are installing the operating system on PCs that are already networked, or for users who want to purchase their own network cards.

The starter kits and user kits are also available in the form of upgrade packages for current Windows 3.1 users. Software-only versions are available in upgrade form for current users of Windows 3.1.

RELATED ENTRIES   Client-Server Computing; Groupware; Networks; Object Linking and Embedding; *and* Peer-to-Peer Communication

Windows NT, Microsoft

Microsoft Windows NT is designed to take advantage—and to allow software vendors to design applications that take advantage—of powerful new desktop systems, including those designed around Intel, DEC, and other processors. Windows NT expands on the features of Windows 3.1 and offers many features that make it unique among operating systems. Windows NT has a wide target audience:

- End users who need performance and the ability to switch among multiple applications

- Workgroup users who need to share their system with other users, connect with other shared computers, exchange electronic mail, and schedule group meetings and appointments

- Software developers who want to create applications to run on the systems supported by Windows NT

- Network administrators who need a secure (government-certified) network environment that takes advantage of new multiprocessor computer systems

The last point is especially important. Windows NT is not restricted to Intel systems as are DOS and Windows. It runs on the following processors, with support for other processors planned, such as the Motorola PowerPC.

- Intel 80386, 80486, and Pentium processor systems
- MIPS R4000 64-bit Reduced Instruction Set Computer (RISC) systems
- DEC Alpha-based 64-bit RISC systems
- "Super server" systems that use a combination of processors and special proprietary bus designs

IBM is working to make Windows NT available on its super server systems, which include features such as fault tolerance, redundant arrays of inexpensive disks (RAID) systems, error-correcting memory, and hardware error logs. The PS/2 Server 195 and Server 295 super server will run adapted version of Windows NT. Another platform for Windows NT is the Intergraph Corporation's Intergraph Ultra SPARC system. The Ultra SPARC is a high-end version of the SPARC chip developed jointly by Sun Microsystems, Inc. and Intergraph. The SPARC-based Windows NT systems are designed for high-end workstations and multiprocessing servers.

Windows NT is a 32-bit operating system with preemptive multitasking and memory protection, as well as support for symmetrical multiprocessing and networking, all with a graphical user front-end. The ability of Windows NT to fully access 32-bit processors allows it to work with larger numbers, memory addresses, and instructions. Overall *throughput,* which is the combination of processor performance, data transfer, and memory access, improves.

Multitasking means that the operating system can do several things at once. *Preemptive* means that the user or another task can interrupt a task if necessary, rather than wait for it to completely finish. As processing speeds get faster, hardware-related activities such as accessing a disk can seem incredibly slow. When a non-preemptive operating system accesses the disk, the processor waits while the mechanical disk is accessed, thus wasting processing cycles. In Windows NT, multiple tasks can occur simultaneously, so if one task gets hung up when accessing a slow device such as a disk, the processor can turn its attention to other tasks. Basically, there are no wasted processing cycles.

Memory protection ensures that multiple programs run in their own memory area and don't corrupt the memory used by other applications. If one application crashes, the other applications and the operating system remain alive so users can close their work and exit properly.

Symmetrical multiprocessing lets Windows NT take advantage of multiple processors. While multiprocessor systems have existed for a while, these systems typically assigned dedicated tasks to each processor, such as network input/output. This *asymmetrical multiprocessing*—having one processor dedicated to one task—meant that each processor sat idle when finished with its specific job. Symmetrical multiprocessing, on the other hand, allocates tasks to any processor; if one processor finishes before another, the operating system can assign it other tasks. Symmetrical multiprocessing is harder to implement, but provides superior performance.

Networking features in Windows NT let you share files on your system with other network users and connect with shared directories on other systems. Computers

W

running Windows for Workgroups can participate in the network. In addition, Windows NT comes with software and drivers to support connections to other types of operating systems, such as UNIX and IBM mainframes.

The Windows NT Advanced Server product is an enhanced version of Windows NT that provides sophisticated file server features for large network environments. It includes additional features for data protection, such as automatic duplication of data to secondary disks.

Windows NT User Interface

The Windows NT user interface is similar to the Microsoft Windows 3.1 user interface. It uses the same familiar graphical interface that provides a consistent look and operation across applications. It also run thousands of Windows 3.1 and MS-DOS applications.

How Windows NT Presents Itself

After you first boot Windows NT and log on, you see the Program Manager window shown in Figure W-4. Your computer name and logon name appear at the top in the title bar of the window.

You start programs from the Program Manager by double-clicking the icon of the program you want. You can see that the window currently open is the Main window. "Group" icons such as Main, Accessories, Administrative Tools, and the other icons at the bottom of the screen in Figure W-4 help organize the program icons. You start the Command Prompt to execute DOS commands or run applications not specifically designed for Windows NT, such as POSIX-compliant programs.

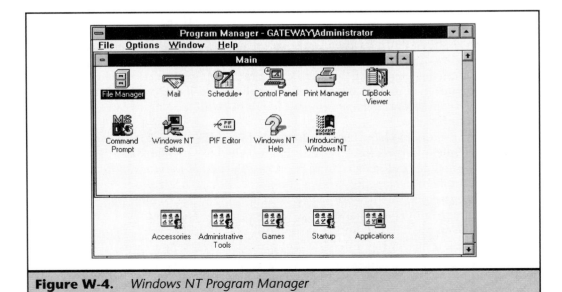

Figure W-4. *Windows NT Program Manager*

Mail, Schedule+, and ClipBook Viewer are network-compatible programs that let you communicate with and share files or graphic objects with other network users.

A File Manager is available to view and manage files, share directories on your system with other network users, or connect with shared drives on other computers. Network administrators can apply security measures to protect directories and files from unauthorized use in Windows NT. The following utilities are available to administer the network:

- *User Manager*   Used to create accounts that other users log onto and groups that provide system security
- *Disk Administrator*   Used to prepare and manage the disks on the system
- *Performance Monitor*   Used to track system usage, monitor performance, perform troubleshooting, and plan for system expansion
- *Backup*   Used to back up directories and files on the system
- *Event Viewer*   Used to view logs that display system, security, and application events for troubleshooting and auditing purposes

Support for Other Environments

Built into Windows NT is the Win32 environment that supports 32-bit NT applications. In addition, NT includes several other *environmental subsystems*. These subsystems allow applications designed for other operating systems to run under Windows NT. You access environmental subsystems by starting the Command Prompt in the Program Manager Main group. The following subsystems are provided:

- The *Virtual DOS Machine (VDM)* subsystem emulates the MS-DOS environment so you can run DOS applications.
- The *Win16 Virtual DOS Machine* subsystem emulates the Windows (16-bit) environment so you can run Windows 3.1 applications. Applications run in an 80286 emulation mode.
- The *OS/2 subsystem* lets you run character-based MS OS/2 1.*x* applications. This subsystem is not supported on MIPS or DEC Alpha computers.
- The *POSIX subsystem* runs applications that meet the Portable Operating System Interface for Computing Environment (POSIX) standard as defined by the Institute of Electrical and Electronic Engineers (IEEE).

Virtual Memory

Virtual memory provides a way to allocate more memory to the operating system and applications than is physically available on your computer. When memory starts to run low, parts of it are swapped to disk storage to make memory available for other processes. For example, if a process has information in memory that it is not currently using, the information is moved to disk and the memory space is made available to another process.

File System Support in Windows NT

The primary file system for Windows NT is the new NT File System (NTFS), but Windows NT also supports the older file systems, described here:

- *File Allocation Table file system (FAT)*   This is the file system for DOS. It uses a filenaming format with an eight-character filename and a three-character extension. Windows NT can access FAT drives, but if you boot the system with DOS, you cannot access NTFS drives.
- *High Performance File System (HPFS)*   This is the file system designed for OS/2 that provides long filenames. It also has performance-enhancing features that FAT does not have. Windows NT can access HPFS drives.
- *NTFS*   This is the new Windows NT file system. It provides long filenames, data protection and recovery, and security through directory and file permissions.

If installing Windows NT on a new system, you will most likely format the entire disk as NTFS. On existing systems, you might want to keep part of the existing file system. You have several installation options:

- You can keep an existing partition for another operating system and install NTFS in a separate partition. When you boot the system, a screen appears that lets you select the operating system you want to start.
- You can convert the existing boot partition to an NTFS volume.
- You can reformat existing partitions to NTFS. This deletes existing files in the partition.

File and System Protection

Windows NT has several features that protect data stored on its file system from unauthorized users and from damage to files. To protect the file system from unauthorized access, all users must log on by typing an account name and password. The system administrator can apply various logon restrictions to accounts that, for example, disable the account after a period of time or force users to change their password.

Windows NT also provides file system protection mechanisms that detect and disable bad disk sectors and restore transactions that were written incompletely due to a power failure. Important file system information is also duplicated on the disk to guard against sector failures. The installation program also creates a repair disk that you can use to bring Windows NT back up in case the boot information is corrupted.

Windows NT also supports *uninterruptable power supplies (UPS)*, which provide backup battery power to the system when AC power is lost. The system will operate for a designated period of time, which allows users to properly shut down the system and write all information in memory to disk.

Networking

The networking services in Windows NT are compatible with networking services in Microsoft Windows for Workgroups, Microsoft LAN Manager, and Windows NT Advanced Server. Computers running any of these operating systems can share directories, files, and resources. Support for Network Basic Input Output System (NetBIOS)/NetBIOS Extended User Interface (NetBEUI) and Transmission Control Protocol/Internet Protocol (TCP/IP) is included. Support is also available for connections to Novell NetWare through the Sequenced Packet Exchange/Internetwork Packet Exchange (SPX/IPX) protocols.

Windows NT uses the Microsoft Network Driver Interface Specification (NDIS) as its network adapter interface. With NDIS, network card vendors simply create drivers that are NDIS-compatible. End users then buy NDIS-compatible cards with the assurance that the cards will work with Windows NT. NDIS supports multiple network interface cards in the same system, thus providing the system with a way to access several different types of networks.

Security and User Hierarchy

Windows NT meets the Department of Defense C2 Controlled Access Protection security rating. The C2 rating requires that computers must implement a security policy and auditing of events, not only for access by network users, but for access by local users. The C2 level security in Windows NT provides the following:

- Users have special accounts that require logon with password identification. The account tracks various actions performed by a user for auditing purposes, such as logons, logoffs, and file accesses. Management tasks such as changing user accounts or server settings are also tracked.
- Administrators and users can control file, directory, and resource (printers) access on their own system.
- System administrators can track and view auditable events.
- Users are prevented from examining the contents of memory.

Because Windows NT provides file- and resource-sharing capabilities, security is a concern if the computer is accessed by multiple users. Administrators and users must be able to protect the files they share on their system against unauthorized use. However, security does require a certain amount of administration. Permissions must be applied to shared directories, and administrators must create user accounts that require logon passwords and provide logon restrictions.

Logon account information is stored in a master database (called a *security account manager* or *SAM*) on each Windows NT system. When users log on, their user name and password are checked in the SAM of the system they log onto.

Trust Relationships

While the SAM database provides adequate security for the local Windows NT system, it introduces some security and maintenance problems for other file- and resource-sharing computers on the network. For example, you can define access rights for groups of network users, but not for individual users who need to access your system from another computer on the network. That's where the Windows NT Advanced Server comes into play.

The Windows NT Advanced Server product can establish *trust relationships* with other computers on the network. That means that one computer can authenticate a user and provide access information about the user to other computers. Users can then log onto one computer and access other computers without logging onto each computer separately.

One interesting feature of the security system is that protection information assigned to files travels with the files. For example, if you grant a user the ability to open and read a file but not change it, the same rights will apply even if the storage device is moved to another system.

Printing

If your Windows NT system is connected to a network, you can share its printers with other network users or access shared printers on the network. The Print Manager in Windows NT contains all the features and functions you need to install, configure, share, and otherwise manage printers. Those users who have Windows 3.1 probably installed printers using the Printer utility in the Control Panel. Selecting this option in Windows NT opens the Print Manager, which includes all printer management options.

Permissions control the type of access users have to printers. For example, administrators can prevent or allow users to access a printer, and grant some users the ability to control documents in the Print Manager queue. Administrators have full control over printers.

Logon and Startup Options

The person that installs Windows NT on a computer specifies the Administrator password and thus gains full control over the system. This administrative user can create accounts with password protections so other users can log onto the system. In addition, rights and permissions can be assigned to each user account to grant or restrict access to the system and its files. If you log onto a Windows NT system and can't access certain files, it is because your logon account has these restrictions.

Every user who logs on with his or her own account can customize the Program Manager to his or her own needs. For example, when John logs on, he can rearrange the Program Manager window and add some startup icons for the programs he uses. When Jane logs on to the same computer, she does not see John's changes and can create her own custom settings that John does not see. Administrators can create common settings that all users see, however.

RELATED ENTRIES   Alpha AXP, DEC; Authentication and Authorization; Client-Server Computing; File and Directory Permissions, Windows NT; Groupware; Multiprocessing; Networks; Object Linking and Embedding; Peer-to-Peer Communication; Permissions in Windows NT; *and* Security

Windows NT Advanced Server, Microsoft

The Microsoft Windows NT Advanced Server operating system provides all the features of Windows NT, such as 32-bit operation, preemptive multitasking, symmetrical multitasking, gigabyte memory addressing capabilities, networking, and security, in a system designed to operate as a network server. The system provides network administration features and the data protection features of advanced fault tolerance.

Features available in Windows NT Advanced Server that are not available in Windows NT include more control over administrative domains and advanced fault-tolerance features, including support for RAID level 5. The Remote Access Server features provide a way for administrators to access and control systems remotely using asynchronous telephone lines, Integrated Services Digital Network (ISDN), and X.25 networks.

RELATED ENTRY   Windows NT, Microsoft

Windows Open System Architecture (WOSA)

WOSA is Microsoft's architectural plan for application development across different platforms in the Windows environment. It sets standards that allow the free flow of information within an enterprise. WOSA includes modular application program interfaces (APIs) that provide an application created by any developer with access to network services such as E-mail, databases, and host connections. WOSA also provides a way to "plug in" back-end services created by any developer. WOSA is a so-called "middleware" strategy that is built directly into the operating system with the intent to stimulate the growth of workgroup applications that let users collaborate over networks. Windows will provide a common interface for messaging systems and directory services that let users quickly locate other users or resources on the network. WOSA also provides common data access services and security enhancements. The WOSA strategy is similar in scope to the Apple Open Collaborative Environment (AOCE) strategy.

W

Windows for Workgroups with its built-in Mail and Schedule+ groupware products implements WOSA architectural components. WOSA is also being used to implement OLE (Object Linking and Embedding) 2.0 and its new Cairo object-oriented operating system.

WOSA implements a standard API for client applications and a Service Providers Interface (SPI) for server applications, as shown in Figure W-5. Using SPI, a database vendor can create a WOSA-compatible database engine for the Windows environment. Developers of client applications can then create interfaces that can access the database engine without writing code specifically for that engine.

The following components have been defined and are individually discussed under the appropriate heading in this book:

- *Messaging Application Programming Interface (MAPI)* Provides access to E-mail functions while working within other applications such as word processors or scheduling packages. It competes with Vendor Independent Messaging (VIM), which is supported by Lotus, IBM, Apple, Novell, and Borland.

- *Open Database Connectivity (ODBC)* Defines Windows operating system component connections to front-end and back-end (client-server) database services. The idea is to create access to any data stored on any server on heterogeneous networks. Database vendors use ODBC to provide interoperability in their products so users can access data using any front-end interface they want.

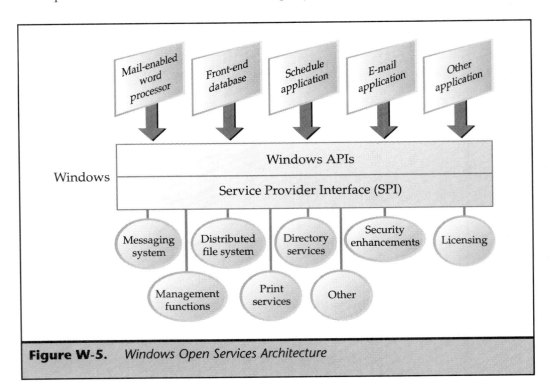

Figure W-5. *Windows Open Services Architecture*

- *Windows Socket API* Transmission Control Protocol/Internet Protocol (TCP/IP) is a network communication standard used to connect dissimilar computers. The Windows Socket API (also known as the Network Transit Protocol) is designed to resolve incompatibilities among the many varieties of TCP/IP that exist for Windows.

- *Remote procedure call (RPC)* WOSA implements the RPC defined by Open Software Foundation's (OSF) Distributed Computing Environment (DCE). RPC provides a way to distribute an application's processing tasks over multiple machines on a network. RPC paves the way for true distributed processing.

- *Systems Network Architecture (SNA) API* Defines the way in which Windows applications access IBM hosts.

- *Licensing Server API (LS API)* Helps administrators monitor and control the use of licensed software and helps a company stay within legal bounds.

WOSA has its roots in Microsoft's strategy of separating printer drivers from applications. In the Windows environment, a printer driver is installed during the initial setup and can be upgraded or changed at any time with a simple procedure. Windows applications use the installed printer driver without any special configuration. They automatically interface to it and take advantage of its special features and available fonts. Likewise, WOSA-compatible server applications automatically make their features available to WOSA-compatible client applications. This approach greatly simplifies application development and the task of network administrators who must integrate all the different applications and data available on a network.

RELATED ENTRIES Cairo; Electronic Software Distribution and Licensing; Messaging Application Programming Interface; Middleware; Object Linking and Embedding; Open Database Connectivity, Microsoft; Remote Procedure Call; Windows for Workgroups, Microsoft; Windows NT, Microsoft; *and* Windows Sockets API

Windows Sockets API

Windows Sockets was developed by a group of software vendors and Transmission Control Protocol/Internet Protocol (TCP/IP) vendors such as Microsoft and Sun Microsystems, Inc. as a standard that could tie together the inconsistencies in PC-based TCP/IP products on the market. The specification is also called Windows Network Transit Protocol. It allows Windows applications to communicate regardless of underlying protocols. The specification was released in June 1992 and is available free to developers. It is designed to ensure interoperability between any networking vendor's TCP/IP software and any Windows or Windows NT application that accesses the protocol stack.

The need for Windows Sockets came about because vendors developed TCP/IP protocol stacks for the PC environment using their own application program interfaces (APIs). With many different TCP/IP APIs available, product developers had

W

to choose one of the APIs to use in their product, or support all the available APIs at great expense. Windows Sockets was developed around the well-known Berkeley Sockets, developed by Berkeley Software Distribution (BSD) at the University of California (Berkeley). Because Windows is the primary software development environment in the PC world, it made sense to add the socket extensions to it.

With Windows Sockets, applications written to operate with one vendor's implementation of the TCP/IP protocol stack will work with other vendors' stacks. This greatly simplifies the job of developers and promotes the development of software. Windows Sockets conforms to Berkeley System Distribution release 4.3 and provides stream-type, connection-oriented TCP services as well as the datagram services of the User Datagram Protocol (UDP).

RELATED ENTRIES   Transmission Control Protocol/Internet Protocol; Windows Open System Architecture

Windows Telephony Applications Interface

The Windows Telephony Applications Interface is an application program interface (API) designed to help developers create products for integrating computers and telephony applications. Specifically, Windows-based PCs use it to perform PBX-like functions such as conferencing, call transfers, and voice recording. It also includes tools for integrating fax, E-mail, and voice.

Wireless LAN Communication

Wireless communication falls into the two categories: wireless local area network (LAN) communication, as covered here, and wireless mobile computing, as covered under "Wireless Mobile Communication." The primary difference between the two is found in the transmission facilities. Wireless LAN communication uses transmitters and receivers that are located within a company's premises and owned by that company. Wireless mobile computing involves telephone carriers or other public services to transmit and receive signals using packet-radio, cellular networks, and satellite stations for users who are "out of the office" and "on the road."

A wireless LAN transceiver (**trans**mitter/re**ceiver**) is typically located in a fixed position within an office. Users with portable computers are allowed some mobility, typically within the immediate area of the transceiver. Wireless LANs can eliminate the need to run cable, especially if the LAN site is a temporary installation or serves a workgroup that might disband in the near future. With a wireless LAN, you'll save the wire and installation costs and, in some cases, avoid the need to get special permits to wire a building as is required in some areas.

A typical wireless LAN configuration consists of a transceiver unit connected to servers and other equipment using standard Ethernet cable. The transceiver broadcasts and receives signals from workstations around it, as shown in Figure W-6.

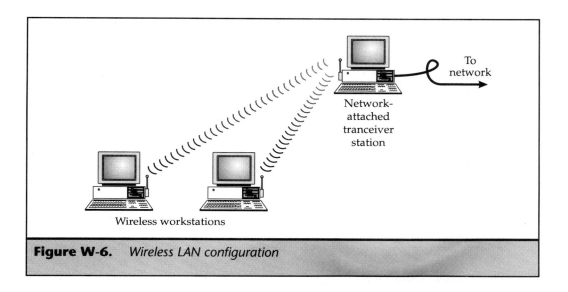

Figure W-6. *Wireless LAN configuration*

There are three techniques for wireless data transmission, as described here:

■ *Infrared light* This method offers a wide bandwidth that transmits signals at extremely high rates. Infrared light transmissions operate by line of sight, so the source and receiver must be aimed at or focused on each other, similar to a television remote control. Obstructions in the office environment must be considered, but mirrors can be used to bend infrared light if necessary. Because infrared light transmissions are susceptible to strong light from windows or other sources, systems that produce stronger beams might be necessary. Note that infrared light is not regulated by the government and there are no restrictions on transmission rates. Typical transmission speeds range up to 10 Mbits/sec.

■ *Narrow-band (or single-frequency) radio* This technique is similar to a broadcast from a radio station. You tune in to a "tight" frequency band on both the transmitter and receiver. The signal can penetrate walls and is spread over a wide area, so focusing is not required. However, narrow-band radio transmissions have problems with radio reflections (ghosting) and are regulated by the FCC. They must be precisely tuned to prevent interference from other frequencies. Motorola uses the narrow-band radio transmission technique in its Altair series. The company received licenses for frequencies in the 19 GHz range, which it allocates to customers based on geographic region. Motorola handles all the FCC licensing for its products. Transmission speeds are in the 4,800 Kbits/sec range.

■ *Spread-spectrum radio* This technique broadcasts signals over a wide range of frequencies, avoiding problems inherent in narrow-band communication. A code is used to spread the signal, and the receiving station uses the same code to retrieve it. Coding allows the spread-spectrum signal to operate in a wide range of frequencies, even if other spread-spectrum signals are in the same range. Spread-spectrum radio does not interfere with conventional radio because its energy levels are too weak. Transmission speeds are in the 250 Kbits/sec range.

Another wireless LAN option is microwave, which is available in small, short-distance systems that can interconnect buildings in a campus environment or in a metropolitan area (see "Microwave Communication").

Black Box sells a wireless LAN bridge for connecting Ethernet networks up to 3 miles apart, eliminating the need for wide area connections such as T1 lines or fiber-optic cable. Transmission rates are in the 2 Mbits/sec range. It is an IEEE 802.1D-compliant Media Access Control-layer bridge that provides protocol transparency. Spread-spectrum radio technology is implemented to provide secure data transmission, even in incremental weather.

The Black Box bridge connects to any Thin Ethernet or 10Base-T network and automatically learns all the addresses on the LAN. Three antennas are available. A short-range antenna and a long-range antenna provide transmission distances of 1/2 mile and 3 miles, respectively, in a point-to-point configuration. An omnidirectional antenna provides multipoint configurations with transmission distances of 1/2 mile. Contact Black Box in Pittsburgh, Pennsylvania at 412/746-5500.

If you're interested in wireless LANs, contact Motorola (800/233-0877) about its narrow-band products, contact NCR (800/237-2870) about its spread-spectrum products, or contact Laser Communications (800/527-3740) about its infrared products. Other vendors are listed here.

- Altair (Arlington Heights, Illinois), a division of Motorola   Provides Ethernet networks that use the narrowband 18GHz frequencies.

- InfraLAN Technology (Cambridge, Massachusetts)   Provides infrared 4 Mbits/sec and 16 Mbits/sec Token Ring networks with ranges of 24 meters (80 feet).

- NCR (Dayton, Ohio)   Provides WaveLAN spread spectrum-type systems.

- Proxim Inc. (Mountain View, California)   Offers spread-spectrum LAN products.

- Telesystems (Don Mills, Ontario)   Offers spread-spectrum Ethernet-based networks.

- Windata (Northborough, Massachusetts)   Offers spread-spectrum Ethernet-based networks.

Wireless Mobile Communication

Wireless communication falls into the two categories: wireless mobile computing, as covered here, and wireless local area network (LAN) communication, as covered under "Wireless LAN Communication." The primary difference between the two is found in the transmission facilities. Wireless LAN communication uses transmitters and receivers that are located within a company's premises and owned by that company. The broadcast range is relatively small. Wireless mobile computing involves telephone carriers or other public services to transmit and receive signals using packet-radio communication, cellular networks, and satellite stations for users who are "out of the office" and "on the road."

Today, mobile communication is used to keep in touch with roving salespeople, delivery trucks, field technicians, and other personnel. Mobile computer users use wireless communication to connect with corporate networks and to exchange electronic mail, transfer files, and receive personalized news or other information directly to their mobile computers or personal digital assistants (PDAs) such as the Apple Newton and devices from EO and General Magic. As the technology grows, transmission rates will improve and costs will go down. Mobile users will spend more time connected over wireless networks to query corporate databases or participate in online meetings and conferences.

Operating system vendors are taking mobile users into consideration by building new features that keep track of mobile user locations and maintain environments from one session to another. For example, as a mobile user travels from site to site, he or she disconnects and reconnects to remote systems on a regular basis. The operating system can restore connections and the desktop of the previous session automatically. If a user was accessing a database, previous queries to that database are waiting for the user the next time he or she connects. PDAs use interfaces that are foreign to most network operating systems and applications. However, vendors are working to integrate these systems as the number of mobile computer users increases.

Mobile computing naturally involves telephone carriers or other service providers. Users must be concerned with the level of access (range and signal penetration), rate of data transfers, and store-and-forward capabilities, which allows users to pick up messages when they come back into range. For example, data transfer rates to and from mobile devices using the communication systems described later are low, from 8 Kbits/sec to 19.2 Kbits/sec. Error-correction requirements can drastically reduce transmission rates.

Wireless devices are either one-way or two-way. One-way communicators include beepers and pagers that receive signals only. Two-way communication devices use packet-radio and cellular transmission methods, as described shortly. SkyTel offers three levels of service that transmit phone numbers, voice-mail message alerts, or E-mail message alerts. It uses the 930 to 931 MHz range in the electromagnetic spectrum. EMBARC competes with SkyTel and provides messaging capabilities as high as 30,000 characters, compared to the SkyTel limit of 240. EMBARC also provides simultaneous transmission, so users can update information on several remote systems, for example.

Two-way communication systems include packet-radio networks and cellular systems, as described next.

W

Packet-Radio Communication

Packet-radio communication breaks a transmission into small digital packets that include the source and destination address, as well as error-correction information. The packets are uplinked to a satellite, then broadcast. The recipient device receives only packets that are addressed to it. Because the transmissions are two-way, error detection and correction methods can be used. See "Packet-Radio Communication."

Cellular Digital Packet Communication

Cellular communicators are mobile computing devices that provide two-way transmissions between users and their home, office, or network. The devices provide E-mail capabilities and the ability to transmit and receive files and other information. Error detection and correction is also possible due to the two-way transmission nature of the devices. See "Cellular Digital Packet Data."

At this writing, the future of mobile computing is still being defined. Bob Metcalfe, writing in *Infoworld* (8-16-93), provides a contrast to the marketing blitz produced by mobile computing vendors. He notes that wireless is a temporary fad, and that "there isn't enough megahertz to go around out there in our increasingly polluted electromagnetic ether. It is an ecologically unsound waste of energy to broadcast bits in all directions when they need to be received in only one."

RELATED ENTRIES   Cellular Digital Packet Data; Mobile Computing; *and* Packet-Radio Communication

Wiring

See EIA/TIA 568 Commercial Building Wiring Standard; Cabling.

Workflow Software

The purpose of workflow software is to automate document procedures in an organization by replacing paper systems with electronic documents. A local area network provides the routing system that moves documents to and from storage, and among users who need to view and make changes to the documents or sign the documents and validate their authenticity. Workflow software encourages workgroup collaboration by automating processes and eliminating footwork.

A typical workflow application combines document imaging with electronic messaging and advanced security features such as digital signatures, which can provide proof that documents are from the specified source and that they have been validated by the person indicated in the form.

In accounting environments, documents typically move from clerks to supervisors in various stages of processing and validation. A workflow package can display the forms used by an organization for a clerk to fill out. Some fields in the form are automatically filled out by the software, based on the job or the clerk manipulating the form. It's possible to assign predefined routing schemes to forms and eliminate some of the management headaches associated with manual paper flow. Forms are sent directly to the person who is supposed to handle the next step in the procedure. Automated features prevent hang ups in forms-processing. For example, users can be alerted when a form must be dealt with to prevent overdue charges or other problems caused by late processing. Publishing is another example of a collaborative environment that can benefit from workflow software. Documents are transferred from writer to editor to production in stages, using the network and its resources to store and eventually print the completed work.

Here are some key features of workflow software:

- Documents are distributed according to predefined routes.

- A number of users can access the document and make changes as necessary. Any changes can be tagged with the name of the person making those changes. Comments can be added for other people to view.

- Document tracking allows users to easily locate documents flowing through the system, and send reminders to users who might be holding them up, or even cancel the document.

- Workflow software typically consists of a central management and filing system that administrators use to assign various levels of access and security, as well as set up workflow procedures and track workflow.

- Locking procedures let users complete and forward a document in a secure way. When a lock is applied, other users can't alter the changes made by the user. This not only protects the user who made the changes; it also protects the recipient from blame for changes he or she did not make.

- Security is assured through authentication and digital signatures:

    - The recipient is sure of the sender's authenticity, that the document is authentic, and that it hasn't been altered in the transmission.

    - The sender is assured that any alterations to the document by the recipient can be detected.

From a management point of view, workflow software can help an organization track how information is flowing and how to better manage that flow. Workflow software can eliminate many time-consuming activities and often expensive activities such as meetings, phone calls, and express mail deliveries. But as users take to the new software, bandwidth requirements will increase. Workflow software allows users to view large image files, graphics, sound, and even video. This type of traffic can saturate the network.

Workflow systems are available from Action Technologies (Alameda, California), DEC (Maynard, Massachusetts), IBM (White Plains, New York), Lotus Development (Cambridge, Massachusetts), and others. Graphical user environments such as Windows are well suited to workflow applications in which graphics, text, and other elements from many different applications are integrated as objects into compound documents. Windows has built-in workflow capabilities with its Object Linking and

W

Embedding (OLE) features and the Windows for Workgroups product is a network groupware package that includes mail and scheduling software.

Multipurpose Internet Mail Extension (MIME) is an Internet standard that provides a way to include different types of data, such as graphics, audio, video, and text in electronic mail messages. Formatting features allow users to specify font styles, font sizes, and page layouts in documents so they can be read and interpreted by users on other systems who don't have similar applications.

Standard Generalized Markup Language (SGML) is a document specification that goes beyond the American Standard Code for Information Interchange (ASCII) format in providing a way to specify the format of documents. It creates "smart" files rather than "dumb" (ASCII) files. A SGML document contains attributes to define each component of the document, thus making the documents hardware and software independent. Using SGML document formats, workflow software developers can concentrate more on features than document conversion. Users and programmers alike can store information in documents that execute events or enable formats that are compliant with the system and the output devices attached to it.

RELATED ENTRIES   Compound Documents; Document Interchange Standards; Electronic Mail; Groupware; Lotus Notes; Mail/Message Enabled Applications; Messaging Application Programming Interface; Object Linking and Embedding; Standard Generalized Markup Language; *and* Workflow Software

Workgroups

A workgroup is a group of users who are physically located in one place and connected by the same local area network. Alternatively, a workgroup is a logical grouping of users who are scattered throughout an organization, but connected to the same network. In either case, users in workgroups share documents, applications, electronic mail, and system resources in a predefined way. A workgroup might be a simple grouping of users with a name such as "Managers" or "Temps" that is used to address E-mail. On the other hand, the workgroup can have special privileges on the network such as access to data servers or special applications.

Workgroups and workgroup-supporting software are becoming more common. For example, the Schedule+ application supplied with Microsoft Windows for Workgroups lets users collaborate on their schedules and set up meetings that fit into the schedules of attendees. Microsoft's Windows Open Software Architecture (WOSA) is a strategy to build workgroup-enabling features directly into the Windows operating system. With these features, developers and users can create or use features that stimulate workgroup and workflow activities on networks. WOSA includes interfaces to common messaging systems, directory services, security features, and access to back-end database services. Apple's Open Collaborative Environment (AOCE) is a similar strategy for the Macintosh environment.

RELATED ENTRIES   Apple Open Collaborative Environment; Electronic Mail; Groupware; Users and Groups; *and* Windows Open System Architecture

Workplace OS

Workplace OS is a powerful microkernel-based operating system. It uses the same Workplace Shell graphical user interface as OS/2, but it provides a 64-bit core that will run applications designed for a number of existing operating systems, including DOS, Windows, UNIX, and of course, OS/2. The microkernel is designed to run on the Motorola PowerPC processor, as well as Intel 80386, 80486, and Pentium processors.

Workplace OS is based on the Mach 3 microkernel technology created at Carnegie-Mellon University. Mach 3 is also used in the OSF Research Institute's OSF/1 MK Microkernel OS. IBM added enhanced features to the Mach 3 microkernel such as symmetrical multiprocessing, memory management, and security. A layered architecture lets the microkernel host a number of diverse operating systems such as these:

- *DOS*, which is the IBM version and is different than MS-DOS, the Microsoft version
- *OS/2*, initially developed by IBM and Microsoft, but now owned by IBM
- *AIX*, based on work done by the Open Software Foundation (OSF)

Workplace OS is also in the hands of Taligent Inc. This independent company, formed by Apple and IBM, will expand the OS/2 graphical user interface with object technology. Workplace OS already supports object technology such as the IBM System Object Model (SOM) and the Distributed System Object Model (DSOM).

RELATED ENTRIES   Distributed Computing Environment, OSF; IBM Operating Systems; Microkernel; OSF/1, Open Software Foundation; Remote Procedure Call; *and* Windows NT, Microsoft

Workstation

Today, a workstation is a general term that applies to computers attached to networks. In the past, a workstation referred to a high-powered engineering and computer-aided design/computer-aided manufacturing (CAD/CAM) system. As desktop PCs have become more powerful, the term is now used generically to refer to systems attached to networks. Similar terms are "nodes" and "clients," although clients assumes a client-server relationship in which the client workstation is the front-end system where users interact with back-end servers.

The Desktop Management Task Force (DMTF) is a group of vendors that is defining a standard for managing and tracking resources on network workstations. The standard is called the Desktop Management Interface (DMI). The DMTF group consists of Digital Equipment Corporation, Hewlett-Packard, Intel, Microsoft, SunConnect, SynOptics Communications, and other companies.

RELATED ENTRIES   Desktop Management Interface; Networks

W

X.25

The X.25 protocol is a CCITT (ITU) recommendation that defines connections of terminals and computers to packet-switching networks. Packet-switching networks route packets of data through a network to destination nodes. X.25 is a well-established packet-switching service traditionally used to connect remote terminals to host systems. The service provides any-to-any connections for simultaneous users. As shown in Figure X-1, signals from multiple users on a network can be multiplexed through the X.25 interface into the packet-switched network and delivered to different remote sites. A communication channel called a *virtual circuit* connects end stations through the network over a predefined path. The X.25 interface supports line speeds up to 64 Kbits/sec, although a major portion of the throughput is error-checking overhead. The CCITT revised the standard in 1992 and boosted the speed to 2 Mbits/sec.

The packet-switching architecture of X.25 has advantages and disadvantages. Packets of information are routed through a mesh network based on destination address information in the packet header. Users can connect with many different sites, unlike circuit-oriented networks in which a dedicated path exists between only two points. Because packets travel through the shared ports of routers, delivery delays are possible. Users may experience slow performance as more and more people access the network, although most networks can support excess traffic by routing around congested areas. In contrast, circuit-oriented networks provide a fixed bandwidth between two points that does not accommodate bursts in traffic over that bandwidth.

The overhead in X.25 is extensive compared to Frame Relay. For example, in X.25, every node along a packet's path must completely receive a packet and perform an

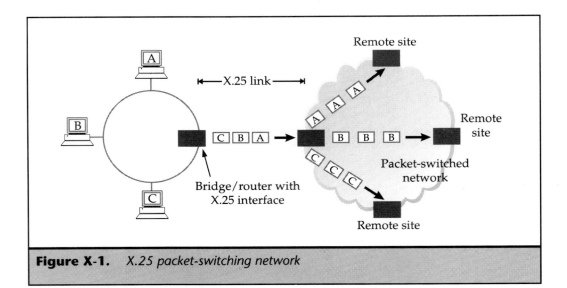

Figure X-1. *X.25 packet-switching network*

error check on the packet before sending it on. Frame Relay nodes simply look at the packet header destination information and immediately forward the packet, in some cases even before it is completely received. Frame Relay does not require the state tables used in X.25 at each intermediate node to deal with management, flow control, and error checking. End nodes must detect missing frames and request a retransmission.

X.25 suffers from poor performance and is not acceptable for most real-time LAN-to-LAN applications. However, X.25 is well established, well understood, and acceptable for remote terminal or computer access, as long as traffic is light. X.25 may be the only reliable way to set up international network links to countries with unreliable phone systems. Almost every country has X.25 services. In contrast, obtaining reliable dedicated circuits in some countries is next to impossible.

In the United States, X.25 is available from most of the carriers and value-added carriers (VACs) including AT&T, US Sprint, CompuServe, Ameritech, Pacific Bell, and others. It's also possible to build private X.25 packet-switching networks by installing X.25 switching equipment on site and connecting the sites with leased lines.

X.25 predates the Open Systems Interconnection (OSI) protocol model, so some of the terminology used to explain X.25 is different. The standard defines protocols in three layers, which closely correspond to the lower three layers of the OSI protocol stack:

- The *Physical layer,* which is called the X.21 interface, defines the physical/electrical interface from the computer/terminal (Data Terminal Equipment, or DTE) to the node of attachment in the X.25 packet-switching network. RS-232-C is often substituted for the X.21 interface.

- The *Link-Access layer* defines data transmission as a sequence of frames. The protocol used is Link Access Procedure-Balanced (LAP-B), which is part of the High-level Data Link Control (HDLC) protocol. LAP-B is designed for point-to-point connections. It provides the frame structure, error, and flow control mechanism for an asynchronous balanced mode session. LAP-B provides a way to acknowledge that a packet has reached each link in the network.

- The *Packet layer* defines reliable virtual circuits through the packet-switched network. Thus, X.25 provides point-to-point data delivery, rather than point-to-multipoint delivery.

The virtual circuit concept is important in X.25. A virtual circuit establishes a temporary or permanent "logical" communication channel between two end points across the packet-switched network. The use of a circuit guarantees that packets arrive in sequence because they follow the same path. It also provides reliable transport of data through the network. There are two types of virtual circuits in X.25:

- *Temporary, call-based virtual circuits* are set up, then dismantled when the data-transfer session is complete.

- *Permanent virtual circuits* maintain a constant connection between the two end nodes.

X.25 uses call setup packets to initially establish a communication channel between two end stations. Once the call is set up, data packets transfer information between the stations. Note that because X.25 is a connection-oriented service, packets do not require source and destination addresses. The virtual circuits provide a pathway for packets through the network to the destination. The packets are assigned a number that identifies them with the channel that links the source and destination, however.

X.25 networks are easy to install and maintain. Charges are based on the number of packets sent and, in some cases, the time connected. Keep in mind that other services are preferable for high-speed local area network traffic, such as Frame Relay or dedicated connections.

RELATED ENTRIES Carrier Services; Connection-Oriented and Connectionless Protocols; Frame Relay; Networks; Packet-Switching Networks; Virtual Circuits; *and* Wide Area Networks

X.400 Message Handling System (MHS)

The Consultative Committee for International Telegraph and Telephone (CCITT) which is part of the International Telecommunications Union (ITU), defined the X.400 MHS standard, an electronic system for exchanging messages among store-and-forward mail systems running on a wide variety of platforms. In the terminology of the International Organization for Standardization (ISO), X.400 is called the Message Oriented Text Interchange System (MOTIS). The goal of the standard is to provide compatibility among multivendor products and interfaces as well as public and private message services.

Electronic mail and messaging systems are an increasingly important part of an enterprise's computing strategy. The systems are designed to help users keep in contact and improve productivity. In addition, messaging systems are becoming an important tool for program development in distributed environments. A message can carry queries from users to remote databases. The remote database then packages a response within a message and sends it back to the user. Of course, this is not a real-time strategy, but in distributed environments, real-time operations are not always practical.

There are many different E-mail systems in use on networks, mainframe systems, and public data networks. For example, the Internet message standard is Simple Mail Transfer Protocol (SMTP). (PROFS) and (SNADs) are used in the IBM mainframe environment. VAXmail and All-In-1 are used in the DEC environment. In addition, numerous E-mail systems are available in the desktop networking environment. A single organization might have numerous E-mail systems that were implemented in the days when departments or workgroups maintained their own local area networks. As the enterprise was interconnected, E-mail gateway systems were often employed to translate messages among the different systems. Recently, X.400-based systems have been gaining in popularity.

X.400 was first introduced in 1984 and has been through several enhancements. It outlines the protocols, procedures, components, terminology, and testing methods required to build interoperable E-mail systems. X.400 is based on a distributed client-server model that includes the components described here and pictured in Figure X-2.

- *User Agent (UA)*   The UA is a software component that runs in the computer of every user attached to the X.400 system. It provides the functions that let users create E-mail messages, read received messages, or browse message lists. UAs communicate with one another through the messaging system, and each UA has a unique name. Users can look up these unique names by accessing a directory service such as the one defined by the X.500 standard described elsewhere in this book.

- *Message Transfer Agent (MTA)*   An MTA accepts messages from UAs and routes them to other MTAs. The MTA must translate the address information in the message and determine how to route the message. The MTA contains an agent of the X.500 directory services system for doing this. Address translation is required because of the many different types of networks possible within the enterprise. The MTA packages the message and addresses it with the address it has translated. It then sends the message to the MTA of the recipient.

- *Message Store (MS)*   The MS is a storage area for messages that can't be delivered directly to a user because the user's system is offline or unavailable. Users can access their messages in the MS at any time.

- *Access Unit (AU)*   An AU provides access to the mail system for other entities, such as fax, teletex, and telex users.

XYZ

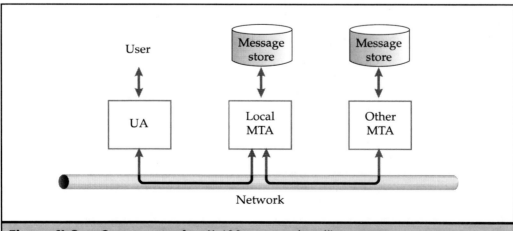

Figure X-2.   *Components of an X.400 message handling system*

■ *Directory System (DS)* The DS contains a complete list of the names and addresses of other X.400 users. It usually follows the X.500 standard.

The X.400 message structure is the same for all systems. An *envelope header* contains a message ID, source and destination address, content type information, and encryption information. This information is in a form used by MTAs to route messages. Following the envelope header is the contents header, which contains To:, From:, cc:, Subject:, and other information that the recipient can read. Below this header is the body of the message.

Other services defined in X.400 include distribution lists, management domains, and security features:

■ *Distribution lists* are groups of users. Mail sent to a distribution list is automatically sent to all users in the list. A user manages the list and only specified users can submit mail to the list.

■ *Management domains* include the local private management domain (PRMD) and public X.400 service providers, called administrative management domains (ADMDs). ADMDs can provide delivery of messages to remote sites on a global scale.

■ *Security* features specified in X.400 include source authentication, proof of correct delivery and receipt, detection of unauthorized users, protection against message alteration during transit, and other features.

The X.400 API Association (XAPIA) is a standards group that is actively defining standard application program interfaces (APIs) for X.400 messaging systems.

RELATED ENTRIES CCITT; Electronic Mail; Groupware; Message-Enabled Applications; Messaging API, E-mail; Workflow Software; *and* X.500 Directory Services

X.500 Directory Services

X.500 is a CCITT (ITU) recommendation for a directory services system that has been adopted by the International Organization for Standardization (ISO). X.500 defines how an organization can share names and the objects associated with them over a global enterprise. A complete X.500 system is called a "Directory." X.500 has been adopted as an international standard to provide worldwide directory services. It is closely linked to the X.400 electronic mail standard. X.500 is hierarchical in that there are administrative domains (organizations, divisions, departments, and workgroups) that provide information about the users and resources in those domains. X.500 is considered the best way to implement a directory service, but it costs more to implement and is slower than other methods.

NOTE: NetWare Directory Services (NDS) provides a good example of an X.500-like implementation. Refer to "Directory Services, NetWare" for further discussion.

X.500 directory services can provide information to electronic mail systems, applications that need to access resources elsewhere on the network, or management systems that need to know the name and location of entities on the network. The directory is database, or directory information base (DIB) as it is called in the X.500 specification. Entries made in the database are called *objects*. For example, there are user objects, and resource objects such as printers. Objects hold information that describe the object.

Objects are organized into a tree structure that is organized in a way that closely resembles the structure of an organization. For example, objects that represent divisions or departments of a company branch from the root of the tree, as pictured in Figure X-3. These are called *organizational object* types because they can "contain" other objects, such as *organizational unit objects*, or *common name objects*. Organizational unit objects define subbranches of a division or department, and common name objects are end nodes that represent physical entities like people, printers, and servers. See "Directory Services Naming, NetWare 4.x" for a complete discussion of object types and object naming in the NetWare 4.x environment.

Each branch in the directory represents a division or department that is typically at a different geographic location. A master copy of the DIB is stored at one of the sites. While it's possible for a remote user to access the master copy of the DIB, this is highly inefficient over wide area links. Therefore, the DIB is divided into partitions at branches in the directory tree, and partitions are stored on servers at each site. Only relevant partitions are copied to each site. When a user needs information about an object, the local partition is queried first. If the information is not available in the partition, the master DIB is queried over the wide area link. This strategy helps reduce long-distance charges, improves access time, and indirectly provides a way to back up the DIB by replicating it to other locations.

RELATED ENTRIES   CCITT; Directory Services; Directory Services, NetWare; Distributed Database; Domain Name Service; Electronic Mail; Partition Management; Replication; *and* X.400 Message Handling System

Xerox Network System (XNS)

XNS is a peer-to-peer network communication standard developed by Xerox and designed for Ethernet networks. Various network operating systems use XNS, and Novell NetWare's Internetwork Packet Exchange (IPX) is fashioned from it.

XYZ

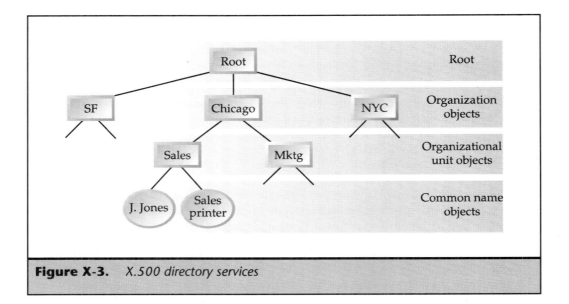

Figure X-3. *X.500 directory services*

XMODEM Protocol

XMODEM is an asynchronous file transfer protocol that is used extensively in personal computer communication using dialup modems. The protocol transfers data in 128-byte blocks and each block is error-checked using a checksum procedure. An acknowledgment byte is sent from the receiver to the sender if its checksum calculation on the block is the same as the sender's checksum. However, this acknowledgment strategy on every block can cause poor performance, especially over satellite connections that have long propagation delays.

An alternative XMODEM protocol that uses cyclic redundancy checking is called XMODEM-CRC. Still another is called XMODEM-1K, which transfers data in 1,024 byte blocks. ZMODEM is the most efficient version of XMODEM. It does not need to acknowledge every block. Instead, it simply requests a retransmission of blocks that are corrupted. ZMODEM is especially useful over packet-switched networks in which charges are incurred by the packet. The lack of acknowledgment packets greatly reduces traffic.

YMODEM is yet another XMODEM implementation. It contains all the features of XMODEM-1K plus a batch file transfer mode for delivering a group of files during a single session.

RELATED ENTRIES   Asynchronous Communications; Communication; *and* Modems

X/Open

X/Open Consortium Ltd. is a European foundation that was established to provide standards for the UNIX environment. Its main goal is to promote open systems protocols for UNIX languages, interfaces, networks, and applications. It also promotes portability of applications between the different UNIX environments and supports the Institute of Electrical and Electronics Engineers (IEEE) Portable Operating System Interface for UNIX (POSIX) specifications.

RELATED ENTRIES   Common Open Software Environment; Open Software Foundation; OSF/1, Open Software Foundation; POSIX; Transmission Control Protocol/Internet Protocol; *and* UNIX

X Window

X Window is a standard graphical user interface (GUI) used on UNIX systems that was developed at the Massachusetts Institute of Technology. A GUI is a mouse and keyboard controlled interface with pull-down menus, onscreen buttons, scroll bars, and overlapping windows for running separate applications. Examples of other GUI environments include Apple's Macintosh, Microsoft's Windows, and IBM's OS/2 Presentation Manager. However, the X Window environment is a client-server design that operates well over remote links.

With regard to developers, X Window provides software tools and standard application program interfaces for creating graphics-based distributed applications. Completed applications are hardware independent, meaning they can execute on any system that supports the X Window environment. The entire environment is often referred to simply as "X."

The X Window system runs programs in one or more windows on a bit-mapped screen. Users can run multiple programs at once in each window and switch among windows by clicking them with the mouse. The X Window environment is pictured in Figure X-4 and described in the following list:

- A program called the *X Server* runs in the local workstation and manages its windows and programs.

- Each program window is called an *X Client,* and it interacts with the X Server program running in the same machine using a client-server relationship.

- The X Server performs all the program processing for the X Clients, interacting with those clients with a messaging system. X Server controls the entire local environment so that programs cooperate when accessing memory and other system resources.

- The X Server runs the *X Window Manager* program, which provides GUI interfacing. Currently, two window managers are available: Motif and Open Look. Both are similar in functionality and run the same programs.

XYZ

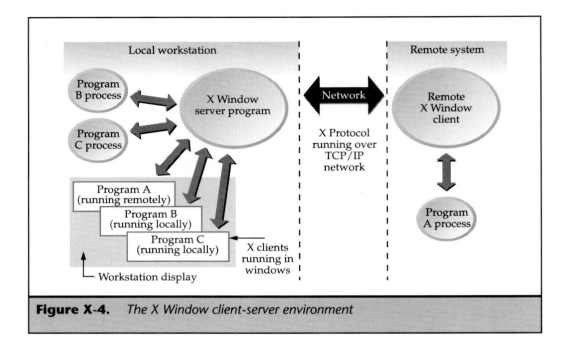

Figure X-4. *The X Window client-server environment*

■ The X Server running in the local machine can interact with programs running on remote computers and display the output of those programs in a local window. This is a client-server relationship, but the local server has complete control and remote processes are called clients, not servers, because they are under the control of the local X Server.

This last point is extremely important on the Internet and in other wide area network environments. Users can work with programs running on remote computers. The remote program runs near the resources it needs to access often, such as disk data. Only the information necessary to update the local user's screen is transmitted over the remote link, reducing bottlenecks that might occur if the entire program and its data were transmitted to the local system for processing.

The interface between the X Server and remote X Clients is event-oriented and based on the X protocols. This protocol runs over Transmission Control Protocol/Internet Protocol (TCP/IP) network protocols. In some cases, vendors have enhanced the X Window environment by adding such features as three-dimensional imaging. An advantage of the X Window environment is that server applications can run on any platform, as long as the application can exchange a common set of messages over a common transport protocol with the client. Thus, developers can build X Window-compliant applications on a number of systems, and those applications are accessible by any workstation that supports X Window.

X Window is the user interface for the Open Software Foundation's (OSF's) Motif and the Open Look system. SunSoft's Solaris 2 operating system also implements an X Window implementation developed by AT&T.

Ymodem

See XMODEM Protocol.

ZMODEM Protocol

See XMODEM Protocol.

Zone, AppleTalk

AppleTalk networks can be divided into logical groups of networks called *zones*. Each zone has a name that makes it easier for users to refer to groups of users or network equipment. The Zone Information Protocol (ZIP) works with Routing Table Maintenance Protocol (RTMP) and AppleTalk Update Routing Protocol (AURP) to maintain a list of network numbers in matching zone names. This information is held in Zone Information Tables (ZITs). When an AppleTalk packet arrives at a router, the zone name in the packet is compared to the ZIT so the router can forward the packet to the port connected to the destination network.

RELATED ENTRIES   Apple Computer; AppleTalk; *and* Domains

XYZ

Zone Information Protocol (ZIP), AppleTalk

ZIP is an AppleTalk session-layer protocol that maintains and discovers the internetwork mapping of network number ranges. The AppleTalk Name Binding Protocol provides internet-to-local translation services and uses ZIP to determine which networks contain nodes belonging to a zone.

RELATED ENTRIES   Apple Computer; AppleTalk

Zone Information Table (ZIT), AppleTalk

ZIT tables on AppleTalk networks hold information about each network. ZIT tables are maintained by routers on an AppleTalk internetwork.

RELATED ENTRIES   Apple Computer; AppleTalk

Zone Multicast Address, AppleTalk

The data-link multicast address where nodes on AppleTalk networks receive Name Binding Protocol broadcast.

RELATED ENTRIES   Apple Computer; AppleTalk

Appendix A

Acronym List

This appendix provides a listing of the most commonly used acronyms. For a more complete list, refer to the index.

ACL	access control list
ADC	analog-to-digital conversion
ADCCP	Advanced Data Communications Control Procedure
ADPCM	adaptive differential pulse code modulation
ADSL	Asymmetrical Digital Subscriber Line
AFP	AppleTalk Filing Protocol
AFS	Andrew File System
AIX	Advanced Interactive Executive
AM	amplitude modulation
ANSI	American National Standards Institute
AOCE	Apple Open Collaborative Environment
API	application program interface
APPC	Advanced Program-to-Program Communications
APPN	Advanced Peer-to-Peer Networking
ARDIS	Advanced National Radio Data Service
ARP	Address Resolution Protocol
ARPANET	Advanced Research Projects Agency Network
ATM	Asynchronous Transfer Mode
AWG	American Wire Gauge
BBS	bulletin board system
BGP	Border Gateway Protocol
B-ISDN	Broadband ISDN
BISYNC	Binary Synchronous Communications
CCITT	Consultative Committee for International Telegraph and Telephone
CDDI	Copper Distributed Data Interface
CDPD	Cellular Digital Packet Data
CISC	Complex Instruction Set Computer
CLNP	Connectionless Network Protocol
CMIP	Common Management Information Protocol
CMIS	Common Management Information Service
COM	Common Object Model
CORBA	Common Object Request Broker Architecture
COS	Corporation for Open Systems
COSE	Common Open Software Environment
CSMA/CD	carrier sense multiple access/collision detection
CSU/DSU	channel service unit/data service unit

DBMS	database management system
DCE	data communication equipment
DCE	Distributed Computing Environment
DDE	Dynamic Data Exchange
DDP	Datagram Delivery Protocol
DEC	Digital Equipment Corporation
DECdns	DEC distributed name service
DECmcc	DEC management control center
DES	Data Encryption Standard
DME	Distributed Management Environment
DMI	Desktop Management Interface
DMTF	Desktop Management Task Force
DNA	DEC Network Architecture
DNS	Domain Name Service
DOE	Distributed Objects Everywhere
DOMF	Distributed Object Management Facility
DOMS	Distributed Object Management System
DPSK	differential phase-shift keying
DQDB	Distributed Queue Dual Bus
DRDA	Distributed Relational Database Architecture
DSOM	Distributed System Object Model
DSU/CSU	data service unit/channel service unit
DTE	data terminal equipment
EDI	Electronic Data Interchange
EGP	Exterior Gateway Protocols
EIA	Electronic Industries Association
EMI	electromagnetic interference
ESCON	Enterprise System Connections
ESD	electronic software distribution
ES-IS	End System-to-Intermediate System routing
ESL	electronic software licensing
FDDI	Fiber Distributed Data Interface
FDM	frequency division multiplexing
FIPS	Federal Information Processing Standard
FTAM	File Transfer Access and Management
FTP	File Transfer Protocol
GOSIP	Government OSI Profile
HCSS	High Capacity Storage System
HDLC	High-level Data Link Control
HDSL	High-bit-rate Digital Subscriber Line

HIPPI	High Performance Parallel Interface
HMI	Hub Management Interface
HPFS	High Performance File System
HSM	hierarchical storage management
HSSI	High-Speed Serial Interface
IDAPI	Integrated Database API
IDRP	Interdomain Routing Protocol
IEEE	Institute of Electrical and Electronic Engineers
IETF	Internet Engineering Task Force
IIA	Information Interchange Architecture
IP	Internet Protocol
IPC	interprocess communication
IPX	Internetwork Packet Exchange
ISDN	Integrated Services Digital Network
IS-IS	Intermediate System-to-Intermediate System Routing
ISO	International Organization for Standardization
ITU	International Telecommunications Union
LAN	local area network
LAP	Link Access Procedure
LAP-B	Link Access Procedure-Balanced
LAP-D	Link Access Procedure D-Channel
LAT	Local Area Transport
LATA	Local Access and Transport Area
LEC	local exchange carrier
LIPX	Large Internetwork Packet Exchange
LS-API	Licensing Server API
LU	logical units
MAC	Media Access Control
MAN	metropolitan area network
MAP	Manufacturing Automation Protocol
MAPI	Messaging Application Programming Interface
MAU	multistation access unit
MHS	Message Handling Service, Novell
MIB	Management information base
MIFF	Management information format file
MIME	Multipurpose Internet Mail Extension
MNP	Microcom Networking Protocol
MPTN	Multiprotocol Transport Network
MQI	Message Queuing Interface, IBM
MTA	Message Transfer Agent

NCP	NetWare Core Protocol
NCP	Network Control Program
NDIS	Network Driver Interface Specification
NetDDE	Network Dynamic Data Exchange
NFS	Network File System
NII	National Information Infrastructure
NLM	NetWare Loadable Module
NLSP	NetWare Link Service Protocol
NREN	National Research and Education Network
NTFS	New Technology File System
OCE	Open Collaborative Environment, Apple
ODBC	Open Database Connectivity, Microsoft
ODI	Open Data-link Interface
OLE	Object Linking and Embedding
OLTP	On-Line Transaction Processing
OMA	Object Management Architecture
OMG	Object Management Group
ONC	Open Network Computing
OSF	Open Software Foundation
OSI	Open Systems Interconnection
OSPF	Open Shortest Path First
PAD	packet assembler-disassembler
PAP	Printer Access Protocol
PCI	Peripheral Component Interface
PDN	public data network
PDS	Premises Distribution System
PEM	Privacy Enhanced Mail
PPP	Point-to-Point Protocol
PSDN	Public switched data network
PU	physical unit
PVC	permanent virtual circuits
QAM	quadrature amplitude modulation
RAID	redundant arrays of inexpensive disks
RBOC	regional Bell operating companies
RIP	Routing Information Protocol
RISC	Reduced Instruction Set Computer
RPC	remote procedure call
RSA	Rivest, Shamir, Adleman
SAA	Systems Application Architecture
SAG	SQL Access Group

SAP	Service Advertising Protocol
SCSI	Small Computer System Interface
SDLC	Synchronous Data Link Control
SFT	System Fault Tolerance
SGML	Standard Generalized Markup Language
SLIP	Serial Line Internet Protocol
SMB	Server Message Block
SMDS	Switched Multimegabit Data Service
SMTP	Simple Mail Transfer Protocol
SNA	Systems Network Architecture
SNMP	Simple Network Management Protocol
SOM	System Object Model
SONET	Synchronous Optical Network
SPARC	Scalable Performance Architecture, Sun Microsystems, Inc.
SPX	Sequenced Packet Exchange
SQL	Structured Query Language
TCP/IP	Transmission Control Protocol/Internet Protocol
TDR	time domain reflectometer
TFTP	Trivial File Transfer Protocol
TLI	Transport Level Interface
TOP	Technical Office Protocol
UNMA	Unified Network Management Architecture
UPS	uninterruptible power supply
USL	UNIX System Laboratories
UTP	Unshielded twisted pair
UUCP	UNIX-to-UNIX Copy Program
VAC	value added carrier
VFS	Virtual File System
VIM	Vendor Independent Messaging
VITAL	Virtually Integrated Technical Architecture Lifecycle, Apple
VMS	Virtual Memory System
VSAT	very small aperture terminals
VT	Virtual Terminal
VTAM	Virtual Telecommunication Access Method
WAN	wide area network
WOSA	Windows Open System Architecture
XNS	Xerox Network System
ZIP	Zone Information Protocol
ZIT	Zone Information Table
ZMA	Zone Multicast Address

Index

G

W

LAN TIMES Free Subscription Form

○ **Yes,** I want to receive (continue to receive) LAN TIMES free of charge.　　　　○ No.

I am ○ a new subscriber　○ renewing my subscription　○ changing my address

Signature required _____ Date _____

Name_____

Title _____ Telephone _____

Company _____

Address _____

City _____

State/County _____ Zip/Postal Code _____

Free in the United States to qualified subscribers only

International Prices (Airmail Delivery)

Canada: $65 Elsewhere: $150

○ Payment enclosed ○ Bill me later

Charge my: ○ Visa ○ Mastercard ○ Amer. Exp

Card number _____

Exp. Date _____

All questions must be completed to qualify for a subscription to LAN TIMES. Publisher reserves the right to serve only those individuals who meet publication criteria.

1. Which of the following best describe your organization?
(Check only one)
○ A. Agriculture/Mining/Construction/Oil/Petrochemical/Environmental
○ B. Manufacturer (non-computer)
○ C. Government/Military/Public Adm.
○ D. Education
○ E. Research/Development
○ F. Engineering/Architecture
○ G. Finance/Banking/Accounting/Insurance/Real Estate
○ H. Health/Medical/Legal
○ I. VAR/VAD Systems House
○ J. Manufacturer Computer Hardware/Software
○ K. Aerospace
○ L. Retailer/Distributor/Wholesaler (non-computer)
○ M. Computer Retailer/Distributor/Sales
○ N. Transportation
○ O. Media/Marketing/Advertising/Publishing/Broadcasting
○ P. Utilities/Telecommunications/VAN
○ Q. Entertainment/Recreation/Hospitality/Non-profit/Trade Association
○ R. Consultant
○ S. Systems Integrator
○ T. Computer/LAN Leasing/Training
○ U. Information/Data Services
○ V. Computer/Communications Services: Outsourcing/3rd Party
○ W. All Other Business Services
○ X. Other _____

2. Which best describes your title? (Check only one)
○ A. Network/LAN Manager
○ B. MIS/DP/IS Manager
○ C. Owner/President/CEO/Partner
○ D. Data Communications Manager
○ E. Engineer/CNE/Technician
○ F. Consultant/Analyst
○ G. Micro Manager/Specialist/Coordinator
○ H. Vice President
○ I. All other Dept. Heads, Directors and Managers
○ J. Educator
○ K. Programmer/Systems Analyst
○ L. Professional
○ M. Other_____

3. Which of the following best describes your job function?
(Check only one)
○ A. Network/LAN Management
○ B. MIS/DP/IS Management
○ C. Systems Engineering/Integration
○ D. Administration/Management
○ E. Technical Services
○ F. Consulting
○ G. Research/Development
○ H. Sales/Marketing
○ I. Accounting/Finance
○ J. Education/Training

○ K. Office Automation
○ L. Manufacturing/Operations/Production
○ M. Personnel
○ N. Technology Assessment
○ O. Other _____

4. How many employees work in your entire ORGANIZATION?
(Check only one)
○ A. Under 25　　○ E. 1,001-5,000
○ B. 25-100　　○ F. 5,001-9,999
○ C. 101-500　　○ G. 10,000 and over
○ D. 501-1,000

5. Which of the following are you or your clients currently using, or planning to purchase in the next 12 months? (1–Own; 2–Plan to purchase in next 12 months) (Check all that apply)

Topologies	1	2
A. Ethernet	○	○
B. Token Ring	○	○
C. Arcnet	○	○
D. LocalTalk	○	○
E. FDDI	○	○
F. Starlan	○	○
G. Other	○	○

Network Operating System	1	2
A. Novell Netware	○	○
B. Novell Netware Lite	○	○
C. Banyan VINES	○	○
D. Digital Pathworks	○	○
E. IBM LAN Server	○	○
F. Microsoft LAN Manager	○	○
G. Microsoft Windows for Workgroups	○	○
H. Artisoft LANtastic	○	○
I. Sitka TOPS	○	○
J. 10NET	○	○
K. AppleTalk	○	○

Client/Workstation Operating Sys.	1	2
A. DOS	○	○
B. DR-DOS	○	○
C. Windows	○	○
D. Windows NT	○	○
E. UNIX	○	○
F. UnixWare	○	○
G. OS/2	○	○
H. Mac System 6	○	○
I. Mac System 7	○	○

Protocols/Standards	1	2
A. IPX	○	○
B. TCP/IP	○	○
C. X.25	○	○
D. XNS	○	○
E. OSI	○	○
F. SAA/SNA	○	○
G. NFS	○	○
H. MHS	○	○

6. Is your Organization/Clients network... (Check all that apply)

- A. International
- B. National
- C. Regional
- D. Metropolitan
- E. Local
- F. Other _____

7. What hardware does your department/client base own/plan to purchase. (Check all that apply)

	Owns	Plan to purchase in next 12 months
A. Bridges	○	○
B. Diskless Workstations	○	○
C. Cabling System	○	○
D. Printers	○	○
E. Disk Drive	○	○
F. Optical Storage	○	○
G. Tape Backup System	○	○
H. Optical Storage	○	○
I. Application Servers	○	○
J. Communication Servers	○	○
K. Fax Servers	○	○
L. Mainframe	○	○
M. Network Adapter Cards	○	○
N. Wireless Adapters/Bridges	○	○
O. Power Conditioners/UPSs	○	○
P. Hubs/Concentrators	○	○
Q. Minicomputers	○	○
R. Modems	○	○
S. 386-based computers	○	○
T. 486-based computers	○	○
U. Pentium-based computers	○	○
V. Macintosh computers	○	○
W. RISC-based workstations	○	○
X. Routers	○	○
Y. Multimedia Cards	○	○
Z. Network Test/Diagnostic Equipment	○	○
1. Notebooks/Laptops	○	○
2. DSU/CSU	○	○
99. None of the Above	○	○

8. What network software/applications do you/your clients own/plan to purchase in the next 12 months? (Check all that apply)

- A. Network Management
- B. Software Metering
- C. Network Inventory
- D. Virus Protection
- E. Menuing
- F. E-mail
- G. Word Processing
- H. Spreadsheet
- I. Database
- J. Accounting
- K. Document Management
- L. Graphics
- M. Communications
- N. Application Development Tools
- O. Desktop Publishing
- P. Integrated Business Applications
- Q. Multimedia
- R. Document Imaging
- S. Groupware
- Z. None of the above

9. What is the annual revenue of your entire organization or budget if non-profit (Check only one)

- A. Under $10 million
- B. $10-$50 million
- C. $50-$100 million
- D. $100-$500 million
- E. $500 million-$1 billion
- F. Over $1 billion

10. How much does your organization (if reseller, your largest client's company) plan to spend on computer products in the next 12 months? (Check only one)

- A. Under $25,000
- B. $25,000-$99,999
- C. $100,000-$499,999
- D. $500,000-$999,999
- E. $1 billion

11. Where do you purchase computer products? (Check all that apply)

- A. Manufacturer
- B. Distributor
- C. Reseller
- D. VAR
- E. System Integrator
- F. Consultant
- G. Other _____

12. In which ways are you involved in acquiring computer products and services? (Check all that apply)

- A. Determine the need
- B. Define product specifications/features
- C. Select brand
- D. Evaluate the supplier
- E. Select vendor/source
- F. Approve the acquisition
- G. None of the above

ICS1639

---

fold here

Place Stamp Here

LAN TIMES

McGraw–Hill, INC.

P.O. Box 652

Hightstown NJ 08520-0652